SMITHSONIAN MISCELLANEOUS COLLECTIONS
VOLUME 109 (WHOLE VOLUME)

Research Corporation Fund

SMITHSONIAN
ELLIPTIC FUNCTIONS TABLES

PREPARED BY

G. W. AND R. M. SPENCELEY
MIAMI UNIVERSITY, OXFORD, OHIO

(PUBLICATION 3863)

CITY OF WASHINGTON
PUBLISHED BY THE SMITHSONIAN INSTITUTION
NOVEMBER 1, 1947

PREFACE

These tables were inspired by the similar work of Sir George Greenhill and Col. R. L. Hippisley as published in *Smithsonian Mathematical Formulae and Tables of Elliptic Functions*. The pattern they designed has been followed closely by us. The chief difference is our inclusion of the three elliptic functions, sn(u,k), cn(u,k), dn(u,k).

Columns A and D were computed first. From them were computed columns sn(u) and cn(u), checked by means of

Check I: $sn^2(u) + cn^2(u) = 1$, with a maximum error of ± 2 in the 15th decimal. Practically all errors in these first four columns were eliminated at this time, but some few managed to elude us.

Column dn(u) was then computed, and checked by means of

Check II: $sn(K-u) \cdot dn(u) = cn(u)$, with a maximum error of ± 2 in the 15th decimal. Those few errors that had eluded us in Check I were discovered at this time.

Column E(u,k) followed, computed by the formula

$$E(u+v) = E(u) + E(v) - k^2 sn(u+v) sn(u) sn(v),$$

where u was taken as r/90 K and tabulated r°, while v was taken as 1/90 K, i.e. 1°. Independent computations for r° = 15°, 30°, 45°, 60°, 75°, 90° were used as Check III, with a maximum divergence of ± 3 in the 15th decimal. In this method of computing the E(u,k) column the errors are additive, and hence Check III is more sensitive than Checks I and II.

The ϕ column was computed last by means of $\sin \phi = sn(u)$, using Andoyer's 15-place Table of Natural Sines and Cosines. This was checked by computing $\cos \phi = cn(u)$. Interpolation into Andoyer's Tables was not used. Instead we developed a rapid method, fitted to machine computation, based on the two formulas

$$\sin(\phi + \epsilon) = \sin \phi + \epsilon \cos \phi - \frac{\epsilon^2}{2} \sin \phi - \frac{\epsilon^3}{6} \cos \phi$$

$$\cos(\phi + \epsilon) = \cos \phi - \epsilon \sin \phi - \frac{\epsilon^2}{2} \cos \phi + \frac{\epsilon^3}{6} \sin \phi$$

Maximum divergence here was kept to ± 4 in the 15th decimal.

Our manuscript columns are all, thus, correct to ± 4 in the 15th decimal. In printing, these have been cut to 12 decimal figures, assuring the accuracy of the 12th decimal digit.

Galley proofs were checked by adding entries in each column of our manuscript in groups of ten and subtracting the entries of the corresponding groups in the galley proofs and demanding that the remainder be equal to zero.

To teachers of mathematics and amateur computers, elliptic functions is a pleasant field of endeavor. Our present tables are not exhaustive. Three more

iii

columns, snh(u,k), cnh(u,k), dnh(u,k), added to ours, would open up the complex argument territory. In the popular field of undergraduate mathematics, a new elementary text on elliptic functions with a wide variety of problems and applications, supplemented by an adequate set of 5-place tables, would be a boon to teachers and students.

It is a pleasant task to acknowledge our indebtedness to Messrs. John Hook, Arthur Gels, Earl Boland, John Brinko, Edward Murphy, and Victor Sutcliffe, who, as N. Y. A. students, shared the work with us in the earlier years. These young men became expert and dependable computers; our thanks to them and to the Federal Government which paid them for their splendid and efficient work.

The considerable cost of printing these tables has been defrayed mainly by a grant from the Research Corporation of New York. Grateful acknowledgement is made for that grant, without which this volume could not have appeared.

We wish to acknowledge here our deep indebtedness to Dr. C. G. Abbot, former Secretary of the Smithsonian, for his invaluable advice and encouragement throughout. Dr. A. Wetmore, who has succeeded Dr. Abbot as Secretary, has assumed full responsibility for the publication of this volume, and for the work of seeing it through the press. We can never repay these two great men, and their corps of advisers, for their critical advice and practical assistance. To have been associated with them, however humbly, has been for us the experience of a lifetime.

G. W. S.
R. M. S.

OXFORD, OHIO,
April 25, 1946.

SMITHSONIAN ELLIPTIC
FUNCTIONS TABLES

K = 1.57091 59581 27243   E = 1.57067 67091 27960
K′= 5.43490 98296 25564   E′= 1.00075 15777 01834

r	u=(r/90)K=F(φ,k)	sn u	cn u	dn u
0	0.00000 00000 00	0.00000 00000 00	1.00000 00000 00	1.00000 00000 00
1	0.01745 46217 57	0.01745 37352 02	0.99984 76719 62	0.99999 99536 06
2	0.03490 92435 14	0.03490 21513 99	0.99939 07343 12	0.99999 98144 82
3	0.05236 38652 71	0.05233 99312 14	0.99862 93264 27	0.99999 95827 97
4	0.06981 84870 28	0.06976 17605 21	0.99756 36805 58	0.99999 92588 34
5	0.08727 31087 85	0.08716 23300 75	0.99619 41217 53	0.99999 88429 86
6	0.10472 77305 42	0.10453 63371 33	0.99452 10677 60	0.99999 83357 62
7	0.12218 23522 99	0.12187 84870 73	0.99254 50288 97	0.99999 77377 78
8	0.13963 69740 56	0.13918 34950 21	0.99026 66078 96	0.99999 70497 64
9	0.15709 15958 13	0.15644 60874 60	0.98768 64997 15	0.99999 62725 58
10	0.17454 62175 70	0.17366 10038 43	0.98480 54913 25	0.99999 54071 08
11	0.19200 08393 27	0.19082 29982 08	0.98162 44614 69	0.99999 44544 67
12	0.20945 54610 84	0.20792 68407 72	0.97814 43803 89	0.99999 34157 97
13	0.22691 00828 41	0.22496 73195 39	0.97436 63095 26	0.99999 22923 64
14	0.24436 47045 98	0.24193 92418 87	0.97029 14011 96	0.99999 10855 37
15	0.26181 93263 55	0.25883 74361 57	0.96592 08982 33	0.99998 97967 85
16	0.27927 39481 12	0.27565 67532 34	0.96125 61336 07	0.99998 84276 80
17	0.29672 85698 68	0.29239 20681 19	0.95629 85300 11	0.99998 69797 90
18	0.31418 31916 25	0.30903 82814 95	0.95104 95994 27	0.99998 54551 80
19	0.33163 78133 82	0.32559 03212 88	0.94551 09426 57	0.99998 38554 06
20	0.34909 24351 39	0.34204 31442 09	0.93968 42488 30	0.99998 21725 20
21	0.36654 70568 96	0.35839 17373 00	0.93357 12948 86	0.99998 04385 58
22	0.38400 16786 53	0.37463 11194 63	0.92717 39450 23	0.99997 86256 47
23	0.40145 63004 10	0.39075 63429 79	0.92049 41501 29	0.99997 67459 95
24	0.41891 09221 67	0.40676 24950 20	0.91353 39471 77	0.99997 48018 93
25	0.43636 55439 24	0.42264 46991 47	0.90629 54586 02	0.99997 27957 10
26	0.45382 01656 81	0.43839 81167 95	0.89878 08916 47	0.99997 07298 90
27	0.47127 47874 38	0.45401 79487 55	0.89099 25376 84	0.99996 86069 51
28	0.48872 94091 95	0.46949 94366 33	0.88293 27715 07	0.99996 64294 79
29	0.50618 40309 52	0.48483 78643 00	0.87460 40506 08	0.99996 42001 28
30	0.52363 86527 09	0.50002 85593 33	0.86600 89144 18	0.99996 19216 14
31	0.54109 32744 66	0.51506 68944 35	0.85714 99835 25	0.99995 95967 14
32	0.55854 78962 23	0.52994 82888 47	0.84802 99588 74	0.99995 72282 60
33	0.57600 25179 80	0.54466 82097 43	0.83865 16209 34	0.99995 48191 38
34	0.59345 71397 37	0.55922 21736 11	0.82901 78288 45	0.99995 23722 85
35	0.61091 17614 94	0.57360 57476 13	0.81913 15195 41	0.99994 98906 80
36	0.62836 63832 51	0.58781 45509 42	0.80899 57068 49	0.99994 73773 48
37	0.64582 10050 08	0.60184 42561 49	0.79861 34805 65	0.99994 48353 51
38	0.66327 56267 65	0.61569 05904 60	0.78798 80055 05	0.99994 22677 86
39	0.68073 02485 22	0.62934 93370 76	0.77712 25205 34	0.99993 96777 82
40	0.69818 48702 79	0.64281 63364 58	0.76602 03375 77	0.99993 70684 95
41	0.71563 94920 36	0.65608 74875 86	0.75468 48406 01	0.99993 44431 03
42	0.73309 41137 93	0.66915 87492 08	0.74311 94845 77	0.99993 18048 06
43	0.75054 87355 50	0.68202 61410 66	0.73132 77944 27	0.99992 91568 17
44	0.76800 33573 07	0.69468 57451 08	0.71931 33639 41	0.99992 65023 63
45	0.78545 79790 64	0.70713 37066 71	0.70707 98546 76	0.99992 38446 78

2

q = 0.00001 90395 55386 95351   D(90) = 1.00007 61611 21696
q′= 0.40330 93063 38377 8   1/D(90) = 0.99992 38446 78379

r	ϕ	$E(\phi,k)$	$A(r)$	$D(r)$
0	0.00000 00000 00	0.00000 00000 00	0.00000 00000 00	1.00000 00000 00
1	0.01745 46214 87	0.01745 46212 17	0.01745 24064 12	1.00000 00231 98
2	0.03490 92413 55	0.03490 92391 96	0.03489 94966 52	1.00000 00927 62
3	0.05236 38579 86	0.05236 38507 01	0.05233 59561 67	1.00000 02086 09
4	0.06981 84697 68	0.06981 84525 07	0.06975 64736 43	1.00000 03705 97
5	0.08727 30750 92	0.08727 30413 99	0.08715 57426 22	1.00000 05785 29
6	0.10472 76723 59	0.10472 76141 77	0.10452 84631 18	1.00000 08321 52
7	0.12218 22599 80	0.12218 21676 62	0.12186 93432 31	1.00000 11311 55
8	0.13963 68363 77	0.13963 66986 99	0.13917 31007 62	1.00000 14751 76
9	0.15709 13999 85	0.15709 12041 58	0.15643 44648 19	1.00000 18637 95
10	0.17454 59492 55	0.17454 56809 42	0.17364 81774 23	1.00000 22965 39
11	0.19200 04826 57	0.19200 01259 89	0.19080 89951 10	1.00000 27728 80
12	0.20945 49986 78	0.20945 45362 75	0.20791 16905 29	1.00000 32922 37
13	0.22690 94958 28	0.22690 89088 19	0.22495 10540 34	1.00000 38539 79
14	0.24436 39726 39	0.24436 32406 85	0.24192 18952 69	1.00000 44574 21
15	0.26181 84276 68	0.26181 75289 88	0.25881 90447 52	1.00000 51018 28
16	0.27927 28594 99	0.27927 17708 95	0.27563 73554 48	1.00000 57864 14
17	0.29672 72667 44	0.29672 59636 29	0.29237 17043 35	1.00000 65103 45
18	0.31418 16480 43	0.31418 01044 75	0.30901 69939 70	1.00000 72727 40
19	0.33163 60020 72	0.33163 41907 80	0.32556 81540 35	1.00000 80726 69
20	0.34909 03275 36	0.34908 82199 56	0.34202 01428 88	1.00000 89091 59
21	0.36654 46231 78	0.36654 21894 88	0.35836 79490 92	1.00000 97811 89
22	0.38399 88877 74	0.38399 60969 31	0.37460 65929 49	1.00001 06876 98
23	0.40145 31201 41	0.40144 99399 16	0.39073 11279 36	1.00001 16275 81
24	0.41890 73191 33	0.41890 37161 54	0.40673 66425 84	1.00001 25996 92
25	0.43636 14836 47	0.43635 74234 36	0.42261 82612 37	1.00001 36028 48
26	0.45381 56126 19	0.45381 10596 38	0.43837 11462 76	1.00001 46358 27
27	0.47126 97050 31	0.47126 46227 21	0.45399 04992 17	1.00001 56973 69
28	0.48872 37599 08	0.48871 81107 36	0.46947 15622 55	1.00001 67861 81
29	0.50617 77763 22	0.50617 15218 27	0.48480 96197 09	1.00001 79009 38
30	0.52363 17533 90	0.52362 48542 30	0.49999 99994 56	1.00001 90402 80
31	0.54108 56902 78	0.54107 81062 77	0.51503 80743 61	1.00002 02028 20
32	0.55853 95862 02	0.55853 12763 98	0.52991 92636 81	1.00002 13871 42
33	0.57599 34404 26	0.57598 43631 23	0.54463 90344 60	1.00002 25918 01
34	0.59344 72522 67	0.59343 73650 85	0.55919 29029 13	1.00002 38153 32
35	0.61090 10210 90	0.61089 02810 17	0.57357 64357 93	1.00002 50562 42
36	0.62835 47463 17	0.62834 31097 60	0.58778 52517 35	1.00002 63130 20
37	0.64580 84274 21	0.64579 58502 60	0.60181 50225 95	1.00002 75841 36
38	0.66326 20639 26	0.66324 85015 71	0.61566 14747 71	1.00002 88680 39
39	0.68071 56554 16	0.68070 10628 54	0.62932 03904 99	1.00003 01631 67
40	0.69816 92015 25	0.69815 35333 82	0.64278 76091 40	1.00003 14679 41
41	0.71562 27019 45	0.71560 59125 36	0.65605 90284 49	1.00003 27807 71
42	0.73307 61564 22	0.73305 81998 12	0.66913 06058 23	1.00003 41000 58
43	0.75052 95647 60	0.75051 03948 15	0.68199 83595 34	1.00003 54241 95
44	0.76798 29268 17	0.76796 24972 62	0.69465 83699 38	1.00003 67515 68
45	0.78543 62425 08	0.78541 45069 86	0.70710 67806 74	1.00003 80805 61

ELLIPTIC FUNCTIONS TABLE $\theta = 1°$

K = 1.57091 59581 27243   E = 1.57067 67091 27960
K'= 5.43490 98296 25563 5   E'= 1.00075 15777 01834

r	u=(r/90)K=F(φ,k)	sn u	cn u	dn u
45	0.78545 79790 64	0.70713 37066 71	0.70707 98546 76	0.99992 38446 78
46	0.80291 26008 21	0.71936 62356 59	0.69463 09948 41	0.99992 11870 01
47	0.82036 72225 78	0.73137 96076 87	0.68197 05781 48	0.99991 85325 68
48	0.83782 18443 35	0.74317 01652 11	0.66910 24626 62	0.99991 58846 14
49	0.85527 64660 91	0.75473 43186 41	0.65603 05696 13	0.99991 32463 66
50	0.87273 10878 48	0.76606 85474 24	0.64275 88822 01	0.99991 06210 37
51	0.89018 57096 05	0.77716 94011 16	0.62929 14443 79	0.99990 80118 25
52	0.90764 03313 62	0.78803 35004 23	0.61563 23596 19	0.99990 54219 10
53	0.92509 49531 19	0.79865 75382 28	0.60178 57896 56	0.99990 28544 47
54	0.94254 95748 76	0.80903 82805 89	0.58775 59532 16	0.99990 03125 63
55	0.96000 41966 33	0.81917 25677 21	0.57354 71247 36	0.99989 77993 55
56	0.97745 88183 90	0.82905 73149 50	0.55916 36330 51	0.99989 53178 86
57	0.99491 34401 47	0.83868 95136 49	0.54460 98600 79	0.99989 28711 78
58	1.01236 80619 04	0.84806 62321 43	0.52989 02394 83	0.99989 04622 11
59	1.02982 26836 61	0.85718 46166 00	0.51500 92553 18	0.99988 80939 21
60	1.04727 73054 18	0.86604 18918 95	0.49997 14406 67	0.99988 57691 92
61	1.06473 19271 75	0.87463 53624 42	0.48478 13762 57	0.99988 34908 57
62	1.08218 65489 32	0.88296 24130 15	0.46944 36890 64	0.99988 12616 91
63	1.09964 11706 89	0.89102 05095 34	0.45396 30509 07	0.99987 90844 10
64	1.11709 57924 46	0.89880 71998 33	0.43834 41770 21	0.99987 69616 65
65	1.13455 04142 03	0.90632 01143 98	0.42259 18246 22	0.99987 48960 43
66	1.15200 50359 60	0.91355 69670 83	0.40671 07914 64	0.99987 28900 61
67	1.16945 96577 17	0.92051 55558 02	0.39070 59143 73	0.99987 09461 60
68	1.18691 42794 74	0.92719 37631 90	0.37458 20677 78	0.99986 90667 11
69	1.20436 89012 31	0.93358 95572 44	0.35834 41622 31	0.99986 72540 02
70	1.22182 35229 88	0.93970 09919 34	0.34199 71429 09	0.99986 55202 39
71	1.23927 81447 45	0.94552 62077 93	0.32554 59881 13	0.99986 38375 52
72	1.25673 27665 02	0.95106 34324 74	0.30899 57077 55	0.99986 22379 73
73	1.27418 73882 59	0.95631 09812 85	0.29235 13418 37	0.99986 07135 53
74	1.29164 20100 16	0.96126 72576 99	0.27561 79589 14	0.99985 92658 48
75	1.30909 66317 73	0.96593 07538 32	0.25880 06545 61	0.99985 78969 21
76	1.32655 12535 30	0.97030 00509 00	0.24190 45498 18	0.99985 66083 42
77	1.34400 58752 87	0.97437 38196 44	0.22493 47896 42	0.99985 54016 78
78	1.36146 04970 44	0.97815 08207 32	0.20789 65413 40	0.99985 42783 99
79	1.37891 51188 01	0.98162 99051 30	0.19079 49930 01	0.99985 32398 75
80	1.39636 97405 58	0.98481 00144 51	0.17363 53519 20	0.99985 22873 70
81	1.41382 43623 15	0.98769 01812 72	0.15642 28430 20	0.99985 14220 44
82	1.43127 89840 71	0.99026 95294 25	0.13916 27072 64	0.99985 06449 52
83	1.44873 36058 28	0.99254 72742 60	0.12186 02000 64	0.99984 99570 39
84	1.46618 82275 85	0.99452 27228 83	0.10452 05896 89	0.99984 93591 44
85	1.48364 28493 42	0.99619 52743 65	0.08714 91556 63	0.99984 88519 95
86	1.50109 74710 99	0.99756 44199 19	0.06975 11871 64	0.99984 84362 10
87	1.51855 20928 56	0.99862 97430 58	0.05233 19814 22	0.99984 81122 96
88	1.53600 67146 13	0.99939 09197 16	0.03489 68421 06	0.99984 78806 46
89	1.55346 13363 70	0.99984 77183 48	0.01745 10777 23	0.99984 77415 43
90	1.57091 59581 27	1.00000 00000 00	0.00000 00000 00	0.99984 76951 56

4

q = 0.00001 90395 55386 95351   D(90) = 1.00007 61611 21696
q' = 0.40330 93063 38377 8   1/D(90) = 0.99992 38446 78379

r	ϕ	$E(\phi,k)$	A(r)	D(r)
45	0.78543 62425 08	0.78541 45069 86	0.70710 67806 74	1.00003 80805 61
46	0.80288 95118 06	0.80286 64239 29	0.71933 97998 35	1.00003 94095 53
47	0.82034 27347 39	0.82031 82481 50	0.73135 37011 26	1.00004 07369 26
48	0.83779 59113 91	0.83776 99798 18	0.74314 48249 95	1.00004 20610 63
49	0.85524 90419 05	0.85522 16192 15	0.75470 95797 52	1.00004 33803 51
50	0.87270 21264 77	0.87267 31667 37	0.76604 44426 60	1.00004 46931 81
51	0.89015 51653 60	0.89012 46228 91	0.77714 59610 11	1.00004 59979 55
52	0.90760 81588 65	0.90757 59882 96	0.78801 07531 74	1.00004 72930 82
53	0.92506 11073 55	0.92502 72636 80	0.79863 55096 28	1.00004 85769 86
54	0.94251 40112 50	0.94247 84498 82	0.80901 69939 70	1.00004 98481 01
55	0.95996 68710 23	0.95992 95478 48	0.81915 20438 98	1.00005 11048 80
56	0.97741 96872 02	0.97738 05586 35	0.82903 75721 79	1.00005 23457 90
57	0.99487 24603 66	0.99483 14834 03	0.83867 05675 85	1.00005 35693 20
58	1.01232 51911 49	1.01228 23234 17	0.84804 80958 11	1.00005 47739 80
59	1.02977 78802 35	1.02973 30800 46	0.85716 73003 72	1.00005 59583 01
60	1.04723 05283 60	1.04718 37547 62	0.86602 54034 71	1.00005 71208 41
61	1.06468 31363 08	1.06463 43491 33	0.87461 97068 41	1.00005 82601 84
62	1.08213 57049 14	1.08208 48648 29	0.88294 75925 77	1.00005 93749 40
63	1.09958 82350 59	1.09953 53036 14	0.89100 65239 22	1.00006 04637 53
64	1.11704 07276 73	1.11698 56673 45	0.89879 40460 49	1.00006 15252 95
65	1.13449 31837 31	1.13443 59579 71	0.90630 77868 02	1.00006 25582 74
66	1.15194 56042 50	1.15188 61775 30	0.91354 54574 23	1.00006 35614 30
67	1.16939 79902 94	1.16933 63281 48	0.92050 48532 49	1.00006 45335 41
68	1.18685 03429 67	1.18678 64120 32	0.92718 38543 78	1.00006 54734 24
69	1.20430 26634 14	1.20423 64314 72	0.93358 04263 23	1.00006 63799 33
70	1.22175 49528 20	1.22168 63888 38	0.93969 26206 27	1.00006 72519 63
71	1.23920 72124 06	1.23913 62865 73	0.94551 85754 54	1.00006 80884 52
72	1.25665 94434 31	1.25658 61271 94	0.95105 65161 63	1.00006 88883 82
73	1.27411 16471 88	1.27403 59132 87	0.95630 47558 45	1.00006 96507 77
74	1.29156 38250 04	1.29148 56475 04	0.96126 16958 32	1.00007 03747 08
75	1.30901 59782 37	1.30893 53325 62	0.96592 58261 95	1.00007 10592 94
76	1.32646 81082 75	1.32638 49712 36	0.97029 57261 94	1.00007 17037 00
77	1.34392 02165 33	1.34383 45663 58	0.97437 00647 14	1.00007 23071 42
78	1.36137 23044 56	1.36128 41208 14	0.97814 76006 72	1.00007 28688 84
79	1.37882 43735 10	1.37873 36375 38	0.98162 71833 96	1.00007 33882 42
80	1.39627 64251 85	1.39618 31195 11	0.98480 77529 69	1.00007 38645 83
81	1.41372 84609 95	1.41363 25697 55	0.98768 83405 60	1.00007 42973 26
82	1.43118 04824 69	1.43108 19913 34	0.99026 80687 14	1.00007 46859 45
83	1.44863 24911 56	1.44853 13873 42	0.99254 61516 20	1.00007 50299 66
84	1.46608 44886 20	1.46598 07609 08	0.99452 18953 53	1.00007 53289 70
85	1.48353 64764 39	1.48343 01151 88	0.99619 46980 81	1.00007 55825 92
86	1.50098 84562 03	1.50087 94533 58	0.99756 40502 53	1.00007 57905 24
87	1.51844 04295 11	1.51832 87786 18	0.99862 95347 51	1.00007 59525 12
88	1.53589 23979 69	1.53577 80941 81	0.99939 08270 17	1.00007 60683 59
89	1.55334 43631 91	1.55322 74032 73	0.99984 76951 56	1.00007 61379 24
90	1.57079 63267 95	1.57067 67091 28	1.00000 00000 00	1.00007 61611 22

K = 1.57127 49523 72225 E = 1.57031 79198 97448
K'= 4.74271 72652 78886 E'= 1.00258 40855 27552

r	u=(r/90)K=F(φ,k)	sn u	cn u	dn u
0	0.00000 00000 00	0.00000 00000 00	1.00000 00000 00	1.00000 00000 00
1	0.01745 86105 82	0.01745 77226 09	0.99984 76023 48	0.99999 98143 98
2	0.03491 72211 64	0.03491 01177 11	0.99939 04560 69	0.99999 92578 17
3	0.05237 58317 46	0.05235 18594 47	0.99862 87011 76	0.99999 83309 36
4	0.06983 44423 28	0.06977 76252 59	0.99756 25709 76	0.99999 70348 86
5	0.08729 30529 10	0.08718 20975 33	0.99619 23919 96	0.99999 53712 47
6	0.10475 16634 91	0.10455 99652 47	0.99451 85838 72	0.99999 33420 48
7	0.12221 02740 73	0.12190 59256 16	0.99254 16592 26	0.99999 09497 63
8	0.13966 88846 55	0.13921 46857 31	0.99026 22234 93	0.99998 81973 10
9	0.15712 74952 37	0.15648 09641 98	0.98768 09747 30	0.99998 50880 45
10	0.17458 61058 19	0.17369 94927 67	0.98479 87033 97	0.99998 16257 58
11	0.19204 47164 01	0.19086 50179 69	0.98161 62921 00	0.99997 78146 73
12	0.20950 33269 83	0.20797 23027 33	0.97813 47153 11	0.99997 36594 37
13	0.22696 19375 65	0.22501 61280 03	0.97435 50390 58	0.99996 91651 16
14	0.24442 05481 47	0.24199 12943 57	0.97027 84205 86	0.99996 43371 90
15	0.26187 91587 29	0.25889 26236 06	0.96590 61079 85	0.99995 91815 46
16	0.27933 77693 11	0.27571 49603 91	0.96123 94397 95	0.99995 37044 71
17	0.29679 63798 93	0.29245 31737 79	0.95627 98445 78	0.99994 79126 43
18	0.31425 49904 74	0.30910 21588 36	0.95102 88404 68	0.99994 18131 24
19	0.33171 36010 56	0.32565 68382 07	0.94548 80346 83	0.99993 54133 50
20	0.34917 22116 38	0.34211 21636 72	0.93965 91230 16	0.99992 87211 24
21	0.36663 08222 20	0.35846 31177 04	0.93354 38892 98	0.99992 17446 06
22	0.38408 94328 02	0.37470 47150 10	0.92714 42048 30	0.99991 44923 02
23	0.40154 80433 84	0.39083 20040 59	0.92046 20277 90	0.99990 69730 52
24	0.41900 66539 66	0.40684 00686 06	0.91349 94026 14	0.99989 91960 25
25	0.43646 52645 48	0.42272 40292 00	0.90625 84593 46	0.99989 11707 00
26	0.45392 38751 30	0.43847 90446 74	0.89874 14129 67	0.99988 29068 62
27	0.47138 24857 12	0.45410 03136 31	0.89095 05626 91	0.99987 44145 84
28	0.48884 10962 94	0.46958 30759 15	0.88288 82912 43	0.99986 57042 19
29	0.50629 97068 75	0.48492 26140 60	0.87455 70641 03	0.99985 67863 85
30	0.52375 83174 57	0.50011 42547 36	0.86595 94287 32	0.99984 76719 52
31	0.54121 69280 39	0.51515 33701 69	0.85709 80137 67	0.99983 83720 29
32	0.55867 55386 21	0.53003 53795 57	0.84797 55281 95	0.99982 88979 52
33	0.57613 41492 03	0.54475 57504 63	0.83859 47605 00	0.99981 92612 69
34	0.59359 27597 85	0.55931 00001 89	0.82895 85777 88	0.99980 94737 26
35	0.61105 13703 67	0.57369 36971 45	0.81906 99248 88	0.99979 95472 50
36	0.62850 99809 49	0.58790 24621 88	0.80893 18234 27	0.99978 94939 40
37	0.64596 85915 31	0.60193 19699 55	0.79854 73708 84	0.99977 93260 47
38	0.66342 72021 13	0.61577 79501 69	0.78791 97396 22	0.99976 90559 64
39	0.68088 58126 95	0.62943 61889 30	0.77705 21758 96	0.99975 86961 96
40	0.69834 44232 77	0.64290 25299 94	0.76594 79988 40	0.99974 82593 96
41	0.71580 30338 58	0.65617 28760 22	0.75461 05994 31	0.99973 77582 53
42	0.73326 16444 40	0.66924 31898 18	0.74304 34394 32	0.99972 72055 73
43	0.75072 02550 22	0.68210 94955 44	0.73125 00503 17	0.99971 66142 14
44	0.76817 88656 04	0.69476 78799 15	0.71923 40321 74	0.99970 59970 80
45	0.78563 74761 86	0.70721 44933 79	0.70699 90525 84	0.99969 53671 09

q = 0.00007 61698 24679 77407
q' = 0.35316 56482 96037 1

D(90) = 1.00030 47257 20529
1/D(90) = 0.99969 53671 08948

r	ϕ	$E(\phi,k)$	A(r)	D(r)
0	0.00000 00000 00	0.00000 00000 00	0.00000 00000 00	1.00000 00000 00
1	0.01745 86095 02	0.01745 86084 22	0.01745 24060 32	1.00000 00928 15
2	0.03491 72125 24	0.03491 72038 84	0.03489 94958 94	1.00000 03711 48
3	0.05237 58025 96	0.05237 57734 45	0.05233 59550 32	1.00000 08346 60
4	0.06983 43732 60	0.06983 43041 93	0.06975 64721 33	1.00000 14827 85
5	0.08729 29180 87	0.08729 27832 64	0.08715 57407 40	1.00000 23147 34
6	0.10475 14306 74	0.10475 11978 57	0.10452 84608 68	1.00000 33294 94
7	0.12220 99046 60	0.12220 95352 49	0.12186 93406 19	1.00000 45258 28
8	0.13966 83337 32	0.13966 77828 13	0.13917 30977 93	1.00000 59022 79
9	0.15712 67116 30	0.15712 59280 30	0.15643 44614 99	1.00000 74571 69
10	0.17458 50321 57	0.17458 39585 08	0.17364 81737 59	1.00000 91886 05
11	0.19204 32891 87	0.19204 18619 91	0.19080 89911 10	1.00001 10944 76
12	0.20950 14766 68	0.20949 96263 83	0.20791 16862 01	1.00001 31724 61
13	0.22695 95886 38	0.22695 72397 54	0.22495 10493 88	1.00001 54200 29
14	0.24441 76192 22	0.24441 46903 61	0.24192 18903 14	1.00001 78344 40
15	0.26187 55626 48	0.26187 19666 56	0.25881 90394 98	1.00002 04127 53
16	0.27933 34132 48	0.27932 90573 08	0.27563 73499 06	1.00002 31518 27
17	0.29679 11654 69	0.29678 59512 09	0.29237 16985 18	1.00002 60483 24
18	0.31424 88138 76	0.31424 26374 94	0.30901 69878 88	1.00002 90987 17
19	0.33170 63531 61	0.33169 91055 49	0.32556 81477 02	1.00003 22992 88
20	0.34916 37781 51	0.34915 53450 28	0.34202 01363 17	1.00003 56461 38
21	0.36662 10838 10	0.36661 13458 62	0.35836 79422 97	1.00003 91351 89
22	0.38407 82652 49	0.38406 70982 74	0.37460 65859 42	1.00004 27621 91
23	0.40153 53177 30	0.40152 25927 92	0.39073 11208 06	1.00004 65227 24
24	0.41899 22366 70	0.41897 78202 56	0.40673 66351 98	1.00005 04122 07
25	0.43644 90176 54	0.43643 27718 32	0.42261 82536 85	1.00005 44259 02
26	0.45390 56564 29	0.45388 74390 25	0.43837 11385 71	1.00005 85589 17
27	0.47136 21489 21	0.47134 18136 83	0.45399 04913 75	1.00006 28062 18
28	0.48881 84912 30	0.48879 58880 14	0.46947 15542 92	1.00006 71626 30
29	0.50627 46796 42	0.50624 96545 92	0.48480 96116 40	1.00007 16228 45
30	0.52373 07106 28	0.52370 31063 64	0.49999 99912 97	1.00007 61814 30
31	0.54118 65808 54	0.54115 62366 64	0.51503 80661 28	1.00008 08328 30
32	0.55864 22871 79	0.55860 90392 15	0.52991 92553 89	1.00008 55713 78
33	0.57609 78266 64	0.57606 15081 43	0.54463 90261 25	1.00009 03913 02
34	0.59355 31965 71	0.59351 36379 77	0.55919 28945 51	1.00009 52867 28
35	0.61100 83943 71	0.61096 54236 62	0.57357 64274 19	1.00010 02516 93
36	0.62846 34177 43	0.62841 68605 63	0.58778 52433 64	1.00010 52801 47
37	0.64591 82645 81	0.64586 79444 68	0.60181 50142 44	1.00011 03659 64
38	0.66337 29329 91	0.66331 86715 97	0.61566 14664 53	1.00011 55029 48
39	0.68082 74212 99	0.68076 90386 04	0.62932 03822 29	1.00012 06848 40
40	0.69828 17280 49	0.69821 90425 82	0.64278 76009 33	1.00012 59053 27
41	0.71573 58520 06	0.71566 86810 68	0.65605 90203 18	1.00013 11580 49
42	0.73318 97921 60	0.73311 79520 43	0.66913 05977 83	1.00013 64366 05
43	0.75064 35477 21	0.75056 68539 35	0.68199 83515 97	1.00014 17345 64
44	0.76809 71181 29	0.76801 53856 24	0.69465 83621 17	1.00014 70454 73
45	0.78555 05030 46	0.78546 35464 39	0.70710 67729 82	1.00015 23628 60

7

K = 1.57127 49523 72225

K′ = 4.74271 72652 78886

E = 1.57031 79198 97448

E′ = 1.00258 40855 27552

r	u=(r/90)K=F(φ,k)	sn u	cn u	dn u
45	0.78563 74761 86	0.70721 44933 79	0.70699 90525 84	0.99969 53671 09
46	0.80309 60867 68	0.71944 55512 67	0.69454 88454 83	0.99968 47372 50
47	0.82055 46973 50	0.73145 73349 29	0.68188 72100 12	0.99967 41204 56
48	0.83801 33079 32	0.74324 61928 51	0.66901 80093 34	0.99966 35296 59
49	0.85547 19185 14	0.75480 85417 41	0.65594 51694 42	0.99965 29777 62
50	0.87293 05290 96	0.76614 08676 05	0.64267 26779 52	0.99964 24776 20
51	0.89038 91396 78	0.77723 97267 92	0.62920 45828 64	0.99963 20420 34
52	0.90784 77502 60	0.78810 17470 20	0.61554 49913 24	0.99962 16836 85
53	0.92530 63608 41	0.79872 36283 84	0.60169 80683 54	0.99961 14152 21
54	0.94276 49714 23	0.80910 21443 32	0.58766 80355 76	0.99960 12491 40
55	0.96022 35820 05	0.81923 41426 25	0.57345 91699 13	0.99959 11978 24
56	0.97768 21925 87	0.82911 65462 75	0.55907 58022 79	0.99958 12735 15
57	0.99514 08031 69	0.83874 63544 51	0.54452 23162 51	0.99957 14883 01
58	1.01259 94137 51	0.84812 06433 74	0.52980 31467 29	0.99956 18540 99
59	1.03005 80243 33	0.85723 65671 74	0.51492 27785 79	0.99955 23826 43
60	1.04751 66349 15	0.86609 13587 39	0.49988 57452 64	0.99954 30854 67
61	1.06497 52454 97	0.87468 23305 22	0.48469 66274 62	0.99953 39738 93
62	1.08243 38560 79	0.88300 68753 40	0.46936 00516 68	0.99952 50590 17
63	1.09989 24666 61	0.89106 24671 42	0.45388 06887 85	0.99951 63516 96
64	1.11735 10772 42	0.89884 66617 43	0.43826 32527 07	0.99950 78625 31
65	1.13480 96878 24	0.90635 70975 55	0.42251 24988 83	0.99949 96018 61
66	1.15226 82984 06	0.91359 14962 69	0.40663 32228 75	0.99949 15797 44
67	1.16972 69089 88	0.92054 76635 30	0.39063 02589 02	0.99948 38059 47
68	1.18718 55195 70	0.92722 34895 76	0.37450 84783 79	0.99947 62899 36
69	1.20464 41301 52	0.93361 69498 60	0.35827 27884 36	0.99946 90408 62
70	1.22210 27407 34	0.93972 61056 37	0.34192 81304 38	0.99946 20675 52
71	1.23956 13513 16	0.94554 91045 33	0.32547 94784 89	0.99945 53784 94
72	1.25701 99618 98	0.95108 41810 86	0.30893 18379 32	0.99944 89818 33
73	1.27447 85724 80	0.95632 96572 62	0.29229 02438 34	0.99944 28853 57
74	1.29193 71830 62	0.96128 39429 43	0.27555 97594 72	0.99943 70964 88
75	1.30939 57936 44	0.96594 55363 88	0.25874 54748 05	0.99943 16222 73
76	1.32685 44042 25	0.97031 30246 75	0.24185 25049 39	0.99942 64693 76
77	1.34431 30148 07	0.97438 50841 10	0.22488 59885 91	0.99942 16440 70
78	1.36177 16253 89	0.97816 04806 09	0.20785 10865 40	0.99941 71522 30
79	1.37923 02359 71	0.98163 80700 61	0.19075 29800 75	0.99941 29993 23
80	1.39668 88465 53	0.98481 67986 59	0.17359 68694 40	0.99940 91904 05
81	1.41414 74571 35	0.98769 57032 04	0.15638 79722 73	0.99940 57301 13
82	1.43160 60677 17	0.99027 39113 89	0.13913 15220 33	0.99940 26226 58
83	1.44906 46782 99	0.99255 06420 44	0.12183 27664 36	0.99939 98718 24
84	1.46652 32888 81	0.99452 52053 73	0.10449 69658 77	0.99939 74809 59
85	1.48398 18994 63	0.99619 70031 45	0.08712 93918 55	0.99939 54529 73
86	1.50144 05100 45	0.99756 55288 72	0.06973 53253 88	0.99939 37903 35
87	1.51889 91206 26	0.99863 03679 54	0.05232 00554 35	0.99939 24950 69
88	1.53635 77312 08	0.99939 11978 00	0.03488 88773 04	0.99939 15687 51
89	1.55381 63417 90	0.99984 77879 22	0.01744 70910 74	0.99939 10125 08
90	1.57127 49523 72	1.00000 00000 00	0.00000 00000 00	0.99939 08270 19

8

q = 0.00007 61698 24679 77407

q' = 0.35316 56482 96037 1

D(90) = 1.00030 47257 20529

1/D(90) = 0.99969 53671 08948

r	φ	E(φ,k)	A(r)	D(r)
45	0.78555 05030 46	0.78546 35464 39	0.70710 67729 82	1.00015 23628 60
46	0.80300 37023 60	0.80291 13361 63	0.71933 97922 83	1.00015 76802 47
47	0.82045 67161 86	0.82035 87550 28	0.73135 36937 25	1.00016 29911 56
48	0.83790 95448 67	0.83780 58037 22	0.74314 48177 56	1.00016 82891 16
49	0.85536 21889 67	0.85525 24833 81	0.75470 95726 84	1.00017 35676 72
50	0.87281 46492 79	0.87269 87955 90	0.76604 44357 74	1.00017 88203 93
51	0.89026 69268 19	0.89014 47423 84	0.77714 59543 14	1.00018 40408 80
52	0.90771 90228 23	0.90759 03262 41	0.78801 07466 75	1.00018 92227 72
53	0.92517 09387 51	0.92503 55500 83	0.79863 55033 35	1.00019 43597 56
54	0.94262 26762 82	0.94248 04172 69	0.80901 69878 88	1.00019 94455 73
55	0.96007 42373 11	0.95992 49315 92	0.81915 20380 35	1.00020 44740 28
56	0.97752 56239 49	0.97736 90972 75	0.82903 75665 39	1.00020 94389 92
57	0.99497 68385 19	0.99481 29189 66	0.83867 05621 72	1.00021 43344 19
58	1.01242 78835 54	1.01225 64017 33	0.84804 80906 30	1.00021 91543 42
59	1.02987 87617 93	1.02969 95510 53	0.85716 72954 25	1.00022 38928 90
60	1.04732 94761 78	1.04714 23728 13	0.86602 53987 60	1.00022 85442 90
61	1.06478 00298 51	1.06458 48732 95	0.87461 97023 69	1.00023 31028 75
62	1.08223 04261 50	1.08202 70591 76	0.88294 75883 43	1.00023 75630 90
63	1.09968 06686 03	1.09946 89375 12	0.89100 65199 26	1.00024 19195 03
64	1.11713 07609 28	1.11691 05157 37	0.89879 40422 91	1.00024 61668 04
65	1.13458 07070 24	1.13435 18016 47	0.90630 77832 80	1.00025 02998 19
66	1.15203 05109 68	1.15179 28033 95	0.91354 54541 35	1.00025 43135 13
67	1.16948 01770 10	1.16923 35294 81	0.92050 48501 91	1.00025 82029 96
68	1.18692 97095 70	1.18667 39887 38	0.92718 38515 47	1.00026 19635 30
69	1.20437 91132 28	1.20411 41903 27	0.93358 04237 15	1.00026 55905 31
70	1.22182 83927 21	1.22155 41437 19	0.93969 26182 35	1.00026 90795 83
71	1.23927 75529 39	1.23899 38586 90	0.94551 85732 73	1.00027 24264 33
72	1.25672 65989 17	1.25643 33453 03	0.95105 65141 88	1.00027 56270 04
73	1.27417 55358 27	1.27387 26139 01	0.95630 47540 66	1.00027 86773 96
74	1.29162 43689 76	1.29131 16750 93	0.96126 16942 43	1.00028 15738 94
75	1.30907 31037 96	1.30875 05397 37	0.96592 58247 87	1.00028 43129 68
76	1.32652 17458 39	1.32618 92189 33	0.97029 57249 58	1.00028 68912 81
77	1.34397 03007 70	1.34362 77240 06	0.97437 00636 41	1.00028 93056 92
78	1.36141 87743 61	1.36106 60664 92	0.97814 75997 53	1.00029 15532 59
79	1.37886 71724 82	1.37850 42581 26	0.98162 71826 18	1.00029 36312 44
80	1.39631 55010 95	1.39594 23108 24	0.98480 77523 23	1.00029 55371 16
81	1.41376 37662 46	1.41338 02366 75	0.98768 83400 34	1.00029 72685 51
82	1.43121 19740 59	1.43081 80479 18	0.99026 80682 96	1.00029 88234 42
83	1.44866 01307 28	1.44825 57569 34	0.99254 61512 99	1.00030 01998 92
84	1.46610 82425 09	1.46569 33762 28	0.99452 18951 16	1.00030 13962 26
85	1.48355 63157 13	1.48313 09184 14	0.99619 46979 16	1.00030 24109 86
86	1.50100 43566 97	1.50056 83961 99	0.99756 40501 47	1.00030 32429 36
87	1.51845 23718 58	1.51800 58223 69	0.99862 95346 91	1.00030 38910 61
88	1.53590 03676 24	1.53544 32097 73	0.99939 08269 91	1.00030 43545 72
89	1.55334 83504 47	1.55288 05713 07	0.99984 76951 49	1.00030 46329 05
90	1.57079 63267 95	1.57031 79198 97	1.00000 00000 00	1.00030 47257 21

K = 1.57187 36105 14009   E = 1.56972 01504 23979
K'= 4.33865 39759 99725   E'= 1.00525 85872 09152

r	u=(r/90)K=F(φ,k)	sn u	cn u	dn u
0	0.00000 00000 00	0.00000 00000 00	1.00000 00000 00	1.00000 00000 00
1	0.01746 52623 39	0.01746 43720 01	0.99984 74862 25	0.99999 95822 89
2	0.03493 05246 78	0.03492 34023 07	0.99938 99919 31	0.99999 83296 64
3	0.05239 57870 17	0.05237 17509 14	0.99862 76581 92	0.99999 62436 56
4	0.06986 10493 56	0.06980 40811 88	0.99756 07200 81	0.99999 33268 11
5	0.08732 63116 95	0.08721 50615 56	0.99618 95065 89	0.99998 95826 90
6	0.10479 15740 34	0.10459 93671 85	0.99451 44405 11	0.99998 50158 64
7	0.12225 68363 73	0.12195 16816 65	0.99253 60383 07	0.99997 96319 08
8	0.13972 20987 12	0.13926 66986 88	0.99025 49099 28	0.99997 34373 95
9	0.15718 73610 51	0.15653 91237 13	0.98767 17586 06	0.99996 64398 87
10	0.17465 26233 90	0.17376 36756 46	0.98478 73806 19	0.99995 86479 26
11	0.19211 78857 29	0.19093 50884 91	0.98160 26650 24	0.99995 00710 23
12	0.20958 31480 69	0.20804 81130 15	0.97811 85933 57	0.99994 07196 49
13	0.22704 84104 08	0.22509 75183 95	0.97433 62392 99	0.99993 06052 18
14	0.24451 36727 47	0.24207 80938 62	0.97025 67683 21	0.99991 97400 76
15	0.26197 89350 86	0.25898 46503 34	0.96588 14372 85	0.99990 81374 85
16	0.27944 41974 25	0.27581 20220 43	0.96121 15940 29	0.99989 58116 07
17	0.29690 94597 64	0.29255 50681 54	0.95624 86769 13	0.99988 27774 84
18	0.31437 47221 03	0.30920 86743 70	0.95099 42143 33	0.99986 90510 24
19	0.33183 99844 42	0.32576 77545 29	0.94544 98242 16	0.99985 46489 80
20	0.34930 52467 81	0.34222 72521 92	0.93961 72134 74	0.99983 95889 26
21	0.36677 05091 20	0.35858 21422 13	0.93349 81774 41	0.99982 38892 40
22	0.38423 57714 59	0.37482 74323 06	0.92709 45992 68	0.99980 75690 80
23	0.40170 10337 98	0.39095 81645 90	0.92040 84492 99	0.99979 06483 59
24	0.41916 62961 37	0.40696 94171 27	0.91344 17844 20	0.99977 31477 23
25	0.43663 15584 76	0.42285 63054 44	0.90619 67473 71	0.99975 50885 22
26	0.45409 68208 15	0.43861 39840 42	0.89867 55660 43	0.99973 64927 90
27	0.47156 20831 54	0.45423 76478 86	0.89088 05527 36	0.99971 73832 11
28	0.48902 73454 93	0.46972 25338 84	0.88281 41034 00	0.99969 77830 96
29	0.50649 26078 32	0.48506 39223 50	0.87447 86968 44	0.99967 77163 54
30	0.52395 78701 71	0.50025 71384 48	0.86587 68939 24	0.99965 72074 59
31	0.54142 31325 10	0.51529 75536 21	0.85701 13367 00	0.99963 62814 25
32	0.55888 83948 49	0.53018 05870 00	0.84788 47475 74	0.99961 49637 73
33	0.57635 36571 88	0.54490 17068 04	0.83849 99283 97	0.99959 32805 00
34	0.59381 89195 28	0.55945 64317 07	0.82885 97595 62	0.99957 12580 45
35	0.61128 41818 67	0.57384 03322 04	0.81896 71990 60	0.99954 89232 62
36	0.62874 94442 06	0.58804 90319 41	0.80882 52815 25	0.99952 63033 82
37	0.64621 47065 45	0.60207 82090 39	0.79843 71172 49	0.99950 34259 81
38	0.66367 99688 84	0.61592 35973 94	0.78780 58911 77	0.99948 03189 51
39	0.68114 52312 23	0.62958 09879 51	0.77693 48618 84	0.99945 70104 57
40	0.69861 04935 62	0.64304 62299 69	0.76582 73605 21	0.99943 35289 11
41	0.71607 57559 01	0.65631 52322 56	0.75448 67897 51	0.99940 99029 33
42	0.73354 10182 40	0.66938 39643 88	0.74291 66226 57	0.99938 61613 16
43	0.75100 62805 79	0.68224 84579 02	0.73112 04016 37	0.99936 23329 93
44	0.76847 15429 18	0.69490 48074 77	0.71910 17372 70	0.99933 84470 01
45	0.78593 68052 57	0.70734 91720 81	0.70686 43071 73	0.99931 45324 44

q = 0.00017 14256 42257 4727   D(90) = 1.00068 59377 43666
q' = 0.32040 03371 34866 4   1/D(90) = 0.99931 45324 44402

r	ϕ	$E(\phi,k)$	$A(r)$	$D(r)$
0	0.00000 00000 00	0.00000 00000 00	1.00000 00000 00	1.00000 00000 00
1	0.01746 52599 07	0.01746 52574 75	0.01745 24043 86	1.00000 02089 27
2	0.03493 05052 26	0.03493 04857 75	0.03489 94926 05	1.00000 08354 55
3	0.05239 57213 88	0.05239 56557 58	0.05233 59501 08	1.00000 18788 19
4	0.06986 08938 56	0.06986 07383 57	0.06975 64655 84	1.00000 33377 49
5	0.08732 60081 51	0.08732 57046 09	0.08715 57325 81	1.00000 52104 68
6	0.10479 10498 62	0.10479 05256 95	0.10452 84511 15	1.00000 74946 93
7	0.12225 60046 68	0.12225 51729 73	0.12186 93292 93	1.00001 01876 41
8	0.13972 08583 53	0.13971 96180 14	0.13917 30849 18	1.00001 32860 32
9	0.15718 55968 26	0.15718 38326 35	0.15643 44471 02	1.00001 67860 91
10	0.17465 02061 34	0.17464 77889 37	0.17364 81578 71	1.00002 06835 54
11	0.19211 46724 84	0.19211 14593 35	0.19080 89737 64	1.00002 49736 71
12	0.20957 89822 58	0.20957 48165 95	0.20791 16674 35	1.00002 96512 17
13	0.22704 31220 26	0.22703 78338 65	0.22495 10292 40	1.00003 47104 92
14	0.24450 70785 69	0.24450 04847 10	0.24192 18688 27	1.00004 01453 32
15	0.26197 08388 89	0.26196 27431 41	0.25881 90167 17	1.00004 59491 16
16	0.27943 43902 30	0.27942 45836 51	0.27563 73258 78	1.00005 21147 73
17	0.29689 77200 89	0.29688 59812 44	0.29237 16732 93	1.00005 86347 91
18	0.31436 08162 33	0.31434 69114 63	0.30901 69615 20	1.00006 55012 26
19	0.33182 36667 17	0.33180 73504 25	0.32556 81202 44	1.00007 27057 13
20	0.34928 62598 93	0.34926 72748 46	0.34202 01078 25	1.00008 02394 73
21	0.36674 85844 28	0.36672 66620 72	0.35836 79128 30	1.00008 80933 29
22	0.38421 06293 18	0.38418 54901 05	0.37460 65555 61	1.00009 62577 12
23	0.40167 23838 97	0.40164 37376 29	0.39073 10895 72	1.00010 47226 74
24	0.41913 38378 57	0.41910 13840 41	0.40673 66031 75	1.00011 34779 03
25	0.43659 49812 54	0.43655 84094 68	0.42261 82209 36	1.00012 25127 31
26	0.45405 58045 25	0.45401 47947 99	0.43837 11051 62	1.00013 18161 50
27	0.47151 62984 96	0.47147 05217 04	0.45399 04573 73	1.00014 13768 27
28	0.48897 64543 94	0.48892 55726 56	0.46947 15197 64	1.00015 11831 13
29	0.50643 62638 62	0.50637 99309 55	0.48480 95766 53	1.00016 12230 60
30	0.52389 57189 61	0.52383 35807 46	0.49999 99559 20	1.00017 14844 36
31	0.54135 48121 88	0.54128 65070 41	0.51503 80304 28	1.00018 19547 40
32	0.55881 35364 79	0.55873 86957 31	0.52991 92194 35	1.00019 26212 14
33	0.57627 18852 20	0.57619 01336 12	0.54463 89899 85	1.00020 34708 64
34	0.59372 98522 57	0.59364 08083 94	0.55919 28582 93	1.00021 44904 71
35	0.61118 74318 98	0.61109 07087 19	0.57357 63911 10	1.00022 56666 09
36	0.62864 46189 28	0.62853 98241 73	0.58778 52070 71	1.00023 69856 62
37	0.64610 13835 57	0.64598 81453 01	0.60181 49780 32	1.00024 84338 39
38	0.66355 77966 78	0.66343 56636 16	0.61566 14303 87	1.00025 99971 92
39	0.68101 37793 79	0.68088 23716 11	0.62932 03463 72	1.00027 16616 34
40	0.69846 93534 39	0.69832 82627 66	0.64278 75653 47	1.00028 34129 52
41	0.71592 45160 74	0.71577 33315 59	0.65605 89850 65	1.00029 52368 30
42	0.73337 92650 44	0.73321 75734 68	0.66913 05629 21	1.00030 71188 63
43	0.75083 35985 50	0.75066 09849 82	0.68199 83171 83	1.00031 90445 73
44	0.76828 75153 43	0.76810 35635 99	0.69465 83282 07	1.00033 09994 31
45	0.78574 10146 69	0.78554 53078 35	0.70710 67396 27	1.00034 29688 72

K = 1.57187 36105 14009   E = 1.56972 01504 23979
K'= 4.33865 39759 99725   E'= 1.00525 85872 09152

r	u=(r/90)K=F(ϕ,k)	sn u	cn u	dn u
45	0.78593 68052 57	0.70734 91720 81	0.70686 43071 73	0.99931 45324 44
46	0.80340 20675 96	0.71957 77761 06	0.69441 18548 34	0.99929 06184 60
47	0.82086 73299 35	0.73158 69104 72	0.68174 81884 28	0.99926 67341 82
48	0.83833 25922 74	0.74337 29337 21	0.66887 71796 16	0.99924 29087 07
49	0.85579 78546 13	0.75493 22730 71	0.65580 27623 27	0.99921 91710 57
50	0.87326 31169 52	0.76626 14254 65	0.64252 89315 23	0.99919 55501 46
51	0.89072 83792 91	0.77735 69585 84	0.62905 97419 50	0.99917 20747 43
52	0.90819 36416 30	0.78821 55118 41	0.61539 93068 67	0.99914 87734 37
53	0.92565 89039 69	0.79883 37973 58	0.60155 17967 72	0.99912 56746 06
54	0.94312 41663 08	0.80920 86009 03	0.58752 14380 98	0.99910 28063 75
55	0.96058 94286 47	0.81933 67828 24	0.57331 25119 10	0.99908 01965 91
56	0.97805 46909 86	0.82921 52789 42	0.55892 93525 74	0.99905 78727 80
57	0.99551 99533 26	0.83884 11014 31	0.54437 63464 28	0.99903 58621 21
58	1.01298 52156 65	0.84821 13396 67	0.52965 79304 23	0.99901 41914 09
59	1.03045 04780 04	0.85732 31610 58	0.51477 85907 68	0.99899 28870 24
60	1.04791 57403 43	0.86617 38118 46	0.49974 28615 52	0.99897 19748 96
61	1.06538 10026 82	0.87476 06178 86	0.48455 53233 59	0.99895 14804 80
62	1.08284 62650 21	0.88308 09854 01	0.46922 06018 74	0.99893 14287 18
63	1.10031 15273 60	0.89113 24017 14	0.45374 33664 70	0.99891 18440 13
64	1.11777 67896 99	0.89891 24359 51	0.43812 83287 95	0.99889 27501 96
65	1.13524 20520 38	0.90641 87397 24	0.42238 02413 43	0.99887 41705 04
66	1.15270 73143 77	0.91364 90477 87	0.40650 38960 19	0.99885 61275 42
67	1.17017 25767 16	0.92060 11786 66	0.39050 41226 91	0.99883 86432 63
68	1.18763 78390 55	0.92727 30352 70	0.37438 57877 38	0.99882 17389 40
69	1.20510 31013 94	0.93366 26054 72	0.35815 37925 86	0.99880 54351 38
70	1.22256 83637 33	0.93976 79626 63	0.34181 30722 39	0.99878 97516 91
71	1.24003 36260 72	0.94558 72662 89	0.32536 85938 00	0.99877 47076 77
72	1.25749 88884 11	0.95111 87623 61	0.30882 53549 92	0.99876 03213 96
73	1.27496 41507 50	0.95636 07839 30	0.29218 83826 58	0.99874 66103 45
74	1.29242 94130 89	0.96131 17515 56	0.27546 27312 72	0.99873 35912 03
75	1.30989 46754 28	0.96597 01737 34	0.25865 34814 31	0.99872 12798 03
76	1.32735 99377 67	0.97033 46473 05	0.24176 57383 48	0.99870 96911 18
77	1.34482 52001 06	0.97440 38578 43	0.22480 46303 38	0.99869 88392 43
78	1.36229 04624 45	0.97817 65800 08	0.20777 53073 00	0.99868 87373 73
79	1.37975 57247 85	0.98165 16778 88	0.19068 29391 92	0.99867 93977 95
80	1.39722 09871 24	0.98482 81053 04	0.17353 27145 05	0.99867 08318 65
81	1.41468 62494 63	0.98770 49060 94	0.15632 98387 32	0.99866 30499 99
82	1.43215 15118 02	0.99028 12143 77	0.13907 95328 32	0.99865 60616 61
83	1.44961 67741 41	0.99255 62547 84	0.12178 70316 93	0.99864 98753 47
84	1.46708 20364 80	0.99452 93426 74	0.10445 75825 94	0.99864 44985 79
85	1.48454 72988 19	0.99619 98843 12	0.08709 64436 56	0.99863 99378 96
86	1.50201 25611 58	0.99756 73770 37	0.06970 88823 02	0.99863 61988 42
87	1.51947 78234 97	0.99863 14093 95	0.05230 01737 07	0.99863 32859 65
88	1.53694 30858 36	0.99939 16612 50	0.03487 55992 52	0.99863 12028 04
89	1.55440 83481 75	0.99984 79038 73	0.01744 04449 71	0.99862 99518 94
90	1.57187 36105 14	1.00000 00000 00	0.00000 00000 00	0.99862 95347 55

12

q = 0.00017 14256 42257 4727   D(90) = 1.00068 59377 43666
q' = 0.32040 03371 34866 4   1/D(90) = 0.99931 45324 44402

r	ϕ	$E(\phi,k)$	A(r)	D(r)
45	0.78574 10146 69	0.78554 53078 35	0.70710 67396 27	1.00034 29688 72
46	0.80319 40962 83	0.80298 62172 20	0.71933 97595 36	1.00035 49383 13
47	0.82064 67604 50	0.82042 62923 04	0.73135 36616 33	1.00036 68931 71
48	0.83809 90079 44	0.83786 55346 51	0.74314 47863 66	1.00037 88188 81
49	0.85555 08400 43	0.85530 39468 40	0.75470 95420 39	1.00039 07009 13
50	0.87300 22585 37	0.87274 15324 62	0.76604 44059 14	1.00040 25247 91
51	0.89045 32657 13	0.89017 82961 12	0.77714 59252 78	1.00041 42761 10
52	0.90790 38643 65	0.90761 42433 88	0.78801 07184 97	1.00042 59405 51
53	0.92535 40577 80	0.92504 93808 81	0.79863 54760 47	1.00043 75039 05
54	0.94280 38497 41	0.94248 37161 68	0.80901 69615 20	1.00044 89520 82
55	0.96025 32445 18	0.95991 72578 01	0.81915 20126 11	1.00046 02711 35
56	0.97770 22468 68	0.97735 00153 00	0.82903 75420 82	1.00047 14472 73
57	0.99515 08620 22	0.99478 19991 36	0.83867 05387 03	1.00048 24668 79
58	1.01259 90956 83	1.01221 32207 24	0.84804 80681 63	1.00049 33165 29
59	1.03004 69540 21	1.02964 36924 04	0.85716 72739 75	1.00050 39830 04
60	1.04749 44436 60	1.04707 34274 30	0.86602 53783 35	1.00051 44533 08
61	1.06494 15716 75	1.06450 24399 50	0.87461 96829 75	1.00052 47146 84
62	1.08238 83455 79	1.08193 07449 90	0.88294 75699 84	1.00053 47546 31
63	1.09983 47733 17	1.09935 83584 39	0.89100 65026 02	1.00054 45609 17
64	1.11728 08632 55	1.11678 52970 24	0.89879 40259 96	1.00055 41215 93
65	1.13472 66241 71	1.13421 15782 93	0.90630 77680 09	1.00056 34250 13
66	1.15217 20652 43	1.15163 72205 93	0.91354 54398 77	1.00057 24598 41
67	1.16961 71960 37	1.16906 22430 47	0.92050 48369 33	1.00058 12150 69
68	1.18706 20264 97	1.18648 66655 31	0.92718 38392 73	1.00058 96800 32
69	1.20450 65669 34	1.20391 05086 52	0.93358 04124 04	1.00059 78444 14
70	1.22195 08280 10	1.22133 37937 18	0.93969 26078 65	1.00060 56982 70
71	1.23939 48207 27	1.23875 65427 16	0.94551 85638 19	1.00061 32320 31
72	1.25683 85564 13	1.25617 87782 83	0.95105 65056 20	1.00062 04365 18
73	1.27428 20467 12	1.27360 05236 82	0.95630 47463 54	1.00062 73029 53
74	1.29172 53035 62	1.29102 18027 68	0.96126 16873 54	1.00063 38229 71
75	1.30916 83391 87	1.30844 26399 66	0.96592 58186 83	1.00063 99886 28
76	1.32661 11660 80	1.32586 30602 34	0.97029 57196 01	1.00064 57924 12
77	1.34405 37969 88	1.34328 30890 37	0.97437 00589 89	1.00065 12272 52
78	1.36149 62448 97	1.36070 27523 17	0.97814 75957 64	1.00065 62865 27
79	1.37893 85230 13	1.37812 20764 58	0.98162 71792 47	1.00066 09640 72
80	1.39638 06447 51	1.39554 10882 55	0.98480 77495 22	1.00066 52541 90
81	1.41382 26237 15	1.41295 98148 85	0.98768 83377 54	1.00066 91516 52
82	1.43126 44736 84	1.43037 82838 67	0.99026 80664 87	1.00067 26517 11
83	1.44870 62085 92	1.44779 65230 37	0.99254 61499 09	1.00067 57501 02
84	1.46614 78425 13	1.46521 45605 07	0.99452 18940 91	1.00067 84430 51
85	1.48358 93896 45	1.48263 24246 34	0.99619 46972 02	1.00068 07272 76
86	1.50103 08642 91	1.50005 01439 87	0.99756 40496 89	1.00068 25999 94
87	1.51847 22808 43	1.51746 77473 09	0.99862 95344 33	1.00068 40589 24
88	1.53591 36537 62	1.53488 52634 83	0.99939 08268 76	1.00068 51022 89
89	1.55335 49975 62	1.55230 27215 02	0.99984 76951 21	1.00068 57288 16
90	1.57079 63267 95	1.56972 01504 24	1.00000 00000 00	1.00068 59377 44

13

K = 1.57271 24349 95227   E = 1.56888 37196 07763
K′= 4.05275 81695 49437   E′= 1.00864 79569 07096

r	u=(r/90)K=F(φ,k)	sn u	cn u	dn u
0	0.00000 00000 00	0.00000 00000 00	1.00000 00000 00	1.00000 00000 00
1	0.01747 45826 11	0.01747 36889 55	0.99984 73234 42	0.99999 92571 38
2	0.03494 91652 22	0.03494 20163 24	0.99938 93412 96	0.99999 70294 59
3	0.05242 37478 33	0.05239 96222 59	0.99862 61961 25	0.99999 33196 87
4	0.06989 83304 44	0.06984 11503 95	0.99755 81254 80	0.99998 81323 59
5	0.08737 29130 55	0.08726 12495 81	0.99618 54618 10	0.99998 14738 18
6	0.10484 74956 66	0.10465 45756 20	0.99450 86323 42	0.99997 33522 06
7	0.12232 20782 77	0.12201 57929 99	0.99252 81589 25	0.99996 37774 52
8	0.13979 66608 88	0.13933 95766 19	0.99024 46578 43	0.99995 27612 64
9	0.15727 12435 00	0.15662 06135 14	0.98765 88395 91	0.99994 03171 10
10	0.17474 58261 11	0.17385 36045 71	0.98477 15086 14	0.99992 64602 06
11	0.19222 04087 22	0.19103 32662 41	0.98158 35630 19	0.99991 12074 92
12	0.20969 49913 33	0.20815 43322 41	0.97809 59942 51	0.99989 45776 14
13	0.22716 95739 44	0.22521 15552 49	0.97430 98867 31	0.99987 65909 02
14	0.24464 41565 55	0.24219 97085 92	0.97022 64174 71	0.99985 72693 42
15	0.26211 87391 66	0.25911 35879 24	0.96584 68556 42	0.99983 66365 51
16	0.27959 33217 77	0.27594 80128 87	0.96117 25621 26	0.99981 47177 49
17	0.29706 79043 88	0.29269 78287 73	0.95620 49890 23	0.99979 15397 22
18	0.31454 24869 99	0.30935 79081 63	0.95094 56791 30	0.99976 71307 97
19	0.33201 70696 10	0.32592 31525 62	0.94539 62653 96	0.99974 15208 02
20	0.34949 16522 21	0.34238 84940 13	0.93955 84703 29	0.99971 47410 28
21	0.36696 62348 32	0.35874 88967 03	0.93343 41053 95	0.99968 68241 97
22	0.38444 08174 43	0.37499 93585 53	0.92702 50703 65	0.99965 78044 13
23	0.40191 54000 54	0.39113 49127 93	0.92033 33526 47	0.99962 77171 29
24	0.41938 99826 65	0.40715 06295 17	0.91336 10265 85	0.99959 65990 94
25	0.43686 45652 76	0.42304 16172 31	0.90611 02527 23	0.99956 44883 18
26	0.45433 91478 88	0.43880 30243 74	0.89858 32770 54	0.99953 14240 14
27	0.47181 37304 99	0.45443 00408 26	0.89078 24302 24	0.99949 74465 60
28	0.48928 83131 10	0.46991 78994 00	0.88271 01267 25	0.99946 25974 43
29	0.50676 28957 21	0.48526 18773 14	0.87436 88640 53	0.99942 69192 11
30	0.52423 74783 32	0.50045 72976 38	0.86576 12218 39	0.99939 04554 18
31	0.54171 20609 43	0.51549 95307 33	0.85688 98609 59	0.99935 32505 73
32	0.55918 66435 54	0.53038 39956 59	0.84775 75226 14	0.99931 53500 86
33	0.57666 12261 65	0.54510 61615 70	0.83836 70273 92	0.99927 68002 08
34	0.59413 58087 76	0.55966 15490 83	0.82872 12743 00	0.99923 76479 79
35	0.61161 03913 87	0.57404 57316 32	0.81882 32397 75	0.99919 79411 69
36	0.62908 49739 98	0.58825 43367 89	0.80867 59766 73	0.99915 77282 16
37	0.64655 95566 09	0.60228 30475 82	0.79828 26132 37	0.99911 70581 74
38	0.66403 41392 20	0.61612 76037 67	0.78764 63520 37	0.99907 59806 44
39	0.68150 87218 31	0.62978 38030 98	0.77677 04689 00	0.99903 45457 20
40	0.69898 33044 42	0.64324 75025 65	0.76565 83118 11	0.99899 28039 27
41	0.71645 78870 53	0.65651 46196 03	0.75431 32997 95	0.99895 08061 56
42	0.73393 24696 64	0.66958 11332 94	0.74273 89217 86	0.99890 86036 03
43	0.75140 70522 75	0.68244 30855 29	0.73093 87354 72	0.99886 62477 08
44	0.76888 16348 87	0.69509 65821 54	0.71891 63661 22	0.99882 37900 92
45	0.78635 62174 98	0.70753 77940 94	0.70667 55053 98	0.99878 12824 94

q = 0.00030 48651 48813 9401

q' = 0.29548 83855 58691 4

D(90) = 1.00122 02045 90964

1/D(90) = 0.99878 12824 93732

r	ϕ	$E(\phi,k)$	$A(r)$	$D(r)$
0	0.00000 00000 00	0.00000 00000 00	0.00000 00000 00	1.00000 00000 00
1	0.01747 45782 84	0.01747 45739 57	0.01745 23999 51	1.00000 03716 58
2	0.03494 91306 10	0.03494 90959 99	0.03489 94837 44	1.00000 14861 79
3	0.05242 36310 55	0.05242 35142 77	0.05233 59368 39	1.00000 33422 04
4	0.06989 80537 54	0.06989 77770 66	0.06975 64479 37	1.00000 59374 74
5	0.08737 23729 43	0.08737 18328 36	0.08715 57105 92	1.00000 92688 25
6	0.10484 65629 79	0.10484 56303 07	0.10452 84248 32	1.00001 33321 99
7	0.12232 05983 82	0.12231 91185 19	0.12186 92987 71	1.00001 81226 46
8	0.13979 44538 57	0.13979 22468 88	0.13917 30502 22	1.00002 36343 28
9	0.15726 81043 32	0.15726 49652 76	0.15643 44083 06	1.00002 98605 32
10	0.17474 15249 83	0.17473 72240 45	0.17364 81150 56	1.00003 67936 70
11	0.19221 46912 69	0.19220 89741 21	0.19080 89270 22	1.00004 44252 97
12	0.20968 75789 59	0.20968 01670 55	0.20791 16168 63	1.00005 27461 15
13	0.22716 01641 63	0.22715 07550 80	0.22495 09749 46	1.00006 17459 85
14	0.24463 24233 60	0.24462 06911 74	0.24192 18109 24	1.00007 14139 42
15	0.26210 43334 29	0.26208 99291 10	0.25881 89553 27	1.00008 17382 09
16	0.27957 58716 75	0.27955 84235 22	0.27563 72611 29	1.00009 27062 05
17	0.29704 70158 56	0.29702 61299 51	0.29237 16053 19	1.00010 43045 69
18	0.31451 77442 14	0.31449 30049 07	0.30901 68904 62	1.00011 65191 70
19	0.33198 80354 98	0.33195 90059 17	0.32556 80462 50	1.00012 93351 26
20	0.34945 78689 90	0.34942 40915 83	0.34202 00310 47	1.00014 27368 22
21	0.36692 72245 34	0.36688 82216 23	0.35836 78334 25	1.00015 67079 32
22	0.38439 60825 55	0.38435 13569 31	0.37460 64736 92	1.00017 12314 32
23	0.40186 44240 87	0.40181 34596 15	0.39073 10054 04	1.00018 62896 29
24	0.41933 22307 97	0.41927 44930 52	0.40673 65168 79	1.00020 18641 77
25	0.43679 94850 02	0.43673 44219 26	0.42261 81326 86	1.00021 79360 99
26	0.45426 61696 95	0.45419 32122 72	0.43837 10151 34	1.00023 44858 16
27	0.47173 22685 65	0.47165 08315 22	0.45399 03657 46	1.00025 14931 64
28	0.48919 77660 16	0.48910 72485 39	0.46947 14267 18	1.00026 89374 21
29	0.50666 26471 87	0.50656 24336 56	0.48480 94823 71	1.00028 67973 36
30	0.52412 68979 67	0.52401 63587 17	0.49999 98605 86	1.00030 50511 48
31	0.54159 05050 18	0.54146 89971 03	0.51503 79342 26	1.00032 36766 17
32	0.55905 34557 85	0.55892 03237 70	0.52991 91225 47	1.00034 26510 53
33	0.57651 57385 14	0.57637 03152 78	0.54463 88925 96	1.00036 19513 36
34	0.59397 73422 69	0.59381 89498 18	0.55919 27605 86	1.00038 15539 53
35	0.61143 82569 39	0.61126 62072 40	0.57357 62932 65	1.00040 14350 21
36	0.62889 84732 56	0.62871 20690 76	0.58778 51092 68	1.00042 15703 18
37	0.64635 79828 03	0.64615 65185 63	0.60181 48804 48	1.00044 19353 12
38	0.66381 67780 25	0.66359 95406 61	0.61566 13331 97	1.00046 25051 92
39	0.68127 48522 38	0.68104 11220 75	0.62932 02497 46	1.00048 32548 96
40	0.69873 21996 38	0.69848 12512 66	0.64278 74694 53	1.00050 41591 44
41	0.71618 88153 07	0.71591 99184 68	0.65605 88900 66	1.00052 51924 67
42	0.73364 46952 18	0.73335 71157 00	0.66913 04689 76	1.00054 63292 40
43	0.75109 98362 43	0.75079 28367 70	0.68199 82244 46	1.00056 75437 11
44	0.76855 42361 52	0.76822 70772 90	0.69465 82368 26	1.00058 88100 32
45	0.78600 78936 20	0.78565 98346 74	0.70710 66497 46	1.00061 01022 95

15

K = 1.57271 24349 95227
K' = 4.05275 81695 49437

E = 1.56888 37196 07763
E' = 1.00864 79569 07096

r	u=(r/90)K=F(ϕ,k)	sn u	cn u	dn u
45	0.78635 62174 98	0.70753 77940 94	0.70667 55053 98	0.99878 12824 94
46	0.80383 08001 09	0.71976 29584 44	0.69421 99101 52	0.99873 87767 04
47	0.82130 53827 20	0.73176 83795 50	0.68155 34012 03	0.99869 63245 07
48	0.83877 99653 31	0.74355 04300 47	0.66867 98620 99	0.99865 39776 13
49	0.85625 45479 42	0.75510 55518 92	0.65560 32378 67	0.99861 17876 00
50	0.87372 91305 53	0.76643 02573 56	0.64232 75337 47	0.99856 98058 47
51	0.89120 37131 64	0.77752 11300 02	0.62885 68139 09	0.99852 80834 71
52	0.90867 82957 75	0.78837 48256 36	0.61519 52001 63	0.99848 66712 71
53	0.92615 28783 86	0.79898 80732 25	0.60134 68706 53	0.99844 56196 59
54	0.94362 74609 97	0.80935 76758 07	0.58731 60585 35	0.99840 49786 02
55	0.96110 20436 08	0.81948 05113 56	0.57310 70506 52	0.99836 47975 63
56	0.97857 66262 19	0.82935 35336 43	0.55872 41861 91	0.99832 51254 37
57	0.99605 12088 30	0.83897 37730 50	0.54417 18553 30	0.99828 60104 95
58	1.01352 57914 41	0.84833 83373 84	0.52945 44978 79	0.99824 75003 25
59	1.03100 03740 52	0.85744 44126 41	0.51457 66019 07	0.99820 96417 73
60	1.04847 49566 63	0.86628 92637 66	0.49954 27023 62	0.99817 24808 87
61	1.06594 95392 75	0.87487 02353 78	0.48435 73796 79	0.99813 60628 62
62	1.08342 41218 86	0.88318 47524 69	0.46902 52583 88	0.99810 04319 84
63	1.10089 87044 97	0.89123 03210 87	0.45355 10057 04	0.99806 56315 76
64	1.11837 32871 08	0.89900 45289 87	0.43793 93301 14	0.99803 17039 49
65	1.13584 78697 19	0.90650 50462 61	0.42219 49799 60	0.99799 86903 48
66	1.15332 24523 30	0.91372 96259 43	0.40632 27420 09	0.99796 66309 02
67	1.17079 70349 41	0.92067 61045 91	0.39032 74400 24	0.99793 55645 77
68	1.18827 16175 52	0.92734 24028 42	0.37421 39333 20	0.99790 55291 28
69	1.20574 62001 63	0.93372 65259 50	0.35798 71153 24	0.99787 65610 53
70	1.22322 07827 74	0.93982 65642 89	0.34165 19121 23	0.99784 86955 53
71	1.24069 53653 85	0.94564 06938 44	0.32521 32810 12	0.99782 19664 82
72	1.25816 99479 96	0.95116 71766 72	0.30867 62090 30	0.99779 64063 13
73	1.27564 45306 07	0.95640 43613 41	0.29204 57115 03	0.99777 20460 98
74	1.29311 91132 18	0.96135 06833 45	0.27532 68305 72	0.99774 89154 25
75	1.31059 36958 29	0.96600 46654 95	0.25852 46337 22	0.99772 70423 90
76	1.32806 82784 40	0.97036 49182 94	0.24164 42123 13	0.99770 64535 59
77	1.34554 28610 51	0.97443 01402 76	0.22469 06800 93	0.99768 71739 34
78	1.36301 74436 63	0.97819 91183 36	0.20766 91717 29	0.99766 92269 30
79	1.38049 20262 74	0.98167 07280 25	0.19058 48413 12	0.99765 26343 40
80	1.39796 66088 85	0.98484 39338 34	0.17344 28608 81	0.99763 74163 10
81	1.41544 11914 96	0.98771 77894 43	0.15624 84189 28	0.99762 35913 19
82	1.43291 57741 07	0.99029 14379 60	0.13900 67189 16	0.99761 11761 51
83	1.45039 03567 18	0.99256 41121 26	0.12172 29777 77	0.99760 01858 81
84	1.46786 49393 29	0.99453 51345 09	0.10440 24244 28	0.99759 06338 50
85	1.48533 95219 40	0.99620 39176 65	0.08705 02982 72	0.99758 25316 55
86	1.50281 41045 51	0.99756 99642 82	0.06967 18477 03	0.99757 58891 32
87	1.52028 86871 62	0.99863 28673 05	0.05227 23286 09	0.99757 07143 44
88	1.53776 32697 73	0.99939 23100 32	0.03485 70028 72	0.99756 70135 74
89	1.55523 78523 84	0.99984 80661 92	0.01743 11368 76	0.99756 47913 13
90	1.57271 24349 95	1.00000 00000 00	0.00000 00000 00	0.99756 40502 60

q = 0.00030 48651 48813 9401   D(90) = 1.00122 02045 90964
q′= 0.29548 83855 58691 4   1/D(90) = 0.99878 12824 93732

r	ϕ	$E(\phi,k)$	A(r)	D(r)
45	0.78600 78936 20	0.78565 98346 74	0.70710 66497 46	1.00061 01022 95
46	0.80346 08082 25	0.80309 11081 44	0.71933 96712 90	1.00063 13945 58
47	0.82091 29804 52	0.82052 08987 31	0.73135 35751 54	1.00065 26608 80
48	0.83836 44116 90	0.83794 92092 71	0.74314 47017 77	1.00067 38753 51
49	0.85581 51042 30	0.85537 60444 02	0.75470 94594 58	1.00069 50121 24
50	0.87326 50612 61	0.87280 14105 59	0.76604 43254 49	1.00071 60454 47
51	0.89071 42868 71	0.89022 53159 65	0.77714 58470 32	1.00073 69496 95
52	0.90816 27860 36	0.90764 77706 20	0.78801 06425 64	1.00075 76993 99
53	0.92561 05646 18	0.92506 87862 89	0.79863 54025 12	1.00077 82692 79
54	0.94305 76293 54	0.94248 83764 87	0.80901 68904 62	1.00079 86342 73
55	0.96050 39878 53	0.95990 65564 62	0.81915 19440 99	1.00081 87695 70
56	0.97794 96485 81	0.97732 33431 77	0.82903 74761 78	1.00083 86506 38
57	0.99539 46208 53	0.99473 87552 87	0.83867 04754 58	1.00085 82532 55
58	1.01283 89148 23	1.01215 28131 18	0.84804 80076 21	1.00087 75535 38
59	1.03028 25414 70	1.02956 55386 41	0.85716 72161 70	1.00089 65279 74
60	1.04772 55125 84	1.04697 69554 44	0.86602 53232 94	1.00091 51534 43
61	1.06516 78407 52	1.06438 70887 07	0.87461 96307 14	1.00093 34072 55
62	1.08260 95393 44	1.08179 59651 63	0.88294 75205 11	1.00095 12671 69
63	1.10005 06224 95	1.09920 36130 76	0.89100 64559 15	1.00096 87114 27
64	1.11749 11050 89	1.11661 00621 97	0.89879 39820 87	1.00098 57187 75
65	1.13493 10027 38	1.13401 53437 31	0.90630 77268 57	1.00100 22684 92
66	1.15237 03317 67	1.15141 94903 01	0.91354 54014 56	1.00101 83404 14
67	1.16980 91091 92	1.16882 25359 06	0.92050 48012 06	1.00103 39149 62
68	1.18724 73527 00	1.18622 45158 80	0.92718 38061 95	1.00104 89731 59
69	1.20468 50806 24	1.20362 54668 46	0.93358 03819 23	1.00106 34966 59
70	1.22212 23119 26	1.22102 54266 78	0.93969 25799 20	1.00107 74677 69
71	1.23955 90661 71	1.23842 44344 47	0.94551 85383 40	1.00109 08694 65
72	1.25699 53635 04	1.25582 25303 82	0.95105 64825 32	1.00110 36854 21
73	1.27443 12246 23	1.27321 97558 13	0.95630 47255 72	1.00111 59000 22
74	1.29186 66707 59	1.29061 61531 25	0.96126 16687 87	1.00112 74983 86
75	1.30930 17236 44	1.30801 17657 07	0.96592 58022 34	1.00113 84663 82
76	1.32673 64054 91	1.32540 66378 97	0.97029 57051 64	1.00114 87906 49
77	1.34417 07389 59	1.34280 08149 29	0.97437 00464 55	1.00115 84586 06
78	1.36160 47471 35	1.36019 43428 81	0.97814 75850 14	1.00116 74584 76
79	1.37903 84534 98	1.37758 72686 13	0.98162 71701 61	1.00117 57792 93
80	1.39647 18818 94	1.39497 96397 16	0.98480 77419 72	1.00118 34109 20
81	1.41390 50565 07	1.41237 15044 52	0.98768 83316 09	1.00119 03440 59
82	1.43133 80018 29	1.42976 29116 95	0.99026 80616 11	1.00119 65702 63
83	1.44877 07426 30	1.44715 39108 74	0.99254 61461 61	1.00120 20819 45
84	1.46620 33039 28	1.46454 45519 10	0.99452 18913 28	1.00120 68723 92
85	1.48363 57109 62	1.48193 48851 57	0.99619 46952 78	1.00121 09357 66
86	1.50106 79891 53	1.49932 49613 44	0.99756 40484 55	1.00121 42671 17
87	1.51850 01640 82	1.51671 48315 08	0.99862 95337 38	1.00121 68623 87
88	1.53593 22614 55	1.53410 45469 36	0.99939 08265 67	1.00121 87184 12
89	1.55336 43070 72	1.55149 41591 03	0.99984 76950 43	1.00121 98329 33
90	1.57079 63267 95	1.56888 37196 08	1.00000 00000 00	1.00122 02045 91

ELLIPTIC FUNCTIONS TABLE $\theta = 5°$

K = 1.57379 21309 24768
K' = 3.83174 19997 84146

E = 1.56780 90739 77622
E' = 1.01266 35062 34396

r	u=(r/90)K=F(ϕ,k)	sn u	cn u	dn u
0	0.00000 00000 00	0.00000 00000 00	1.00000 00000 00	1.00000 00000 00
1	0.01748 65792 32	0.01748 56813 02	0.99984 71137 88	0.99999 88387 46
2	0.03497 31584 65	0.03496 59753 86	0.99938 85033 19	0.99999 53564 05
3	0.05245 97376 97	0.05243 54968 41	0.99862 43130 78	0.99998 95572 46
4	0.06994 63169 30	0.06988 88638 73	0.99755 47838 12	0.99998 14483 73
5	0.08743 28961 62	0.08732 07001 10	0.99618 02524 30	0.99997 10397 22
6	0.10491 94753 95	0.10472 56364 05	0.99450 11518 74	0.99995 83440 46
7	0.12240 60546 27	0.12209 83126 34	0.99251 80109 46	0.99994 33769 00
8	0.13989 26338 60	0.13943 33794 88	0.99023 14540 98	0.99992 61566 21
9	0.15737 92130 92	0.15672 55002 64	0.98764 22011 88	0.99990 67043 04
10	0.17486 57923 25	0.17396 93526 42	0.98475 10671 95	0.99988 50437 79
11	0.19235 23715 57	0.19115 96304 59	0.98155 89618 98	0.99986 12015 79
12	0.20983 89507 90	0.20829 10454 72	0.97806 68895 20	0.99983 52069 06
13	0.22732 55300 22	0.22535 83291 12	0.97427 59483 33	0.99980 70915 99
14	0.24481 21092 55	0.24235 62342 28	0.97018 73302 26	0.99977 68900 89
15	0.26229 86884 87	0.25927 95368 14	0.96580 23202 44	0.99974 46393 59
16	0.27978 52677 20	0.27612 30377 32	0.96112 22960 86	0.99971 03788 98
17	0.29727 18469 52	0.29288 15644 14	0.95614 87275 66	0.99967 41506 53
18	0.31475 84261 85	0.30954 99725 54	0.95088 31760 48	0.99963 59989 72
19	0.33224 50054 17	0.32612 31477 83	0.94532 72938 41	0.99959 59705 57
20	0.34973 15846 50	0.34259 60073 26	0.93948 28235 60	0.99955 41143 98
21	0.36721 81638 82	0.35896 35016 50	0.93335 15974 61	0.99951 04817 16
22	0.38470 47431 15	0.37522 06160 83	0.92693 55367 37	0.99946 51259 02
23	0.40219 13223 47	0.39136 23724 25	0.92023 66507 86	0.99941 81024 44
24	0.41967 79015 80	0.40738 38305 35	0.91325 70364 46	0.99936 94688 66
25	0.43716 44808 12	0.42328 00898 96	0.90599 88772 05	0.99931 92846 51
26	0.45465 10600 45	0.43904 62911 69	0.89846 44423 74	0.99926 76111 70
27	0.47213 76392 77	0.45467 76177 12	0.89065 60862 37	0.99921 45116 05
28	0.48962 42185 10	0.47016 92970 94	0.88257 62471 71	0.99916 00508 73
29	0.50711 07977 42	0.48551 66025 71	0.87422 74467 37	0.99910 42955 43
30	0.52459 73769 75	0.50071 48545 51	0.86561 22887 48	0.99904 73137 55
31	0.54208 39562 07	0.51575 94220 30	0.85673 34583 10	0.99898 91751 38
32	0.55957 05354 40	0.53064 57240 07	0.84759 37208 32	0.99892 99507 19
33	0.57705 71146 72	0.54536 92308 73	0.83819 59210 21	0.99886 97128 43
34	0.59454 36939 05	0.55992 54657 79	0.82854 29818 50	0.99880 85350 77
35	0.61203 02731 37	0.57431 00059 72	0.81863 79034 96	0.99874 64921 22
36	0.62951 68523 70	0.58851 84841 17	0.80848 37622 69	0.99868 36597 22
37	0.64700 34316 02	0.60254 65895 82	0.79808 37095 09	0.99862 01145 73
38	0.66449 00108 35	0.61639 00697 07	0.78744 09704 65	0.99855 59342 22
39	0.68197 65900 67	0.63004 47310 39	0.77655 88431 60	0.99849 11969 79
40	0.69946 31693 00	0.64350 64405 47	0.76544 06972 29	0.99842 59818 17
41	0.71694 97485 32	0.65677 11268 06	0.75408 99727 44	0.99836 03682 77
42	0.73443 63277 65	0.66983 47811 60	0.74251 01790 20	0.99829 44363 70
43	0.75192 29069 97	0.68269 34588 51	0.73070 48934 02	0.99822 82664 79
44	0.76940 94862 30	0.69534 32801 28	0.71867 77600 43	0.99816 19392 63
45	0.78689 60654 62	0.70778 04313 26	0.70643 24886 58	0.99809 55355 53

18

q = 0.00047 65699 16866 8574　　　　　　D(90) = 1.00190 80983 52013
q' = 0.27517 98048 73562 8　　　　　　　1/D(90) = 0.99809 55355 53459

r	ϕ	$E(\phi,k)$	$A(r)$	$D(r)$
0	0.00000 00000 00	0.00000 00000 00	0.00000 00000 00	1.00000 00000 00
1	0.01748 65724 63	0.01748 65656 94	0.01745 23905 87	1.00000 05811 81
2	0.03497 31043 22	0.03497 30501 80	0.03489 94650 36	1.00000 23240 16
3	0.05245 95550 22	0.05245 93723 48	0.05233 59088 27	1.00000 52263 81
4	0.06994 58841 08	0.06994 54512 90	0.06975 64106 80	1.00000 92847 41
5	0.08743 20512 73	0.08743 12063 97	0.08715 56641 70	1.00001 44941 51
6	0.10491 80164 09	0.10491 65574 60	0.10452 83693 44	1.00002 08482 64
7	0.12240 37396 57	0.12240 14247 65	0.12186 92343 34	1.00002 83393 38
8	0.13988 91814 52	0.13988 57291 97	0.13917 29769 74	1.00003 69582 47
9	0.15737 43025 75	0.15736 93923 32	0.15643 43264 01	1.00004 66944 90
10	0.17485 90642 00	0.17485 23365 39	0.17364 80246 69	1.00005 75362 05
11	0.19234 34279 40	0.19233 44850 70	0.19080 88283 42	1.00006 94701 84
12	0.20982 73558 99	0.20981 57621 56	0.20791 15101 00	1.00008 24818 85
13	0.22731 08107 09	0.22729 60931 04	0.22495 08603 23	1.00009 65554 57
14	0.24479 37555 87	0.24477 54043 84	0.24192 16886 82	1.00011 16737 53
15	0.26227 61543 71	0.26225 36237 20	0.25881 88257 23	1.00012 78183 53
16	0.27975 79715 69	0.27973 06801 82	0.27563 71244 32	1.00014 49695 89
17	0.29723 91724 01	0.29720 65042 70	0.29237 14618 15	1.00016 31065 63
18	0.31471 97228 41	0.31468 10279 99	0.30901 67404 48	1.00018 22071 79
19	0.33219 95896 60	0.33215 41849 84	0.32556 78900 37	1.00020 22481 66
20	0.34967 87404 66	0.34962 59105 21	0.34201 98689 56	1.00022 32051 06
21	0.36715 71438 46	0.36709 61416 66	0.35836 76657 89	1.00024 50524 68
22	0.38463 47688 86	0.38456 48173 10	0.37460 63008 52	1.00026 77636 32
23	0.40211 15862 49	0.40203 18782 57	0.39073 08277 13	1.00029 13109 30
24	0.41958 75671 70	0.41949 72672 93	0.40673 63346 95	1.00031 56656 72
25	0.43706 26840 10	0.43696 09292 58	0.42261 79463 76	1.00034 07981 87
26	0.45453 69101 88	0.45442 28111 12	0.43837 08250 71	1.00036 66778 53
27	0.47201 02202 12	0.47188 28619 99	0.45399 01723 07	1.00039 32731 40
28	0.48948 25897 09	0.48934 10333 12	0.46947 12302 85	1.00042 05516 47
29	0.50695 39954 57	0.50679 72787 46	0.48480 92833 29	1.00044 84801 38
30	0.52442 44154 11	0.52425 15543 59	0.49999 96593 22	1.00047 70245 88
31	0.54189 38287 31	0.54170 38186 24	0.51503 77311 28	1.00050 61502 18
32	0.55936 22158 09	0.55915 40324 77	0.52991 89180 04	1.00053 58215 44
33	0.57682 95582 86	0.57660 21593 67	0.54463 86869 95	1.00056 60024 17
34	0.59429 58390 83	0.59404 81652 96	0.55919 25543 12	1.00059 66560 64
35	0.61176 10424 16	0.61149 20188 66	0.57357 60867 01	1.00062 77451 40
36	0.62922 51538 17	0.62893 36913 08	0.58778 49027 93	1.00065 92317 67
37	0.64668 81601 49	0.64637 31565 24	0.60181 46744 35	1.00069 10775 84
38	0.66415 00496 27	0.66381 03911 14	0.61566 11280 14	1.00072 32437 91
39	0.68161 08118 27	0.68124 53744 03	0.62932 00457 55	1.00075 56911 99
40	0.69907 04376 99	0.69867 80884 67	0.64278 72670 07	1.00078 83802 75
41	0.71652 89195 82	0.71610 85181 53	0.65605 86895 09	1.00082 12711 94
42	0.73398 62512 08	0.73353 66510 98	0.66913 02706 44	1.00085 43238 82
43	0.75144 24277 13	0.75096 24777 40	0.68199 80286 63	1.00088 74980 70
44	0.76889 74456 39	0.76838 59913 31	0.69465 80439 07	1.00092 07533 40
45	0.78635 13029 43	0.78580 71879 43	0.70710 64599 92	1.00095 40491 76

K = 1.57379 21309 24768
K' = 3.83174 19997 84146

E = 1.56780 90739 77622
E' = 1.01266 35062 34396

r	u=(r/90)K=F(φ,k)	sn u	cn u	dn u
45	0.78689 60654 62	0.70778 04313 26	0.70643 24886 58	0.99809 55355 53
46	0.80438 26446 95	0.72000 11659 17	0.69397 28532 72	0.99802 91362 62
47	0.82186 92239 27	0.73200 18055 38	0.68130 26909 45	0.99796 28222 77
48	0.83935 58031 60	0.74377 87409 90	0.66842 59004 95	0.99789 66743 66
49	0.85684 23823 92	0.75532 84332 05	0.65534 64411 99	0.99783 07730 82
50	0.87432 89616 25	0.76664 74141 99	0.64206 83314 89	0.99776 51986 57
51	0.89181 55408 57	0.77773 22879 86	0.62859 56476 34	0.99770 00309 13
52	0.90930 21200 90	0.78857 97314 68	0.61493 25224 10	0.99763 53491 58
53	0.92678 86993 22	0.79918 64953 07	0.60108 31437 66	0.99757 12320 97
54	0.94427 52785 55	0.80954 94047 57	0.58705 17534 74	0.99750 77577 30
55	0.96176 18577 87	0.81966 53604 83	0.57284 26457 80	0.99744 50032 62
56	0.97924 84370 20	0.82953 13393 44	0.55846 01660 34	0.99738 30450 05
57	0.99673 50162 52	0.83914 43951 54	0.54390 87093 27	0.99732 19582 93
58	1.01422 15954 85	0.84850 16594 22	0.52919 27191 09	0.99726 18173 82
59	1.03170 81747 17	0.85760 03420 58	0.51431 66858 10	0.99720 26953 69
60	1.04919 47539 50	0.86643 77320 58	0.49928 51454 49	0.99714 46640 97
61	1.06668 13331 82	0.87501 11981 67	0.48410 26782 43	0.99708 77940 73
62	1.08416 79124 15	0.88331 81895 13	0.46877 39072 05	0.99703 21543 79
63	1.10165 44916 47	0.89135 62362 16	0.45330 34967 42	0.99697 78125 93
64	1.11914 10708 80	0.89912 29499 80	0.43769 61512 51	0.99692 48347 05
65	1.13662 76501 12	0.90661 60246 49	0.42195 66137 06	0.99687 32850 38
66	1.15411 42293 45	0.91383 32367 53	0.40608 96642 43	0.99682 32261 71
67	1.17160 08085 77	0.92077 24460 22	0.39010 01187 48	0.99677 47188 64
68	1.18908 73878 10	0.92743 15958 76	0.37399 28274 33	0.99672 78219 87
69	1.20657 39670 42	0.93380 87139 00	0.35777 26734 17	0.99668 25924 44
70	1.22406 05462 75	0.93990 19122 90	0.34144 45713 04	0.99663 90851 11
71	1.24154 71255 07	0.94570 93882 78	0.32501 34657 56	0.99659 73527 65
72	1.25903 37047 40	0.95122 94245 36	0.30848 43300 66	0.99655 74460 26
73	1.27652 02839 72	0.95646 03895 60	0.29186 21647 34	0.99651 94132 92
74	1.29400 68632 05	0.96140 07380 27	0.27515 19960 34	0.99648 33006 83
75	1.31149 34424 37	0.96604 90111 39	0.25835 88745 86	0.99644 91519 86
76	1.32898 00216 70	0.97040 38369 40	0.24148 78739 25	0.99641 70086 02
77	1.34646 66009 02	0.97446 39306 11	0.22454 40890 74	0.99638 69094 97
78	1.36395 31801 35	0.97822 80947 54	0.20753 26351 04	0.99635 88911 56
79	1.38143 97593 67	0.98169 52196 45	0.19045 86457 12	0.99633 29875 37
80	1.39892 63386 00	0.98486 42834 71	0.17332 72717 81	0.99630 92300 36
81	1.41641 29178 32	0.98773 43525 52	0.15614 36799 52	0.99628 76474 41
82	1.43389 94970 65	0.99030 45815 35	0.13891 30511 92	0.99626 82659 07
83	1.45138 60762 97	0.99257 42135 75	0.12164 05793 59	0.99625 11089 18
84	1.46887 26555 30	0.99454 25804 94	0.10433 14697 68	0.99623 61972 61
85	1.48635 92347 62	0.99620 91029 23	0.08699 09377 65	0.99622 35490 03
86	1.50384 58139 95	0.99757 32904 20	0.06962 42072 88	0.99621 31794 67
87	1.52133 23932 27	0.99863 47415 76	0.05223 65094 38	0.99620 51012 17
88	1.53881 89724 60	0.99939 31440 95	0.03483 30810 44	0.99619 93240 38
89	1.55630 55516 92	0.99984 82748 66	0.01741 91632 34	0.99619 58549 29
90	1.57379 21309 25	1.00000 00000 00	0.00000 00000 00	0.99619 46980 92

20

q = 0.00047 65699 16866 8574

q' = 0.27517 98048 73562 8

D(90) = 1.00190 80983 52013

1/D(90) = 0.99809 55355 53459

r	ϕ	$E(\phi,k)$	A(r)	D(r)
45	0.78635 13029 43	0.78580 71879 43	0.70710 64599 92	1.00095 40491 76
46	0.80380 39989 93	0.80322 60664 72	0.71933 94849 91	1.00098 73450 12
47	0.82125 55345 75	0.82064 26286 39	0.73135 33925 84	1.00102 06002 82
48	0.83870 59118 87	0.83805 68789 84	0.74314 45231 98	1.00105 37744 70
49	0.85615 51345 37	0.85546 88248 63	0.75470 92851 16	1.00108 68271 58
50	0.87360 32075 40	0.87287 84764 36	0.76604 41555 76	1.00111 97180 77
51	0.89105 01373 11	0.89028 58466 53	0.77714 56818 43	1.00115 24071 53
52	0.90849 59316 55	0.90769 09512 39	0.78801 04822 57	1.00118 48545 61
53	0.92594 05997 59	0.92509 38086 72	0.79863 52472 70	1.00121 70207 68
54	0.94338 41521 81	0.94249 44401 60	0.80901 67404 48	1.00124 88665 85
55	0.96082 66008 37	0.95989 28696 15	0.81915 17994 61	1.00128 03532 12
56	0.97826 79589 82	0.97728 91236 22	0.82903 73370 44	1.00131 14422 88
57	0.99570 82412 00	0.99468 32314 07	0.83867 03419 38	1.00134 20959 35
58	1.01314 74633 83	1.01207 52247 97	0.84804 78798 08	1.00137 22768 07
59	1.03058 56427 10	1.02946 51381 86	0.85716 70941 37	1.00140 19481 33
60	1.04797 43162 60	1.04685 30084 88	0.86602 52070 94	1.00143 10737 64
61	1.06545 89478 29	1.06423 88750 93	0.87461 95203 83	1.00145 96182 13
62	1.08289 41142 25	1.08162 27798 19	0.88294 74160 65	1.00148 75467 05
63	1.10032 83189 24	1.09900 47668 57	0.89100 63573 53	1.00151 48252 11
64	1.11776 15852 01	1.11638 48827 23	0.89879 38893 87	1.00154 14204 99
65	1.13519 39374 71	1.13376 31761 95	0.90630 76399 80	1.00156 73001 65
66	1.15262 54012 58	1.15113 96982 58	0.91354 53203 43	1.00159 24326 80
67	1.17005 60031 66	1.16851 45020 36	0.92050 47257 81	1.00161 67874 22
68	1.18748 57708 43	1.18588 76427 33	0.92718 37363 63	1.00164 03347 20
69	1.20491 47329 50	1.20325 91775 63	0.93358 03175 73	1.00166 30458 84
70	1.22234 29191 26	1.22062 91656 78	0.93969 25209 23	1.00168 48932 46
71	1.23977 03599 52	1.23799 76681 02	0.94551 84845 52	1.00170 58501 86
72	1.25719 70869 12	1.25536 47476 51	0.95105 64337 89	1.00172 58911 73
73	1.27462 31323 55	1.27273 04688 59	0.95630 46816 99	1.00174 49917 89
74	1.29204 85294 59	1.29009 48979 00	0.96126 16295 90	1.00176 31287 63
75	1.30947 33121 86	1.30745 81025 08	0.96592 57675 06	1.00178 02799 99
76	1.32689 75152 43	1.32482 01518 93	0.97029 56746 86	1.00179 64245 99
77	1.34432 11740 41	1.34218 11166 59	0.97437 00199 92	1.00181 15428 95
78	1.36174 43246 50	1.35954 10687 19	0.97814 75623 21	1.00182 56164 67
79	1.37916 70037 56	1.37690 00812 06	0.98162 71509 80	1.00183 86281 68
80	1.39658 92486 17	1.39425 82283 87	0.98480 77260 34	1.00185 05621 47
81	1.41401 10970 16	1.41161 55855 70	0.98768 83186 37	1.00186 14038 62
82	1.43143 25872 18	1.42897 22290 18	0.99026 80513 16	1.00187 11401 05
83	1.44885 37579 21	1.44632 82358 51	0.99254 61382 49	1.00187 97590 14
84	1.46627 46482 09	1.46368 36839 59	0.99452 18854 96	1.00188 72500 88
85	1.48369 52975 10	1.48103 86519 04	0.99619 46912 17	1.00189 36042 01
86	1.50111 57455 38	1.49839 32188 26	0.99756 40458 50	1.00189 88136 11
87	1.51853 60322 56	1.51574 74643 48	0.99862 95322 70	1.00190 28719 71
88	1.53595 61978 20	1.53310 14684 80	0.99939 08259 13	1.00190 57743 36
89	1.55337 62825 32	1.55045 53115 25	0.99984 76948 80	1.00190 75171 71
90	1.57079 63267 95	1.56780 90739 78	1.00000 00000 00	1.00190 80983 52

K = 1.57511 36077 77251   E = 1.56649 67877 60132
K'= 3.65185 59694 78752   E'= 1.01723 69183 41019

r	u=(r/90)K=F(φ,k)	sn u	cn u	dn u
0	0.00000 00000 00	0.00000 00000 00	1.00000 00000 00	1.00000 00000 00
1	0.01750 12623 09	0.01750 03591 40	0.99984 68569 89	0.99999 83268 56
2	0.03500 25246 17	0.03499 52996 49	0.99938 74769 09	0.99999 33094 78
3	0.05250 37869 26	0.05247 94047 86	0.99862 20066 04	0.99998 49540 30
4	0.07000 50492 35	0.06994 72615 98	0.99755 06907 40	0.99997 32707 75
5	0.08750 63115 43	0.08739 34628 04	0.99617 38717 01	0.99995 82740 64
6	0.10500 75738 52	0.10481 26086 81	0.99449 19894 41	0.99993 99823 16
7	0.12250 88361 60	0.12219 93089 47	0.99250 55812 91	0.99991 84179 99
8	0.14001 00984 69	0.13954 81846 31	0.99021 52817 27	0.99989 36075 96
9	0.15751 13607 78	0.15685 38699 44	0.98762 18220 98	0.99986 55815 75
10	0.17501 26230 86	0.17411 10141 34	0.98472 60303 03	0.99983 43743 51
11	0.19251 38853 95	0.19131 42833 36	0.98152 88304 43	0.99980 00242 42
12	0.21001 51477 04	0.20845 83624 09	0.97803 12424 16	0.99976 25734 19
13	0.22751 64100 12	0.22553 79567 60	0.97423 43814 81	0.99972 20678 57
14	0.24501 76723 21	0.24254 77941 56	0.97013 94577 84	0.99967 85572 76
15	0.26251 89346 30	0.25948 26265 23	0.96574 77758 36	0.99963 20950 74
16	0.28002 01969 38	0.27633 72317 28	0.96106 07339 61	0.99958 27382 67
17	0.29752 14592 47	0.29310 64153 42	0.95607 98237 00	0.99953 05474 14
18	0.31502 27215 55	0.30978 50123 89	0.95080 66291 83	0.99947 55865 40
19	0.33252 39838 64	0.32636 78890 79	0.94524 28264 62	0.99941 79230 59
20	0.35002 52461 73	0.34284 99445 13	0.93939 01828 03	0.99935 76276 86
21	0.36752 65084 81	0.35922 61123 75	0.93325 05559 54	0.99929 47743 55
22	0.38502 77707 90	0.37549 13626 02	0.92682 58933 65	0.99922 94401 16
23	0.40252 90330 99	0.39164 07030 25	0.92011 82313 89	0.99916 17050 50
24	0.42003 02954 07	0.40766 91809 98	0.91312 96944 38	0.99909 16521 61
25	0.43753 15577 16	0.42357 18849 97	0.90586 24941 13	0.99901 93672 78
26	0.45503 28200 25	0.43934 39461 90	0.89831 89283 02	0.99894 49389 44
27	0.47253 40823 33	0.45498 05399 93	0.89050 13802 50	0.99886 84583 09
28	0.49003 53446 42	0.47047 68875 90	0.88241 23175 95	0.99879 00190 14
29	0.50753 66069 50	0.48582 82574 36	0.87405 42913 78	0.99870 97170 75
30	0.52503 78692 59	0.50102 99667 20	0.86542 99350 32	0.99862 76507 68
31	0.54253 91315 68	0.51607 73828 16	0.85654 19633 30	0.99854 39205 01
32	0.56004 03938 76	0.53096 59246 96	0.84739 31713 27	0.99845 86286 92
33	0.57754 16561 85	0.54569 10643 15	0.83798 64332 59	0.99837 18796 45
34	0.59504 29184 94	0.56024 83279 71	0.82832 47014 34	0.99828 37794 17
35	0.61254 41808 02	0.57463 32976 36	0.81841 10050 88	0.99819 44356 89
36	0.63004 54431 11	0.58884 16122 51	0.80824 84492 29	0.99810 39576 33
37	0.64754 67054 20	0.60286 89690 02	0.79784 02134 60	0.99801 24557 77
38	0.66504 79677 28	0.61671 11245 57	0.78718 95507 74	0.99792 00418 69
39	0.68254 92300 37	0.63036 38962 73	0.77629 97863 42	0.99782 68287 41
40	0.70005 04923 45	0.64382 31633 85	0.76517 43162 77	0.99773 29301 67
41	0.71755 17546 54	0.65708 48681 44	0.75381 66063 81	0.99763 84607 27
42	0.73505 30169 63	0.67014 50169 47	0.74223 01908 85	0.99754 35356 65
43	0.75255 42792 71	0.68299 96814 20	0.73041 86711 61	0.99744 82707 46
44	0.77005 55415 80	0.69564 49994 76	0.71838 57144 35	0.99735 27821 19
45	0.78755 68038 89	0.70807 71763 48	0.70613 50524 76	0.99725 71861 70

22

q = 0.00068 66451 27304 8341   D(90) = 1.00275 03575 48436
q′ = 0.25794 01957 66336 7   1/D(90) = 0.99725 71861 70284

r	ϕ	$E(\phi,k)$	$A(r)$	$D(r)$
0	0.00000 00000 00	0.00000 00000 00	0.00000 00000 00	1.00000 00000 00
1	0.01750 12525 48	0.01750 12427 86	0.01745 23735 33	1.00000 08377 22
2	0.03500 24465 43	0.03500 23684 69	0.03489 94309 65	1.00000 33498 66
3	0.05250 35235 05	0.05250 32600 87	0.05233 58578 12	1.00000 75333 73
4	0.07000 44250 99	0.07000 38009 73	0.06975 63428 29	1.00001 33831 45
5	0.08750 50932 02	0.08750 38748 90	0.08715 55796 27	1.00002 08920 56
6	0.10500 54699 80	0.10500 33661 83	0.10452 82682 89	1.00003 00509 56
7	0.12250 54979 56	0.12250 21599 16	0.12186 91169 82	1.00004 08486 87
8	0.14000 51200 83	0.14000 01420 16	0.13917 28435 74	1.00005 32720 93
9	0.15750 42798 11	0.15749 71994 16	0.15643 41772 36	1.00006 73060 40
10	0.17500 29211 57	0.17499 32201 94	0.17364 78600 54	1.00008 29334 28
11	0.19250 09887 77	0.19248 80937 09	0.19080 86486 27	1.00010 01352 17
12	0.20999 84280 29	0.20998 17107 41	0.20791 13156 62	1.00011 88904 51
13	0.22749 51850 43	0.22747 39636 24	0.22495 06515 71	1.00013 91762 79
14	0.24499 12067 88	0.24496 47463 77	0.24192 14660 55	1.00016 09679 86
15	0.26248 64411 34	0.26245 39548 39	0.25881 85896 87	1.00018 42390 21
16	0.27998 08369 17	0.27994 14867 94	0.27563 68754 80	1.00020 89610 33
17	0.29747 43440 03	0.29742 72420 99	0.29237 12004 65	1.00023 51039 01
18	0.31496 69133 48	0.31491 11228 02	0.30901 64672 43	1.00026 26357 75
19	0.33245 84970 58	0.33239 30332 71	0.32556 76055 40	1.00029 15231 12
20	0.34994 90484 48	0.34987 28803 04	0.34201 95737 55	1.00032 17307 16
21	0.36743 85321 00	0.36735 05732 44	0.35836 73604 89	1.00035 32217 84
22	0.38492 68739 14	0.38482 60240 94	0.37460 59860 76	1.00038 59579 49
23	0.40241 40611 69	0.40229 91476 22	0.39073 05041 01	1.00041 98993 27
24	0.41990 00425 70	0.41976 98614 64	0.40673 60029 02	1.00045 50045 67
25	0.43738 47782 97	0.43723 80862 25	0.42261 76070 68	1.00049 12308 97
26	0.45486 82300 61	0.45470 37455 77	0.43837 04789 27	1.00052 85341 81
27	0.47235 03611 41	0.47216 67663 50	0.45398 98200 15	1.00056 68689 71
28	0.48983 11364 36	0.48962 70786 21	0.46947 08725 40	1.00060 61885 62
29	0.50731 05225 02	0.50708 46158 00	0.48480 89208 33	1.00064 64450 49
30	0.52478 84876 00	0.52453 93147 09	0.49999 92927 78	1.00068 75893 86
31	0.54226 50017 24	0.54199 11156 56	0.51503 73612 44	1.00072 95714 45
32	0.55974 00366 48	0.55943 99625 10	0.52991 85454 88	1.00077 23400 77
33	0.57721 35659 53	0.57688 58027 68	0.54463 83125 51	1.00081 58431 75
34	0.59468 55650 60	0.59432 85876 15	0.55919 21786 43	1.00086 00277 38
35	0.61215 60112 63	0.61176 82719 83	0.57357 57105 05	1.00090 48399 32
36	0.62962 48837 51	0.62920 48146 07	0.58778 45267 57	1.00095 02251 62
37	0.64709 21636 37	0.64663 81780 68	0.60181 42992 42	1.00099 61281 32
38	0.66455 78339 81	0.66406 83288 43	0.61566 07543 33	1.00104 24929 18
39	0.68202 18798 06	0.68149 52373 38	0.62931 96742 44	1.00108 92630 29
40	0.69948 42881 19	0.69891 88779 26	0.64278 68983 09	1.00113 63814 85
41	0.71694 50479 25	0.71633 92289 77	0.65605 83242 53	1.00118 37908 79
42	0.73440 41502 42	0.73375 62728 76	0.66912 99094 40	1.00123 14334 49
43	0.75186 15881 07	0.75116 99960 50	0.68199 76721 03	1.00127 92511 51
44	0.76931 73565 88	0.76858 03889 76	0.69465 76925 62	1.00132 71857 26
45	0.78677 14527 89	0.78598 74461 96	0.70710 61144 11	1.00137 51787 73

K = 1.57511 36077 77251
K' = 3.65185 59694 78752

E = 1.56649 67877 60132
E' = 1.01723 69183 41019

r	u=(r/90)K=F(φ,k)	sn u	cn u	dn u
45	0.78755 68038 89	0.70807 71763 48	0.70613 50524 76	0.99725 71861 70
46	0.80505 80661 97	0.72029 24855 82	0.69367 04802 81	0.99716 15993 85
47	0.82255 93285 06	0.73228 72700 10	0.68099 58547 46	0.99706 61382 01
48	0.84006 05908 15	0.74405 79426 84	0.66811 50933 25	0.99697 09188 74
49	0.85756 18531 23	0.75560 09877 89	0.65503 21726 85	0.99687 60573 28
50	0.87506 31154 32	0.76691 29615 16	0.64175 11273 52	0.99678 16690 20
51	0.89256 43777 40	0.77799 04929 22	0.62827 60483 45	0.99668 78687 99
52	0.91006 56400 49	0.78883 02847 39	0.61461 10818 06	0.99659 47707 65
53	0.92756 69023 58	0.79942 91141 78	0.60076 04276 29	0.99650 24881 32
54	0.94506 81646 66	0.80978 38336 86	0.58672 83380 75	0.99641 11330 92
55	0.96256 94269 75	0.81989 13716 88	0.57251 91163 90	0.99632 08166 78
56	0.98007 06892 84	0.82974 87332 89	0.55813 71154 16	0.99623 16486 29
57	0.99757 19515 92	0.83935 30009 65	0.54358 67361 98	0.99614 37372 64
58	1.01507 32139 01	0.84870 13352 14	0.52887 24265 89	0.99605 71893 41
59	1.03257 44762 10	0.85779 09751 84	0.51399 86798 55	0.99597 21099 39
60	1.05007 57385 18	0.86661 92392 79	0.49897 00332 80	0.99588 86023 27
61	1.06757 70008 27	0.87518 35257 38	0.48379 10667 61	0.99580 67678 37
62	1.08507 82631 35	0.88348 13131 86	0.46846 64014 12	0.99572 67057 50
63	1.10257 95254 44	0.89151 01611 66	0.45300 06981 65	0.99564 85131 71
64	1.12008 07877 53	0.89926 77106 43	0.43739 86563 72	0.99557 22849 14
65	1.13758 20500 61	0.90675 16844 85	0.42166 50124 01	0.99549 81133 93
66	1.15508 33123 70	0.91395 98879 27	0.40580 45382 45	0.99542 60885 05
67	1.17258 45746 79	0.92089 02090 01	0.38982 20401 23	0.99535 62975 26
68	1.19008 58369 87	0.92754 06189 57	0.37372 23570 85	0.99528 88250 10
69	1.20758 70992 96	0.93390 91726 53	0.35751 03596 20	0.99522 37526 82
70	1.22508 83616 05	0.93999 40089 30	0.34119 09482 63	0.99516 11593 45
71	1.24258 96239 13	0.94579 33509 63	0.32476 90522 11	0.99510 11207 85
72	1.26009 08862 22	0.95130 55065 96	0.30824 96279 32	0.99504 37096 83
73	1.27759 21485 30	0.95652 88686 51	0.29163 76577 83	0.99498 89955 26
74	1.29509 34108 39	0.96146 19152 26	0.27493 81486 27	0.99493 70445 24
75	1.31259 46731 48	0.96610 32099 66	0.25815 61304 57	0.99488 79195 35
76	1.33009 59354 56	0.97045 14023 27	0.24129 66550 15	0.99484 16799 88
77	1.34759 71977 65	0.97450 52278 07	0.22436 47944 22	0.99479 83818 14
78	1.36509 84600 74	0.97826 35081 76	0.20736 56398 03	0.99475 80773 78
79	1.38259 97223 82	0.98172 51516 75	0.19030 42999 21	0.99472 08154 18
80	1.40010 09846 91	0.98488 91532 08	0.17318 58998 08	0.99468 66409 89
81	1.41760 22470 00	0.98775 45945 14	0.15601 55794 01	0.99465 55954 07
82	1.43510 35093 08	0.99032 06443 21	0.13879 84921 79	0.99462 77162 02
83	1.45260 47716 17	0.99258 65584 88	0.12153 98038 07	0.99460 30370 74
84	1.47010 60339 25	0.99455 16801 29	0.10424 46907 69	0.99458 15878 51
85	1.48760 72962 34	0.99621 54397 23	0.08691 83390 20	0.99456 33944 57
86	1.50510 85585 43	0.99757 73552 09	0.06956 59426 24	0.99454 84788 79
87	1.52260 98208 51	0.99863 70320 67	0.05219 27024 06	0.99453 68591 40
88	1.54011 10831 60	0.99939 41633 78	0.03480 38245 91	0.99452 85492 84
89	1.55761 23454 69	0.99984 85298 80	0.01740 45194 62	0.99452 35593 50
90	1.57511 36077 77	1.00000 00000 00	0.00000 00000 00	0.99452 18953 68

24

q = 0.00068 66451 27304 8341   D(90) = 1.00275 03575 48436
q′= 0.25794 01957 66336 7   1/D(90) = 0.99725 71861 70284

r	ϕ	$E(\phi,k)$	A(r)	D(r)
45	0.78677 14527 89	0.78598 74461 96	0.70710 61144 11	1.00137 51787 73
46	0.80422 38758 50	0.80339 11663 15	0.71933 91457 01	1.00142 31718 20
47	0.82167 46269 51	0.82079 15520 05	0.73135 30600 87	1.00147 11063 95
48	0.83912 37093 09	0.83818 86099 98	0.74314 41979 69	1.00151 89240 97
49	0.85657 11281 69	0.85558 23510 76	0.75470 89676 04	1.00156 65666 68
50	0.87401 68908 06	0.87297 27900 54	0.76604 38462 03	1.00161 39760 61
51	0.89146 10065 08	0.89035 99457 61	0.77714 53809 99	1.00166 10945 17
52	0.90890 34865 66	0.90774 38410 16	0.78801 01903 06	1.00170 78646 29
53	0.92634 43442 62	0.92512 45025 95	0.79863 49645 42	1.00175 42294 14
54	0.94378 35948 50	0.94250 19611 98	0.80901 64672 43	1.00180 01323 85
55	0.96122 12555 37	0.95987 62514 11	0.81915 15360 46	1.00184 55176 15
56	0.97865 73454 62	0.97724 74116 58	0.82903 70836 53	1.00189 03298 09
57	0.99609 18856 74	0.99461 54841 56	0.83867 00987 72	1.00193 45143 72
58	1.01352 48991 02	1.01198 05148 62	0.84804 76470 34	1.00197 80174 70
59	1.03095 64105 31	1.02934 25534 13	0.85716 68718 88	1.00202 07861 02
60	1.04838 64465 68	1.04670 16530 64	0.86602 49954 70	1.00206 27681 61
61	1.06581 50356 11	1.06405 78706 24	0.87461 93194 48	1.00210 39124 98
62	1.08324 22078 14	1.08141 12663 83	0.88294 72258 49	1.00214 41689 85
63	1.10066 79950 48	1.09876 19040 42	0.89100 61778 51	1.00218 34885 76
64	1.11809 24308 66	1.11610 98506 29	0.89879 37205 61	1.00222 18233 67
65	1.13551 55504 58	1.13345 51764 17	0.90630 74817 58	1.00225 91266 51
66	1.15293 73906 10	1.15079 79548 44	0.91354 51726 19	1.00229 53529 81
67	1.17035 79896 58	1.16813 82624 16	0.92050 45884 15	1.00233 04582 20
68	1.18777 73874 43	1.18547 61786 16	0.92718 36091 86	1.00236 43995 99
69	1.20519 56252 59	1.20281 17858 08	0.93358 02003 80	1.00239 71357 64
70	1.22261 27458 08	1.22014 51691 35	0.93969 24134 79	1.00242 86268 32
71	1.24002 87931 42	1.23747 64164 18	0.94551 83865 92	1.00245 88344 36
72	1.25744 38126 14	1.25480 56180 45	0.95105 63450 20	1.00248 77217 73
73	1.27485 78508 20	1.27213 28668 67	0.95630 46017 96	1.00251 52536 47
74	1.29227 09555 44	1.28945 82580 79	0.96126 15582 04	1.00254 13965 15
75	1.30968 31757 00	1.30678 18891 11	0.96592 57042 61	1.00256 61185 27
76	1.32709 45612 72	1.32410 38595 07	0.97029 56191 79	1.00258 93895 62
77	1.34450 51632 54	1.34142 42708 05	0.97436 99717 98	1.00261 11812 69
78	1.36191 50335 86	1.35874 32264 14	0.97814 75209 92	1.00263 14670 97
79	1.37932 42250 95	1.37606 08314 92	0.98162 71160 46	1.00265 02223 31
80	1.39673 27914 28	1.39337 71928 18	0.98480 76970 09	1.00266 74241 21
81	1.41414 07869 87	1.41069 24186 60	0.98768 82950 11	1.00268 30515 08
82	1.43154 82668 65	1.42800 66186 51	0.99026 80325 68	1.00269 70854 55
83	1.44895 52867 77	1.44531 99036 54	0.99254 61238 40	1.00270 95088 62
84	1.46636 19029 97	1.46263 23856 29	0.99452 18748 75	1.00272 03065 93
85	1.48376 81722 85	1.47994 41774 96	0.99619 46838 21	1.00272 94654 93
86	1.50117 41518 18	1.49725 53930 06	0.99756 40411 05	1.00273 69744 03
87	1.51857 98991 27	1.51456 61466 00	0.99862 95295 96	1.00274 28241 75
88	1.53598 54720 23	1.53187 65532 71	0.99939 08247 23	1.00274 70076 82
89	1.55339 09285 25	1.54918 67284 28	0.99984 76945 82	1.00274 95198 27
90	1.57079 63267 95	1.56649 67877 60	1.00000 00000 00	1.00275 03575 48

K = 1.57667 79815 92838   E = 1.56494 75629 69419
K'= 3.50042 24991 71838   E'= 1.02231 25881 67584

r	u=(r/90)K=F(ϕ,k)	sn u	cn u	dn u
0	0.00000 00000 00	0.00000 00000 00	1.00000 00000 00	1.00000 00000 00
1	0.01751 86442 40	0.01751 77348 61	0.99984 65527 10	0.99999 77211 52
2	0.03503 72884 80	0.03503 00138 44	0.99938 62607 27	0.99999 08874 16
3	0.05255 59327 20	0.05253 13830 66	0.99861 92736 94	0.99997 95072 11
4	0.07007 45769 60	0.07001 63926 27	0.99754 58409 33	0.99996 35945 57
5	0.08759 32212 00	0.08747 95986 01	0.99616 63113 30	0.99994 31690 58
6	0.10511 18654 40	0.10491 55650 17	0.99448 11331 63	0.99991 82558 76
7	0.12263 05096 79	0.12231 88658 40	0.99249 08538 92	0.99988 88856 97
8	0.14014 91539 19	0.13968 40869 39	0.99019 61198 95	0.99985 50946 97
9	0.15766 77981 59	0.15700 58280 49	0.98759 76761 61	0.99981 69244 91
10	0.17518 64423 99	0.17427 87047 19	0.98469 63659 33	0.99977 44220 84
11	0.19270 50866 39	0.19149 73502 56	0.98149 31303 10	0.99972 76398 08
12	0.21022 37308 79	0.20865 64176 44	0.97798 90077 99	0.99967 66352 59
13	0.22774 23751 19	0.22575 05814 56	0.97418 51338 28	0.99962 14712 19
14	0.24526 10193 59	0.24277 45397 49	0.97008 27402 08	0.99956 22155 82
15	0.26277 96635 99	0.25972 30159 41	0.96568 31545 55	0.99949 89412 64
16	0.28029 83078 39	0.27659 07606 66	0.96098 77996 70	0.99943 17261 12
17	0.29781 69520 79	0.29337 25536 12	0.95599 81928 79	0.99936 06528 05
18	0.31533 55963 19	0.31006 32053 40	0.95071 59453 25	0.99928 58087 52
19	0.33285 42405 58	0.32665 75590 74	0.94514 27612 27	0.99920 72859 75
20	0.35037 28847 98	0.34315 04924 72	0.93928 04370 99	0.99912 51810 02
21	0.36789 15290 38	0.35953 69193 74	0.93313 08609 23	0.99903 95947 35
22	0.38541 01732 78	0.37581 17915 19	0.92669 60112 98	0.99895 06323 32
23	0.40292 88175 18	0.39197 01002 35	0.91997 79565 41	0.99885 84030 70
24	0.42044 74617 58	0.40800 68781 11	0.91297 88537 60	0.99876 30202 06
25	0.43796 61059 98	0.42391 72006 30	0.90570 09478 91	0.99866 46008 38
26	0.45548 47502 38	0.43969 61877 73	0.89814 65706 99	0.99856 32657 58
27	0.47300 33944 78	0.45533 90056 02	0.89031 81397 55	0.99845 91392 98
28	0.49052 20387 18	0.47084 08678 04	0.88221 81573 77	0.99835 23491 75
29	0.50804 06829 58	0.48619 70372 02	0.87384 92095 42	0.99824 30263 33
30	0.52555 93271 98	0.50140 28272 43	0.86521 39647 70	0.99813 13047 76
31	0.54307 79714 38	0.51645 36034 45	0.85631 51729 87	0.99801 73214 07
32	0.56059 66156 77	0.53134 47848 15	0.84715 56643 56	0.99790 12158 49
33	0.57811 52599 17	0.54607 18452 28	0.83773 83480 83	0.99778 31302 77
34	0.59563 39041 57	0.56063 03147 84	0.82806 62112 08	0.99766 32092 42
35	0.61315 25483 97	0.57501 57811 15	0.81814 23173 68	0.99754 15994 86
36	0.63067 11926 37	0.58922 38906 69	0.80796 98055 41	0.99741 84497 66
37	0.64818 98368 77	0.60325 03499 54	0.79755 18887 70	0.99729 39106 65
38	0.66570 84811 17	0.61709 09267 53	0.78689 18528 74	0.99716 81344 11
39	0.68322 71253 57	0.63074 14512 94	0.77599 30551 36	0.99704 12746 84
40	0.70074 57695 97	0.64419 78173 94	0.76485 89229 82	0.99691 34864 31
41	0.71826 44138 37	0.65745 59835 63	0.75349 29526 39	0.99678 49256 71
42	0.73578 30580 77	0.67051 19740 80	0.74189 87077 87	0.99665 57493 09
43	0.75330 17023 17	0.68336 18800 21	0.73007 98181 94	0.99652 61149 38
44	0.77082 03465 56	0.69600 18602 69	0.71803 99783 45	0.99639 61806 48
45	0.78833 89907 96	0.70842 81424 76	0.70578 29460 59	0.99626 61048 34

q = 0.00093 52197 97815 9662   D(90) = 1.00374 78893 91977
q'= 0.24291 29743 06665 4   1/D(90) = 0.99626 61048 34106

r	ϕ	$E(\phi,k)$	A(r)	D(r)
0	0.00000 00000 00	0.00000 00000 00	0.00000 00000 00	1.00000 00000 00
1	0.01751 86309 32	0.01751 86176 24	0.01745 23453 98	1.00000 11415 56
2	0.03503 71820 36	0.03503 70755 92	0.03489 93747 54	1.00000 45648 35
3	0.05255 55735 81	0.05255 52144 47	0.05233 57736 45	1.00001 02656 65
4	0.07007 37260 35	0.07007 28751 29	0.06975 62308 86	1.00001 82371 01
5	0.08759 15601 59	0.08758 98991 75	0.08715 54401 46	1.00002 84694 31
6	0.10510 89971 06	0.10510 61289 13	0.10452 81015 66	1.00004 09501 88
7	0.12262 59585 18	0.12262 14076 61	0.12186 89233 73	1.00005 56641 66
8	0.14014 23666 25	0.14013 55799 22	0.13917 26234 88	1.00007 25934 39
9	0.15765 81443 36	0.15764 84915 74	0.15643 39311 41	1.00009 17173 81
10	0.17517 32153 36	0.17515 99900 67	0.17364 75884 70	1.00011 30126 93
11	0.19268 75041 83	0.19266 99246 07	0.19080 83521 28	1.00013 64534 29
12	0.21020 09363 96	0.21017 81463 48	0.20791 09948 73	1.00016 20110 31
13	0.22771 34385 49	0.22768 45085 71	0.22495 03071 68	1.00018 96543 60
14	0.24522 49383 60	0.24518 88668 72	0.24192 10987 61	1.00021 93497 37
15	0.26273 53647 82	0.26269 10793 36	0.25881 82002 70	1.00025 10609 83
16	0.28024 46480 87	0.28019 10067 15	0.27563 64647 54	1.00028 47494 63
17	0.29775 27199 55	0.29768 85125 98	0.29237 07692 85	1.00032 03741 33
18	0.31525 95135 54	0.31518 34635 82	0.30901 60165 03	1.00035 78915 89
19	0.33276 49636 27	0.33267 57294 33	0.32556 71361 73	1.00039 72561 23
20	0.35026 90065 65	0.35016 51832 49	0.34201 90867 26	1.00043 84197 74
21	0.36777 15804 91	0.36765 17016 14	0.35836 68567 98	1.00048 13323 91
22	0.38527 26253 32	0.38513 51647 49	0.37460 54667 53	1.00052 59416 91
23	0.40277 20828 95	0.40261 54566 61	0.39072 99702 00	1.00057 21933 26
24	0.42026 98969 35	0.42009 24652 81	0.40673 54550 02	1.00062 00309 44
25	0.43776 60132 25	0.43756 60826 05	0.42261 70472 71	1.00066 93962 62
26	0.45526 03796 22	0.45503 62048 19	0.43836 99078 52	1.00072 02291 38
27	0.47275 29461 31	0.47250 27324 32	0.45398 92387 96	1.00077 24676 38
28	0.49024 36649 66	0.48996 55703 92	0.46947 02823 26	1.00082 60481 18
29	0.50773 24906 03	0.50742 46281 99	0.48480 83227 78	1.00088 09052 99
30	0.52521 93798 44	0.52487 98200 20	0.49999 86880 47	1.00093 69723 46
31	0.54270 42918 61	0.54233 10647 84	0.51503 67510 03	1.00099 41809 49
32	0.56018 71882 49	0.55977 82862 86	0.52991 79309 03	1.00105 24614 08
33	0.57766 80330 72	0.57722 14132 71	0.54463 76947 87	1.00111 17427 18
34	0.59514 67929 06	0.59466 03795 24	0.55919 15588 58	1.00117 19526 55
35	0.61262 34368 79	0.61209 51239 44	0.57357 50898 48	1.00123 30178 60
36	0.63009 79367 05	0.62952 55906 17	0.58778 39063 67	1.00129 48639 36
37	0.64757 02667 24	0.64695 17288 80	0.60181 36802 41	1.00135 74155 32
38	0.66504 04039 28	0.66437 34933 79	0.61566 01378 27	1.00142 05964 40
39	0.68250 83279 85	0.68179 08441 24	0.62931 90613 18	1.00148 43296 83
40	0.69997 40212 73	0.69920 37465 29	0.64278 62900 25	1.00154 85376 12
41	0.71743 74688 88	0.71661 21714 54	0.65605 77216 47	1.00161 31419 99
42	0.73489 86586 71	0.73401 60952 33	0.66912 93135 19	1.00167 80641 34
43	0.75235 75812 17	0.75141 54997 03	0.68199 70838 43	1.00174 32249 19
44	0.76981 42298 86	0.76881 03722 18	0.69465 71129 06	1.00180 85449 66
45	0.78726 86008 12	0.78620 07056 64	0.70710 55442 65	1.00187 39446 93

27

K = 1.57667 79815 92838

K' = 3.50042 24991 71838

E = 1.56494 75629 69419

E' = 1.02231 25881 67584

r	u=(r/90)K=F(ϕ,k)	sn u	cn u	dn u
45	0.78833 89907 96	0.70842 81424 76	0.70578 29460 59	0.99626 61048 34
46	0.80585 76350 36	0.72063 70239 98	0.69331 25410 98	0.99613 60460 01
47	0.82337 62792 76	0.73262 48727 95	0.68063 26437 67	0.99600 61625 71
48	0.84089 49235 16	0.74438 81282 99	0.66774 71935 16	0.99587 66126 91
49	0.85841 35677 56	0.75592 33022 43	0.65466 01875 22	0.99574 75540 40
50	0.87593 22119 96	0.76722 69794 65	0.64137 56792 87	0.99561 91436 38
51	0.89345 08562 36	0.77829 58186 78	0.62789 77772 12	0.99549 15376 56
52	0.91096 95004 76	0.78912 65532 05	0.61423 06431 84	0.99536 48912 26
53	0.92848 81447 16	0.79971 59916 86	0.60037 84911 55	0.99523 93582 55
54	0.94600 67889 56	0.81006 10187 53	0.58634 55857 22	0.99511 50912 38
55	0.96352 54331 96	0.82015 85956 81	0.57213 62407 07	0.99499 22410 78
56	0.98104 40774 36	0.83000 57610 00	0.55775 48177 36	0.99487 09568 99
57	0.99856 27216 75	0.83959 96310 84	0.54320 57248 26	0.99475 13858 70
58	1.01608 13659 15	0.84893 74007 18	0.52849 34149 66	0.99463 36730 31
59	1.03360 00101 55	0.85801 63436 25	0.51362 23847 08	0.99451 79611 13
60	1.05111 86543 95	0.86683 38129 76	0.49859 71727 57	0.99440 43903 76
61	1.06863 72986 35	0.87538 72418 74	0.48342 23585 68	0.99429 30984 33
62	1.08615 59428 75	0.88367 41438 09	0.46810 25609 45	0.99418 42200 92
63	1.10367 45871 15	0.89169 21130 90	0.45264 24366 45	0.99407 78871 92
64	1.12119 32313 55	0.89943 88252 57	0.43704 66789 94	0.99397 42284 51
65	1.13871 18755 95	0.90691 20374 65	0.42132 00164 96	0.99387 33693 05
66	1.15623 05198 35	0.91410 95888 52	0.40546 72114 60	0.99377 54317 70
67	1.17374 91640 75	0.92102 94008 78	0.38949 30586 27	0.99368 05342 89
68	1.19126 78083 15	0.92766 94776 54	0.37340 23838 02	0.99358 87915 94
69	1.20878 64525 55	0.93402 79062 42	0.35720 00425 00	0.99350 03145 74
70	1.22630 50967 94	0.94010 28569 38	0.34089 09185 89	0.99341 52101 40
71	1.24382 37410 34	0.94589 25835 44	0.32447 99229 49	0.99333 35811 02
72	1.26134 23852 74	0.95139 54236 10	0.30797 19921 27	0.99325 55260 45
73	1.27886 10295 14	0.95660 97986 70	0.29137 20870 11	0.99318 11392 16
74	1.29637 96737 54	0.96153 42144 57	0.27468 51915 00	0.99311 05104 12
75	1.31389 83179 94	0.96616 72611 01	0.25791 63111 86	0.99304 37248 75
76	1.33141 69622 34	0.97050 76133 19	0.24107 04720 41	0.99298 08631 91
77	1.34893 56064 74	0.97455 40305 78	0.22415 27191 10	0.99292 20011 96
78	1.36645 42507 14	0.97830 53572 58	0.20716 81152 12	0.99286 72098 90
79	1.38397 28949 54	0.98176 05227 94	0.19012 17396 40	0.99281 65553 49
80	1.40149 15391 94	0.98491 85418 05	0.17301 86868 77	0.99277 00986 51
81	1.41901 01834 34	0.98777 85142 15	0.15586 40653 08	0.99272 78958 06
82	1.43652 88276 73	0.99033 96253 59	0.13866 29959 40	0.99268 99976 87
83	1.45404 74719 13	0.99260 11460 77	0.12142 06111 29	0.99265 64499 71
84	1.47156 61161 53	0.99456 24327 98	0.10414 20533 06	0.99262 72930 90
85	1.48908 47603 93	0.99622 29276 17	0.08683 24737 10	0.99260 25621 79
86	1.50660 34046 33	0.99758 21583 53	0.06949 70311 24	0.99258 22870 39
87	1.52412 20488 73	0.99863 97386 07	0.05214 08906 15	0.99256 64920 97
88	1.54164 06931 13	0.99939 53678 01	0.03476 92222 70	0.99255 51963 84
89	1.55915 93373 53	0.99984 88312 13	0.01738 71999 44	0.99254 84135 08
90	1.57667 79815 93	1.00000 00000 00	0.00000 00000 00	0.99254 61516 41

q = 0.00093 52197 97815 9662   D(90) = 1.00374 78893 91977
q′= 0.24291 29743 06665 4   1/D(90) = 0.99626 61048 34106

r	ϕ	$E(\phi,k)$	A(r)	D(r)
45	0.78726 86008 12	0.78620 07056 64	0.70710 55442 65	1.00187 39446 93
46	0.80472 06929 03	0.80358 64984 58	0.71933 85859 33	1.00193 93444 20
47	0.82217 05078 45	0.82096 77545 52	0.73135 25115 26	1.00200 46644 67
48	0.83961 80500 97	0.83834 44834 17	0.74314 36613 99	1.00206 98252 52
49	0.85706 33268 83	0.85571 67000 35	0.75470 84437 67	1.00213 47473 87
50	0.87450 63481 86	0.87308 44248 68	0.76604 33357 92	1.00219 93517 75
51	0.89194 71267 32	0.89044 76838 36	0.77714 48846 62	1.00226 35597 03
52	0.90938 56779 74	0.90780 65082 78	0.78800 97086 38	1.00232 72929 46
53	0.92682 20200 71	0.92516 09349 09	0.79863 44980 91	1.00239 04738 54
54	0.94425 61738 68	0.94251 10057 74	0.80901 60165 03	1.00245 30254 51
55	0.96168 81628 68	0.95985 67681 91	0.81915 11014 57	1.00251 48715 27
56	0.97911 80131 99	0.97719 82746 91	0.82903 66656 03	1.00257 59367 32
57	0.99654 57535 89	0.99453 55829 50	0.83866 96975 91	1.00263 61466 68
58	1.01397 14153 23	1.01186 87557 15	0.84804 72629 99	1.00269 54279 79
59	1.03139 50322 08	1.02919 78607 26	0.85716 65052 18	1.00275 37084 39
60	1.04881 66405 29	1.04652 29706 30	0.86602 46463 28	1.00281 09170 42
61	1.06623 62790 07	1.06384 41628 90	0.87461 89879 41	1.00286 69840 88
62	1.08365 39887 47	1.08116 15196 87	0.88294 69120 26	1.00292 18412 69
63	1.10106 98131 93	1.09847 51278 22	0.89100 58817 06	1.00297 54217 50
64	1.11848 37980 69	1.11578 50786 02	0.89879 34420 29	1.00302 76602 50
65	1.13589 59913 26	1.13309 14677 34	0.90630 72207 20	1.00307 84931 26
66	1.15330 64430 83	1.15039 43952 03	0.91354 49289 01	1.00312 78584 45
67	1.17071 52055 66	1.16769 39651 51	0.92050 43617 88	1.00317 56960 63
68	1.18812 23330 43	1.18499 02857 49	0.92718 33993 65	1.00322 19476 98
69	1.20552 78817 59	1.20228 34690 64	0.93358 00070 31	1.00326 65569 99
70	1.22293 19098 65	1.21957 36309 26	0.93969 22362 15	1.00330 94696 16
71	1.24033 44773 52	1.23686 08907 83	0.94551 82249 76	1.00335 06332 67
72	1.25773 56459 74	1.25414 53715 58	0.95105 61985 65	1.00338 99978 01
73	1.27513 54791 74	1.27142 71995 00	0.95630 44699 71	1.00342 75152 57
74	1.29253 40420 08	1.28870 65040 31	0.96126 14404 30	1.00346 31399 27
75	1.30993 14010 64	1.30598 34175 92	0.96592 55999 17	1.00349 68284 07
76	1.32732 76243 84	1.32325 80754 80	0.97029 55276 02	1.00352 85396 54
77	1.34472 27813 79	1.34053 06156 86	0.97436 98922 86	1.00355 82350 31
78	1.36211 69427 49	1.35780 11787 33	0.97814 74528 06	1.00358 58783 60
79	1.37951 01803 92	1.37506 99075 02	0.98162 70584 13	1.00361 14359 62
80	1.39690 25673 21	1.39233 69470 62	0.98480 76491 21	1.00363 48766 98
81	1.41429 41775 74	1.40960 24445 01	0.98768 82560 34	1.00365 61720 10
82	1.43168 50861 27	1.42686 65487 42	0.99026 80016 37	1.00367 52959 52
83	1.44907 53688 00	1.44412 94103 72	0.99254 61000 68	1.00369 22252 26
84	1.46646 51021 68	1.46139 11814 59	0.99452 18573 52	1.00370 69392 04
85	1.48385 43634 68	1.47865 20153 70	0.99619 46716 18	1.00371 94199 61
86	1.50124 32305 05	1.49591 20665 89	0.99756 40332 78	1.00372 96522 91
87	1.51863 17815 62	1.51317 14905 33	0.99862 95251 85	1.00373 76237 27
88	1.53592 00952 99	1.53043 04433 65	0.99939 08227 61	1.00374 33245 57
89	1.55340 82506 64	1.54768 90818 11	0.99984 76940 91	1.00374 67478 35
90	1.57079 63267 95	1.56494 75629 69	1.00000 00000 00	1.00374 78893 92

K = 1.57848 65776 88648   E = 1.56316 22295 18261
K′ = 3.36986 80266 68445   E′ = 1.02784 36197 40833

r	u=(r/90)K=F(φ,k)	sn u	cn u	dn u
0	0.00000 00000 00	0.00000 00000 00	1.00000 00000 00	1.00000 00000 00
1	0.01753 87397 52	0.01753 78231 79	0.99984 62005 52	0.99999 70212 60
2	0.03507 74795 04	0.03507 01473 42	0.99938 48531 80	0.99998 80887 21
3	0.05261 62192 56	0.05259 14755 83	0.99861 61107 73	0.99997 32134 28
4	0.07015 49590 08	0.07009 63152 12	0.99754 02280 58	0.99995 24137 67
5	0.08769 36987 60	0.08757 91798 62	0.99615 75614 60	0.99992 57154 51
6	0.10523 24385 13	0.10503 45915 85	0.99446 85689 20	0.99989 31514 79
7	0.12277 11782 65	0.12245 70829 42	0.99247 38096 48	0.99985 47620 97
8	0.14030 99180 17	0.13984 11990 89	0.99017 39438 29	0.99981 05947 46
9	0.15784 86577 69	0.15718 14998 42	0.98756 97322 76	0.99976 07040 02
10	0.17538 73975 21	0.17447 25617 41	0.98466 20360 30	0.99970 51515 03
11	0.19292 61372 73	0.19170 89800 86	0.98145 18159 11	0.99964 40058 71
12	0.21046 48770 25	0.20888 53709 70	0.97794 01320 10	0.99957 73426 24
13	0.22800 36167 77	0.22599 63732 85	0.97412 81431 42	0.99950 52440 79
14	0.24554 23565 29	0.24303 66507 11	0.97001 71062 47	0.99942 77992 47
15	0.26308 10962 81	0.26000 08936 85	0.96560 83757 31	0.99934 51037 16
16	0.28061 98360 34	0.27688 38213 46	0.96090 34027 81	0.99925 72595 33
17	0.29815 85757 86	0.29368 01834 55	0.95590 37346 12	0.99916 43750 68
18	0.31569 73155 38	0.31038 47622 88	0.95061 10136 85	0.99906 65648 80
19	0.33323 60552 90	0.32699 23745 11	0.94502 69768 70	0.99896 39495 68
20	0.35077 47950 42	0.34349 78730 10	0.93915 34545 74	0.99885 66556 19
21	0.36831 35347 94	0.35989 61487 07	0.93299 23698 22	0.99874 48152 44
22	0.38585 22745 46	0.37618 21323 38	0.92654 57373 00	0.99862 85662 11
23	0.40339 10142 98	0.39235 07961 96	0.91981 56623 61	0.99850 80516 72
24	0.42092 97540 50	0.40839 71558 49	0.91280 43399 85	0.99838 34199 76
25	0.43846 84938 02	0.42431 62718 13	0.90551 40537 15	0.99825 48244 86
26	0.45600 72335 54	0.44010 32512 01	0.89794 71745 50	0.99812 24233 82
27	0.47354 59733 07	0.45575 32493 32	0.89010 61598 05	0.99798 63794 62
28	0.49108 47130 59	0.47126 14712 95	0.88199 35519 45	0.99784 68599 35
29	0.50862 34528 11	0.48662 31734 89	0.87361 19773 81	0.99770 40362 11
30	0.52616 21925 63	0.50183 36651 16	0.86496 41452 43	0.99755 80836 87
31	0.54370 09323 15	0.51688 83096 37	0.85605 28461 26	0.99740 91815 21
32	0.56123 96720 67	0.53178 25261 92	0.84688 09508 05	0.99725 75124 15
33	0.57877 84118 19	0.54651 17909 72	0.83745 14089 36	0.99710 32623 81
34	0.59631 71515 71	0.56107 16385 65	0.82776 72477 20	0.99694 66205 08
35	0.61385 58913 23	0.57545 76632 47	0.81783 15705 64	0.99678 77787 28
36	0.63139 46310 75	0.58966 55202 40	0.80764 75557 08	0.99662 69315 78
37	0.64893 33708 28	0.60369 09269 31	0.79721 84548 43	0.99646 42759 55
38	0.66647 21105 80	0.61752 96640 46	0.78654 75917 09	0.99630 00108 73
39	0.68401 08503 32	0.63117 75767 85	0.77563 83606 83	0.99613 43372 17
40	0.70154 95900 84	0.64463 05759 21	0.76449 42253 47	0.99596 74574 95
41	0.71908 83298 36	0.65788 46388 45	0.75311 87170 50	0.99579 95755 85
42	0.73662 70695 88	0.67093 58105 93	0.74151 54334 63	0.99563 08964 88
43	0.75416 58093 40	0.68378 02048 10	0.72968 80371 16	0.99546 16260 73
44	0.77170 45490 92	0.69641 40046 92	0.71764 02539 36	0.99529 19708 27
45	0.78924 32888 44	0.70883 34638 79	0.70537 58717 77	0.99512 21376 00

q = 0.00122 24470 64293 800   D(90) = 1.00490 17725 72135
q' = 0.22956 71598 81194 2   1/D(90) = 0.99512 21375 99988

r	ϕ	$E(\phi,k)$	A(r)	D(r)
0	0.00000 00000 00	0.00000 00000 00	0.00000 00000 00	1.00000 00000 00
1	0.01753 87223 37	0.01753 87049 22	0.01745 23021 47	1.00000 14930 14
2	0.03507 73402 09	0.03507 72009 14	0.03489 92883 45	1.00000 59702 36
3	0.05261 57492 79	0.05261 52793 10	0.05233 56442 62	1.00001 34262 11
4	0.07015 38454 71	0.07015 27319 65	0.06975 60588 04	1.00002 38518 57
5	0.08769 15250 92	0.08768 93515 20	0.08715 52257 32	1.00003 72344 70
6	0.10522 86849 67	0.10522 49316 62	0.10452 78452 76	1.00005 35577 45
7	0.12276 52225 61	0.12275 92673 77	0.12186 86257 51	1.00007 28017 97
8	0.14030 10361 10	0.14029 21552 15	0.13917 22851 66	1.00009 49431 77
9	0.15783 60247 45	0.15782 33935 37	0.15643 35528 37	1.00011 99549 12
10	0.17537 00886 13	0.17535 27827 72	0.17364 71709 84	1.00014 78065 28
11	0.19290 31290 07	0.19288 01256 65	0.19080 78963 42	1.00017 84640 91
12	0.21033 80857 45	0.21040 52275 22	0.20791 05017 48	1.00021 18902 51
13	0.22796 57509 78	0.22792 78964 53	0.22494 97777 42	1.00024 80442 82
14	0.24549 51419 38	0.24544 79436 13	0.24192 05341 46	1.00028 68821 37
15	0.26302 31284 24	0.26296 51834 36	0.25881 76016 48	1.00032 83564 98
16	0.28054 96192 30	0.28047 94338 61	0.27563 58333 75	1.00037 24168 35
17	0.29807 45249 97	0.29799 05165 67	0.29237 01064 63	1.00041 90094 66
18	0.31559 77583 19	0.31549 82571 84	0.30901 53236 13	1.00046 80776 26
19	0.33311 92338 56	0.33300 24855 16	0.32556 64146 48	1.00051 95615 33
20	0.35063 88684 32	0.35050 30357 44	0.34201 83380 53	1.00057 33984 62
21	0.36815 65811 41	0.36799 97466 36	0.35836 60825 12	1.00062 95228 21
22	0.38567 22934 44	0.38549 24617 43	0.37460 46684 34	1.00068 78662 30
23	0.40318 59292 66	0.40298 10295 90	0.39072 91494 72	1.00074 83576 08
24	0.42069 74150 90	0.42046 53038 59	0.40673 46140 24	1.00081 09232 54
25	0.43820 66800 43	0.43794 51435 72	0.42261 61867 36	1.00087 54869 43
26	0.45571 36559 86	0.45542 04132 58	0.43836 90299 79	1.00094 19700 14
27	0.47321 82775 95	0.47289 09831 19	0.45398 83453 31	1.00101 02914 66
28	0.49072 04824 37	0.49035 67291 87	0.46946 93750 31	1.00108 03680 62
29	0.50822 02110 54	0.50781 75334 70	0.48480 74034 33	1.00115 21144 22
30	0.52571 74070 26	0.52527 32840 97	0.49999 77584 38	1.00122 54431 36
31	0.54321 20170 44	0.54272 38754 49	0.51503 58129 24	1.00130 02648 64
32	0.56070 39909 72	0.56016 92082 84	0.52991 69861 47	1.00137 64884 47
33	0.57819 32819 07	0.57760 91898 53	0.54463 67451 44	1.00145 40210 18
34	0.59567 98462 38	0.59504 37340 13	0.55919 06061 08	1.00153 27681 16
35	0.61316 36436 93	0.61247 27613 22	0.57357 41357 58	1.00161 26337 99
36	0.63064 46373 92	0.62989 61991 33	0.58778 29526 86	1.00169 35207 64
37	0.64812 27938 85	0.64731 39816 78	0.60181 27286 96	1.00177 53304 62
38	0.66559 80831 98	0.66472 60501 37	0.61565 91901 18	1.00185 79632 21
39	0.68307 04788 62	0.68213 23527 13	0.62931 81191 12	1.00194 13183 66
40	0.70053 99579 44	0.69953 28446 78	0.64278 53549 55	1.00202 52943 40
41	0.71795 80197 11	0.71692 74884 28	0.65605 67953 05	1.00210 97888 33
42	0.73547 00924 86	0.73431 62535 20	0.66912 83974 53	1.00219 46989 00
43	0.75293 07199 88	0.75169 91167 01	0.68199 61795 54	1.00227 99210 92
44	0.77038 83750 22	0.76907 60619 29	0.69465 62218 42	1.00236 53515 79
45	0.78784 30526 55	0.78644 70803 88	0.70710 46678 22	1.00245 08862 77

K = 1.57848 65776 88648   E = 1.56316 22295 18261
K'= 3.36986 80266 68445   E'= 1.02784 36197 40833

r	u=(r/90)K=F(ϕ,k)	sn u	cn u	dn u
45	0.78924 32888 44	0.70883 34638 79	0.70537 58717 77	0.99512 21376 00
46	0.80678 20285 96	0.72103 49073 14	0.69289 87389 47	0.99495 23333 52
47	0.82432 07683 49	0.73301 47320 64	0.68021 27627 28	0.99478 27649 04
48	0.84185 95081 01	0.74476 94081 00	0.66732 19078 97	0.99461 36386 83
49	0.85939 82478 53	0.75629 54790 45	0.65423 01952 49	0.99444 51604 73
50	0.87693 69876 05	0.76758 95628 85	0.64094 17001 17	0.99427 75351 64
51	0.89447 57273 57	0.77864 83526 41	0.62746 05508 95	0.99411 09665 07
52	0.91201 44671 09	0.78946 86170 08	0.61379 09275 63	0.99394 56568 65
53	0.92955 32068 61	0.80004 72009 68	0.59993 70602 18	0.99378 18069 72
54	0.94709 19466 13	0.81038 10263 57	0.58590 32276 07	0.99361 96156 91
55	0.96463 06863 65	0.82046 70924 11	0.57169 37556 69	0.99345 92797 73
56	0.98216 94261 17	0.83030 24762 73	0.55731 30160 82	0.99330 09936 25
57	0.99970 81658 69	0.83988 43334 80	0.54276 54248 15	0.99314 49490 77
58	1.01724 69056 22	0.84920 98984 09	0.52805 54406 92	0.99299 13351 50
59	1.03478 56453 74	0.85827 64847 02	0.51318 75639 64	0.99284 03378 35
60	1.05232 43851 26	0.86708 14856 68	0.49816 63348 84	0.99269 21398 72
61	1.06986 31248 78	0.87562 23746 46	0.48299 63323 05	0.99254 69205 30
62	1.08740 18646 30	0.88389 67053 55	0.46768 21722 74	0.99240 48553 96
63	1.10494 06043 82	0.89190 21122 16	0.45222 85066 47	0.99226 61161 72
64	1.12247 93441 34	0.89963 63106 51	0.43664 00217 09	0.99213 08704 66
65	1.14001 80838 86	0.90709 70973 58	0.42092 14368 08	0.99199 92815 98
66	1.15755 68236 38	0.91428 23505 69	0.40507 75030 01	0.99187 15084 09
67	1.17509 55633 90	0.92119 00302 87	0.38911 30017 11	0.99174 77050 72
68	1.19263 43031 43	0.92781 81785 00	0.37303 27433 94	0.99162 80209 16
69	1.21017 30428 95	0.93416 49193 89	0.35684 15662 22	0.99151 26002 43
70	1.22771 17826 47	0.94022 84595 00	0.34054 43347 74	0.99140 15821 70
71	1.24525 05223 99	0.94600 70879 22	0.32414 59387 40	0.99129 51004 59
72	1.26278 92621 51	0.95149 91764 33	0.30765 12916 38	0.99119 32833 63
73	1.28032 80019 03	0.95670 31796 42	0.29106 53295 44	0.99109 62534 81
74	1.29786 67416 55	0.96161 76351 13	0.27439 30098 23	0.99100 41276 10
75	1.31540 54814 07	0.96624 11634 79	0.25763 93098 88	0.99091 70166 13
76	1.33294 42211 59	0.97057 24685 44	0.24080 92259 53	0.99083 50252 89
77	1.35048 29609 11	0.97461 03373 77	0.22390 77718 11	0.99075 82522 53
78	1.36802 17006 63	0.97835 36403 92	0.20693 99776 07	0.99068 67898 21
79	1.38556 04404 16	0.98180 13314 21	0.18991 08886 31	0.99062 07239 03
80	1.40309 91801 68	0.98495 24477 79	0.17282 55641 21	0.99056 01339 08
81	1.42063 79199 20	0.98780 61103 25	0.15568 90760 64	0.99050 50926 46
82	1.43817 66596 72	0.99036 15235 05	0.13850 65080 13	0.99045 56662 48
83	1.45571 53994 24	0.99261 79754 02	0.12128 29539 11	0.99041 19140 92
84	1.47325 41391 76	0.99457 48377 71	0.10402 35169 19	0.99037 38887 27
85	1.49079 28789 28	0.99623 15660 73	0.08673 33082 49	0.99034 16358 23
86	1.50833 16186 80	0.99758 76994 98	0.06941 74460 06	0.99031 51941 11
87	1.52587 03584 32	0.99864 28609 92	0.05208 10540 31	0.99029 45953 39
88	1.54340 90981 84	0.99939 67572 73	0.03472 92607 49	0.99027 98642 41
89	1.56094 78379 37	0.99984 91788 43	0.01736 71980 22	0.99027 10185 02
90	1.57848 65776 89	1.00000 00000 00	0.00000 00000 00	0.99026 80687 42

32

q = 0.00122 24470 64293 800   D(90) = 1.00490 17725 72135
q′= 0.22956 71598 81194 2   1/D(90) = 0.99512 21375 99988

r	ϕ	$E(\phi,k)$	A(r)	D(r)
45	0.78784 30526 55	0.78644 70803 88	0.70710 46678 22	1.00245 08862 77
46	0.80529 47515 78	0.80381 21704 89	0.71933 77254 44	1.00253 64209 75
47	0.82274 34741 14	0.82117 13378 63	0.73135 16682 62	1.00262 18514 62
48	0.84018 92262 10	0.83852 45953 51	0.74314 28365 69	1.00270 70736 54
49	0.85763 20174 28	0.85587 19629 78	0.75470 76385 09	1.00279 19837 22
50	0.87507 18609 31	0.87321 34679 23	0.76604 25511 74	1.00287 64782 15
51	0.89250 87734 67	0.89054 91444 76	0.77714 41216 78	1.00296 04541 89
52	0.90994 27753 45	0.90787 90339 93	0.78800 89682 07	1.00304 38093 34
53	0.92737 38904 08	0.92520 31848 35	0.79863 37810 51	1.00312 64420 93
54	0.94480 21460 07	0.94252 16523 07	0.80901 53236 13	1.00320 82517 92
55	0.96222 75729 60	0.95983 44985 80	0.81915 04333 96	1.00328 91387 57
56	0.97965 02055 16	0.97714 17926 11	0.82903 60229 64	1.00336 90044 41
57	0.99707 00813 11	0.99444 36100 52	0.83866 90808 86	1.00344 77515 39
58	1.01448 72413 22	1.01174 00331 56	0.84804 66726 50	1.00352 52841 11
59	1.03190 17298 16	1.02903 11506 68	0.85716 59415 64	1.00360 15076 94
60	1.04931 35942 90	1.04631 70577 13	0.86602 41096 18	1.00367 63294 22
61	1.06672 28854 20	1.06359 78556 77	0.87461 84783 39	1.00374 96581 37
62	1.08412 96569 93	1.08087 36520 79	0.88294 64296 09	1.00382 14044 98
63	1.10153 39658 40	1.09814 45604 35	0.89100 54264 63	1.00389 14810 94
64	1.11893 58717 70	1.11541 07001 21	0.89879 30138 62	1.00395 98025 47
65	1.13633 54374 94	1.13267 21962 20	0.90630 68194 46	1.00402 62856 18
66	1.15373 27285 47	1.14992 91793 72	0.91354 45542 51	1.00409 08493 08
67	1.17112 78132 11	1.16718 17856 10	0.92050 40134 09	1.00415 34149 55
68	1.18852 07624 28	1.18443 01561 95	0.92718 30768 24	1.00421 39063 33
69	1.20591 16497 17	1.20167 44374 43	0.93357 97098 10	1.00427 22497 43
70	1.22330 05510 81	1.21891 47805 49	0.93969 19637 20	1.00432 83741 03
71	1.24068 75449 17	1.23615 13413 99	0.94551 79765 35	1.00438 22110 32
72	1.25807 27119 21	1.25338 42803 84	0.95105 59734 32	1.00443 36949 40
73	1.27545 61349 88	1.27061 37622 06	0.95630 42673 26	1.00448 27631 00
74	1.29283 78991 11	1.28783 99556 79	0.96126 12593 85	1.00452 93557 32
75	1.31021 80912 82	1.30506 30335 27	0.96592 54395 16	1.00457 34160 69
76	1.32759 68003 83	1.32228 31721 73	0.97029 53868 27	1.00461 48904 31
77	1.34497 41170 82	1.33950 05515 32	0.97436 97700 59	1.00465 37282 86
78	1.36235 01337 19	1.35671 53547 94	0.97814 73479 89	1.00468 98823 18
79	1.37972 49441 98	1.37392 77682 03	0.98162 69698 17	1.00472 33084 79
80	1.39709 86438 73	1.39113 79808 39	0.98480 75755 07	1.00475 39660 42
81	1.41447 13294 33	1.40834 61843 88	0.98768 81961 16	1.00478 18176 58
82	1.43184 30987 86	1.42555 25729 19	0.99026 79540 89	1.00480 68293 93
83	1.44921 40509 40	1.44275 73426 49	0.99254 60635 24	1.00482 89707 75
84	1.46658 42858 85	1.45996 06917 12	0.99452 18304 15	1.00484 82148 26
85	1.48395 39044 72	1.47716 28199 23	0.99619 46528 59	1.00486 45381 02
86	1.50132 30082 93	1.49436 39285 44	0.99756 40212 44	1.00487 79207 15
87	1.51869 16995 57	1.51156 42200 42	0.99862 95184 04	1.00488 83463 61
88	1.53606 00809 69	1.52876 38978 50	0.99939 08197 43	1.00489 58023 36
89	1.55342 82556 07	1.54596 31661 27	0.99984 76933 36	1.00490 02795 58
90	1.57079 63267 95	1.56316 22295 18	1.00000 00000 00	1.00490 17725 72

K = 1.58054 09338 95721   E = 1.56114 17453 51334
K'= 3.25530 29421 43555   E'= 1.03378 94623 90754

r	u=(r/90)K=F(φ,k)	sn u	cn u	dn u
0	0.00000 00000 00	0.00000 00000 00	1.00000 00000 00	1.00000 00000 00
1	0.01756 15659 32	0.01756 06411 71	0.99984 58000 52	0.99999 62267 43
2	0.03512 31318 64	0.03511 57342 22	0.99938 32524 16	0.99998 49116 53
3	0.05268 46977 97	0.05265 97332 78	0.99861 25136 86	0.99996 60687 73
4	0.07024 62637 29	0.07018 70969 45	0.99753 38447 50	0.99993 97214 86
5	0.08780 78296 61	0.08769 22905 49	0.99614 76106 37	0.99990 59024 86
6	0.10536 93955 93	0.10516 97883 68	0.99445 42803 04	0.99986 46537 34
7	0.12293 09615 25	0.12261 40758 46	0.99245 44263 61	0.99981 60264 04
8	0.14049 25274 57	0.14001 96518 08	0.99014 87247 42	0.99976 00808 17
9	0.15805 40933 90	0.15738 10306 52	0.98753 79543 04	0.99969 68863 58
10	0.17561 56593 22	0.17469 27445 33	0.98462 29963 84	0.99962 65213 93
11	0.19317 72252 54	0.19194 93455 22	0.98140 48342 83	0.99954 90731 59
12	0.21073 87911 86	0.20914 54077 54	0.97788 45527 03	0.99946 46376 55
13	0.22830 03571 18	0.22627 55295 42	0.97406 33371 25	0.99937 33195 16
14	0.24586 19230 50	0.24333 43354 85	0.96994 24731 26	0.99927 52318 75
15	0.26342 34889 83	0.26031 64785 29	0.96552 33456 56	0.99917 04962 19
16	0.28098 50549 15	0.27721 66420 22	0.96080 74382 45	0.99905 92422 28
17	0.29854 66208 47	0.29402 95417 22	0.95579 63321 73	0.99894 16076 09
18	0.31610 81867 79	0.31074 99277 88	0.95049 17055 82	0.99881 77379 19
19	0.33366 97527 11	0.32737 25867 27	0.94489 53325 42	0.99868 77863 71
20	0.35123 13186 43	0.34389 23433 13	0.93900 90820 70	0.99855 19136 43
21	0.36879 28845 76	0.36030 40624 75	0.93283 49171 01	0.99841 02876 66
22	0.38635 44505 08	0.37660 26511 35	0.92637 48934 19	0.99826 30834 09
23	0.40391 60164 40	0.39278 30600 19	0.91963 11585 42	0.99811 04826 55
24	0.42147 75823 72	0.40884 02854 24	0.91260 59505 69	0.99795 26737 65
25	0.43903 91483 04	0.42476 93709 46	0.90530 15969 87	0.99778 98514 40
26	0.45660 07142 37	0.44056 54091 60	0.89772 05134 40	0.99762 22164 69
27	0.47416 22801 69	0.45622 35432 71	0.88986 52024 69	0.99744 99754 74
28	0.49172 38461 01	0.47173 89687 03	0.88173 82522 08	0.99727 33406 47
29	0.50928 54120 33	0.48710 69346 61	0.87334 23350 58	0.99709 25294 77
30	0.52684 69779 65	0.50232 27456 36	0.86468 02063 29	0.99690 77644 78
31	0.54440 85438 97	0.51738 17628 68	0.85575 47028 51	0.99671 92729 06
32	0.56197 01098 30	0.53227 94057 67	0.84656 87415 66	0.99652 72864 68
33	0.57953 16757 62	0.54701 11532 80	0.83712 53180 90	0.99633 20410 35
34	0.59709 32416 94	0.56157 25452 17	0.82742 75052 59	0.99613 37763 41
35	0.61465 48076 26	0.57595 91835 25	0.81747 84516 51	0.99593 27356 85
36	0.63221 63735 58	0.59016 67335 23	0.80728 13800 92	0.99572 91656 24
37	0.64977 79394 90	0.60419 09250 79	0.79683 95861 48	0.99552 33156 64
38	0.66733 95054 23	0.61802 75537 48	0.78615 64366 01	0.99531 54379 52
39	0.68490 10713 55	0.63167 24818 58	0.77523 53679 13	0.99510 57869 60
40	0.70246 26372 87	0.64512 16395 57	0.76407 98846 82	0.99489 46191 68
41	0.72002 42032 19	0.65837 10258 02	0.75269 35580 86	0.99468 21927 51
42	0.73758 57691 51	0.67141 67093 11	0.74108 00243 28	0.99446 87672 54
43	0.75514 73350 84	0.68425 48294 70	0.72924 29830 64	0.99425 46032 79
44	0.77270 89010 16	0.69688 15971 84	0.71718 61958 42	0.99403 99621 58
45	0.79027 04669 48	0.70929 32957 03	0.70491 34845 29	0.99382 51056 37

q = 0.00154 85045 16579 192   D(90) = 1.00621 32605 90419
q'= 0.21754 89496 99726 3   1/D(90) = 0.99382 51056 37374

r	ϕ	$E(\phi,k)$	A(r)	D(r)
0	0.00000 00000 00	0.00000 00000 00	0.00000 00000 00	1.00000 00000 00
1	0.01756 15438 43	0.01756 15217 54	0.01745 22390 95	1.00000 18924 75
2	0.03512 29551 85	0.03512 27785 07	0.03489 91623 74	1.00000 75675 95
3	0.05268 41016 89	0.05268 35055 94	0.05233 54556 41	1.00001 70184 46
4	0.07024 48513 47	0.07024 34390 16	0.06975 58079 35	1.00003 02335 12
5	0.08780 50726 43	0.08780 23157 81	0.08715 49131 48	1.00004 71966 94
6	0.10536 46347 17	0.10535 98742 29	0.10452 74716 43	1.00006 78873 25
7	0.12292 34075 28	0.12291 58543 65	0.12186 81918 63	1.00009 22801 95
8	0.14048 12620 11	0.14046 99981 88	0.13917 17919 45	1.00012 03455 87
9	0.15803 80702 43	0.15802 20500 16	0.15643 30013 26	1.00015 20493 07
10	0.17559 37055 98	0.17557 17568 03	0.17364 65623 53	1.00018 73527 29
11	0.19314 80429 03	0.19311 88684 65	0.19080 72318 75	1.00022 62128 40
12	0.21070 09585 96	0.21066 31381 89	0.20790 97828 47	1.00026 85822 97
13	0.22825 23308 74	0.22820 43227 42	0.22494 90059 20	1.00031 44094 77
14	0.24580 20398 49	0.24574 21827 81	0.24191 97110 23	1.00036 36385 49
15	0.26334 99676 94	0.26327 64831 44	0.25881 67289 47	1.00041 62095 34
16	0.28089 59987 84	0.28080 69931 53	0.27563 49129 19	1.00047 20583 81
17	0.29844 00198 46	0.29833 34868 93	0.29236 91401 69	1.00053 11170 49
18	0.31598 19200 92	0.31585 57434 98	0.30901 43134 85	1.00059 33135 83
19	0.33352 15913 59	0.33337 35474 22	0.32556 53627 75	1.00065 85722 06
20	0.35105 89282 41	0.35088 66887 08	0.34201 72466 01	1.00072 68134 11
21	0.36859 38282 16	0.36839 49632 45	0.35836 49537 20	1.00079 79540 56
22	0.38612 61917 74	0.38589 81730 19	0.37460 35046 07	1.00087 19074 68
23	0.40365 59225 38	0.40339 61263 60	0.39072 79529 75	1.00094 85835 45
24	0.42118 29273 82	0.42088 86381 69	0.40673 33872 77	1.00102 78888 69
25	0.43870 71165 44	0.43837 55301 49	0.42261 49322 06	1.00110 97268 20
26	0.45622 84037 34	0.45585 66310 19	0.43836 77501 75	1.00119 39976 90
27	0.47374 67062 40	0.47333 17767 23	0.45398 70427 95	1.00128 05988 08
28	0.49126 19450 28	0.49080 08106 25	0.46946 80523 34	1.00136 94246 65
29	0.50877 40448 39	0.50826 35836 95	0.48480 60631 66	1.00146 03670 38
30	0.52628 29342 76	0.52571 99546 91	0.49999 64032 09	1.00155 33151 30
31	0.54378 85458 92	0.54316 97903 23	0.51503 44453 46	1.00164 81556 98
32	0.56129 08162 71	0.56061 29654 10	0.52991 56088 36	1.00174 47731 91
33	0.57878 96861 03	0.57804 93630 27	0.54463 53607 08	1.00184 30498 98
34	0.59628 51002 54	0.59547 88746 39	0.55918 92171 43	1.00194 28660 83
35	0.61377 70078 33	0.61290 14002 25	0.57357 27448 39	1.00204 41001 36
36	0.63126 53622 50	0.63031 68483 96	0.58778 15623 65	1.00214 66287 18
37	0.64875 01212 71	0.64772 51364 90	0.60181 13414 88	1.00225 03269 14
38	0.66623 12470 69	0.66512 61906 70	0.61565 78085 01	1.00235 50683 84
39	0.68370 87062 64	0.68251 99460 00	0.62931 67455 18	1.00246 07255 16
40	0.70118 24699 64	0.69990 63465 16	0.64278 39917 63	1.00256 71695 83
41	0.71865 25137 96	0.71728 53452 82	0.65605 54448 37	1.00267 42709 01
42	0.73611 88179 35	0.73465 69044 36	0.66912 70619 67	1.00278 18989 82
43	0.75358 13671 21	0.75202 09952 25	0.68199 48612 38	1.00288 99226 98
44	0.77104 01506 79	0.76937 75980 31	0.69465 49228 08	1.00299 82104 38
45	0.78849 51625 29	0.78672 67023 78	0.70710 33901 00	1.00310 66302 72

K = 1.58054 09338 95721   E = 1.56114 17453 51334
K' = 3.25530 29421 43555   E' = 1.03378 94623 90754

r	u=(r/90)K=F(ϕ,k)	sn u	cn u	dn u
45	0.79027 04669 48	0.70929 32957 03	0.70491 34845 29	0.99382 51056 37
46	0.80783 20328 80	0.72148 62813 81	0.69242 87297 47	0.99361 02955 57
47	0.82539 35988 12	0.73345 69844 17	0.67973 58692 98	0.99339 57935 30
48	0.84295 51647 44	0.74520 19095 32	0.66683 88966 09	0.99318 18606 25
49	0.86051 67306 77	0.75671 76366 20	0.65374 18591 68	0.99296 87570 50
50	0.87807 82966 09	0.76800 08213 54	0.64044 88569 74	0.99275 67418 36
51	0.89563 98625 41	0.77904 81957 52	0.62696 40409 91	0.99254 60725 26
52	0.91320 14284 73	0.78985 65687 06	0.61329 16116 11	0.99233 70048 67
53	0.93076 29944 05	0.80042 28264 77	0.59943 58171 27	0.99212 97924 96
54	0.94832 45603 37	0.81074 39331 51	0.58540 09522 19	0.99192 46866 45
55	0.96588 61262 70	0.82081 69310 63	0.57119 13564 47	0.99172 19358 35
56	0.98344 76922 02	0.83063 89411 85	0.55681 14127 66	0.99152 17855 81
57	1.00100 92581 34	0.84020 71634 88	0.54226 55460 41	0.99132 44781 02
58	1.01857 08240 66	0.84951 88772 67	0.52755 82215 90	0.99113 02520 34
59	1.03613 23899 98	0.85857 14414 41	0.51269 39437 34	0.99093 93421 44
60	1.05369 39559 30	0.86736 22948 27	0.49767 72543 64	0.99075 19790 58
61	1.07125 55218 63	0.87588 89563 81	0.48251 27315 32	0.99056 83889 87
62	1.08881 70877 95	0.88414 90254 18	0.46720 49880 43	0.99038 87934 62
63	1.10637 86537 27	0.89214 01818 13	0.45175 86700 82	0.99021 34090 74
64	1.12394 02196 59	0.89986 01861 71	0.43617 84558 46	0.99004 24472 21
65	1.14150 17855 91	0.90730 68799 81	0.42046 90542 00	0.98987 61138 63
66	1.15906 33515 24	0.91447 81857 50	0.40463 52033 47	0.98971 46092 80
67	1.17662 49174 56	0.92137 21071 20	0.38868 16695 21	0.98955 81278 42
68	1.19418 64833 88	0.92798 67289 65	0.37261 32456 92	0.98940 68577 81
69	1.21174 80493 20	0.93432 02174 75	0.35643 47502 95	0.98926 09809 78
70	1.22930 96152 52	0.94037 08202 25	0.34015 10259 71	0.98912 06727 47
71	1.24687 11811 84	0.94613 68662 33	0.32376 69383 29	0.98898 61016 36
72	1.26443 27471 17	0.95161 67660 00	0.30728 73747 28	0.98885 74292 38
73	1.28199 43130 49	0.95680 90115 50	0.29071 72430 68	0.98873 48099 95
74	1.29955 58789 81	0.96171 21764 49	0.27406 14706 03	0.98861 83910 31
75	1.31711 74449 13	0.96632 49158 27	0.25732 50027 71	0.98850 83119 78
76	1.33467 90108 45	0.97064 59663 83	0.24051 28020 37	0.98840 47048 20
77	1.35224 05767 77	0.97467 41463 90	0.22362 98467 52	0.98830 76937 39
78	1.36980 21427 10	0.97840 83556 95	0.20668 11300 22	0.98821 73949 77
79	1.38736 37086 42	0.98184 75757 08	0.18967 16585 99	0.98813 39167 01
80	1.40492 52745 74	0.98499 08694 02	0.17260 64517 79	0.98805 73588 81
81	1.42248 68405 06	0.98783 73812 90	0.15549 05403 10	0.98798 78131 79
82	1.44004 84064 38	0.99038 63374 23	0.13832 89653 17	0.98792 53628 41
83	1.45760 99723 70	0.99263 70453 68	0.12112 67772 35	0.98787 00826 06
84	1.47517 15383 03	0.99458 88941 97	0.10388 90347 47	0.98782 20386 19
85	1.49273 31042 35	0.99624 13544 72	0.08662 08037 38	0.98778 12883 59
86	1.51029 46701 67	0.99759 39782 33	0.06932 71562 50	0.98774 78805 69
87	1.52785 62360 99	0.99864 63989 84	0.05201 31694 48	0.98772 18552 10
88	1.54541 78020 31	0.99939 83316 85	0.03468 39245 86	0.98770 32434 05
89	1.56297 93679 64	0.99984 95727 42	0.01734 45059 83	0.98769 20674 12
90	1.58054 09338 96	1.00000 00000 00	0.00000 00000 00	0.98768 83405 95

q = 0.00154 85045 16579 192   D(90) = 1.00621 32605 90419
q' = 0.21754 89496 99726 3   1/D(90) = 0.99382 51056 37374

r	ϕ	$E(\phi, k)$	A(r)	D(r)
45	0.78849 51625 29	0.78672 67023 78	0.70710 33901 00	1.00310 66302 72
46	0.80594 64011 87	0.80406 83069 39	0.71933 64709 80	1.00321 50501 06
47	0.82339 38697 65	0.82140 24195 21	0.73135 04389 13	1.00332 33378 47
48	0.84083 75759 68	0.83872 90570 45	0.74314 16340 93	1.00343 13615 63
49	0.85827 75320 76	0.85604 82455 16	0.75470 64645 66	1.00353 89896 44
50	0.87571 37549 30	0.87336 00199 76	0.76604 14073 21	1.00364 60909 62
51	0.89314 62659 08	0.89066 44244 52	0.77714 30093 63	1.00375 25350 31
52	0.91057 50908 93	0.90796 15118 91	0.78800 78887 69	1.00385 81921 63
53	0.92800 02602 45	0.92525 13440 85	0.79863 27357 14	1.00396 29336 34
54	0.94542 18087 54	0.94253 39915 83	0.80901 43134 85	1.00406 66318 31
55	0.96283 97756 00	0.95980 95335 99	0.81914 94594 65	1.00416 91604 14
56	0.98025 42043 03	0.97707 80579 00	0.82903 50860 95	1.00427 03944 67
57	0.99766 51426 63	0.99433 96606 96	0.83866 81818 22	1.00437 02106 54
58	1.01507 26427 06	1.01159 44465 10	0.84804 58120 11	1.00446 84873 62
59	1.03247 67606 13	1.02884 25280 44	0.85716 51198 40	1.00456 51048 57
60	1.04987 75566 53	1.04608 40260 34	0.86602 33271 76	1.00465 99454 26
61	1.06727 50951 06	1.06331 90690 97	0.87461 77354 18	1.00475 28935 19
62	1.08466 94441 85	1.08054 77935 66	0.88294 57263 18	1.00484 38358 94
63	1.10206 06759 48	1.09777 03433 22	0.89100 47627 87	1.00493 26617 52
64	1.11944 88662 15	1.11498 68696 09	0.89879 23896 60	1.00501 92628 72
65	1.13683 40944 69	1.13219 75308 51	0.90630 62344 49	1.00510 35337 43
66	1.15421 64437 60	1.14940 24924 54	0.91354 40080 68	1.00518 53716 96
67	1.17159 60006 05	1.16660 19265 99	0.92050 35055 27	1.00526 46770 22
68	1.18897 28548 80	1.18379 60120 38	0.92718 26066 07	1.00534 13531 00
69	1.20634 70997 11	1.20098 49338 67	0.93357 92765 07	1.00541 53065 13
70	1.22371 88313 62	1.21816 88833 06	0.93969 15664 64	1.00548 64471 60
71	1.24108 81491 15	1.23534 80574 67	0.94551 76143 46	1.00555 46883 67
72	1.25845 51551 53	1.25252 26591 12	0.95105 56452 21	1.00561 99469 91
73	1.27581 99544 33	1.26969 28964 12	0.95630 39719 00	1.00568 21435 27
74	1.29318 26545 60	1.28685 89826 96	0.96126 09954 49	1.00574 12021 96
75	1.31054 33656 59	1.30402 11361 92	0.96592 52056 77	1.00579 70510 45
76	1.32790 22002 38	1.32117 95797 72	0.97029 51816 00	1.00584 96220 31
77	1.34525 92730 56	1.33833 45406 79	0.97436 95918 69	1.00589 88511 04
78	1.36261 47009 82	1.35548 62502 64	0.97814 71951 82	1.00594 46782 86
79	1.37996 86028 58	1.37263 49437 04	0.98162 68406 58	1.00598 70477 44
80	1.39732 10993 51	1.38978 08597 26	0.98480 74681 89	1.00602 59078 56
81	1.41467 23128 13	1.40692 42403 27	0.98768 81087 66	1.00606 12112 79
82	1.43202 23671 31	1.42406 53304 83	0.99026 78847 71	1.00609 29150 00
83	1.44937 13875 79	1.44120 43778 63	0.99254 60102 50	1.00612 09803 92
84	1.46671 95006 69	1.45834 16325 37	0.99452 17911 44	1.00614 53732 64
85	1.48406 68339 98	1.47547 73466 77	0.99619 46255 11	1.00616 60638 95
86	1.50141 35160 96	1.49261 17742 69	0.99756 40037 02	1.00618 30270 77
87	1.51875 96762 73	1.50974 51708 04	0.99862 95085 19	1.00619 62421 44
88	1.53610 54444 62	1.52687 77929 87	0.99939 08153 44	1.00620 56929 95
89	1.55345 09510 64	1.54400 98984 30	0.99984 76922 35	1.00621 13681 15
90	1.57079 63267 95	1.56114 17453 51	1.00000 00000 00	1.00621 32605 90

K = 1.58284 28043 38351

K' = 3.15338 52518 87839

E = 1.55888 71966 01596

E' = 1.04011 43957 06010

r	u=(r/90)K=F(φ,k)	sn u	cn u	dn u
0	0.00000 00000 00	0.00000 00000 00	1.00000 00000 00	1.00000 00000 00
1	0.01758 71422 70	0.01758 62083 12	0.99984 53506 80	0.99999 53371 02
2	0.03517 42845 41	0.03516 68133 56	0.99938 14563 21	0.99998 13542 20
3	0.05276 14268 11	0.05273 62142 55	0.99860 84776 86	0.99995 80687 83
4	0.07034 85690 82	0.07028 88149 19	0.99752 66825 99	0.99992 55098 10
5	0.08793 57113 52	0.08781 90264 27	0.99613 64457 73	0.99988 37178 77
6	0.10552 28536 23	0.10532 12694 03	0.99443 82485 66	0.99983 27450 60
7	0.12310 99958 93	0.12278 99763 89	0.99243 26786 73	0.99977 26548 64
8	0.14069 71381 63	0.14021 95941 89	0.99012 04297 48	0.99970 35221 45
9	0.15828 42804 34	0.15760 45862 16	0.98750 23009 61	0.99962 54330 02
10	0.17587 14227 04	0.17493 94348 03	0.98457 91964 85	0.99953 84846 71
11	0.19345 85649 75	0.19221 86435 05	0.98135 21249 22	0.99944 27853 90
12	0.21104 57072 45	0.20943 67393 71	0.97782 21986 65	0.99933 84542 61
13	0.22863 28495 16	0.22658 82751 95	0.97399 06331 91	0.99922 56210 87
14	0.24621 99917 86	0.24366 78317 34	0.96985 87463 02	0.99910 44262 06
15	0.26380 71340 56	0.26067 00198 98	0.96542 79572 95	0.99897 50203 02
16	0.28139 42763 27	0.27758 94829 09	0.96069 97860 82	0.99883 75642 09
17	0.29898 14185 97	0.29442 08984 19	0.95567 58522 50	0.99869 22286 96
18	0.31656 85608 68	0.31115 89806 02	0.95035 78740 62	0.99853 91942 48
19	0.33415 57031 38	0.32779 84821 93	0.94474 76674 07	0.99837 86508 24
20	0.35174 28454 09	0.34433 41965 02	0.93884 71447 04	0.99821 07976 10
21	0.36932 99876 79	0.36076 09593 73	0.93265 83137 42	0.99803 58427 62
22	0.38691 71299 49	0.37707 36511 06	0.92618 32764 86	0.99785 40031 30
23	0.40450 42722 20	0.39326 71983 30	0.91942 42278 28	0.99766 55039 78
24	0.42209 14144 90	0.40933 65758 35	0.91238 34543 02	0.99747 05786 88
25	0.43967 85567 61	0.42527 68083 46	0.90506 33327 47	0.99726 94684 64
26	0.45726 56990 31	0.44108 29722 59	0.89746 63289 41	0.99706 24220 13
27	0.47485 28413 02	0.45675 01973 17	0.88959 49961 93	0.99684 96952 29
28	0.49243 99835 72	0.47227 36682 41	0.88145 19738 97	0.99663 15508 59
29	0.51002 71258 42	0.48764 86263 06	0.87303 99860 61	0.99640 82581 69
30	0.52761 42681 13	0.50287 03708 64	0.86436 18398 03	0.99618 00925 98
31	0.54520 14103 83	0.51793 42608 14	0.85542 04238 12	0.99594 73354 05
32	0.56278 85526 54	0.53283 57160 19	0.84621 87067 98	0.99571 02733 11
33	0.58037 56949 24	0.54757 02186 68	0.83675 97359 03	0.99546 91981 33
34	0.59796 28371 94	0.56213 33145 82	0.82704 66351 04	0.99522 44064 16
35	0.61554 99794 65	0.57652 06144 65	0.81708 26035 94	0.99497 61990 59
36	0.63313 71217 35	0.59072 77951 07	0.80687 09141 42	0.99472 48809 30
37	0.65072 42640 06	0.60475 06005 20	0.79641 49114 44	0.99447 07604 88
38	0.66831 14062 76	0.61858 48430 33	0.78571 80104 65	0.99421 41493 96
39	0.68589 85485 47	0.63222 64043 21	0.77478 36947 69	0.99395 53621 28
40	0.70348 56908 17	0.64567 12363 90	0.76361 55148 36	0.99369 47155 78
41	0.72107 28330 87	0.65891 53625 03	0.75221 70863 90	0.99343 25286 70
42	0.73865 99753 58	0.67195 48780 55	0.74059 20887 09	0.99316 91219 57
43	0.75624 71176 28	0.68478 59513 97	0.72874 42629 41	0.99290 48172 30
44	0.77383 42598 99	0.69740 48246 07	0.71667 74104 26	0.99263 99371 21
45	0.79142 14021 69	0.70980 78142 16	0.70439 53910 11	0.99237 48047 04

q = 0.00191 35945 90170 284   D(90) = 1.00768 37856 61824
q'= 0.20660 97552 00965 0   1/D(90) = 0.99237 48047 04456

r	ϕ	$E(\phi,k)$	A(r)	D(r)
0	0.00000 00000 00	0.00000 00000 00	0.00000 00000 00	1.00000 00000 00
1	0.01758 71149 34	0.01758 70875 97	0.01745 21508 84	1.00000 23403 77
2	0.03517 40658 87	0.03517 38472 36	0.03489 89861 41	1.00000 93586 58
3	0.05276 06890 85	0.05275 99513 78	0.05233 51917 61	1.00002 10462 90
4	0.07034 68211 60	0.07034 50733 17	0.06975 54569 70	1.00003 73890 36
5	0.08793 22993 57	0.08792 88876 01	0.08715 44758 47	1.00005 83669 83
6	0.10551 69617 37	0.10551 10704 42	0.10452 69489 34	1.00008 39545 74
7	0.12310 06473 74	0.12309 13001 31	0.12186 75848 57	1.00011 41206 33
8	0.14068 31965 62	0.14066 92574 43	0.13917 11019 31	1.00014 88284 09
9	0.15826 44510 10	0.15824 46260 49	0.15643 22297 67	1.00018 80356 14
10	0.17584 42540 39	0.17581 70929 10	0.17364 57108 81	1.00023 16944 82
11	0.19342 24507 76	0.19338 63486 77	0.19080 63022 90	1.00027 97518 20
12	0.21099 88883 49	0.21095 20880 84	0.20790 87771 10	1.00033 21490 78
13	0.22857 34160 74	0.22851 40103 31	0.22494 79261 46	1.00038 88224 18
14	0.24614 58856 44	0.24607 18194 63	0.24191 85594 80	1.00044 97027 92
15	0.26371 61513 10	0.26362 52247 43	0.25881 55080 46	1.00051 47160 27
16	0.28128 40700 62	0.28117 39410 18	0.27563 36252 09	1.00058 37829 15
17	0.29884 95018 09	0.29871 76890 73	0.29236 77883 30	1.00065 68193 08
18	0.31641 23095 47	0.31625 61959 83	0.30901 29003 24	1.00073 37362 22
19	0.33397 23595 30	0.33378 91954 52	0.32556 38912 12	1.00081 44399 46
20	0.35152 95214 36	0.35131 64281 41	0.34201 57196 67	1.00089 88321 54
21	0.36908 36685 23	0.36883 76419 92	0.35836 33745 47	1.00098 68100 29
22	0.38663 46777 89	0.38635 25925 36	0.37460 18764 21	1.00107 82663 83
23	0.40418 24301 17	0.40386 10431 97	0.39072 62790 84	1.00117 30897 90
24	0.42172 68104 28	0.42136 27655 77	0.40673 16710 67	1.00127 11647 22
25	0.43926 77078 13	0.43885 75397 35	0.42261 31771 27	1.00137 23716 90
26	0.45680 50156 74	0.45634 51544 58	0.43836 59597 37	1.00147 65873 89
27	0.47433 86318 49	0.47382 54075 09	0.45398 52205 55	1.00158 36848 49
28	0.49186 84587 37	0.49129 81058 73	0.46946 62018 89	1.00169 35335 87
29	0.50939 44034 18	0.50876 30659 86	0.48480 41881 43	1.00180 59997 70
30	0.52691 63777 61	0.52622 01139 52	0.49999 45072 54	1.00192 09463 75
31	0.54443 42985 30	0.54366 90857 50	0.51503 25321 15	1.00203 82333 58
32	0.56194 80874 86	0.56110 98274 19	0.52991 36819 88	1.00215 77178 21
33	0.57945 76714 77	0.57854 21952 43	0.54463 34238 91	1.00227 92541 93
34	0.59696 29825 24	0.59596 60559 08	0.55918 72739 90	1.00240 26943 99
35	0.61446 39579 06	0.61338 12866 58	0.57357 07989 54	1.00252 78880 47
36	0.63196 05402 24	0.63078 77754 30	0.58777 96173 14	1.00265 46826 07
37	0.64945 26774 78	0.64818 54209 76	0.60180 94007 94	1.00278 29236 00
38	0.66684 03231 20	0.66557 41329 72	0.61565 58756 29	1.00291 24547 84
39	0.68442 34361 06	0.68295 38321 13	0.62931 48238 70	1.00304 31183 45
40	0.70190 19809 48	0.70032 44501 95	0.64278 20846 69	1.00317 47550 90
41	0.71937 59277 48	0.71768 59301 82	0.65605 35555 44	1.00330 72046 39
42	0.73684 52522 32	0.73503 82262 53	0.66912 51936 32	1.00344 03056 24
43	0.75430 99357 76	0.75238 13038 49	0.68199 30169 23	1.00357 38958 81
44	0.77176 99654 22	0.76971 51396 92	0.69465 31054 67	1.00370 78126 51
45	0.78922 53338 92	0.78703 97217 95	0.70710 16025 76	1.00384 18927 77

K = 1.58284 28043 38351
K' = 3.15338 52518 87839

E = 1.55888 71966 01596
E' = 1.04011 43957 06010

r	u=(r/90)K=F(φ,k)	sn u	cn u	dn u
45	0.79142 14021 69	0.70980 78142 16	0.70439 53910 11	0.99237 48047 04
46	0.80900 85444 40	0.72199 13118 79	0.69190 21213 81	0.99210 97431 04
47	0.82659 56867 10	0.73395 17850 00	0.67920 15733 90	0.99184 50750 99
48	0.84418 28289 80	0.74568 57773 12	0.66629 77724 07	0.99158 11227 32
49	0.86176 99712 51	0.75718 99094 12	0.65319 47956 66	0.99131 82069 15
50	0.87935 71135 21	0.76846 08792 47	0.63989 67706 34	0.99105 66470 50
51	0.89694 42557 92	0.77949 54625 63	0.62640 78733 89	0.99079 67606 35
52	0.91453 13980 62	0.79029 05133 09	0.61273 23270 19	0.99053 88628 90
53	0.93211 85403 33	0.80084 29640 03	0.59887 44000 26	0.99028 32663 76
54	0.94970 56826 03	0.81114 98260 58	0.58483 84047 63	0.99003 02806 26
55	0.96729 28248 73	0.82120 81900 73	0.57062 86958 76	0.98978 02117 72
56	0.98487 99671 44	0.83101 52260 86	0.55624 96687 76	0.98953 33621 88
57	1.00246 71094 14	0.84056 81837 99	0.54170 57581 23	0.98929 00301 28
58	1.02005 42516 85	0.84986 43927 66	0.52700 14363 44	0.98905 05093 79
59	1.03764 13939 55	0.85890 12625 50	0.51214 12121 58	0.98881 50889 14
60	1.05522 85362 26	0.86767 62828 58	0.49712 96291 36	0.98858 40525 52
61	1.07281 56784 96	0.87618 70236 46	0.48197 12642 83	0.98835 76786 30
62	1.09040 28207 66	0.88443 11351 95	0.46667 07266 36	0.98813 62396 80
63	1.10798 99630 37	0.89240 63481 69	0.45123 26558 96	0.98792 00021 09
64	1.12557 71053 07	0.90011 04736 54	0.43566 17210 84	0.98770 92258 92
65	1.14316 42475 78	0.90754 14031 69	0.41996 26192 11	0.98750 41642 75
66	1.16075 13898 48	0.91469 71086 63	0.40414 00739 90	0.98730 50634 81
67	1.17833 85321 19	0.92157 56425 00	0.38819 88345 56	0.98711 21624 29
68	1.19592 56743 89	0.92817 51374 25	0.37214 36742 26	0.98692 56924 59
69	1.21351 28166 59	0.93449 38065 15	0.35597 93892 69	0.98674 58770 68
70	1.23109 99589 30	0.94052 99431 26	0.33971 07977 14	0.98657 29316 59
71	1.24868 71012 00	0.94628 19208 20	0.32334 27381 72	0.98640 70632 92
72	1.26627 42434 71	0.95174 81932 97	0.30688 00686 85	0.98624 84704 51
73	1.28386 13857 41	0.95692 72943 05	0.29032 76656 02	0.98609 73428 20
74	1.30144 85280 12	0.96181 78375 61	0.27369 04224 66	0.98595 38610 69
75	1.31903 56702 82	0.96641 85166 54	0.25697 32489 37	0.98581 81966 49
76	1.33662 28125 52	0.97072 81049 54	0.24018 10697 23	0.98569 05116 03
77	1.35420 99548 23	0.97474 54555 18	0.22331 88235 41	0.98557 09583 80
78	1.37179 70970 93	0.97846 95009 94	0.20639 14620 90	0.98545 96796 65
79	1.38938 42393 64	0.98189 92535 32	0.18940 39490 45	0.98535 68082 22
80	1.40697 13816 34	0.98503 38046 86	0.17236 12590 65	0.98526 24667 44
81	1.42455 85239 05	0.98787 23253 33	0.15526 83768 26	0.98517 67677 17
82	1.44214 56661 75	0.99041 40655 86	0.13813 02960 56	0.98509 98132 92
83	1.45973 28084 45	0.99265 83547 21	0.12095 20185 93	0.98503 16951 77
84	1.47731 99507 16	0.99460 46010 99	0.10373 85534 51	0.98497 24945 28
85	1.49490 70929 86	0.99625 22921 05	0.08649 49158 99	0.98492 22818 66
86	1.51249 42352 57	0.99760 09940 87	0.06922 61265 50	0.98488 11169 94
87	1.53008 13775 27	0.99865 03523 11	0.05193 72104 54	0.98484 90489 32
88	1.54766 85197 97	0.99940 00909 15	0.03463 31962 05	0.98482 61158 63
89	1.56525 56620 68	0.99985 00128 79	0.01731 91150 49	0.98481 23450 92
90	1.58284 28043 38	1.00000 00000 00	0.00000 00000 00	0.98480 77530 12

q = 0.00191 35945 90170 284   D(90) = 1.00768 37856 61824
q'= 0.20660 97552 00965 0   1/D(90) = 0.99237 48047 04456

r	ϕ	$E(\phi,k)$	$A(r)$	$D(r)$
45	0.78922 53338 92	0.78703 97217 95	0.70710 16025 76	1.00384 18927 77
46	0.80667 60395 89	0.80435 50494 62	0.71933 47159 95	1.00397 59729 03
47	0.82412 20865 99	0.82166 11332 70	0.73134 87190 61	1.00410 98896 74
48	0.84156 34846 77	0.83895 79950 36	0.74313 99518 37	1.00424 34799 31
49	0.85900 02492 32	0.85624 56677 73	0.75470 48222 28	1.00437 65809 17
50	0.87643 24013 07	0.87352 41956 33	0.76603 98070 78	1.00450 90304 68
51	0.89385 99675 43	0.89079 36338 39	0.77714 14532 44	1.00464 06672 14
52	0.91128 29801 46	0.90805 40485 91	0.78800 63786 44	1.00477 13307 77
53	0.92870 14768 46	0.92530 55169 82	0.79863 12732 96	1.00490 08619 62
54	0.94611 55008 40	0.94254 81268 75	0.80901 29003 24	1.00502 91029 58
55	0.96352 51007 41	0.95978 19767 92	0.81914 80969 41	1.00515 58975 20
56	0.98093 03305 15	0.97700 71757 69	0.82903 37754 22	1.00528 10911 70
57	0.99833 12494 08	0.99422 38432 17	0.83866 69240 39	1.00540 45313 79
58	1.01572 79218 72	1.01143 21087 60	0.84804 46079 82	1.00552 60677 54
59	1.03312 04174 88	1.02863 21120 64	0.85716 39702 55	1.00564 55522 20
60	1.05050 88108 71	1.04582 40026 59	0.86602 22325 46	1.00576 28392 06
61	1.06789 31815 79	1.06300 79397 43	0.87461 66960 75	1.00587 77858 14
62	1.08527 36140 19	1.08018 40919 80	0.88294 47424 20	1.00599 02520 01
63	1.10265 01973 33	1.09735 26372 86	0.89100 38343 10	1.00610 01007 43
64	1.12002 30252 94	1.11451 37626 06	0.89879 15164 05	1.00620 71982 06
65	1.13739 21961 90	1.13166 76636 81	0.90630 54160 42	1.00631 14139 09
66	1.15475 78127 00	1.14881 45448 03	0.91354 32439 62	1.00641 26208 81
67	1.17211 99817 69	1.16595 46185 62	0.92050 27950 02	1.00651 06958 16
68	1.18947 88144 78	1.18308 81055 89	0.92718 19487 77	1.00660 55192 27
69	1.20683 44259 09	1.20021 52342 80	0.93357 86703 20	1.00669 69755 84
70	1.22418 69350 03	1.21733 62405 25	0.93969 10107 06	1.00678 49534 63
71	1.24153 64644 18	1.23445 13674 16	0.94551 71076 46	1.00686 93456 75
72	1.25888 31403 74	1.25156 08649 55	0.95105 51860 57	1.00695 00494 03
73	1.27622 70925 11	1.26866 49897 57	0.95630 35586 02	1.00702 69663 21
74	1.29356 84537 21	1.28576 40047 37	0.96126 06262 04	1.00710 00027 17
75	1.31090 73599 94	1.30285 81788 00	0.96592 48785 38	1.00716 90696 08
76	1.32824 39502 55	1.31994 77865 18	0.97029 48944 88	1.00723 40828 46
77	1.34557 83661 92	1.33703 31078 08	0.97436 93425 84	1.00729 49632 24
78	1.36291 07520 91	1.35411 44275 94	0.97814 69814 06	1.00735 16365 66
79	1.38024 12546 57	1.37119 20354 77	0.98162 66599 65	1.00740 40338 27
80	1.39757 00228 45	1.38826 62253 90	0.98480 73180 51	1.00745 20911 68
81	1.41489 72076 77	1.40533 72952 53	0.98768 79865 63	1.00749 57500 38
82	1.43222 29620 62	1.42240 55466 24	0.99026 77877 96	1.00753 49572 45
83	1.44954 74406 15	1.43947 12843 44	0.99254 59357 19	1.00756 96650 22
84	1.46687 07994 70	1.45653 48161 84	0.99452 17362 05	1.00759 98310 83
85	1.48419 31960 95	1.47359 64524 81	0.99619 45872 52	1.00762 54186 75
86	1.50151 47891 06	1.49065 65057 79	0.99756 39791 60	1.00764 63966 24
87	1.51883 57380 74	1.50771 52904 62	0.99862 94946 90	1.00766 27393 70
88	1.53615 62033 38	1.52477 31223 91	0.99939 08091 90	1.00767 44270 04
89	1.55347 63458 12	1.54183 03185 35	0.99984 76906 96	1.00768 14452 84
90	1.57079 63267 95	1.55888 71966 02	1.00000 00000 00	1.00768 37856 62

41

ELLIPTIC FUNCTIONS   TABLE $\theta = 11°$

K = 1.58539 41637 75538

K' = 3.06172 86120 38789

E = 1.55639 97977 70947

E' = 1.04678 64993 44049

r	u=(r/90)K=F(φ,k)	sn u	cn u	dn u
0	0.00000 00000 00	0.00000 00000 00	1.00000 00000 00	1.00000 00000 00
1	0.01761 54907 09	0.01761 45465 30	0.99984 48518 40	0.99999 43517 77
2	0.03523 09814 17	0.03522 34285 04	0.99937 94625 09	0.99997 74141 81
3	0.05284 64721 26	0.05282 09839 28	0.99860 39974 17	0.99994 92084 23
4	0.07046 19628 34	0.07040 15559 26	0.99751 87321 16	0.99990 97698 24
5	0.08807 74535 43	0.08795 94952 99	0.99612 40521 07	0.99985 91477 66
6	0.10569 29442 52	0.10548 91630 61	0.99442 04525 64	0.99979 74056 25
7	0.12330 84349 60	0.12298 49329 73	0.99240 85379 83	0.99972 46206 86
8	0.14092 39256 69	0.14044 11940 56	0.99008 90217 61	0.99964 08840 38
9	0.15853 94163 78	0.15785 23530 85	0.98746 27256 89	0.99954 63004 53
10	0.17615 49070 86	0.17521 28370 66	0.98453 05793 76	0.99944 09882 42
11	0.19377 03977 95	0.19251 70956 79	0.98129 36196 02	0.99932 50790 97
12	0.21138 58885 03	0.20975 96037 02	0.97775 29895 91	0.99919 87179 15
13	0.22900 13792 12	0.22693 48634 03	0.97390 99382 24	0.99906 20626 00
14	0.24661 68699 21	0.24403 74068 92	0.96976 58191 74	0.99891 52838 55
15	0.26423 23606 29	0.26106 17984 43	0.96532 20899 75	0.99875 85649 49
16	0.28184 78513 38	0.27800 26367 78	0.96058 03110 33	0.99859 21014 77
17	0.29946 33420 46	0.29485 45573 04	0.95554 21445 63	0.99841 61010 93
18	0.31707 88327 55	0.31161 22343 16	0.95020 93534 71	0.99823 07832 38
19	0.33469 43234 64	0.32827 03831 44	0.94458 38001 74	0.99803 63788 43
20	0.35230 98141 72	0.34482 37622 57	0.93866 74453 62	0.99783 31300 29
21	0.36992 53048 81	0.36126 71753 21	0.93246 23467 12	0.99762 12897 78
22	0.38754 07955 90	0.37759 54732 00	0.92597 06575 37	0.99740 11216 05
23	0.40515 62862 98	0.39380 35559 02	0.91919 46253 97	0.99717 28992 07
24	0.42277 17770 07	0.40988 63744 79	0.91213 65906 57	0.99693 69061 04
25	0.44038 72677 15	0.42583 89328 60	0.90479 89850 02	0.99669 34352 66
26	0.45800 27584 24	0.44165 62896 34	0.89718 43299 05	0.99644 27887 28
27	0.47561 82491 33	0.45733 35597 67	0.88929 52350 66	0.99618 52772 00
28	0.49323 37398 41	0.47286 59162 70	0.88113 43968 03	0.99592 12196 56
29	0.51084 92305 50	0.48824 85917 92	0.87270 45964 20	0.99565 09429 27
30	0.52846 47212 59	0.50347 68801 62	0.86400 86985 34	0.99537 47812 70
31	0.54608 02119 67	0.51854 61378 65	0.85504 96493 80	0.99509 30759 44
32	0.56369 57026 76	0.53345 17854 54	0.84583 04750 93	0.99480 61747 65
33	0.58131 11933 84	0.54818 93089 01	0.83635 42799 59	0.99451 44316 63
34	0.59892 66840 93	0.56275 42608 87	0.82662 42446 56	0.99421 82062 28
35	0.61654 21748 02	0.57714 22620 19	0.81664 36244 72	0.99391 78632 54
36	0.63415 76655 10	0.59134 90019 98	0.80641 57475 12	0.99361 37722 71
37	0.65177 31562 19	0.60537 02407 12	0.79594 40128 93	0.99330 63070 85
38	0.66938 86469 27	0.61920 18092 74	0.78523 18889 29	0.99299 58452 98
39	0.68700 41376 36	0.63283 96109 94	0.77428 29113 17	0.99268 27678 39
40	0.70461 96283 45	0.64627 96222 89	0.76310 06813 09	0.99236 74584 86
41	0.72223 51190 53	0.65951 78935 39	0.75168 88638 94	0.99205 03033 87
42	0.73985 06097 62	0.67255 05498 75	0.74005 11859 74	0.99173 16905 80
43	0.75746 61004 71	0.68537 37919 13	0.72819 14345 54	0.99141 20095 11
44	0.77508 15911 79	0.69798 38964 29	0.71611 34549 26	0.99109 16505 58
45	0.79269 70818 88	0.71037 72169 78	0.70382 11488 71	0.99077 10045 45

42

q = 0.00231 79450 15820 765   D(90) = 1.00931 49632 07826
q' = 0.19656 76611 43642 2   1/D(90) = 0.99077 10045 45280

r	ϕ	$E(\phi,k)$	$A(r)$	$D(r)$
0	0.00000 00000 00	0.00000 00000 00	0.00000 00000 00	1.00000 00000 00
1	0.01761 54575 42	0.01761 54243 75	0.01745 20314 76	1.00000 28372 12
2	0.03523 07161 33	0.03523 04508 52	0.03489 87475 78	1.00001 13453 91
3	0.05284 55770 71	0.05284 46820 43	0.05233 48345 53	1.00002 55141 70
4	0.07045 98421 53	0.07045 77215 86	0.06975 49818 77	1.00004 53262 89
5	0.08807 33139 20	0.08806 91746 48	0.08715 38838 80	1.00007 07576 07
6	0.10568 57959 10	0.10567 86484 37	0.10452 62413 54	1.00010 17771 43
7	0.12329 70928 95	0.12328 57527 05	0.12186 67631 67	1.00013 83471 02
8	0.14090 70111 34	0.14089 01002 48	0.13917 01678 74	1.00018 04229 30
9	0.15851 53586 10	0.15849 13074 02	0.15643 11853 24	1.00022 79533 64
10	0.17612 19452 72	0.17608 89945 33	0.17364 45582 63	1.00028 08804 96
11	0.19372 65832 69	0.19368 27865 24	0.19080 50439 32	1.00033 91398 42
12	0.21132 90871 88	0.21127 23132 52	0.20790 74156 65	1.00040 26604 21
13	0.22892 92742 84	0.22885 72100 57	0.22494 64644 80	1.00047 13648 45
14	0.24652 69647 05	0.24643 71182 09	0.24191 70006 60	1.00054 51694 07
15	0.26412 19817 17	0.26401 16853 58	0.25881 38553 37	1.00062 39841 88
16	0.28171 41519 26	0.28158 05659 80	0.27563 18820 63	1.00070 77131 64
17	0.29930 33054 86	0.29914 34218 15	0.29236 59583 75	1.00079 62543 25
18	0.31688 92763 17	0.31669 99222 88	0.30901 09873 57	1.00088 94997 95
19	0.33447 19023 04	0.33424 97449 23	0.32556 18991 89	1.00098 73359 71
20	0.35205 10254 99	0.35179 25757 46	0.34201 36526 90	1.00108 96436 54
21	0.36962 64923 16	0.36932 81096 75	0.35836 12368 56	1.00119 62981 98
22	0.38719 81537 18	0.38685 60508 95	0.37459 96723 81	1.00130 71696 61
23	0.40476 58654 02	0.40437 61132 22	0.39072 40131 75	1.00142 21229 62
24	0.42232 94879 70	0.42188 80204 55	0.40672 93478 70	1.00154 10180 50
25	0.43988 88871 05	0.43939 15067 12	0.42261 08013 15	1.00166 37100 68
26	0.45744 39337 30	0.45688 63167 48	0.43836 35360 60	1.00179 00495 36
27	0.47499 45041 67	0.47437 22062 66	0.45398 27538 29	1.00191 98825 28
28	0.49254 04802 81	0.49184 89422 09	0.46946 36969 83	1.00205 30508 63
29	0.51008 17496 30	0.50931 63030 30	0.48480 16499 65	1.00218 93922 96
30	0.52761 82055 93	0.52677 40789 61	0.49999 19407 40	1.00232 87407 15
31	0.54514 97474 99	0.54422 20722 51	0.51502 99422 16	1.00247 09263 46
32	0.56267 62807 49	0.56166 00973 95	0.52991 10736 54	1.00261 57759 58
33	0.58019 77169 24	0.57908 79813 47	0.54463 08020 65	1.00276 31130 74
34	0.59771 39738 90	0.59650 55637 14	0.55918 46435 86	1.00291 27581 87
35	0.61522 49758 94	0.61391 26969 35	0.57356 81648 51	1.00306 45289 76
36	0.63273 06536 52	0.63130 92464 40	0.58777 69843 42	1.00321 82405 32
37	0.65023 09444 27	0.64869 50907 93	0.60180 67737 18	1.00337 37055 83
38	0.66772 57921 03	0.66607 01218 22	0.61565 32591 41	1.00353 07347 16
39	0.68521 51472 41	0.68343 42447 28	0.62931 22225 76	1.00368 91366 18
40	·0.70269 89671 43	0.70078 73781 72	0.64277 95030 75	1.00384 87182 98
41	0.72017 72158 92	0.71812 94543 57	0.65605 09980 47	1.00400 92853 33
42	0.73764 98643 87	0.73546 04190 82	0.66912 26645 08	1.00417 06420 94
43	0.75511 68903 81	0.75278 02317 82	0.68199 05203 13	1.00433 25919 95
44	0.77257 82784 91	0.77008 88655 54	0.69465 06453 72	1.00449 49377 24
45	0.79003 40202 19	0.78738 63071 62	0.70709 91828 43	1.00465 74814 88

43

K = 1.58539 41637 75538   E = 1.55639 97977 70947
K' = 3.06172 86120 38789   E' = 1.04678 64993 44049

r	u=(r/90)K=F(φ,k)	sn u	cn u	dn u
45	0.79269 70818 88	0.71037 72169 78	0.70382 11488 71	0.99077 10045 45
46	0.81031 25725 96	0.72255 01844 58	0.69131 84728 76	0.99045 04622 71
47	0.82792 80633 05	0.73449 93076 22	0.67860 94363 50	0.99013 04140 26
48	0.84554 35540 14	0.74622 11735 33	0.66569 80998 70	0.98981 12491 23
49	0.86315 90447 22	0.75771 24479 75	0.65258 85734 40	0.98949 33554 23
50	0.88077 45354 31	0.76896 98758 09	0.63928 50147 62	0.98917 71188 72
51	0.89839 00261 39	0.77999 02812 88	0.62579 16275 37	0.98886 29230 31
52	0.91600 55168 48	0.79077 05683 24	0.61211 26597 88	0.98855 11486 24
53	0.93362 10075 57	0.80130 77207 06	0.59825 24022 00	0.98824 21730 80
54	0.95123 64982 65	0.81159 88022 88	0.58421 51864 89	0.98793 63700 88
55	0.96885 19889 74	0.82164 09571 30	0.57000 53838 05	0.98763 41091 55
56	0.98646 74796 83	0.83143 14096 02	0.55562 74031 46	0.98733 57551 67
57	1.00408 29703 91	0.84096 74644 55	0.54108 56898 21	0.98704 16679 69
58	1.02169 84611 00	0.85024 65068 56	0.52638 47239 22	0.98675 22019 35
59	1.03931 39518 08	0.85926 60023 98	0.51152 90188 48	0.98646 77055 62
60	1.05692 94425 17	0.86802 34970 70	0.49652 31198 38	0.98618 85210 66
61	1.07454 49332 26	0.87651 66172 14	0.48137 16025 56	0.98591 49839 82
62	1.09216 04239 34	0.88474 30694 44	0.46607 90716 93	0.98564 74227 82
63	1.10977 59146 43	0.89270 06405 53	0.45065 01596 09	0.98538 61584 94
64	1.12739 14053 51	0.90038 71973 93	0.43508 95250 08	0.98513 15043 39
65	1.14500 68960 60	0.90780 06867 38	0.41940 18516 38	0.98488 37653 74
66	1.16262 23867 69	0.91493 91351 37	0.40359 18470 37	0.98464 32381 40
67	1.18023 78774 77	0.92180 06487 42	0.38766 42412 96	0.98441 02103 34
68	1.19785 33681 86	0.92838 34131 31	0.37162 37858 68	0.98418 49604 78
69	1.21546 88588 95	0.93468 56931 24	0.35547 52523 99	0.98396 77576 11
70	1.23308 43496 03	0.94070 58325 83	0.33922 34315 98	0.98375 88609 83
71	1.25069 98403 12	0.94644 22542 08	0.32287 31321 28	0.98355 85197 66
72	1.26831 53310 20	0.95189 34593 36	0.30642 91795 41	0.98336 69727 80
73	1.28593 08217 29	0.95705 80277 27	0.28989 64152 29	9.98318 44482 21
74	1.30354 63124 38	0.96193 46173 60	0.27327 96954 11	0.98301 11634 13
75	1.32116 18031 46	0.96652 19642 19	0.25658 38901 46	0.98284 73245 66
76	1.33877 72938 55	0.97081 88820 89	0.23981 38823 74	0.98269 31265 48
77	1.35639 27845 64	0.97482 42623 58	0.22297 45669 74	0.98254 87526 70
78	1.37400 82752 72	0.97853 70738 18	0.20607 08498 64	0.98241 43744 86
79	1.39162 37659 81	0.98195 63624 77	0.18910 76471 00	0.98229 01516 04
80	1.40923 92566 89	0.98508 12513 79	0.17208 98840 21	0.98217 62315 09
81	1.42685 47473 98	0.98791 09404 35	0.15502 24943 95	0.98207 27494 09
82	1.44447 02381 07	0.99044 47062 65	0.13791 04195 94	0.98197 98280 78
83	1.46208 57288 15	0.99268 19020 44	0.12075 86077 83	0.98189 75777 29
84	1.47970 12195 24	0.99462 19573 77	0.10357 20131 27	0.98182 60958 92
85	1.49731 67102 32	0.99626 43781 70	0.08635 55950 06	0.98176 54673 07
86	1.51493 22009 41	0.99760 87465 29	0.06911 43172 51	0.98171 57638 33
87	1.53254 76916 50	0.99865 47206 65	0.05185 31473 83	0.98167 70443 73
88	1.55016 31823 58	0.99940 20348 23	0.03457 70558 65	0.98164 93548 03
89	1.56777 86730 67	0.99985 04992 19	0.01729 10153 62	0.98163 27279 28
90	1.58539 41637 76	1.00000 00000 00	0.00000 00000 00	0.98162 71834 48

ELLIPTIC FUNCTIONS TABLE $\theta = 11°$

q = 0.00231 79450 15820 765

q' = 0.19656 76611 43642 2

D(90) = 1.00931 49632 07826

1/D(90) = 0.99077 10045 45280

r	ϕ	$E(\phi,k)$	$A(r)$	$D(r)$
45	0.79003 40202 19	0.78738 63071 62	0.70709 91828 43	1.00465 74814 88
46	0.80748 41139 50	0.80467 25570 27	0.71933 23403 09	1.00482 00252 52
47	0.82492 85649 51	0.82194 76292 00	0.73134 63909 35	1.00498 23709 82
48	0.84236 73853 54	0.83921 15513 21	0.74313 76746 03	1.00514 43208 84
49	0.85980 05941 40	0.85646 43645 52	0.75470 25990 30	1.00530 56776 48
50	0.87722 82171 02	0.87370 61235 10	0.76603 76408 64	1.00546 62446 84
51	0.89465 02868 16	0.89093 68961 68	0.77713 93467 57	1.00562 58263 68
52	0.91206 68425 87	0.90815 67637 52	0.78800 43344 20	1.00578 42282 73
53	0.92947 79303 99	0.92536 58206 14	0.79862 92936 53	1.00594 12574 11
54	0.94688 36028 52	0.94256 41740 96	0.80901 09873 57	1.00609 67224 66
55	0.96428 39190 94	0.95975 19443 77	0.81914 62525 23	1.00625 04340 27
56	0.98167 89447 40	0.97692 92643 02	0.82903 20011 92	1.00640 22048 22
57	0.99906 87517 92	0.99409 62792 05	0.83866 52214 05	1.00655 18499 40
58	1.01645 34185 39	1.01125 31467 07	0.84804 29781 15	1.00669 91870 62
59	1.03383 30294 64	1.02840 00365 10	0.85716 24140 86	1.00684 40366 81
60	1.05120 76751 34	1.04553 71301 71	0.86602 07507 68	1.00698 62223 19
61	1.06857 74520 85	1.06266 46208 71	0.87461 52891 40	1.00712 55707 45
62	1.08594 24627 04	1.07978 27131 59	0.88294 34105 37	1.00726 19121 85
63	1.10330 28150 97	1.09689 16226 95	0.89100 25774 50	1.00739 50805 28
64	1.12065 86229 58	1.11399 15759 79	0.89879 03342 99	1.00752 49135 27
65	1.13801 00054 27	1.13108 28100 60	0.90630 43081 83	1.00765 12530 03
66	1.15535 70869 42	1.14816 55722 48	0.91354 22096 08	1.00777 39450 30
67	1.17269 99970 89	1.16524 01198 01	0.92050 18331 81	1.00789 28401 25
68	1.19003 88704 42	1.18230 67196 15	0.92718 10582 87	1.00800 77934 35
69	1.20737 38463 95	1.19936 56478 90	0.93357 78497 37	1.00811 86649 06
70	1.22470 50690 00	1.21641 71898 01	0.93969 02583 88	1.00822 53194 58
71	1.24203 26867 84	1.23346 16391 48	0.94551 64217 38	1.00832 76271 49
72	1.25935 68525 73	1.25049 92980 02	0.95105 45644 97	1.00842 54633 32
73	1.27667 77233 08	1.26753 04763 47	0.95630 29991 28	1.00851 87088 11
74	1.29399 54598 54	1.28455 54917 05	0.96126 01263 65	1.00860 72499 78
75	1.31131 02268 07	1.30157 46687 62	0.96592 44356 96	1.00869 09789 62
76	1.32862 21922 94	1.31858 83389 79	0.97029 45058 30	1.00876 97937 49
77	1.34593 15277 75	1.33559 68402 07	0.97436 90051 32	1.00884 35983 18
78	1.36323 84078 36	1.35260 05162 82	0.97814 66920 22	1.00891 23027 48
79	1.38054 30099 79	1.36959 97166 27	0.98162 64153 65	1.00897 58233 34
80	1.39784 55144 12	1.38659 47958 41	0.98480 71148 14	1.00903 40826 85
81	1.41514 61038 32	1.40358 61132 85	0.98768 78211 39	1.00908 70098 22
82	1.43239 64818 42	1.42057 40326 65	0.99026 76565 23	1.00913 45402 60
83	1.44974 22795 68	1.43755 89216 08	0.99254 58348 28	1.00917 66160 93
84	1.46703 82417 58	1.45454 11512 36	0.99452 16618 36	1.00921 31860 55
85	1.48433 30402 38	1.47152 10957 35	0.99619 45354 62	1.00924 42055 93
86	1.50162 68668 46	1.48849 91319 28	0.99756 39459 38	1.00926 96369 15
87	1.51891 99145 70	1.50547 56388 31	0.99862 94759 69	1.00928 94490 35
88	1.53621 23773 22	1.52245 09972 25	0.99939 08008 59	1.00930 36178 16
89	1.55350 44497 08	1.53942 55892 10	0.99984 76886 11	1.00931 21259 96
90	1.57079 63267 95	1.55639 97977 71	1.00000 00000 00	1.00931 49632 08

45

K = 1.58819 72125 27520   E = 1.55368 08919 36509
K'= 2.97856 89511 81384   E'= 1.05377 69204 07046

r	u=(r/90)K=F(φ,k)	sn u	cn u	dn u
0	0.00000 00000 00	0.00000 00000 00	1.00000 00000 00	1.00000 00000 00
1	0.01764 66356 95	0.01764 56802 56	0.99984 43028 63	0.99999 32701 39
2	0.03529 32713 90	0.03528 56284 26	0.99937 72683 16	0.99997 30890 28
3	0.05293 99070 84	0.05291 41151 76	0.99859 90669 01	0.99993 94820 73
4	0.07058 65427 79	0.07052 54166 63	0.99750 99827 09	0.99989 24915 77
5	0.08823 31784 74	0.08811 38172 75	0.99611 04131 60	0.99983 21766 83
6	0.10587 98141 69	0.10567 36123 59	0.99440 08686 90	0.99975 86132 92
7	0.12352 64498 63	0.12319 91109 31	0.99238 19723 60	0.99967 18939 60
8	0.14117 30855 58	0.14068 46383 66	0.99005 44593 75	0.99957 21277 67
9	0.15881 97212 53	0.15812 45390 73	0.98741 91765 12	0.99945 94401 73
10	0.17646 63569 48	0.17551 31791 35	0.98447 70814 75	0.99933 39728 39
11	0.19411 29926 42	0.19284 49489 28	0.98122 92421 62	0.99919 58834 37
12	0.21175 96283 37	0.21011 42657 00	0.97767 68358 46	0.99904 53454 33
13	0.22940 62640 32	0.22731 55761 21	0.97382 11482 88	0.99888 25478 50
14	0.24705 28997 27	0.24444 33587 86	0.96966 35727 64	0.99870 76950 10
15	0.26469 95354 21	0.26149 21266 86	0.96520 56090 19	0.99852 10062 55
16	0.28234 61711 16	0.27845 64296 22	0.96044 88621 48	0.99832 27156 45
17	0.29999 28068 11	0.29533 08565 78	0.95539 50414 11	0.99811 30716 50
18	0.31763 94425 06	0.31211 00380 43	0.95004 59589 69	0.99789 23368 00
19	0.33528 60782 00	0.32878 86482 81	0.94440 35285 63	0.99766 07873 43
20	0.35293 27138 95	0.34536 14075 33	0.93846 97641 30	0.99741 87128 61
21	0.37057 93495 90	0.36182 30841 82	0.93224 67783 55	0.99716 64158 89
22	0.38822 59852 85	0.37816 84968 37	0.92573 67811 64	0.99690 42115 03
23	0.40587 26209 79	0.39439 25163 66	0.91894 20781 72	0.99663 24269 01
24	0.42351 92566 74	0.41049 00678 67	0.91186 50690 66	0.99635 14009 68
25	0.44116 58923 69	0.42645 61325 61	0.90450 82459 55	0.99606 14838 18
26	0.45881 25280 64	0.44228 57496 30	0.89687 41916 65	0.99576 30363 39
27	0.47645 91637 58	0.45797 40179 82	0.88896 55779 91	0.99545 64297 08
28	0.49410 57994 53	0.47351 60979 46	0.88078 51639 23	0.99514 20449 06
29	0.51175 24351 48	0.48890 72128 94	0.87233 57938 21	0.99482 02722 15
30	0.52939 90708 43	0.50414 26507 97	0.86362 03955 72	0.99449 15107 07
31	0.54704 57065 37	0.51921 77657 06	0.85464 19787 11	0.99415 61677 28
32	0.56469 23422 32	0.53412 79791 59	0.84540 36325 21	0.99381 46583 61
33	0.58233 89779 27	0.54886 87815 20	0.83590 85241 05	0.99346 74048 95
34	0.59998 56136 22	0.56343 57332 40	0.82615 98964 54	0.99311 48362 78
35	0.61763 22493 16	0.57782 44660 46	0.81616 10664 81	0.99275 73875 64
36	0.63527 88850 11	0.59203 06840 63	0.80591 54230 61	0.99239 54993 60
37	0.65292 55207 06	0.60605 01648 61	0.79542 64250 53	0.99202 96172 61
38	0.67057 21564 01	0.61987 87604 23	0.78469 75993 19	0.99166 01912 88
39	0.68821 87920 95	0.63351 23980 57	0.77373 25387 42	0.99128 76753 16
40	0.70586 54277 90	0.64694 70812 25	0.76253 49002 47	0.99091 25265 06
41	0.72351 20634 85	0.66017 88903 11	0.75110 84028 21	0.99053 52047 30
42	0.74115 86991 80	0.67320 39833 19	0.73945 68255 44	0.99015 61719 99
43	0.75880 53348 74	0.68601 85965 04	0.72758 40056 32	0.98977 58918 86
44	0.77645 19705 69	0.69861 90449 39	0.71549 38364 86	0.98939 48289 60
45	0.79409 86062 64	0.71100 17230 19	0.70319 02657 64	0.98901 34482 07

q = 0.00276 18093 29251 567   D(90) = 1.01110 85969 69203
q' = 0.18728 51836 10216 8   1/D(90) = 0.98901 34482 06750

r	ϕ	$E(\phi, k)$	A(r)	D(r)
0	0.00000 00000 00	0.00000 00000 00	0.00000 00000 00	1.00000 00000 00
1	0.01764 65961 07	0.01764 65565 19	0.01745 18741 24	1.00000 33835 28
2	0.03529 29547 44	0.03529 26381 04	0.03489 84332 11	1.00001 35299 91
3	0.05293 88387 43	0.05293 77704 40	0.05233 43638 40	1.00003 04270 26
4	0.07058 40115 30	0.07058 14804 44	0.06975 43558 21	1.00005 40540 47
5	0.08822 82374 28	0.08822 32968 80	0.08715 31038 14	1.00008 43822 67
6	0.10587 12819 52	0.10586 27509 72	0.10452 53089 36	1.00012 13747 38
7	0.12351 29121 02	0.12349 93770 08	0.12186 56803 80	1.00016 49863 89
8	0.14115 28966 58	0.14113 27129 48	0.13916 89370 16	1.00021 51640 86
9	0.15879 10064 71	0.15876 23010 16	0.15642 98090 04	1.00027 18466 95
10	0.17642 70147 47	0.17638 76882 96	0.17364 30393 94	1.00033 49651 58
11	0.19406 06973 34	0.19400 84273 13	0.19080 33857 23	1.00040 44425 73
12	0.21169 18330 04	0.21162 40766 05	0.20790 56216 13	1.00048 01942 95
13	0.22932 02037 25	0.22923 42012 96	0.22494 45383 61	1.00056 21280 30
14	0.24694 55949 37	0.24683 83736 46	0.24191 49465 17	1.00065 01439 56
15	0.26456 77958 19	0.26443 61736 01	0.25881 16774 72	1.00074 41348 38
16	0.28218 65995 51	0.28202 71893 25	0.27562 95850 23	1.00084 39861 64
17	0.29980 18035 71	0.29961 10177 19	0.29236 35469 42	1.00094 95762 79
18	0.31741 32098 25	0.31718 72649 36	0.30900 84665 34	1.00106 07765 38
19	0.33502 06250 15	0.33475 55468 69	0.32555 92741 88	1.00117 74514 61
20	0.35262 38608 34	0.35231 54896 37	0.34201 09289 19	1.00129 94588 98
21	0.37022 27342 03	0.36986 67300 47	0.35835 84199 01	1.00142 66502 02
22	0.38781 70674 91	0.38740 89160 46	0.37459 67679 94	1.00155 88704 09
23	0.40540 66887 34	0.40494 17071 54	0.39072 10272 60	1.00169 59584 29
24	0.42299 14318 48	0.42246 47748 80	0.40672 62864 64	1.00183 77472 42
25	0.44057 11368 26	0.43997 78031 22	0.42260 76705 75	1.00198 40641 01
26	0.45814 56499 37	0.45748 04885 50	0.43836 03422 46	1.00213 47307 40
27	0.47571 48239 11	0.47497 25409 67	0.45397 95032 87	1.00228 95635 95
28	0.49327 85181 13	0.49245 36836 57	0.46946 03961 28	1.00244 83740 27
29	0.51083 65987 14	0.50992 36537 08	0.48479 83052 66	1.00261 09685 50
30	0.52838 89388 52	0.52738 22023 21	0.49998 85587 01	1.00277 71490 67
31	0.54593 54187 81	0.54482 90950 96	0.51502 65293 61	1.00294 67131 12
32	0.56347 59260 10	0.56226 41122 97	0.52990 76365 09	1.00311 94540 99
33	0.58101 03554 40	0.57968 70491 04	0.54462 73471 38	1.00329 51615 69
34	0.59853 86094 82	0.59709 77158 33	0.55918 11773 56	1.00347 36214 49
35	0.61606 05981 71	0.61449 59381 49	0.57356 46937 47	1.00365 46163 14
36	0.63357 62392 70	0.63188 15572 45	0.58777 35147 27	1.00383 79256 49
37	0.65108 54583 62	0.64925 44300 11	0.60180 33118 73	1.00402 33261 21
38	0.66858 81889 32	0.66661 44291 77	0.61564 98112 50	1.00421 05918 46
39	0.68608 43724 42	0.68396 14434 37	0.62930 87947 07	1.00439 94946 71
40	0.70357 39583 94	0.70129 53775 49	0.64277 61011 66	1.00458 98044 48
41	0.72105 69043 81	0.71861 61524 18	0.65604 76278 92	1.00478 12893 11
42	0.73853 31761 31	0.73592 37051 61	0.66911 93317 40	1.00497 37159 68
43	0.75600 27475 40	0.75321 79891 38	0.68198 72303 92	1.00516 68499 75
44	0.77346 56006 94	0.77049 89739 85	0.69464 74035 68	1.00536 04560 29
45	0.79092 17258 80	0.78776 66456 01	0.70709 59942 27	1.00555 42982 51

K = 1.58819 72125 27520   E = 1.55368 08919 36509
K'= 2.97856 89511 81384   E'= 1.05377 69204 07046

r	u=(r/90)K=F(ϕ,k)	sn u	cn u	dn u
45	0.79409 86062 64	0.71100 17230 19	0.70319 02657 64	0.98901 34482 07
46	0.81174 52419 59	0.72316 31049 03	0.69067 72934 64	0.98863 22144 64
47	0.82939 18776 53	0.73509 97448 98	0.67795 89700 35	0.98825 15918 52
48	0.84703 85133 48	0.74680 82777 80	0.66503 93945 01	0.98787 20432 14
49	0.86468 51490 43	0.75828 54190 68	0.65192 27126 19	0.98749 40295 53
50	0.88233 17847 38	0.76952 79652 34	0.63861 31150 57	0.98711 80094 80
51	0.89997 84204 32	0.78053 27938 69	0.62511 48356 07	0.98674 44386 63
52	0.91762 50561 27	0.79129 68637 97	0.61143 21494 20	0.98637 37692 88
53	0.93527 16918 22	0.80181 72151 44	0.59756 93712 85	0.98600 64495 20
54	0.95291 83275 17	0.81209 09693 57	0.58353 08539 30	0.98564 29229 73
55	0.97056 49632 11	0.82211 53291 88	0.56932 09863 64	0.98528 36281 92
56	0.98821 15989 06	0.83188 75786 31	0.55494 41922 56	0.98492 89981 41
57	1.00585 82346 01	0.84140 50828 31	0.54040 49283 52	0.98457 94596 92
58	1.02350 48702 96	0.85066 52879 47	0.52570 76829 21	0.98423 54331 41
59	1.04115 15059 90	0.85966 57209 95	0.51085 69742 56	0.98389 73317 13
60	1.05879 81416 85	0.86840 39896 51	0.49585 73492 03	0.98356 55610 96
61	1.07644 47773 80	0.87687 77820 33	0.48071 33817 34	0.98324 05189 70
62	1.09409 14130 75	0.88508 48664 58	0.46542 96715 58	0.98292 25945 59
63	1.11173 80487 69	0.89302 30911 78	0.45001 08427 84	0.98261 21681 89
64	1.12938 46844 64	0.90069 03840 92	0.43446 15426 07	0.98230 96108 59
65	1.14703 13201 59	0.90808 47524 47	0.41878 64400 53	0.98201 52838 20
66	1.16467 79558 54	0.91520 42825 26	0.40299 02247 53	0.98172 95381 77
67	1.18232 45915 48	0.92204 71393 14	0.38707 76057 63	0.98145 27144 93
68	1.19997 12272 43	0.92861 15661 69	0.37105 33104 24	0.98118 51424 11
69	1.21761 78629 38	0.93489 58844 79	0.35492 20832 58	0.98092 71402 93
70	1.23526 44986 33	0.94089 84933 10	0.33868 86849 11	0.98067 90148 62
71	1.25291 11343 27	0.94661 78690 64	0.32235 78911 23	0.98044 10608 73
72	1.27055 77700 22	0.95205 25651 24	0.30593 44917 47	0.98021 35607 84
73	1.28820 44057 17	0.95720 12115 14	0.28942 32897 95	0.97999 67844 50
74	1.30585 10414 12	0.96206 25145 52	0.27282 91005 25	0.97979 09888 30
75	1.32349 76771 06	0.96663 52565 17	0.25615 67505 61	0.97959 64177 09
76	1.34114 43128 01	0.97091 82953 21	0.23941 10770 42	0.97941 33014 30
77	1.35879 09484 96	0.97491 05641 94	0.22259 69268 06	0.97924 18566 52
78	1.37643 75841 91	0.97861 10713 75	0.20571 91556 06	0.97908 22861 10
79	1.39408 42198 85	0.98201 88998 25	0.18878 26273 45	0.97893 47784 04
80	1.41173 08555 80	0.98513 32069 49	0.17179 22133 48	0.97879 95077 92
81	1.42937 74912 75	0.98795 32243 36	0.15475 27916 53	0.97867 66340 06
82	1.44702 41269 70	0.99047 82575 18	0.13766 92463 26	0.97856 63020 82
83	1.46467 07626 64	0.99270 76857 48	0.12054 64667 93	0.97846 86422 05
84	1.48231 73983 59	0.99464 09617 97	0.10338 93472 04	0.97838 37695 71
85	1.49996 40340 54	0.99627 76117 73	0.08620 27857 96	0.97831 17842 63
86	1.51761 06697 49	0.99761 72349 65	0.06899 16842 87	0.97825 27711 47
87	1.53525 73054 43	0.99865 95037 04	0.05176 09472 70	0.97820 67997 81
88	1.55290 39411 38	0.99940 41632 53	0.03451 54816 31	0.97817 39243 45
89	1.57055 05768 33	0.99985 10317 22	0.01726 01959 64	0.97815 41835 76
90	1.58819 72125 28	1.00000 00000 00	0.00000 00000 00	0.97814 76007 34

q = 0.00276 18093 29251 567
q' = 0.18728 51836 10216 8

D(90) = 1.01110 85969 69203
1/D(90) = 0.98901 34482 06750

r	ϕ	$E(\phi,k)$	$A(r)$	$D(r)$
45	0.79092 17258 80	0.78776 66456 01	0.70709 59942 27	1.00555 42982 51
46	0.80837 11215 94	0.80502 10061 38	0.71932 92097 35	1.00574 81404 73
47	0.82581 37945 25	0.82226 20739 54	0.73134 33230 33	1.00594 17465 28
48	0.84324 97595 44	0.83948 98835 57	0.74313 46737 65	1.00613 48805 38
49	0.86067 90396 74	0.85670 44855 25	0.75469 96693 99	1.00632 73071 99
50	0.87810 16660 52	0.87390 59464 05	0.76603 47863 24	1.00651 87920 68
51	0.89551 76778 84	0.89109 43486 02	0.77713 65709 23	1.00670 91018 50
52	0.91292 71223 85	0.90826 97902 37	0.78800 16406 32	1.00689 80046 82
53	0.93033 00547 19	0.92543 23849 96	0.79862 66849 66	1.00708 52704 16
54	0.94772 65379 14	0.94258 22619 60	0.80900 84665 34	1.00727 06708 97
55	0.96511 66427 85	0.95971 95654 12	0.81914 38220 29	1.00745 39802 42
56	0.98250 04478 39	0.97684 44546 34	0.82902 96631 91	1.00763 49751 18
57	0.99987 80391 67	0.99395 71036 83	0.83866 29777 49	1.00781 34350 10
58	1.01724 95103 38	1.01105 77011 52	0.84804 08303 48	1.00798 91424 92
59	1.03461 49622 75	1.02814 64499 17	0.85716 03634 36	1.00816 18834 92
60	1.05197 45031 26	1.04522 35668 61	0.86601 87981 47	1.00833 14475 51
61	1.06932 82481 32	1.06228 92825 97	0.87461 34351 43	1.00849 76280 83
62	1.08667 63194 73	1.07934 38411 60	0.88294 16554 42	1.00866 02226 20
63	1.10401 88461 23	1.09638 74996 97	0.89100 09212 16	1.00881 90330 68
64	1.12135 59636 85	1.11342 05281 40	0.89878 87765 71	1.00897 38659 39
65	1.13868 78142 22	1.13044 32088 65	0.90630 28482 95	1.00912 45325 94
66	1.15601 45460 85	1.14745 58363 35	0.91354 08465 82	1.00927 08494 68
67	1.17333 63137 27	1.16445 87167 38	0.92050 05657 35	1.00941 26382 98
68	1.19065 32775 16	1.18145 21676 08	0.92717 98848 39	1.00954 97263 35
69	1.20796 56035 37	1.19843 65174 39	0.93357 67684 09	1.00968 19465 58
70	1.22527 34633 91	1.21541 21052 80	0.93968 92670 16	1.00980 91378 77
71	1.24257 70339 87	1.23237 92803 28	0.94551 55178 78	1.00993 11453 31
72	1.25987 64973 28	1.24933 84015 12	0.95105 37454 32	1.01004 78202 70
73	1.27717 20402 89	1.26628 98370 56	0.95630 22618 79	1.01015 90205 44
74	1.29446 38543 96	1.28323 39640 48	0.96125 94676 99	1.01026 46106 74
75	1.31175 21355 91	1.30017 11679 90	0.96592 38521 38	1.01036 44620 14
76	1.32903 70840 01	1.31710 18423 45	0.97029 39936 75	1.01045 84529 10
77	1.34631 89036 97	1.33402 63880 75	0.97436 85604 52	1.01054 64688 49
78	1.36359 78024 53	1.35094 52131 72	0.97814 63106 85	1.01062 84025 97
79	1.38087 39914 93	1.36785 87321 82	0.98162 60930 41	1.01070 41543 30
80	1.39814 76852 44	1.38476 73657 28	0.98480 68469 96	1.01077 36317 57
81	1.41541 91010 81	1.40167 15400 18	0.98768 76031 51	1.01083 67502 29
82	1.43268 84590 67	1.41857 16863 54	0.99026 74835 37	1.01089 34328 48
83	1.44995 59816 95	1.43546 82406 39	0.99254 57018 78	1.01094 36105 53
84	1.46722 18936 23	1.45236 16428 73	0.99452 15638 35	1.01098 72222 11
85	1.48448 64214 07	1.46925 23366 51	0.99619 44672 15	1.01102 42146 88
86	1.50160 43491 32	1.48614 07686 55	0.99756 39021 60	1.01105 45429 14
87	1.51901 22386 64	1.50302 73881 41	0.99862 94513 00	1.01107 81699 38
88	1.53627 39883 32	1.51991 26464 30	0.99939 07898 81	1.01109 50669 76
89	1.55353 52737 06	1.53679 69963 94	0.99984 76858 65	1.01110 52134 40
90	1.57079 63267 95	1.55368 08919 37	1.00000 00000 00	1.01110 85969 69

K = 1.59125 43820 13687   E = 1.55073 19509 84013
K' = 2.90256 49406 70027   E' = 1.06105 93337 53857

r	u=(r/90)K=F(ϕ,k)	sn u	cn u	dn u
0	0.00000 00000 00	0.00000 00000 00	1.00000 00000 00	1.00000 00000 00
1	0.01768 06042 45	0.01767 96364 85	0.99984 37030 13	0.99999 20914 94
2	0.03536 12084 89	0.03535 34670 01	0.99937 48707 92	0.99996 83759 89
3	0.05304 18127 34	0.05301 56885 35	0.99859 36795 16	0.99992 88835 08
4	0.07072 24169 78	0.07066 05039 79	0.99750 04226 45	0.99987 36640 45
5	0.08840 30212 23	0.08828 21250 70	0.99609 55106 78	0.99980 27874 93
6	0.10608 36254 68	0.10587 47753 22	0.99437 94708 01	0.99971 63435 43
7	0.12376 42297 12	0.12343 26929 33	0.99235 29464 44	0.99961 44415 64
8	0.14144 48339 57	0.14095 01336 76	0.99001 66967 36	0.99949 72104 44
9	0.15912 54382 01	0.15842 13737 64	0.98737 15958 72	0.99936 47984 13
10	0.17680 60424 46	0.17584 07126 78	0.98441 86323 74	0.99921 73728 33
11	0.19448 66466 91	0.19320 24759 70	0.98115 89082 71	0.99905 51199 65
12	0.21216 72509 35	0.21050 10180 21	0.97759 36381 81	0.99887 82447 11
13	0.22984 78551 80	0.22773 07247 60	0.97372 41483 09	0.99868 69703 25
14	0.24752 84594 24	0.24488 60163 38	0.96955 18753 54	0.99848 15381 04
15	0.26520 90636 69	0.26196 13497 50	0.96507 83653 35	0.99826 22070 53
16	0.28288 96679 14	0.27895 12214 07	0.96030 52723 36	0.99802 92535 26
17	0.30057 02721 58	0.29585 01696 49	0.95523 43571 70	0.99778 29708 44
18	0.31825 08764 03	0.31265 27772 02	0.94986 74859 72	0.99752 36688 91
19	0.33593 14806 47	0.32935 36735 70	0.94420 66287 13	0.99725 16736 86
20	0.35361 20848 92	0.34594 75373 65	0.93825 38576 48	0.99696 73269 38
21	0.37129 26891 37	0.36242 90985 65	0.93201 13457 00	0.99667 09855 77
22	0.38897 32933 81	0.37879 31407 08	0.92548 13647 79	0.99636 30212 68
23	0.40665 38976 26	0.39503 45030 09	0.91866 62840 40	0.99604 38199 06
24	0.42433 45018 70	0.41114 80824 04	0.91156 85680 93	0.99571 37810 91
25	0.44201 51061 15	0.42712 88355 20	0.90419 07751 50	0.99537 33175 92
26	0.45969 57103 60	0.44297 17805 63	0.89653 55551 37	0.99502 28547 89
27	0.47737 63146 04	0.45867 19991 29	0.88860 56477 51	0.99466 28301 03
28	0.49505 69188 49	0.47422 46379 42	0.88040 38804 83	0.99429 36924 13
29	0.51273 75230 93	0.48962 49104 92	0.87193 31666 05	0.99391 59014 58
30	0.53041 81273 38	0.50486 80986 13	0.86319 65031 23	0.99352 99272 28
31	0.54809 87315 82	0.51994 95539 63	0.85419 69686 99	0.99313 62493 43
32	0.56577 93358 27	0.53486 46994 25	0.84493 77215 56	0.99273 53564 27
33	0.58345 99400 72	0.54960 90304 30	0.83542 19973 58	0.99232 77454 62
34	0.60114 05443 16	0.56417 81161 86	0.82565 31070 71	0.99191 39211 50
35	0.61882 11485 61	0.57856 76008 36	0.81563 44348 20	0.99149 43952 49
36	0.63650 17528 05	0.59277 32045 22	0.80536 94357 26	0.99106 96859 21
37	0.65418 23570 50	0.60679 07243 78	0.79486 16337 51	0.99064 03170 62
38	0.67186 29612 95	0.62061 60354 34	0.78411 46195 31	0.99020 68176 36
39	0.68954 35655 39	0.63424 50914 44	0.77313 20482 16	0.98976 97210 00
40	0.70722 41697 84	0.64767 39256 31	0.76191 76373 19	0.98932 95642 31
41	0.72490 47740 28	0.66089 86513 57	0.75047 51645 68	0.98888 68874 48
42	0.74258 53782 73	0.67391 54627 23	0.73880 84657 77	0.98844 22331 39
43	0.76026 59825 18	0.68672 06350 79	0.72692 14327 27	0.98799 61454 84
44	0.77794 65867 62	0.69931 05254 78	0.71481 80110 74	0.98754 91696 80
45	0.79562 71910 07	0.71168 15730 50	0.70250 21982 74	0.98710 18512 72

ELLIPTIC FUNCTIONS TABLE $\theta = 13°$

q = 0.00324 54674 43524 990   D(90) = 1.01306 66847 71240
q'= 0.17865 56628 04652 6   1/D(90) = 0.98710 18512 72317

r	ϕ	$E(\phi,k)$	A(r)	D(r)
0	0.00000 00000 00	0.00000 00000 00	0.00000 00000 00	1.00000 00000 00
1	0.01768 05576 34	0.01768 05110 23	0.01745 16713 60	1.00000 39799 35
2	0.03536 08356 72	0.03536 04628 62	0.03489 80281 15	1.00001 59148 92
3	0.05304 05548 73	0.05303 92970 67	0.05233 37572 75	1.00003 57903 28
4	0.07071 94367 05	0.07071 64566 57	0.06975 35490 80	1.00006 35820 30
5	0.08839 72036 91	0.08839 13868 48	0.08715 20986 13	1.00009 92561 38
6	0.10607 35797 70	0.10606 35357 84	0.10452 41074 15	1.00014 27691 87
7	0.12374 82906 39	0.12373 23552 56	0.12186 42850 91	1.00019 40681 64
8	0.14142 10641 01	0.14139 73014 23	0.13916 73509 21	1.00025 30905 70
9	0.15909 16304 09	0.15905 78355 20	0.15642 80354 66	1.00031 97644 94
10	0.17675 97226 07	0.17671 34245 59	0.17364 10821 66	1.00039 40087 05
11	0.19442 50768 67	0.19436 35420 26	0.19080 12489 41	1.00047 57327 47
12	0.21208 74328 16	0.21200 76685 59	0.20790 33097 83	1.00056 48370 52
13	0.22974 65338 68	0.22964 52926 25	0.22494 20563 47	1.00066 12130 61
14	0.24740 21275 46	0.24727 59111 77	0.24191 22995 31	1.00076 47433 54
15	0.26505 39657 93	0.26489 90303 00	0.25880 88710 56	1.00087 53017 96
16	0.28270 18052 88	0.28251 41658 44	0.27562 66250 37	1.00099 27536 89
17	0.30034 54077 46	0.30012 08440 41	0.29236 04395 49	1.00111 69559 34
18	0.31798 45402 14	0.31771 86021 09	0.30900 52181 81	1.00124 77572 11
19	0.33561 89753 63	0.33530 69888 32	0.32555 58915 91	1.00138 49981 59
20	0.35324 84917 67	0.35288 55651 31	0.34200 74190 45	1.00152 85115 72
21	0.37087 28741 75	0.37045 39046 09	0.35835 47899 49	1.00167 81225 99
22	0.38849 19137 80	0.38801 15940 85	0.37459 30253 77	1.00183 36489 63
23	0.40610 54084 72	0.40555 82341 00	0.39071 71795 85	1.00199 49011 79
24	0.42371 31630 86	0.42309 34394 08	0.40672 23415 11	1.00216 16827 87
25	0.44131 49896 40	0.44061 68394 43	0.42260 36362 78	1.00233 37905 88
26	0.45891 07075 61	0.45812 80787 69	0.43835 62266 71	1.00251 10148 96
27	0.47650 01439 04	0.47562 68174 98	0.45397 53146 11	1.00269 31397 91
28	0.49408 31335 62	0.49311 27317 01	0.46945 61426 19	1.00287 99433 81
29	0.51165 95194 61	0.51058 55137 78	0.48479 39952 59	1.00307 11980 74
30	0.52922 91527 44	0.52804 48728 21	0.49998 42005 78	1.00326 66708 58
31	0.54679 18929 54	0.54549 05349 41	0.51502 21315 28	1.00346 61235 77
32	0.56434 76081 92	0.56292 22435 76	0.52990 32073 74	1.00366 93132 31
33	0.58189 61752 73	0.58033 97597 80	0.54462 28950 90	1.00387 59922 63
34	0.59943 74798 69	0.59774 28624 76	0.55917 67107 43	1.00408 59088 67
35	0.61697 14166 38	0.61513 13486 93	0.57356 02208 54	1.00429 88072 92
36	0.63449 78893 45	0.63250 50337 77	0.58776 90437 52	1.00451 44281 54
37	0.65201 68109 67	0.64986 37515 76	0.60179 88509 12	1.00473 25087 53
38	0.66952 81037 90	0.66720 73545 99	0.61564 53682 69	1.00495 27833 91
39	0.68703 16994 92	0.68453 57141 53	0.62930 43775 26	1.00517 49836 96
40	0.70452 75392 15	0.70184 87204 52	0.64277 17174 38	1.00539 88389 53
41	0.72201 55736 25	0.71914 62827 07	0.65604 32850 81	1.00562 40764 28
42	0.73949 57629 59	0.73642 83291 85	0.66911 50371 07	1.00585 04217 04
43	0.75696 80770 63	0.75369 48072 48	0.68198 29909 71	1.00607 75990 15
44	0.77443 24954 12	0.77094 56833 63	0.69464 32261 53	1.00630 53315 78
45	0.79188 90071 26	0.78818 09430 99	0.70709 18853 49	1.00653 33419 39

K = 1.59125 43820 13687   E = 1.55073 19509 84013
K′ = 2.90256 49406 70027   E′ = 1.06105 93337 53857

r	u=(r/90)K=F(ϕ,k)	sn u	cn u	dn u
45	0.79562 71910 07	0.71168 15730 50	0.70250 21982 74	0.98710 18512 72
46	0.81330 77952 51	0.72383 02993 11	0.68997 80415 34	0.98665 47354 81
47	0.83098 83994 96	0.73575 33084 00	0.67724 96357 90	0.98620 83665 40
48	0.84866 90037 41	0.74744 72872 64	0.66432 11217 19	0.98576 32870 37
49	0.86634 96079 85	0.75890 90057 67	0.65119 66837 80	0.98532 00372 60
50	0.88403 02122 30	0.77013 53167 50	0.63788 05482 95	0.98487 91545 44
51	0.90171 08164 74	0.78112 31560 35	0.62437 69815 63	0.98444 11726 40
52	0.91939 14207 19	0.79186 95423 67	0.61069 02880 11	0.98400 66210 72
53	0.93707 20249 64	0.80237 15773 13	0.59682 48083 99	0.98357 60245 20
54	0.95475 26292 08	0.81262 64451 10	0.58278 49180 51	0.98314 99021 99
55	0.97243 32334 53	0.82263 14124 70	0.56857 50251 44	0.98272 87672 57
56	0.99011 38376 97	0.83238 38283 41	0.55419 95690 33	0.98231 31261 79
57	1.00779 44419 42	0.84188 11236 29	0.53966 30186 30	0.98190 34782 01
58	1.02547 50461 87	0.85112 08108 85	0.52496 98708 29	0.98150 03147 39
59	1.04315 56504 31	0.86010 04839 60	0.51012 46489 74	0.98110 41188 25
60	1.06083 62546 76	0.86881 78176 28	0.49513 19013 87	0.98071 53645 63
61	1.07851 68589 20	0.87727 05671 84	0.47999 61999 36	0.98033 45165 88
62	1.09619 74631 65	0.88545 65680 14	0.46472 21386 59	0.97996 20295 49
63	1.11387 80674 10	0.89337 37351 56	0.44931 43324 36	0.97959 83475 97
64	1.13155 86716 54	0.90102 00628 28	0.43377 74157 12	0.97924 39038 92
65	1.14923 92758 99	0.90839 36239 50	0.41811 60412 70	0.97889 91201 23
66	1.16691 98801 43	0.91549 25696 56	0.40233 48790 55	0.97856 44060 46
67	1.18460 04843 88	0.92231 51287 94	0.38643 86150 46	0.97824 01590 30
68	1.20228 10886 33	0.92885 96074 16	0.37043 19501 76	0.97792 67636 26
69	1.21996 16928 77	0.93512 43882 76	0.35431 95993 05	0.97762 45911 49
70	1.23764 22971 22	0.94110 79303 17	0.33810 62902 33	0.97733 39992 77
71	1.25532 29013 66	0.94680 87681 65	0.32179 67627 65	0.97705 53316 63
72	1.27300 35056 11	0.95222 55116 30	0.30539 57678 18	0.97678 89175 69
73	1.29068 41098 56	0.95735 68452 09	0.28890 80665 75	0.97653 50715 11
74	1.30836 47141 00	0.96220 15276 03	0.27233 84296 75	0.97629 40929 27
75	1.32604 53183 45	0.96675 83912 49	0.25569 16364 50	0.97606 62658 58
76	1.34372 59225 89	0.97102 63418 54	0.23897 24742 00	0.97585 18586 49
77	1.36140 65268 34	0.97500 43579 64	0.22218 57375 04	0.97565 11236 63
78	1.37908 71310 79	0.97869 14905 37	0.20533 62275 65	0.97546 42970 20
79	1.39676 77353 23	0.98208 68625 40	0.18842 87515 93	0.97529 15983 45
80	1.41444 83395 68	0.98518 96685 74	0.17146 81222 15	0.97513 32305 43
81	1.43212 89438 12	0.98799 91745 16	0.15445 91569 20	0.97498 93795 87
82	1.44980 95480 57	0.99051 47171 91	0.13740 66775 24	0.97486 02143 19
83	1.46749 01523 02	0.99273 57040 69	0.12031 55096 69	0.97474 58862 84
84	1.48517 07565 46	0.99466 16129 90	0.10319 04823 36	0.97464 65295 66
85	1.50285 13607 91	0.99629 19919 20	0.08603 64273 84	0.97456 22606 52
86	1.52053 19650 35	0.99762 64587 36	0.06885 81791 04	0.97449 31783 11
87	1.53821 25692 80	0.99866 47010 46	0.05166 05737 92	0.97443 93634 94
88	1.55589 31735 24	0.99940 64760 34	0.03444 84493 30	0.97440 08792 50
89	1.57357 37777 69	0.99985 16103 45	0.01722 66447 84	0.97437 77706 58
90	1.59125 43820 14	1.00000 00000 00	0.00000 00000 00	0.97437 00647 85

q = 0.00324 54674 43524 990   D(90) = 1.01306 66847 71240
q' = 0.17865 56628 04652 6   1/D(90) = 0.98710 18512 72317

r	ϕ	$E(\phi,k)$	$A(r)$	$D(r)$
45	0.79188 90071 26	0.78818 09430 99	0.70709 18853 49	1.00653 33419 39
46	0.80933 76109 69	0.80540 05910 86	0.71932 51756 52	1.00676 13523 01
47	0.82677 83153 36	0.82260 46509 59	0.73133 93697 10	1.00698 90848 68
48	0.84421 11382 32	0.83979 31652 80	0.74313 08068 60	1.00721 62621 83
49	0.86163 61072 34	0.85696 61954 35	0.75469 58942 51	1.00744 26074 67
50	0.87905 32594 49	0.87412 38215 06	0.76603 11079 39	1.00766 78449 52
51	0.89646 26414 52	0.89126 61421 26	0.77713 29939 61	1.00789 17002 20
52	0.91386 43092 18	0.90839 32743 08	0.78799 81693 95	1.00811 39005 40
53	0.93125 83280 44	0.92550 53532 61	0.79862 33233 90	1.00833 41751 93
54	0.94864 47724 56	0.94260 25321 72	0.80900 52181 81	1.00855 22558 09
55	0.96602 37261 07	0.95968 49819 81	0.81914 06900 76	1.00876 78766 90
56	0.98339 52816 63	0.97675 28911 30	0.82902 66504 22	1.00898 07751 36
57	1.00075 95406 85	0.99380 64652 95	0.83866 00865 56	1.00919 06917 63
58	1.01811 66134 91	1.01084 59270 93	0.84803 80627 17	1.00939 73708 19
59	1.03546 66190 12	1.02787 15157 85	0.85715 77209 52	1.00960 05604 97
60	1.05280 96846 45	1.04488 34869 45	0.86601 62819 84	1.00980 00132 43
61	1.07014 59460 85	1.06188 21121 23	0.87461 10460 67	1.00999 54860 54
62	1.08747 55471 53	1.07886 76784 90	0.88293 93938 11	1.01018 67407 77
63	1.10479 86396 19	1.09584 04884 60	0.89099 87869 79	1.01037 35443 96
64	1.12211 53830 06	1.11280 08593 10	0.89878 67692 71	1.01055 56693 20
65	1.13942 59443 99	1.12974 91227 68	0.90630 09670 71	1.01073 28936 59
66	1.15673 04982 31	1.14668 56246 04	0.91353 90901 76	1.01090 50014 91
67	1.17402 92260 72	1.16361 07241 94	0.92049 89324 94	1.01107 17831 30
68	1.19132 23164 04	1.18052 47940 78	0.92717 83727 23	1.01123 30353 77
69	1.20860 99643 93	1.19742 82195 06	0.93357 53750 01	1.01138 85617 73
70	1.22589 23716 50	1.21432 13979 65	0.93968 79895 26	1.01153 81728 31
71	1.24316 97459 84	1.23120 47387 04	0.94551 43531 56	1.01168 16862 73
72	1.26044 23011 57	1.24807 86622 38	0.95105 26899 78	1.01181 89272 51
73	1.27771 02566 21	1.26494 35998 53	0.95630 13118 54	1.01194 97285 58
74	1.29497 38372 56	1.28179 99930 92	0.96125 86189 37	1.01207 39308 32
75	1.31223 32731 00	1.29864 82932 34	0.96592 31001 62	1.01219 13827 52
76	1.32948 87990 76	1.31548 89607 69	0.97029 33337 07	1.01230 19412 20
77	1.34674 06547 09	1.33232 24648 58	0.97436 79874 34	1.01240 54715 38
78	1.36398 90838 45	1.34914 92827 90	0.97814 58192 90	1.01250 18475 71
79	1.38123 43343 57	1.36596 98994 32	0.98162 56776 93	1.01259 09518 99
80	1.39847 66578 55	1.38278 48066 68	0.98480 65018 84	1.01267 26759 62
81	1.41561 93466 50	1.39959 45028 38	0.98768 73222 51	1.01274 69201 92
82	1.43295 35471 35	1.41639 94921 67	0.99026 72606 26	1.01281 35941 33
83	1.45018 86321 19	1.43320 02841 90	0.99254 55305 58	1.01287 26165 55
84	1.46742 18278 81	1.44999 73931 76	0.99452 14375 50	1.01292 39155 46
85	1.48465 34001 79	1.46679 13375 41	0.99619 43792 71	1.01296 74286 07
86	1.50188 36166 72	1.48358 26392 65	0.99756 38457 47	1.01300 31027 24
87	1.51911 27466 11	1.50037 18233 01	0.99862 94195 12	1.01303 08944 33
88	1.53634 10605 19	1.51715 94169 86	0.99939 07757 35	1.01305 07698 75
89	1.55356 88298 75	1.53394 59494 41	0.99984 76823 26	1.01306 27048 35
90	1.57079 63267 95	1.55073 19509 84	1.00000 00000 00	1.01306 66847 71

K = 1.59456 83409 31825   E = 1.54755 45758 69993
K'= 2.83267 25829 18100   E'= 1.06860 95329 78401

r	u=(r/90)K=F(ϕ,k)	sn u	cn u	dn u
0	0.00000 00000 00	0.00000 00000 00	1.00000 00000 00	1.00000 00000 00
1	0.01771 74260 10	0.01771 64448 49	0.99984 30514 75	0.99999 08150 77
2	0.03543 48520 21	0.03542 70033 65	0.99937 22666 92	0.99996 32720 09
3	0.05315 22780 31	0.05312 57923 96	0.99858 78279 76	0.99991 74058 79
4	0.07086 97040 41	0.07080 69351 46	0.99749 00390 16	0.99985 32751 03
5	0.08858 71300 52	0.08846 45643 39	0.99607 93245 80	0.99977 09613 46
6	0.10630 45560 62	0.10609 28253 73	0.99435 62301 33	0.99967 05694 06
7	0.12402 19820 72	0.12368 58794 44	0.99232 14213 28	0.99955 22270 60
8	0.14173 94080 83	0.14123 79066 55	0.98997 56834 00	0.99941 60848 87
9	0.15945 68340 93	0.15874 31090 85	0.98731 99204 50	0.99926 23160 45
10	0.17717 42601 04	0.17619 57138 36	0.98435 51546 19	0.99909 11160 31
11	0.19489 16861 14	0.19358 99760 22	0.98108 25251 65	0.99890 27023 97
12	0.21260 91121 24	0.21092 01817 35	0.97750 32874 30	0.99869 73144 42
13	0.23032 65381 35	0.22818 06509 41	0.97361 88117 21	0.99847 52128 72
14	0.24804 39641 45	0.24536 57403 42	0.96943 05820 77	0.99823 66794 30
15	0.26576 13901 55	0.26246 98461 67	0.96494 01949 62	0.99798 20164 94
16	0.28347 88161 66	0.27948 74069 10	0.96014 93578 50	0.99771 15466 57
17	0.30119 62421 76	0.29641 29059 97	0.95505 98877 34	0.99742 56122 66
18	0.31891 36681 86	0.31324 08743 94	0.94967 37095 49	0.99712 45749 43
19	0.33663 10941 97	0.32996 58931 30	0.94399 28545 13	0.99680 88150 79
20	0.35434 85202 07	0.34658 25957 56	0.93801 94583 90	0.99647 87313 05
21	0.37206 59462 17	0.36308 56707 22	0.93175 57596 90	0.99613 47399 33
22	0.38978 33722 28	0.37946 98636 73	0.92520 40977 88	0.99577 72743 81
23	0.40750 07982 38	0.39572 99796 61	0.91836 69109 88	0.99540 67845 76
24	0.42521 82242 48	0.41186 08852 76	0.91124 67345 24	0.99502 37363 29
25	0.44293 56502 59	0.42785 75106 80	0.90384 61985 06	0.99462 86107 03
26	0.46065 30762 69	0.44371 48515 66	0.89616 80258 19	0.99422 19033 50
27	0.47837 05022 80	0.45942 79710 13	0.88821 50299 62	0.99380 41238 41
28	0.49608 79282 90	0.47499 20012 54	0.87999 01128 68	0.99337 57949 76
29	0.51380 53543 00	0.49040 21453 53	0.87149 62626 62	0.99293 74520 77
30	0.53152 27803 11	0.50565 36787 85	0.86273 65514 06	0.99248 96422 71
31	0.54924 02063 21	0.52074 19509 23	0.85371 41328 04	0.99203 29237 59
32	0.56695 76323 31	0.53566 23864 30	0.84443 22398 89	0.99156 78650 77
33	0.58467 50583 42	0.55041 04865 53	0.83489 41826 92	0.99109 50443 41
34	0.60239 24843 52	0.56498 18303 30	0.82510 33458 89	0.99061 50484 88
35	0.62010 99103 62	0.57937 20756 93	0.81506 31864 51	0.99012 84725 09
36	0.63782 73363 73	0.59357 69604 87	0.80477 72312 75	0.98963 59186 75
37	0.65554 47623 83	0.60759 23033 90	0.79424 90748 26	0.98913 79957 58
38	0.67326 21883 93	0.62141 40047 39	0.78348 23767 73	0.98863 53182 45
39	0.69097 96144 04	0.63503 80472 77	0.77248 08596 40	0.98812 85055 56
40	0.70869 70404 14	0.64846 04967 99	0.76124 83064 62	0.98761 81812 53
41	0.72641 44664 24	0.66167 75027 18	0.74978 85584 60	0.98710 49722 54
42	0.74413 18924 35	0.67468 52985 41	0.73810 55127 37	0.98658 95080 44
43	0.76184 93184 45	0.68748 02022 67	0.72620 31199 95	0.98607 24198 88
44	0.77956 67444 56	0.70005 86167 03	0.71408 53822 76	0.98555 43400 50
45	0.79728 41704 66	0.71241 70296 94	0.70175 63507 39	0.98503 59010 09

54

q = 0.00376 92262 86977 846   D(90) = 1.01519 14249 78510
q′= 0.17059 45383 49476 6   1/D(90) = 0.98503 59010 08687

r	ϕ	$E(\phi,k)$	A(r)	D(r)
0	0.00000 00000 00	0.00000 00000 00	0.00000 00000 00	1.00000 00000 00
1	0.01771 73717 64	0.01771 73175 17	0.01745 14149 63	1.00000 46271 02
2	0.03543 44181 30	0.03543 39842 49	0.03489 75158 68	1.00001 85027 70
3	0.05315 08141 16	0.05314 93502 74	0.05233 29902 70	1.00004 16100 99
4	0.07086 62355 68	0.07086 27674 00	0.06975 25289 50	1.00007 39209 36
5	0.08858 03595 72	0.08857 35900 24	0.08715 08275 31	1.00011 53959 16
6	0.10629 28648 67	0.10628 11759 85	0.10452 25880 83	1.00016 59845 07
7	0.12400 34322 52	0.12398 48874 21	0.12186 25207 39	1.00022 56250 75
8	0.14171 17449 93	0.14168 40916 07	0.13916 53452 94	1.00029 42449 58
9	0.15941 74892 23	0.15937 81617 94	0.15642 57928 15	1.00037 17605 53
10	0.17712 03543 43	0.17706 64780 32	0.17363 86072 38	1.00045 80774 18
11	0.19482 00334 11	0.19474 84279 86	0.19079 85469 66	1.00055 30903 91
12	0.21251 62235 34	0.21242 34077 38	0.20790 03864 59	1.00065 66837 13
13	0.23020 86262 50	0.23009 08225 74	0.22493 89178 25	1.00076 87311 70
14	0.24789 69479 01	0.24775 00877 60	0.24190 89524 00	1.00088 90962 52
15	0.26558 09000 05	0.26540 06292 97	0.25880 53223 25	1.00101 76323 10
16	0.28326 01996 18	0.28304 18846 65	0.27562 28821 16	1.00115 41827 45
17	0.30093 45696 86	0.30067 33035 43	0.29235 65102 30	1.00129 85811 91
18	0.31860 37393 92	0.31829 43485 12	0.30900 11106 17	1.00145 06517 20
19	0.33626 74444 93	0.33590 44957 39	0.32555 16142 75	1.00161 02090 58
20	0.35392 54276 49	0.35350 32356 35	0.34200 29807 86	1.00177 70588 09
21	0.37157 74387 40	0.37109 00735 01	0.35835 01998 51	1.00195 09976 93
22	0.38922 32351 72	0.38866 45301 34	0.37458 82928 14	1.00213 18137 91
23	0.40686 25821 81	0.40622 61424 31	0.39071 23141 74	1.00231 92868 08
24	0.42449 52531 13	0.42377 44639 46	0.40671 73530 92	1.00251 31883 36
25	0.44212 10297 06	0.44130 90654 38	0.42259 85348 82	1.00271 32821 37
26	0.45973 97023 47	0.45882 95353 86	0.43835 10224 99	1.00291 93244 27
27	0.47735 10703 34	0.47633 54804 80	0.45397 00180 03	1.00313 10641 75
28	0.49495 49421 08	0.49382 65260 79	0.46945 07640 29	1.00334 82434 09
29	0.51255 11354 86	0.51130 23166 51	0.48478 85452 27	1.00357 05975 31
30	0.53013 94778 76	0.52876 25161 79	0.49997 86897 03	1.00379 78556 35
31	0.54771 98064 77	0.54620 68085 38	0.51501 65704 39	1.00402 97408 42
32	0.56529 19684 72	0.56363 48978 47	0.52989 76067 04	1.00426 59706 37
33	0.58285 58212 02	0.58104 65087 88	0.54461 72654 47	1.00450 62572 11
34	0.60041 12323 30	0.59844 13869 00	0.55917 10626 82	1.00475 03078 10
35	0.61795 80799 92	0.61581 92988 43	0.57355 45648 50	1.00499 78250 97
36	0.63549 62529 30	0.63318 00326 29	0.58776 33901 75	1.00524 85075 10
37	0.65302 56506 15	0.65052 33978 28	0.60179 32099 96	1.00550 20496 31
38	0.67054 61833 57	0.66784 92257 44	0.61563 97500 89	1.00575 81425 60
39	0.68805 77723 97	0.68515 73695 60	0.62929 87919 71	1.00601 64742 84
40	0.70556 03499 89	0.70244 77044 54	0.64276 61741 84	1.00627 67300 68
41	0.72305 38594 66	0.71972 01276 89	0.65603 77935 69	1.00653 85928 30
42	0.74053 82552 91	0.73697 45586 74	0.66910 96065 15	1.00680 17435 31
43	0.75801 35030 97	0.75421 09389 88	0.68197 76301 96	1.00706 58615 61
44	0.77547 95797 14	0.77142 92323 92	0.69463 79437 83	1.00733 06251 34
45	0.79293 64731 74	0.78862 94247 97	0.70708 66896 45	1.00759 57116 76

55

K = 1.59456 83409 31825   E = 1.54755 45758 69993
K′= 2.83267 25829 18100   E′= 1.06860 95329 78401

r	$u=(r/90)K=F(\phi,k)$	sn u	cn u	dn u
45	0.79728 41704 66	0.71241 70296 94	0.70175 63507 39	0.98503 59010 09
46	0.81500 15964 76	0.72455 20142 91	0.68922 01234 64	0.98451 77346 86
47	0.83271 90224 87	0.73646 02288 31	0.67648 08432 98	0.98400 04716 75
48	0.85043 64484 97	0.74813 84169 60	0.66354 26957 39	0.98348 47404 77
49	0.86815 38745 07	0.75958 34075 76	0.65040 99068 55	0.98297 11667 45
50	0.88587 13005 18	0.77079 21147 18	0.63708 67412 60	0.98246 03725 35
51	0.90358 87265 28	0.78176 15373 88	0.62357 75001 24	0.98195 29755 70
52	0.92130 61525 38	0.79248 87593 17	0.60988 65192 44	0.98144 95885 08
53	0.93902 35785 49	0.80297 09486 77	0.59601 81671 57	0.98095 08182 25
54	0.95674 10045 59	0.81320 53577 36	0.58197 68433 10	0.98045 72651 07
55	0.97445 84305 69	0.82318 93224 78	0.56776 69762 84	0.97996 95223 56
56	0.99217 58565 80	0.83292 02621 63	0.55339 30220 72	0.97948 81753 08
57	1.00989 32825 90	0.84239 56788 59	0.53885 94624 19	0.97901 38007 62
58	1.02761 07086 01	0.85161 31569 30	0.52417 08032 15	0.97854 69663 24
59	1.04532 81346 11	0.86057 03624 92	0.50933 15729 47	0.97808 82297 73
60	1.06304 55606 21	0.86926 50428 39	0.49434 63212 15	0.97763 81384 25
61	1.08076 29866 32	0.87769 50258 43	0.47921 96173 05	0.97719 72285 32
62	1.09848 04126 42	0.88585 82193 34	0.46395 60488 21	0.97676 60246 84
63	1.11619 78386 52	0.89375 26104 53	0.44856 02203 81	0.97634 50392 27
64	1.13391 52646 63	0.90137 62649 96	0.43303 67523 68	0.97593 47717 11
65	1.15163 26906 73	0.90872 73267 44	0.41739 02797 49	0.97553 57083 39
66	1.16935 01166 83	0.91580 40167 82	0.40162 54509 44	0.97514 83214 42
67	1.18706 75426 94	0.92260 46328 18	0.38574 69267 59	0.97477 30689 71
68	1.20478 49687 04	0.92912 75484 90	0.36975 93793 76	0.97441 03940 10
69	1.22250 23947 14	0.93537 12126 87	0.35366 74914 05	0.97406 07242 97
70	1.24021 98207 25	0.94133 41488 60	0.33747 59549 79	0.97372 44717 76
71	1.25793 72467 35	0.94701 49543 55	0.32118 94709 17	0.97340 20321 63
72	1.27565 46727 45	0.95241 22997 41	0.30481 27479 33	0.97309 37845 27
73	1.29337 20987 56	0.95752 49281 64	0.28835 05018 97	0.97280 00908 98
74	1.31108 95247 66	0.96235 16547 10	0.27180 74551 52	0.97252 12958 86
75	1.32880 69507 77	0.96689 13657 90	0.25518 83358 65	0.97225 77263 31
76	1.34652 43767 87	0.97114 30185 38	0.23849 78774 41	0.97200 96909 59
77	1.36424 18027 97	0.97510 56402 49	0.22174 08179 72	0.97177 74800 69
78	1.38195 92288 08	0.97877 83278 22	0.20492 18997 22	0.97156 13652 35
79	1.39967 66548 18	0.98216 02472 50	0.18804 58686 65	0.97136 15990 30
80	1.41739 40808 28	0.98525 06331 25	0.17111 74740 52	0.97117 84147 68
81	1.43511 15068 39	0.98804 87881 88	0.15414 14680 09	0.97101 20262 68
82	1.45282 89328 49	0.99055 40829 00	0.13712 26051 77	0.97086 26276 37
83	1.47054 63588 59	0.99276 59550 58	0.12006 56423 71	0.97073 03930 78
84	1.48826 37848 70	0.99468 39094 44	0.10297 53382 75	0.97061 54767 09
85	1.50598 12108 80	0.99630 75175 13	0.08585 64531 52	0.97051 80124 15
86	1.52369 86368 90	0.99763 64171 16	0.06871 37485 80	0.97043 81137 08
87	1.54141 60629 01	0.99867 03122 73	0.05155 19872 08	0.97037 58736 18
88	1.55913 34889 11	0.99940 89729 75	0.03437 59325 19	0.97033 13645 97
89	1.57685 09149 21	0.99985 22350 40	0.01719 03486 14	0.97030 46384 49
90	1.59456 83409 32	1.00000 00000 00	0.00000 00000 00	0.97029 57262 76

q = 0.00376 92262 86977 846   D(90) = 1.01519 14249 78510
q' = 0.17059 45383 49476 6   1/D(90) = 0.98503 59010 08687

r	ϕ	$E(\phi,k)$	A(r)	D(r)
45	0.79293 64731 74	0.78862 94247 97	0.70708 66896 45	1.00759 57116 76
46	0.81038 41827 12	0.80581 15242 16	0.71932 00745 27	1.00786 07982 20
47	0.82782 27187 50	0.82297 55606 82	0.73133 43707 06	1.00812 55617 99
48	0.84525 21028 62	0.84012 15861 43	0.74312 59171 33	1.00838 96798 39
49	0.86267 23677 35	0.85724 96743 31	0.75469 11205 52	1.00865 28305 53
50	0.88008 35571 12	0.87435 99206 03	0.76602 64565 97	1.00891 46933 32
51	0.89748 57257 17	0.89145 24417 57	0.77712 84708 68	1.00917 49491 38
52	0.91487 89391 76	0.90852 73758 29	0.78799 37799 92	1.00943 32808 87
53	0.93226 32739 19	0.92558 48818 56	0.79861 90726 55	1.00968 93738 44
54	0.94963 88170 72	0.94262 51396 27	0.80900 11106 17	1.00994 29159 97
55	0.96700 56663 37	0.95964 83494 00	0.81913 67296 99	1.01019 35984 45
56	0.98436 39298 55	0.97665 47316 05	0.82902 28407 57	1.01044 11157 70
57	1.00171 37260 65	0.99364 45265 24	0.83865 64306 23	1.01068 51664 10
58	1.01905 51835 44	1.01061 79939 46	0.84803 45630 30	1.01092 54530 27
59	1.03638 84408 39	1.02757 54128 05	0.85715 43795 12	1.01116 16828 68
60	1.05371 36462 88	1.04451 70807 98	0.86601 31002 78	1.01139 35681 24
61	1.07103 09578 30	1.06144 33139 85	0.87460 80250 65	1.01162 08262 78
62	1.08834 05428 00	1.07835 44463 67	0.88293 65339 63	1.01184 31804 51
63	1.10564 25777 24	1.09525 08294 50	0.89099 60882 22	1.01206 03597 39
64	1.12293 72480 87	1.11213 28317 92	0.89878 42310 27	1.01227 20995 41
65	1.14022 47481 13	1.12900 08385 29	0.90629 85882 52	1.01247 81418 87
66	1.16750 52805 15	1.14585 52508 94	0.91353 68691 88	1.01267 82357 44
67	1.17477 90562 48	1.16269 64857 09	0.92049 68672 49	1.01287 21373 29
68	1.19204 62942 51	1.17952 49748 76	0.92717 64606 44	1.01305 96104 02
69	1.20930 72211 77	1.19634 11648 45	0.93357 36130 28	1.01324 04265 57
70	1.22656 20711 18	1.21314 55160 68	0.93968 63741 32	1.01341 43654 97
71	1.24381 10853 23	1.22993 85024 52	0.94551 28803 58	1.01358 12153 04
72	1.26105 45119 03	1.24672 06107 87	0.95105 13553 49	1.01374 07726 96
73	1.27829 26055 37	1.26349 23401 68	0.95630 01105 40	1.01389 28432 79
74	1.29552 56271 62	1.28025 42014 10	0.96125 75456 71	1.01403 72417 76
75	1.31275 38436 66	1.29700 67164 51	0.96592 21492 82	1.01417 37922 61
76	1.32997 75275 66	1.31375 04177 39	0.97029 24991 74	1.01430 23283 68
77	1.34719 69566 87	1.33048 58476 21	0.97436 72628 49	1.01442 26934 96
78	1.36441 24138 33	1.34721 35577 17	0.97814 51979 18	1.01453 47409 97
79	1.38162 41864 49	1.36393 41082 90	0.98162 51524 82	1.01463 83343 59
80	1.39883 25662 87	1.38064 80676 06	0.98480 60654 87	1.01473 33473 70
81	1.41603 78490 59	1.39735 60112 89	0.98768 69670 50	1.01481 96642 70
82	1.43324 03340 91	1.41405 85216 70	0.99026 69787 54	1.01489 71798 97
83	1.45044 03239 73	1.43075 61871 34	0.99254 53139 23	1.01496 57998 08
84	1.46763 81242 04	1.44744 96014 56	0.99452 12778 62	1.01502 54404 01
85	1.48483 40428 32	1.46413 93631 38	0.99619 42680 66	1.01507 60290 14
86	1.50202 83901 00	1.48082 60747 38	0.99756 37744 13	1.01511 75040 11
87	1.51922 14780 79	1.49751 03422 04	0.99862 93793 15	1.01514 98148 62
88	1.53641 36203 06	1.51419 27741 92	0.99939 07578 47	1.01517 29222 01
89	1.55360 51314 21	1.53087 39813 97	0.99984 76778 50	1.01518 67978 75
90	1.57079 63267 95	1.54755 45758 70	1.00000 00000 00	1.01519 14249 79

K = 1.59814 20021 12540   E = 1.54415 04969 14673
K'= 2.76806 31453 68768   E'= 1.07640 51130 76403

r	u=(r/90)K=F(ϕ,k)	sn u	cn u	dn u
0	0.00000 00000 00	0.00000 00000 00	1.00000 00000 00	1.00000 00000 00
1	0.01775 71333 57	0.01775 61376 90	0.99984 23473 60	0.99998 94400 52
2	0.03551 42667 14	0.03550 63020 63	0.99936 94524 62	0.99995 77737 49
3	0.05327 14000 70	0.05324 45232 32	0.99858 15043 08	0.99990 50416 91
4	0.07102 85334 27	0.07096 48381 54	0.99747 88176 93	0.99983 13114 79
5	0.08878 56667 84	0.08866 12940 48	0.99606 18328 89	0.99973 66776 15
6	0.10654 28001 41	0.10632 79517 79	0.99433 11152 08	0.99962 12613 63
7	0.12429 99334 98	0.12395 88892 33	0.99228 73544 39	0.99948 52105 75
8	0.14205 70668 54	0.14154 82046 50	0.98993 13641 66	0.99932 86994 68
9	0.15981 42002 11	0.15909 00199 31	0.98726 40809 62	0.99915 19283 74
10	0.17757 13335 68	0.17657 84839 04	0.98428 65634 67	0.99895 51234 46
11	0.19532 84669 25	0.19400 77755 37	0.98099 99913 51	0.99873 85363 30
12	0.21308 56002 82	0.21137 21071 09	0.97740 56641 62	0.99850 24437 95
13	0.23084 27336 38	0.22866 57273 19	0.97350 50000 64	0.99824 71473 35
14	0.24859 98669 95	0.24588 29243 34	0.96929 95344 69	0.99797 29727 30
15	0.26635 70003 52	0.26301 80287 78	0.96479 09185 61	0.99768 02695 78
16	0.28411 41337 09	0.28006 54166 40	0.95998 09177 28	0.99736 94107 88
17	0.30187 12670 66	0.29701 95121 16	0.95487 14098 89	0.99704 07920 44
18	0.31962 84004 23	0.31387 47903 68	0.94946 43837 30	0.99669 48312 43
19	0.33738 55337 79	0.33062 57802 05	0.94376 19368 59	0.99633 19678 95
20	0.35514 26671 36	0.34726 70666 68	0.93776 62738 70	0.99595 26624 96
21	0.37289 98004 93	0.36379 32935 39	0.93147 97043 29	0.99555 73958 80
22	0.39065 69338 50	0.38019 91657 47	0.92490 46406 88	0.99514 66685 36
23	0.40841 40672 07	0.39647 94516 82	0.91804 35961 29	0.99472 09999 09
24	0.42617 12005 63	0.41262 89854 13	0.91089 91823 45	0.99428 09276 68
25	0.44392 83339 20	0.42864 26688 06	0.90347 41072 54	0.99382 70069 60
26	0.46168 54672 77	0.44451 54735 33	0.89577 11726 72	0.99335 98096 37
27	0.47944 26006 34	0.46024 24429 88	0.88779 32719 23	0.99287 99234 70
28	0.49719 97339 91	0.47581 86940 91	0.87954 33874 19	0.99238 79513 40
29	0.51495 68673 47	0.49123 94189 89	0.87102 45881 90	0.99188 45104 14
30	0.53271 40007 04	0.50649 98866 46	0.86224 00273 87	0.99137 02313 03
31	0.55047 11340 61	0.52159 54443 31	0.85319 29397 58	0.99084 57572 17
32	0.56822 82674 18	0.53652 15189 97	0.84388 66391 01	0.99031 17430 91
33	0.58598 54007 75	0.55127 36185 49	0.83432 45156 96	0.98976 88547 18
34	0.60374 25341 31	0.56584 73330 10	0.82451 00337 32	0.98921 77678 58
35	0.62149 96674 88	0.58023 83355 77	0.81444 67287 23	0.98865 91673 48
36	0.63925 68008 45	0.59444 23835 73	0.80413 82049 20	0.98809 37462 04
37	0.65701 39342 02	0.60845 53192 95	0.79358 81327 37	0.98752 22047 14
38	0.67477 10675 59	0.62227 30707 59	0.78280 02461 73	0.98694 52495 34
39	0.69252 82009 15	0.63589 16523 39	0.77177 83402 54	0.98636 35927 73
40	0.71028 53342 72	0.64930 71653 18	0.76052 62684 92	0.98577 79510 90
41	0.72804 24676 29	0.66251 57983 27	0.74904 79403 67	0.98518 90447 74
42	0.74579 96009 86	0.67551 38277 01	0.73734 73188 30	0.98459 75968 43
43	0.76355 67343 43	0.68829 76177 38	0.72542 84178 45	0.98400 43321 34
44	0.78131 38676 99	0.70086 36208 66	0.71329 52999 62	0.98340 99764 01
45	0.79907 10010 56	0.71320 83777 27	0.70095 20739 25	0.98281 52554 21

58

ELLIPTIC FUNCTIONS TABLE $\theta = 15°$

q = 0.00433 34205 09983 127   D(90) = 1.01748 52236 81446
q'= 0.16303 35348 21580 5   1/D(90) = 0.98281 52554 21419

r	ϕ	$E(\phi,k)$	A(r)	D(r)
0	0.00000 00000 00	0.00000 00000 00	0.00000 00000 00	1.00000 00000 00
1	0.01775 70708 49	0.01775 70083 42	0.01745 10959 39	1.00000 53257 61
2	0.03551 37667 50	0.03551 32667 99	0.03489 68784 99	1.00002 12965 56
3	0.05326 97132 34	0.05326 80264 94	0.05233 20359 14	1.00004 78929 27
4	0.07102 45367 95	0.07102 05405 67	0.06975 12596 41	1.00008 50824 70
5	0.08877 78653 64	0.08877 00651 77	0.08714 92459 71	1.00013 28198 75
6	0.10652 93287 90	0.10651 58605 02	0.10452 06976 36	1.00019 10469 83
7	0.12427 85593 10	0.12425 71917 31	0.12186 03254 22	1.00025 96928 52
8	0.14202 51920 24	0.14199 33300 47	0.13916 28497 68	1.00033 86738 48
9	0.15976 88653 53	0.15972 35535 97	0.15642 30023 70	1.00042 78937 44
10	0.17750 92215 09	0.17744 71484 62	0.17363 55277 80	1.00052 72438 41
11	0.19524 59069 45	0.19516 34095 93	0.19079 51850 01	1.00063 66030 96
12	0.21297 85728 07	0.21287 16417 56	0.20789 67490 77	1.00075 58382 70
13	0.23070 68753 75	0.23057 11604 41	0.22493 50126 80	1.00088 48040 96
14	0.24843 04764 98	0.24826 12927 65	0.24190 47876 91	1.00102 33434 47
15	0.26614 90440 25	0.26594 13783 48	0.25880 09067 73	1.00117 12875 36
16	0.28386 22522 19	0.28361 07701 76	0.27561 82249 41	1.00132 84561 14
17	0.30156 97821 66	0.30126 88354 38	0.29235 16211 27	1.00149 46576 98
18	0.31927 13221 79	0.31891 49563 34	0.30899 59997 31	1.00166 96897 95
19	0.33696 65681 84	0.33654 85308 72	0.32554 62921 72	1.00185 33391 56
20	0.35465 52240 97	0.35416 89736 26	0.34199 74584 28	1.00204 53820 34
21	0.37233 70021 95	0.37177 57164 78	0.35834 44885 66	1.00224 55844 53
22	0.39001 16234 66	0.38936 82093 24	0.37458 24042 64	1.00245 37024 98
23	0.40767 88179 58	0.40694 59207 54	0.39070 62603 28	1.00266 94826 10
24	0.42533 83251 04	0.42450 83387 10	0.40671 11461 91	1.00289 26618 93
25	0.44298 98940 39	0.44205 49710 98	0.42259 21874 09	1.00312 29684 38
26	0.46063 32839 08	0.45958 53463 88	0.43834 45471 44	1.00336 01216 53
27	0.47826 82641 52	0.47709 90141 64	0.45396 34276 34	1.00360 38326 03
28	0.49589 46147 85	0.49459 55456 55	0.46944 40716 52	1.00385 38043 64
29	0.51351 21266 52	0.51207 45342 30	0.48478 17639 58	1.00410 97323 83
30	0.53112 06016 82	0.52953 55958 56	0.49997 18327 29	1.00437 13048 53
31	0.54871 98531 12	0.54697 83695 22	0.51500 96509 86	1.00463 82030 88
32	0.56630 97057 06	0.56440 25176 41	0.52989 06380 02	1.00491 01019 13
33	0.58388 99959 57	0.58180 77264 01	0.54461 02606 95	1.00518 66700 61
34	0.60146 05722 68	0.59919 37060 91	0.55916 40350 13	1.00546 75705 78
35	0.61902 12951 27	0.61656 01913 97	0.57354 75272 99	1.00575 24612 29
36	0.63657 20372 53	0.63390 69416 52	0.58775 63556 44	1.00604 09949 20
37	0.65411 26837 40	0.65123 37410 61	0.60178 61912 19	1.00633 28201 15
38	0.67164 31321 72	0.66854 03988 88	0.61563 27596 02	1.00662 75812 72
39	0.68916 32927 34	0.68582 67496 08	0.62929 18420 76	1.00692 49192 69
40	0.70667 30882 95	0.70309 26530 31	0.64275 92769 23	1.00722 44718 47
41	0.72417 24544 85	0.72033 79943 83	0.65603 09606 88	1.00752 58740 45
42	0.74166 13397 50	0.73756 26843 63	0.66910 28494 36	1.00782 87586 53
43	0.75913 97053 91	0.75476 66591 60	0.68197 09599 87	1.00813 27566 51
44	0.77660 75255 91	0.77194 98804 42	0.69463 13711 31	1.00843 74976 66
45	0.79406 47874 20	0.78911 23353 13	0.70708 02248 29	1.00874 26104 18

59

K = 1.59814 20021 12540   E = 1.54415 04969 14673
K'= 2.76806 31453 68768   E'= 1.07640 51130 76403

r	u=(r/90)K=F(ϕ,k)	sn u	cn u	dn u
45	0.79907 10010 56	0.71320 83777 27	0.70095 20739 25	0.98281 52554 21
46	0.81682 81344 13	0.72532 85171 78	0.68840 28923 30	0.98222 08941 01
47	0.83458 52677 70	0.73722 07562 05	0.67565 19493 20	0.98162 76155 96
48	0.85234 24011 27	0.74888 18997 67	0.66270 34783 38	0.98103 61404 36
49	0.87009 95344 83	0.76030 88405 62	0.64956 17499 23	0.98044 71856 57
50	0.88785 66678 40	0.77149 85587 29	0.63623 10695 65	0.97986 14639 55
51	0.90561 38011 97	0.78244 81214 72	0.62271 57756 19	0.97927 96828 33
52	0.92337 09345 54	0.79315 46826 36	0.60902 02372 77	0.97870 25437 79
53	0.94112 80679 11	0.80361 54822 13	0.59514 88525 98	0.97813 07414 43
54	0.95888 52012 68	0.81382 78457 98	0.58110 60466 07	0.97756 49628 39
55	0.97664 23346 24	0.82378 91839 99	0.56689 62694 59	0.97700 58865 48
56	0.99439 94679 81	0.83349 69917 87	0.55252 39946 66	0.97645 41819 55
57	1.01215 66013 38	0.84294 88478 23	0.53799 37173 92	0.97591 05084 83
58	1.02991 37346 95	0.85214 24137 28	0.52330 99528 25	0.97537 55148 60
59	1.04767 08680 52	0.86107 54333 29	0.50847 72346 10	0.97484 98383 87
60	1.06542 80014 08	0.86974 57318 78	0.49350 01133 54	0.97433 41042 42
61	1.08318 51347 65	0.87815 12152 32	0.47838 31552 07	0.97382 89247 87
62	1.10094 22681 22	0.88628 98690 29	0.46313 09405 09	0.97333 48989 02
63	1.11869 94014 79	0.89415 97578 29	0.44774 80625 07	0.97285 26113 34
64	1.13645 65348 36	0.90175 90242 55	0.43223 91261 50	0.97238 26320 72
65	1.15421 36681 92	0.90908 58881 15	0.41660 87469 44	0.97192 55157 33
66	1.17197 08015 49	0.91613 86455 25	0.40086 15498 85	0.97148 18009 78
67	1.18972 79349 06	0.92291 56680 25	0.38500 21684 55	0.97105 20099 38
68	1.20748 50682 63	0.92941 54017 00	0.36903 52436 88	0.97063 66476 71
69	1.22524 22016 20	0.93563 63663 05	0.35296 54233 04	0.97023 62016 36
70	1.24299 93349 76	0.94157 71544 00	0.33679 73609 04	0.96985 11411 86
71	1.26075 64683 33	0.94723 64304 97	0.32053 57152 31	0.96948 19170 86
72	1.27851 36016 90	0.95261 29302 24	0.30418 51494 90	0.96912 89610 52
73	1.29627 07350 47	0.95770 54595 04	0.28775 03307 32	0.96879 26853 11
74	1.31402 78684 04	0.96251 28937 63	0.27123 59292 92	0.96847 34821 84
75	1.33178 50017 60	0.96703 41771 61	0.25464 66182 84	0.96817 17236 90
76	1.34954 21351 17	0.97126 83218 43	0.23798 70731 45	0.96788 77611 75
77	1.36729 92684 74	0.97521 44072 37	0.22126 19712 40	0.96762 19249 59
78	1.38505 64018 31	0.97887 15793 70	0.20447 59915 04	0.96737 45240 10
79	1.40281 35351 88	0.98223 90502 29	0.18763 38141 32	0.96714 58456 37
80	1.42057 06685 44	0.98531 60971 55	0.17074 01203 18	0.96693 61552 07
81	1.43832 78019 01	0.98810 20622 85	0.15379 95920 26	0.96674 56958 84
82	1.45608 49352 58	0.99059 63520 25	0.13681 69118 02	0.96657 46883 92
83	1.47384 20686 15	0.99279 84365 76	0.11979 67626 15	0.96642 33308 00
84	1.49159 92019 72	0.99470 78495 02	0.10274 38277 37	0.96629 17983 27
85	1.50935 63353 29	0.99632 41873 50	0.08566 27906 44	0.96618 02431 75
86	1.52711 34686 85	0.99764 71093 08	0.06855 83349 36	0.96608 87943 79
87	1.54487 06020 42	0.99867 63369 24	0.05143 51442 92	0.96601 75576 83
88	1.56262 77353 99	0.99941 16538 69	0.03429 79024 31	0.96596 66154 38
89	1.58038 48687 56	0.99985 29057 54	0.01715 12930 87	0.96593 60265 23
90	1.59814 20021 13	1.00000 00000 00	0.00000 00000 00	0.96592 58262 89

q = 0.00433 34205 09983 127   D(90) = 1.01748 52236 81446
q′ = 0.16303 35348 21580 5   1/D(90) = 0.98281 52554 21419

r	ϕ	$E(\phi,k)$	A(r)	D(r)
45	0.79406 47874 20	0.78911 23353 13	0.70708 02248 29	1.00874 26104 18
46	0.81151 14908 31	0.80625 40362 33	0.71931 37273 90	1.00904 77231 73
47	0.82894 76486 35	0.82337 50209 15	0.73132 81506 35	1.00935 24641 98
48	0.84637 32864 60	0.84047 53521 84	0.74311 98330 32	1.00965 64622 14
49	0.86378 84427 01	0.85755 51178 16	0.75468 51808 20	1.00995 93468 46
50	0.88119 31684 48	0.87461 44303 32	0.76602 06691 08	1.01026 07490 75
51	0.89858 75274 00	0.89165 34267 84	0.77712 28429 54	1.01056 03016 89
52	0.91597 15957 69	0.90867 22684 93	0.78798 83184 24	1.01085 76397 30
53	0.93334 54621 63	0.92567 11407 77	0.79861 37836 27	1.01115 24009 37
54	0.95070 92274 58	0.94265 02526 40	0.80899 59997 31	1.01144 42261 88
55	0.96806 30046 56	0.95960 98364 43	0.81913 18019 53	1.01173 27599 39
56	0.98540 69187 29	0.97655 01475 46	0.82901 81005 34	1.01201 76506 57
57	1.00274 11064 46	0.99347 14639 29	0.83865 18816 83	1.01229 85512 45
58	1.02006 57161 94	1.01037 40857 89	0.84803 02085 02	1.01257 51194 70
59	1.03738 09077 78	1.02725 83351 11	0.85715 02218 86	1.01284 70183 75
60	1.05468 68522 12	1.04412 45552 22	0.86600 91414 03	1.01311 39166 94
61	1.07198 37315 01	1.06097 31103 25	0.87460 42661 47	1.01337 54892 52
62	1.08927 17384 02	1.07780 43850 03	0.88293 29755 64	1.01363 14173 62
63	1.10655 10761 84	1.09461 87837 19	0.89099 27302 62	1.01388 13892 16
64	1.12382 19583 70	1.11141 67302 85	0.89878 10727 85	1.01412 51002 61
65	1.14108 46084 67	1.12819 86673 16	0.90629 56283 76	1.01436 22535 73
66	1.15833 92596 90	1.14496 50556 74	0.91353 41056 98	1.01459 25602 17
67	1.17558 61546 73	1.16171 63738 87	0.92049 42975 44	1.01481 57395 99
68	1.19282 55451 71	1.17845 31175 57	0.92717 40815 15	1.01503 15198 10
69	1.21005 76917 53	1.19517 57987 51	0.93357 14206 71	1.01523 96379 54
70	1.22728 28634 83	1.21188 49453 82	0.93968 43641 58	1.01543 98404 72
71	1.24450 13375 94	1.22858 11005 74	0.94551 10478 11	1.01563 18834 47
72	1.26171 33991 56	1.24526 48220 13	0.95104 96947 22	1.01581 55329 04
73	1.27891 93407 32	1.26193 66812 90	0.95629 86157 92	1.01599 05650 94
74	1.29611 94620 30	1.27859 72632 32	0.96125 62102 48	1.01615 67667 68
75	1.31331 40695 43	1.29524 71652 17	0.96592 09661 38	1.01631 39354 35
76	1.33050 34761 89	1.31188 69964 90	0.97029 14607 95	1.01646 18796 07
77	1.34768 80009 37	1.32851 73774 61	0.97436 63612 75	1.01660 04190 39
78	1.36486 79684 33	1.34513 89389 96	0.97814 44247 69	1.01672 93849 40
79	1.38204 37086 18	1.36175 23217 06	0.98162 44989 83	1.01684 86201 87
80	1.39921 55563 41	1.37835 81752 21	0.98480 55224 96	1.01695 79795 07
81	1.41638 38509 64	1.39495 71574 60	0.98768 65250 87	1.01705 73296 65
82	1.43354 89359 69	1.41154 99339 01	0.99026 66280 31	1.01714 65496 18
83	1.45071 11585 59	1.42813 71768 36	0.99254 50443 72	1.01722 55306 63
84	1.46787 08692 48	1.44471 95646 27	0.99452 10791 68	1.01729 41765 75
85	1.48502 84214 59	1.46129 77809 58	0.99619 41296 97	1.01735 24037 20
86	1.50218 41711 13	1.47787 25140 80	0.99756 36856 54	1.01740 01411 56
87	1.51933 84762 13	1.49444 44560 53	0.99862 93292 99	1.01743 73307 23
88	1.53649 16964 35	1.51101 43019 92	0.99939 07355 89	1.01746 39271 11
89	1.55364 41927 07	1.52758 27493 02	0.99984 76722 82	1.01747 98979 17
90	1.57079 63267 95	1.54415 04969 15	1.00000 00000 00	1.01748 52236 81

3   61

K = 1.60197 85300 86952   E = 1.54052 15741 27631
K' = 2.70806 76145 90486   E' = 1.08442 52193 72543

r	u=(r/90)K=F(ϕ,k)	sn u	cn u	dn u
0	0.00000 00000 00	0.00000 00000 00	1.00000 00000 00	1.00000 00000 00
1	0.01779 97614 45	0.01779 87501 44	0.99984 15897 00	0.99998 79655 07
2	0.03559 95228 91	0.03559 14332 19	0.99936 64242 32	0.99995 18775 69
3	0.05339 92843 36	0.05337 19858 50	0.99857 46998 23	0.99989 17827 79
4	0.07119 90457 82	0.07113 43520 48	0.99746 67432 85	0.99980 77587 15
5	0.08899 88072 27	0.08887 24868 82	0.99604 30116 59	0.99969 99138 25
6	0.10679 85686 72	0.10658 03601 33	0.99430 40917 31	0.99956 83872 60
7	0.12459 83301 18	0.12425 19599 25	0.99225 06993 97	0.99941 33486 71
8	0.14239 80915 63	0.14188 12963 18	0.98988 36789 01	0.99923 49979 48
9	0.16019 78530 09	0.15946 24048 59	0.98720 40019 35	0.99903 35649 27
10	0.17799 76144 54	0.17698 93500 92	0.98421 27666 08	0.99880 93090 42
11	0.19579 73759 00	0.19445 62290 15	0.98091 11962 85	0.99856 25189 42
12	0.21359 71373 45	0.21185 71744 74	0.97730 06383 01	0.99829 35120 60
13	0.23139 68987 90	0.22918 63584 94	0.97338 25625 52	0.99800 26341 41
14	0.24919 66602 36	0.24643 79955 44	0.96915 85599 64	0.99769 02587 33
15	0.26699 64216 81	0.26360 63457 23	0.96463 03408 53	0.99735 67866 32
16	0.28479 61831 27	0.28068 57178 66	0.95979 97331 66	0.99700 26452 96
17	0.30259 59445 72	0.29767 04725 62	0.95466 86806 24	0.99662 82882 13
18	0.32039 57060 17	0.31455 50250 90	0.94923 92407 56	0.99623 41942 46
19	0.33819 54674 63	0.33133 38482 51	0.94351 35828 40	0.99582 08669 26
20	0.35599 52289 08	0.34800 14751 10	0.93749 39857 52	0.99538 88337 31
21	0.37379 49903 54	0.36455 25016 26	0.93118 28357 30	0.99493 86453 17
22	0.39159 47517 99	0.38098 15891 89	0.92458 26240 52	0.99447 08747 30
23	0.40939 45132 44	0.39728 34670 37	0.91769 59446 46	0.99398 61165 86
24	0.42719 42746 90	0.41345 29345 69	0.91052 54916 24	0.99348 49862 21
25	0.44499 40361 35	0.42948 48635 39	0.90307 40567 59	0.99296 81188 20
26	0.46279 37975 81	0.44537 42001 41	0.89534 45268 99	0.99243 61685 23
27	0.48059 35590 26	0.46111 59669 67	0.88733 98813 35	0.99188 98075 06
28	0.49839 33204 71	0.47670 52648 53	0.87906 31891 18	0.99132 97250 41
29	0.51619 30819 17	0.49213 72746 04	0.87051 76063 38	0.99075 66265 47
30	0.53399 28433 62	0.50740 72585 97	0.86170 63733 80	0.99017 12326 10
31	0.55179 26048 08	0.52251 05622 58	0.85263 28121 35	0.98957 42779 99
32	0.56959 23662 53	0.53744 26154 30	0.84330 03232 06	0.98896 65106 69
33	0.58739 21276 99	0.55219 89336 07	0.83371 23830 93	0.98834 86907 44
34	0.60519 18891 44	0.56677 51190 53	0.82387 25413 70	0.98772 15894 96
35	0.62299 16505 89	0.58116 68618 03	0.81378 44178 54	0.98708 59883 22
36	0.64079 14120 35	0.59536 99405 45	0.80345 16997 90	0.98644 26776 99
37	0.65859 11734 80	0.60938 02233 81	0.79287 81390 31	0.98579 24561 54
38	0.67639 09349 26	0.62319 36684 77	0.78206 75492 37	0.98513 61292 13
39	0.69419 06963 71	0.63680 63246 01	0.77102 38031 01	0.98447 45083 59
40	0.71199 04578 16	0.65021 43315 46	0.75975 08295 83	0.98380 84099 90
41	0.72979 02192 62	0.66341 39204 47	0.74825 26111 93	0.98313 86543 74
42	0.74758 99807 07	0.67640 14139 95	0.73653 31812 93	0.98246 60646 11
43	0.76538 97421 53	0.68917 32265 45	0.72459 66214 48	0.98179 14655 97
44	0.78318 95035 98	0.70172 58641 26	0.71244 70588 17	0.98111 56829 95
45	0.80098 92650 43	0.71405 59243 57	0.70008 86635 92	0.98043 95422 15

q = 0.00493 84132 64213 395   D(90) = 1.01995 07026 62439
q' = 0.15591 66592 65792 2   1/D(90) = 0.98043 95422 14776

r	ϕ	$E(\phi, k)$	A(r)	D(r)
0	0.00000 00000 00	0.00000 00000 00	0.00000 00000 00	1.00000 00000 00
1	0.01779 96980 39	0.01779 96186 32	0.01745 07044 85	1.00000 60767 12
2	0.03559 89517 47	0.03559 83806 20	0.03489 60964 27	1.00002 42994 43
3	0.05339 73573 49	0.05339 54304 87	0.05233 08648 90	1.00005 46459 92
4	0.07119 44801 72	0.07118 99150 89	0.06974 97021 59	1.00009 70793 87
5	0.08898 98952 01	0.08898 09847 80	0.08714 73053 46	1.00015 15479 29
6	0.10678 31796 23	0.10676 77945 61	0.10451 83779 98	1.00021 79852 56
7	0.12457 39133 75	0.12454 95052 35	0.12185 76316 99	1.00029 63104 26
8	0.14236 16796 84	0.14232 52845 37	0.13915 97876 79	1.00038 64280 10
9	0.16014 60655 99	0.16009 43082 64	0.15641 95784 05	1.00048 82282 16
10	0.17792 66625 27	0.17785 57613 83	0.17363 17491 86	1.00060 15870 14
11	0.19570 30667 53	0.19560 88391 29	0.19079 10597 62	1.00072 63662 96
12	0.21347 48799 55	0.21335 27480 78	0.20789 22858 93	1.00086 24140 37
13	0.23124 17097 15	0.23108 67072 07	0.22493 02209 44	1.00100 95644 83
14	0.24900 31700 19	0.24880 99489 28	0.24189 96774 61	1.00116 76383 56
15	0.26675 88817 42	0.26652 17201 05	0.25879 54887 50	1.00133 64430 66
16	0.28450 84731 34	0.28422 12830 38	0.27561 25104 39	1.00151 57729 52
17	0.30225 15802 85	0.30190 79164 26	0.29234 56220 42	1.00170 54095 27
18	0.31998 78475 85	0.31958 09163 03	0.30898 97285 10	1.00190 51217 49
19	0.33771 69281 66	0.33723 95969 41	0.32553 97617 82	1.00211 46663 00
20	0.35543 84843 41	0.35488 32917 24	0.34199 06823 19	1.00233 37878 83
21	0.37315 21880 14	0.37251 13539 96	0.35833 74806 37	1.00256 22195 31
22	0.39085 77210 96	0.39012 31578 65	0.37457 51788 26	1.00279 96829 37
23	0.40855 47758 88	0.40771 80989 81	0.39069 88320 65	1.00304 58887 87
24	0.42624 30554 62	0.42529 55952 79	0.40670 35301 25	1.00330 05371 19
25	0.44392 22740 21	0.44285 50876 84	0.42258 43988 57	1.00356 33176 83
26	0.46159 21572 43	0.46039 60407 77	0.43833 66016 78	1.00383 39103 22
27	0.47925 24426 14	0.47791 79434 28	0.45395 53410 41	1.00411 19853 60
28	0.49690 28797 35	0.49542 03093 89	0.46943 58598 93	1.00439 72040 06
29	0.51454 32306 23	0.51290 26778 50	0.48477 34431 25	1.00468 92187 65
30	0.53217 32699 86	0.53036 46139 53	0.49996 34190 04	1.00498 76738 63
31	0.54979 27854 89	0.54780 57092 68	0.51500 11605 97	1.00529 22056 79
32	0.56740 15779 91	0.56522 55822 31	0.52988 20871 82	1.00560 24431 87
33	0.58499 94617 77	0.58262 38785 37	0.54460 16656 40	1.00591 80084 12
34	0.60258 62647 61	0.60000 02715 04	0.55915 54118 39	1.00623 85168 85
35	0.62016 18286 78	0.61735 44623 79	0.57353 88920 00	1.00656 35781 17
36	0.63772 60092 54	0.63468 61806 26	0.58774 77240 49	1.00689 27960 72
37	0.65517 86763 57	0.65199 51841 52	0.60177 75789 55	1.00722 57696 47
38	0.67281 97141 36	0.66928 12595 11	0.61562 41820 50	1.00756 20931 66
39	0.69034 90211 29	0.68654 42220 60	0.62928 33143 34	1.00790 13568 70
40	0.70786 65103 65	0.70378 39160 74	0.64275 08137 64	1.00824 31474 21
41	0.72537 21094 40	0.72100 02148 31	0.65602 25765 25	1.00858 70483 97
42	0.74286 57605 80	0.73819 30206 49	0.66909 45582 84	1.00893 26408 09
43	0.76034 74206 75	0.75536 22648 91	0.68196 27754 27	1.00927 95036 07
44	0.77781 70613 11	0.77250 79079 34	0.69462 33062 77	1.00962 72141 90
45	0.79527 46687 66	0.78962 99390 95	0.70707 22922 93	1.00997 53489 28

63

ELLIPTIC FUNCTIONS   TABLE $\theta = 16°$

K = 1.60197 85300 86952   E = 1.54052 15741 27631
K' = 2.70806 76145 90486   E' = 1.08442 52193 72543

r	u=(r/90)K=F(φ,k)	sn u	cn u	dn u
45	0.80098 92650 43	0.71405 59243 57	0.70008 86635 92	0.98043 95422 15
46	0.81878 90264 89	0.72616 00962 72	0.68752 56464 91	0.97976 38674 01
47	0.83658 87879 34	0.73803 51600 50	0.67476 22563 02	0.97908 94804 26
48	0.85438 85493 80	0.74967 79866 73	0.66180 27774 93	0.97841 71999 05
49	0.87218 83108 25	0.76108 55374 91	0.64865 15278 81	0.97774 78402 07
50	0.88998 80722 71	0.77225 48637 20	0.63531 28563 64	0.97708 22104 97
51	0.90778 78337 16	0.78318 31058 65	0.62179 11407 28	0.97642 11137 79
52	0.92558 75951 61	0.79386 74930 77	0.60809 07855 21	0.97576 53459 60
53	0.94338 73566 07	0.80430 53424 49	0.59421 62199 98	0.97511 56949 29
54	0.96118 71180 52	0.81449 40582 50	0.58017 18961 45	0.97447 29396 54
55	0.97898 68794 98	0.82443 11311 09	0.56596 22867 81	0.97383 78492 97
56	0.99678 66409 43	0.83411 41371 52	0.55159 18837 35	0.97321 11823 42
57	1.01458 64023 88	0.84354 07370 91	0.53706 51961 05	0.97259 36857 52
58	1.03238 61638 34	0.85270 86752 77	0.52238 67485 95	0.97198 60941 37
59	1.05018 59252 79	0.86161 57787 15	0.50756 10799 40	0.97138 91289 51
60	1.06798 56867 25	0.87025 99560 57	0.49259 27414 03	0.97080 34976 99
61	1.08578 54481 70	0.87863 91965 63	0.47748 62953 67	0.97022 98931 76
62	1.10358 52096 15	0.88675 15690 41	0.46224 63139 96	0.96966 89927 24
63	1.12138 49710 61	0.89459 52207 80	0.44687 73779 87	0.96912 14575 09
64	1.13918 47325 06	0.90216 83764 62	0.43138 40754 03	0.96858 79318 25
65	1.15698 44939 52	0.90946 93370 74	0.41577 10005 79	0.96806 90424 18
66	1.17478 42553 97	0.91649 64788 12	0.40004 27531 23	0.96756 53978 37
67	1.19258 40168 43	0.92324 82519 95	0.38420 39369 76	0.96707 75878 03
68	1.21038 37782 88	0.92972 31799 80	0.36825 91595 70	0.96660 61826 08
69	1.22818 35397 33	0.93591 98580 87	0.35221 30310 46	0.96615 17325 35
70	1.24598 33011 79	0.94183 69525 39	0.33607 01635 55	0.96571 47672 99
71	1.26378 30626 24	0.94747 31994 24	0.31983 51706 32	0.96529 57955 24
72	1.28158 28240 70	0.95282 74036 75	0.30351 26666 30	0.96489 53042 27
73	1.29938 25855 15	0.95789 84380 78	0.28710 72662 39	0.96451 37583 46
74	1.31718 23469 60	0.96268 52423 06	0.27062 35840 54	0.96415 16002 73
75	1.33498 21084 06	0.96718 68219 90	0.25406 62342 17	0.96380 92494 30
76	1.35278 18698 51	0.97140 22478 23	0.23743 98301 14	0.96348 71018 58
77	1.37058 16312 97	0.97533 06547 03	0.22074 89841 36	0.96318 55298 31
78	1.38838 13927 42	0.97897 12409 18	0.20399 83074 83	0.96290 48815 06
79	1.40618 11541 87	0.98232 32673 75	0.18719 24100 33	0.96264 54805 83
80	1.42398 09156 33	0.98538 60568 76	0.17033 59002 49	0.96240 76259 97
81	1.44178 06770 78	0.98815 89934 44	0.15343 33851 38	0.96219 15916 40
82	1.45958 04385 24	0.99064 15216 98	0.13648 94702 45	0.96199 76260 96
83	1.47738 01999 69	0.99283 31462 82	0.11950 87596 94	0.96182 59524 11
84	1.49517 99614 14	0.99473 34313 53	0.10249 58562 52	0.96167 67678 83
85	1.51297 97228 60	0.99634 20001 19	0.08545 53614 35	0.96155 02438 73
86	1.53077 94843 05	0.99765 85344 43	0.06839 18756 31	0.96144 65256 54
87	1.54857 92457 51	0.99868 27744 98	0.05130 99982 59	0.96136 57322 67
88	1.56637 90071 96	0.99941 45184 88	0.03421 43279 33	0.96130 79564 14
89	1.58417 87686 42	0.99985 36224 31	0.01710 94626 53	0.96127 32643 74
90	1.60197 85300 87	1.00000 00000 00	0.00000 00000 00	0.96126 16959 38

q = 0.00493 84132 64213 395   D(90) = 1.01995 07026 62439
q'= 0.15591 66592 65792 2   1/D(90) = 0.98043 95422 14776

r	ϕ	$E(\phi,k)$	A(r)	D(r)
45	0.79527 46687 66	0.78962 99390 95	0.70707 22922 93	1.00997 53489 28
46	0.81272 02440 02	0.80672 83765 27	0.71930 59392 51	1.01032 34836 72
47	0.83015 38026 33	0.82380 32670 79	0.73132 05184 10	1.01067 11942 73
48	0.84757 53748 72	0.84085 46861 19	0.74311 23676 45	1.01101 80571 00
49	0.86498 50054 69	0.85788 27373 24	0.75467 78925 78	1.01136 36495 53
50	0.88238 27536 23	0.87488 75524 43	0.76601 35676 74	1.01170 75505 81
51	0.89976 86928 84	0.89186 92910 17	0.77711 59373 25	1.01204 93411 94
52	0.91714 29110 33	0.90882 81400 76	0.78798 16169 07	1.01238 86049 72
53	0.93450 55099 48	0.92576 43138 08	0.79860 72938 21	1.01272 49285 75
54	0.95185 66054 52	0.94267 80531 87	0.80898 97285 10	1.01305 79022 44
55	0.96919 63271 50	0.95956 96255 89	0.81912 57554 51	1.01338 71203 02
56	0.98652 48182 41	0.97643 93243 65	0.82901 22841 30	1.01371 21816 46
57	1.00384 22353 26	0.99328 74683 96	0.83864 62999 90	1.01403 26902 40
58	1.02114 87481 91	1.01011 44016 25	0.84802 48653 57	1.01434 82555 93
59	1.03844 45395 85	1.02692 04925 53	0.85714 51203 45	1.01465 84932 37
60	1.05572 98049 73	1.04370 61337 26	0.86600 42837 36	1.01496 30251 95
61	1.07300 47522 85	1.06047 17411 88	0.87459 96538 34	1.01526 14804 41
62	1.09026 96016 45	1.07721 77539 16	0.88292 86092 94	1.01555 34953 54
63	1.10752 45850 91	1.09394 46332 37	0.89098 86099 37	1.01583 87141 57
64	1.12476 99462 81	1.11065 28622 21	0.89877 71975 23	1.01611 67893 57
65	1.14200 59401 86	1.12734 29450 58	0.90629 19965 14	1.01638 73821 59
66	1.15923 28327 71	1.14401 54064 14	0.91353 07148 07	1.01665 01628 89
67	1.17645 09006 69	1.16067 07907 75	0.92049 11444 34	1.01690 48113 88
68	1.19366 04308 34	1.17730 96617 66	0.92717 11622 48	1.01715 10174 07
69	1.21086 17201 96	1.19393 26014 66	0.93356 87305 79	1.01738 84809 80
70	1.22805 50752 98	1.21054 02096 98	0.93968 18978 56	1.01761 69127 94
71	1.24524 08119 24	1.22713 31033 13	0.94550 87992 17	1.01783 60345 40
72	1.26241 92547 21	1.24371 19154 53	0.95104 76570 79	1.01804 55792 53
73	1.27959 07368 07	1.26027 72948 14	0.95629 67816 87	1.01824 52916 33
74	1.29675 55993 77	1.27682 99048 82	0.96125 45716 41	1.01843 49283 61
75	1.31391 41912 97	1.29337 04231 73	0.96591 95143 83	1.01861 42583 95
76	1.33106 68686 90	1.30989 95404 54	0.97029 01866 72	1.01878 30632 47
77	1.34821 39945 19	1.32641 79599 56	0.97436 52550 16	1.01894 11372 56
78	1.36535 59381 58	1.34292 63965 83	0.97814 34760 90	1.01908 82878 31
79	1.38249 30749 61	1.35942 55761 08	0.98162 36971 17	1.01922 43356 92
80	1.39962 57858 25	1.37591 62343 64	0.98480 48562 28	1.01934 91150 86
81	1.41675 44567 43	1.39239 91164 27	0.98768 59827 84	1.01946 24739 88
82	1.43387 94783 62	1.40887 49757 99	0.99026 61976 82	1.01956 42742 87
83	1.45100 12455 23	1.42534 45735 74	0.99254 47136 25	1.01965 43919 55
84	1.46812 01568 10	1.44180 86776 11	0.99452 08353 64	1.01973 27171 98
85	1.48523 66140 90	1.45826 80616 95	0.99619 39599 15	1.01979 91545 89
86	1.50235 10220 46	1.47472 35046 99	0.99756 35767 44	1.01985 36231 82
87	1.51946 37877 13	1.49117 57897 39	0.99862 92679 28	1.01989 60566 18
88	1.53657 53200 12	1.50762 57033 30	0.99939 07082 79	1.01992 64031 96
89	1.55368 60292 79	1.52407 40345 37	0.99984 76654 49	1.01994 46259 45
90	1.57079 63267 95	1.54052 15741 28	1.00000 00000 00	1.01995 07026 62

K = 1.60608 13494 10364   E = 1.53666 97975 68556
K′= 2.65213 80046 30204   E′= 1.09265 03455 37715

r	u=(r/90)K=F(ϕ,k)	sn u	cn u	dn u
0	0.00000 00000 00	0.00000 00000 00	1.00000 00000 00	1.00000 00000 00
1	0.01784 53483 27	0.01784 43202 34	0.99984 07774 42	0.99998 63904 53
2	0.03569 06966 54	0.03568 24727 13	0.99936 31777 99	0.99994 55795 18
3	0.05353 60449 80	0.05350 82936 65	0.99856 74050 90	0.99987 76202 78
4	0.07138 13933 07	0.07131 56272 85	0.99745 37990 83	0.99978 26011 17
5	0.08922 67416 34	0.08909 83296 96	0.99602 28349 02	0.99966 06455 84
6	0.10707 20899 61	0.10685 02728 87	0.99427 51224 81	0.99951 19121 97
7	0.12491 74382 87	0.12456 53486 24	0.99221 14058 62	0.99933 65942 05
8	0.14276 27866 14	0.14223 74723 18	0.98983 25623 40	0.99913 49192 93
9	0.16060 81349 41	0.15986 05868 52	0.98713 96014 60	0.99890 71492 25
10	0.17845 34832 68	0.17742 86663 53	0.98413 36638 67	0.99865 35794 53
11	0.19629 88315 95	0.19493 57199 00	0.98081 60200 09	0.99837 45386 60
12	0.21414 41799 21	0.21237 57951 71	0.97718 80687 08	0.99807 03882 62
13	0.23198 95282 48	0.22974 29820 15	0.97325 13355 83	0.99774 15218 60
14	0.24983 48765 75	0.24703 14159 43	0.96900 74713 53	0.99738 83646 42
15	0.26768 02249 02	0.26423 52815 30	0.96445 82500 01	0.99701 13727 44
16	0.28552 55732 29	0.28134 88157 33	0.95960 55668 27	0.99661 10325 60
17	0.30337 09215 55	0.29836 63111 05	0.95445 14363 75	0.99618 78600 18
18	0.32121 62698 82	0.31528 21189 08	0.94899 79902 49	0.99574 23998 05
19	0.33906 16182 09	0.33209 06521 19	0.94324 74748 31	0.99527 52245 61
20	0.35690 69665 36	0.34878 63883 29	0.93720 22488 86	0.99478 69340 30
21	0.37475 23148 62	0.36536 38725 13	0.93086 47810 84	0.99427 81541 76
22	0.39259 76631 89	0.38181 77196 96	0.92423 76474 29	0.99374 95362 65
23	0.41044 30115 16	0.39814 26174 86	0.91732 35286 10	0.99320 17559 16
24	0.42828 83598 43	0.41433 33284 81	0.91012 52072 71	0.99263 55121 21
25	0.44613 37081 70	0.43038 46925 51	0.90264 55652 24	0.99205 15262 35
26	0.46397 90564 96	0.44629 16289 88	0.89488 75805 91	0.99145 05409 41
27	0.48182 44048 23	0.46204 91385 20	0.88685 43249 00	0.99083 33191 93
28	0.49966 97531 50	0.47765 23051 94	0.87854 89601 28	0.99020 06431 34
29	0.51751 51014 77	0.49309 62981 25	0.86997 47357 11	0.98955 33129 93
30	0.53536 04498 03	0.50837 63731 00	0.86113 49855 13	0.98889 21459 69
31	0.55320 57981 30	0.52348 78740 56	0.85203 31247 76	0.98821 79750 90
32	0.57105 11464 57	0.53842 62344 20	0.84267 26470 51	0.98753 16480 74
33	0.58889 64947 84	0.55318 69783 06	0.83305 71211 11	0.98683 40261 56
34	0.60674 18431 11	0.56776 57215 83	0.82319 01878 64	0.98612 59829 28
35	0.62458 71914 37	0.58215 81728 11	0.81307 55572 70	0.98540 84031 55
36	0.64243 25397 64	0.59636 01340 40	0.80271 70052 56	0.98468 21815 91
37	0.66027 78880 91	0.61036 75014 82	0.79211 83706 58	0.98394 82217 94
38	0.67812 32364 18	0.62417 62660 51	0.78128 35521 75	0.98320 74349 34
39	0.69596 85847 44	0.63778 25137 84	0.77021 65053 49	0.98246 07386 03
40	0.71381 39330 71	0.65118 24261 33	0.75892 12395 86	0.98170 90556 27
41	0.73165 92813 98	0.66437 22801 43	0.74740 18152 09	0.98095 33128 84
42	0.74950 46297 25	0.67734 84485 06	0.73566 23405 52	0.98019 44401 20
43	0.76734 99780 52	0.69010 73995 12	0.72370 69691 10	0.97943 33687 78
44	0.78519 53263 78	0.70264 56968 84	0.71153 98967 38	0.97867 10308 37
45	0.80304 06747 05	0.71495 99995 12	0.69916 53589 09	0.97790 83576 51

66

ELLIPTIC FUNCTIONS TABLE $\theta = 17°$

q = 0.00558 45970 58516 804   D(90) = 1.02259 07081 95194
q' = 0.14919 73690 67429 2   1/D(90) = 0.97790 83576 50672

r	ϕ	$E(\phi, k)$	$A(r)$	$D(r)$
0	0.00000 00000 00	0.00000 00000 00	0.00000 00000 00	1.00000 00000 00
1	0.01784 52673 68	0.01784 51864 09	0.01745 02299 65	1.00000 68808 20
2	0.03569 00491 06	0.03568 94015 80	0.03489 51483 97	1.00002 75148 96
3	0.05353 38602 19	0.05353 16756 18	0.05232 94453 72	1.00006 18770 89
4	0.07137 62169 71	0.07137 10413 10	0.06974 78141 76	1.00010 99255 33
5	0.08921 66375 18	0.08920 65354 61	0.08714 49529 18	1.00017 16016 91
6	0.10705 46425 35	0.10703 72002 23	0.10451 55661 28	1.00024 68304 18
7	0.12488 97558 34	0.12486 20844 10	0.12185 43663 64	1.00033 55200 60
8	0.14272 15049 84	0.14268 02448 07	0.13915 60758 08	1.00043 75625 63
9	0.16054 94219 22	0.16049 07474 60	0.15641 54278 68	1.00055 28336 03
10	0.17837 30435 57	0.17829 26689 52	0.17362 71687 69	1.00068 11927 43
11	0.19619 19123 69	0.19608 50976 55	0.19078 60591 41	1.00082 24835 95
12	0.21400 55769 94	0.21386 71349 69	0.20788 68756 15	1.00097 65340 18
13	0.23181 35928 07	0.23163 78965 29	0.22492 44123 92	1.00114 31563 28
14	0.24961 55224 90	0.24939 65133 94	0.24189 34828 32	1.00132 21475 19
15	0.26741 09365 90	0.26714 21332 02	0.25878 89210 14	1.00151 32895 21
16	0.28519 94140 63	0.28487 39213 00	0.27560 55833 10	1.00171 63494 55
17	0.30298 05428 12	0.30259 10618 42	0.29233 83499 41	1.00193 10799 25
18	0.32075 39202 02	0.32029 27588 53	0.30898 21265 27	1.00215 72193 16
19	0.33851 91535 72	0.33797 82372 59	0.32553 18456 33	1.00239 44921 12
20	0.35627 58607 21	0.35564 67438 81	0.34198 24683 09	1.00264 26092 32
21	0.37402 36703 85	0.37329 75483 92	0.35832 89856 14	1.00290 12683 86
22	0.39176 22227 00	0.39092 99442 35	0.37456 64201 38	1.00317 01544 38
23	0.40949 11696 42	0.40854 32494 99	0.39068 98275 14	1.00344 89397 90
24	0.42721 01754 53	0.42613 68077 59	0.40669 42979 18	1.00373 72847 88
25	0.44491 89170 50	0.44370 99888 63	0.42257 49575 61	1.00403 48381 28
26	0.46261 70844 16	0.46126 21896 92	0.43832 69701 71	1.00434 12372 86
27	0.48030 43809 69	0.47879 28348 61	0.45394 55384 60	1.00465 61089 64
28	0.49798 05239 13	0.49630 13773 84	0.46942 59055 85	1.00497 90695 40
29	0.51564 52445 76	0.51378 72992 91	0.48476 33565 98	1.00530 97255 35
30	0.53329 82887 19	0.53125 01121 97	0.49995 32198 73	1.00564 76740 98
31	0.55093 94168 26	0.54868 93578 35	0.51499 08685 34	1.00599 25034 90
32	0.56856 84043 82	0.56610 46085 25	0.52987 17218 65	1.00634 37935 90
33	0.58618 50421 23	0.58349 54676 18	0.54459 12467 02	1.00670 11164 06
34	0.60378 91362 64	0.60086 15698 74	0.55914 49588 14	1.00706 40365 95
35	0.62138 05087 12	0.61820 25818 06	0.57352 84242 76	1.00743 21119 96
36	0.63895 89972 54	0.63551 82019 75	0.58773 72608 16	1.00780 48941 65
37	0.65652 44557 24	0.65280 81612 35	0.60176 71391 55	1.00818 19289 25
38	0.67407 67541 49	0.67007 22229 36	0.61561 37843 29	1.00856 27569 18
39	0.69161 57788 78	0.68731 01830 81	0.62927 29769 92	1.00894 69141 64
40	0.70914 14326 81	0.70452 18704 40	0.64274 05547 10	1.00933 39326 26
41	0.72665 36348 35	0.72170 71466 15	0.65601 24132 30	1.00972 33407 83
42	0.74415 23211 84	0.73886 59060 64	0.66908 45077 37	1.01011 46642 00
43	0.76163 74441 80	0.75599 80760 83	0.68195 28540 91	1.01050 74261 11
44	0.77910 89729 07	0.77310 36167 46	0.69461 35300 48	1.01090 11479 95
45	0.79656 68930 72	0.79018 25208 03	0.70706 26764 59	1.01129 53501 63

K = 1.60608 13494 10364   E = 1.53666 97975 68556
K′ = 2.65213 80046 30204   E′ = 1.09265 03455 37715

r	u=(r/90)K=F(φ,k)	sn u	cn u	dn u
45	0.80304 06747 05	0.71495 99995 12	0.69916 53589 09	0.97790 83576 51
46	0.82088 60230 32	0.72704 70610 85	0.68658 76280 33	0.97714 62788 12
47	0.83873 13713 59	0.73890 37296 26	0.67381 10108 52	0.97638 57210 17
48	0.85657 67196 86	0.75052 69469 41	0.66083 98458 89	0.97562 76069 53
49	0.87442 20680 12	0.76191 37479 76	0.64767 85009 91	0.97487 28541 94
50	0.89226 74163 39	0.77306 12600 91	0.63433 13709 30	0.97412 23741 20
51	0.91011 27646 66	0.78396 67022 66	0.62080 28751 04	0.97337 70708 47
52	0.92795 81129 93	0.79462 73842 27	0.60709 74553 03	0.97263 78401 80
53	0.94580 34613 19	0.80504 07055 10	0.59321 95735 75	0.97190 55685 87
54	0.96364 88096 46	0.81520 41544 60	0.57917 37101 69	0.97118 11321 88
55	0.98149 41579 73	0.82511 53071 83	0.56496 43615 78	0.97046 53957 70
56	0.99933 95063 00	0.83477 18264 35	0.55059 60386 62	0.96975 92118 23
57	1.01718 48546 27	0.84417 14604 79	0.53607 32648 74	0.96906 34195 98
58	1.03503 02029 53	0.85331 20418 92	0.52140 05745 70	0.96837 88441 90
59	1.05287 55512 80	0.86219 14863 45	0.50658 25114 17	0.96770 62956 43
60	1.07072 08996 07	0.87080 77913 49	0.49162 36269 00	0.96704 65680 83
61	1.08856 62479 34	0.87915 90349 78	0.47652 84789 14	0.96640 04388 71
62	1.10641 15962 60	0.88724 33745 83	0.46130 16304 54	0.96576 86677 88
63	1.12425 69445 87	0.89505 90454 73	0.44594 76484 04	0.96515 19962 43
64	1.14210 22929 14	0.90260 43596 10	0.43047 11024 14	0.96455 11465 01
65	1.15994 76412 41	0.90987 77042 86	0.41487 65638 64	0.96396 68209 50
66	1.17779 29895 68	0.91687 75408 07	0.39916 86049 33	0.96339 97013 87
67	1.19563 83378 94	0.92360 24031 83	0.38335 17977 45	0.96285 04483 27
68	1.21348 36862 21	0.93005 08968 32	0.36743 07136 07	0.96231 97003 52
69	1.23132 90345 48	0.93622 16972 93	0.35140 99223 38	0.96180 80734 72
70	1.24917 43828 75	0.94211 35489 68	0.33529 39916 72	0.96131 61605 26
71	1.26701 97312 02	0.94772 52638 81	0.31908 74867 53	0.96084 45306 02
72	1.28486 50795 28	0.95305 57204 71	0.30279 49697 04	0.96039 37284 89
73	1.30271 04278 55	0.95810 38624 16	0.28642 09992 72	0.95996 42741 54
74	1.32055 57761 82	0.96286 86974 92	0.26997 01305 52	0.95955 66622 48
75	1.33840 11245 09	0.96734 92964 74	0.25344 69147 78	0.95917 13616 38
76	1.35624 64728 35	0.97154 47920 83	0.23685 58991 79	0.95880 88149 65
77	1.37409 18211 62	0.97545 43779 73	0.22020 16269 11	0.95846 94382 37
78	1.39193 71694 89	0.97907 73077 74	0.20348 86370 36	0.95815 36204 36
79	1.40978 25178 16	0.98241 28941 89	0.18672 14645 69	0.95786 17231 63
80	1.42762 78661 43	0.98546 05081 44	0.16990 46405 77	0.95759 40803 09
81	1.44547 32144 69	0.98821 95779 92	0.15304 26923 23	0.95735 09977 43
82	1.46331 85627 96	0.99068 95887 90	0.13614 01434 65	0.95713 27530 42
83	1.48116 39111 23	0.99287 00816 27	0.11920 15142 92	0.95693 95952 36
84	1.49900 92594 50	0.99476 06530 23	0.10223 13219 99	0.95677 17445 82
85	1.51685 46077 76	0.99636 09543 92	0.08523 40809 98	0.95662 93923 72
86	1.53469 99561 03	0.99767 06915 76	0.06821 43032 60	0.95651 27007 55
87	1.55254 53044 30	0.99868 96244 49	0.05117 64986 81	0.95642 18025 98
88	1.57039 06527 57	0.99941 75665 85	0.03412 51754 68	0.95635 68013 61
89	1.58823 60010 84	0.99985 43850 07	0.01706 48405 52	0.95631 77710 14
90	1.60608 13494 10	1.00000 00000 00	0.00000 00000 00	0.95630 47559 63

q = 0.00558 45970 58516 804   D(90) = 1.02259 07081 95194
q'= 0.14919 73690 67429 2   1/D(90) = 0.97790 83576 50672

r	ϕ	$E(\phi,k)$	A(r)	D(r)
45	0.79656 68930 72	0.79018 25208 03	0.70706 26764 59	1.01129 53501 63
46	0.81401 12069 91	0.80723 48135 32	0.71929 64984 57	1.01168 95523 41
47	0.83144 19335 44	0.82426 05525 62	0.73131 12666 14	1.01208 32742 54
48	0.84885 91081 14	0.84125 98276 50	0.74310 33180 92	1.01247 60362 12
49	0.86626 27825 06	0.85823 27604 24	0.75466 90577 60	1.01286 73596 95
50	0.88365 30248 46	0.87517 95040 82	0.76600 49593 05	1.01325 67679 37
51	0.90102 99194 60	0.89210 02430 69	0.77710 75663 10	1.01364 37865 02
52	0.91839 35667 36	0.90899 51927 05	0.78797 34933 16	1.01402 79438 68
53	0.93574 40829 65	0.92586 45987 91	0.79859 94268 68	1.01440 87719 98
54	0.95308 16001 69	0.94270 87371 75	0.80898 21265 27	1.01478 58069 12
55	0.97040 62659 04	0.95952 79132 93	0.81911 84258 72	1.01515 85892 51
56	0.98771 82430 48	0.97632 24616 75	0.82900 52334 76	1.01552 66648 35
57	1.00501 77095 77	0.99309 27454 25	0.83863 95338 52	1.01588 95852 22
58	1.02230 48583 20	1.00983 91556 73	0.84801 83883 88	1.01624 69082 48
59	1.03957 98966 95	1.02656 21110 00	0.85713 89362 50	1.01659 81985 71
60	1.05684 30464 36	1.04326 20568 39	0.86599 83952 65	1.01694 30281 95
61	1.07409 45432 99	1.05993 94648 47	0.87459 40627 80	1.01728 09770 01
62	1.09133 46367 58	1.07659 48322 64	0.88292 33164 95	1.01761 16332 47
63	1.10856 35896 81	1.09322 86812 36	0.89098 36152 72	1.01793 45940 80
64	1.12578 16780 00	1.10984 15581 32	0.89877 24999 23	1.01824 94660 22
65	1.14298 91903 55	1.12643 40328 27	0.90628 75939 66	1.01855 58654 50
66	1.16018 64277 43	1.14300 66979 78	0.91352 66043 64	1.01885 34190 61
67	1.17737 37031 36	1.15956 01682 73	0.92048 73222 28	1.01914 17643 33
68	1.19455 13410 98	1.17609 50796 70	0.92716 76235 09	1.01942 05499 60
69	1.21171 96773 91	1.19261 20886 18	0.93356 54696 45	1.01968 94362 85
70	1.22887 90585 60	1.20911 18712 58	0.93967 89082 01	1.01994 80957 11
71	1.24602 98415 21	1.22559 51226 19	0.94550 60734 69	1.02019 62131 01
72	1.26317 23931 31	1.24206 25557 95	0.95104 51870 44	1.02043 34861 61
73	1.28030 70897 44	1.25851 49011 10	0.95629 45583 83	1.02065 96258 09
74	1.29743 43167 72	1.27495 29052 71	0.96125 25853 19	1.02087 43565 31
75	1.31455 44682 21	1.29137 73305 18	0.96591 77545 64	1.02107 74167 07
76	1.33166 79462 35	1.30778 89537 51	0.97028 86421 77	1.02126 85589 41
77	1.34877 51606 15	1.32418 85656 59	0.97436 39140 06	1.02144 75503 55
78	1.36587 65283 51	1.34057 69698 37	0.97814 23261 00	1.02161 41728 75
79	1.38297 24731 25	1.35695 49818 91	0.98162 27250 95	1.02176 82234 96
80	1.40006 34248 30	1.37332 34285 43	0.98480 40485 77	1.02190 95145 32
81	1.41714 98190 64	1.38968 31467 25	0.98768 53254 03	1.02203 78738 40
82	1.43423 20966 34	1.40603 49826 71	0.99026 56760 13	1.02215 31450 35
83	1.45131 07030 44	1.42237 97909 96	0.99254 43126 92	1.02225 51876 75
84	1.46838 60879 87	1.43871 84337 83	0.99452 05398 24	1.02234 38774 38
85	1.48545 87048 29	1.45505 17796 50	0.99619 37541 04	1.02241 91062 67
86	1.50252 90100 87	1.47138 07028 31	0.99756 34447 24	1.02248 07825 09
87	1.51959 74629 14	1.48770 60822 40	0.99862 91935 34	1.02252 88310 21
88	1.53666 45245 69	1.50402 88005 37	0.99939 06751 73	1.02256 31932 61
89	1.55373 06578 96	1.52034 97431 97	0.99984 76571 66	1.02258 38273 66
90	1.57079 63267 95	1.53666 97975 69	1.00000 00000 00	1.02259 07081 95

K = 1.61045 41537 89663

K' = 2.59981 97300 61099

E = 1.53259 72877 45636

E' = 1.10106 21687 57941

r	u=(r/90)K=F(φ,k)	sn u	cn u	dn u
0	0.00000 00000 00	0.00000 00000 00	1.00000 00000 00	1.00000 00000 00
1	0.01789 39350 42	0.01789 28889 73	0.99983 99094 48	0.99998 47138 19
2	0.03578 78700 84	0.03577 95023 91	0.99935 97086 18	0.99993 88753 20
3	0.05368 18051 26	0.05365 35689 99	0.99855 96099 05	0.99986 25445 97
4	0.07157 57401 68	0.07150 88261 37	0.99743 99670 08	0.99975 58217 05
5	0.08946 96752 11	0.08933 90240 11	0.99600 12744 92	0.99961 88464 98
6	0.10736 36102 53	0.10713 79299 41	0.99424 41671 78	0.99945 17984 10
7	0.12525 75452 95	0.12489 93325 77	0.99216 94193 64	0.99925 48961 71
8	0.14315 14803 37	0.14261 70460 63	0.98977 79438 70	0.99902 83974 67
9	0.16104 54153 79	0.16028 49141 59	0.98707 07909 23	0.99877 25985 30
10	0.17893 93504 21	0.17789 68142 94	0.98404 91468 74	0.99848 78336 78
11	0.19683 32854 63	0.19544 66615 54	0.98071 43327 63	0.99817 44747 91
12	0.21472 72205 05	0.21292 84125 97	0.97706 78027 18	0.99783 29307 31
13	0.23262 11555 47	0.23033 60694 78	0.97311 11422 12	0.99746 36467 05
14	0.25051 50905 90	0.24766 36833 90	0.96884 60661 68	0.99706 71035 78
15	0.26840 90256 32	0.26490 53583 02	0.96427 44169 29	0.99664 38171 30
16	0.28630 29606 74	0.28205 52544 93	0.95939 81620 85	0.99619 43372 59
17	0.30419 68957 16	0.29910 75919 83	0.95421 93921 83	0.99571 92471 41
18	0.32209 08307 58	0.31605 66538 36	0.94874 03182 99	0.99521 91623 43
19	0.33998 47658 00	0.33289 67893 50	0.94296 32695 08	0.99469 47298 80
20	0.35787 87008 42	0.34962 24171 19	0.93689 06902 34	0.99414 66272 44
21	0.37577 26358 84	0.36622 80279 60	0.93052 51375 09	0.99357 55613 84
22	0.39366 65709 26	0.38270 81877 11	0.92386 92781 23	0.99298 22676 45
23	0.41156 05059 68	0.39905 75398 79	0.91692 58856 99	0.99236 75086 77
24	0.42945 44410 11	0.41527 08081 59	0.90969 78376 86	0.99173 20733 07
25	0.44734 83760 53	0.43134 27987 99	0.90218 81122 71	0.99107 67753 79
26	0.46524 23110 95	0.44726 84028 18	0.89439 97852 42	0.99040 24525 65
27	0.48313 62461 37	0.46304 25980 77	0.88633 60267 79	0.98970 99651 51
28	0.50103 01811 79	0.47866 04511 97	0.87800 00982 12	0.98900 01947 98
29	0.51892 41162 21	0.49411 71193 29	0.86939 53487 26	0.98827 40432 77
30	0.53681 80512 63	0.50940 78517 64	0.86052 52120 42	0.98753 24311 95
31	0.55471 19863 05	0.52452 79913 97	0.85139 32030 74	0.98677 62966 92
32	0.57260 59213 47	0.53947 29760 35	0.84200 29145 60	0.98600 65941 32
33	0.59049 98563 90	0.55423 83395 55	0.83235 80136 98	0.98522 42927 78
34	0.60839 37914 32	0.56881 97129 13	0.82246 22387 70	0.98443 03754 61
35	0.62628 77264 74	0.58321 28249 98	0.81231 93957 78	0.98362 58372 38
36	0.64418 16615 16	0.59741 35033 48	0.80193 33550 97	0.98281 16840 45
37	0.66207 55965 58	0.61141 76747 14	0.79130 80481 38	0.98198 89313 53
38	0.67996 95316 00	0.62522 13654 86	0.78044 74640 49	0.98115 86028 17
39	0.69786 34666 42	0.63882 07019 78	0.76935 56464 50	0.98032 17289 28
40	0.71575 74016 84	0.65221 19105 82	0.75803 66902 03	0.97947 93456 73
41	0.73365 13367 26	0.66539 13177 85	0.74649 47382 37	0.97863 24931 97
42	0.75154 52717 69	0.67835 53500 60	0.73473 39784 20	0.97778 22144 71
43	0.76943 92068 11	0.69110 05336 35	0.72275 86404 94	0.97692 95539 76
44	0.78733 31418 53	0.70362 34941 44	0.71057 29930 76	0.97607 55563 91
45	0.80522 70768 95	0.71592 09561 60	0.69818 13407 21	0.97522 12653 01

ELLIPTIC FUNCTIONS TABLE $\theta = 18°$

q = 0.00627 23946 95993 661   D(90) = 1.02540 83207 37777
q'= 0.14283 65198 36280 4   1/D(90) = 0.97522 12653 00933

r	ϕ	$E(\phi,k)$	A(r)	D(r)
0	0.00000 00000 00	0.00000 00000 00	0.00000 00000 00	1.00000 00000 00
1	0.01789 38438 61	0.01789 37798 19	0.01744 96608 66	1.00000 77390 24
2	0.03578 71407 83	0.03578 64657 82	0.03489 40114 13	1.00003 09466 66
3	0.05367 93445 40	0.05367 69655 68	0.05232 77429 25	1.00006 95946 51
4	0.07156 99103 44	0.07156 41899 22	0.06974 55498 93	1.00012 36358 94
5	0.08945 82955 51	0.08944 70541 80	0.08714 21316 20	1.00019 30045 53
6	0.10734 39603 75	0.10732 44797 85	0.10451 21938 16	1.00027 76161 14
7	0.12522 63685 91	0.12519 53957 96	0.12185 04502 04	1.00037 73674 90
8	0.14310 49882 40	0.14305 87403 73	0.13915 16241 13	1.00049 21371 51
9	0.16097 92923 17	0.16091 34622 56	0.15641 04500 75	1.00062 17852 67
10	0.17884 87594 61	0.17875 85222 17	0.17362 16754 13	1.00076 61538 83
11	0.19671 28746 29	0.19659 28944 88	0.19078 00618 31	1.00092 50671 09
12	0.21457 11297 64	0.21441 55681 72	0.20788 03869 96	1.00109 83313 33
13	0.23242 30244 53	0.23222 55486 19	0.22491 74461 20	1.00128 57354 61
14	0.25026 80665 68	0.25002 18587 72	0.24188 60535 30	1.00148 70511 70
15	0.26810 57729 00	0.26780 35404 87	0.25878 10442 40	1.00170 20331 88
16	0.28593 56697 75	0.28556 96558 10	* 0.27559 72755 13	1.00193 04195 94
17	0.30375 72936 58	0.30331 92882 24	0.29232 96284 14	1.00217 19321 35
18	0.32157 01917 41	0.32105 15438 54	0.30897 30093 67	1.00242 62765 65
19	0.33937 39225 14	0.33876 55526 29	0.32552 23516 91	1.00269 31430 06
20	0.35716 80563 18	0.35646 04694 08	0.34197 26171 38	1.00297 22063 23
21	0.37495 21758 82	0.37413 54750 56	0.35831 87974 20	1.00326 31265 21
22	0.39272 58768 41	0.39178 97774 79	0.37455 59157 27	1.00356 55491 60
23	0.41048 87682 34	0.40942 26126 04	0.39067 90282 35	1.00387 91057 85
24	0.42824 04729 85	0.42703 32453 21	0.40668 32256 09	1.00420 34143 75
25	0.44598 06283 54	0.44462 09703 72	0.42256 36344 90	1.00453 80798 13
26	0.46370 88863 84	0.46218 51131 80	0.43831 54189 76	1.00488 26943 60
27	0.48142 49143 08	0.47972 50306 47	0.45393 37820 94	1.00523 68381 57
28	0.49912 83949 47	0.49724 01118 76	0.46941 39672 52	1.00560 00797 37
29	0.51681 90270 81	0.51472 97788 61	0.48475 12596 92	1.00597 19765 44
30	0.53449 65257 96	0.53219 34871 13	0.49994 09879 19	1.00635 20754 82
31	0.55216 06228 08	0.54963 07262 33	0.51497 85251 26	1.00673 99134 58
32	0.56981 10667 72	0.56704 10204 35	0.52985 92906 03	1.00713 50179 54
33	0.58744 76235 51	0.58442 39290 13	0.54457 87511 30	1.00753 69075 95
34	0.60507 00764 78	0.60177 90467 58	0.55913 24223 62	1.00794 50927 41
35	0.62267 82265 83	0.61910 60043 13	0.57351 58701 96	1.00835 90760 82
36	0.64027 18928 01	0.63640 44684 87	0.58772 47121 22	1.00877 83532 44
37	0.65785 09121 55	0.65367 41425 05	0.60175 46185 65	1.00920 24134 03
38	0.67541 51399 12	0.67091 47662 12	0.61560 13142 03	1.00963 07399 07
39	0.69296 44497 22	0.68812 61162 23	0.62926 05792 80	1.01006 28109 07
40	0.71049 87337 25	0.70530 80060 25	0.64272 82508 89	1.01049 80999 91
41	0.72801 79026 38	0.72246 02860 23	0.65600 02242 54	1.01093 60768 27
42	0.74552 18858 15	0.73958 28435 40	0.66907 24539 81	1.01137 62078 07
43	0.76301 06312 93	0.75667 56027 71	0.68194 09553 00	1.01181 79567 00
44	0.78048 41057 99	0.77373 85246 86	0.69460 18052 86	1.01226 07853 04
45	0.79794 22947 48	0.79077 16068 83	0.70705 11440 63	1.01270 41540 99

71

K = 1.61045 41537 89663   E = 1.53259 72877 45636
K'= 2.59981 97300 61099   E'= 1.10106 21687 57941

r	u=(r/90)K=F(ϕ,k)	sn u	cn u	dn u
45	0.80522 70768 95	0.71592 09561 60	0.69818 13407 21	0.97522 12653 01
46	0.82312 10119 37	0.72798 97426 21	0.68558 80210 73	0.97436 77219 12
47	0.84101 49469 79	0.73982 67741 55	0.67279 74020 78	0.97351 59637 92
48	0.85890 88820 21	0.75142 90683 00	0.65981 38792 97	0.97266 70236 17
49	0.87680 28170 63	0.76279 37386 37	0.64664 18732 93	0.97182 19279 52
50	0.89469 67521 05	0.77391 79938 32	0.63328 58271 13	0.97098 16960 38
51	0.91259 06871 47	0.78479 91365 97	0.61975 02038 69	0.97014 73386 04
52	0.93048 46221 90	0.79543 45625 76	0.60603 94844 07	0.96931 98567 13
53	0.94837 85572 32	0.80582 17591 59	0.59215 81650 76	0.96850 02406 13
54	0.96627 24922 74	0.81595 83042 36	0.57811 07556 06	0.96768 94686 28
55	0.98416 64273 16	0.82584 18648 90	0.56390 17770 61	0.96688 85060 66
56	1.00206 03623 58	0.83547 01960 35	0.54953 57600 17	0.96609 83041 58
57	1.01995 42974 00	0.84484 11390 17	0.53501 72425 49	0.96531 97990 21
58	1.03784 82324 42	0.85395 26201 66	0.52035 07687 24	0.96455 39106 48
59	1.05574 21674 84	0.86280 26493 22	0.50554 08868 96	0.96380 15419 33
60	1.07363 61025 26	0.87138 93183 24	0.49059 21482 36	0.96306 35777 13
61	1.09153 00375 69	0.87971 07994 89	0.47550 91053 42	0.96234 08838 52
62	1.10942 39726 11	0.88776 53440 62	0.46029 63109 60	0.96163 43063 41
63	1.12731 79076 53	0.89555 12806 66	0.44495 83168 09	0.96094 46704 42
64	1.14521 18426 95	0.90306 70137 43	0.42949 96725 13	0.96027 27798 50
65	1.16310 57777 37	0.91031 10219 96	0.41392 49246 34	0.95961 94158 94
66	1.18099 97127 79	0.91728 18568 35	0.39823 86158 09	0.95898 53367 59
67	1.19889 36478 21	0.92397 81408 42	0.38244 52839 90	0.95837 12767 49
68	1.21678 75828 63	0.93039 85662 44	0.36654 94617 80	0.95777 79455 73
69	1.23468 15179 05	0.93654 18934 14	0.35055 56758 63	0.95720 60276 63
70	1.25257 54529 48	0.94240 69493 97	0.33446 84465 36	0.95665 61815 25
71	1.27046 93879 90	0.94799 26264 63	0.31829 22873 26	0.95612 90391 18
72	1.28836 33230 32	0.95329 78807 06	0.30203 17046 96	0.95562 52052 63
73	1.30625 72580 74	0.95832 17306 71	0.28569 11978 41	0.95514 52570 85
74	1.32415 11931 16	0.96306 32560 36	0.26927 52585 60	0.95468 97434 82
75	1.34204 51281 58	0.96752 15963 37	0.25278 83712 16	0.95425 91846 24
76	1.35993 90632 00	0.97169 59497 42	0.23623 50127 62	0.95385 40714 88
77	1.37783 29982 42	0.97558 55718 92	0.21961 96528 45	0.95347 48654 12
78	1.39572 69332 84	0.97918 97747 88	0.20294 67539 78	0.95312 19976 86
79	1.41362 08683 26	0.98250 79257 49	0.18622 07717 72	0.95279 58691 73
80	1.43151 48033 69	0.98553 94464 34	0.16944 61552 32	0.95249 68499 53
81	1.44940 87384 11	0.98828 38119 26	0.15262 73471 05	0.95222 52790 02
82	1.46730 26734 53	0.99074 05498 98	0.13576 87842 88	0.95198 14638 97
83	1.48519 66084 95	0.99290 92398 41	0.11887 48982 70	0.95176 56805 48
84	1.50309 05435 37	0.99478 95123 71	0.10195 01156 29	0.95157 81729 63
85	1.52098 44785 79	0.99638 10486 17	0.08499 88585 58	0.95141 91530 37
86	1.53887 84136 21	0.99768 35796 83	0.06802 55454 32	0.95128 88003 72
87	1.55677 23486 63	0.99869 68861 88	0.05103 45914 00	0.95118 72621 23
88	1.57466 62837 05	0.99942 07978 94	0.03403 04089 96	0.95111 46528 74
89	1.59256 02187 48	0.99985 51934 15	0.01701 74087 84	0.95107 10545 39
90	1.61045 41537 90	1.00000 00000 00	0.00000 00000 00	0.95105 65162 95

q = 0.00627 23946 95993 661
q' = 0.14283 65198 36280 4

D(90) = 1.02540 83207 37777
1/D(90) = 0.97522 12653 00933

r	φ	E(φ,k)	A(r)	D(r)
45	0.79794 22947 48	0.79077 16068 83	0.70705 11440 63	1.01270 41540 99
46	0.81538 52022 06	0.80777 48834 07	0.71928 51759 86	1.01314 75229 09
47	0.83281 28508 43	0.82474 84245 12	0.73130 01708 12	1.01359 03515 58
48	0.85022 52818 52	0.84169 23363 88	0.74309 24648 41	1.01403 21005 28
49	0.86762 25548 52	0.85860 67608 43	0.75465 84620 45	1.01447 22316 14
50	0.88500 47477 67	0.87549 18749 47	0.76599 46351 74	1.01491 02085 85
51	0.90237 19566 85	0.89234 78906 33	0.77709 75268 40	1.01534 54978 33
52	0.91972 42956 96	0.90917 50542 67	0.78796 37505 86	1.01577 75690 24
53	0.93706 18967 06	0.92597 36461 70	0.79858 99919 26	1.01620 58957 47
54	0.95438 49092 38	0.94274 39801 18	0.80897 30093 67	1.01662 99561 51
55	0.97169 35002 04	0.95948 64028 00	0.81910 96354 11	1.01704 92335 82
56	0.98898 78536 66	0.97620 12932 48	0.82899 67775 32	1.01746 32172 17
57	1.00626 81705 72	0.99288 90622 29	0.83863 14191 33	1.01787 14026 78
58	1.02353 46684 81	1.00955 01516 18	0.84801 06204 73	1.01827 32926 54
59	1.04078 75812 59	1.02618 50337 35	0.85713 15195 82	1.01866 83975 03
60	1.05802 71587 72	1.04279 42106 56	0.86599 13331 43	1.01905 62358 51
61	1.07525 36665 47	1.05937 82135 02	0.87458 73573 56	1.01943 63351 75
62	1.09246 73854 32	1.07593 76017 00	0.88291 69687 70	1.01980 82323 82
63	1.10966 86112 26	1.09247 29622 23	0.89097 76251 04	1.02017 14743 73
64	1.12685 76543 05	1.10898 49088 07	0.89876 68660 29	1.02052 56185 91
65	1.14403 48392 26	1.12547 40811 50	0.90628 23139 31	1.02087 02335 66
66	1.16120 05043 23	1.14194 11440 87	0.91352 16746 54	1.02120 48994 37
67	1.17835 50012 83	1.15838 67867 52	0.92048 27382 07	1.02152 92084 64
68	1.19549 86947 13	1.17481 17217 21	0.92716 33794 51	1.02184 27655 26
69	1.21263 19616 96	1.19121 66841 37	0.93356 15587 64	1.02214 51886 02
70	1.22975 51913 30	1.20760 24308 20	0.93967 53226 68	1.02243 61092 33
71	1.24686 87842 61	1.22396 97393 69	0.94550 28044 42	1.02271 51729 78
72	1.26397 31521 99	1.24031 94072 44	0.95104 22247 00	1.02298 20398 40
73	1.28106 87174 31	1.25665 22508 39	0.95629 18919 44	1.02323 63846 82
74	1.29815 59123 20	1.27296 91045 44	0.96125 02030 96	1.02347 78976 22
75	1.31523 51787 94	1.28927 08197 97	0.96591 56439 89	1.02370 62844 15
76	1.33230 69678 27	1.30555 82641 22	0.97028 67898 44	1.02392 12668 04
77	1.34937 17389 16	1.32183 23201 67	0.97436 23057 15	1.02412 25828 67
78	1.36642 99595 44	1.33809 38847 26	0.97814 09469 01	1.02430 99873 30
79	1.38348 21046 39	1.35434 38677 57	0.98162 15593 36	1.02448 32518 69
80	1.40052 86560 30	1.37058 31913 93	0.98480 30799 50	1.02464 21653 87
81	1.41757 01018 87	1.38681 27889 50	0.98768 45369 98	1.02478 65342 73
82	1.43460 69361 66	1.40303 36039 21	0.99026 50503 68	1.02491 61826 34
83	1.45163 96580 45	1.41924 65889 78	0.99254 38318 48	1.02503 09525 14
84	1.46866 87713 53	1.43545 27049 55	0.99452 01853 80	1.02513 07040 82
85	1.48569 47839 99	1.45165 29198 44	0.99619 35072 72	1.02521 53158 07
86	1.50271 82073 94	1.46784 82077 69	0.99756 32863 90	1.02528 46846 01
87	1.51973 95558 74	1.48403 95479 77	0.99862 91043 13	1.02533 87259 50
88	1.53675 93461 15	1.50022 79238 09	0.99939 06354 69	1.02537 73740 11
89	1.55377 80965 52	1.51641 43216 81	0.99984 76472 32	1.02540 05816 99
90	1.57079 63267 95	1.53259 97300 61	1.00000 00000 00	1.02540 83207 38

K = 1.61510 09160 67722   E = 1.52830 62960 54359
K'= 2.55073 14496 27254   E'= 1.10964 34135 42761

r	u=(r/90)K=F(ϕ,k)	sn u	cn u	dn u
0	0.00000 00000 00	0.00000 00000 00	1.00000 00000 00	1.00000 00000 00
1	0.01794 55657 34	0.01794 45004 70	0.99983 89844 88	0.99998 29344 50
2	0.03589 11314 68	0.03588 26102 81	0.99935 60117 79	0.99993 17603 62
3	0.05383 66972 02	0.05380 79434 16	0.99855 13032 52	0.99984 65453 87
4	0.07178 22629 36	0.07171 41231 28	0.99742 52275 45	0.99972 74021 52
5	0.08972 78286 70	0.08959 47865 51	0.99597 83000 76	0.99957 44880 84
6	0.10767 33944 05	0.10744 35892 82	0.99421 11823 56	0.99938 80051 48
7	0.12561 89601 39	0.12525 42099 19	0.99212 46811 25	0.99916 81995 25
8	0.14356 45258 73	0.14302 03545 55	0.98971 97472 94	0.99891 53612 14
9	0.16151 00916 07	0.16073 57612 04	0.98699 74747 03	0.99862 98235 64
10	0.17945 56573 41	0.17839 42041 70	0.98395 90987 02	0.99831 19627 42
11	0.19740 12230 75	0.19598 94983 32	0.98060 59945 48	0.99796 21971 23
12	0.21534 67888 09	0.21351 55033 40	0.97693 96756 37	0.99758 09866 30
13	0.23329 23545 43	0.23096 61277 23	0.97296 17915 65	0.99716 88319 93
14	0.25123 79202 77	0.24833 53328 90	0.96867 41260 29	0.99672 62739 63
15	0.26918 34860 11	0.26561 71370 21	0.96407 85945 76	0.99625 38924 48
16	0.28712 90517 45	0.28280 56188 43	0.95917 72421 98	0.99575 23056 05
17	0.30507 46174 79	0.29989 49212 75	0.95397 22407 88	0.99522 21688 70
18	0.32302 01832 14	0.31687 92549 49	0.94846 58864 63	0.99466 41739 32
19	0.34096 57489 48	0.33375 29015 87	0.94266 05967 59	0.99407 90476 62
20	0.35891 13146 82	0.35051 02172 42	0.93655 89077 09	0.99346 75509 88
21	0.37685 68804 16	0.36714 56353 84	0.93016 34708 04	0.99283 04777 29
22	0.39480 24461 50	0.38365 36698 38	0.92347 70498 61	0.99216 86533 77
23	0.41274 80118 84	0.40002 89175 64	0.91650 25177 89	0.99148 29338 50
24	0.43069 35776 18	0.41626 60612 76	0.90924 28532 74	0.99077 42041 95
25	0.44863 91433 52	0.43235 98719 01	0.90170 11373 89	0.99004 33772 70
26	0.46658 47090 86	0.44830 52108 69	0.89388 05501 34	0.98929 13923 79
27	0.48453 02748 20	0.46409 70322 35	0.88578 43669 15	0.98851 92138 87
28	0.50247 58405 54	0.47973 03846 35	0.87741 59549 82	0.98772 78298 09
29	0.52042 14062 88	0.49520 04130 72	0.86877 87698 22	0.98691 82503 70
30	0.53836 69720 23	0.51050 23605 25	0.85987 63515 17	0.98609 15065 51
31	0.55631 25377 57	0.52563 15693 98	0.85071 23210 88	0.98524 86486 13
32	0.57425 81034 91	0.54058 34827 94	0.84129 03768 20	0.98439 07446 07
33	0.59220 36692 25	0.55535 36456 14	0.83161 42905 84	0.98351 88788 74
34	0.61014 92349 59	0.56993 77055 03	0.82168 79041 62	0.98263 41505 35
35	0.62809 48006 93	0.58433 14136 21	0.81151 51255 87	0.98173 76719 74
36	0.64604 03664 27	0.59853 06252 50	0.80109 99255 01	0.98083 05673 19
37	0.66398 59321 61	0.61253 13002 51	0.79044 63335 44	0.97991 39709 21
38	0.68193 14978 95	0.62632 95033 56	0.77955 84347 73	0.97898 90258 33
39	0.69987 70636 29	0.63992 14043 07	0.76844 03661 38	0.97805 68822 96
40	0.71782 26293 63	0.65330 32778 55	0.75709 63129 91	0.97711 86962 31
41	0.73576 81950 98	0.66647 15036 05	0.74553 05056 68	0.97617 56277 38
42	0.75371 37608 32	0.67942 25657 27	0.73374 72161 32	0.97522 88396 03
43	0.77165 93265 66	0.69215 30525 29	0.72175 07546 76	0.97427 94958 30
44	0.78960 48923 00	0.70465 96559 02	0.70954 54667 20	0.97332 87601 71
45	0.80755 04580 34	0.71693 91706 46	0.69713 57296 77	0.97237 77946 86

q = 0.00700 22602 97383 134   D(90) = 1.02840 68655 87094
q' = 0.13680 08474 28618 9   1/D(90) = 0.97237 77946 86467

r	ϕ	$E(\phi,k)$	$A(r)$	$D(r)$
0	0.00000 00000 00	0.00000 00000 00	0.00000 00000 00	1.00000 00000 00
1	0.01794 54636 46	0.01794 53615 59	0.01744 89847 67	1.00000 86523 36
2	0.03589 03149 25	0.03588 94984 15	0.03489 26606 55	1.00003 45988 01
3	0.05383 39422 80	0.05383 11876 11	0.05232 57203 87	1.00007 78077 84
4	0.07177 57357 71	0.07176 92096 73	0.06974 28598 84	1.00013 82266 43
5	0.08971 50878 82	0.08970 23503 47	0.08713 87798 65	1.00021 57817 65
6	0.10765 13943 22	0.10762 94023 23	0.10450 81874 46	1.00031 03786 63
7	0.12558 40548 22	0.12554 91669 42	0.12184 57977 33	1.00042 19020 85
8	0.14351 24739 24	0.14346 04558 91	0.13914 63354 17	1.00055 02161 57
9	0.16143 60617 65	0.16136 20928 78	0.15640 45363 65	1.00069 51645 50
10	0.17935 42348 49	0.17925 29152 75	0.17361 51492 05	1.00085 65706 67
11	0.19726 64168 08	0.19713 17757 46	0.19077 29369 15	1.00103 42378 59
12	0.21517 20391 59	0.21499 75438 37	0.20787 26783 97	1.00122 79496 69
13	0.23307 05420 38	0.23284 91075 39	0.22490 91700 60	1.00143 74700 87
14	0.25096 13749 28	0.25068 53748 09	0.24187 72273 83	1.00166 25438 49
15	0.26884 39973 67	0.26850 52750 58	0.25877 16864 88	1.00190 28967 35
16	0.28671 78796 48	0.28630 77606 01	0.27558 74056 96	1.00215 82359 15
17	0.30458 25034 89	0.30409 18080 51	0.29231 92670 79	1.00242 82502 99
18	0.32243 73627 00	0.32185 64196 84	0.30896 21780 12	1.00271 26109 16
19	0.34028 19638 20	0.33960 06247 44	0.32551 10727 11	1.00301 09713 17
20	0.35811 58267 39	0.35732 34807 06	0.34196 09137 64	1.00332 29679 99
21	0.37593 84853 00	0.37502 40744 78	0.35830 66936 58	1.00364 82208 42
22	0.39374 94878 77	0.39270 15235 63	0.37454 34362 93	1.00398 63335 77
23	0.41154 83979 34	0.41035 49771 52	0.39066 61984 93	1.00433 68942 68
24	0.42933 47945 56	0.42798 36171 72	0.40667 00715 02	1.00469 94758 10
25	0.44710 82729 64	0.44558 66592 68	0.42255 01824 72	1.00507 36364 56
26	0.46486 84450 00	0.46316 33537 33	0.43830 16959 44	1.00545 89203 49
27	0.48261 49395 88	0.48071 29863 75	0.45391 98153 14	1.00585 48580 82
28	0.50034 74031 74	0.49823 48793 22	0.46939 97842 92	1.00626 09672 67
29	0.51806 55001 36	0.51572 83917 69	0.48473 68883 44	1.00667 67531 24
30	0.53576 89131 68	0.53319 29206 65	0.49992 64561 32	1.00710 17090 82
31	0.55345 73436 42	0.55062 79013 35	0.51496 38609 30	1.00753 53174 00
32	0.57113 05119 38	0.56803 28080 40	0.52984 45220 34	1.00797 70497 93
33	0.58878 81577 52	0.58540 71544 79	0.54456 39061 60	1.00842 63680 79
34	0.60643 00403 76	0.60275 04942 28	0.55911 75288 26	1.00888 27248 36
35	0.62405 59389 44	0.62006 24211 13	0.57350 09557 17	1.00934 55640 62
36	0.64166 56526 62	0.63734 25695 31	0.58770 98040 42	1.00981 43218 60
37	0.65925 90010 04	0.65459 06147 02	0.60173 97438 72	1.01028 84271 23
38	0.67683 58238 78	0.67180 62728 71	0.61558 64994 64	1.01076 73022 26
39	0.69439 59817 74	0.68898 93014 38	0.62924 58505 68	1.01125 03637 35
40	0.71193 93558 77	0.70613 94990 47	0.64271 36337 23	1.01173 70231 13
41	0.72946 58481 54	0.72325 67056 01	0.65598 57435 26	1.01222 66874 43
42	0.74697 53814 18	0.74034 08022 36	0.66905 81338 97	1.01271 87601 44
43	0.76446 78993 61	0.75739 17112 29	0.68192 68193 18	1.01321 26417 01
44	0.78194 33665 64	0.77440 93958 62	0.69458 78760 53	1.01370 77303 96
45	0.79940 17684 80	0.79139 38602 28	0.70703 74433 63	1.01420 34230 41

75

K = 1.61510 09160 67722   E = 1.52830 62960 54359
K' = 2.55073 14496 27254   E' = 1.10964 34135 42761

r	u=(r/90)K=F(ϕ,k)	sn u	cn u	dn u
45	0.80755 04580 34	0.71693 91706 46	0.69713 57296 77	0.97237 77946 86
46	0.82549 60237 68	0.72898 84936 67	0.68452 59499 10	0.97142 77583 18
47	0.84344 15895 02	0.74080 46230 73	0.67172 05597 82	0.97047 98054 83
48	0.86138 71552 36	0.75238 46571 54	0.65872 40148 04	0.96953 50846 92
49	0.87933 27209 70	0.76372 57932 74	0.64554 07908 79	0.96859 47371 89
50	0.89727 82867 04	0.77482 53266 58	0.63217 53816 55	0.96765 98956 16
51	0.91522 38524 38	0.78568 06490 99	0.61863 22959 82	0.96673 16827 01
52	0.93316 94181 72	0.79628 92475 84	0.60491 60554 84	0.96581 12099 83
53	0.95111 49839 07	0.80664 87028 45	0.59103 11922 38	0.96489 95765 52
54	0.96906 05496 41	0.81675 66878 45	0.57698 22465 73	0.96399 78678 31
55	0.98700 61153 75	0.82661 09662 01	0.56277 37649 85	0.96310 71543 77
56	1.00495 16811 09	0.83620 93905 59	0.54841 02981 71	0.96222 84907 20
57	1.02289 72468 43	0.84554 99009 19	0.53389 63991 78	0.96136 29142 35
58	1.04084 28125 77	0.85463 05229 19	0.51923 66216 81	0.96051 14440 37
59	1.05878 83783 11	0.86344 93660 93	0.50443 55183 71	0.95967 50799 21
60	1.07673 39440 45	0.87200 46220 91	0.48949 76394 75	0.95885 48013 22
61	1.09467 95097 79	0.88029 45628 95	0.47442 75313 87	0.95805 15663 23
62	1.11262 50755 13	0.88831 75390 05	0.45922 97354 22	0.95726 63106 83
63	1.13057 06412 47	0.89607 19776 32	0.44390 87866 92	0.95649 99469 07
64	1.14851 62069 81	0.90355 63808 80	0.42846 92130 95	0.95575 33633 50
65	1.16646 17727 16	0.91076 93239 42	0.41291 55344 22	0.95502 74233 50
66	1.18440 73384 50	0.91770 94532 98	0.39725 22615 76	0.95432 29644 01
67	1.20235 29041 84	0.92437 54849 42	0.38148 38959 10	0.95364 07973 54
68	1.22029 84699 18	0.93076 62026 18	0.36561 49286 66	0.95298 17056 62
69	1.23824 40356 52	0.93688 04560 99	0.34964 98405 25	0.95234 64446 44
70	1.25618 96013 86	0.94271 71594 86	0.33359 31012 65	0.95173 57407 99
71	1.27413 51671 20	0.94827 52895 52	0.31744 91695 13	0.95115 02911 40
72	1.29208 07328 54	0.95355 38841 35	0.30122 24926 05	0.95059 07625 71
73	1.31002 62985 88	0.95855 20405 67	0.28491 75065 26	0.95005 77912 90
74	1.32797 18643 22	0.96326 89141 65	0.26853 86359 59	0.94955 19822 32
75	1.34591 74300 56	0.96770 37167 78	0.25209 02944 07	0.94907 39085 35
76	1.36386 29957 91	0.97185 57153 89	0.23557 68844 05	0.94862 41110 51
77	1.38180 85615 25	0.97572 42307 90	0.21900 27978 11	0.94820 30978 74
78	1.39975 41272 59	0.97930 86363 22	0.20237 24161 67	0.94781 13439 13
79	1.41769 96929 93	0.98260 83566 84	0.18569 01111 38	0.94744 92904 89
80	1.43564 52587 27	0.98562 28668 24	0.16896 02450 11	0.94711 73449 66
81	1.45359 08244 61	0.98835 16909 00	0.15218 71712 57	0.94681 58804 07
82	1.47153 63901 95	0.99079 44013 30	0.13537 52351 51	0.94654 52352 74
83	1.48948 19559 29	0.99295 06179 21	0.11852 87744 42	0.94630 57131 41
84	1.50742 75216 63	0.99482 00070 79	0.10165 21200 69	0.94609 75824 49
85	1.52537 30873 97	0.99640 22811 20	0.08474 95969 24	0.94592 10762 89
86	1.54331 86531 31	0.99769 71976 54	0.06782 55246 42	0.94577 63922 08
87	1.56126 42188 65	0.99870 45590 74	0.05088 42184 32	0.94566 36920 56
88	1.57920 97846 00	0.99942 42121 26	0.03392 99899 32	0.94558 31018 48
89	1.59715 53503 34	0.99985 60475 82	0.01696 71480 78	0.94553 47116 69
90	1.61510 09160 68	1.00000 00000 00	0.00000 00000 00	0.94551 85755 99

q = 0.00700 22602 97383 134   D(90) = 1.02840 68655 87094
q'= 0.13680 08474 28618 9   1/D(90) = 0.97237 77946 86467

r	φ	E(φ,k)	A(r)	D(r)
45	0.79940 17684 80	0.79139 38602 28	0.70703 74433 63	1.01420 34230 41
46	0.81684 31113 88	0.80834 51489 86	0.71927 17246 82	1.01469 91157 08
47	0.83426 74223 30	0.82526 33470 74	0.73128 69887 95	1.01519 42044 75
48	0.85167 47490 09	0.84214 85793 69	0.74307 95709 80	1.01568 80861 50
49	0.86906 51596 80	0.85900 10102 98	0.75464 58741 41	1.01618 01590 16
50	0.88643 87429 99	0.87582 08434 13	0.76598 23699 15	1.01666 98235 56
51	0.90379 56078 64	0.89260 83209 17	0.77708 55997 65	1.01715 64831 90
52	0.92113 58832 20	0.90936 37231 50	0.78795 21760 43	1.01763 95449 97
53	0.93845 97178 53	0.92608 73680 39	0.79857 87830 41	1.01811 84204 40
54	0.95576 72801 47	0.94277 96105 04	0.80896 21780 12	1.01859 25260 84
55	0.97305 87578 37	0.95944 08418 32	0.81909 91921 80	1.01906 12843 01
56	0.99033 43577 26	0.97607 14890 16	0.82898 67317 15	1.01952 41239 83
57	1.00759 43053 89	0.99267 20140 62	0.83862 17786 96	1.01998 04812 29
58	1.02483 88448 55	1.00924 29132 62	0.84800 13920 46	1.02042 98000 37
59	1.04206 82382 70	1.02578 47164 36	0.85712 27084 44	1.02087 15329 81
60	1.05928 27655 41	1.04229 79861 54	0.86598 29432 12	1.02130 51418 76
61	1.07648 27239 60	1.05878 33169 22	0.87457 93911 87	1.02173 00984 35
62	1.09366 84278 16	1.07524 13343 47	0.88290 94275 56	1.02214 58849 13
63	1.11084 02079 80	1.09167 26942 80	0.89097 05086 75	1.02255 19947 38
64	1.12799 84114 87	1.10807 80819 34	0.89876 01728 59	1.02294 79331 26
65	1.14514 34010 87	1.12445 82109 81	0.90627 60411 52	1.02333 32176 85
66	1.16227 55547 96	1.14081 38226 32	0.91351 58180 68	1.02370 73790 05
67	1.17939 52654 18	1.15714 56846 99	0.92047 72923 04	1.02406 99612 26
68	1.19650 29400 66	1.17345 45906 35	0.92715 83374 33	1.02442 05225 97
69	1.21359 89996 60	1.18974 13585 64	0.93355 69125 65	1.02475 86360 11
70	1.23068 38784 17	1.20600 68302 96	0.93967 10629 88	1.02508 38895 29
71	1.24775 80233 29	1.22225 18703 23	0.94549 89207 78	1.02539 58868 76
72	1.26482 18936 25	1.23847 73648 10	0.95103 87053 79	1.02569 42479 32
73	1.28187 59602 29	1.25468 42205 68	0.95628 87241 66	1.02597 86091 89
74	1.29892 07052 01	1.27087 33640 23	0.96124 73729 71	1.02624 86241 94
75	1.31595 66211 74	1.28704 57401 67	0.96591 31365 87	1.02650 39639 75
76	1.33298 42107 76	1.30320 23115 11	0.97028 45892 39	1.02674 43174 39
77	1.35000 39860 48	1.31934 40570 18	0.97436 03950 36	1.02696 93917 51
78	1.36701 64678 52	1.33547 19710 40	0.97813 93083 88	1.02717 89126 92
79	1.38402 21852 71	1.35158 70622 41	0.98162 01743 93	1.02737 26249 91
80	1.40102 16750 04	1.36769 03525 15	0.98480 19292 03	1.02755 02926 39
81	1.41801 54807 54	1.38378 28759 04	0.98768 36003 59	1.02771 16991 74
82	1.43500 41526 08	1.39986 56775 06	0.99026 43070 90	1.02785 66479 48
83	1.45198 82464 14	1.41593 98123 77	0.99254 32605 96	1.02798 49623 61
84	1.46896 83231 54	1.43200 63444 40	0.99451 97642 94	1.02809 64860 81
85	1.48594 49483 08	1.44806 63453 75	0.99619 32140 32	1.02819 10832 34
86	1.50291 86912 24	1.46412 08935 23	0.99756 30982 86	1.02826 86385 67
87	1.51989 01244 71	1.48017 10727 74	0.99862 89983 16	1.02832 90575 90
88	1.53685 98232 04	1.49621 79714 65	0.99939 05882 99	1.02837 22666 91
89	1.55382 83645 16	1.51226 26812 61	0.99984 76354 31	1.02839 82132 28
90	1.57079 63267 95	1.52830 62960 54	1.00000 00000 00	1.02840 68655 87

K = 1.62002 58991 24204
K'= 2.50455 00790 01634

E = 1.52379 92052 59774
E'= 1.11837 77379 69864

r	u=(r/90)K=F(ϕ,k)	sn u	cn u	dn u
0	0.00000 00000 00	0.00000 00000 00	1.00000 00000 00	1.00000 00000 00
1	0.01800 02877 68	0.01799 92020 55	0.99983 80012 41	0.99998 10511 00
2	0.03600 05755 36	0.03599 18908 36	0.99935 20819 98	0.99992 42296 74
3	0.05400 08633 04	0.05397 15580 74	0.99854 24732 67	0.99982 96114 98
4	0.07200 11510 72	0.07193 17055 04	0.99740 95596 81	0.99969 73227 22
5	0.09000 14388 40	0.08986 58498 32	0.99595 38789 69	0.99952 75396 68
6	0.10800 17266 08	0.10776 75276 80	0.99417 61212 07	0.99932 04885 30
7	0.12600 20143 76	0.12563 03004 73	0.99207 71278 50	0.99907 64449 99
8	0.14400 23021 44	0.14344 77592 81	0.98965 78905 65	0.99879 57338 12
9	0.16200 25899 12	0.16121 35295 84	0.98691 95498 51	0.99847 87282 09
10	0.18000 28776 80	0.17892 12759 73	0.98386 33934 67	0.99812 58493 22
11	0.19800 31654 49	0.19656 47067 46	0.98049 08546 55	0.99773 75654 79
12	0.21600 34532 17	0.21413 75784 23	0.97680 35101 84	0.99731 43914 41
13	0.23400 37409 85	0.23163 37001 44	0.97280 30782 01	0.99685 68875 56
14	0.25200 40287 53	0.24904 69379 54	0.96849 14159 12	0.99636 56588 49
15	0.27000 43165 21	0.26637 12189 66	0.96387 05170 85	0.99584 13540 44
16	0.28800 46042 89	0.28360 05353 85	0.95894 25093 97	0.99528 46645 13
17	0.30600 48920 57	0.30072 89483 96	0.95370 96516 22	0.99469 63231 68
18	0.32400 51798 25	0.31775 05919 05	0.94817 43306 71	0.99407 71032 91
19	0.34200 54675 93	0.33465 96761 21	0.94233 90585 02	0.99342 78173 01
20	0.36000 57553 61	0.35145 04909 81	0.93620 64688 89	0.99274 93154 77
21	0.37800 60431 29	0.36811 74094 08	0.92977 93140 80	0.99204 24846 15
22	0.39600 63308 97	0.38465 48903 97	0.92306 04613 42	0.99130 82466 51
23	0.41400 66186 65	0.40105 74819 24	0.91605 28894 08	0.99054 75572 27
24	0.43200 69064 33	0.41731 98236 80	0.90875 96848 25	0.98976 14042 24
25	0.45000 71942 01	0.43343 66496 20	0.90118 40382 33	0.98895 08062 51
26	0.46800 74819 69	0.44940 27903 25	0.89332 92405 65	0.98811 68111 01
27	0.48600 77697 37	0.46521 31751 77	0.88519 86791 91	0.98726 04941 73
28	0.50400 80575 05	0.48086 28343 51	0.87679 58340 12	0.98638 29568 74
29	0.52200 83452 73	0.49634 69006 10	0.86812 42735 09	0.98548 53249 83
30	0.54000 86330 41	0.51166 06109 16	0.85918 76507 71	0.98456 87470 05
31	0.55800 89208 09	0.52679 93078 47	0.84998 96994 98	0.98363 43925 03
32	0.57600 92085 77	0.54175 84408 32	0.84053 42299 91	0.98268 34504 13
33	0.59400 94963 46	0.55653 35671 93	0.83082 51251 54	0.98171 71273 54
34	0.61200 97841 14	0.57112 03530 04	0.82086 63364 91	0.98073 66459 21
35	0.63001 00718 82	0.58551 45737 73	0.81066 18801 32	0.97974 32429 84
36	0.64801 03596 50	0.59971 21149 35	0.80021 58328 85	0.97873 81679 76
37	0.66601 06474 18	0.61370 89721 77	0.78953 23283 25	0.97772 26811 85
38	0.68401 09351 86	0.62750 12515 88	0.77861 55529 24	0.97669 80520 54
39	0.70201 12229 54	0.64108 51696 44	0.76746 97422 45	0.97566 55574 83
40	0.72001 15107 22	0.65445 70530 27	0.75609 91771 87	0.97462 64801 44
41	0.73801 17984 90	0.66761 33382 85	0.74450 81803 07	0.97358 21068 05
42	0.75601 20862 58	0.68055 05713 51	0.73270 11122 10	0.97253 37266 72
43	0.77401 23740 26	0.69326 54068 96	0.72068 23680 38	0.97148 26297 48
44	0.79201 26617 94	0.70575 46075 66	0.70845 63740 27	0.97043 01052 08
45	0.81001 29495 62	0.71801 50430 62	0.69602 75841 78	0.96937 74397 96

ELLIPTIC FUNCTIONS TABLE $\theta = 20°$

q = 0.00777 46804 16441 809   D(90) = 1.03158 99245 70763
q' = 0.13106 18244 99858 3   1/D(90) = 0.96937 74397 96238

r	ϕ	$E(\phi,k)$	A(r)	D(r)
0	0.00000 00000 00	0.00000 00000 00	0.00000 00000 00	1.00000 00000 00
1	0.01800 01740 68	0.01800 00603 69	0.01744 81882 89	1.00000 96218 46
2	0.03599 96661 16	0.03599 87567 37	0.03489 10693 97	1.00003 84756 62
3	0.05399 77950 34	0.05399 47270 78	0.05232 33377 41	1.00008 65262 94
4	0.07199 38815 31	0.07198 66133 10	0.06973 96909 24	1.00015 37152 00
5	0.08998 72490 35	0.08997 30632 54	0.08713 48313 39	1.00023 99605 21
6	0.10797 72246 01	0.10795 27325 90	0.10450 34677 52	1.00034 51571 81
7	0.12596 31397 99	0.12592 42867 84	0.12184 03169 02	1.00046 91770 14
8	0.14394 43316 06	0.14388 64030 06	0.13914 01050 82	1.00061 18689 24
9	0.16192 01432 80	0.16183 77720 18	0.15639 75697 33	1.00077 30590 62
10	0.17988 99252 30	0.17977 71000 36	0.17360 74610 22	1.00095 25510 44
11	0.19785 30358 71	0.19770 31105 60	0.19076 45434 25	1.00115 01261 88
12	0.21580 88424 67	0.21561 45461 73	0.20786 35973 02	1.00136 55437 80
13	0.23375 67219 62	0.23351 01702 96	0.22489 94204 68	1.00159 85413 69
14	0.25169 60617 86	0.25138 87689 04	0.24186 68297 63	1.00184 88350 84
15	0.26962 62606 56	0.26924 91522 00	0.25876 06626 12	1.00211 61199 83
16	0.28754 67293 54	0.28709 01562 35	0.27557 57785 82	1.00240 00704 22
17	0.30545 68914 79	0.30491 06444 87	0.29230 70609 34	1.00270 03404 52
18	0.32335 61841 90	0.32270 95093 73	0.30894 94181 62	1.00301 65642 42
19	0.34124 40589 18	0.34048 56737 20	0.32549 77855 38	1.00334 83565 25
20	0.35911 99820 61	0.35823 80921 69	0.34194 71266 34	1.00369 53130 64
21	0.37698 34356 54	0.37596 57525 19	0.35829 24348 51	1.00405 70111 48
22	0.39483 39180 11	0.39366 76770 14	0.37452 87349 27	1.00443 30101 05
23	0.41267 09443 49	0.41134 29235 60	0.39065 10844 48	1.00482 28518 41
24	0.43049 40473 77	0.42899 05868 83	0.40665 45753 39	1.00522 60613 95
25	0.44830 27778 67	0.44660 97996 13	0.42253 43353 56	1.00564 21475 21
26	0.46609 67051 88	0.46419 97333 07	0.43828 55295 60	1.00607 06032 84
27	0.48387 54178 25	0.48175 95993 98	0.45390 33617 84	1.00651 09066 77
28	0.50163 85238 54	0.49928 86500 80	0.46938 30760 90	1.00696 25212 61
29	0.51938 56513 98	0.51678 61791 13	0.48471 99582 14	1.00742 48968 16
30	0.53711 64490 53	0.53425 15225 69	0.49990 93369 97	1.00789 74700 09
31	0.55483 05862 80	0.55168 40594 99	0.51494 65858 09	1.00837 96650 84
32	0.57252 77537 69	0.56908 32125 35	0.52982 71239 57	1.00887 08945 62
33	0.59020 76637 74	0.58644 84484 14	0.54454 64180 80	1.00937 05599 58
34	0.60787 00504 13	0.60377 92784 42	0.55909 99835 33	1.00987 80525 08
35	0.62551 46699 44	0.62107 52588 75	0.57348 33857 52	1.01039 27539 12
36	0.64314 13010 03	0.63833 59912 45	0.58769 22416 15	1.01091 40370 86
37	0.66074 97448 17	0.65556 11226 09	0.60172 22207 77	1.01144 12669 28
38	0.67833 98253 84	0.67275 03457 31	0.61556 90469 97	1.01197 38010 92
39	0.69591 13896 21	0.68990 33992 00	0.62922 84994 47	1.01251 09907 66
40	0.71346 43074 86	0.70702 00674 82	0.64269 64140 07	1.01305 21814 70
41	0.73099 84720 62	0.72410 01809 12	0.65596 86845 41	1.01359 67138 47
42	0.74851 37996 21	0.74114 36156 13	0.66904 12641 58	1.01414 39244 67
43	0.76601 02296 50	0.75815 02933 68	0.68191 01664 58	1.01469 31466 40
44	0.78348 77248 50	0.77512 01814 24	0.69457 14667 55	1.01524 37112 24
45	0.80094 62711 10	0.79205 32922 37	0.70702 13032 87	1.01579 49474 40

79

ELLIPTIC FUNCTIONS   TABLE $\theta = 20°$

K = 1.62002 58991 24204
K'= 2.50455 00790 01634

E = 1.52379 92052 59774
E'= 1.11837 77379 69864

r	u=(r/90)K=F(ϕ,k)	sn u	cn u	dn u
45	0.81001 29495 62	0.71801 50430 62	0.69602 75841 78	0.96937 74397 96
46	0.82801 32373 30	0.73004 36891 08	0.68340 04770 22	0.96832 59162 54
47	0.84601 35250 98	0.74183 76262 93	0.67057 95524 88	0.96727 68117 63
48	0.86401 38128 66	0.75339 40388 04	0.65756 93288 89	0.96623 13964 18
49	0.88201 41006 34	0.76471 02130 40	0.64437 43400 17	0.96519 09317 33
50	0.90001 43884 02	0.77578 35361 46	0.63099 91323 65	0.96415 66691 76
51	0.91801 46761 70	0.78661 14944 40	0.61744 82624 60	0.96312 98487 26
52	0.93601 49639 38	0.79719 16717 63	0.60372 62943 36	0.96211 16974 79
53	0.95401 52517 06	0.80752 17477 49	0.58983 77971 20	0.96110 34282 72
54	0.97201 55394 75	0.81759 94960 33	0.57578 73427 64	0.96010 62383 51
55	0.99001 58272 43	0.82742 27823 84	0.56157 95038 93	0.95912 13080 72
56	1.00801 61150 11	0.83698 95627 99	0.54721 88518 00	0.95814 97996 37
57	1.02601 64027 79	0.84629 78815 43	0.53270 99545 67	0.95719 28558 68
58	1.04401 66905 47	0.85534 58691 48	0.51805 73753 27	0.95625 15990 18
59	1.06201 69783 15	0.86413 17403 87	0.50326 56706 51	0.95532 71296 21
60	1.08001 72660 83	0.87265 37922 16	0.48833 93890 84	0.95442 05253 77
61	1.09801 75538 51	0.88091 04017 09	0.47328 30698 02	0.95353 28400 78
62	1.11601 78416 19	0.88890 00239 73	0.45810 12414 10	0.95266 51025 72
63	1.13401 81293 87	0.89662 11900 66	0.44279 84208 69	0.95181 83157 66
64	1.15201 84171 55	0.90407 25049 20	0.42737 91125 55	0.95099 34556 62
65	1.17001 87049 23	0.91125 26452 65	0.41184 78074 46	0.95019 14704 41
66	1.18801 89926 91	0.91816 03575 84	0.39620 89824 34	0.94941 32795 80
67	1.20601 92804 59	0.92479 44560 81	0.38046 70997 62	0.94865 97730 01
68	1.22401 95682 27	0.93115 38206 82	0.36462 66065 84	0.94793 18102 73
69	1.24201 98559 95	0.93723 73950 70	0.34869 19346 38	0.94723 02198 33
70	1.26002 01437 63	0.94304 41847 64	0.33266 75000 41	0.94655 57982 63
71	1.27802 04315 31	0.94857 32552 39	0.31655 77031 86	0.94590 93095 85
72	1.29602 07192 99	0.95382 37301 04	0.30036 69287 57	0.94529 14846 09
73	1.31402 10070 67	0.95879 47893 33	0.28409 95458 44	0.94470 30203 08
74	1.33202 12948 35	0.96348 56675 57	0.26775 99081 49	0.94414 45792 25
75	1.35002 15826 04	0.96789 56524 26	0.25135 23543 04	0.94361 67889 29
76	1.36802 18703 72	0.97202 40830 37	0.23488 12082 66	0.94312 02414 90
77	1.38602 21581 40	0.97587 03484 37	0.21835 07798 04	0.94265 54929 97
78	1.40402 24459 08	0.97943 38862 11	0.20176 53650 68	0.94222 30631 08
79	1.42202 27336 76	0.98271 41811 42	0.18512 92472 36	0.94182 34346 37
80	1.44002 30214 44	0.98571 07639 64	0.16844 66972 25	0.94145 70531 61
81	1.45802 33092 12	0.98842 32101 99	0.15172 19744 81	0.94112 43266 76
82	1.47602 35969 80	0.99085 11390 89	0.13495 93278 19	0.94082 56252 75
83	1.49402 38847 48	0.99299 42126 21	0.11816 29963 28	0.94056 12808 61
84	1.51202 41725 16	0.99485 21346 44	0.10133 72103 18	0.94033 15868 85
85	1.53002 44602 84	0.99642 46500 90	0.08448 61923 22	0.94013 67981 29
86	1.54802 47480 52	0.99771 15442 95	0.06761 41581 32	0.93997 71305 05
87	1.56602 50358 20	0.99871 26424 19	0.05072 53178 66	0.93985 27608 90
88	1.58402 53235 88	0.99942 78089 69	0.03382 38770 73	0.93976 38269 97
89	1.60202 56113 56	0.99985 69474 30	0.01691 40378 54	0.93971 04272 64
90	1.62002 58991 24	1.00000 00000 00	0.00000 00000 00	0.93969 26207 86

q = 0.00777 46804 16441 809   D(90) = 1.03158 99245 70763
q'= 0.13106 18244 99858 3   1/D(90) = 0.96937 74397 96238

r	ϕ	$E(\phi,k)$	$A(r)$	$D(r)$
45	0.80094 62711 10	0.79205 32922 37	0.70702 13032 87	1.01579 49474 40
46	0.81838 58774 47	0.80894 96831 70	0.71925 58784 07	1.01634 61836 92
47	0.83580 65759 18	0.82580 94561 27	0.73127 14597 52	1.01689 67483 84
48	0.85320 84215 10	0.84263 27571 44	0.74306 43813 98	1.01744 59707 37
49	0.87059 14919 96	0.85941 97759 22	0.75463 10449 91	1.01799 31816 08
50	0.88795 58877 70	0.87617 07453 16	0.76596 79208 58	1.01853 77143 05
51	0.90530 17316 49	0.89288 59407 74	0.77707 15491 04	1.01907 89053 97
52	0.92262 91686 59	0.90956 56797 42	0.78793 85406 82	1.01961 60955 26
53	0.93993 83657 85	0.92621 03210 09	0.79856 55784 41	1.02014 86302 07
54	0.95722 95117 07	0.94282 02640 27	0.80894 94181 62	1.02067 58606 29
55	0.97450 28165 04	0.95939 59481 86	0.81908 68895 58	1.02119 71444 41
56	0.99175 85113 42	0.97593 78520 53	0.82897 48972 65	1.02171 18465 38
57	1.00899 68481 34	0.99244 64925 76	0.83861 04218 05	1.02221 93398 33
58	1.02621 80991 80	1.00892 24242 57	0.84799 05205 22	1.02271 90060 23
59	1.04342 25567 87	1.02536 62382 92	0.85711 23285 04	1.02321 02363 40
60	1.06061 05328 69	1.04177 85616 83	0.86597 30594 75	1.02369 24322 94
61	1.07778 23585 25	1.05816 00563 25	0.87457 00066 63	1.02416 50064 02
62	1.09493 83835 98	1.07451 14180 62	0.88290 05436 48	1.02462 73829 03
63	1.11207 89762 22	1.09083 33757 24	0.89096 21251 82	1.02507 89984 61
64	1.12920 45223 40	1.10712 66901 41	0.89875 22879 86	1.02551 93028 50
65	1.14631 54252 14	1.12339 21531 33	0.90626 86515 20	1.02594 77596 26
66	1.16341 21049 19	1.13963 05864 88	0.91350 89187 32	1.02636 38467 78
67	1.18049 49978 15	1.15584 28409 13	0.92047 08767 72	1.02676 70573 66
68	1.19756 45560 07	1.17202 97949 74	0.92715 23976 95	1.02715 69001 38
69	1.21462 12467 96	1.18819 23540 24	0.93355 14391 22	1.02753 29001 29
70	1.23166 55521 09	1.20433 14491 10	0.93966 60448 83	1.02789 45992 40
71	1.24869 79679 17	1.22044 80358 73	0.94549 43456 37	1.02824 15567 92
72	1.26571 90036 50	1.23654 30934 33	0.95103 45594 52	1.02857 33500 71
73	1.28272 91815 86	1.25261 76232 68	0.95628 49923 73	1.02888 95748 35
74	1.29972 90362 41	1.26867 26480 79	0.96124 40389 50	1.02918 98458 12
75	1.31671 91137 43	1.28470 92106 46	0.96591 01827 48	1.02947 37971 65
76	1.33369 99711 96	1.30072 83726 84	0.97028 19968 21	1.02974 10829 43
77	1.35067 21760 40	1.31673 12136 85	0.97435 81441 65	1.02999 13774 96
78	1.36763 63053 98	1.33271 88297 51	0.97813 73781 41	1.03022 43758 79
79	1.38459 29454 14	1.34869 23324 34	0.98161 85428 64	1.03043 97942 17
80	1.40154 26905 91	1.36465 28475 59	0.98480 05735 69	1.03063 73700 54
81	1.41848 61431 11	1.38060 15140 48	0.98768 24969 53	1.03081 68626 74
82	1.43542 39121 64	1.39653 94827 38	0.99026 34314 73	1.03097 80533 91
83	1.45235 66132 53	1.41246 79152 04	0.99254 25876 35	1.03112 07458 19
84	1.46928 48675 15	1.42838 79825 65	0.99451 92682 34	1.03124 47661 07
85	1.48620 93010 18	1.44430 08642 99	0.99619 28685 81	1.03134 99631 55
86	1.50313 05440 68	1.46020 77470 52	0.99756 28766 91	1.03143 62087 96
87	1.52004 92305 07	1.47610 98234 47	0.99862 88734 47	1.03150 33979 53
88	1.53696 59970 05	1.49200 82908 86	0.99939 05327 31	1.03155 14487 64
89	1.55388 14823 63	1.50790 43503 63	0.99984 76215 28	1.03158 03026 88
90	1.57079 63267 95	1.52379 92052 60	1.00000 00000 00	1.03158 99245 71

ELLIPTIC FUNCTIONS   TABLE $\theta = 21°$

K = 1.62523 36677 58843
K′= 2.46099 94583 04126

E = 1.51907 85300 25531
E′= 1.12724 96377 57702

r	u=(r/90)K=F(φ,k)	sn u	cn u	dn u
0	0.00000 00000 00	0.00000 00000 00	1.00000 00000 00	1.00000 00000 00
1	0.01805 81518 64	0.01805 70444 13	0.99983 69582 82	0.99997 90624 33
2	0.03611 63037 28	0.03610 74451 97	0.99934 79135 92	0.99991 62779 16
3	0.05417 44555 92	0.05414 45641 26	0.99853 31072 01	0.99981 17309 48
4	0.07223 26074 56	0.07216 17737 60	0.99739 29408 25	0.99966 55622 02
5	0.09029 07593 20	0.09015 24628 08	0.99592 79760 35	0.99947 79682 82
6	0.10834 89111 84	0.10811 00414 53	0.99413 89334 18	0.99924 92013 90
7	0.12640 70630 48	0.12602 79466 24	0.99202 66915 11	0.99897 95688 94
8	0.14446 52149 12	0.14389 96472 03	0.98959 22855 07	0.99866 94328 06
9	0.16252 33667 76	0.16171 86491 63	0.98683 69057 31	0.99831 92091 68
10	0.18058 15186 40	0.17947 85006 10	0.98376 18958 97	0.99792 93673 46
11	0.19863 96705 04	0.19717 27967 35	0.98036 87511 48	0.99750 04292 41
12	0.21669 78223 68	0.21479 51846 52	0.97665 91158 90	0.99703 29684 05
13	0.23475 59742 32	0.23233 93681 11	0.97263 47814 19	0.99652 76090 86
14	0.25281 41260 96	0.24979 91120 93	0.96829 76833 59	0.99598 50251 83
15	0.27087 22779 60	0.26716 82472 52	0.96364 98989 05	0.99540 59391 24
16	0.28893 04298 24	0.28444 06742 15	0.95869 36438 99	0.99479 11206 77
17	0.30698 85816 88	0.30161 03677 22	0.95343 12697 21	0.99414 13856 75
18	0.32504 67335 52	0.31867 13805 98	0.94786 52600 38	0.99345 75946 89
19	0.34310 48854 16	0.33561 78475 57	0.94199 82273 87	0.99274 06516 23
20	0.36116 30372 80	0.35244 39888 20	0.93583 29096 29	0.99199 15022 52
21	0.37922 11891 44	0.36914 41135 50	0.92937 21662 67	0.99121 11327 08
22	0.39727 93410 08	0.38571 26230 97	0.92261 89746 50	0.99040 05679 02
23	0.41533 74928 72	0.40214 40140 41	0.91557 64260 68	0.98956 08699 03
24	0.43339 56447 36	0.41843 28810 43	0.90824 77217 49	0.98869 31362 68
25	0.45145 37966 00	0.43457 39194 82	0.90063 61687 75	0.98779 84983 36
26	0.46951 19484 64	0.45056 19278 96	0.89274 51759 21	0.98687 81194 69
27	0.48757 01003 28	0.46639 18102 09	0.88457 82494 33	0.98593 31932 81
28	0.50562 82521 92	0.48205 85777 46	0.87613 89887 58	0.98496 49418 16
29	0.52368 64040 56	0.49755 73510 46	0.86743 10822 31	0.98397 46137 12
30	0.54174 45559 20	0.51288 33614 55	0.85845 83027 40	0.98296 34823 42
31	0.55980 27077 84	0.52803 19525 19	0.84922 45033 67	0.98193 28439 34
32	0.57786 08596 48	0.54299 85811 58	0.83973 36130 35	0.98088 40156 78
33	0.59591 90115 12	0.55777 88186 46	0.82998 96321 46	0.97981 83338 23
34	0.61397 71633 76	0.57236 83513 79	0.81999 66282 49	0.97873 71517 69
35	0.63203 53152 40	0.58676 29814 41	0.80975 87317 29	0.97764 18381 51
36	0.65009 34671 04	0.60095 86269 81	0.79928 01315 29	0.97653 37749 33
37	0.66815 16189 68	0.61495 13223 93	0.78856 50709 27	0.97541 43554 96
38	0.68620 97708 32	0.62873 72183 05	0.77761 78433 64	0.97428 49827 39
39	0.70426 79226 95	0.64231 25813 88	0.76644 27883 35	0.97314 70671 93
40	0.72232 60745 59	0.65567 37939 90	0.75504 42873 60	0.97200 20251 39
41	0.74038 42264 23	0.66881 73535 94	0.74342 67600 32	0.97085 12767 57
42	0.75844 23782 87	0.68173 98721 17	0.73159 46601 54	0.96969 62442 82
43	0.77650 05301 51	0.69443 80750 40	0.71955 24719 82	0.96853 83501 84
44	0.79455 86820 15	0.70690 88003 99	0.70730 47065 57	0.96737 90153 84
45	0.81261 68338 79	0.71914 89976 27	0.69485 58981 63	0.96621 96574 78

82

q = 0.00859 01752 53625 654
q' = 0.12559 47852 09818 5

D(90) = 1.03496 13488 61410
1/D(90) = 0.96621 96574 78154

r	ϕ	$E(\phi, k)$	A(r)	D(r)
0	0.00000 00000 00	0.00000 00000 00	0.00000 00000 00	1.00000 00000 00
1	0.01805 80258 27	0.01805 78997 92	0.01744 72570 56	1.00001 06487 28
2	0.03611 52956 36	0.03611 42875 95	0.03488 92089 18	1.00004 25819 37
3	0.05417 10544 27	0.05416 76536 47	0.05232 05519 78	1.00009 57607 21
4	0.07222 45492 33	0.07221 64926 28	0.06973 59858 14	1.00017 01202 93
5	0.09027 50301 33	0.09025 93058 75	0.08713 02147 68	1.00026 55700 55
6	0.10832 17512 58	0.10829 46035 76	0.10449 79495 41	1.00038 19937 19
7	0.12636 39717 94	0.12632 09069 47	0.12183 39087 77	1.00051 92494 41
8	0.14440 09569 69	0.14433 67503 89	0.13913 28206 46	1.00067 71699 98
9	0.16243 19790 40	0.16234 06836 10	0.15638 94244 28	1.00085 55629 88
10	0.18045 63182 57	0.18033 12737 21	0.17359 84720 88	1.00105 42110 69
11	0.19847 32638 24	0.19830 71072 95	0.19075 47298 54	1.00127 28722 22
12	0.21648 21148 35	0.21626 67923 79	0.20785 29797 89	1.00151 12800 42
13	0.23448 21812 02	0.23420 89604 70	0.22488 80213 56	1.00176 91440 68
14	0.25247 27845 59	0.25213 22684 37	0.24185 46729 84	1.00204 61501 36
15	0.27045 32591 50	0.27003 54003 88	0.25874 77736 22	1.00234 19607 58
16	0.28842 29526 93	0.28791 70694 95	0.27556 21842 95	1.00265 62155 37
17	0.30638 12272 25	0.30577 60197 39	0.29229 27896 50	1.00298 85316 04
18	0.32432 74599 22	0.32361 10276 14	0.30893 44994 93	1.00333 85040 87
19	0.34226 10438 92	0.34142 09037 53	0.32548 22503 28	1.00370 57065 99
20	0.36018 13889 49	0.35920 44944 89	0.34193 10068 80	1.00408 96917 65
21	0.37808 79223 49	0.37696 06833 50	0.35827 57636 18	1.00448 99917 59
22	0.39598 00895 12	0.39468 83924 78	0.37451 15462 59	1.00490 61188 82
23	0.41385 73547 01	0.41238 65839 76	0.39063 34132 79	1.00533 75661 49
24	0.43171 92016 83	0.43005 42611 82	0.40663 64574 03	1.00578 38079 10
25	0.44956 51343 51	0.44769 04698 56	0.42251 58070 90	1.00624 43004 93
26	0.46739 46773 20	0.46529 42993 01	0.43826 66280 10	1.00671 84828 60
27	0.48520 73764 90	0.48286 48834 00	0.45388 41245 06	1.00720 57772 95
28	0.50300 27995 75	0.50040 14015 68	0.46936 35410 53	1.00770 55901 10
29	0.52078 05365 98	0.51790 30796 29	0.48470 01637 00	1.00821 73123 60
30	0.53854 02003 57	0.53536 91906 13	0.49988 93215 01	1.00874 03205 94
31	0.55628 14268 55	0.55279 90554 68	0.51492 63879 37	1.00927 39776 10
32	0.57400 38756 93	0.57019 20436 93	0.52980 67823 27	1.00981 76332 31
33	0.59170 72304 35	0.58754 75738 90	0.54452 59712 19	1.01037 06250 99
34	0.60939 11989 31	0.60486 51142 39	0.55907 94697 77	1.01093 22794 80
35	0.62705 55136 12	0.62214 41828 90	0.57346 28431 51	1.01150 19120 88
36	0.64469 99317 48	0.63938 43482 76	0.58767 17078 27	1.01207 88289 13
37	0.66232 42356 69	0.65658 52293 57	0.60170 17329 76	1.01266 23270 75
38	0.67992 82329 57	0.67374 64957 77	0.61554 86417 73	1.01325 16956 72
39	0.69751 17566 00	0.69086 78679 53	0.62920 82127 15	1.01384 62166 50
40	0.71507 46651 10	0.70794 91170 92	0.64267 62809 13	1.01444 51656 78
41	0.73261 68426 15	0.72499 00651 31	0.65594 87393 71	1.01504 78130 31
42	0.75013 81989 09	0.74199 05846 16	0.66902 15402 53	1.01565 34244 76
43	0.76763 86694 72	0.75895 05985 03	0.68189 06961 26	1.01626 12621 70
44	0.78511 82154 65	0.77587 00799 05	0.69455 22811 92	1.01687 05855 57
45	0.80257 68236 74	0.79274 90517 64	0.70700 24324 96	1.01748 06522 69

ELLIPTIC FUNCTIONS TABLE $\theta = 21°$

K = 1.62523 36677 58843
K'= 2.46099 94583 04126

E = 1.51907 85300 25531
E'= 1.12724 96377 57702

r	u=(r/90)K=F(ϕ,k)	sn u	cn u	dn u
45	0.81261 68338 79	0.71914 89976 27	0.69485 58981 63	0.96621 96574 78
46	0.83067 49857 43	0.73115 57262 56	0.68221 06008 88	0.96506 16890 08
47	0.84873 31376 07	0.74292 61544 94	0.66937 33853 16	0.96390 65157 51
48	0.86679 12894 71	0.75445 75576 82	0.65634 88353 43	0.96275 55350 48
49	0.88484 94413 35	0.76574 73166 38	0.64314 15451 22	0.96161 01341 65
50	0.90290 75931 99	0.77679 29158 91	0.62975 61161 44	0.96047 16886 92
51	0.92096 57450 63	0.78759 19418 29	0.61619 71544 61	0.95934 15609 73
52	0.93902 38969 27	0.79814 20807 47	0.60246 92680 47	0.95822 10985 87
53	0.95708 20487 91	0.80844 11168 28	0.58857 70643 01	0.95711 16328 53
54	0.97514 02006 55	0.81848 69300 44	0.57452 51477 07	0.95601 44773 91
55	0.99319 83525 19	0.82827 74939 95	0.56031 81176 27	0.95493 09267 11
56	1.01125 65043 83	0.83781 08737 03	0.54596 05662 54	0.95386 22548 56
57	1.02931 46562 47	0.84708 52233 47	0.53145 70767 12	0.95280 97140 77
58	1.04737 28081 11	0.85609 87839 67	0.51681 22213 05	0.95177 45335 59
59	1.06543 09599 75	0.86484 98811 44	0.50203 05599 12	0.95075 79181 86
60	1.08348 91118 39	0.87333 69226 44	0.48711 66385 45	0.94976 10473 51
61	1.10154 72637 03	0.88155 83960 64	0.47207 49880 37	0.94878 50738 10
62	1.11960 54155 67	0.88951 28664 61	0.45691 01228 91	0.94783 11225 74
63	1.13766 35674 31	0.89719 89739 89	0.44162 65402 73	0.94690 02898 57
64	1.15572 17192 95	0.90461 54315 40	0.42622 87191 40	0.94599 36420 51
65	1.17377 98711 59	0.91176 10224 08	0.41072 11195 18	0.94511 22147 59
66	1.19183 80230 23	0.91863 45979 67	0.39510 81819 17	0.94425 70118 58
67	1.20989 61748 87	0.92523 50753 90	0.37939 43268 79	0.94342 90046 14
68	1.22795 43267 51	0.93156 14353 94	0.36358 39546 61	0.94262 91308 32
69	1.24601 24786 15	0.93761 27200 34	0.34768 14450 48	0.94185 82940 51
70	1.26407 06304 79	0.94338 80305 47	0.33169 11572 85	0.94111 73627 77
71	1.28212 87823 43	0.94888 65252 45	0.31561 74301 42	0.94040 71697 59
72	1.30018 69342 07	0.95410 74174 73	0.29946 45820 84	0.93972 85113 00
73	1.31824 50860 71	0.95904 99736 35	0.28323 69115 61	0.93908 21466 13
74	1.33630 32379 35	0.96371 35112 81	0.26693 86974 09	0.93846 87972 10
75	1.35436 13897 99	0.96809 73972 82	0.25057 41993 42	0.93788 91463 30
76	1.37241 95416 63	0.97220 10460 76	0.23414 76585 59	0.93734 38384 04
77	1.39047 76935 27	0.97602 39180 04	0.21766 32984 33	0.93683 34785 56
78	1.40853 58453 91	0.97956 55177 30	0.20112 53252 91	0.93635 86321 43
79	1.42659 39972 55	0.98282 53927 61	0.18453 79292 82	0.93591 98243 23
80	1.44465 21491 19	0.98580 31320 52	0.16790 52853 13	0.93551 75396 63
81	1.46271 03009 83	0.98849 83647 20	0.15123 15540 68	0.93515 22217 78
82	1.48076 84528 47	0.99091 07588 55	0.13452 08830 83	0.93482 42730 07
83	1.49882 66047 11	0.99304 00204 38	0.11777 74078 90	0.93453 40541 16
84	1.51688 47565 75	0.99488 58923 63	0.10100 52532 12	0.93428 18840 38
85	1.53494 29084 39	0.99644 81535 77	0.08420 85342 04	0.93406 80396 41
86	1.55300 10603 03	0.99772 66183 19	0.06739 13577 41	0.93389 27555 34
87	1.57105 92121 67	0.99872 11354 82	0.05055 78237 43	0.93375 62238 96
88	1.58911 73640 31	0.99943 15880 88	0.03371 20265 28	0.93365 85943 40
89	1.60717 55158 95	0.99985 78928 74	0.01685 80561 91	0.93359 99738 09
90	1.62523 36677 59	1.00000 00000 00	0.00000 00000 00	0.93358 04264 97

84

q = 0.00859 01752 53625 654   D(90) = 1.03496 13488 61410
q′= 0.12559 47852 09818 5   1/D(90) = 0.96621 96574 78154

r	φ	E(φ,k)	A(r)	D(r)
45	0.80257 68236 74	0.79274 90517 64	0.70700 24324 96	1.01748 06522 69
46	0.82001 45064 47	0.80958 75864 72	0.71923 73511 24	1.01809 07190 36
47	0.83743 13015 78	0.82638 58054 25	0.73125 33033 74	1.01870 00425 84
48	0.85482 72721 74	0.84314 38785 24	0.74304 66219 14	1.01930 78805 47
49	0.87220 25064 87	0.85986 20236 24	0.75461 37069 19	1.01991 34923 66
50	0.88955 71177 17	0.87654 05059 20	0.76595 10271 86	1.02051 61401 97
51	0.90689 12437 88	0.89317 96373 01	0.77705 51212 32	1.02111 50898 05
52	0.92420 50470 95	0.90977 97756 38	0.78792 25983 73	1.02170 96114 61
53	0.94149 87142 20	0.92634 13240 37	0.79855 01397 76	1.02229 89808 31
54	0.95877 24556 32	0.94286 47300 50	0.80893 44994 92	1.02288 24798 58
55	0.97602 65053 50	0.95935 04848 40	0.81907 25054 73	1.02345 93976 36
56	0.99326 11205 86	0.97579 91223 09	0.82896 10605 62	1.02402 90312 78
57	1.01047 65813 65	0.99221 12181 96	0.83859 71434 57	1.02459 06867 72
58	1.02767 31901 18	1.00858 73891 32	0.84797 78096 60	1.02514 36798 25
59	1.04485 12712 56	1.02492 82916 72	0.85710 01923 98	1.02568 73366 97
60	1.06201 11707 18	1.04123 46212 89	0.86596 15035 22	1.02622 09950 25
61	1.07915 32555 05	1.05750 71113 50	0.87455 90343 84	1.02674 40046 25
62	1.09627 79131 83	1.07374 65320 57	0.88289 01566 84	1.02725 57282 89
63	1.11338 55513 76	1.08995 36893 73	0.89095 23232 99	1.02775 55425 56
64	1.13047 65972 36	1.10612 94239 18	0.89874 30690 84	1.02824 28384 79
65	1.14755 14968 95	1.12227 46098 53	0.90626 00116 48	1.02871 70223 59
66	1.16461 07149 03	1.13839 01537 41	0.91350 08521 07	1.02917 75164 73
67	1.18165 47336 41	1.15447 69933 89	0.92046 33758 06	1.02962 37597 78
68	1.19868 40527 32	1.17053 60966 84	0.92714 54530 22	1.03005 52085 92
69	1.21569 91884 25	1.18656 84604 04	0.93354 50396 34	1.03047 13372 57
70	1.23270 06729 69	1.20257 51090 24	0.93966 01777 73	1.03087 16387 84
71	1.24968 90539 75	1.21855 70935 09	0.94548 89964 35	1.03125 56254 62
72	1.26666 48937 66	1.23451 54900 98	0.95102 97120 83	1.03162 28294 62
73	1.28362 87687 07	1.25045 13990 75	0.95628 06292 03	1.03197 28033 98
74	1.30058 12685 37	1.26636 59435 36	0.96124 01408 51	1.03230 51208 78
75	1.31752 29956 79	1.28226 02681 50	0.96590 67291 53	1.03261 93770 23
76	1.33445 45645 41	1.29813 55379 10	0.97027 89657 95	1.03291 51889 56
77	1.35137 66008 18	1.31399 29368 84	0.97435 55124 73	1.03319 21962 76
78	1.36828 97407 72	1.32983 36669 54	0.97813 51213 19	1.03345 00614 87
79	1.38519 46305 13	1.34565 89465 58	0.98161 66352 98	1.03368 84704 20
80	1.40209 19252 67	1.36147 00094 27	0.98479 89885 77	1.03390 71326 07
81	1.41898 22886 44	1.37726 81033 16	0.98768 12068 63	1.03410 57816 41
82	1.43586 63918 88	1.39305 44887 37	0.99026 24077 13	1.03428 41754 96
83	1.45274 49131 39	1.40883 04376 84	0.99254 18008 16	1.03444 20968 26
84	1.46961 85366 70	1.42459 72323 67	0.99451 86882 46	1.03457 93532 26
85	1.48648 79521 36	1.44035 61639 32	0.99619 24646 83	1.03469 57774 70
86	1.50335 38538 10	1.45610 85311 87	0.99756 26176 04	1.03479 12277 10
87	1.52021 69398 19	1.47185 56393 29	0.99862 87274 51	1.03486 55876 56
88	1.53707 79113 75	1.48759 87986 64	0.99939 04677 62	1.03491 87667 09
89	1.55393 74720 09	1.50333 93233 31	0.99984 76052 74	1.03495 07000 80
90	1.57079 63267 95	1.51907 85300 26	1.00000 00000 00	1.03496 13488 61

ELLIPTIC FUNCTIONS TABLE $\theta = 22°$

K = 1.63072 91016 30788
K' = 2.41984 16537 39137

E = 1.51414 69174 93342
E' = 1.13624 43646 84239

r	u=(r/90)K=F(φ,k)	sn u	cn u	dn u
0	0.00000 00000 00	0.00000 00000 00	1.00000 00000 00	1.00000 00000 00
1	0.01811 92122 40	0.01811 80817 19	0.99983 58540 85	0.99997 69670 13
2	0.03623 84244 81	0.03622 93814 78	0.99934 35004 63	0.99990 78993 54
3	0.05435 76367 21	0.05432 71231 40	0.99852 31913 64	0.99979 28908 77
4	0.07247 68489 61	0.07240 45422 00	0.99737 53467 32	0.99963 20978 22
5	0.09059 60612 02	0.09045 48915 65	0.99590 05535 65	0.99942 57385 40
6	0.10871 52734 42	0.10847 14472 95	0.99409 95649 94	0.99917 40931 11
7	0.12683 44856 82	0.12644 75142 75	0.99197 32991 03	0.99887 75028 51
8	0.14495 36979 23	0.14437 64318 29	0.98952 28374 99	0.99853 63697 17
9	0.16307 29101 63	0.16225 15792 44	0.98674 94236 29	0.99815 11556 06
10	0.18119 21224 03	0.18006 63811 93	0.98365 44608 57	0.99772 23815 50
11	0.19931 13346 44	0.19781 43130 51	0.98023 95103 00	0.99725 06268 16
12	0.21743 05468 84	0.21548 89060 86	0.97650 62884 35	0.99673 65279 00
13	0.23554 97591 24	0.23308 37525 18	0.97245 66644 90	0.99618 07774 34
14	0.25366 89713 65	0.25059 25104 28	0.96809 26576 10	0.99558 41230 01
15	0.27178 81836 05	0.26800 89085 08	0.96341 64338 23	0.99494 73658 58
16	0.28990 73958 45	0.28532 67506 51	0.95843 03028 20	0.99427 13595 78
17	0.30802 66080 86	0.30253 99203 57	0.95313 67145 33	0.99355 70086 07
18	0.32614 58203 26	0.31964 23849 55	0.94753 82555 55	0.99280 52667 52
19	0.34426 50325 67	0.33662 81996 35	0.94163 76453 87	0.99201 71355 86
20	0.36238 42448 07	0.35349 15112 73	0.93543 77325 39	0.99119 36627 96
21	0.38050 34570 47	0.37022 65620 50	0.92894 14904 89	0.99033 59404 56
22	0.39862 26692 88	0.38682 76928 62	0.92215 20135 18	0.98944 51032 46
23	0.41674 18815 28	0.40328 93465 05	0.91507 25124 25	0.98852 23266 19
24	0.43486 10937 68	0.41960 60706 38	0.90770 63101 49	0.98756 88249 11
25	0.45298 03060 09	0.43577 25205 23	0.90005 68372 93	0.98658 58494 09
26	0.47109 95182 49	0.45178 34615 32	0.89212 76275 77	0.98557 46863 79
27	0.48921 87304 89	0.46763 37714 25	0.88392 23132 28	0.98453 66550 52
28	0.50733 79427 30	0.48331 84423 95	0.87544 46203 16	0.98347 31055 89
29	0.52545 71549 70	0.49883 25828 79	0.86669 83640 56	0.98238 54170 09
30	0.54357 63672 10	0.51417 14191 38	0.85768 74440 85	0.98127 49951 00
31	0.56169 55794 51	0.52933 02966 07	0.84841 58397 24	0.98014 32703 11
32	0.57981 47916 91	0.54430 46810 10	0.83888 76052 43	0.97899 16956 30
33	0.59793 40039 31	0.55909 01592 58	0.82910 68651 39	0.97782 17444 57
34	0.61605 32161 72	0.57368 24401 12	0.81907 78094 34	0.97663 49084 70
35	0.63417 24284 12	0.58807 73546 32	0.80880 46890 13	0.97546 26954 89
36	0.65229 16406 52	0.60227 08564 14	0.79829 18110 03	0.97421 66273 47
37	0.67041 08528 93	0.61625 90216 05	0.78754 35342 19	0.97298 82377 69
38	0.68853 00651 33	0.63003 80487 25	0.77656 42646 68	0.97174 90702 61
39	0.70664 92773 73	0.64360 42582 84	0.76535 84511 31	0.97050 06760 13
40	0.72476 84896 14	0.65695 40922 06	0.75393 05808 45	0.96924 46118 25
41	0.74288 77018 54	0.67008 41130 69	0.74228 51752 61	0.96798 24380 51
42	0.76100 69140 94	0.68299 10031 66	0.73042 67859 23	0.96671 57165 68
43	0.77912 61263 35	0.69567 15633 98	0.71835 99904 50	0.96544 60087 77
44	0.79724 53385 75	0.70812 27119 99	0.70608 93886 41	0.96417 48736 31
45	0.81536 45508 15	0.72034 14831 11	0.69361 95987 06	0.96290 38656 93

86

q = 0.00944 92999 75082 239

q′= 0.12037 82455 07893 9

D(90) = 1.03852 52730 08598

1/D(90) = 0.96290 38656 93137

r	φ	E(φ,k)	A(r)	D(r)
0	0.00000 00000 00	0.00000 00000 00	0.00000 00000 00	1.00000 00000 00
1	0.01811 90731 21	0.01811 89340 03	0.01744 61756 42	1.00001 17342 38
2	0.03623 73117 52	0.03623 61990 84	0.03488 70483 93	1.00004 69226 56
3	0.05435 38825 36	0.05435 01288 18	0.05231 73169 49	1.00010 55223 83
4	0.07246 79543 85	0.07245 90617 72	0.06973 16831 70	1.00018 74620 25
5	0.09057 86996 01	0.09056 13439 85	0.08712 48536 70	1.00029 26417 51
6	0.10868 52950 06	0.10865 53314 36	0.10449 15413 93	1.00042 09334 19
7	0.12678 69230 50	0.12673 93924 82	0.12182 64671 97	1.00057 21807 25
8	0.14488 27729 19	0.14481 19102 78	0.13912 43614 30	1.00074 61994 00
9	0.16297 20416 26	0.16287 12851 60	0.15637 99655 07	1.00094 27774 32
10	0.18105 39350 90	0.18091 59369 87	0.17358 80334 84	1.00116 16753 22
11	0.19912 76691 99	0.19894 43074 49	0.19074 33336 22	1.00140 26263 80
12	0.21719 24708 59	0.21695 48623 18	0.20784 06499 62	1.00166 53370 46
13	0.23524 75790 17	0.23494 60936 54	0.22487 47838 81	1.00194 94872 52
14	0.25329 22456 71	0.25291 65219 53	0.24184 05556 50	1.00225 47308 07
15	0.27132 57368 52	0.27086 46982 29	0.25873 28059 91	1.00258 06958 22
16	0.28934 73335 86	0.28878 92060 41	0.27554 63976 22	1.00292 69851 62
17	0.30735 63328 28	0.30668 86634 43	0.29227 62167 98	1.00329 31769 32
18	0.32535 20483 69	0.32456 17248 66	0.30891 71748 50	1.00367 88249 86
19	0.34333 38117 20	0.34240 70829 26	0.32546 42097 13	1.00408 34594 76
20	0.36130 09729 57	0.36022 34701 51	0.34191 22874 51	1.00450 65874 20
21	0.37925 29015 48	0.37800 96606 31	0.35825 64037 71	1.00494 76933 08
22	0.39718 89871 33	0.39576 44715 77	0.37449 15855 29	1.00540 62397 22
23	0.41510 86402 86	0.41348 67648 08	0.39061 28922 35	1.00588 16680 00
24	0.43301 12932 35	0.43117 54481 36	0.40661 54175 40	1.00637 33989 09
25	0.45089 64005 46	0.44882 94766 74	0.42249 42907 22	1.00688 08333 55
26	0.46876 34397 80	0.46644 78540 48	0.43824 46781 57	1.00740 33531 11
27	0.48661 19121 05	0.48402 96335 19	0.45386 17847 81	1.00794 03215 72
28	0.50444 13428 74	0.50157 39190 15	0.46934 08555 50	1.00849 10845 28
29	0.52225 12821 71	0.51907 98660 68	0.48467 71768 73	1.00905 49709 64
30	0.54004 13053 11	0.53654 66826 64	0.49986 60780 53	1.00963 12938 74
31	0.55781 10133 07	0.55397 36299 91	0.51490 29327 01	1.01021 93511 01
32	0.57556 00333 00	0.57136 00231 08	0.52978 31601 47	1.01081 84261 92
33	0.59328 80189 44	0.58870 52315 13	0.54450 22268 38	1.01142 77892 69
34	0.61099 46507 59	0.60600 86796 22	0.55905 56477 15	1.01204 66979 20
35	0.62867 96364 44	0.62326 98471 64	0.57343 89875 90	1.01267 43981 04
36	0.64634 27111 47	0.64048 82695 82	0.58764 78625 01	1.01331 01250 67
37	0.66398 36377 02	0.65766 35377 48	0.60167 79410 53	1.01395 31042 77
38	0.68160 22068 24	0.67479 52991 98	0.61552 49457 45	1.01460 25523 65
39	0.69919 82372 70	0.69188 32567 75	0.62918 46542 89	1.01525 76780 80
40	0.71677 15759 55	0.70892 71696 00	0.64265 29009 01	1.01591 76832 54
41	0.73432 20980 39	0.72592 68528 59	0.65592 55775 91	1.01658 17637 74
42	0.75184 97069 68	0.74288 21771 09	0.66899 86354 21	1.01724 91105 63
43	0.76935 43344 92	0.75979 30684 21	0.68186 80857 62	1.01791 89105 60
44	0.78683 59406 28	0.77665 95079 35	0.69453 00015 22	1.01859 03477 20
45	0.80429 45136 05	0.79348 15314 63	0.70698 05183 63	1.01926 26040 00

87

K = 1.63072 91016 30788   E = 1.51414 69174 93342
K'= 2.41984 16537 39137   E'= 1.13624 43646 84239

r	u=(r/90)K=F(ϕ,k)	sn u	cn u	dn u
45	0.81536 45508 15	0.72034 14831 11	0.69361 95987 06	0.96290 38656 93
46	0.83348 37630 56	0.73232 50252 13	0.68095 52536 31	0.96163 45332 41
47	0.85160 29752 96	0.74407 05994 11	0.66810 09976 74	0.96036 84163 97
48	0.86972 21875 36	0.75557 55776 02	0.65506 14830 16	0.95910 70453 04
49	0.88784 13997 77	0.76683 74405 18	0.64184 13665 54	0.95785 19383 40
50	0.90596 06120 17	0.77785 37756 58	0.62844 53068 44	0.95660 46003 81
51	0.92407 98242 57	0.78862 22751 28	0.61487 79612 01	0.95536 65210 99
52	0.94219 90364 98	0.79914 07333 78	0.60114 39829 66	0.95413 91733 13
53	0.96031 82487 38	0.80940 70448 63	0.58724 80189 21	0.95292 40113 86
54	0.97843 74609 78	0.81941 92016 38	0.57319 47068 73	0.95172 24696 64
55	0.99655 66732 19	0.82917 52908 77	0.55898 86734 09	0.95053 59609 69
56	1.01467 58854 59	0.83867 34923 46	0.54463 45318 06	0.94936 58751 35
57	1.03279 50976 99	0.84791 20758 35	0.53013 68801 11	0.94821 35776 00
58	1.05091 43099 40	0.85688 93985 39	0.51550 02993 90	0.94708 04080 42
59	1.06903 35221 80	0.86560 39024 32	0.50072 93521 40	0.94596 76790 65
60	1.08715 27344 21	0.87405 41116 07	0.48582 85808 62	0.94487 66749 34
61	1.10527 19466 61	0.88223 86296 15	0.47080 25068 06	0.94380 86503 66
62	1.12339 11589 01	0.89015 61367 98	0.45565 56288 69	0.94276 48293 56
63	1.14151 03711 42	0.89780 53876 34	0.44039 24226 60	0.94174 64040 67
64	1.15962 95833 82	0.90518 52080 89	0.42501 73397 12	0.94075 45337 57
65	1.17774 87956 22	0.91229 44930 05	0.40953 48068 64	0.93979 03437 62
66	1.19586 80078 63	0.91913 22035 00	0.39394 92257 75	0.93885 49245 16
67	1.21398 72201 03	0.92569 73644 23	0.37826 49726 05	0.93794 93306 31
68	1.23210 64323 43	0.93198 90618 41	0.36248 63978 25	0.93707 45800 10
69	1.25022 56445 84	0.93800 64405 84	0.34661 78261 76	0.93623 16530 09
70	1.26834 48568 24	0.94374 87018 43	0.33066 35567 60	0.93542 14916 50
71	1.28646 40690 64	0.94921 51008 37	0.31462 78632 67	0.93464 49988 68
72	1.30458 32813 05	0.95440 49445 42	0.29851 49943 21	0.93390 30378 04
73	1.32270 24935 45	0.95931 75895 05	0.28232 91739 55	0.93319 64311 41
74	1.34082 17057 85	0.96395 24397 31	0.26607 46022 01	0.93252 59604 79
75	1.35894 09180 26	0.96830 89446 57	0.24975 54557 92	0.93189 23657 51
76	1.37706 01302 66	0.97238 65972 18	0.23337 58889 64	0.93129 63446 75
77	1.39517 93425 06	0.97618 49320 12	0.21694 00343 72	0.93073 85522 49
78	1.41329 85547 47	0.97970 35235 51	0.20045 20040 84	0.93021 96002 80
79	1.43141 77669 87	0.98294 19846 33	0.18391 58906 81	0.92974 00569 47
80	1.44953 69792 27	0.98589 99648 06	0.16733 57684 26	0.92930 04464 09
81	1.46765 61914 68	0.98857 71489 50	0.15071 56945 20	0.92890 12484 33
82	1.48577 54037 08	0.99097 32559 67	0.13405 97104 24	0.92854 28980 72
83	1.50389 46159 48	0.99308 80375 94	0.11737 18432 45	0.92822 57853 65
84	1.52201 38281 89	0.99492 12773 31	0.10065 61071 86	0.92795 02550 75
85	1.54013 30404 29	0.99647 27894 84	0.08391 65050 41	0.92771 66064 59
86	1.55825 22526 69	0.99774 24183 41	0.06715 70297 42	0.92752 50930 68
87	1.57637 14649 10	0.99873 00374 66	0.05038 16659 43	0.92737 59225 81
88	1.59449 06771 50	0.99943 55491 23	0.03359 43916 33	0.92726 92566 65
89	1.61260 98893 90	0.99985 88838 22	0.01679 91797 81	0.92720 52108 73
90	1.63072 91016 31	1.00000 00000 00	0.00000 00000 00	0.92718 38545 67

q = 0.00944 92999 75082 239   D(90) = 1.03852 52730 08598
q′ = 0.12037 82455 07893 9   1/D(90) = 0.96290 38656 93137

r	ϕ	$E(\phi,k)$	A(r)	D(r)
45	0.80429 45136 05	0.79348 15314 63	0.70698 05183 63	1.01926 26040 00
46	0.82173 00697 68	0.81025 92290 11	0.71921 58358 97	1.01993 48603 58
47	0.83914 26534 40	0.82699 27442 42	0.73123 22188 69	1.02060 62977 55
48	0.85653 23367 65	0.84368 22738 78	0.74302 59983 11	1.02127 60981 47
49	0.87389 92195 06	0.86032 80670 43	0.75459 35726 90	1.02194 34454 84
50	0.89124 34288 22	0.87693 04245 49	0.76593 14090 26	1.02260 75267 06
51	0.90856 51189 99	0.89348 96981 28	0.77703 60439 94	1.02326 75327 30
52	0.92586 44711 67	0.91000 62896 16	0.78790 40850 07	1.02392 26594 39
53	0.94314 16929 78	0.92648 06500 88	0.79853 22112 75	1.02457 21086 61
54	0.96039 70182 56	0.94291 32789 46	0.80891 71748 48	1.02521 50891 40
55	0.97763 07066 22	0.95930 47229 70	0.81905 58016 29	1.02585 08175 00
56	0.99484 30430 89	0.97565 55753 24	0.82894 49923 77	1.02647 85192 02
57	1.01203 43376 34	0.99196 64745 27	0.83858 17236 75	1.02709 74294 86
58	1.02920 49247 45	1.00823 81033 90	0.84796 30488 83	1.02770 67943 01
59	1.04635 51629 40	1.02447 11879 25	0.85708 60990 69	1.02830 58712 27
60	1.06348 54342 63	1.04066 64962 13	0.86594 80839 11	1.02889 39303 78
61	1.08059 61437 64	1.05682 48372 59	0.87454 62925 77	1.02947 02552 91
62	1.09768 77189 53	1.07294 70598 12	0.88287 80945 87	1.03003 41437 99
63	1.11476 06092 26	1.08903 40511 67	0.89094 09406 40	1.03058 49088 87
64	1.13181 15285 88	1.10508 67359 44	0.89873 23634 24	1.03112 18795 29
65	1.14885 22385 42	1.12110 60748 50	0.90624 99784 00	1.03164 44015 05
66	1.16587 19804 63	1.13709 30634 22	0.91349 14845 56	1.03215 18381 97
67	1.18287 50419 67	1.15304 87307 59	0.92045 46651 39	1.03264 35713 70
68	1.19986 19727 41	1.16897 41382 35	0.92713 73883 63	1.03311 90019 16
69	1.21683 33405 81	1.18487 03782 03	0.93353 76080 85	1.03357 75505 94
70	1.23378 97306 99	1.20073 85726 90	0.93965 33644 57	1.03401 86587 28
71	1.25073 17450 21	1.21657 98720 80	0.94548 27845 53	1.03444 17888 92
72	1.26766 00014 77	1.23239 54537 89	0.95102 40829 64	1.03484 64255 63
73	1.28457 51332 69	1.24818 65209 39	0.95627 55623 74	1.03523 20757 49
74	1.30147 77881 33	1.26395 43010 15	0.96123 56140 95	1.03559 82695 91
75	1.32122 90283 12	1.27970 00445 31	0.96590 27185 88	1.03594 45609 35
76	1.33524 83261 97	1.29542 50236 80	0.97027 54459 48	1.03627 05278 74
77	1.35211 75707 48	1.31113 05309 88	0.97435 24563 61	1.03657 57732 64
78	1.36897 70595 29	1.32681 78779 62	0.97813 25005 33	1.03685 99252 08
79	1.38582 75015 10	1.34248 83937 38	0.98161 44200 95	1.03712 26375 06
80	1.40266 96155 62	1.35814 34237 27	0.98479 71479 70	1.03736 35900 82
81	1.41950 41296 48	1.37378 43282 61	0.98767 97087 17	1.03758 24893 69
82	1.43633 17800 21	1.38941 24812 32	0.99026 12188 47	1.03777 90686 69
83	1.45315 33104 10	1.40502 92687 40	0.99254 08871 05	1.03795 30884 79
84	1.46996 94712 01	1.42063 60877 38	0.99451 80147 23	1.03810 43367 80
85	1.48678 10186 14	1.43623 43446 70	0.99619 19956 48	1.03823 26292 97
86	1.50358 87138 79	1.45182 54541 15	0.99756 23167 34	1.03833 78097 25
87	1.52039 33224 02	1.46741 08374 37	0.99862 85579 11	1.03841 97499 15
88	1.53719 56129 40	1.48299 19214 20	0.99939 03923 15	1.03847 83500 36
89	1.55399 63567 57	1.49857 01369 17	0.99984 75863 97	1.03851 35386 91
90	1.57079 63267 95	1.51414 69174 93	1.00000 00000 00	1.03852 52730 09

K = 1.63651 74093 35819   E = 1.50900 71479 16775
K'= 2.38087 01906 04429   E'= 1.14534 78566 80849

r	u=(r/90)K=F(φ,k)	sn u	cn u	dn u
0	0.00000 00000 00	0.00000 00000 00	1.00000 00000 00	1.00000 00000 00
1	0.01818 35267 70	0.01818 23718 06	0.99983 46870 14	0.99997 47632 99
2	0.03636 70535 41	0.03635 78150 79	0.99933 88360 72	0.99989 90878 42
3	0.05455 05803 11	0.05451 94075 66	0.99851 27110 85	0.99977 30774 99
4	0.07273 41070 82	0.07266 02395 51	0.99735 67514 13	0.99959 69051 79
5	0.09091 76338 52	0.09077 34200 87	0.99587 15711 40	0.99937 08125 19
6	0.10910 11606 22	0.10885 20831 75	0.99405 79580 63	0.99909 51094 43
7	0.12728 46873 93	0.12688 93938 82	0.99191 68723 84	0.99877 01736 07
8	0.14546 82141 63	0.14487 85543 75	0.98944 94451 37	0.99839 64497 21
9	0.16365 17409 34	0.16281 28098 65	0.98665 69763 32	0.99797 44487 48
10	0.18183 52677 04	0.18068 54544 36	0.98354 09328 32	0.99750 47469 91
11	0.20001 87944 74	0.19848 98367 55	0.98010 29459 73	0.99698 79850 68
12	0.21820 23212 45	0.21621 93656 36	0.97634 48089 30	0.99642 48667 73
13	0.23638 58480 15	0.23386 75154 66	0.97226 84738 33	0.99581 61578 32
14	0.25456 93747 86	0.25142 78314 51	0.96787 60486 61	0.99516 26845 55
15	0.27275 29015 56	0.26889 39346 97	0.96316 97939 01	0.99446 53323 92
16	0.29093 64283 26	0.28625 95271 02	0.95815 21189 99	0.99372 50443 89
17	0.30911 99550 97	0.30351 83960 48	0.95282 55786 14	0.99294 28195 56
18	0.32730 34818 67	0.32066 44188 83	0.94719 28686 72	0.99211 97111 50
19	0.34548 70086 38	0.33769 15671 98	0.94125 68222 56	0.99125 68248 77
20	0.36367 05354 08	0.35459 39108 64	0.93502 04053 27	0.99035 53170 17
21	0.38185 40621 78	0.37136 56218 51	0.92848 67122 94	0.98941 63924 73
22	0.40003 75889 49	0.38800 09778 01	0.92165 89614 52	0.98844 13027 68
23	0.41822 11157 19	0.40449 43653 61	0.91454 04902 96	0.98743 13439 69
24	0.43640 46424 90	0.42084 02832 68	0.90713 47507 28	0.98638 78545 60
25	0.45458 81692 60	0.43703 33451 82	0.89944 53041 73	0.98531 22132 67
26	0.47277 16960 30	0.45306 82822 65	0.89147 58166 13	0.98420 58368 42
27	0.49095 52228 01	0.46893 99455 06	0.88323 00535 58	0.98307 01778 00
28	0.50913 87495 71	0.48464 33077 85	0.87471 18749 73	0.98190 67221 32
29	0.52732 22763 42	0.50017 34656 86	0.86592 52301 58	0.98071 69869 87
30	0.54550 58031 12	0.51552 56410 47	0.85687 41526 17	0.97950 25183 33
31	0.56368 93298 82	0.53069 51822 60	0.84756 27549 19	0.97826 48885 98
32	0.58187 28566 53	0.54567 75653 22	0.83799 52235 57	0.97700 56943 04
33	0.60005 63834 23	0.56046 83946 25	0.82817 58138 38	0.97572 65536 93
34	0.61823 99101 94	0.57506 34035 16	0.81810 88447 98	0.97442 91043 51
35	0.63642 34369 64	0.58945 84546 05	0.80779 86941 65	0.97311 50008 36
36	0.65460 69637 34	0.60364 95398 44	0.79724 97933 81	0.97178 59123 14
37	0.67279 04905 05	0.61763 27803 70	0.78646 66226 94	0.97044 35202 06
38	0.69097 40172 75	0.63140 44261 38	0.77545 37063 25	0.96908 95158 53
39	0.70915 75440 46	0.64496 08553 22	0.76421 56077 33	0.96772 55982 01
40	0.72734 10708 16	0.65829 85735 17	0.75275 69249 80	0.96635 34715 14
41	0.74552 45975 86	0.67141 42127 43	0.74108 22862 05	0.96497 48431 09
42	0.76370 81243 57	0.68430 45302 47	0.72919 63452 21	0.96359 14211 25
43	0.78189 16511 27	0.69696 64071 31	0.71710 37772 39	0.96220 49123 31
44	0.80007 51778 98	0.70939 68468 05	0.70480 92747 28	0.96081 70199 66
45	0.81825 87046 68	0.72159 29732 68	0.69231 75434 22	0.95942 94416 23

q = 0.01035 26461 44729 26   D(90) = 1.04228 61302 94986
q' = 0.11539 33684 49986 6   1/D(90) = 0.95942 94416 22697

r	ϕ	$E(\phi,k)$	A(r)	D(r)
0	0.00000 00000 00	0.00000 00000 00	0.00000 00000 00	1.00000 00000 00
1	0.01818 33737 99	0.01818 32208 31	0.01744 49275 12	1.00001 28797 27
2	0.03636 58300 24	0.03636 46065 82	0.03488 45547 94	1.00005 15032 16
3	0.05454 64523 60	0.05454 23249 70	0.05231 35831 95	1.00011 58234 10
4	0.07272 43270 08	0.07271 45493 00	0.06972 67172 14	1.00020 57619 48
5	0.09089 85439 40	0.09087 94612 38	0.08711 86660 84	1.00032 12092 53
6	0.10906 81981 43	0.10903 52535 72	0.10448 41453 40	1.00046 20246 73
7	0.12723 23908 55	0.12718 01329 44	0.12181 78783 94	1.00062 80366 48
8	0.14539 02307 95	0.14531 23225 51	0.13911 45981 08	1.00081 90429 22
9	0.16354 08353 68	0.16343 00648 05	0.15636 90483 63	1.00103 48107 84
10	0.18168 33318 69	0.18153 16239 53	0.17357 59856 24	1.00127 50773 59
11	0.19981 68586 57	0.19961 52886 49	0.19073 01805 03	1.00153 95499 22
12	0.21794 05663 15	0.21767 93744 66	0.20782 64193 22	1.00182 79062 59
13	0.23605 36187 91	0.23572 22263 47	0.22485 95056 65	1.00213 97950 56
14	0.25415 51945 07	0.25374 22210 01	0.24182 42619 34	1.00247 48363 29
15	0.27224 44874 52	0.27173 77692 13	0.25871 55308 93	1.00283 26218 86
16	0.29032 07082 42	0.28970 73180 94	0.27552 81772 14	1.00321 27158 27
17	0.30838 30851 49	0.30764 93532 40	0.29225 70890 11	1.00361 46550 70
18	0.32643 08651 10	0.32556 24008 20	0.30889 71793 73	1.00403 79499 20
19	0.34446 33146 93	0.34344 50295 61	0.32544 33878 88	1.00448 20846 63
20	0.36247 97210 31	0.36129 58526 64	0.34189 06821 63	1.00494 65181 95
21	0.38047 93927 32	0.37911 35296 05	0.35823 40593 35	1.00543 06846 81
22	0.39846 16607 38	0.39689 67678 57	0.37446 85475 76	1.00593 39942 45
23	0.41642 58791 56	0.41464 43245 08	0.39058 92075 87	1.00645 58336 87
24	0.43437 14260 49	0.43235 50077 74	0.40659 11340 91	1.00699 55672 33
25	0.45229 77041 89	0.45002 76784 22	0.42246 94573 08	1.00755 25373 06
26	0.47020 41417 65	0.46766 12510 76	0.43821 93444 30	1.00812 60653 31
27	0.48809 01930 58	0.48525 46954 30	0.45383 60010 79	1.00871 54525 56
28	0.50595 53390 69	0.50280 70373 55	0.46931 46727 61	1.00931 99809 12
29	0.52379 90881 04	0.52031 73598 93	0.48465 06463 08	1.00993 89138 77
30	0.54162 09763 24	0.53778 48041 56	0.49983 92513 05	1.01057 14973 84
31	0.55942 05682 43	0.55520 85701 12	0.51487 58615 15	1.01121 69607 32
32	0.57719 74571 93	0.57258 79172 77	0.52975 58962 82	1.01187 45175 29
33	0.59495 12657 36	0.58992 21652 93	0.54447 48219 31	1.01254 33666 48
34	0.61268 16460 37	0.60721 06944 10	0.55902 81531 51	1.01322 26932 03
35	0.63038 82801 98	0.62445 29458 65	0.57341 14543 64	1.01391 16695 45
36	0.64807 08805 44	0.64164 84221 67	0.58762 03410 88	1.01460 94562 65
37	0.66572 91898 64	0.65879 66872 77	0.60165 04812 75	1.01531 52032 22
38	0.68336 29816 17	0.67589 73667 00	0.61549 75966 46	1.01602 80505 75
39	0.70097 20600 86	0.69295 01474 79	0.62915 74640 04	1.01674 71298 32
40	0.71855 62605 02	0.70995 47781 02	0.64262 59165 37	1.01747 15649 10
41	0.73611 54491 16	0.72691 10683 21	0.65589 88451 01	1.01820 04731 97
42	0.75364 95232 33	0.74381 88888 86	0.66897 21994 93	1.01893 29666 32
43	0.77115 84112 10	0.76067 81711 95	0.68184 19896 98	1.01966 81527 88
44	0.78864 20724 12	0.77748 89068 64	0.69450 42871 33	1.02040 51359 53
45	0.80610 04971 23	0.79425 11472 32	0.70695 52258 62	1.02114 30182 28

91

K = 1.63651 74093 35819

K' = 2.38087 01906 04429

E = 1.50900 71479 16775

E' = 1.14534 78566 80849

r	u=(r/90)K=F(φ,k)	sn u	cn u	dn u
45	0.81825 87046 68	0.72159 29732 68	0.69231 75434 22	0.95942 94416 23
46	0.83644 22314 38	0.73355 20292 44	0.67963 32984 72	0.95804 38671 71
47	0.85462 57582 09	0.74527 13741 63	0.66676 12607 62	0.95666 19767 33
48	0.87280 92849 79	0.75674 84820 17	0.65370 61533 78	0.95528 54386 96
49	0.89099 28117 50	0.76798 09390 86	0.64047 26982 48	0.95391 59077 84
50	0.90917 63385 20	0.77896 64415 45	0.62706 56129 52	0.95255 50231 74
51	0.92735 98652 90	0.78970 27929 75	0.61348 96077 09	0.95120 44066 66
52	0.94554 33920 61	0.80018 79017 78	0.59974 93825 33	0.94986 56609 06
53	0.96372 69188 31	0.81041 97785 02	0.58584 96245 73	0.94854 03676 63
54	0.98191 04456 01	0.82039 65331 03	0.57179 50056 38	0.94723 00861 62
55	1.00009 39723 72	0.83011 63721 35	0.55759 01798 32	0.94593 63514 71
56	1.01827 74991 42	0.83957 75958 91	0.54323 97817 51	0.94466 06729 44
57	1.03646 10259 13	0.84877 85955 03	0.52874 84239 38	0.94340 45327 23
58	1.05464 45526 83	0.85771 78500 01	0.51412 06957 42	0.94216 93842 92
59	1.07282 80794 53	0.86639 39233 61	0.49936 11614 48	0.94095 66510 88
60	1.09101 16062 24	0.87480 54615 27	0.48447 43589 53	0.93976 77251 70
61	1.10919 51329 94	0.88295 11894 33	0.46946 47985 52	0.93860 39659 41
62	1.12737 86597 65	0.89082 99080 32	0.45433 69619 07	0.93746 66989 28
63	1.14556 21865 35	0.89844 04913 34	0.43909 53011 94	0.93635 72146 12
64	1.16374 57133 05	0.90578 18834 66	0.42374 42384 09	0.93527 67673 13
65	1.18192 92400 76	0.91285 30957 62	0.40828 81648 51	0.93422 65741 33
66	1.20011 27668 46	0.91965 32038 94	0.39273 14407 67	0.93320 78139 42
67	1.21829 62936 17	0.92618 13450 44	0.37707 83951 54	0.93222 16264 19
68	1.23647 98203 87	0.93243 67151 30	0.36133 33257 22	0.93126 91111 49
69	1.25466 33471 57	0.93841 85660 94	0.34550 04990 01	0.93035 13267 57
70	1.27284 68739 28	0.94412 62032 54	0.32958 41506 04	0.92946 92900 98
71	1.29103 04006 98	0.94955 89827 31	0.31358 84856 22	0.92862 39754 93
72	1.30921 39274 69	0.95471 63089 56	0.29751 76791 61	0.92781 63140 07
73	1.32739 74542 39	0.95959 76322 59	0.28137 58770 11	0.92704 71927 72
74	1.34558 09810 09	0.96420 24465 52	0.26516 71964 32	0.92631 74543 60
75	1.36376 45077 80	0.96853 02871 08	0.24889 57270 71	0.92562 78961 86
76	1.38194 80345 50	0.97258 07284 40	0.23256 55319 83	0.92497 92699 61
77	1.40013 15613 21	0.97635 33822 85	0.21618 06487 66	0.92437 22811 82
78	1.41831 50880 91	0.97984 78956 99	0.19974 50907 90	0.92380 75886 58
79	1.43649 86148 61	0.98306 39492 67	0.18326 28485 30	0.92328 58040 81
80	1.45468 21416 32	0.98600 12554 31	0.16673 78909 81	0.92280 74916 22
81	1.47286 56684 02	0.98865 95569 35	0.15017 41671 57	0.92237 31675 77
82	1.49104 91951 73	0.99103 86254 01	0.13357 56076 66	0.92198 33000 30
83	1.50923 27219 43	0.99313 82600 28	0.11694 61263 53	0.92163 83085 69
84	1.52741 62487 13	0.99495 82864 21	0.10028 96220 03	0.92133 85640 19
85	1.54559 97754 84	0.99649 85555 57	0.08360 99801 07	0.92108 43882 19
86	1.56378 33022 54	0.99775 89428 75	0.06691 10746 68	0.92087 60538 20
87	1.58196 68290 25	0.99873 93475 16	0.05019 67700 49	0.92071 37841 27
88	1.60015 03557 95	0.99943 96916 89	0.03347 09228 64	0.92059 77529 58
89	1.61833 38825 65	0.99985 99201 79	0.01673 73838 91	0.92052 80845 44
90	1.63651 74093 36	1.00000 00000 00	0.00000 00000 00	0.92050 48534 52

q = 0.01035 26461 44729 26   D(90) = 1.04228 61302 94986
q′= 0.11539 33684 49986 6   1/D(90) = 0.95942 94416 22697

r	φ	E(φ,k)	A(r)	D(r)
45	0.80610 04971 23	0.79425 11472 32	0.70695 52258 62	1.02114 30182 28
46	0.82353 37064 32	0.81096 50027 75	0.71919 10038 00	1.02188 09006 18
47	0.84094 17520 67	0.82763 06424 65	0.73120 78838 94	1.02261 78841 25
48	0.85832 47162 04	0.84424 82930 58	0.74300 21952 94	1.02335 30708 49
49	0.87568 27112 37	0.86081 82383 19	0.75457 03344 91	1.02408 55650 77
50	0.89301 58795 07	0.87734 08181 84	0.76590 87664 56	1.02481 44743 76
51	0.91032 43930 06	0.89381 64278 72	0.77701 40257 35	1.02553 89106 80
52	0.92760 84530 47	0.91024 55169 40	0.78788 27175 48	1.02625 79913 73
53	0.94486 82898 95	0.92662 85882 88	0.79851 15188 48	1.02697 08403 64
54	0.96210 41623 77	0.94296 61971 17	0.80889 71793 70	1.02767 65891 52
55	0.97931 63574 53	0.95925 89498 48	0.81903 65226 56	1.02837 43778 89
56	0.99650 51897 64	0.97550 75029 92	0.82892 64470 59	1.02906 33564 22
57	1.01367 10011 54	0.99171 25619 93	0.83856 39267 20	1.02974 26853 33
58	1.03081 41601 57	1.00787 48800 27	0.84794 60125 29	1.03041 15369 60
59	1.04793 50614 66	1.02399 52567 75	0.85706 98330 59	1.03106 90964 06
60	1.06503 41253 74	1.04007 45371 68	0.86593 25954 80	1.03171 45625 32
61	1.08211 17971 90	1.05611 36100 97	0.87453 15864 44	1.03234 71489 30
62	1.09916 85466 38	1.07211 34071 13	0.88286 41729 51	1.03296 60848 88
63	1.11620 48672 26	1.08807 49010 94	0.89092 78031 87	1.03357 06163 20
64	1.13322 12756 01	1.10399 91048 97	0.89872 00073 39	1.03416 00066 94
65	1.15021 83108 81	1.11988 70699 97	0.90623 83983 88	1.03473 35379 22
66	1.16719 65339 70	1.13573 98851 02	0.91348 06728 67	1.03529 05112 38
67	1.18415 65268 52	1.15155 86747 68	0.92044 46116 02	1.03583 02480 51
68	1.20109 88918 72	1.16734 45979 87	0.92712 80804 25	1.03635 20907 68
69	1.21802 42509 97	1.18309 88467 83	0.93352 90308 59	1.03685 54035 99
70	1.23493 32450 66	1.19882 26447 82	0.93964 55007 75	1.03733 95733 28
71	1.25182 65330 22	1.21451 72457 95	0.94547 56150 23	1.03780 40100 64
72	1.26870 47911 33	1.23018 39323 75	0.95101 75860 40	1.03824 81479 55
73	1.28556 87121 98	1.24582 40143 88	0.95626 97144 22	1.03867 14458 82
74	1.30241 90047 43	1.26143 88275 71	0.96123 03894 76	1.03907 33881 17
75	1.31925 63922 05	1.27702 97320 88	0.96589 80897 39	1.03945 34849 49
76	1.33608 16121 07	1.29259 81110 90	0.97027 13834 68	1.03981 12732 84
77	1.35289 54152 21	1.30814 53692 69	0.97434 89291 06	1.04014 63172 06
78	1.36969 85647 23	1.32367 29314 16	0.97812 94757 17	1.04045 82085 12
79	1.38649 18353 41	1.33918 22409 75	0.98161 18633 88	1.04074 65672 04
80	1.40327 60124 95	1.35467 47586 04	0.98479 50236 07	1.04101 10419 59
81	1.42005 18914 28	1.37015 19607 29	0.98767 79796 11	1.04125 13105 50
82	1.43682 02763 34	1.38561 53381 07	0.99025 98467 02	1.04146 70802 44
83	1.45358 19794 76	1.40106 63943 88	0.99253 98325 32	1.04165 80881 54
84	1.47033 78203 06	1.41650 66446 73	0.99451 72373 66	1.04182 41015 65
85	1.48708 86245 73	1.43193 76140 83	0.99619 14543 04	1.04196 49182 12
86	1.50383 52234 31	1.44736 08363 24	0.99756 19694 80	1.04208 03665 30
87	1.52057 84525 43	1.46277 78522 51	0.99862 83622 33	1.04217 03058 59
88	1.53731 91511 84	1.47819 02084 40	0.99939 03052 36	1.04223 46266 23
89	1.55405 81613 37	1.49359 94557 54	0.99984 75646 11	1.04227 32504 54
90	1.57079 63267 95	1.50900 71479 17	1.00000 00000 00	1.04228 61302 95

K = 1.64260 41437 12491   E = 1.50366 21353 53715
K'= 2.34390 47244 46913   E'= 1.15454 66775 24465

r	u=(r/90)K=F(ϕ,k)	sn u	cn u	dn u
0	0.00000 00000 00	0.00000 00000 00	1.00000 00000 00	1.00000 00000 00
1	0.01825 11571 52	0.01824 99763 23	0.99983 34553 14	0.99997 24496 45
2	0.03650 23143 05	0.03649 28690 23	0.99933 39134 20	0.99988 98368 00
3	0.05475 34714 57	0.05472 16012 43	0.99850 16506 53	0.99975 22760 51
4	0.07300 46286 09	0.07292 91096 36	0.99733 71270 38	0.99955 99581 40
5	0.09125 57857 62	0.09110 83510 78	0.99584 09854 81	0.99931 31496 07
6	0.10950 69429 14	0.10925 23093 22	0.99401 40506 59	0.99901 21922 98
7	0.12775 81000 67	0.12735 40015 83	0.99185 73275 83	0.99865 75027 26
8	0.14600 92572 19	0.14540 64850 33	0.98937 19998 62	0.99824 95713 06
9	0.16426 04143 71	0.16340 28631 88	0.98655 94276 59	0.99778 89614 49
10	0.18251 15715 24	0.18133 62921 74	0.98342 11453 60	0.99727 63085 21
11	0.20076 27286 76	0.19919 99868 54	0.97995 88589 51	0.99671 23186 85
12	0.21901 38858 28	0.21698 72267 97	0.97617 44431 23	0.99609 77676 08
13	0.23726 50429 81	0.23469 13620 85	0.97206 99381 03	0.99543 34990 53
14	0.25551 62001 33	0.25230 58189 28	0.96764 75462 35	0.99472 04233 54
15	0.27376 73572 85	0.26982 41050 90	0.96290 96283 21	0.99395 95157 80
16	0.29201 85144 38	0.28723 98151 03	0.95785 86997 15	0.99315 18147 88
17	0.31026 96715 90	0.30454 66352 61	0.95249 74262 18	0.99229 84201 85
18	0.32852 08287 42	0.32173 83483 80	0.94682 86197 52	0.99140 04911 83
19	0.34677 19858 95	0.33880 88383 24	0.94085 52338 56	0.99045 92443 70
20	0.36502 31430 47	0.35575 20942 75	0.93458 03589 95	0.98947 59515 97
21	0.38327 43002 00	0.37256 22147 47	0.92800 72177 21	0.98845 19377 86
22	0.40152 54573 52	0.38923 34113 44	0.92113 91596 79	0.98738 85786 64
23	0.41977 66145 04	0.40576 00122 31	0.91397 96564 88	0.98628 72984 37
24	0.43802 77716 57	0.42213 64653 51	0.90653 22965 13	0.98514 95673 95
25	0.45627 89288 09	0.43835 73413 47	0.89880 07795 32	0.98397 68994 78
26	0.47453 00859 61	0.45441 73362 13	0.89078 89113 30	0.98277 08497 82
27	0.49278 12431 14	0.47031 12736 60	0.88250 05982 26	0.98153 30120 31
28	0.51103 24002 66	0.48603 41071 97	0.87393 98415 46	0.98026 50160 21
29	0.52928 35574 18	0.50158 09219 31	0.86511 07320 77	0.97896 85250 21
30	0.54753 47145 71	0.51694 69360 86	0.85601 74444 90	0.97764 52331 71
31	0.56578 58717 23	0.53212 75022 42	0.84666 42317 69	0.97629 68628 51
32	0.58403 70288 76	0.54711 81082 94	0.83705 54196 56	0.97492 51620 49
33	0.60228 81860 28	0.56191 43781 47	0.82719 54011 18	0.97353 19017 21
34	0.62053 93431 80	0.57651 20721 33	0.81708 86308 62	0.97211 88731 56
35	0.63879 05003 33	0.59090 70871 75	0.80673 96199 06	0.97068 78853 47
36	0.65704 16574 85	0.60509 54566 87	0.79615 29302 19	0.96924 07623 77
37	0.67529 28146 37	0.61907 33502 35	0.78533 31694 44	0.96777 93408 19
38	0.69354 39717 90	0.63283 70729 43	0.77428 49857 18	0.96630 54671 64
39	0.71179 51289 42	0.64638 30646 79	0.76301 30625 99	0.96482 09952 72
40	0.73004 62860 94	0.65970 78990 06	0.75152 21141 06	0.96332 77838 58
41	0.74829 74432 47	0.67280 82819 24	0.73981 68798 93	0.96182 76940 10
42	0.76654 86003 99	0.68568 10504 06	0.72790 21205 59	0.96032 25867 47
43	0.78479 97575 52	0.69832 31707 31	0.71578 26131 03	0.95881 43206 24
44	0.80305 09147 04	0.71073 17366 40	0.70346 31465 35	0.95730 47493 77
45	0.82130 20718 56	0.72290 39673 11	0.69094 85176 52	0.95579 57196 19

ELLIPTIC FUNCTIONS   TABLE $\theta = 24°$

q = 0.01130 08432 78049 37
q' = 0.11062 35386 78854 3

D(90) = 1.04624 86695 36094
1/D(90) = 0.95579 57196 19313

r	ϕ	$E(\phi,k)$	$A(r)$	$D(r)$
0	0.00000 00000 00	0.00000 00000 00	0.00000 00000 00	1.00000 00000 00
1	0.01825 09895 36	0.01825 08219 22	0.01744 34949 69	1.00001 40866 39
2	0.03650 09736 53	0.03649 96330 89	0.03488 16927 63	1.00005 63293 92
3	0.05474 89483 26	0.05474 44258 67	0.05230 92977 74	1.00012 66767 96
4	0.07299 39123 18	0.07298 31988 56	0.06972 10175 33	1.00022 50431 44
5	0.09123 48685 63	0.09121 39599 90	0.08711 15642 76	1.00035 13085 93
6	0.10947 08255 52	0.10943 47296 12	0.10447 56565 11	1.00050 53193 11
7	0.12770 07986 94	0.12764 35435 22	0.12180 80205 85	1.00068 68876 63
8	0.14592 38116 76	0.14583 84559 88	0.13910 33922 44	1.00089 57924 40
9	0.16413 88978 05	0.16401 75427 05	0.15635 65181 98	1.00113 17791 28
10	0.18234 51013 27	0.18217 89037 20	0.17356 21576 79	1.00139 45602 18
11	0.20054 14787 34	0.20032 06662 83	0.19071 50839 95	1.00168 38155 57
12	0.21872 71000 41	0.21844 09876 44	0.20781 00860 87	1.00199 91927 37
13	0.23690 10500 45	0.23653 80577 77	0.22484 19700 74	1.00234 03075 27
14	0.25506 24295 51	0.25461 01020 27	0.24180 55608 01	1.00270 67443 37
15	0.27321 03565 75	0.27265 53836 82	0.25869 57033 78	1.00309 80567 27
16	0.29134 39675 11	0.29067 22064 49	0.27550 72647 19	1.00351 37679 50
17	0.30946 24182 71	0.30865 89168 49	0.29223 51350 71	1.00395 33715 33
18	0.32756 48853 83	0.32661 39065 06	0.30887 42295 40	1.00441 63318 97
19	0.34565 05670 58	0.34453 56143 47	0.32541 94896 13	1.00490 20850 01
20	0.36371 86842 20	0.36242 25286 90	0.34186 58846 67	1.00541 00390 40
21	0.38176 84814 94	0.38027 31892 27	0.35820 84134 83	1.00593 95751 58
22	0.39979 92281 53	0.39808 61889 04	0.37444 21057 38	1.00649 00482 04
23	0.41781 02190 23	0.41586 01756 75	0.39056 20235 04	1.00706 07875 22
24	0.43580 07753 50	0.43359 38541 58	0.40656 32627 33	1.00765 10977 61
25	0.45377 02456 14	0.45128 59871 60	0.42244 09547 27	1.00826 02597 28
26	0.47171 80063 10	0.46893 53970 94	0.43819 02676 14	1.00888 75312 62
27	0.48964 34626 66	0.48654 09672 74	0.45380 64078 02	1.00953 21481 36
28	0.50754 60493 34	0.50410 16430 92	0.46928 46214 34	1.01019 33249 93
29	0.52542 52310 21	0.52161 64330 73	0.48462 01958 19	1.01087 02562 98
30	0.54328 05030 74	0.53908 44098 19	0.49980 84608 73	1.01156 21173 24
31	0.56111 13910 25	0.55650 47108 22	0.51484 47905 28	1.01226 80651 50
32	0.57891 74560 76	0.57387 65391 71	0.52972 46041 47	1.01298 72396 97
33	0.59669 82855 47	0.59119 91641 38	0.54444 33679 16	1.01371 87647 66
34	0.61445 35032 70	0.60847 19216 51	0.55899 65962 31	1.01446 17491 15
35	0.63218 27649 35	0.62569 42146 48	0.57337 98530 71	1.01521 52875 37
36	0.64988 57593 89	0.64286 55133 31	0.58758 87533 52	1.01597 84619 68
37	0.66756 22088 89	0.65998 53553 02	0.60161 89642 81	1.01675 03426 02
38	0.68521 18693 08	0.67705 33456 00	0.61546 62066 83	1.01752 99890 26
39	0.70283 45302 89	0.69406 91566 31	0.62912 62563 21	1.01831 64513 66
40	0.72043 00153 56	0.71103 25279 98	0.64259 49452 00	1.01910 87714 41
41	0.73799 81819 87	0.72794 32662 41	0.65586 81628 54	1.01990 59839 37
42	0.75553 89216 26	0.74480 12444 72	0.66894 18576 22	1.02070 71175 73
43	0.77305 21596 66	0.76160 64019 33	0.68181 20379 07	1.02151 11962 95
44	0.79053 78553 79	0.77835 87434 57	0.69447 47734 10	1.02231 72404 57
45	0.80799 60018 09	0.79505 83388 56	0.70692 61963 63	1.02312 42680 21

K = 1.64260 41437 12491   E = 1.50366 21353 53715
K' = 2.34390 47244 46913   E' = 1.15454 66775 24465

r	u=(r/90)K=F(ϕ,k)	sn u	cn u	dn u
45	0.82130 20718 56	0.72290 39673 11	0.69094 85176 52	0.95579 57196 19
46	0.83955 32290 09	0.73483 72051 78	0.67824 35269 78	0.95428 90685 93
47	0.85780 43861 61	0.74652 89135 82	0.66535 29748 83	0.95278 66219 68
48	0.87605 55433 13	0.75797 66743 01	0.65228 16578 87	0.95129 01917 02
49	0.89430 67004 66	0.76917 81849 28	0.63903 43651 40	0.94980 15739 53
50	0.91255 78576 18	0.78013 12561 50	0.62561 58751 01	0.94832 25470 60
51	0.93080 90147 70	0.79083 38089 01	0.61203 09524 02	0.94685 48695 76
52	0.94906 01719 23	0.80128 38714 36	0.59828 43449 21	0.94540 02783 66
53	0.96731 13290 75	0.81147 95763 05	0.58438 07810 33	0.94396 04867 67
54	0.98556 24862 27	0.82141 91572 66	0.57032 49670 82	0.94253 71828 18
55	1.00381 36433 80	0.83110 09461 27	0.55612 15850 39	0.94113 20275 37
56	1.02206 48005 32	0.84052 33695 44	0.54177 52903 65	0.93974 66532 84
57	1.04031 59576 85	0.84968 49457 69	0.52729 07100 76	0.93838 26621 68
58	1.05856 71148 37	0.85858 42813 80	0.51267 24410 07	0.93704 16245 31
59	1.07681 82719 89	0.86722 00679 79	0.49792 50482 69	0.93572 50774 88
60	1.09506 94291 42	0.87559 10788 97	0.48305 30639 14	0.93443 45235 34
61	1.11332 05862 94	0.88369 61658 79	0.46806 09857 81	0.93317 14292 07
62	1.13157 17434 46	0.89153 42558 01	0.45295 32765 45	0.93193 72238 25
63	1.14982 29005 99	0.89910 43473 91	0.43773 43629 44	0.93073 32982 64
64	1.16807 40577 51	0.90640 55079 86	0.42240 86352 01	0.92956 10038 14
65	1.18632 52149 03	0.91343 68703 26	0.40698 04466 19	0.92842 16510 85
66	1.20457 63720 56	0.92019 76293 91	0.39145 41133 55	0.92731 65089 62
67	1.22282 75292 08	0.92668 70393 01	0.37583 39143 72	0.92624 68036 35
68	1.24107 86863 61	0.93290 44102 62	0.36012 40915 48	0.92521 37176 62
69	1.25932 98435 13	0.93884 91056 02	0.34432 88499 53	0.92421 83890 99
70	1.27758 10006 65	0.94452 05388 64	0.32845 23582 88	0.92326 19106 79
71	1.29583 21578 18	0.94991 81709 94	0.31249 87494 63	0.92234 53290 33
72	1.31408 33149 70	0.95504 15076 17	0.29647 21213 34	0.92146 96439 70
73	1.33233 44721 22	0.95989 00964 08	0.28037 65375 65	0.92063 58077 97
74	1.35058 56292 75	0.96446 35245 61	0.26421 60286 42	0.91984 47246 83
75	1.36883 67864 27	0.96876 14163 69	0.24799 45929 93	0.91909 72500 79
76	1.38708 79435 79	0.97278 34309 19	0.23171 61982 47	0.91839 41901 61
77	1.40533 91007 32	0.97652 92598 93	0.21538 47825 94	0.91773 63013 32
78	1.42359 02578 84	0.97999 86255 04	0.19900 42562 62	0.91712 42897 54
79	1.44184 14150 37	0.98319 12785 47	0.18257 85030 86	0.91655 88109 19
80	1.46009 25721 89	0.98610 69965 84	0.16611 13821 78	0.91604 04692 63
81	1.47834 37293 41	0.98874 55822 58	0.14960 67296 78	0.91556 98178 06
82	1.49659 48864 94	0.99110 68617 51	0.13306 83605 90	0.91514 73578 37
83	1.51484 60436 46	0.99319 06833 69	0.11650 00706 86	0.91477 35386 25
84	1.53309 72007 98	0.99499 69162 77	0.09990 56384 77	0.91444 87571 68
85	1.55134 83579 51	0.99652 54493 77	0.08328 88272 44	0.91417 33579 72
86	1.56959 95151 03	0.99777 61903 28	0.06665 33871 19	0.91394 76328 59
87	1.58785 06722 55	0.99874 90647 16	0.05000 30572 05	0.91377 18208 06
88	1.60610 18294 08	0.99944 40153 71	0.03334 15677 46	0.91364 61078 22
89	1.62435 29865 60	0.99986 10018 39	0.01667 26423 09	0.91357 06268 38
90	1.64260 41437 12	1.00000 00000 00	0.00000 00000 00	0.91354 54576 43

q = 0.01130 08432 78049 37   D(90) = 1.04624 86695 36094
q'= 0.11062 35386 78854 3   1/D(90) = 0.95579 57196 19313

r	ϕ	$E(\phi,k)$	A(r)	D(r)
45	0.80799 60018 09	0.79505 83388 56	0.70692 61963 63	1.02312 42680 21
46	0.82542 66256 21	0.81170 53222 20	0.71916 25027 29	1.02393 12957 47
47	0.84282 97869 10	0.82829 98911 54	0.73117 99533 97	1.02473 73403 97
48	0.86020 55789 67	0.84484 23059 31	0.74297 48753 51	1.02554 14199 28
49	0.87755 41280 15	0.86133 28885 87	0.75454 36628 20	1.02634 25546 91
50	0.89487 55928 98	0.87777 20219 49	0.76588 27784 17	1.02713 97686 26
51	0.91217 01647 41	0.89416 01486 04	0.77698 87542 51	1.02793 20904 47
52	0.92943 80665 67	0.91049 77698 14	0.78785 81930 21	1.02871 85548 29
53	0.94667 95528 87	0.92678 54443 77	0.79848 77690 89	1.02949 82035 83
54	0.96389 49092 57	0.94302 37874 43	0.80887 42295 35	1.03027 00868 22
55	0.98108 44517 96	0.95921 34692 81	0.81901 43951 91	1.03103 32641 21
56	0.99824 85266 77	0.97535 52140 13	0.82890 51616 47	1.03178 68056 60
57	1.01538 75095 96	0.99144 97983 01	0.83854 35002 42	1.03252 97933 60
58	1.03250 18051 99	1.00749 80500 07	0.84792 64590 31	1.03326 13219 99
59	1.04959 18464 92	1.02350 08468 21	0.85705 11637 25	1.03398 05003 14
60	1.06665 80942 22	1.03945 91148 58	0.86591 48186 14	1.03468 64520 92
61	1.08370 10362 32	1.05537 38272 34	0.87451 47074 61	1.03537 83172 31
62	1.10072 11867 91	1.07124 60026 23	0.88284 81943 75	1.03605 52527 92
63	1.11771 90859 10	1.08707 67037 81	0.89091 27246 58	1.03671 64340 27
64	1.13469 52986 22	1.10286 70360 75	0.89870 58256 27	1.03736 10553 80
65	1.15165 04142 53	1.11861 81459 76	0.90622 51074 15	1.03798 83314 70
66	1.16858 50456 73	1.13433 12195 54	0.91346 82637 37	1.03859 74980 51
67	1.18549 98285 20	1.15000 74809 62	0.92043 30726 42	1.03918 78129 38
68	1.20239 54204 14	1.16564 81909 02	0.92711 73972 28	1.03975 85569 14
69	1.21927 25001 56	1.18125 46450 97	0.93351 91863 37	1.04030 90346 09
70	1.23613 17669 02	1.19682 81727 50	0.93963 64752 23	1.04083 85753 40
71	1.25297 39393 35	1.21237 01350 06	0.94546 73861 86	1.04134 65339 36
72	1.26979 97548 13	1.22788 19234 05	0.95101 01291 86	1.04183 22915 18
73	1.28660 99685 08	1.24336 49583 39	0.95626 30024 28	1.04229 52562 60
74	1.30340 53525 37	1.25882 06875 12	0.96122 43929 14	1.04273 48640 99
75	1.32018 66950 72	1.27425 05843 92	0.96589 27769 72	1.04315 05794 36
76	1.33695 47994 52	1.28965 61466 74	0.97026 67207 51	1.04354 18957 77
77	1.35371 04832 75	1.30503 88947 41	0.97434 48806 96	1.04390 83363 55
78	1.37045 45774 87	1.32040 03701 27	0.97812 60039 80	1.04424 94547 14
79	1.38718 79254 59	1.33574 21339 88	0.98160 89289 23	1.04456 48352 46
80	1.40391 13820 61	1.35106 57655 73	0.98479 25853 67	1.04485 40937 02
81	1.42062 58127 28	1.36637 28606 97	0.98767 59950 27	1.04511 68776 60
82	1.43733 20925 13	1.38166 50302 23	0.99025 82718 20	1.04535 28669 53
83	1.45403 11051 46	1.39694 38985 42	0.99253 86221 45	1.04556 17740 60
84	1.47072 37420 80	1.41221 11020 63	0.99451 63451 54	1.04574 33444 55
85	1.48741 09015 34	1.42746 82876 99	0.99619 08329 76	1.04589 73569 18
86	1.50409 34875 36	1.44271 71113 65	0.99756 15709 20	1.04602 36238 07
87	1.52077 24089 55	1.45795 92364 66	0.99862 81376 43	1.04612 19912 81
88	1.53744 85785 41	1.47319 63324 04	0.99939 02052 92	1.04619 23394 94
89	1.55412 29119 54	1.48843 00730 71	0.99984 75396 06	1.04623 45827 35
90	1.57079 63267 95	1.50366 21353 54	1.00000 00000 00	1.04624 86695 36

K = 1.64899 52184 78530   E = 1.49811 49284 22116
K'= 2.30878 67981 67196   E'= 1.16382 79644 93139

r	u=(r/90)K=F(φ,k)	sn u	cn u	dn u
0	0.00000 00000 00	0.00000 00000 00	1.00000 00000 00	1.00000 00000 00
1	0.01832 21690 94	0.01832 09609 29	0.99983 21571 10	0.99997 00242 86
2	0.03664 43381 88	0.03663 46743 26	0.99932 87250 13	0.99988 01391 86
3	0.05496 65072 83	0.05493 38999 45	0.99848 99932 58	0.99973 04707 40
4	0.07328 86763 77	0.07321 14120 95	0.99731 64438 33	0.99952 12287 46
5	0.09161 08454 71	0.09146 00068 64	0.99580 87502 85	0.99925 27063 61
6	0.10993 30145 65	0.10967 25092 84	0.99396 77764 93	0.99892 52795 35
7	0.12825 51836 59	0.12784 17804 19	0.99179 45750 91	0.99853 94062 98
8	0.14657 73527 54	0.14596 07243 45	0.98929 03855 54	0.99809 56258 86
9	0.16489 95218 48	0.16402 22950 21	0.98645 66319 59	0.99759 45577 14
10	0.18322 16909 42	0.18201 95030 12	0.98329 49204 20	0.99703 69002 10
11	0.20154 38600 36	0.19994 54220 71	0.97980 70362 03	0.99642 34294 94
12	0.21986 60291 30	0.21779 31955 28	0.97599 49405 51	0.99575 49979 20
13	0.23818 81982 25	0.23555 60425 15	0.97186 07672 06	0.99503 25324 89
14	0.25651 03673 19	0.25322 72639 65	0.96740 68186 57	0.99425 70331 20
15	0.27483 25364 13	0.27080 02484 06	0.96263 55621 23	0.99342 95708 10
16	0.29315 47055 07	0.28826 84775 17	0.95754 96252 78	0.99255 12856 61
17	0.31147 68746 02	0.30562 55314 37	0.95215 17917 51	0.99162 33848 07
18	0.32979 90436 96	0.32286 50938 25	0.94644 49963 89	0.99064 71402 25
19	0.34812 12127 90	0.33998 09566 42	0.94043 23203 30	0.98962 38864 50
20	0.36644 33818 84	0.35696 70246 63	0.93411 69858 77	0.98855 50182 02
21	0.38476 55509 78	0.37381 73197 04	0.92750 23512 04	0.98744 19879 19
22	0.40308 77200 73	0.39052 59845 51	0.92059 19049 12	0.98628 63032 13
23	0.42140 98891 67	0.40708 72865 98	0.91338 92604 42	0.98508 95242 65
24	0.43973 20582 61	0.42349 56211 72	0.90589 81503 72	0.98385 32611 41
25	0.45805 42273 55	0.43974 55145 62	0.89812 24206 21	0.98257 91710 62
26	0.47637 63964 49	0.45583 16267 32	0.89006 60245 57	0.98126 89556 23
27	0.49469 85655 44	0.47174 87537 18	0.88173 30170 55	0.97992 43579 66
28	0.51302 07346 38	0.48749 18297 28	0.87312 75484 99	0.97854 71599 26
29	0.53134 29037 32	0.50305 59289 16	0.86425 38587 61	0.97713 91791 47
30	0.54966 50728 26	0.51843 62668 57	0.85511 62711 63	0.97570 22661 73
31	0.56798 72419 20	0.53362 82017 12	0.84571 91864 55	0.97423 83015 33
32	0.58630 94110 15	0.54862 72350 93	0.83606 70768 03	0.97274 91928 21
33	0.60463 15801 09	0.56342 90126 27	0.82616 44798 28	0.97123 68717 66
34	0.62295 37492 03	0.57802 93242 36	0.81601 59926 89	0.96970 32913 24
35	0.64127 59182 97	0.59242 41041 20	0.80562 62662 41	0.96815 04227 70
36	0.65959 80873 91	0.60660 94304 77	0.79499 99992 81	0.96658 02528 16
37	0.67792 02564 86	0.62058 15249 40	0.78414 19328 82	0.96499 47807 50
38	0.69624 24255 80	0.63433 67517 61	0.77305 68448 48	0.96339 60156 13
39	0.71456 45946 74	0.64787 16167 40	0.76174 95442 88	0.96178 59733 97
40	0.73288 67637 68	0.66118 27659 17	0.75022 48663 26	0.96016 66742 96
41	0.75120 89328 62	0.67426 69840 27	0.73848 76669 59	0.95854 01399 92
42	0.76953 11019 57	0.68712 11927 38	0.72654 28180 71	0.95690 83909 98
43	0.78785 32710 51	0.69974 24486 81	0.71439 52026 11	0.95527 34440 42
44	0.80617 54401 45	0.71212 79412 80	0.70204 97099 55	0.95363 73095 18
45	0.82449 76092 39	0.72427 49904 02	0.68951 12314 37	0.95200 19889 88

q = 0.01229 45605 27181 44   D(90) = 1.05041 79734 57467
q'= 0.10605 40201 85995 5   1/D(90) = 0.95200 19889 87760

r	ϕ	$E(\phi,k)$	A(r)	D(r)
0	0.00000 00000 00	0.00000 00000 00	0.00000 00000 00	1.00000 00000 00
1	0.01832 19860 12	0.01832 18029 34	0.01744 18590 87	1.00001 53565 19
2	0.03664 28738 41	0.03664 14095 99	0.03487 84244 85	1.00006 14073 69
3	0.05496 15668 43	0.05495 66272 03	0.05230 44040 66	1.00013 80964 43
4	0.07327 69714 52	0.07326 52698 91	0.06971 45088 19	1.00024 53303 11
5	0.09158 79987 11	0.09156 51621 99	0.08710 34544 12	1.00038 29783 27
6	0.10989 35657 91	0.10985 41424 73	0.10446 59627 49	1.00055 08727 93
7	0.12819 25975 07	0.12813 00662 57	0.12179 67635 24	1.00074 88091 58
8	0.14648 40278 12	0.14639 08096 42	0.13909 05957 80	1.00097 65462 74
9	0.16476 68012 72	0.16463 42725 59	0.15634 22094 58	1.00123 38066 84
10	0.18303 98745 31	0.18285 83820 13	0.17354 63669 47	1.00152 02769 62
11	0.20130 22177 41	0.20106 10952 59	0.19069 78446 37	1.00183 56080 95
12	0.21955 28159 77	0.21924 04028 93	0.20779 14344 56	1.00217 94159 10
13	0.23779 06706 17	0.23739 43318 71	0.22482 19454 21	1.00255 12815 38
14	0.25601 48006 93	0.25552 09484 39	0.24178 42051 64	1.00295 07519 27
15	0.27422 42442 13	0.27361 83609 64	0.25867 30614 76	1.00337 73403 94
16	0.29241 80594 43	0.29168 47226 78	0.27548 33838 31	1.00383 05272 16
17	0.31059 53261 58	0.30971 82343 00	0.29221 00649 12	1.00430 97602 66
18	0.32875 51468 45	0.32771 71465 66	0.30884 80221 29	1.00481 44556 83
19	0.34689 66478 74	0.34567 97626 29	0.32539 21991 33	1.00534 39985 84
20	0.36501 89806 22	0.36360 44403 52	0.34183 75673 29	1.00589 77438 15
21	0.38312 13225 53	0.38148 95944 70	0.35817 91273 68	1.00647 50167 34
22	0.40120 28782 51	0.39933 36986 35	0.37441 19106 52	1.00707 51140 35
23	0.41926 28804 10	0.41713 52873 20	0.39053 09808 18	1.00769 73046 03
24	0.43730 05907 69	0.43489 29576 10	0.40653 14352 16	1.00834 08304 08
25	0.45531 53010 06	0.45260 53708 43	0.42240 84063 89	1.00900 49074 23
26	0.47330 63335 71	0.47027 12541 29	0.43815 70635 33	1.00968 87265 86
27	0.49127 30424 76	0.48788 94017 31	0.45377 26139 53	1.01039 14547 79
28	0.50921 48140 32	0.50545 86763 06	0.46925 03045 16	1.01111 22358 48
29	0.52713 10675 29	0.52297 80100 25	0.48458 54230 82	1.01185 01916 44
30	0.54502 12558 64	0.54044 64055 40	0.49977 32999 39	1.01260 44230 92
31	0.56288 48661 21	0.55786 29368 33	0.51480 93092 17	1.01337 40112 87
32	0.58072 14200 92	0.57522 67499 24	0.52968 88702 97	1.01415 80186 16
33	0.59853 04747 44	0.59253 70634 56	0.54440 74492 08	1.01495 54898 95
34	0.61631 16226 39	0.60979 31691 40	0.55896 05600 12	1.01576 54535 39
35	0.63406 44922 91	0.62699 44320 86	0.57334 37661 78	1.01658 69227 38
36	0.65178 87484 79	0.64414 02910 06	0.58755 26819 42	1.01741 88966 69
37	0.66948 40925 03	0.66123 02582 94	0.60158 29736 55	1.01826 03617 06
38	0.68715 02623 88	0.67826 39199 90	0.61543 03611 20	1.01911 02926 60
39	0.70478 70330 34	0.69524 09356 36	0.62909 06189 11	1.01996 76540 28
40	0.72239 42163 26	0.71216 10380 11	0.64255 95776 82	1.02083 14012 51
41	0.73997 16611 77	0.72902 40327 75	0.65583 31254 60	1.02170 04819 92
42	0.75751 92535 36	0.74582 97979 93	0.66890 72089 21	1.02257 38374 12
43	0.77503 69163 42	0.76257 82835 79	0.68177 78346 54	1.02345 04034 67
44	0.79252 46094 30	0.77926 95106 32	0.69444 10704 07	1.02432 91121 97
45	0.80998 23293 94	0.79590 35706 93	0.70689 30463 15	1.02520 88930 32

99

K = 1.64899 52184 78530

K′= 2.30878 67981 67196

E = 1.49811 49284 22116

E′= 1.16382 79644 93139

r	u=(r/90)K=F(ϕ,k)	sn u	cn u	dn u
45	0.82449 76092 39	0.72427 49904 02	0.68951 12314 37	0.95200 19889 88
46	0.84281 97783 33	0.73618 10438 29	0.67678 46560 81	0.95036 94727 45
47	0.86114 19474 28	0.74784 36745 70	0.66387 48665 27	0.94874 17374 46
48	0.87946 41165 22	0.75926 05780 30	0.65078 67351 52	0.94712 07438 07
49	0.89778 62856 16	0.77042 95690 37	0.63752 51204 09	0.94550 84343 62
50	0.91610 84547 10	0.78134 85787 52	0.62409 48633 68	0.94390 67312 99
51	0.93443 06238 05	0.79201 56514 62	0.61050 07844 70	0.94231 75343 63
52	0.95275 27928 99	0.80242 89412 86	0.59674 76805 04	0.94074 27188 28
53	0.97107 49619 93	0.81258 67087 82	0.58284 03217 96	0.93918 41335 47
54	0.98939 71310 87	0.82248 73174 94	0.56878 34496 20	0.93764 35990 67
55	1.00771 93001 81	0.83212 92304 31	0.55458 17738 28	0.93612 29058 22
56	1.02604 14692 76	0.84151 10065 00	0.54023 99706 98	0.93462 38124 02
57	1.04436 36383 70	0.85063 12969 01	0.52576 26810 01	0.93314 80438 84
58	1.06268 58074 64	0.85948 88414 96	0.51115 45082 89	0.93169 72902 43
59	1.08100 79765 58	0.86808 24651 67	0.49642 00173 95	0.93027 32048 31
60	1.09933 01456 52	0.87641 10741 66	0.48156 37331 43	0.92887 74029 31
61	1.11765 23147 47	0.88447 36524 79	0.46659 01392 77	0.92751 14603 71
62	1.13597 44838 41	0.89226 92581 98	0.45150 36775 87	0.92617 69122 14
63	1.15429 66529 35	0.89979 70199 31	0.43630 87472 46	0.92487 52515 13
64	1.17261 88220 29	0.90705 61332 42	0.42100 97043 40	0.92360 79281 26
65	1.19094 09911 23	0.91404 58571 40	0.40561 08615 98	0.92237 63476 05
66	1.20926 31602 18	0.92076 55106 23	0.39011 64883 05	0.92118 18701 35
67	1.22758 53293 12	0.92721 44692 87	0.37453 08104 08	0.92002 58095 45
68	1.24590 74984 06	0.93339 21620 05	0.35885 80107 89	0.91890 94323 67
69	1.26422 96675 00	0.93929 80676 86	0.34310 22297 23	0.91783 39569 57
70	1.28255 18365 94	0.94493 17121 22	0.32726 75654 97	0.91680 05526 74
71	1.30087 40056 89	0.95029 26649 27	0.31135 80751 91	0.91581 03391 05
72	1.31919 61747 83	0.95538 05365 79	0.29537 77756 12	0.91486 43853 46
73	1.33751 83438 77	0.96019 49755 71	0.27933 06443 78	0.91396 37093 30
74	1.35584 05129 71	0.96473 56656 64	0.26322 06211 45	0.91310 92772 02
75	1.37416 26820 65	0.96900 23232 73	0.24705 16089 65	0.91230 20027 46
76	1.39248 48511 60	0.97299 46949 65	0.23082 74757 70	0.91154 27468 41
77	1.41080 70202 54	0.97671 25550 92	0.21455 20559 82	0.91083 23169 80
78	1.42912 91893 48	0.98015 57035 51	0.19822 91522 34	0.91017 14668 06
79	1.44745 13584 42	0.98332 39636 90	0.18186 25371 92	0.90956 08957 10
80	1.46577 35275 36	0.98621 71803 39	0.16545 59554 80	0.90900 12484 45
81	1.48409 56966 31	0.98883 52180 06	0.14901 31256 98	0.90849 31147 91
82	1.50241 78657 25	0.99117 79592 02	0.13253 77425 21	0.90803 70292 50
83	1.52074 00348 19	0.99324 53029 24	0.11603 34788 71	0.90763 34707 67
84	1.53906 22039 13	0.99503 71632 96	0.09950 39881 61	0.90728 28624 96
85	1.55738 43730 08	0.99655 34683 53	0.08295 29066 03	0.90698 55715 85
86	1.57570 65421 02	0.99779 41589 93	0.06638 38555 64	0.90674 19089 97
87	1.59402 87111 96	0.99875 91880 83	0.04980 04439 69	0.90655 21293 61
88	1.61235 08802 90	0.99944 85197 26	0.03320 62707 48	0.90641 64308 48
89	1.63067 30493 84	0.99986 21286 90	0.01660 49273 01	0.90633 49550 74
90	1.64899 52184 79	1.00000 00000 00	0.00000 00000 00	0.90630 77870 37

304946

q = 0.01229 45605 27181 44   D(90) = 1.05041 79734 57467
q′= 0.10605 40201 85995 5   1/D(90) = 0.95200 19889 87760

r	φ	E(φ,k)	A(r)	D(r)
45	0.80998 23293 94	0.79590 35706 93	0.70689 30463 15	1.02520 88930 32
46	0.82741 01094 01	0.81248 06249 13	0.71912 99561 17	1.02608 86740 95
47	0.84480 80189 60	0.82900 09031 40	0.73114 80583 48	1.02696 73835 09
48	0.86217 61636 59	0.84546 47029 35	0.74294 36775 19	1.02784 39506 99
49	0.87951 46848 43	0.86187 23885 13	0.75451 32052 77	1.02871 73077 02
50	0.89682 37592 69	0.87822 43896 17	0.76585 31015 45	1.02958 63904 64
51	0.91410 35987 08	0.89452 12003 35	0.77695 98956 44	1.03045 01401 37
52	0.93135 44495 18	0.91076 33778 58	0.78783 01873 96	1.03130 75043 71
53	0.94857 65921 75	0.92695 15411 79	0.79846 06482 05	1.03215 74385 95
54	0.96577 03407 78	0.94308 63697 51	0.80884 80221 20	1.03299 89072 89
55	0.98293 60425 04	0.95916 86020 97	0.81898 91268 75	1.03383 08852 46
56	1.00007 40770 50	0.97519 90343 81	0.82888 08549 08	1.03465 23588 22
57	1.01718 48560 26	0.99117 85189 39	0.83852 01743 58	1.03546 23271 70
58	1.03426 88223 33	1.00710 79627 81	0.84790 41300 41	1.03625 98034 59
59	1.05132 64495 00	1.02298 83260 62	0.85702 98444 00	1.03704 38160 79
60	1.06835 82410 05	1.03882 06205 28	0.86589 45184 37	1.03781 34098 21
61	1.08536 47295 60	1.05460 59079 41	0.87449 54326 16	1.03856 76470 43
62	1.10234 64763 79	1.07034 52984 77	0.88282 99477 44	1.03930 56088 13
63	1.11930 40704 19	1.08603 99491 24	0.89089 55058 29	1.04002 63960 28
64	1.13623 81275 98	1.10169 10620 46	0.89868 96309 13	1.04072 91305 08
65	1.15314 92899 95	1.11729 98829 56	0.90620 99298 73	1.04141 29560 67
66	1.17003 82250 29	1.13286 76994 63	0.91345 40932 12	1.04207 70395 59
67	1.18690 56246 14	1.14839 58394 29	0.92041 98958 01	1.04272 05718 87
68	1.20375 22043 07	1.16388 56693 05	0.92710 51976 19	1.04334 27689 96
69	1.22057 87024 31	1.17933 85924 83	0.93350 79444 49	1.04394 28728 20
70	1.23738 58791 82	1.19475 60476 30	0.93962 61685 53	1.04452 01522 16
71	1.25417 45157 27	1.21013 95070 36	0.94545 79893 18	1.04507 39038 44
72	1.27094 54132 87	1.22549 04749 56	0.95100 16138 80	1.04560 34530 32
73	1.28769 93922 00	1.24081 04859 58	0.95625 53377 10	1.04610 81545 94
74	1.30443 72909 84	1.25610 11032 80	0.96121 75451 78	1.04658 73936 19
75	1.32115 99653 78	1.27136 39171 80	0.96588 67100 91	1.04704 05862 15
76	1.33786 82873 81	1.28660 05433 05	0.97026 13961 92	1.04746 71802 28
77	1.35456 31442 77	1.30181 26210 59	0.97434 02576 39	1.04786 66559 08
78	1.37124 54376 51	1.31700 18119 79	0.97812 20394 53	1.04823 85265 46
79	1.38791 60824 01	1.33216 97981 16	0.98160 55779 31	1.04858 23390 65
80	1.40457 60057 39	1.34731 82804 26	0.98478 98010 34	1.04889 76745 75
81	1.42122 61461 88	1.36244 89771 65	0.98767 37287 45	1.04918 41488 79
82	1.43786 74525 69	1.37756 36222 96	0.99025 64733 94	1.04944 14129 46
83	1.45537 35476 16	1.39266 39638 94	0.99253 72399 52	1.04966 91533 32
84	1.47112 74038 22	1.40775 17625 60	0.99451 53262 98	1.04986 70925 64
85	1.48774 79886 77	1.42282 87898 47	0.99619 01234 55	1.05003 49894 79
86	1.50436 36173 79	1.43789 68266 84	0.99756 11157 86	1.05017 26395 17
87	1.52097 52749 35	1.45295 76618 04	0.99862 78811 75	1.05027 98749 67
88	1.53758 39504 99	1.46801 30901 80	0.99939 00911 61	1.05035 65651 77
89	1.55419 06363 38	1.48306 49114 64	0.99984 75110 52	1.05040 26167 10
90	1.57079 63267 95	1.49811 49284 22	1.00000 00000 00	1.05041 79734 57

K = 1.65569 69263 10344
K'= 2.27537 64296 11676

E = 1.49236 87111 24151
E'= 1.17317 93826 83722

r	u=(r/90)K=F(ϕ,k)	sn u	cn u	dn u
0	0.00000 00000 00	0.00000 00000 00	1.00000 00000 00	1.00000 00000 00
1	0.01839 66325 15	0.01839 53954 89	0.99983 07903 96	0.99996 74853 38
2	0.03679 32650 29	0.03678 33703 94	0.99932 32628 45	0.99986 99874 73
3	0.05518 98975 44	0.05515 65119 79	0.99847 77209 26	0.99970 76446 78
4	0.07358 65300 58	0.07350 74231 76	0.99729 46699 64	0.99948 06871 05
5	0.09198 31625 73	0.09182 87303 66	0.99577 48160 50	0.99918 94363 30
6	0.11037 97950 87	0.11011 30910 89	0.99391 90646 98	0.99883 43047 22
7	0.12877 64276 02	0.12835 32016 64	0.99172 85191 13	0.99841 57946 27
8	0.14717 30601 16	0.14654 18046 97	0.98920 44780 91	0.99793 44973 87
9	0.16556 96926 31	0.16467 16964 61	0.98634 84335 59	0.99739 10921 85
10	0.18396 63251 46	0.18273 57341 17	0.98316 20677 57	0.99678 63447 18
11	0.20236 29576 60	0.20072 68427 63	0.97964 72500 83	0.99612 11057 14
12	0.22075 95901 75	0.21863 80222 96	0.97580 60335 98	0.99539 63092 87
13	0.23915 62226 89	0.23646 23540 57	0.97164 06512 25	0.99461 29711 46
14	0.25755 28552 04	0.25419 30072 53	0.96715 35116 33	0.99377 21866 51
15	0.27594 94877 18	0.27182 32451 36	0.96234 71948 33	0.99287 51287 34
16	0.29434 61202 33	0.28934 64309 19	0.95722 44475 12	0.99192 30456 88
17	0.31274 27527 48	0.30675 60334 26	0.95178 81780 93	0.99091 72588 28
18	0.33113 93852 62	0.32404 56324 52	0.94604 14515 70	0.98985 91600 35
19	0.34953 60177 77	0.34120 89238 29	0.93998 74841 19	0.98875 02091 93
20	0.36793 26502 91	0.35823 97241 80	0.93362 96375 01	0.98759 19315 20
21	0.38632 92828 06	0.37513 19753 68	0.92697 14132 90	0.98638 59148 07
22	0.40472 59153 20	0.39187 97486 12	0.92001 64469 33	0.98513 38065 72
23	0.42312 25478 35	0.40847 72482 73	0.91276 85016 71	0.98383 73111 38
24	0.44151 91803 49	0.42491 88153 14	0.90523 14623 30	0.98249 81866 37
25	0.45991 58128 64	0.44119 89304 14	0.89740 93290 14	0.98111 82419 65
26	0.47831 24453 79	0.45731 22167 43	0.88930 62107 16	0.97969 93336 75
27	0.49670 90778 93	0.47325 34423 95	0.88092 63188 61	0.97824 33628 36
28	0.51510 57104 08	0.48901 75224 83	0.87227 39608 09	0.97675 22718 48
29	0.53350 23429 22	0.50459 95208 86	0.86335 35333 35	0.97522 80412 42
30	0.55189 89754 37	0.51999 46516 67	0.85416 95161 02	0.97367 26864 58
31	0.57029 56079 51	0.53519 82801 49	0.84472 64651 51	0.97208 82546 09
32	0.58869 22404 66	0.55020 59236 66	0.83502 90064 20	0.97047 68212 46
33	0.60708 88729 80	0.56501 32519 92	0.82508 18293 20	0.96884 04871 34
34	0.62548 55054 95	0.57961 60874 47	0.81488 96803 70	0.96718 13750 32
35	0.64388 21380 10	0.59401 04046 98	0.80445 73569 25	0.96550 16264 98
36	0.66227 87705 24	0.60819 23302 65	0.79378 97009 96	0.96380 33987 18
37	0.68067 54030 39	0.62215 81417 20	0.78289 15931 92	0.96208 88613 70
38	0.69907 20355 53	0.63590 42666 26	0.77176 79467 86	0.96036 01935 21
39	0.71746 86680 68	0.64942 72811 86	0.76042 37019 26	0.95861 95805 78
40	0.73586 53005 82	0.66272 39086 49	0.74886 38200 00	0.95686 92112 78
41	0.75426 19330 97	0.67579 10174 57	0.73709 32781 71	0.95511 12747 37
42	0.77265 85656 11	0.68862 56191 68	0.72511 70640 83	0.95334 79575 60
43	0.79105 51981 26	0.70122 48661 50	0.71294 01707 66	0.95158 14410 07
44	0.80945 18306 41	0.71358 60490 69	0.70056 75917 24	0.94981 38982 31
45	0.82784 84631 55	0.72570 65941 80	0.68800 43162 39	0.94804 74915 84

q = 0.01333 45085 07947 30   D(90) = 1.05479 94787 99259
q'= 0.10167 16783 93444 1   1/D(90) = 0.94804 74915 84239

r	ϕ	$E(\phi,k)$	A(r)	D(r)
0	0.00000 00000 00	0.00000 00000 00	0.00000 00000 00	1.00000 00000 00
1	0.01839 64331 18	0.01839 62337 26	0.01743 99996 37	1.00001 66910 23
2	0.03679 16701 99	0.03679 00754 93	0.03487 47095 48	1.00006 67437 56
3	0.05518 45169 01	0.05517 91372 01	0.05229 88415 59	1.00015 00972 20
4	0.07357 37822 71	0.07356 10384 57	0.06970 71105 92	1.00026 66498 64
5	0.09195 82804 35	0.09193 34104 04	0.08709 42362 14	1.00041 62596 91
6	0.11033 68322 67	0.11029 38995 18	0.10445 49441 90	1.00059 87444 29
7	0.12870 82670 60	0.12864 01713 71	0.12178 39680 19	1.00081 38817 55
8	0.14707 14241 66	0.14696 99143 37	0.13907 60504 90	1.00106 14095 65
9	0.16542 51546 27	0.16528 08432 48	0.15632 59452 15	1.00134 10262 92
10	0.18376 83227 78	0.18357 07029 73	0.17352 84181 77	1.00165 23912 75
11	0.20209 98078 22	0.20183 72719 31	0.19067 82492 63	1.00199 51251 76
12	0.22041 85053 86	0.22007 83655 11	0.20777 02338 03	1.00236 88104 36
13	0.23872 33290 32	0.23829 18394 04	0.22479 91841 00	1.00277 29917 89
14	0.25701 32117 46	0.25647 55928 35	0.24175 99309 61	1.00320 71768 15
15	0.27528 71073 78	0.27462 75716 84	0.25864 73252 21	1.00367 08365 40
16	0.29354 39920 57	0.29274 57714 95	0.27545 62392 65	1.00416 34060 81
17	0.31178 28655 49	0.31082 82403 67	0.29218 15685 43	1.00468 42853 31
18	0.33000 27525 82	0.32887 30817 14	0.30881 82330 84	1.00523 28396 94
19	0.34820 27041 17	0.34687 84569 00	0.32536 11790 04	1.00580 84008 58
20	0.36638 17985 81	0.36484 25877 32	0.34180 53800 04	1.00641 02676 06
21	0.38453 91430 36	0.38276 37588 18	0.35814 58388 70	1.00703 77066 71
22	0.40267 38743 11	0.40064 03197 78	0.37437 75889 59	1.00768 99536 33
23	0.42078 51600 68	0.41847 06873 16	0.39049 56956 86	1.00836 62138 45
24	0.43887 21998 24	0.43625 33471 30	0.40649 52579 96	1.00906 56634 06
25	0.45693 42259 12	0.45398 68556 85	0.42237 14098 37	1.00978 74501 59
26	0.47497 05043 83	0.47166 98418 32	0.43811 93216 20	1.01053 06947 36
27	0.49298 03358 61	0.48930 10082 62	0.45373 42016 71	1.01129 44916 24
28	0.51096 30563 23	0.50687 91328 29	0.46921 12976 80	1.01207 79102 69
29	0.52901 80378 40	0.52440 30696 99	0.48454 58981 33	1.01287 99962 13
30	0.54684 46892 42	0.54187 17503 64	0.49973 33337 40	1.01369 97722 53
31	0.56474 24567 32	0.55928 41844 97	0.51476 89788 56	1.01453 62396 31
32	0.58261 08244 41	0.57663 94606 64	0.52964 82528 84	1.01538 83792 56
33	0.60044 93149 20	0.59393 67468 83	0.54436 66216 73	1.01625 51529 40
34	0.61825 74895 72	0.61117 52910 48	0.55891 95989 07	1.01713 55046 66
35	0.63603 49490 32	0.62835 44212 06	0.57330 27474 75	1.01802 83618 73
36	0.65378 13334 81	0.64547 35457 02	0.58751 16808 36	1.01893 26367 61
37	0.67149 63229 02	0.66253 21531 87	0.60154 20643 73	1.01984 72276 24
38	0.68917 96372 86	0.67952 98124 95	0.61538 96167 25	1.02077 10201 80
39	0.70683 10367 75	0.69646 61724 03	0.62905 01111 17	1.02170 28889 40
40	0.72445 03217 48	0.71334 09612 61	0.64251 93766 65	1.02264 16985 73
41	0.74203 73328 60	0.73015 39865 13	0.65579 32996 84	1.02358 63052 89
42	0.75959 19510 18	0.74690 51341 00	0.66886 78249 57	1.02453 55582 36
43	0.77711 40973 10	0.76359 43677 66	0.68173 89570 16	1.02548 83009 00
44	0.79460 37328 83	0.78022 17282 54	0.69440 27613 84	1.02644 33725 14
45	0.81206 08587 66	0.79678 73324 12	0.70685 53658 18	1.02739 96094 70

K = 1.65569 69263 10344
K' = 2.27537 64296 11676

E = 1.49236 87111 24151
E' = 1.17317 93826 83722

r	u=(r/90)K=F(φ,k)	sn u	cn u	dn u
45	0.82784 84631 55	0.72570 65941 80	0.68800 43162 39	0.94804 74915 84
46	0.84624 50956 70	0.73758 40604 45	0.67525 53248 79	0.94628 43699 94
47	0.86464 17281 84	0.74921 61364 68	0.66232 55852 34	0.94452 66664 17
48	0.88303 83606 99	0.76060 06372 94	0.64922 00478 63	0.94277 64953 73
49	0.90143 49932 13	0.77173 55010 53	0.63594 36424 83	0.94103 59505 46
50	0.91983 16257 28	0.78261 87854 87	0.62250 12743 78	0.93930 71024 82
51	0.93822 82582 43	0.79324 86643 64	0.60889 78210 55	0.93759 19963 55
52	0.95662 48907 57	0.80362 34237 87	0.59513 81291 26	0.93589 26498 23
53	0.97502 15232 72	0.81374 14584 32	0.58122 70114 41	0.93421 10509 62
54	0.99341 81557 86	0.82360 12676 98	0.56716 92444 47	0.93254 91562 85
55	1.01181 47883 01	0.83320 14518 11	0.55296 95657 99	0.93090 88888 42
56	1.03021 14208 15	0.84254 07078 82	0.53863 26722 01	0.92929 21364 10
57	1.04860 80533 30	0.85161 78259 23	0.52416 32174 90	0.92770 07497 47
58	1.06700 46858 44	0.86043 16848 58	0.50956 58109 54	0.92613 65409 48
59	1.08540 13183 59	0.86898 12485 09	0.49484 50158 79	0.92460 12818 67
60	1.10379 79508 74	0.87726 55616 01	0.48000 53483 33	0.92309 67026 18
61	1.12219 45833 88	0.88528 37457 74	0.46505 12761 71	0.92162 44901 59
62	1.14059 12159 03	0.89303 49956 17	0.44998 72182 66	0.92018 62869 48
63	1.15898 78484 17	0.90051 85747 51	0.43481 75439 52	0.91878 36896 68
64	1.17738 44809 32	0.90773 38119 44	0.41954 65726 88	0.91741 82480 33
65	1.19578 11134 46	0.91468 00972 91	0.40417 85739 26	0.91609 14636 54
66	1.21417 77459 61	0.92135 68784 58	0.38871 77671 77	0.91480 47889 80
67	1.23257 43784 75	0.92776 36569 97	0.37316 83222 83	0.91355 96262 96
68	1.25097 10109 90	0.93389 99847 49	0.35753 43598 68	0.91235 73267 94
69	1.26936 76435 05	0.93976 54603 28	0.34181 99519 84	0.91119 91896 95
70	1.28776 42760 19	0.94535 97257 16	0.32602 91229 24	0.91008 64614 35
71	1.30616 09085 34	0.95068 24629 51	0.31016 58502 12	0.90902 03349 06
72	1.32455 75410 48	0.95573 33909 37	0.29423 40657 51	0.90800 19487 50
73	1.34295 41735 63	0.96051 22623 65	0.27823 76571 34	0.90703 23867 03
74	1.36135 08060 77	0.96501 88607 60	0.26218 04690 98	0.90611 26769 93
75	1.37974 74385 92	0.96925 29976 66	0.24606 63051 21	0.90524 37917 80
76	1.39814 40711 07	0.97321 45099 49	0.22989 89291 50	0.90442 66466 42
77	1.41654 07036 21	0.97690 32572 60	0.21368 20674 63	0.90366 21001 07
78	1.43493 73361 36	0.98031 91196 25	0.19741 94106 42	0.90295 09532 17
79	1.45333 39686 50	0.98346 19951 96	0.18111 46156 56	0.90229 39491 43
80	1.47173 06011 65	0.98633 17981 50	0.16477 13080 55	0.90169 17728 28
81	1.49012 72336 79	0.98892 84567 38	0.14839 30842 50	0.90114 50506 64
82	1.50852 38661 94	0.99125 19115 05	0.13198 35138 88	0.90065 43502 13
83	1.52692 04987 08	0.99330 21136 59	0.11554 61422 98	0.90022 01799 46
84	1.54531 71312 23	0.99507 90236 18	0.09908 44930 16	0.89984 29890 23
85	1.56371 37637 38	0.99658 26097 07	0.08260 20703 70	0.89952 31670 98
86	1.58211 03962 52	0.99781 28470 42	0.06610 23621 19	0.89926 10441 56
87	1.60065 70287 67	0.99876 97165 69	0.04958 88421 44	0.89905 68903 66
88	1.61890 36612 81	0.99945 32042 82	0.03306 49731 74	0.89891 09159 79
89	1.63730 02937 96	0.99986 33006 14	0.01653 42095 49	0.89882 32712 34
90	1.65569 69263 10	1.00000 00000 00	0.00000 00000 00	0.89879 40462 99

q = 0.01333 45085 07947 30   D(90) = 1.05479 94787 99259
q'= 0.10167 16783 93444 1   1/D(90) = 0.94804 74915 84239

r	ϕ	$E(\phi,k)$	A(r)	D(r)
45	0.81206 08587 66	0.79678 73324 12	0.70685 53658 18	1.02739 96094 70
46	0.82948 55156 49	0.81329 13722 10	0.71909 29615 23	1.02835 58467 43
47	0.84687 77836 12	0.82973 41136 63	0.73111 18043 63	1.02931 09193 04
48	0.86423 77818 09	0.84611 58956 85	0.74290 82160 38	1.03026 36635 43
49	0.88185 65563 13	0.86243 71288 60	0.75447 85852 56	1.03121 29186 85
50	0.89886 16386 71	0.87869 82941 53	0.76581 93688 85	1.03215 75282 03
51	0.91612 59275 44	0.89489 99415 47	0.77692 70930 77	1.03309 63412 33
52	0.93335 88061 30	0.91104 26886 27	0.78779 83543 83	1.03402 82139 69
53	0.95056 05826 86	0.92712 72191 10	0.79842 98208 47	1.03495 20110 60
54	0.96773 16017 58	0.94315 42813 25	0.80881 82330 70	1.03586 66069 93
55	0.98487 22435 76	0.95912 46866 47	0.81896 04052 66	1.03677 08874 66
56	1.00198 29234 30	0.97503 93078 98	0.82885 32262 90	1.03766 37507 40
57	1.01906 40909 97	0.99089 90777 04	0.83849 36606 44	1.03854 41089 90
58	1.03611 62296 51	1.00670 49868 28	0.84787 87494 61	1.03941 08896 21
59	1.05313 98557 35	1.02245 80824 72	0.85700 56114 71	1.04026 30365 83
60	1.07013 55178 05	1.03815 94665 60	0.86587 14439 38	1.04109 95116 52
61	1.08710 37958 51	1.05381 02940 01	0.87447 35235 75	1.04191 92956 99
62	1.10404 53004 90	1.06941 17709 31	0.88280 92074 38	1.04272 13899 28
63	1.12096 06721 36	1.08496 51529 52	0.89087 59337 90	1.04350 48170 95
64	1.13785 05801 45	1.10047 17433 51	0.89867 12229 48	1.04426 86227 01
65	1.15471 57219 43	1.11593 28913 25	0.90619 26780 94	1.04501 18761 49
66	1.17155 68221 29	1.13134 99901 86	0.91343 79860 72	1.04573 36718 83
67	1.18837 46315 64	1.14672 44755 81	0.92040 49181 48	1.04643 31304 90
68	1.20516 99264 36	1.16205 78237 02	0.92709 13307 52	1.04710 93997 71
69	1.22194 35073 14	1.17735 15495 01	0.93349 51661 89	1.04776 16557 80
70	1.23869 61981 85	1.19260 72049 10	0.93961 44533 22	1.04838 91038 26
71	1.25542 88454 72	1.20782 63770 64	0.94544 73082 28	1.04899 09794 44
72	1.27214 23170 49	1.22301 06865 40	0.95099 19348 30	1.04956 65493 26
73	1.28883 75012 30	1.23816 17855 87	0.95624 66254 93	1.05011 51122 12
74	1.30551 53057 59	1.25328 13563 86	0.96120 97615 97	1.05063 59997 47
75	1.32217 66567 79	1.26837 11093 01	0.96587 98140 81	1.05112 85772 94
76	1.33882 24977 99	1.28343 27811 51	0.97025 53439 52	1.05159 22447 11
77	1.35545 37886 46	1.29846 81334 91	0.97433 50027 73	1.05202 64370 74
78	1.37207 15044 15	1.31347 89509 01	0.97811 75331 14	1.05243 06253 74
79	1.38867 66344 03	1.32846 70392 86	0.98160 17689 75	1.05280 43171 57
80	1.40527 01810 47	1.34343 42241 89	0.98478 66361 80	1.05314 70571 26
81	1.42185 31588 44	1.35838 23491 15	0.98767 11527 41	1.05345 84276 93
82	1.43842 65932 75	1.37331 32738 60	0.99025 44291 86	1.05373 80494 92
83	1.45499 15197 18	1.38822 88728 52	0.99253 56688 61	1.05398 55818 36
84	1.47154 89823 62	1.40313 10335 05	0.99451 41682 01	1.05420 07231 38
85	1.48810 00331 09	1.41802 16545 74	0.99618 93169 67	1.05438 32112 73
86	1.50464 57304 83	1.43290 26445 22	0.99756 05984 52	1.05453 28239 02
87	1.52118 71385 28	1.44777 59198 94	0.99862 75896 56	1.05464 93787 40
88	1.53772 53257 07	1.46264 34036 87	0.99938 99614 32	1.05473 27337 79
89	1.55426 13637 99	1.47750 70237 43	0.99984 74785 95	1.05478 27874 60
90	1.57079 63267 95	1.49236 87111 24	1.00000 00000 00	1.05479 94787 99

K = 1.66271 59584 91370
K′= 2.24354 93416 98626

E = 1.48642 68037 44253
E′= 1.18258 90849 45384

r	u=(r/90)K=F(φ,k)	sn u	cn u	dn u
0	0.00000 00000 00	0.00000 00000 00	1.00000 00000 00	1.00000 00000 00
1	0.01847 46217 61	0.01847 33542 92	0.99982 93530 30	0.99996 48307 84
2	0.03694 92435 22	0.03693 91054 62	0.99931 75183 53	0.99985 93736 13
3	0.05542 38652 83	0.05538 96588 33	0.99846 48144 50	0.99968 37798 17
4	0.07389 84870 44	0.07381 74365 93	0.99727 17714 12	0.99943 83012 70
5	0.09237 31088 05	0.09221 48861 65	0.99573 91298 78	0.99912 32898 80
6	0.11084 77305 66	0.11057 44884 99	0.99386 78395 51	0.99873 91968 70
7	0.12932 23523 27	0.12888 87662 69	0.99165 90573 02	0.99828 65718 69
8	0.14779 69740 88	0.14715 02919 40	0.98911 41448 70	0.99776 60617 99
9	0.16627 15958 49	0.16535 16956 89	0.98623 46661 59	0.99717 84095 73
10	0.18474 62176 10	0.18348 56731 59	0.98302 23841 53	0.99652 44526 06
11	0.20322 08393 71	0.20154 49930 15	0.97947 92574 58	0.99580 51211 39
12	0.22169 54611 32	0.21952 25042 91	0.97560 74364 77	0.99502 14363 94
13	0.24017 00828 93	0.23741 11435 01	0.97140 92592 42	0.99417 45085 53
14	0.25864 47046 54	0.25520 39414 96	0.96688 72469 14	0.99326 55345 78
15	0.27711 93264 15	0.27289 40300 56	0.96204 40989 68	0.99229 57958 73
16	0.29559 39481 76	0.29047 46481 89	0.95688 26880 86	0.99126 66557 99
17	0.31406 85699 37	0.30793 91481 33	0.95140 60547 67	0.99017 95570 54
18	0.33254 31916 98	0.32528 10010 38	0.94561 74016 82	0.98903 60189 15
19	0.35101 78134 59	0.34249 38023 22	0.93952 00877 95	0.98783 76343 70
20	0.36949 24352 20	0.35957 12766 87	0.93311 76222 65	0.98658 60671 28
21	0.38796 70569 81	0.37650 72827 88	0.92641 36581 50	0.98528 30485 31
22	0.40644 16787 42	0.39329 58175 41	0.91941 19859 48	0.98393 03743 77
23	0.42491 63005 03	0.40993 10200 70	0.91211 65269 77	0.98252 99016 51
24	0.44339 09222 64	0.42640 71752 90	0.90453 13266 34	0.98108 35451 95
25	0.46186 55440 25	0.44271 87171 04	0.89666 05475 46	0.97959 32743 08
26	0.48034 01657 86	0.45886 02312 45	0.88850 84626 39	0.97806 11092 92
27	0.49881 47875 47	0.47482 64577 26	0.88007 94481 43	0.97648 91179 59
28	0.51728 94093 08	0.49061 22929 23	0.87137 79765 59	0.97487 94121 03
29	0.53576 40310 69	0.50621 27912 92	0.86240 86096 12	0.97323 41439 48
30	0.55423 86528 30	0.52162 31667 01	0.85317 59912 00	0.97155 55025 80
31	0.57271 32745 91	0.53683 87934 14	0.84368 48403 79	0.96984 57103 75
32	0.59118 78963 52	0.55185 52067 08	0.83393 99443 78	0.96810 70194 30
33	0.60966 25181 14	0.56666 81031 40	0.82394 61516 90	0.96634 17080 05
34	0.62813 71398 75	0.58127 33404 71	0.81370 83652 37	0.96455 20769 85
35	0.64661 17616 36	0.59566 69372 60	0.80323 15356 45	0.96274 04463 70
36	0.66508 63833 97	0.60984 50721 23	0.79252 06546 25	0.96090 91517 99
37	0.68356 10051 58	0.62380 40826 92	0.78158 07484 94	0.95906 05411 18
38	0.70203 56269 19	0.63754 04642 61	0.77041 68718 49	0.95719 69709 94
39	0.72051 02486 80	0.65105 08681 52	0.75903 41013 94	0.95532 08035 84
40	0.73898 48704 41	0.66433 20997 94	0.74743 75299 54	0.95343 44032 68
41	0.75745 94922 02	0.67738 11165 51	0.73563 22606 71	0.95154 01334 42
42	0.77593 41139 63	0.69019 50252 94	0.72362 34014 04	0.94964 03533 87
43	0.79440 87357 24	0.70277 10797 36	0.71141 60593 40	0.94773 74152 07
44	0.81288 33574 85	0.71510 66775 58	0.69901 53358 21	0.94583 36608 52
45	0.83135 79792 46	0.72719 93573 16	0.68642 63214 06	0.94393 14192 19

q = 0.01442 14412 80637 80   D(90) = 1.05939 89983 16669
q'= 0.09746 47524 70351 77   1/D(90) = 0.94393 14192 18773

r	ϕ	$E(\phi,k)$	A(r)	D(r)
0	0.00000 00000 00	0.00000 00000 00	0.00000 00000 00	1.00000 00000 00
1	0.01847 44051 71	0.01847 41885 86	0.01743 78950 14	1.00001 80919 15
2	0.03694 75111 78	0.03694 57789 79	0.03487 05047 90	1.00007 23456 20
3	0.05541 80207 18	0.05541 21772 62	0.05229 25456 25	1.00016 26950 17
4	0.07388 46402 18	0.07387 07980 60	0.06969 87368 94	1.00028 90300 33
5	0.09234 60816 79	0.09231 90687 77	0.08708 38025 79	1.00045 11967 55
6	0.11080 10645 25	0.11075 44338 12	0.10444 24728 11	1.00064 89976 12
7	0.12924 83174 25	0.12917 43587 12	0.12176 94854 01	1.00088 21916 26
8	0.14768 65801 04	0.14757 63342 82	0.13905 95873 73	1.00115 04946 93
9	0.16611 46051 26	0.16595 78806 23	0.15630 75364 99	1.00145 35799 41
10	0.18453 11596 56	0.18431 65510 92	0.17350 81028 25	1.00179 10781 18
11	0.20293 50271 92	0.20264 99361 75	0.19065 60702 00	1.00216 25780 49
12	0.22132 50092 59	0.22095 56672 61	0.20774 62378 00	1.00256 76271 34
13	0.23969 99270 73	0.23923 14203 16	0.22477 34216 54	1.00300 57319 00
14	0.25805 86231 68	0.25747 49194 35	0.24173 24561 57	1.00347 63586 01
15	0.27639 99629 74	0.27568 39402 72	0.25861 81955 90	1.00397 89338 68
16	0.29472 28363 54	0.29385 63133 45	0.27542 55156 33	1.00451 28454 11
17	0.31302 61590 97	0.31198 99271 96	0.29214 93148 70	1.00507 74427 61
18	0.33130 88743 57	0.33008 27314 12	0.30878 45162 94	1.00567 20380 63
19	0.34956 99540 42	0.34813 27394 94	0.32532 60688 07	1.00629 59069 16
20	0.36780 84001 46	0.36613 80315 73	0.34176 89487 16	1.00694 82892 54
21	0.38602 32460 30	0.38409 67569 63	0.35810 81612 16	1.00762 83902 72
22	0.40421 35576 42	0.40200 71365 56	0.37433 87418 81	1.00833 53813 93
23	0.42237 84346 77	0.41986 74650 50	0.39045 57581 38	1.00906 84012 82
24	0.44051 70116 74	0.43767 61130 02	0.40645 43107 36	1.00982 65568 88
25	0.45862 84590 59	0.45543 15287 18	0.42232 95352 14	1.01060 89245 38
26	0.47671 19841 16	0.47313 22399 69	0.43807 66033 59	1.01141 45510 61
27	0.49476 68318 98	0.49077 68555 35	0.45369 07246 52	1.01224 24549 47
28	0.51279 22860 70	0.50836 40665 77	0.46916 71477 14	1.01309 16275 44
29	0.53078 76696 92	0.52589 26478 33	0.48450 11617 38	1.01396 10342 88
30	0.54875 23459 33	0.54336 14586 56	0.49968 80979 16	1.01484 96159 61
31	0.56668 57187 13	0.56076 94438 69	0.51472 33308 54	1.01575 62899 83
32	0.58458 72332 94	0.57811 56344 67	0.52960 22799 82	1.01667 99517 32
33	0.60245 63767 90	0.59539 91481 46	0.54432 04109 44	1.01761 94758 85
34	0.62029 26786 20	0.61261 91896 80	0.55887 32369 96	1.01857 37177 95
35	0.63809 57108 91	0.62977 50511 38	0.57325 63203 70	1.01954 15148 82
36	0.65586 50887 24	0.64686 61119 47	0.58746 52736 51	1.02052 16880 49
37	0.67360 04705 06	0.66389 18388 18	0.60149 57611 19	1.02151 30431 19
38	0.69130 15580 86	0.68085 17855 14	0.61534 35000 99	1.02251 43722 93
39	0.70896 80969 08	0.69774 55924 96	0.62900 42622 86	1.02352 44556 15
40	0.72659 98760 83	0.71457 29864 26	0.64247 38750 62	1.02454 20624 66
41	0.74419 67283 96	0.73133 37795 50	0.65574 82227 96	1.02556 59530 56
42	0.76175 85302 63	0.74802 78689 59	0.66882 32481 37	1.02659 48799 40
43	0.77928 52016 25	0.76465 52357 34	0.68169 49532 81	1.02762 75895 34
44	0.79677 67057 89	0.78121 59439 83	0.69435 94012 38	1.02866 28236 44
45	0.81423 30492 10	0.79771 01397 78	0.70681 27170 69	1.02969 93210 00

K = 1.66271 59584 91370

K′= 2.24354 93416 98626

E = 1.48642 68037 44253

E′= 1.18258 90849 45384

r	u=(r/90)K=F(φ,k)	sn u	cn u	dn u
45	0.83135 79792 46	0.72719 93573 16	0.68642 63214 06	0.94393 14192 19
46	0.84983 26010 07	0.73904 67951 74	0.67365 40911 65	0.94203 30033 35
47	0.86830 72227 68	0.75064 68014 50	0.66070 37002 11	0.94014 07076 39
48	0.88678 18445 29	0.76199 73170 09	0.64758 01794 92	0.93825 68053 38
49	0.90525 64662 90	0.77309 64095 12	0.63428 85318 21	0.93638 35458 68
50	0.92373 10880 51	0.78394 22695 38	0.62083 37281 68	0.93452 31524 42
51	0.94220 57098 12	0.79453 32065 90	0.60722 07042 13	0.93267 78196 87
52	0.96068 03315 73	0.80486 76450 04	0.59345 43571 54	0.93084 97113 85
53	0.97915 49533 34	0.81494 41197 77	0.57953 95427 76	0.92904 09583 00
54	0.99762 95750 95	0.82476 12723 23	0.56548 10727 83	0.92725 36561 03
55	1.01610 41968 56	0.83431 78461 80	0.55128 37123 89	0.92548 98633 88
56	1.03457 88186 17	0.84361 26826 67	0.53695 21781 71	0.92375 15997 83
57	1.05305 34403 78	0.85264 47165 27	0.52249 11361 73	0.92204 08441 52
58	1.07152 80621 39	0.86141 29715 42	0.50790 52002 68	0.92035 95328 88
59	1.09000 26839 00	0.86991 65561 63	0.49319 89307 71	0.91870 95582 90
60	1.10847 73056 61	0.87815 46591 36	0.47837 68332 99	0.91709 27670 34
61	1.12695 19274 22	0.88612 65451 63	0.46344 33578 74	0.91551 09587 23
62	1.14542 65491 83	0.89383 15505 91	0.44840 28982 61	0.91396 58845 25
63	1.16390 11709 44	0.90126 90791 50	0.43325 97915 43	0.91245 92458 86
64	1.18237 57927 05	0.90843 85977 50	0.41801 83179 21	0.91099 26933 23
65	1.20085 04144 66	0.91533 96323 38	0.40268 27007 35	0.90956 78252 97
66	1.21932 50362 27	0.92197 17638 35	0.38725 71067 01	0.90818 61871 52
67	1.23779 96579 88	0.92833 46241 62	0.37174 56463 53	0.90684 92701 25
68	1.25627 42797 49	0.93442 78923 50	0.35615 23746 91	0.90555 85104 31
69	1.27474 89015 10	0.94025 12907 65	0.34048 12920 19	0.90431 52884 00
70	1.29322 35232 71	0.94580 45814 30	0.32473 63449 71	0.90312 09276 88
71	1.31169 81450 32	0.95108 75624 76	0.30892 14277 18	0.90197 66945 37
72	1.33017 27667 93	0.95610 00647 07	0.29304 03833 40	0.90088 37971 00
73	1.34864 73885 54	0.96084 19483 01	0.27709 70053 72	0.89984 33848 10
74	1.36712 20103 15	0.96531 30996 47	0.26109 50394 97	0.89885 65478 07
75	1.38559 66320 76	0.96951 34283 24	0.24503 81853 91	0.89792 43164 12
76	1.40407 12538 37	0.97344 28642 23	0.22893 00987 05	0.89704 76606 41
77	1.42254 58755 98	0.97710 13548 28	0.21277 43931 82	0.89622 74897 65
78	1.44102 04973 59	0.98048 88626 45	0.19657 46428 93	0.89546 46519 15
79	1.45949 51191 20	0.98360 53628 03	0.18033 43845 92	0.89475 99337 20
80	1.47796 97408 81	0.98645 08408 02	0.16405 71201 76	0.89411 40599 80
81	1.49644 43626 42	0.98902 52904 50	0.14774 63192 44	0.89352 76933 74
82	1.51491 89844 03	0.99132 87119 50	0.13140 54217 46	0.89300 14342 06
83	1.53339 36061 64	0.99336 11101 73	0.11503 78407 13	0.89253 58201 71
84	1.55186 82279 25	0.99512 24931 05	0.09864 69650 64	0.89213 13261 57
85	1.57034 28496 86	0.99661 28704 67	0.08223 61624 76	0.89178 83640 72
86	1.58881 74714 47	0.99783 22525 21	0.06580 87823 13	0.89150 72826 97
87	1.60729 20932 08	0.99878 06490 50	0.04936 81586 01	0.89128 83675 59
88	1.62576 67149 69	0.99945 80685 31	0.03291 76130 50	0.89113 18408 40
89	1.64424 13367 30	0.99986 45174 82	0.01646 04580 99	0.89103 78612 92
90	1.66271 59584 91	1.00000 00000 00	0.00000 00000 00	0.89100 65241 88

q = 0.01442 14412 80637 80   D(90) = 1.05939 89983 16669
q'= 0.09746 47524 70351 77   1/D(90) = 0.94393 14192 18773

r	ϕ	$E(\phi,k)$	$A(r)$	$D(r)$
45	0.81423 30492 10	0.79771 01397 78	0.70681 27170 69	1.02969 93210 00
46	0.83165 42812 29	0.81413 80499 94	0.71905 10891 16	1.03073 58187 90
47	0.84904 04937 50	0.83049 99810 57	0.73107 07702 15	1.03177 10542 01
48	0.86639 18208 74	0.84679 63176 10	0.74286 80788 86	1.03280 37659 54
49	0.88370 84384 83	0.86302 75211 02	0.75443 94005 14	1.03383 26958 46
50	0.90099 05637 78	0.87919 41283 00	0.76578 11885 03	1.03485 65902 79
51	0.91823 84547 72	0.89529 67497 49	0.77688 99654 23	1.03587 42017 88
52	0.93545 24097 43	0.91133 60681 52	0.78776 23241 22	1.03688 42905 62
53	0.95263 27666 41	0.92731 28367 17	0.79839 49288 38	1.03788 56259 53
54	0.96977 99024 60	0.94322 78774 39	0.80878 45162 71	1.03887 69879 77
55	0.98689 42325 72	0.95908 20793 51	0.81892 78966 53	1.03985 71688 00
56	1.00397 62100 22	0.97487 63967 30	0.82882 19547 81	1.04082 49742 07
57	1.02102 63247 94	0.99061 18472 72	0.83846 36510 40	1.04177 92250 63
58	1.03804 51030 43	1.00628 95102 43	0.84785 00223 98	1.04271 87587 42
59	1.05503 31062 90	1.02191 05245 99	0.85697 81833 79	1.04364 24305 51
60	1.07199 09305 98	1.03747 60870 95	0.86584 53270 17	1.04454 91151 19
61	1.08891 92057 13	1.05298 74503 74	0.87444 87257 80	1.04543 77077 72
62	1.10581 85941 85	1.06844 59210 43	0.88278 57324 78	1.04630 71258 76
63	1.12268 97904 56	1.08385 28577 51	0.89085 37811 37	1.04715 63101 58
64	1.13953 35199 34	1.09920 96692 51	0.89865 03878 54	1.04798 42259 97
65	1.15635 05380 42	1.11451 78124 66	0.90617 31516 31	1.04878 98646 84
66	1.17314 16292 41	1.12977 87905 59	0.91341 97551 71	1.04957 22446 48
67	1.18990 76060 47	1.14499 41510 00	0.92038 79656 59	1.05033 04126 59
68	1.20664 93080 18	1.16016 54836 48	0.92707 56355 09	1.05106 34449 83
69	1.22336 76007 31	1.17529 44188 33	0.93348 07030 88	1.05177 04485 09
70	1.24006 33747 40	1.19038 26254 52	0.93960 11934 13	1.05245 05618 41
71	1.25673 75445 26	1.20543 18090 77	0.94543 52188 14	1.05310 29563 43
72	1.27339 10474 26	1.22044 37100 73	0.95098 09795 77	1.05372 68371 50
73	1.29002 48425 56	1.23542 01017 32	0.95623 67645 52	1.05432 14441 37
74	1.30663 99097 23	1.25036 27884 19	0.96120 09517 34	1.05488 60528 47
75	1.32323 72483 18	1.26527 36037 37	0.96587 20088 16	1.05541 99753 70
76	1.33981 78762 13	1.28015 44087 04	0.97024 84937 11	1.05592 25611 83
77	1.35638 28286 40	1.29500 70899 44	0.97432 90550 41	1.05639 31979 43
78	1.37293 31570 65	1.30983 35578 99	0.97811 24326 04	1.05683 13122 35
79	1.38946 99280 54	1.32463 57450 52	0.98159 74578 00	1.05723 63702 66
80	1.40599 42221 39	1.33941 56041 68	0.98478 30540 34	1.05760 78785 18
81	1.42250 71326 63	1.35417 51065 44	0.98766 82370 86	1.05794 53843 51
82	1.43900 97646 42	1.36891 62402 80	0.99025 21154 45	1.05824 84765 52
83	1.45550 32335 99	1.38364 10085 56	0.99253 38906 18	1.05851 67858 37
84	1.47198 86644 16	1.39835 14279 29	0.99451 28574 06	1.05874 99853 02
85	1.48846 71901 63	1.41304 95266 32	0.99618 84041 41	1.05894 77908 18
86	1.50493 99509 37	1.42773 73428 86	0.99756 00129 05	1.05910 99613 82
87	1.52140 80926 98	1.44241 69232 27	0.99862 72597 00	1.05923 62994 06
88	1.53787 27660 92	1.45709 03208 31	0.99938 98145 99	1.05932 66509 63
89	1.55433 51252 87	1.47175 95938 49	0.99984 74418 59	1.05938 09059 67
90	1.57079 63267 95	1.48642 68037 44	1.00000 00000 00	1.05939 89983 17

K = 1.67005 94262 69580   E = 1.48029 26638 27039
K′ = 2.21319 46949 79374   E′ = 1.19204 56765 79886

r	u=(r/90)K=F(ϕ,k)	sn u	cn u	dn u
0	0.00000 00000 00	0.00000 00000 00	1.00000 00000 00	1.00000 00000 00
1	0.01855 62158 47	0.01855 49162 91	0.99982 78427 22	0.99996 20584 71
2	0.03711 24316 95	0.03710 20370 62	0.99931 14823 95	0.99984 82890 10
3	0.05566 86475 42	0.05563 35758 80	0.99845 12533 09	0.99965 88568 76
4	0.07422 48633 90	0.07414 17644 56	0.99724 77118 37	0.99939 40371 16
5	0.09278 10792 37	0.09261 88616 47	0.99570 16352 64	0.99905 42139 86
6	0.11133 72950 85	0.11105 71623 75	0.99381 40201 69	0.99863 98801 52
7	0.12989 35109 32	0.12944 90064 32	0.99158 60803 45	0.99815 16356 57
8	0.14844 97267 80	0.14778 67871 51	0.98901 92442 74	0.99759 01866 74
9	0.16700 59426 27	0.16606 29599 04	0.98611 51521 74	0.99695 63440 41
10	0.18556 21584 74	0.18427 00504 23	0.98287 56526 22	0.99625 10215 86
11	0.20411 83743 22	0.20240 06628 96	0.97930 27987 60	0.99547 52342 45
12	0.22267 45901 69	0.22044 74878 28	0.97539 88441 20	0.99463 00959 91
13	0.24123 08060 17	0.23840 33096 53	0.97116 62380 59	0.99371 68175 61
14	0.25978 70218 64	0.25626 10140 47	0.96660 76208 47	0.99273 67040 12
15	0.27834 32377 12	0.27401 35949 59	0.96172 58184 00	0.99169 11521 01
16	0.29689 94535 59	0.29165 41613 14	0.95652 38367 07	0.99058 16474 97
17	0.31545 56694 06	0.30917 59433 82	0.95100 48559 47	0.98940 97618 50
18	0.33401 18852 54	0.32657 22988 05	0.94517 22243 35	0.98817 71497 04
19	0.35256 81011 01	0.34383 67182 51	0.93902 94517 12	0.98688 55452 87
20	0.37112 43169 49	0.36096 28307 01	0.93258 02029 06	0.98553 67591 74
21	0.38968 05327 96	0.37794 44083 48	0.92582 82908 83	0.98413 26748 42
22	0.40823 67486 44	0.39477 53711 00	0.91877 76697 18	0.98267 52451 22
23	0.42679 29644 91	0.41144 97906 91	0.91143 24274 13	0.98116 64885 64
24	0.44534 91803 39	0.42796 18943 77	0.90379 67785 74	0.97960 84857 27
25	0.46390 53961 86	0.44430 60682 30	0.89587 50569 88	0.97800 33754 00
26	0.48246 16120 33	0.46047 68600 22	0.88767 17081 13	0.97635 33507 70
27	0.50101 78278 81	0.47646 89816 90	0.87919 12815 12	0.97466 06555 49
28	0.51957 40437 28	0.49227 73114 06	0.87043 84232 53	0.97292 75800 66
29	0.53813 02595 76	0.50789 68952 27	0.86141 78682 95	0.97115 64573 38
30	0.55668 64754 23	0.52332 29483 50	0.85213 44328 98	0.96934 96591 35
31	0.57524 26912 71	0.53855 08559 72	0.84259 30070 51	0.96750 95920 35
32	0.59379 89071 18	0.55357 61737 56	0.83279 85469 78	0.96563 86934 98
33	0.61235 51229 66	0.56839 46279 21	0.82275 60677 08	0.96373 94279 58
34	0.63091 13388 13	0.58300 21149 58	0.81247 06357 49	0.96181 42829 35
35	0.64946 75546 60	0.59739 47009 85	0.80194 73618 85	0.95986 57651 95
36	0.66802 37705 08	0.61156 86207 58	0.79119 13941 04	0.95789 63969 47
37	0.68657 99863 55	0.62552 02763 37	0.78020 79106 82	0.95590 87120 96
38	0.70513 62022 03	0.63924 62354 37	0.76900 21134 43	0.95390 52525 58
39	0.72369 24180 50	0.65274 32294 66	0.75757 92211 95	0.95188 85646 41
40	0.74224 86338 98	0.66600 81512 67	0.74594 44633 79	0.94986 11954 93
41	0.76080 48497 45	0.67903 80525 87	0.73410 30739 20	0.94782 56896 40
42	0.77936 10655 92	0.69183 01412 77	0.72206 02853 09	0.94578 45855 99
43	0.79791 72814 40	0.70438 17782 46	0.70982 13229 22	0.94374 04125 84
44	0.81647 34972 87	0.71669 04741 90	0.69739 13995 78	0.94169 56873 01
45	0.83502 97131 35	0.72875 38860 97	0.68477 57103 60	0.93965 29108 45

ELLIPTIC FUNCTIONS   TABLE $\theta = 28°$

q = 0.01555 61584 97708 09   D(90) = 1.06422 27448 65491
q' = 0.09342 26672 88483 19   1/D(90) = 0.93965 29108 44705

r	ϕ	$E(\phi,k)$	A(r)	D(r)
0	0.00000 00000 00	0.00000 00000 00	0.00000 00000 00	1.00000 00000 00
1	0.01855 59811 52	0.01855 57464 63	0.01743 55221 54	1.00001 95610 86
2	0.03711 05545 43	0.03710 86775 63	0.03486 57641 28	1.00007 82205 13
3	0.05566 23144 57	0.05565 59826 67	0.05228 54472 65	1.00017 59068 16
4	0.07420 98592 62	0.07419 48605 91	0.06968 92959 56	1.00031 25009 86
5	0.09275 17934 47	0.09272 25242 84	0.08707 20391 62	1.00048 78366 11
6	0.11128 67296 37	0.11123 62054 85	0.10442 84119 38	1.00070 17000 80
7	0.12981 42905 97	0.12973 31593 19	0.12175 31569 52	1.00095 38308 47
8	0.14833 01112 15	0.14821 06688 32	0.13904 10260 09	1.00124 39217 41
9	0.16683 58404 54	0.16666 60494 45	0.15628 67815 67	1.00157 16193 47
10	0.18532 91432 84	0.18509 66533 26	0.17348 51982 53	1.00193 65244 33
11	0.20380 87025 70	0.20349 98736 53	0.19063 10643 84	1.00233 81924 38
12	0.22227 32209 35	0.22187 31487 74	0.20771 91834 73	1.00277 61340 12
13	0.24072 14225 75	0.24021 39662 38	0.22474 43757 47	1.00324 98156 12
14	0.25915 20550 30	0.25851 98667 00	0.24170 14796 49	1.00375 86601 54
15	0.27756 38909 12	0.27678 84476 82	0.25858 53533 45	1.00430 20477 14
16	0.29595 57295 83	0.29501 73671 89	0.27539 08762 30	1.00487 93162 85
17	0.31432 63987 74	0.31320 43471 58	0.29211 29504 20	1.00548 97625 80
18	0.33267 47561 54	0.33134 71767 58	0.30874 65022 50	1.00613 26428 94
19	0.35099 96908 38	0.34944 37155 04	0.32528 64837 66	1.00680 71740 04
20	0.36930 01248 37	0.36749 18962 05	0.34172 78742 07	1.00751 25341 28
21	0.38757 50144 40	0.38548 97277 30	0.35806 56814 91	1.00824 78639 23
22	0.40582 33515 34	0.40343 52975 82	0.37429 49436 87	1.00901 22675 34
23	0.42404 41648 62	0.42132 67742 92	0.39041 07304 92	1.00980 48136 83
24	0.44223 65212 02	0.43916 24096 16	0.40640 81446 88	1.01062 45368 07
25	0.46039 95264 86	0.45694 05405 45	0.42228 23236 10	1.01147 04382 29
26	0.47853 23268 46	0.47465 95911 15	0.43802 84405 94	1.01234 14873 79
27	0.49663 41095 82	0.49231 80740 28	0.45364 17064 23	1.01323 66230 48
28	0.51470 41040 73	0.50991 45920 78	0.46911 73707 69	1.01415 47546 81
29	0.53274 15825 96	0.52744 78393 82	0.48445 07236 24	1.01509 47637 05
30	0.55074 58610 87	0.54491 66024 27	0.49963 70967 20	1.01605 55048 92
31	0.56871 62998 21	0.56231 97609 22	0.51467 18649 48	1.01703 58077 53
32	0.58665 23040 25	0.57965 62884 70	0.52955 04477 66	1.01803 44779 68
33	0.60455 33244 09	0.59692 52530 57	0.54426 83105 90	1.01905 02988 35
34	0.62241 88576 38	0.61412 58173 58	0.55882 09661 91	1.02008 20327 57
35	0.64024 84467 15	0.63125 72388 85	0.57320 39760 63	1.02112 84227 46
36	0.65804 16813 13	0.64831 88699 50	0.58741 29518 00	1.02218 81939 59
37	0.67579 81980 20	0.66531 01574 81	0.60144 35564 45	1.02326 00552 46
38	0.69351 76805 24	0.68223 06426 68	0.61529 15058 40	1.02434 27007 27
39	0.71119 98597 26	0.69907 99604 72	0.62895 25699 54	1.02543 48113 80
40	0.72884 45137 93	0.71585 78389 81	0.64242 25742 11	1.02653 50566 51
41	0.74645 14681 36	0.73256 40986 34	0.65569 74007 93	1.02764 20960 72
42	0.76402 05953 33	0.74919 86513 12	0.66877 29899 34	1.02875 45808 94
43	0.78155 18149 87	0.76576 14993 08	0.68164 53412 04	1.02987 11557 35
44	0.79904 50935 20	0.78225 27341 77	0.69431 05147 76	1.03099 04602 24
45	0.81650 04439 17	0.79867 25354 84	0.70676 46326 73	1.03211 11306 66

K = 1.67005 94262 69580   E = 1.48029 26638 27039
K'= 2.21319 46949 79374   E'= 1.19204 56765 79886

r	u=(r/90)K=F(ϕ,k)	sn u	cn u	dn u
45	0.83502 97131 35	0.72875 38860 97	0.68477 57103 60	0.93965 29108 45
46	0.85358 59289 82	0.74056 98135 63	0.67197 94276 90	0.93761 45656 88
47	0.87214 21448 30	0.75213 61949 29	0.65900 76966 75	0.93558 31127 77
48	0.89069 83606 77	0.76345 11032 47	0.64586 56307 25	0.93356 09887 32
49	0.90925 45765 25	0.77451 27421 05	0.63255 83074 45	0.93155 06031 44
50	0.92781 07923 72	0.78531 94413 24	0.61909 07648 15	0.92955 43359 90
51	0.94636 70082 19	0.79586 96525 38	0.60546 79976 42	0.92757 45351 48
52	0.96492 32240 67	0.80616 19446 80	0.59169 49543 05	0.92561 35140 16
53	0.98347 94399 14	0.81619 49993 86	0.57777 65337 71	0.92367 35492 49
54	1.00203 56557 62	0.82596 76063 36	0.56371 75829 12	0.92175 68785 87
55	1.02059 18716 09	0.83547 86585 41	0.54952 28940 83	0.91986 56988 04
56	1.03914 80874 57	0.84472 71476 04	0.53519 72030 01	0.91800 21637 48
57	1.05770 43033 04	0.85371 21589 50	0.52074 51868 82	0.91616 83824 95
58	1.07626 05191 52	0.86243 28670 60	0.50617 14628 60	0.91436 64175 89
59	1.09481 67349 99	0.87088 85307 06	0.49148 05866 81	0.91259 82833 95
60	1.11337 29508 46	0.87907 84882 08	0.47667 70516 50	0.91086 59445 42
61	1.13192 91666 94	0.88700 21527 29	0.46176 52878 41	0.90917 13144 54
62	1.15048 53825 41	0.89465 90076 05	0.44674 96615 69	0.90751 62539 84
63	1.16904 15983 89	0.90204 86017 44	0.43163 44750 97	0.90590 25701 23
64	1.18759 78142 36	0.90917 05450 83	0.41642 39665 92	0.90433 20148 01
65	1.20615 40300 84	0.91602 45041 30	0.40112 23103 15	0.90280 62837 70
66	1.22471 02459 31	0.92261 01975 87	0.38573 36170 32	0.90132 70155 61
67	1.24326 64617 78	0.92892 73920 75	0.37026 19346 53	0.89989 57905 21
68	1.26182 26776 26	0.93497 58979 67	0.35471 12490 75	0.89851 41299 14
69	1.28037 88934 73	0.94075 55653 32	0.33908 54852 36	0.89718 34951 02
70	1.29893 51093 21	0.94626 62799 99	0.32338 85083 56	0.89590 52867 79
71	1.31749 13251 68	0.95150 79597 60	0.30762 41253 77	0.89468 08442 74
72	1.33604 75410 16	0.95648 05506 97	0.29179 60865 72	0.89351 14449 10
73	1.35460 37568 63	0.96118 40236 63	0.27590 80873 31	0.89239 83034 17
74	1.37315 99727 11	0.96561 83709 07	0.25996 37701 04	0.89134 25713 97
75	1.39171 61885 58	0.96978 36028 51	0.24396 67265 03	0.89034 53368 40
76	1.41027 24044 05	0.97367 97450 32	0.22792 04995 46	0.88940 76236 84
77	1.42882 86202 53	0.97730 68352 04	0.21182 85860 40	0.88853 03914 11
78	1.44738 48361 00	0.98066 49206 08	0.19569 44390 83	0.88771 45346 98
79	1.46594 10519 48	0.98375 40554 21	0.17952 14707 00	0.88696 08830 89
80	1.48449 72677 95	0.98657 42983 71	0.16331 30545 74	0.88627 02007 11
81	1.50305 34836 43	0.98912 57105 37	0.14707 25288 90	0.88564 31860 20
82	1.52160 96994 90	0.99140 83533 35	0.13080 31992 64	0.88508 04715 74
83	1.54016 59153 38	0.99342 22866 77	0.11450 83417 63	0.88458 26238 39
84	1.55872 21311 85	0.99516 75673 30	0.09819 12059 97	0.88415 01430 17
85	1.57727 83470 32	0.99664 42474 54	0.08185 50182 76	0.88378 34628 97
86	1.59583 45628 80	0.99785 23733 39	0.06550 29848 34	0.88348 29507 36
87	1.61439 07787 27	0.99879 19843 27	0.04913 82950 97	0.88324 89071 50
88	1.63294 69945 75	0.99946 31119 32	0.03276 41249 92	0.88308 15660 37
89	1.65150 32104 22	0.99986 57791 58	0.01638 36402 95	0.88298 10945 11
90	1.67005 94262 70	1.00000 00000 00	0.00000 00000 00	0.88294 75928 59

q = 0.01555 61584 97708 09   D(90) = 1.06422 27448 65491
q' = 0.09342 26672 88483 19   1/D(90) = 0.93965 29108 44705

r	φ	E(φ,k)	A(r)	D(r)
45	0.81650 04439 17	0.79867 25354 84	0.70676 46326 73	1.03211 11306 66
46	0.83391 79254 05	0.81502 11694 45	0.71900 38800 07	1.03323 18016 97
47	0.85129 76430 79	0.83129 89874 73	0.73102 45062 03	1.03435 11079 51
48	0.86863 97474 81	0.84750 64246 41	0.74282 28261 94	1.03546 76857 22
49	0.88594 44341 19	0.86364 39980 61	0.75439 52216 16	1.03658 01746 27
50	0.90321 19429 45	0.87971 23051 91	0.76573 81419 74	1.03768 72192 62
51	0.92044 25577 78	0.89571 20220 76	0.77684 81057 92	1.03878 74708 54
52	0.93763 66056 90	0.91164 39015 27	0.78772 17017 49	1.03987 95889 05
53	0.95479 44563 43	0.92750 87712 53	0.79835 55897 88	1.04096 22428 24
54	0.97191 65212 87	0.94330 75319 36	0.80874 65022 15	1.04203 41135 47
55	0.98900 32532 19	0.95904 11552 76	0.81889 12447 67	1.04309 38951 49
56	1.00605 51452 06	0.97471 06819 91	0.82878 66976 70	1.04414 02964 30
57	1.02307 27298 66	0.99031 72197 98	0.83842 98166 66	1.04517 20424 91
58	1.04005 65785 29	1.00586 19413 59	0.84781 76340 26	1.04618 78762 85
59	1.05700 73003 50	1.02134 60822 17	0.85694 72595 33	1.04718 65601 52
60	1.07392 55414 05	1.03677 09387 11	0.86581 58814 53	1.04816 68773 24
61	1.09081 19837 55	1.05213 78658 89	0.87442 07674 68	1.04912 76334 11
62	1.10766 73444 77	1.06744 82754 05	0.88275 92655 98	1.05006 76578 51
63	1.12449 23746 85	1.08270 36334 23	0.89082 88050 92	1.05098 58053 41
64	1.14128 78585 12	1.09790 54585 20	0.89862 68972 95	1.05188 09572 32
65	1.15805 46120 82	1.11305 53195 90	0.90615 11364 90	1.05275 20228 88
66	1.17479 34824 56	1.12815 48337 63	0.91339 92007 14	1.05359 79410 21
67	1.19150 53465 61	1.14320 56643 27	0.92036 88525 49	1.05441 76809 78
68	1.20819 11101 02	1.15820 95186 71	0.92705 79398 82	1.05521 02440 03
69	1.22485 17064 62	1.17316 81462 35	0.93346 43966 42	1.05597 46644 48
70	1.24148 80955 74	1.18808 33364 80	0.93958 62435 07	1.05671 00109 54
71	1.25810 12627 98	1.20295 69168 76	0.94542 15885 84	1.05741 53875 84
72	1.27469 22177 73	1.21779 07509 11	0.95096 86280 59	1.05808 99349 15
73	1.29126 19932 57	1.23258 67361 17	0.95622 56468 18	1.05873 28310 86
74	1.30781 16439 67	1.24734 68021 16	0.96119 10190 40	1.05934 32927 98
75	1.32434 22453 98	1.26207 29086 92	0.96586 32087 59	1.05992 05762 68
76	1.34085 48926 43	1.27676 70438 81	0.97024 07703 96	1.06046 39781 39
77	1.35735 06991 93	1.29143 12220 78	0.97432 23492 61	1.06097 28363 34
78	1.37383 07957 49	1.30606 74821 75	0.97810 66820 26	1.06144 65308 61
79	1.39029 63290 04	1.32067 78857 14	0.98159 25971 59	1.06188 44845 73
80	1.40674 84604 42	1.33526 45150 56	0.98477 90153 38	1.06228 61638 70
81	1.42318 83651 15	1.34982 94715 73	0.98766 49498 26	1.06265 10793 45
82	1.43961 72304 26	1.36437 48738 63	0.99024 95068 14	1.06297 87863 88
83	1.45603 62549 02	1.37890 28559 72	0.99253 18857 35	1.06326 88857 19
84	1.47244 66469 66	1.39341 55656 38	0.99451 13795 47	1.06352 10238 83
85	1.48884 96237 10	1.40791 51625 46	0.99618 73749 75	1.06373 48936 74
86	1.50524 64096 56	1.42240 38165 98	0.99755 93527 30	1.06391 02345 14
87	1.52163 82355 22	1.43688 37061 94	0.99862 68876 91	1.06404 68327 66
88	1.53802 63369 87	1.45135 70165 21	0.99938 96490 51	1.06414 45220 00
89	1.55441 19534 52	1.46582 59378 47	0.99984 74004 40	1.06420 31831 91
90	1.57079 63267 95	1.48029 26638 27	1.00000 00000 00	1.06422 27448 65

113

K = 1.67773 48840 80745   E = 1.47396 98872 41625
K′= 2.18421 32169 49248   E′= 1.20153 81841 13662

r	u=(r/90)K=F(φ,k)	sn u	cn u	dn u
0	0.00000 00000 00	0.00000 00000 00	1.00000 00000 00	1.00000 00000 00
1	0.01864 14987 12	0.01864 01653 57	0.99982 62570 24	0.99995 91661 01
2	0.03728 29974 24	0.03727 23325 39	0.99930 51452 02	0.99983 67244 85
3	0.05592 44961 36	0.05588 85131 44	0.99843 70155 89	0.99963 28552 64
4	0.07456 59948 48	0.07448 07382 84	0.99722 24524 27	0.99934 78581 93
5	0.09320 74935 60	0.09304 10682 63	0.99566 22718 66	0.99898 21520 23
6	0.11184 89922 72	0.11156 16021 62	0.99375 75201 84	0.99853 62735 92
7	0.13049 04909 84	0.13003 44873 02	0.99150 94715 19	0.99801 08766 78
8	0.14913 19896 96	0.14845 19285 49	0.98891 96251 01	0.99740 67305 91
9	0.16777 34884 08	0.16680 61974 42	0.98598 97020 23	0.99672 47185 30
10	0.18641 49871 20	0.18508 96411 04	0.98272 16415 42	0.99596 58357 03
11	0.20505 64858 32	0.20329 46909 22	0.97911 75969 43	0.99513 11872 20
12	0.22369 79845 44	0.22141 38709 60	0.97517 99309 60	0.99422 19857 61
13	0.24233 94832 56	0.23943 98060 82	0.97091 12108 03	0.99323 95490 41
14	0.26098 09819 68	0.25736 52297 72	0.96631 42027 85	0.99218 52970 62
15	0.27962 24806 80	0.27518 29916 13	0.96139 18665 80	0.99106 07491 87
16	0.29826 39793 92	0.29288 60644 24	0.95614 73491 39	0.98986 75210 20
17	0.31690 54781 04	0.31046 75510 14	0.95058 39782 82	0.98860 73211 24
18	0.33554 69768 16	0.32792 06905 68	0.94470 52559 91	0.98728 19475 84
19	0.35418 84755 28	0.34523 88646 11	0.93851 48514 34	0.98589 32844 14
20	0.37282 99742 40	0.36241 56025 78	0.93201 65937 41	0.98444 32978 41
21	0.39147 14729 52	0.37944 45869 49	0.92521 44645 62	0.98293 40324 67
22	0.41011 29716 64	0.39631 96579 54	0.91811 25904 37	0.98136 76073 19
23	0.42875 44703 76	0.41303 48178 38	0.91071 52349 96	0.97974 62118 09
24	0.44739 59690 88	0.42958 42346 85	0.90302 67910 26	0.97807 21016 13
25	0.46603 74678 00	0.44596 22457 84	0.89505 17724 33	0.97634 75944 79
26	0.48467 89665 12	0.46216 33605 62	0.88679 48061 16	0.97457 50659 85
27	0.50332 04652 24	0.47818 22630 49	0.87826 06237 93	0.97275 69452 47
28	0.52196 19639 36	0.49401 38139 16	0.86945 40537 95	0.97089 57106 06
29	0.54060 34626 48	0.50965 30520 54	0.86038 00128 62	0.96899 38852 90
30	0.55924 49613 60	0.52509 51957 23	0.85104 34979 65	0.96705 40330 78
31	0.57788 64600 72	0.54033 56432 78	0.84144 95781 71	0.96507 87539 62
32	0.59652 79587 84	0.55536 99734 56	0.83160 33865 87	0.96307 06798 34
33	0.61516 94574 96	0.57019 39452 71	0.82151 01124 01	0.96103 24701 96
34	0.63381 09562 08	0.58480 34974 92	0.81117 49930 33	0.95896 68079 09
35	0.65245 24549 20	0.59919 47477 43	0.80060 33064 36	0.95687 63949 95
36	0.67109 39536 32	0.61336 39912 29	0.78980 03635 50	0.95476 39484 88
37	0.68973 54523 44	0.62730 76990 89	0.77877 15009 31	0.95263 21963 59
38	0.70837 69510 56	0.64102 25164 23	0.76752 20735 84	0.95048 38735 07
39	0.72701 84497 68	0.65450 52599 69	0.75605 74479 97	0.94832 17178 36
40	0.74565 99484 80	0.66775 29154 90	0.74438 29954 09	0.94614 84664 21
41	0.76430 14471 92	0.68076 26348 43	0.73250 40853 14	0.94396 68517 61
42	0.78294 29459 04	0.69353 17327 88	0.72042 60792 17	0.94177 95981 40
43	0.80158 44446 16	0.70605 76835 31	0.70815 43246 54	0.93958 94180 83
44	0.82022 59433 28	0.71833 81170 24	0.69569 41494 87	0.93739 90089 32
45	0.83886 74420 40	0.73037 08150 45	0.68305 08564 75	0.93521 10495 17

114

q = 0.01673 95077 33022 71   D(90) = 1.06927 73577 85771
q'= 0.08953 58769 52552 59   1/D(90) = 0.93521 10495 17378

r	ϕ	$E(\phi,k)$	$A(r)$	$D(r)$
0	0.00000 00000 00	0.00000 00000 00	0.00000 00000 00	1.00000 00000 00
1	0.01864 12449 65	0.01864 09912 23	0.01743 28564 42	1.00002 11005 51
2	0.03728 09678 92	0.03727 89385 59	0.03486 04383 85	1.00008 43765 00
3	0.05591 76489 86	0.05591 08033 44	0.05227 74728 42	1.00018 97507 57
4	0.07454 97729 20	0.07453 35573 42	0.06967 86898 39	1.00033 70949 48
5	0.09317 58310 71	0.09314 41879 29	0.08705 88239 30	1.00052 62295 67
6	0.11179 43237 20	0.11173 97032 16	0.10441 26157 03	1.00075 69241 94
7	0.13040 37622 49	0.13031 71371 28	0.12173 48132 83	1.00102 88977 81
8	0.14900 26713 06	0.14887 35544 02	0.13902 01738 43	1.00134 18189 87
9	0.16758 95909 47	0.16740 60554 92	0.15626 34651 06	1.00169 53065 86
10	0.18616 30787 35	0.18591 17813 79	0.17345 94668 49	1.00208 89299 31
11	0.20472 17118 16	0.20438 79182 69	0.19060 29724 05	1.00252 22094 79
12	0.22326 40889 43	0.22283 17021 49	0.20768 87901 61	1.00299 46173 73
13	0.24178 88324 57	0.24124 04232 25	0.22471 17450 58	1.00350 55780 86
14	0.26029 45902 23	0.25961 14301 89	0.24166 66800 88	1.00405 44691 24
15	0.27878 00375 05	0.27794 21343 42	0.25854 84577 83	1.00464 06217 80
16	0.29724 38787 95	0.29623 00135 34	0.27535 19617 08	1.00526 33219 53
17	0.31568 48495 71	0.31447 26159 37	0.29207 20979 49	1.00592 18110 16
18	0.33410 17180 05	0.33266 75636 19	0.30870 37965 96	1.00661 52867 38
19	0.35249 32865 92	0.35081 25559 36	0.32524 20132 25	1.00734 29042 65
20	0.37085 83937 19	0.36890 53727 15	0.34168 17303 72	1.00810 37771 48
21	0.38919 59151 65	0.38694 38772 35	0.35801 79590 10	1.00889 69784 20
22	0.40750 47655 24	0.40492 60189 97	0.37424 57400 16	1.00972 15417 28
23	0.42578 38995 51	0.42284 98362 87	0.39036 01456 31	1.01057 64625 12
24	0.44403 23134 42	0.44071 34585 12	0.40635 62809 27	1.01146 06992 22
25	0.46224 90460 25	0.45851 51083 30	0.42222 92852 52	1.01237 31745 95
26	0.48043 31798 84	0.47625 31035 56	0.43797 43336 84	1.01331 27769 60
27	0.49858 38423 87	0.49392 58588 50	0.45358 66384 70	1.01427 83615 97
28	0.51670 02066 56	0.51153 18871 90	0.46906 14504 62	1.01526 87521 30
29	0.53478 14924 33	0.52906 98011 29	0.48439 40605 47	1.01628 27419 59
30	0.55282 69668 84	0.54653 83138 38	0.49957 98010 66	1.01731 90957 32
31	0.57083 59453 13	0.56393 62399 42	0.51461 40472 30	1.01837 65508 49
32	0.58880 77917 94	0.58126 24961 45	0.52949 22185 29	1.01945 38189 97
33	0.60674 19197 27	0.59851 61016 62	0.54420 97801 22	1.02054 95877 26
34	0.62463 77923 15	0.61569 61784 46	0.55876 22442 35	1.02166 25220 41
35	0.64249 49229 57	0.63280 19512 30	0.57314 51715 34	1.02279 12660 33
36	0.66031 28755 69	0.64983 27473 82	0.58735 41724 99	1.02393 44445 30
37	0.67809 12648 25	0.66678 79965 83	0.60138 49087 82	1.02509 06647 70
38	0.69582 97563 23	0.68366 72303 38	0.61523 30945 59	1.02625 85181 00
39	0.71352 80666 78	0.70047 00813 12	0.62889 44978 64	1.02743 65816 91
40	0.73118 59635 41	0.71719 62825 26	0.64236 49419 18	1.02862 34202 73
41	0.74880 32655 48	0.73384 56663 90	0.65564 03064 44	1.02981 75878 80
42	0.76637 98422 06	0.75041 81636 09	0.66871 65289 69	1.03101 76296 17
43	0.78391 56136 99	0.76691 38019 43	0.68158 96061 09	1.03222 20834 27
44	0.80141 05506 40	0.78333 27048 58	0.69425 55948 49	1.03342 94818 77
45	0.81886 46737 61	0.79967 50900 51	0.70671 06138 01	1.03463 83539 41

K = 1.67773 48840 80745   E = 1.47396 98872 41625
K' = 2.18421 32169 49248   E' = 1.20153 81841 13662

r	u=(r/90)K=F(φ,k)	sn u	cn u	dn u
45	0.83886 74420 40	0.73037 08150 45	0.68305 08564 75	0.93521 10495 17
46	0.85750 89407 52	0.74215 37070 75	0.67022 97181 37	0.93302 81969 64
47	0.87615 04394 64	0.75368 48659 90	0.65723 59719 13	0.93085 30835 98
48	0.89479 19381 76	0.76496 25035 84	0.64407 48156 16	0.92868 83139 82
49	0.91343 34368 88	0.77598 49659 42	0.63075 14031 95	0.92653 64620 67
50	0.93207 49356 00	0.78675 07286 94	0.61727 08407 98	0.92440 00684 67
51	0.95071 64343 12	0.79725 83921 44	0.60363 81831 49	0.92228 16378 55
52	0.96935 79330 24	0.80750 66763 13	0.58985 84302 27	0.92018 36364 80
53	0.98799 94317 36	0.81749 44159 01	0.57593 65242 54	0.91810 84898 05
54	1.00664 09304 48	0.82722 05551 96	0.56187 73469 90	0.91605 85802 64
55	1.02528 24291 60	0.83668 41429 30	0.54768 57173 32	0.91403 62451 35
56	1.04392 39278 72	0.84588 43271 14	0.53336 63892 14	0.91204 37745 35
57	1.06256 54265 84	0.85482 03498 61	0.51892 40498 02	0.91008 34095 24
58	1.08120 69252 96	0.86349 15422 10	0.50436 33179 88	0.90815 73403 21
59	1.09984 84240 08	0.87189 73189 66	0.48968 87431 63	0.90626 77046 29
60	1.11848 99227 20	0.88003 71735 76	0.47490 48042 77	0.90441 65860 68
61	1.13713 14214 33	0.88791 06730 43	0.46001 59091 78	0.90260 60127 07
62	1.15577 29201 45	0.89551 74529 02	0.44502 63942 16	0.90083 79557 00
63	1.17441 44188 57	0.90285 72122 61	0.42994 05241 06	0.89911 43280 07
64	1.19305 59175 69	0.90992 97089 24	0.41476 24920 58	0.89743 69832 21
65	1.21169 74162 81	0.91673 47546 04	0.39949 64201 36	0.89580 77144 71
66	1.23033 89149 93	0.92327 22102 36	0.38414 63598 77	0.89422 82534 15
67	1.24898 04137 05	0.92954 19814 02	0.36871 62931 20	0.89270 02693 12
68	1.26762 19124 17	0.93554 40138 74	0.35321 01330 72	0.89122 53681 66
69	1.28626 34111 29	0.94127 82892 86	0.33763 17255 80	0.88980 50919 49
70	1.30490 49098 41	0.94674 48209 40	0.32198 48506 10	0.88844 09178 85
71	1.32354 64085 53	0.95194 36497 55	0.30627 32239 20	0.88713 42578 01
72	1.34218 79072 65	0.95687 48403 66	0.29050 04989 21	0.88588 64575 41
73	1.36082 94059 77	0.96153 84773 82	0.27467 02687 13	0.88469 87964 29
74	1.37947 09046 89	0.96593 46617 96	0.25878 60682 89	0.88357 24867 89
75	1.39811 24034 01	0.97006 35075 79	0.24285 13769 03	0.88250 86735 16
76	1.41675 39021 13	0.97392 51384 26	0.22686 96205 81	0.88150 84336 86
77	1.43539 54008 25	0.97751 96846 93	0.21084 41747 77	0.88057 27762 09
78	1.45403 68995 37	0.98084 72805 12	0.19477 83671 54	0.87970 26415 28
79	1.47267 83982 49	0.98390 80610 85	0.17867 54805 01	0.87889 89013 43
80	1.49131 98969 61	0.98670 21601 69	0.16253 87557 42	0.87816 23583 72
81	1.50996 13956 73	0.98922 97077 55	0.14637 13950 74	0.87749 37461 47
82	1.52860 28943 85	0.99149 08279 35	0.13017 65651 76	0.87689 37288 22
83	1.54724 43930 97	0.99348 56369 70	0.11395 74005 25	0.87636 29010 25
84	1.56588 58918 09	0.99521 42415 52	0.09771 70067 74	0.87590 17877 17
85	1.58452 73905 21	0.99667 67372 67	0.08145 84642 09	0.87551 08440 81
86	1.60316 88892 33	0.99787 32072 63	0.06518 48312 59	0.87519 04554 24
87	1.62181 03879 45	0.99880 37211 18	0.04889 91480 64	0.87494 09370 99
88	1.64045 18866 57	0.99946 83339 09	0.03260 44400 76	0.87476 25344 43
89	1.65909 33853 69	0.99986 70854 96	0.01630 37217 10	0.87465 54227 31
90	1.67773 48840 81	1.00000 00000 00	0.00000 00000 00	0.87461 97071 39

q = 0.01673 95077 33022 71   D(90) = 1.06927 73577 85771
q'= 0.08953 58769 52552 59   1/D(90) = 0.93521 10495 17378

r	ϕ	$E(\phi, k)$	A(r)	D(r)
45	0.81886 46737 61	0.79967 50900 51	0.70671 06138 01	1.03463 83539 41
46	0.83627 80535 29	0.81594 12678 74	0.71895 08444 49	1.03584 72267 96
47	0.85365 08097 20	0.83213 16396 55	0.73097 25323 83	1.03705 46276 17
48	0.87098 31109 27	0.84824 66959 33	0.74277 19885 08	1.03825 90853 66
49	0.88827 51740 14	0.86428 70146 06	0.75434 55902 51	1.03945 91325 90
50	0.90552 72635 19	0.88025 32590 08	0.76568 97827 31	1.04065 33072 06
51	0.92273 96910 12	0.89614 61759 22	0.77680 10799 33	1.04184 01542 84
52	0.93991 28143 99	0.91196 65935 24	0.78767 60658 46	1.04301 82278 18
53	0.95704 70371 85	0.92771 54192 86	0.79831 13955 94	1.04418 60924 88
54	0.97414 28076 88	0.94339 36378 31	0.80870 37965 41	1.04534 23254 12
55	0.99120 06182 25	0.95900 23087 46	0.81885 00693 80	1.04648 55178 73
56	1.00822 10042 45	0.97454 25643 71	0.82874 70891 98	1.04761 42770 42
57	1.02520 45434 31	0.99001 56075 56	0.83839 18065 23	1.04872 72276 73
58	1.04215 18547 77	1.00542 27094 05	0.84778 12483 47	1.04982 30137 76
59	1.05906 35976 14	1.02076 52070 02	0.85691 25191 30	1.05090 03002 74
60	1.07594 04706 24	1.03604 45011 32	0.86578 28017 79	1.05195 77746 25
61	1.09278 32108 16	1.05126 20539 95	0.87438 93585 98	1.05299 41484 25
62	1.10959 25924 73	1.06641 93869 21	0.88272 95322 30	1.05400 81589 75
63	1.12636 94260 86	1.08151 80780 98	0.89080 07465 56	1.05499 85708 21
64	1.14311 45572 54	1.09655 97602 96	0.89860 05075 79	1.05596 41772 61
65	1.15982 88655 69	1.11154 61186 15	0.90612 64042 85	1.05690 38018 11
66	1.17651 32634 75	1.12647 88882 41	0.91337 61094 67	1.05781 62996 45
67	1.19316 86951 20	1.14135 98522 22	0.92034 73805 38	1.05870 05589 81
68	1.20979 61351 78	1.15619 08392 67	0.92703 80602 96	1.05955 55024 46
69	1.22639 65876 69	1.17097 37215 65	0.93344 60776 87	1.06038 00883 81
70	1.24297 10847 52	1.18571 04126 27	0.93956 94485 14	1.06117 33121 13
71	1.25952 06855 18	1.20040 28651 59	0.94540 62761 39	1.06193 42071 82
72	1.27604 64747 59	1.21505 30689 52	0.95095 47521 42	1.06266 18465 12
73	1.29254 95617 41	1.22966 30488 13	0.95621 31569 56	1.06335 53435 47
74	1.30903 10789 49	1.24423 48625 09	0.96117 98604 73	1.06401 38533 30
75	1.32549 21808 46	1.25877 05987 50	0.96585 33226 16	1.06463 65735 30
76	1.34193 40426 00	1.27327 23751 95	0.97023 20938 85	1.06522 27454 21
77	1.35835 78588 26	1.28774 23364 87	0.97431 48158 68	1.06577 16548 08
78	1.37476 48423 06	1.30218 26523 16	0.97810 02217 23	1.06628 26328 96
79	1.39115 62227 23	1.31659 55155 06	0.98158 71366 27	1.06675 50571 05
80	1.40753 32453 50	1.33098 31401 27	0.98477 44781 94	1.06718 83518 30
81	1.42389 71697 92	1.34534 77596 38	0.98766 12568 58	1.06758 19891 40
82	1.44024 92686 79	1.35969 16250 40	0.99024 65762 30	1.06793 54894 22
83	1.45659 08263 72	1.37401 70030 65	0.99252 96334 14	1.06824 84219 68
84	1.47292 31376 69	1.38832 61743 70	0.99450 97192 95	1.06852 04054 98
85	1.48924 75065 04	1.40262 14317 64	0.99618 62187 91	1.06875 11086 22
86	1.50556 52446 45	1.41690 50784 34	0.99755 86110 78	1.06894 02502 50
87	1.52187 76703 90	1.43117 94262 00	0.99862 64697 68	1.06908 75999 28
88	1.53818 61072 64	1.44544 67937 72	0.99938 94630 72	1.06919 29781 24
89	1.55449 18827 13	1.45970 95050 17	0.99984 73539 10	1.06925 62564 43
90	1.57079 63267 95	1.47396 98872 42	1.00000 00000 00	1.06927 73577 86

K = 1.68575 03548 12596
K' = 2.15651 56474 99643

E = 1.46746 22093 39427
E' = 1.21105 60275 68459

r	u=(r/90)K=F(ϕ,k)	sn u	cn u	dn u
0	0.00000 00000 00	0.00000 00000 00	1.00000 00000 00	1.00000 00000 00
1	0.01873 05594 98	0.01872 91905 62	0.99982 45933 27	0.99995 61512 16
2	0.03746 11189 96	0.03745 01696 09	0.99929 84963 44	0.99982 46702 29
3	0.05619 16784 94	0.05615 47361 35	0.99842 20778 86	0.99960 57529 86
4	0.07492 22379 92	0.07483 47101 10	0.99719 59517 38	0.99929 97255 78
5	0.09365 27974 90	0.09348 19428 89	0.99562 09752 48	0.99890 70435 17
6	0.11238 33569 88	0.11208 83275 04	0.99369 82473 76	0.99842 82907 20
7	0.13111 39164 85	0.13064 58088 30	0.99142 91062 07	0.99786 41782 12
8	0.14984 44759 83	0.14914 63935 73	0.98881 51259 38	0.99721 55425 59
9	0.16857 50354 81	0.16758 21600 60	0.98585 81133 36	0.99648 33440 19
10	0.18730 55949 79	0.18594 52677 91	0.98256 01037 02	0.99566 86644 39
11	0.20603 61544 77	0.20422 79667 31	0.97892 33563 49	0.99477 27048 94
12	0.22476 67139 75	0.22242 26063 08	0.97495 03496 09	0.99379 67830 75
13	0.24349 72734 73	0.24052 16440 96	0.97064 37753 99	0.99274 23304 57
14	0.26222 78329 71	0.25851 76541 49	0.96600 65333 59	0.99161 08892 22
15	0.28095 83924 69	0.27640 33349 70	0.96104 17245 97	0.99040 41089 90
16	0.29968 89519 67	0.29417 15170 95	0.95575 26450 55	0.98912 37433 37
17	0.31841 95114 65	0.31181 51702 59	0.95014 27785 32	0.98777 16461 30
18	0.33715 00709 63	0.32932 74101 49	0.94421 57893 85	0.98634 97676 95
19	0.35588 06304 60	0.34670 15047 04	0.93797 55149 45	0.98486 01508 13
20	0.37461 11899 58	0.36393 08799 62	0.93142 59576 64	0.98330 49265 88
21	0.39334 17494 56	0.38100 91254 49	0.92457 12770 38	0.98168 63101 73
22	0.41207 23089 54	0.39792 99990 81	0.91741 57813 29	0.98000 65963 85
23	0.43080 28684 52	0.41468 74315 91	0.90996 39191 09	0.97826 81552 21
24	0.44953 34279 50	0.43127 55304 66	0.90222 02706 77	0.97647 34272 91
25	0.46826 39874 48	0.44768 85833 92	0.89418 95393 60	0.97462 49191 74
26	0.48699 45469 46	0.46392 10612 13	0.88587 65427 32	0.97272 51987 28
27	0.50572 51064 44	0.47996 76203 96	0.87728 62037 96	0.97077 68903 53
28	0.52445 56659 42	0.49582 31050 10	0.86842 35421 37	0.96878 26702 28
29	0.54318 62254 40	0.51148 25482 27	0.85929 36650 87	0.96674 52615 42
30	0.56191 67849 38	0.52694 11733 44	0.84990 17589 32	0.96466 74297 18
31	0.58064 73444 35	0.54219 43943 41	0.84025 30801 76	0.96255 19776 54
32	0.59937 79039 33	0.55723 78159 85	0.83035 29469 06	0.96040 17409 96
33	0.61810 84634 31	0.57206 72334 88	0.82020 67302 63	0.95821 95834 42
34	0.63683 90229 29	0.58667 86317 33	0.80981 98460 57	0.95600 83921 01
35	0.65556 95824 27	0.60106 81840 83	0.79919 77465 45	0.95377 10729 10
36	0.67430 01419 25	0.61523 22507 93	0.78834 59123 91	0.95151 05461 30
37	0.69303 07014 23	0.62916 73770 33	0.77726 98448 27	0.94922 97419 06
38	0.71176 12609 21	0.64287 02905 40	0.76597 50580 41	0.94693 15959 38
39	0.73049 18204 19	0.65633 78989 29	0.75446 70717 99	0.94461 90452 28
40	0.74922 23799 17	0.66956 72866 67	0.74275 14043 24	0.94229 50239 48
41	0.76795 29394 15	0.68255 57117 39	0.73083 35654 39	0.93996 24594 06
42	0.78668 34989 13	0.69530 06020 16	0.71871 90500 02	0.93762 42681 42
43	0.80541 40584 10	0.70779 95513 65	0.70641 33316 17	0.93528 33521 30
44	0.82414 46179 08	0.72005 03154 93	0.69392 18566 66	0.93294 25951 20
45	0.84287 51774 06	0.73205 08075 69	0.68125 00386 33	0.93060 48591 02

q = 0.01797 23870 08967 24

q' = 0.08579 57337 02194 77

D(90) = 1.07456 99318 23542

1/D(90) = 0.93060 48591 02100

r	ϕ	$E(\phi,k)$	A(r)	D(r)
0	0.00000 00000 00	0.00000 00000 00	0.00000 00000 00	1.00000 00000 00
1	0.01873 02857 14	0.01873 00119 36	0.01742 98716 10	1.00002 27124 67
2	0.03745 89292 11	0.03745 67396 56	0.03485 44750 85	1.00009 08221 97
3	0.05618 42907 23	0.05617 69047 00	0.05226 85437 81	1.00020 42462 15
4	0.07490 47353 71	0.07488 72401 07	0.06966 68140 38	1.00036 28463 40
5	0.09361 86355 99	0.09358 44961 22	0.08704 40266 71	1.00056 64293 58
6	0.11232 43735 83	0.11226 54458 45	0.10439 49284 62	1.00081 47472 49
7	0.13102 03436 35	0.13092 68908 22	0.12171 42736 48	1.00110 74974 98
8	0.14970 49545 57	0.14956 56665 45	0.13899 68254 13	1.00144 43234 57
9	0.16837 66319 87	0.16817 86478 47	0.15623 73573 76	1.00182 48147 84
10	0.18703 38206 88	0.18676 27541 94	0.17343 06550 77	1.00224 85079 39
11	0.20567 49868 09	0.20531 49548 28	0.19057 15174 67	1.00271 48867 52
12	0.22429 86200 90	0.22383 22737 85	0.20765 47583 91	1.00322 33830 49
13	0.24290 32360 26	0.24231 17947 33	0.22467 52080 71	1.00377 33773 45
14	0.26148 73779 62	0.26075 06656 57	0.24162 77145 88	1.00436 41995 99
15	0.28004 96191 43	0.27914 61033 52	0.25850 71453 63	1.00499 51300 30
16	0.29858 85646 89	0.29749 53977 22	0.27530 83886 34	1.00566 53999 92
17	0.31710 28535 16	0.31579 59158 79	0.29202 63549 30	1.00637 41929 15
18	0.33559 11601 66	0.33404 51060 30	0.30865 59785 45	1.00712 06452 93
19	0.35405 21965 90	0.35224 05011 42	0.32519 22190 08	1.00790 38477 42
20	0.37248 47138 32	0.37037 97223 77	0.34163 00625 47	1.00872 28461 02
21	0.39088 75036 47	0.38846 04823 04	0.35796 45235 56	1.00957 66426 04
22	0.40925 94000 35	0.40648 05878 67	0.37419 06460 52	1.01046 41970 84
23	0.42759 92806 91	0.42443 79431 10	0.39030 35051 34	1.01138 44282 48
24	0.44590 60683 67	0.44233 05516 69	0.40629 82084 28	1.01233 62149 92
25	0.46417 87321 56	0.46015 65190 10	0.42216 98975 42	1.01331 83977 64
26	0.48241 62886 83	0.47791 40544 23	0.43791 37495 04	1.01432 97799 81
27	0.50061 78032 06	0.49560 14727 79	0.45352 49781 97	1.01536 91294 84
28	0.51878 23906 30	0.51321 71960 38	0.46899 88357 98	1.01643 51800 39
29	0.53690 92164 39	0.53075 97545 12	0.48433 06141 93	1.01752 66328 78
30	0.55499 74975 21	0.54822 77879 04	0.49951 56464 07	1.01864 21582 86
31	0.57304 65029 25	0.56562 00460 98	0.51454 93080 10	1.01978 03972 15
32	0.59105 55545 12	0.58293 53897 35	0.52942 70185 25	1.02093 99629 42
33	0.60902 40275 25	0.60017 27905 55	0.54414 42428 26	1.02211 94427 62
34	0.62695 13510 74	0.61733 13315 29	0.55869 64925 27	1.02331 73997 00
35	0.64483 70085 30	0.63441 02067 75	0.57307 93273 67	1.02453 23742 72
36	0.66268 05378 32	0.65140 87212 83	0.58728 83565 80	1.02576 28862 55
37	0.68048 15317 20	0.66832 62904 32	0.60131 92402 61	1.02700 74364 92
38	0.69823 96378 74	0.68516 24393 27	0.61516 76907 18	1.02826 45087 23
39	0.71595 45589 81	0.70191 68019 61	0.62882 94738 18	1.02953 25714 26
40	0.73362 60527 18	0.71858 91202 04	0.64230 04103 17	1.03081 00796 87
41	0.75125 39316 64	0.73517 92426 33	0.65557 63771 87	1.03209 54770 78
42	0.76883 80631 34	0.75168 71232 12	0.66865 33089 19	1.03338 71975 58
43	0.78637 83689 38	0.76811 28198 38	0.68152 71988 24	1.03468 36673 79
44	0.80387 48250 80	0.78445 64927 40	0.69419 41003 18	1.03598 33070 01
45	0.82132 74613 77	0.80071 84027 77	0.70665 01281 92	1.03728 45330 18

K = 1.68575 03548 12596   E = 1.46746 22093 39427
K'= 2.15651 56474 99643   E'= 1.21105 60275 68459

r	u=(r/90)K=F(ϕ,k)	sn u	cn u	dn u
45	0.84287 51774 06	0.73205 08075 69	0.68125 00386 33	0.93060 48591 02
46	0.86160 57369 04	0.74379 90936 37	0.66840 32527 63	0.92827 29809 04
47	0.88033 62964 02	0.75529 33878 37	0.65538 68310 32	0.92594 97689 25
48	0.89906 68559 00	0.76653 20474 54	0.64220 60574 50	0.92363 80000 07
49	0.91779 74153 98	0.77751 35678 30	0.62886 61636 95	0.92134 04164 37
50	0.93652 79748 96	0.78823 65771 31	0.61537 23250 79	0.91905 97230 97
51	0.95525 85343 94	0.79869 98310 17	0.60172 96568 50	0.91679 85847 41
52	0.97398 90938 92	0.80890 22072 21	0.58794 32108 23	0.91455 96234 19
53	0.99271 96533 90	0.81884 27000 47	0.57401 79723 50	0.91234 54160 27
54	1.01145 02128 88	0.82852 04148 26	0.55995 88576 10	0.91015 84919 97
55	1.03018 07723 85	0.83793 45623 33	0.54577 07112 40	0.90800 13311 18
56	1.04891 13318 83	0.84708 44531 79	0.53145 83042 74	0.90587 63614 84
57	1.06764 18913 81	0.85596 94922 08	0.51702 63324 13	0.90378 59575 71
58	1.08637 24508 79	0.86458 91729 07	0.50247 94145 96	0.90173 24384 33
59	1.10510 30103 77	0.87294 30718 37	0.48782 20918 86	0.89971 80660 26
60	1.12383 35698 75	0.88103 08431 17	0.47305 88266 56	0.89774 50436 34
61	1.14256 41293 73	0.88885 22129 57	0.45819 40020 58	0.89581 55144 23
62	1.16129 46888 71	0.89640 69742 62	0.44323 19217 90	0.89393 15600 89
63	1.18002 52483 69	0.90369 49813 23	0.42817 68101 28	0.89209 51996 19
64	1.19875 58078 67	0.91071 61445 91	0.41303 28122 34	0.89030 83881 42
65	1.21748 63673 65	0.91747 04255 64	0.39780 39947 21	0.88857 30158 82
66	1.23621 69268 63	0.92395 78317 87	0.38249 43464 67	0.88689 09071 98
67	1.25494 74863 60	0.93017 84119 74	0.36710 77796 73	0.88526 38197 02
68	1.27367 80458 58	0.93613 22512 66	0.35164 81311 49	0.88369 34434 72
69	1.29240 86053 56	0.94181 94666 23	0.33611 91638 24	0.88218 14003 21
70	1.31113 91648 54	0.94724 02023 81	0.32052 45684 70	0.88072 92431 55
71	1.32986 97243 52	0.95239 46259 48	0.30486 79656 25	0.87933 84553 83
72	1.34860 02838 50	0.95728 29236 75	0.28915 29077 14	0.87801 04503 99
73	1.36733 08433 48	0.96190 52968 91	0.27338 28813 45	0.87674 65711 10
74	1.38606 14028 46	0.96626 19581 16	0.25756 13097 86	0.87554 80895 27
75	1.40479 19623 44	0.97035 31274 50	0.24169 15556 01	0.87441 62063 98
76	1.42352 25218 42	0.97417 90291 53	0.22577 69234 42	0.87335 20508 88
77	1.44225 30813 40	0.97773 98884 09	0.20982 06629 83	0.87235 66802 94
78	1.46098 36408 38	0.98103 59282 83	0.19382 59719 89	0.87143 10798 07
79	1.47971 42003 36	0.98406 73668 80	0.17779 59995 10	0.87057 61622 97
80	1.49844 47598 33	0.98683 44146 94	0.16173 38491 93	0.86979 27681 31
81	1.51717 53193 31	0.98933 72721 71	0.14564 25826 93	0.86908 16650 20
82	1.53590 58788 29	0.99157 61274 65	0.12952 52231 89	0.86844 35478 84
83	1.55463 64383 27	0.99355 11544 10	0.11338 47589 83	0.86787 90387 45
84	1.57336 69978 25	0.99526 25107 00	0.09722 41471 80	0.86738 86866 33
85	1.59209 75573 23	0.99671 03362 71	0.08104 63174 35	0.86697 29675 10
86	1.61082 81168 21	0.99789 47519 08	0.06485 41757 61	0.86663 22842 06
87	1.62955 86763 19	0.99881 58580 55	0.04865 06083 93	0.86636 69663 74
88	1.64828 92358 17	0.99947 37338 45	0.03243 84856 90	0.86617 72704 47
89	1.66701 97953 15	0.99986 84363 42	0.01622 06660 75	0.86606 33796 10
90	1.68575 03548 13	1.00000 00000 00	0.00000 00000 00	0.86602 54037 84

$q = 0.01797\ 23870\ 08967\ 24$

$q' = 0.08579\ 57337\ 02194\ 77$

$D(90) = 1.07456\ 99318\ 23542$

$1/D(90) = 0.93060\ 48591\ 02100$

r	ϕ	$E(\phi,k)$	$A(r)$	$D(r)$
45	0.82132 74613 77	0.80071 84027 77	0.70665 01281 92	1.03728 45330 18
46	0.83873 63610 24	0.81689 89096 08	0.71889 14598 69	1.03858 57600 90
47	0.85610 16600 90	0.83299 84697 67	0.73091 43366 43	1.03988 54028 70
48	0.87342 35469 55	0.84901 76346 42	0.74271 50649 13	1.04118 18779 38
49	0.89070 22616 92	0.86495 70483 76	0.75429 00173 87	1.04247 36057 28
50	0.90793 80953 93	0.88081 74456 86	0.76563 56342 78	1.04375 90124 57
51	0.92513 13894 44	0.89659 96496 19	0.77674 84244 86	1.04503 65320 36
52	0.94228 25347 44	0.91230 45692 56	0.78762 49667 51	1.04630 46079 85
53	0.95939 19708 87	0.92793 31973 55	0.79826 19107 99	1.04756 16953 23
54	0.97646 01852 93	0.94348 66079 66	0.80865 59784 61	1.04880 62624 57
55	0.99348 77122 98	0.95896 59540 05	0.81880 39647 81	1.05003 67930 42
56	1.01047 51322 04	0.97437 24647 99	0.82870 27390 93	1.05125 17878 32
57	1.02742 30702 95	0.98970 74436 24	0.83834 92460 86	1.05244 97665 06
58	1.04433 21958 10	1.00497 22652 13	0.84774 05068 44	1.05362 92694 72
59	1.06120 32208 99	1.02016 83732 73	0.85687 36198 63	1.05478 88596 45
60	1.07803 68995 27	1.03529 72779 92	0.86574 57620 49	1.05592 71241 98
61	1.09483 40263 70	1.05036 05535 48	0.87435 41896 90	1.05704 26762 84
62	1.11159 54356 71	1.06535 98356 35	0.88269 62394 02	1.05813 41567 27
63	1.12832 20000 83	1.08029 68189 98	0.89076 93290 57	1.05920 02356 74
64	1.14501 46294 74	1.09517 32549 82	0.89857 09586 80	1.06023 96142 23
65	1.16167 42697 29	1.10999 09491 11	0.90609 87113 21	1.06125 10259 95
66	1.17830 19015 24	1.12475 17586 78	0.91335 02539 06	1.06223 32386 89
67	1.19489 85390 80	1.13945 75903 75	0.92032 33380 55	1.06318 50555 74
68	1.21146 52289 09	1.15411 03979 44	0.92701 58008 73	1.06410 53169 54
69	1.22800 30485 40	1.16871 21798 62	0.93342 55657 21	1.06499 29015 75
70	1.24451 31052 36	1.18326 49770 60	0.93955 06429 48	1.06584 67279 99
71	1.26099 65346 96	1.19777 08706 70	0.94538 91306 01	1.06666 57559 15
72	1.27745 44997 51	1.21223 19798 18	0.95093 92151 02	1.06744 89874 08
73	1.29388 81890 43	1.22665 04594 41	0.95619 91718 99	1.06819 54681 80
74	1.31029 88157 07	1.24102 84981 50	0.96116 73660 83	1.06890 42887 06
75	1.32668 76160 35	1.25536 83161 19	0.96584 22529 76	1.06957 45853 47
76	1.34305 58481 41	1.26967 21630 17	0.97022 23786 85	1.07020 55414 02
77	1.35940 47906 14	1.28394 23159 71	0.97430 63806 31	1.07079 63881 01
78	1.37573 57411 74	1.29818 10775 67	0.97809 29880 40	1.07134 64055 43
79	1.39205 00153 17	1.31239 07738 77	0.98158 10224 00	1.07185 49235 75
80	1.40834 89449 57	1.32657 37525 22	0.98476 93978 96	1.07232 13226 06
81	1.42463 38770 71	1.34073 23807 67	0.98765 71217 96	1.07274 50343 64
82	1.44090 61723 32	1.35486 90436 36	0.99024 32948 19	1.07312 55425 88
83	1.45716 72037 48	1.36898 61420 62	0.99252 71114 62	1.07346 23836 55
84	1.47341 83552 93	1.38308 60910 57	0.99450 78602 89	1.07375 51471 49
85	1.48966 10205 41	1.39717 13179 01	0.99618 49241 98	1.07400 34763 59
86	1.50589 66012 98	1.41124 42603 52	0.99755 77806 40	1.07420 70687 14
87	1.52212 65062 27	1.42530 73648 79	0.99862 60018 16	1.07436 56761 49
88	1.53835 21494 81	1.43936 30848 96	0.99938 92548 29	1.07447 91054 14
89	1.55457 49493 32	1.45341 38790 23	0.99984 73018 09	1.07454 72183 02
90	1.57079 63267 95	1.46746 22093 39	1.00000 00000 00	1.07456 99318 24

K = 1.69411 43573 05914   E = 1.46077 35062 13127
K'= 2.13002 14383 99325   E'= 1.22058 89957 54247

r	u=(r/90)K=F(φ,k)	sn u	cn u	dn u
0	0.00000 00000 00	0.00000 00000 00	1.00000 00000 00	1.00000 00000 00
1	0.01882 34928 59	0.01882 20864 83	0.99982 28488 39	0.99995 30111 94
2	0.03764 69857 18	0.03763 57369 68	0.99929 15246 83	0.99981 21157 71
3	0.05647 04785 77	0.05643 25267 52	0.99840 64152 06	0.99957 75265 54
4	0.07529 39714 36	0.07520 40536 76	0.99716 81655 12	0.99924 95977 00
5	0.09411 74642 95	0.09394 19493 06	0.99557 76766 08	0.99882 88238 93
6	0.11294 09571 54	0.11263 78899 95	0.99363 61032 78	0.99831 58392 02
7	0.13176 44500 13	0.13128 36077 88	0.99134 48513 64	0.99771 14156 34
8	0.15058 79428 72	0.14987 09011 46	0.98870 55744 71	0.99701 64613 75
9	0.16941 14357 31	0.16839 16454 38	0.98572 01701 02	0.99623 20187 22
10	0.18823 49285 90	0.18683 78031 80	0.98239 07752 53	0.99535 92617 32
11	0.20705 84214 49	0.20520 14339 77	0.97871 97614 71	0.99439 94935 77
12	0.22588 19143 07	0.22347 47041 45	0.97470 97294 10	0.99335 41436 34
13	0.24470 54071 66	0.24164 98959 80	0.97036 35029 06	0.99222 47643 05
14	0.26352 89000 25	0.25971 94166 44	0.96568 41225 88	0.99101 30276 01
15	0.28235 23928 84	0.27767 58066 53	0.96067 48390 58	0.98972 07214 78
16	0.30117 58857 43	0.29551 17479 23	0.95533 91056 79	0.98834 97459 62
17	0.31999 93786 02	0.31322 00713 76	0.94968 05709 75	0.98690 21090 66
18	0.33882 28714 61	0.33079 37640 74	0.94370 30707 00	0.98537 99225 19
19	0.35764 63643 20	0.34822 59758 64	0.93741 06195 97	0.98378 53973 20
20	0.37646 98571 79	0.36551 00255 21	0.93080 74028 73	0.98212 08391 35
21	0.39529 33500 38	0.38263 94063 84	0.92389 77674 41	0.98038 86435 61
22	0.41411 68428 97	0.39960 77914 69	0.91668 62129 42	0.97859 12912 60
23	0.43294 03357 56	0.41640 90380 47	0.90917 73826 01	0.97673 13429 88
24	0.45176 38286 15	0.43303 71916 95	0.90137 60539 36	0.97481 14345 44
25	0.47058 73214 74	0.44948 64898 10	0.89328 71293 59	0.97283 42716 39
26	0.48941 08143 33	0.46575 13645 84	0.88491 56267 06	0.97080 26247 12
27	0.50823 43071 92	0.48182 64454 50	0.87626 66697 22	0.96871 93237 14
28	0.52705 78000 51	0.49770 65609 92	0.86734 54785 41	0.96658 72528 65
29	0.54588 12929 10	0.51338 67403 43	0.85815 73601 85	0.96440 93454 06
30	0.56470 47857 69	0.52886 22140 58	0.84870 76991 18	0.96218 85783 60
31	0.58352 82786 28	0.54412 84144 88	0.83900 19478 80	0.95992 79673 22
32	0.60235 17714 87	0.55918 09756 62	0.82904 56178 39	0.95763 05612 81
33	0.62117 52643 46	0.57401 57326 93	0.81884 42700 67	0.95529 94374 92
34	0.63999 87572 04	0.58862 87207 12	0.80840 35063 96	0.95293 76964 24
35	0.65882 22500 63	0.60301 61733 66	0.79772 89606 50	0.95054 84567 70
36	0.67764 57429 22	0.61717 45208 81	0.78682 62900 89	0.94813 48505 50
37	0.69646 92357 81	0.63110 03877 14	0.77570 11670 91	0.94570 00183 17
38	0.71529 27286 40	0.64479 05898 18	0.76435 92710 77	0.94324 71044 58
39	0.73411 62214 99	0.65824 21315 34	0.75280 62807 08	0.94077 92526 20
40	0.75293 97143 58	0.67145 22021 34	0.74104 78663 68	0.93829 96012 57
41	0.77176 32072 17	0.68441 81720 40	0.72908 96829 48	0.93581 12793 06
42	0.79058 67000 76	0.69713 75887 32	0.71693 73629 39	0.93331 74019 97
43	0.80941 01929 35	0.70960 81723 80	0.70459 65098 49	0.93082 10668 10
44	0.82823 36857 94	0.72182 78112 14	0.69207 26919 61	0.92832 53495 73
45	0.84705 71786 53	0.73379 45566 50	0.67937 14364 26	0.92583 33007 09

q = 0.01925 57475 39635 14   D(90) = 1.08010 80488 61469
q′= 0.08219 43773 66407 71   1/D(90) = 0.92583 33007 09211

r	φ	E(φ,k)	A(r)	D(r)
0	0.00000 00000 00	0.00000 00000 00	0.00000 00000 00	1.00000 00000 00
1	0.01882 31980 13	0.01882 29031 75	0.01742 65396 37	1.00002 43991 33
2	0.03764 46274 84	0.03764 22695 17	0.03484 78182 40	1.00009 75668 07
3	0.05646 25225 45	0.05645 45685 30	0.05225 85762 52	1.00021 94138 88
4	0.07527 51226 62	0.07525 62823 77	0.06965 35570 57	1.00038 97919 34
5	0.09408 06752 94	0.09404 39121 58	0.08702 75084 61	1.00060 84933 86
6	0.11287 74385 24	0.11281 39841 29	0.10437 51841 59	1.00087 52518 10
7	0.13166 36836 72	0.13156 30558 46	0.12169 13452 12	1.00118 97422 31
8	0.15043 76978 76	0.15028 77222 10	0.13897 07615 13	1.00155 15815 23
9	0.16919 77866 32	0.16898 46213 96	0.15620 82132 63	1.00196 03288 76
10	0.18794 22763 02	0.18765 04406 51	0.17339 84924 36	1.00241 54863 35
11	0.20666 95165 65	0.20628 19219 45	0.19053 64042 56	1.00291 64994 06
12	0.22537 78828 26	0.22487 58674 49	0.20761 67686 57	1.00346 27577 32
13	0.24406 57785 56	0.24342 91448 41	0.22463 44217 57	1.00405 35958 31
14	0.26273 16375 81	0.26193 86924 11	0.24158 42173 20	1.00468 82939 16
15	0.28137 39262 96	0.28040 15239 62	0.25846 10282 24	1.00536 60787 63
16	0.29999 11458 14	0.29881 47334 90	0.27525 97479 22	1.00608 61246 57
17	0.31858 18340 33	0.31717 54996 33	0.29197 52919 03	1.00684 75543 99
18	0.33714 45676 36	0.33548 10898 76	0.30860 25991 55	1.00764 94403 70
19	0.35567 79639 95	0.35372 88645 18	0.32513 66336 19	1.00849 08056 63
20	0.37418 06829 98	0.37191 62803 66	0.34157 23856 45	1.00937 06252 75
21	0.39265 14287 91	0.39004 08941 81	0.35790 48734 46	1.01028 78273 53
22	0.41108 89514 18	0.40810 03658 52	0.37412 91445 45	1.01124 12945 00
23	0.42949 20483 82	0.42609 24612 92	0.39024 02772 27	1.01222 98651 34
24	0.44785 95661 03	0.44401 50550 74	0.40623 33819 75	1.01325 23349 09
25	0.46619 04012 80	0.46186 61327 79	0.42210 36029 16	1.01430 74581 75
26	0.48448 35021 61	0.47964 37930 80	0.43784 61192 55	1.01539 39494 99
27	0.50273 78697 12	0.49734 62495 46	0.45345 61467 04	1.01651 04852 30
28	0.52095 25586 89	0.51497 18321 74	0.46892 89389 14	1.01765 57051 11
29	0.53912 66786 05	0.53251 89886 60	0.48425 97888 93	1.01882 82139 37
30	0.55725 93946 11	0.54998 62853 96	0.49944 40304 25	1.02002 65832 54
31	0.57534 99282 65	0.56737 24082 17	0.51447 70394 80	1.02124 93530 96
32	0.59339 75582 11	0.58467 61628 91	0.52935 42356 21	1.02249 50337 70
33	0.61140 16207 62	0.60189 64753 59	0.54407 10834 00	1.02376 21076 63
34	0.62936 15103 79	0.61903 23917 48	0.55862 30937 53	1.02504 90310 99
35	0.64727 66800 66	0.63608 30781 37	0.57300 58253 80	1.02635 42362 10
36	0.66514 66416 65	0.65304 78201 20	0.58721 48861 26	1.02767 61328 56
37	0.68297 09660 60	0.66992 60221 40	0.60124 59343 46	1.02901 31105 52
38	0.70074 92832 95	0.68671 72066 32	0.61509 46802 66	1.03036 35404 39
39	0.71848 12826 03	0.70342 10129 68	0.62875 68873 32	1.03172 57772 62
40	0.73616 67123 48	0.72003 71962 22	0.64222 83735 49	1.03309 81613 77
41	0.75380 53798 90	0.73656 56257 66	0.65550 50128 16	1.03447 90207 74
42	0.77139 71513 62	0.75300 62836 97	0.66858 27362 37	1.03586 66731 10
43	0.78894 19513 76	0.76935 92631 28	0.68145 75334 33	1.03725 94277 61
44	0.80643 97626 52	0.78562 47663 31	0.69412 54538 36	1.03865 55878 85
45	0.82389 06255 76	0.80180 31027 56	0.70658 26079 72	1.04005 34524 82

K = 1.69411 43573 05914   E = 1.46077 35062 13127
K'= 2.13002 14383 99325   E'= 1.22058 89957 54247

r	u=(r/90)K=F(ϕ,k)	sn u	cn u	dn u
45	0.84705 71786 53	0.73379 45566 50	0.67937 14364 26	0.92583 33007 09
46	0.86588 06715 12	0.74550 66182 13	0.66649 82237 04	0.92334 79416 42
47	0.88470 41643 71	0.75696 23582 58	0.65345 84823 69	0.92087 22613 46
48	0.90352 76572 30	0.76816 02865 27	0.64025 75842 60	0.91840 92130 58
49	0.92235 11500 89	0.77909 90545 54	0.62690 08400 00	0.91596 17111 45
50	0.94117 46429 48	0.78977 74499 48	0.61339 34948 74	0.91353 26281 22
51	0.95999 81358 07	0.80019 43905 67	0.59974 07250 69	0.91112 47918 31
52	0.97882 16286 66	0.81034 89186 08	0.58594 76342 74	0.90874 09827 72
53	0.99764 51215 25	0.82024 01946 36	0.57201 92506 41	0.90638 39315 85
54	1.01646 86143 84	0.82986 74915 62	0.55796 05240 95	0.90405 63166 77
55	1.03529 21072 43	0.83923 01886 01	0.54377 63239 97	0.90176 07620 08
56	1.05411 56001 01	0.84832 77652 14	0.52947 14371 58	0.89949 98350 03
57	1.07293 90929 60	0.85715 97950 65	0.51505 05661 81	0.89727 60446 22
58	1.09176 25858 19	0.86572 59400 01	0.50051 83281 45	0.89509 18395 46
59	1.11058 60786 78	0.87402 59440 72	0.48587 92536 10	0.89294 96065 14
60	1.12940 95715 37	0.88205 96276 09	0.47113 77859 42	0.89085 16687 69
61	1.14823 30643 96	0.88982 68813 69	0.45629 82809 45	0.88880 02846 36
62	1.16705 65572 55	0.89732 76607 67	0.44136 50067 94	0.88679 76462 15
63	1.18588 00501 14	0.90456 19802 05	0.42634 21442 54	0.88484 58781 80
64	1.20470 35429 73	0.91152 99075 01	0.41123 37871 95	0.88294 70366 92
65	1.22352 70358 32	0.91823 15584 48	0.39604 39433 57	0.88110 31084 03
66	1.24235 05286 91	0.92466 70914 95	0.38077 65353 94	0.87931 60095 65
67	1.26117 40215 50	0.93083 67025 67	0.36543 54021 63	0.87758 75852 20
68	1.27999 75144 09	0.93674 06200 41	0.35002 43002 49	0.87591 96084 80
69	1.29882 10072 68	0.94237 90998 69	0.33454 69057 26	0.87431 37798 78
70	1.31764 45001 27	0.94775 24208 66	0.31900 68161 38	0.87277 17268 04
71	1.33646 79929 86	0.95286 08801 79	0.30340 75526 83	0.87129 50029 93
72	1.35529 14858 45	0.95770 47889 18	0.28775 25626 01	0.86988 50880 89
73	1.37411 49787 04	0.96228 44679 84	0.27204 52217 51	0.86854 33872 60
74	1.39293 84715 63	0.96660 02440 76	0.25628 88373 55	0.86727 12308 61
75	1.41176 19644 22	0.97065 24458 98	0.24048 66509 25	0.86606 98741 58
76	1.43058 54572 81	0.97444 14005 59	0.22464 18413 33	0.86494 04970 76
77	1.44940 89501 40	0.97796 74301 78	0.20875 75280 36	0.86388 42040 01
78	1.46823 24429 98	0.98123 08486 93	0.19283 67744 32	0.86290 20236 09
79	1.48705 59358 57	0.98423 19588 78	0.17688 25913 52	0.86199 49087 25
80	1.50587 94287 16	0.98697 10495 72	0.16089 79406 52	0.86116 37362 08
81	1.52470 29215 75	0.98944 83931 23	0.14488 57389 33	0.86040 93068 62
82	1.54352 64144 34	0.99166 42430 43	0.12884 88613 44	0.85973 23453 62
83	1.56234 99072 93	0.99361 88318 88	0.11279 01454 78	0.85913 35001 99
84	1.58117 34001 52	0.99531 23693 52	0.09671 23953 49	0.85861 33436 36
85	1.59999 68930 11	0.99674 50405 84	0.08061 83854 36	0.85817 23716 79
86	1.61882 03858 70	0.99791 70047 27	0.06451 08647 92	0.85781 10040 52
87	1.63764 38787 29	0.99882 83936 80	0.04839 25612 00	0.85752 95841 81
88	1.65646 73715 88	0.99947 93110 82	0.03226 61853 74	0.85732 83791 83
89	1.67529 08644 47	0.99986 98315 28	0.01613 44352 02	0.85720 75798 63
90	1.69411 43573 06	1.00000 00000 00	0.00000 00000 00	0.85716 73007 02

$q = 0.01925\ 57475\ 39635\ 14$
$q' = 0.08219\ 43773\ 66407\ 71$

$D(90) = 1.08010\ 80488\ 61469$
$1/D(90) = 0.92583\ 33007\ 09211$

r	ϕ	$E(\phi, k)$	$A(r)$	$D(r)$
45	0.82389 06255 76	0.80180 31027 56	0.70658 26079 72	1.04005 34524 82
46	0.84129 46376 83	0.81789 46869 31	0.71882 51687 28	1.04145 13184 72
47	0.85865 19530 85	0.83390 00362 67	0.73084 93726 08	1.04284 74827 68
48	0.87596 27818 22	0.84981 97687 50	0.74265 15209 75	1.04424 02443 52
49	0.89322 73891 66	0.86565 46005 67	0.75422 79812 73	1.04562 79063 46
50	0.91044 60948 58	0.88140 53436 49	0.76557 51882 38	1.04700 87780 79
51	0.92761 92722 92	0.89707 29031 50	0.77668 96450 91	1.04838 11771 49
52	0.94474 73476 53	0.91265 82748 74	0.78756 79247 14	1.04974 34314 72
53	0.96183 07989 95	0.92816 25426 53	0.79820 66708 08	1.05109 38813 20
54	0.97887 01552 89	0.94358 68756 96	0.80860 25990 28	1.05243 08813 40
55	0.99586 59954 11	0.95893 25259 01	0.81875 24981 11	1.05375 28025 64
56	1.01281 89471 01	0.97420 08251 53	0.82865 32309 68	1.05505 80343 88
57	1.02972 96858 79	0.98939 31826 07	0.83830 17357 72	1.05634 49865 41
58	1.04659 89339 29	1.00451 10819 66	0.84769 50270 08	1.05761 20910 16
59	1.06342 74589 45	1.01955 60787 62	0.85683 01965 19	1.05885 78039 87
60	1.08021 60729 56	1.03452 97976 40	0.86570 44145 12	1.06008 06076 84
61	1.09696 56311 11	1.04943 39296 59	0.87431 49305 55	1.06127 90122 49
62	1.11367 70304 47	1.06427 02296 11	0.88265 90745 40	1.06245 15575 45
63	1.13035 12086 33	1.07904 05133 59	0.89073 42576 30	1.06359 68149 41
64	1.14698 91426 87	1.09374 66552 08	0.89853 79731 74	1.06471 33890 46
65	1.16359 18476 80	1.10839 05852 98	0.90606 77976 01	1.06579 99194 19
66	1.18016 03754 17	1.12297 42870 43	0.91332 13912 82	1.06685 50822 18
67	1.19669 58131 02	1.13749 97945 95	0.92029 64993 73	1.06787 75918 17
68	1.21319 92819 97	1.15196 91903 52	0.92699 09526 25	1.06886 62023 73
69	1.22967 19360 56	1.16638 46025 15	0.93340 26681 64	1.06981 97093 44
70	1.24611 49605 56	1.18074 82026 68	0.93952 96502 49	1.07073 69509 55
71	1.26252 95707 14	1.19506 22034 25	0.94536 99909 95	1.07161 68096 16
72	1.27891 70102 98	1.20932 88561 03	0.95092 18710 66	1.07245 82132 85
73	1.29527 85502 26	1.22355 04484 51	0.95618 35603 46	1.07326 01367 69
74	1.31161 54871 65	1.23772 93024 15	0.96115 34185 66	1.07402 16029 81
75	1.32792 91421 16	1.25186 77719 58	0.96582 98959 10	1.07474 16841 24
76	1.34422 08590 00	1.26596 82409 13	0.97021 15335 84	1.07541 95028 27
77	1.36049 20032 38	1.28003 31208 87	0.97429 69643 56	1.07605 42332 08
78	1.37674 39603 26	1.29406 48491 99	0.97808 49130 62	1.07664 51018 90
79	1.39297 81344 11	1.30806 58868 65	0.98157 41970 74	1.07719 13889 32
80	1.40919 59468 60	1.32203 87166 15	0.98476 37267 47	1.07769 24287 16
81	1.42539 88348 29	1.33598 58409 53	0.98765 25058 15	1.07814 76107 53
82	1.44158 82498 34	1.34990 97802 40	0.99023 96317 72	1.07855 63804 30
83	1.45776 56563 13	1.36381 30708 21	0.99252 42962 00	1.07891 82396 82
84	1.47393 25301 93	1.37769 82631 72	0.99450 57850 76	1.07923 27476 04
85	1.49009 03574 58	1.39156 79200 73	0.99618 34790 39	1.07949 95209 83
86	1.50624 06327 07	1.40542 46148 13	0.99755 68536 20	1.07971 82347 71
87	1.52238 48577 24	1.41927 09294 00	0.99862 54794 39	1.07988 86224 75
88	1.53852 45400 39	1.43310 94528 02	0.99938 90223 66	1.08001 04764 88
89	1.55466 11914 92	1.44694 27791 93	0.99984 72436 49	1.08008 36483 35
90	1.57079 63267 95	1.46077 35062 13	1.00000 00000 00	1.08010 80488 61

K = 1.70283 59363 12341   E = 1.45390 77960 65210
K' = 2.10465 76584 91159   E' = 1.23012 72241 85949

r	u=(r/90)K=F(ϕ,k)	sn u	cn u	dn u
0	0.00000 00000 00	0.00000 00000 00	1.00000 00000 00	1.00000 00000 00
1	0.01892 03992 92	0.01891 89535 35	0.99982 10205 82	0.99994 97432 32
2	0.03784 07985 85	0.03782 92349 54	0.99928 42183 20	0.99979 90499 24
3	0.05676 11978 77	0.05672 21842 74	0.99839 00008 57	0.99954 81508 79
4	0.07568 15971 69	0.07558 91657 37	0.99713 90464 84	0.99919 74301 60
5	0.09460 19964 62	0.09442 15798 18	0.99553 23024 72	0.99874 74241 80
6	0.11352 23957 54	0.11321 08750 95	0.99357 09827 49	0.99819 88204 31
7	0.13244 27950 47	0.13194 85599 64	0.99125 65649 33	0.99755 24558 61
8	0.15136 31943 39	0.15062 62141 37	0.98859 07867 34	0.99680 93149 11
9	0.17028 35936 31	0.16923 54998 88	0.98557 56417 33	0.99597 05272 00
10	0.18920 39929 24	0.18776 81730 18	0.98221 33745 79	0.99503 73649 01
11	0.20812 43922 16	0.20621 60934 97	0.97850 64755 96	0.99401 12397 88
12	0.22704 47915 08	0.22457 12357 41	0.97445 76748 52	0.99289 36999 82
13	0.24596 51908 01	0.24282 56985 08	0.97006 99356 98	0.99168 64264 12
14	0.26488 55900 93	0.26097 17143 71	0.96534 64478 10	0.99039 12289 97
15	0.28380 59893 85	0.27900 16587 38	0.96029 06197 72	0.98901 00425 69
16	0.30272 63886 78	0.29690 80584 08	0.95490 60712 20	0.98754 49225 60
17	0.32164 67879 70	0.31468 35996 17	0.94919 66245 89	0.98599 80404 53
18	0.34056 71872 62	0.33232 11355 83	0.94316 62964 95	0.98437 16790 37
19	0.35948 75865 55	0.34981 36934 99	0.93681 92887 85	0.98266 82274 71
20	0.37840 79858 47	0.36715 44809 91	0.93015 99792 98	0.98089 01761 73
21	0.39732 83851 40	0.38433 68920 02	0.92319 29123 68	0.97904 01115 71
22	0.41624 87844 32	0.40135 45121 08	0.91592 27891 10	0.97712 07107 10
23	0.43516 91837 24	0.41820 11232 61	0.90835 44575 24	0.97513 47357 66
24	0.45408 95830 17	0.43487 07079 37	0.90049 29024 59	0.97308 50284 47
25	0.47300 99823 09	0.45135 74527 05	0.89234 32354 69	0.97097 45043 46
26	0.49193 03816 01	0.46765 57512 19	0.88391 06846 01	0.96880 61472 20
27	0.51085 07808 94	0.48376 02066 12	0.87520 05841 51	0.96658 30032 54
28	0.52977 11801 86	0.49966 56333 35	0.86621 83644 23	0.96430 81752 93
29	0.54869 15794 78	0.51536 70584 15	0.85696 95415 25	0.96198 48170 90
30	0.56761 19787 71	0.53085 97221 61	0.84745 97072 35	0.95961 61275 64
31	0.58653 23780 63	0.54613 90783 28	0.83769 45189 76	0.95720 53450 99
32	0.60545 27773 55	0.56120 07937 50	0.82767 96899 13	0.95475 57418 92
33	0.62437 31766 48	0.57604 07474 55	0.81742 09792 21	0.95227 06183 66
34	0.64329 35759 40	0.59065 50292 89	0.80692 41825 45	0.94975 32976 71
35	0.66221 39752 33	0.60503 99380 55	0.79619 51226 67	0.94720 71202 67
36	0.68113 43745 25	0.61919 19792 04	0.78523 96404 21	0.94463 54386 22
37	0.70005 47738 17	0.63310 78620 83	0.77406 35858 69	0.94204 16120 25
38	0.71897 51731 10	0.64678 44967 66	0.76267 28097 58	0.93942 90015 19
39	0.73789 55724 02	0.66021 89905 03	0.75107 31552 78	0.93680 09649 81
40	0.75681 59716 94	0.67340 86437 98	0.73927 04501 45	0.93416 08523 38
41	0.77573 63709 87	0.68635 09461 39	0.72727 04990 12	0.93151 20009 41
42	0.79465 67702 79	0.69904 35714 18	0.71507 90762 28	0.92885 77310 91
43	0.81357 71695 71	0.71148 43730 51	0.70270 19189 56	0.92620 13417 34
44	0.83249 75688 64	0.72367 13788 36	0.69014 47206 59	0.92354 61063 20
45	0.85141 79681 56	0.73560 27855 62	0.67741 31249 64	0.92089 52688 32

ELLIPTIC FUNCTIONS TABLE $\theta = 32°$

q = 0.02059 05967 10436 76   D(90) = 1.08589 98127 64555
q′= 0.07872 46415 92072 55   1/D(90) = 0.92089 52688 31601

r	ϕ	$E(\phi,k)$	A(r)	D(r)
0	0.00000 00000 00	0.00000 00000 00	0.00000 00000 00	1.00000 00000 00
1	0.01892 00823 17	0.01891 97653 51	0.01742 28306 23	1.00002 61630 09
2	0.03783 82633 63	0.03783 57284 47	0.03484 04081 20	1.00010 46201 64
3	0.05675 26447 80	0.05674 40940 03	0.05224 74808 16	1.00023 52758 88
4	0.07566 13340 29	0.07564 10806 49	0.06963 87999 41	1.00041 79710 12
5	0.09456 24472 77	0.09452 29278 32	0.08700 91210 81	1.00065 24829 74
6	0.11345 41122 76	0.11338 59026 51	0.10435 32056 29	1.00093 85260 87
7	0.13233 44712 00	0.13222 63066 01	0.12166 58222 38	1.00127 57518 87
8	0.15120 16834 57	0.15104 04822 06	0.13894 17482 72	1.00166 37495 59
9	0.17005 39284 58	0.16982 48195 29	0.15617 57712 57	1.00210 20464 35
10	0.18888 94083 42	0.18857 57625 17	0.17336 26903 32	1.00259 01085 71
11	0.20770 63506 41	0.20728 98151 87	0.19049 73177 00	1.00312 73413 97
12	0.22650 30108 95	0.22596 35476 24	0.20757 44800 76	1.00371 30904 42
13	0.24527 76751 98	0.24459 36017 64	0.22458 90201 40	1.00434 66421 30
14	0.26402 86626 72	0.26317 66969 66	0.24153 57979 83	1.00502 72246 50
15	0.28275 43278 74	0.28170 96353 43	0.25840 96925 56	1.00575 40088 92
16	0.30145 30631 14	0.30018 93068 47	0.27520 56031 18	1.00652 61094 64
17	0.32012 33007 01	0.31861 26940 88	0.29191 84506 80	1.00734 25857 65
18	0.33876 35150 86	0.33697 68768 87	0.30854 31794 54	1.00820 24431 31
19	0.35737 22249 27	0.35527 90365 38	0.32507 47582 92	1.00910 46340 48
20	0.37594 79950 51	0.37351 64597 93	0.34150 81821 33	1.01004 80594 28
21	0.39448 94383 24	0.39168 65425 40	0.35783 84734 40	1.01103 15699 46
22	0.41299 52174 12	0.40978 67931 88	0.37406 06836 42	1.01205 39674 40
23	0.43146 40464 45	0.42781 48357 39	0.39016 98945 67	1.01311 40063 72
24	0.44989 46925 78	0.44576 84125 62	0.40616 12198 80	1.01421 03953 43
25	0.46828 59774 39	0.46364 53868 53	0.42202 98065 11	1.01534 17986 68
26	0.48663 67784 73	0.48144 37447 88	0.43777 08360 90	1.01650 68380 00
27	0.50494 60301 82	0.49916 15973 76	0.45337 95263 64	1.01770 40940 12
28	0.52321 27252 44	0.51679 71820 02	0.46885 11326 25	1.01893 21081 25
29	0.54143 59155 37	0.53434 88636 74	0.48418 09491 29	1.02018 93842 81
30	0.55961 47130 45	0.55181 51359 83	0.49936 43105 06	1.02147 43907 72
31	0.57774 82906 60	0.56919 46217 65	0.51439 65931 71	1.02278 55620 98
32	0.59583 58828 72	0.58648 60734 95	0.52927 32167 32	1.02412 13008 81
33	0.61387 67863 62	0.60368 83734 00	0.54398 96453 84	1.02547 99798 06
34	0.63187 03604 75	0.62080 05333 20	0.55854 13893 03	1.02685 99436 05
35	0.64981 60276 08	0.63782 16943 04	0.57292 40060 37	1.02825 95110 74
36	0.66771 32734 80	0.65475 11259 80	0.58713 31018 84	1.02967 69771 19
37	0.68556 16473 13	0.67158 82256 77	0.60116 43332 62	1.03111 06148 36
38	0.70336 07619 13	0.68833 25173 43	0.61501 34080 78	1.03255 86776 10
39	0.72111 02936 57	0.70498 36502 45	0.62867 60870 84	1.03401 94012 49
40	0.73880 99823 84	0.72154 13974 75	0.64214 81852 24	1.03549 10061 28
41	0.75645 96312 06	0.73800 56542 83	0.65542 55729 74	1.03697 16993 57
42	0.77405 91062 22	0.75437 64362 23	0.66850 41776 69	1.03845 96769 72
43	0.79160 83361 60	0.77065 38771 56	0.68137 99848 23	1.03995 31261 22
44	0.80910 73119 28	0.78683 82271 02	0.69404 90394 33	1.04145 02272 87
45	0.82655 60860 97	0.80292 98499 54	0.70650 74472 76	1.04294 91564 90

127

ELLIPTIC FUNCTIONS TABLE $\theta = 32°$

K = 1.70283 59363 12341   E = 1.45390 77960 65210
K' = 2.10465 76584 91159   E' = 1.23012 72241 85949

r	u=(r/90)K=F(ϕ,k)	sn u	cn u	dn u
45	0.85141 79681 56	0.73560 27855 62	0.67741 31249 64	0.92089 52688 32
46	0.87033 83674 49	0.74727 69534 05	0.66451 27199 01	0.91825 20399 94
47	0.88925 87667 41	0.75869 24001 22	0.65144 90325 40	0.91561 95936 49
48	0.90817 91660 33	0.76984 77950 85	0.63822 75240 09	0.91300 10633 17
49	0.92709 95653 26	0.78074 19531 66	0.62485 35849 03	0.91039 95389 21
50	0.94601 99646 18	0.79137 38284 95	0.61133 25310 93	0.90781 80637 02
51	0.96494 03639 10	0.80174 25081 25	0.59766 95999 18	0.90525 96312 96
52	0.98386 07632 03	0.81184 72056 16	0.58386 99467 64	0.90272 71829 86
53	1.00278 11624 95	0.82168 72545 63	0.56993 86420 38	0.90022 36051 26
54	1.02170 15617 87	0.83126 21020 94	0.55588 06685 10	0.89775 17267 33
55	1.04062 19610 80	0.84057 13023 39	0.54170 09190 36	0.89531 43172 30
56	1.05954 23603 72	0.84961 45099 20	0.52740 41946 49	0.89291 40843 59
57	1.07846 27596 64	0.85839 14734 49	0.51299 52030 09	0.89055 36722 45
58	1.09738 31589 57	0.86690 20290 71	0.49847 85572 05	0.88823 56596 00
59	1.11630 35582 49	0.87514 60940 59	0.48385 87749 06	0.88596 25580 85
60	1.13522 39575 42	0.88312 36604 85	0.46914 02778 39	0.88373 68107 90
61	1.15414 43568 34	0.89083 47889 70	0.45432 73916 03	0.88156 07908 68
62	1.17306 47561 26	0.89827 96025 35	0.43942 43457 87	0.87943 68002 73
63	1.19198 51554 19	0.90545 82805 67	0.42443 52743 97	0.87736 70686 34
64	1.21090 55547 11	0.91237 10529 06	0.40936 42165 83	0.87535 37522 34
65	1.22982 59540 03	0.91901 81940 67	0.39421 51176 37	0.87339 89330 94
66	1.24874 63562 96	0.92540 00176 08	0.37899 18302 70	0.87150 46181 62
67	1.26766 67525 88	0.93151 68706 51	0.36369 81161 52	0.86967 27385 99
68	1.28658 71518 80	0.93736 91285 73	0.34833 76476 89	0.86790 51491 40
69	1.30550 75511 73	0.94295 71898 61	0.33291 40100 52	0.86620 36275 47
70	1.32442 79504 65	0.94828 14711 50	0.31743 07034 19	0.86456 98741 37
71	1.34334 83497 58	0.95334 24024 47	0.30189 11454 43	0.86300 55113 71
72	1.36226 87490 50	0.95814 04225 46	0.28629 86739 10	0.86151 20835 11
73	1.38118 91483 42	0.96267 59746 43	0.27065 65496 06	0.86009 10563 34
74	1.40010 95476 35	0.96694 95021 50	0.25496 79593 44	0.85874 38168 97
75	1.41902 99469 27	0.97096 14447 16	0.23923 60191 84	0.85747 16733 45
76	1.43795 03462 19	0.97471 22344 65	0.22346 37777 91	0.85627 58547 61
77	1.45687 07455 12	0.97820 22924 40	0.20765 42199 56	0.85515 75110 54
78	1.47579 11448 04	0.98143 20252 71	0.19181 02702 48	0.85411 77128 75
79	1.49471 15440 96	0.98440 18220 60	0.17593 47967 98	0.85315 74515 57
80	1.51363 19433 89	0.98711 20514 92	0.16003 06151 95	0.85227 76390 82
81	1.53255 23426 81	0.98956 30591 64	0.14410 04924 97	0.85147 91080 62
82	1.55147 27419 73	0.99175 51651 52	0.12814 71513 35	0.85076 26117 36
83	1.57039 31412 66	0.99368 86617 93	0.11217 32741 08	0.85012 88239 77
84	1.58931 35405 58	0.99536 38117 10	0.09618 15072 54	0.84957 83393 04
85	1.60823 39398 51	0.99678 08460 57	0.08017 44655 97	0.84911 16729 06
86	1.62715 43391 43	0.99793 99630 00	0.06415 47367 51	0.84872 92606 63
87	1.64607 47384 35	0.99884 13264 32	0.04812 48855 70	0.84843 14591 65
88	1.66499 51377 28	0.99948 50649 19	0.03208 74586 59	0.84821 85457 38
89	1.68391 55370 20	0.99987 12708 80	0.01604 49888 96	0.84809 07184 55
90	1.70283 59363 12	1.00000 00000 00	0.00000 00000 00	0.84804 80961 56

128

q = 0.02059 05967 10436 76   D(90) = 1.08589 98127 64555
q' = 0.07872 46415 92072 55   1/D(90) = 0.92089 52688 31601

r	ϕ	$E(\phi,k)$	A(r)	D(r)
45	0.82655 60860 97	0.80292 98499 54	0.70650 74472 76	1.04294 91564 90
46	0.84395 47723 07	0.81892 92210 88	0.71875 13761 92	1.04444 80875 19
47	0.86130 35446 04	0.83483 69248 47	0.73077 70573 50	1.04594 51941 56
48	0.87860 26367 05	0.85065 36519 40	0.74258 07865 09	1.04743 86523 95
49	0.89585 23412 11	0.86638 01967 58	0.75415 89252 53	1.04892 66426 72
50	0.91305 30087 46	0.88201 74546 12	0.76550 79022 21	1.05040 73520 76
51	0.93020 50470 49	0.89756 64189 16	0.77662 42143 15	1.05187 89765 62
52	0.94730 89200 09	0.91302 81783 14	0.78750 44278 93	1.05333 97231 46
53	0.96436 51466 49	0.92840 39137 68	0.79814 51799 48	1.05478 78120 91
54	0.98137 43000 66	0.94369 48956 21	0.80854 31792 63	1.05622 14790 77
55	0.99833 70063 21	0.95890 24806 35	0.81869 52075 53	1.05763 89773 47
56	1.01525 39432 93	0.97402 81090 10	0.82859 81205 82	1.05903 85798 40
57	1.03212 58394 96	0.98907 33014 12	0.83824 88492 64	1.06041 85812 90
58	1.04895 34728 53	1.00403 96559 97	0.84764 44007 46	1.06177 73003 11
59	1.06573 76694 47	1.01892 88454 42	0.85678 18594 57	1.06311 30814 40
60	1.08247 93022 35	1.03374 26140 04	0.86565 83881 52	1.06442 42971 54
61	1.09917 92897 41	1.04848 27745 92	0.87427 12289 16	1.06570 93498 59
62	1.11583 85947 16	1.06315 12058 74	0.88261 77041 58	1.06696 66738 32
63	1.13245 82227 84	1.07774 98494 14	0.89069 52175 73	1.06819 47371 30
64	1.14903 92210 61	1.09228 07068 52	0.89850 12550 78	1.06939 20434 57
65	1.16558 26767 59	1.10674 58371 18	0.90603 33857 30	1.07055 71339 87
66	1.18208 97157 76	1.12114 73537 00	0.91328 92626 06	1.07168 85891 44
67	1.19856 15012 64	1.13548 74219 56	0.92026 66236 67	1.07278 50303 29
68	1.21499 92321 93	1.14976 82564 73	0.92696 32925 87	1.07384 51216 03
69	1.23140 41418 96	1.16399 21184 86	0.93337 71795 54	1.07486 75713 11
70	1.24777 74966 13	1.17816 13133 41	0.93950 62820 48	1.07585 11336 61
71	1.26412 05940 15	1.19227 81880 21	0.94534 86855 79	1.07679 46102 39
72	1.28043 47617 35	1.20634 51287 24	0.95090 25644 05	1.07769 68514 71
73	1.29672 13558 79	1.22036 45584 92	0.95616 61822 13	1.07855 67580 22
74	1.31298 17595 43	1.23433 89348 99	0.96113 78927 69	1.07937 32821 39
75	1.32921 73813 21	1.24827 07477 92	0.96581 61405 37	1.08014 54289 26
76	1.34542 96538 09	1.26216 25170 84	0.97019 94612 67	1.08087 22575 57
77	1.36162 00321 09	1.27601 67905 99	0.97428 64825 50	1.08155 28824 21
78	1.37778 99923 31	1.28983 61419 66	0.97807 59243 31	1.08218 64742 06
79	1.39394 10300 90	1.30362 31685 59	0.98156 65994 04	1.08277 22609 03
80	1.41007 46590 08	1.31738 04894 88	0.98475 74138 58	1.08330 95287 52
81	1.42619 24092 11	1.33111 07436 24	0.98764 73674 97	1.08379 76231 13
82	1.44229 58258 28	1.34481 65876 74	0.99023 55542 19	1.08423 59492 58
83	1.45838 64674 88	1.35850 06942 84	0.99252 11623 67	1.08462 39731 01
84	1.47446 59048 20	1.37216 57501 82	0.99450 34750 35	1.08496 12218 46
85	1.49053 57189 49	1.38581 44543 49	0.99618 18703 49	1.08524 72845 67
86	1.50659 75000 01	1.39944 95162 17	0.99755 58217 00	1.08548 18127 03
87	1.52265 28455 95	1.41307 36538 90	0.99862 48979 51	1.08566 45204 90
88	1.53870 33593 49	1.42668 95923 88	0.99938 87635 99	1.08579 51853 02
89	1.55475 06493 78	1.44030 00619 02	0.99984 71789 08	1.08587 36479 29
90	1.57079 63267 95	1.45390 77960 65	1.00000 00000 00	1.08589 98127 65

K = 1.71192 46951 55678   E = 1.44686 92406 95183
K' = 2.08035 80666 91578   E' = 1.23966 11752 88672

r	u=(r/90)K=F(φ,k)	sn u	cn u	dn u
0	0.00000 00000 00	0.00000 00000 00	1.00000 00000 00	1.00000 00000 00
1	0.01902 13855 02	0.01901 98983 34	0.99981 91053 72	0.99994 63443 37
2	0.03804 27710 03	0.03803 08762 67	0.99927 65645 46	0.99978 54607 36
3	0.05706 41565 05	0.05702 40264 36	0.99837 28063 25	0.99951 75991 58
4	0.07608 55420 07	0.07599 04674 93	0.99710 85441 67	0.99914 31755 26
5	0.09510 69275 09	0.09492 13570 08	0.99548 47743 61	0.99866 27707 03
6	0.11412 83130 10	0.11380 79042 09	0.99350 27734 94	0.99807 71290 78
7	0.13314 96985 12	0.13264 13825 51	0.99116 40952 11	0.99738 71567 51
8	0.15217 10840 14	0.15141 31420 44	0.98847 05662 87	0.99659 39193 38
9	0.17119 24695 16	0.17011 46213 08	0.98542 42820 31	0.99569 86393 93
10	0.19021 38550 17	0.18873 73593 08	0.98202 76010 38	0.99470 26934 75
11	0.20923 52405 19	0.20727 30067 39	0.97828 31393 20	0.99360 76088 52
12	0.22825 66260 21	0.22571 33370 04	0.97419 37638 37	0.99241 50598 81
13	0.24727 80115 22	0.24405 02567 73	0.96976 25854 66	0.99112 68640 59
14	0.26629 93970 24	0.26227 58160 71	0.96499 29514 27	0.98974 49777 73
15	0.28532 07825 26	0.28038 22178 72	0.95988 84372 16	0.98827 14917 64
16	0.30434 21680 28	0.29836 18271 74	0.95445 28380 62	0.98670 86263 27
17	0.32336 35535 29	0.31620 71795 26	0.94869 01599 66	0.98505 87262 62
18	0.34238 49390 31	0.33391 09889 83	0.94260 46103 41	0.98332 42556 03
19	0.36140 63245 33	0.35146 61554 74	0.93620 05883 12	0.98150 77921 41
20	0.38042 77100 35	0.36886 57715 71	0.92948 26746 98	0.97961 20217 67
21	0.39944 90955 36	0.38610 31286 32	0.92245 56217 30	0.97763 97326 52
22	0.41847 04810 38	0.40317 17223 26	0.91512 43425 44	0.97559 38092 93
23	0.43749 18665 40	0.42006 52575 22	0.90749 39004 88	0.97347 72264 41
24	0.45651 32520 42	0.43677 76525 34	0.89956 94982 86	0.97129 30429 41
25	0.47553 46375 43	0.45330 30427 42	0.89135 64671 00	0.96904 43954 90
26	0.49455 60230 45	0.46963 57835 64	0.88286 02555 31	0.96673 44923 62
27	0.51357 74085 47	0.48577 04528 03	0.87408 64186 01	0.96436 66070 88
28	0.53259 87940 48	0.50170 18523 75	0.86504 06067 48	0.96194 40721 39
29	0.55162 01795 50	0.51742 50094 10	0.85572 85548 80	0.95947 02726 18
30	0.57064 15650 52	0.53293 51767 67	0.84615 60715 17	0.95694 86399 83
31	0.58966 29505 54	0.54822 78329 52	0.83632 90280 61	0.95438 26458 22
32	0.60868 43360 55	0.56329 86814 72	0.82625 33482 25	0.95177 57956 91
33	0.62770 57215 57	0.57814 36496 29	0.81593 49976 52	0.94913 16230 43
34	0.64672 71070 59	0.59275 88867 95	0.80537 99737 55	0.94645 36832 45
35	0.66574 84925 61	0.60714 07621 63	0.79459 42958 01	0.94374 55477 20
36	0.68476 98780 62	0.62128 58620 22	0.78358 39952 75	0.94101 07982 10
37	0.70379 12635 64	0.63519 09865 64	0.77235 51065 33	0.93825 30211 77
38	0.72281 26490 66	0.64885 31462 54	0.76091 36577 80	0.93547 58023 57
39	0.74183 40345 67	0.66226 95577 89	0.74926 56623 83	0.93268 27214 72
40	0.76085 54200 69	0.67543 76396 70	0.73741 71105 40	0.92987 73471 11
41	0.77987 68055 71	0.68835 50074 21	0.72537 39613 18	0.92706 32317 88
42	0.79889 81910 73	0.70101 94684 72	0.71314 21350 78	0.92424 39071 79
43	0.81791 95765 74	0.71342 90167 40	0.70072 75062 91	0.92142 28795 50
44	0.83694 09620 76	0.72558 18269 39	0.68813 58967 65	0.91860 36253 76
45	0.85596 23475 78	0.73747 62486 34	0.67537 30692 74	0.91578 95871 57

q = 0.02197 80013 16900 53   D(90) = 1.09195 38876 87547
q' = 0.07537 99738 58803 37   1/D(90) = 0.91578 95871 57129

r	ϕ	$E(\phi,k)$	A(r)	D(r)
0	0.00000 00000 00	0.00000 00000 00	0.00000 00000 00	1.00000 00000 00
1	0.01902 10452 82	0.01902 07050 74	0.01741 87126 70	1.00002 80067 23
2	0.03804 00498 83	0.03803 73291 14	0.03483 21809 92	1.00011 19927 74
3	0.05705 49762 93	0.05704 57987 38	0.05223 51620 46	1.00025 18558 43
4	0.07606 37933 35	0.07604 20558 47	0.06962 24157 70	1.00044 74255 49
5	0.09506 44793 15	0.09502 20651 98	0.08698 87063 88	1.00069 84636 51
6	0.11405 50251 46	0.11398 18219 03	0.10432 88038 41	1.00100 46643 36
7	0.13303 34374 42	0.13291 73588 33	0.12163 74852 11	1.00136 56545 92
8	0.15199 77415 71	0.15182 47538 83	0.13890 95361 56	1.00178 09946 63
9	0.17094 59846 69	0.17070 01371 01	0.15613 97523 36	1.00225 01785 84
10	0.18987 62385 97	0.18953 96976 40	0.17332 29408 42	1.00277 26347 95
11	0.20878 66028 37	0.20833 96905 12	0.19045 39216 28	1.00334 77268 41
12	0.22767 52073 29	0.22709 64431 41	0.20752 75289 38	1.00397 47541 43
13	0.24654 02152 26	0.24580 63616 69	0.22453 86127 36	1.00465 29528 56
14	0.26537 98255 84	0.26446 59370 19	0.24148 20401 37	1.00538 14967 94
15	0.28419 22759 55	0.28307 17506 91	0.25835 26968 37	1.00615 94984 39
16	0.30297 58449 01	0.30162 04802 76	0.27514 54885 38	1.00698 60100 22
17	0.32172 88544 09	0.32010 89046 68	0.29185 53423 85	1.00786 00246 74
18	0.34044 96722 09	0.33853 39089 76	0.30847 72083 88	1.00878 04776 59
19	0.35913 67139 92	0.35689 24891 15	0.32500 60608 53	1.00974 62476 63
20	0.37778 84455 19	0.37518 17560 72	0.34143 68998 12	1.01075 61581 62
21	0.39640 33846 24	0.39339 89398 38	0.35776 47524 50	1.01180 89788 60
22	0.41498 01030 98	0.41154 13929 97	0.37398 46745 27	1.01290 34271 78
23	0.43351 72284 71	0.42960 65939 87	0.39009 17518 11	1.01403 81698 25
24	0.45201 34456 65	0.44759 21499 96	0.40608 11014 94	1.01521 18244 16
25	0.47046 74985 35	0.46549 57995 37	0.42194 78736 24	1.01642 29611 58
26	0.48887 81912 92	0.48331 54146 56	0.43768 72525 18	1.01767 01045 90
27	0.50724 43898 03	0.50104 90028 21	0.45329 44581 84	1.01895 17353 82
28	0.52556 50227 73	0.51869 47084 59	0.46876 47477 39	1.02026 62921 84
29	0.54383 90828 07	0.53625 08141 69	0.48409 34168 20	1.02161 21735 28
30	0.56206 56273 47	0.55371 57416 09	0.49927 58009 99	1.02298 77397 79
31	0.58024 37795 00	0.57108 80520 65	0.51430 72771 86	1.02439 13151 30
32	0.59837 27287 40	0.58836 64467 13	0.52918 32650 35	1.02582 11896 48
33	0.61645 17314 95	0.60554 97665 83	0.54389 92283 46	1.02727 56213 51
34	0.63448 01116 25	0.62263 69922 37	0.55845 06764 56	1.02875 28383 33
35	0.65245 72607 75	0.63962 72431 68	0.57283 31656 29	1.03025 10409 23
36	0.67038 26386 36	0.65651 97769 39	0.58704 23004 45	1.03176 84038 74
37	0.68825 57730 78	0.67331 39880 70	0.60107 37351 74	1.03330 30785 90
38	0.70607 62601 95	0.69000 94066 88	0.61492 31751 48	1.03485 31953 77
39	0.72384 37642 36	0.70660 56969 55	0.62858 63781 28	1.03641 68657 18
40	0.74155 80174 44	0.72310 26552 86	0.64205 91556 58	1.03799 21845 76
41	0.75921 88197 96	0.73950 02083 71	0.65533 73744 15	1.03957 72327 14
42	0.77682 60386 53	0.75579 84110 18	0.66841 69575 50	1.04117 00790 33
43	0.79437 96083 17	0.77199 74438 31	0.68129 38860 14	1.04276 87829 27
44	0.81187 95295 09	0.78809 76107 38	0.69396 41998 83	1.04437 13966 42
45	0.82932 58687 60	0.80409 93363 75	0.70642 39996 61	1.04597 59676 53

K = 1.71192 46951 55678   E = 1.44686 92406 95183
K'= 2.08035 80666 91578   E'= 1.23966 11752 88672

r	u=(r/90)K=F(ϕ,k)	sn u	cn u	dn u
45	0.85596 23475 78	0.73747 62486 34	0.67537 30692 74	0.91578 95871 57
46	0.87498 37330 80	0.74911 08000 83	0.66244 47216 18	0.91298 41694 25
47	0.89400 51185 81	0.76048 41618 79	0.64935 64810 88	0.91019 07349 59
48	0.91302 65040 83	0.77159 51704 29	0.63611 38993 69	0.90741 26011 88
49	0.93204 78895 85	0.78244 28112 83	0.62272 24478 62	0.90465 30368 03
50	0.95106 92750 86	0.79302 62123 61	0.60918 75134 21	0.90191 52585 56
51	0.97009 06605 88	0.80334 46370 71	0.59551 43945 28	0.89920 24282 62
52	0.98911 20460 90	0.81339 74773 72	0.58170 82978 64	0.89651 76499 84
53	1.00813 34315 92	0.82318 42467 87	0.56777 43353 15	0.89386 39674 12
54	1.02715 48170 93	0.83270 45733 86	0.55371 75213 61	0.89124 43614 26
55	1.04617 62025 95	0.84195 81927 79	0.53954 27708 84	0.88866 17478 32
56	1.06519 75880 97	0.85094 49411 13	0.52525 48973 54	0.88611 89752 78
57	1.08421 89735 99	0.85966 47481 16	0.51085 86114 05	0.88361 88233 37
58	1.10324 03591 00	0.86811 76301 87	0.49635 85197 81	0.88116 40007 47
59	1.12226 17446 02	0.87630 36835 61	0.48175 91246 43	0.87875 71438 11
60	1.14128 31301 04	0.88422 30775 65	0.46706 48232 33	0.87640 08149 49
61	1.16030 45156 06	0.89187 60479 63	0.45227 99078 78	0.87409 75013 82
62	1.17932 59011 07	0.89926 28904 35	0.43740 85663 16	0.87184 96139 60
63	1.19834 72866 09	0.90638 39541 69	0.42245 48823 54	0.86965 94861 14
64	1.21736 86721 11	0.91323 96356 04	0.40742 28368 19	0.86752 93729 26
65	1.23639 00576 12	0.91983 03723 21	0.39231 63088 06	0.86546 14503 20
66	1.25541 14431 14	0.92615 66370 98	0.37713 90772 12	0.86345 78143 44
67	1.27443 28286 16	0.93221 89321 32	0.36189 48225 30	0.86152 04805 68
68	1.29345 42141 18	0.93801 77834 54	0.34658 71289 08	0.85965 13835 54
69	1.31247 55996 19	0.94355 37355 13	0.33121 94864 43	0.85785 23764 27
70	1.33149 69851 21	0.94882 73459 74	0.31579 52937 13	0.85612 52305 10
71	1.35051 83706 23	0.95383 91807 06	0.30031 78605 26	0.85447 16350 30
72	1.36953 97561 25	0.95858 98089 77	0.28479 04108 72	0.85289 31968 95
73	1.38856 11416 26	0.96307 97988 73	0.26921 60860 79	0.85139 14405 17
74	1.40758 25271 28	0.96730 97129 14	0.25359 79481 41	0.84996 78076 88
75	1.42660 39126 30	0.97128 01039 14	0.23793 89832 29	0.84862 36575 02
76	1.44562 52981 31	0.97499 15110 44	0.22224 21053 53	0.84736 02663 11
77	1.46464 66836 33	0.97844 44561 36	0.20651 01601 80	0.84617 88277 14
78	1.48366 80691 35	0.98163 94402 09	0.19074 59289 88	0.84508 04525 74
79	1.50268 94546 37	0.98457 69402 38	0.17495 21327 46	0.84406 61690 53
80	1.52171 08401 38	0.98725 74061 38	0.15913 14363 20	0.84313 69226 68
81	1.54073 22256 40	0.98968 12580 08	0.14328 64527 72	0.84229 35763 54
82	1.55975 36111 42	0.99184 88835 90	0.12741 97477 72	0.84153 69105 43
83	1.57877 49966 44	0.99376 06359 80	0.11153 38440 89	0.84086 76232 38
84	1.59779 63821 45	0.99541 68315 75	0.09563 12261 64	0.84028 63300 96
85	1.61681 77676 47	0.99681 77482 58	0.07971 43447 49	0.83979 35645 03
86	1.63583 91531 49	0.99796 36238 24	0.06378 56216 13	0.83938 97776 50
87	1.65486 05386 50	0.99885 46546 51	0.04784 74542 90	0.83907 53385 95
88	1.67388 19241 52	0.99949 09946 08	0.03190 22208 78	0.83885 05343 22
89	1.69290 33096 54	0.99987 27542 08	0.01595 22848 68	0.83871 55697 86
90	1.71192 46951 56	1.00000 00000 00	0.00000 00000 00	0.83867 05679 45

ELLIPTIC FUNCTIONS TABLE $\theta = 33°$

q = 0.02197 80013 16900 53
q'= 0.07537 99738 58803 37

D(90) = 1.09195 38876 87547
1/D(90) = 0.91578 95871 57129

r	ϕ	$E(\phi,k)$	A(r)	D(r)
45	0.82932 58687 60	0.80409 93363 75	0.70642 39996 61	1.04597 59676 53
46	0.84671 87577 27	0.82000 31633 55	0.71866 94475 84	1.04758 05410 42
47	0.86405 83924 36	0.83580 97494 26	0.73069 67688 99	1.04918 31618 79
48	0.88134 50324 50	0.85151 98645 32	0.74250 22531 41	1.05078 18776 05
49	0.89857 89999 78	0.86713 43877 92	0.75408 22553 90	1.05237 47404 08
50	0.91576 06789 13	0.88265 43044 14	0.76543 31975 13	1.05395 98096 02
51	0.93289 05138 18	0.89808 07025 46	0.77655 15693 97	1.05553 51539 84
52	0.94996 90088 52	0.91341 47700 86	0.78743 39301 60	1.05709 88541 94
53	0.96699 67266 51	0.92865 77914 60	0.79807 69093 45	1.05864 90050 50
54	0.98397 42871 48	0.94381 11443 70	0.80847 72081 06	1.06018 37178 68
55	1.00090 23663 64	0.95887 62965 39	0.81863 16003 60	1.06170 11227 69
56	1.01778 16951 45	0.97385 48024 45	0.82853 69339 37	1.06319 93709 51
57	1.03461 30578 71	0.98874 83000 64	0.83819 01316 95	1.06467 66369 47
58	1.05139 72911 20	1.00355 85076 30	0.84758 81926 27	1.06613 11208 46
59	1.06813 52823 08	1.01828 72204 07	0.85672 81929 37	1.06756 10504 87
60	1.08482 79682 97	1.03293 63075 05	0.86560 72871 01	1.06896 46836 23
61	1.10147 63339 76	1.04750 77087 17	0.87422 27089 01	1.07034 03100 35
62	1.11808 14108 21	1.06200 34314 04	0.88257 17724 36	1.07168 62536 25
63	1.13464 42754 29	1.07642 55474 29	0.89065 18731 07	1.07300 08744 55
64	1.15116 60480 39	1.09077 61901 30	0.89846 04885 84	1.07428 25707 45
65	1.16764 78910 36	1.10505 75513 62	0.90599 51797 37	1.07552 97808 26
66	1.18409 10074 30	1.11927 18785 88	0.91325 35915 44	1.07674 09850 41
67	1.20049 66393 41	1.13342 14720 32	0.92023 34539 78	1.07791 47076 03
68	1.21686 60664 57	1.14750 86818 94	0.92693 25828 57	1.07904 95183 87
69	1.23320 06044 88	1.16153 59056 34	0.93334 88806 66	1.08014 40346 77
70	1.24950 16036 19	1.17550 55853 18	0.93948 03373 56	1.08119 69228 48
71	1.26577 04469 44	1.18942 02050 27	0.94532 50311 08	1.08220 68999 96
72	1.28200 85489 09	1.20328 22883 39	0.95088 11290 64	1.08317 27354 97
73	1.29821 73537 39	1.21709 43958 75	0.95614 68880 32	1.08409 32525 10
74	1.31439 83338 72	1.23085 91229 05	0.96112 06551 54	1.08496 73294 09
75	1.33055 29883 81	1.24457 90970 25	0.96580 08685 47	1.08579 39011 53
76	1.34668 28414 09	1.25825 69758 94	0.97018 60579 02	1.08657 19605 82
77	1.36278 94405 85	1.27189 54450 31	0.97427 48450 57	1.08730 05596 44
78	1.37887 43554 58	1.28549 72156 71	0.97806 59445 36	1.08797 88105 53
79	1.39493 91759 19	1.29906 50226 77	0.98155 81640 43	1.08860 58868 69
80	1.41098 55106 31	1.31260 16225 06	0.98475 04049 35	1.08918 10245 07
81	1.42701 49854 56	1.32610 97912 25	0.98764 16626 47	1.08970 35226 68
82	1.44302 92418 86	1.33959 23225 70	0.99023 10270 91	1.09017 27446 90
83	1.45902 99354 72	1.35305 20260 57	0.99251 76830 09	1.09058 81188 30
84	1.47501 87342 62	1.36649 17251 21	0.99450 09102 98	1.09094 91389 56
85	1.49099 73172 28	1.37991 42553 00	0.99618 00842 90	1.09125 53651 65
86	1.50696 73727 10	1.39332 24624 46	0.99755 46760 04	1.09150 64243 23
87	1.52293 05968 46	1.40671 92009 63	0.99862 42523 50	1.09170 20105 12
88	1.53888 86920 14	1.42010 73320 69	0.99938 84763 00	1.09184 18854 13
89	1.55484 33652 72	1.43348 97220 79	0.99984 71070 29	1.09192 58785 87
90	1.57079 63267 95	1.44686 92406 95	1.00000 00000 00	1.09195 38876 88

133

K = 1.72139 08313 74249

E = 1.43966 21471 15459

K′ = 2.05706 23227 97365

E′ = 1.24918 16206 07472

r	u=(r/90)K=F(φ,k)	sn u	cn u	dn u
0	0.00000 00000 00	0.00000 00000 00	1.00000 00000 00	1.00000 00000 00
1	0.01912 65647 93	0.01912 50340 90	0.99981 70998 09	0.99994 28113 08
2	0.03825 31295 86	0.03824 08867 64	0.99926 85497 80	0.99977 13354 33
3	0.05737 96943 79	0.05733 83906 03	0.99835 48011 42	0.99948 58427 47
4	0.07650 62591 72	0.07640 84061 33	0.99707 66046 16	0.99908 67831 09
5	0.09563 28239 65	0.09544 18356 61	0.99543 50084 29	0.99857 47847 32
6	0.11475 93887 58	0.11442 96369 64	0.99343 13555 47	0.99795 06525 99
7	0.13388 59535 51	0.13336 28367 58	0.99106 72801 44	0.99721 53664 37
8	0.15301 25183 44	0.15223 25439 22	0.98834 47033 15	0.99637 00782 74
9	0.17213 90831 37	0.17102 99624 08	0.98526 58280 68	0.99541 61095 59
10	0.19126 56479 30	0.18974 64038 08	0.98183 31336 04	0.99435 49478 96
11	0.21039 22127 24	0.20837 32995 14	0.97804 93689 23	0.99318 82433 71
12	0.22951 87775 17	0.22690 22124 55	0.97391 75457 82	0.99191 78045 21
13	0.24864 53423 10	0.24532 48483 51	0.96944 09310 43	0.99054 55939 40
14	0.26777 19071 03	0.26363 30664 53	0.96462 30384 31	0.98907 37235 47
15	0.28689 84718 96	0.28181 88897 44	0.95946 76197 68	0.98750 44495 52
16	0.30602 50366 89	0.29987 45145 60	0.95397 86556 93	0.98584 01671 21
17	0.32515 16014 82	0.31779 23196 13	0.94816 03459 31	0.98408 34047 72
18	0.34427 81662 75	0.33556 48743 83	0.94201 70991 44	0.98223 68185 31
19	0.36340 47310 68	0.35318 49468 70	0.93555 35224 16	0.98030 31858 65
20	0.38253 12958 61	0.37064 55106 78	0.92877 44104 00	0.97828 53994 20
21	0.40165 78606 54	0.38793 97514 27	0.92168 47342 03	0.97618 64605 90
22	0.42078 44254 47	0.40506 10724 78	0.91428 96300 20	0.97400 94729 39
23	0.43991 09902 40	0.42200 30999 66	0.90659 43875 95	0.97175 76355 02
24	0.45903 75550 33	0.43875 96871 40	0.89860 44385 27	0.96943 42360 01
25	0.47816 41198 26	0.45532 49180 01	0.89032 53444 93	0.96704 26439 78
26	0.49729 06846 19	0.47169 31102 62	0.88176 27854 08	0.96458 63038 95
27	0.51641 72494 12	0.48785 88176 09	0.87292 25475 85	0.96206 87282 06
28	0.53554 38142 05	0.50381 68312 93	0.86381 05119 22	0.95949 34904 35
29	0.55467 03789 98	0.51956 21810 62	0.85443 26421 73	0.95686 42182 73
30	0.57379 69437 91	0.53509 01354 39	0.84479 49733 25	0.95418 45867 29
31	0.59292 35085 84	0.55039 62013 67	0.83490 36001 36	0.95145 83113 42
32	0.61205 00733 78	0.56547 61232 48	0.82476 46658 51	0.94868 91414 75
33	0.63117 66381 71	0.58032 58813 87	0.81438 43511 46	0.94588 08537 25
34	0.65030 32029 64	0.59494 16898 67	0.80376 88633 30	0.94303 72454 38
35	0.66942 97677 57	0.60931 99938 84	0.79292 44258 15	0.94016 21283 75
36	0.68855 63325 50	0.62345 74665 61	0.78185 72679 13	0.93725 93225 17
37	0.70768 28973 43	0.63735 10052 80	0.77057 36149 57	0.93433 26500 43
38	0.72680 94621 36	0.65099 77275 42	0.75907 96787 79	0.93138 59294 81
39	0.74593 60269 29	0.66439 49664 01	0.74738 16485 71	0.92842 29700 38
40	0.76506 25917 22	0.67754 02654 96	0.73548 56821 39	0.92544 75661 40
41	0.78418 91565 15	0.69043 13737 09	0.72339 78975 63	0.92246 34921 59
42	0.80331 57213 08	0.70306 62394 79	0.71112 43652 87	0.91947 44973 63
43	0.82244 22861 01	0.71544 30048 08	0.69867 11006 42	0.91648 43010 70
44	0.84156 88508 94	0.72755 99989 81	0.68604 40568 09	0.91349 65880 31
45	0.86069 54156 87	0.73941 57320 43	0.67324 91182 37	0.91051 50040 25

134

q = 0.02341 90910 88188 44
q' = 0.07215 43668 98737 07

D(90) = 1.09827 95402 37323
1/D(90) = 0.91051 50040 25217

r	ϕ	$E(\phi,k)$	A(r)	D(r)
0	0.00000 00000 00	0.00000 00000 00	0.00000 00000 00	1.00000 00000 00
1	0.01912 62001 66	0.01912 58355 52	0.01741 41517 35	1.00002 99330 83
2	0.03825 02132 61	0.03824 72973 36	0.03482 30688 44	1.00011 96958 68
3	0.05736 98556 62	0.05736 00199 81	0.05222 15181 04	1.00026 91790 10
4	0.07648 29506 37	0.07645 96548 77	0.06960 42690 99	1.00047 82004 15
5	0.09558 73317 63	0.09554 18784 85	0.08696 60956 19	1.00074 65054 61
6	0.11468 08463 30	0.11460 24005 57	0.10430 17770 71	1.00107 37673 09
7	0.13376 13586 96	0.13363 69722 42	0.12160 60998 75	1.00145 95873 03
8	0.15282 67536 11	0.15264 13940 50	0.13887 38588 75	1.00190 34954 50
9	0.17187 49394 85	0.17161 15236 45	0.15609 98587 39	1.00240 49509 96
10	0.19090 38515 97	0.19054 32834 46	0.17327 89153 67	1.00296 33430 86
11	0.20991 14552 37	0.20943 26680 05	0.19040 58572 96	1.00357 79915 04
12	0.22889 57487 81	0.22827 57511 44	0.20747 55271 08	1.00424 81475 04
13	0.24785 47666 73	0.24706 86928 31	0.22448 27828 38	1.00497 29947 18
14	0.26678 65823 33	0.26580 77457 72	0.24142 24993 79	1.00575 16501 57
15	0.28568 93109 62	0.28448 92616 93	0.25828 95698 96	1.00658 31652 77
16	0.30456 11122 52	0.30310 96973 14	0.27507 89072 31	1.00746 65271 43
17	0.32340 01929 91	0.32166 56199 82	0.29178 54453 18	1.00840 06596 57
18	0.34220 48095 58	0.34015 37129 57	0.30840 41405 91	1.00938 44248 68
19	0.36097 32703 04	0.35857 07803 48	0.32492 99733 97	1.01041 66243 63
20	0.37970 39378 13	0.37691 37516 70	0.34135 79494 11	1.01149 60007 18
21	0.39839 52310 49	0.39517 96860 36	0.35768 31010 41	1.01262 12390 39
22	0.41704 56273 68	0.41336 57759 64	0.37390 04888 52	1.01379 09685 55
23	0.43565 36644 10	0.43146 93508 04	0.39000 52029 70	1.01500 37642 90
24	0.45421 79418 62	0.44948 78797 77	0.40599 23644 99	1.01625 81488 03
25	0.47273 71230 86	0.46741 89746 34	0.42185 71269 34	1.01755 25939 77
26	0.49120 99366 21	0.48526 03919 25	0.43759 46775 72	1.01888 55228 92
27	0.50963 51775 44	0.50301 00348 96	0.45320 02389 25	1.02025 53117 36
28	0.52801 17087 14	0.52066 59550 09	0.46866 90701 29	1.02166 02917 86
29	0.54633 84618 64	0.53822 63530 94	0.48399 64683 55	1.02309 87514 43
30	0.56461 44385 76	0.55568 95801 45	0.49917 77702 14	1.02456 89383 11
31	0.58283 87111 23	0.57305 41377 67	0.51420 83531 65	1.02606 90613 37
32	0.60101 04231 75	0.59031 86782 78	0.52908 36369 17	1.02759 72929 89
33	0.61912 87903 87	0.60748 20044 90	0.54379 90848 28	1.02915 17714 81
34	0.63719 31008 56	0.62454 30691 80	0.55835 02053 05	1.03073 06030 45
35	0.65520 27154 55	0.64150 09742 47	0.57273 25531 94	1.03233 18642 33
36	0.67315 70680 53	0.65835 49695 99	0.58694 17311 70	1.03395 36042 63
37	0.69105 56656 14	0.67510 44517 57	0.60097 33911 24	1.03559 38473 94
38	0.70889 80881 77	0.69174 89622 12	0.61482 32355 36	1.03725 05953 31
39	0.72668 39887 40	0.70828 81855 34	0.62848 70188 54	1.03892 18296 63
40	0.74441 30930 25	0.72472 19472 70	0.64196 05488 57	1.04060 55143 20
41	0.76208 51991 42	0.74105 02116 22	0.65523 96880 15	1.04229 95980 50
42	0.77970 01771 63	0.75727 30789 47	0.66832 03548 43	1.04400 20169 24
43	0.79725 79685 88	0.77339 07830 76	0.68119 85252 40	1.04571 06968 46
44	0.81475 85857 35	0.78940 36884 77	0.69387 02338 29	1.04742 35560 80
45	0.83220 21110 31	0.80531 22872 80	0.70633 15752 77	1.04913 85077 88

K = 1.72139 08313 74249   E = 1.43966 21471 15459
K' = 2.05706 23227 97365   E' = 1.24918 16206 07472

r	u=(r/90)K=F(ϕ,k)	sn u	cn u	dn u
45	0.86069 54156 87	0.73941 57320 43	0.67324 91182 37	0.91051 50040 25
46	0.87982 19804 80	0.75100 88880 44	0.66029 20945 15	0.90754 31516 85
47	0.89894 85452 73	0.76233 83180 99	0.64717 87146 98	0.90458 45865 42
48	0.91807 51100 66	0.77340 30332 83	0.63391 46220 97	0.90164 28132 95
49	0.93720 16748 59	0.78420 21973 89	0.62050 53695 25	0.89872 12823 08
50	0.95632 82396 52	0.79473 51195 77	0.60695 64150 01	0.89582 33863 13
51	0.97545 48044 45	0.80500 12469 43	0.59327 31178 98	0.89295 24573 49
52	0.99458 13692 38	0.81500 01570 26	0.57946 07355 53	0.89011 17638 93
53	1.01370 79340 32	0.82473 15502 90	0.56552 44203 00	0.88730 45082 14
54	1.03283 44988 25	0.83419 52425 87	0.55146 92169 52	0.88453 38239 25
55	1.05196 10636 18	0.84339 11576 35	0.53730 00606 95	0.88180 27737 28
56	1.07108 76284 11	0.85231 93195 37	0.52302 17754 02	0.87911 43473 55
57	1.09021 41932 04	0.86097 98453 36	0.50863 90723 54	0.87647 14596 88
58	1.10934 07579 97	0.86937 29376 60	0.49415 65493 48	0.87387 69490 56
59	1.12846 73227 90	0.87749 88774 43	0.47957 86901 91	0.87133 35757 05
60	1.14759 38875 83	0.88535 80167 56	0.46490 98645 61	0.86884 40204 18
61	1.16672 04523 76	0.89295 07717 56	0.45015 43282 25	0.86641 08833 03
62	1.18584 70171 69	0.90027 76157 77	0.43531 62236 03	0.86403 66827 08
63	1.20497 35819 62	0.90733 90725 55	0.42039 95806 56	0.86172 38542 83
64	1.22410 01467 55	0.91413 57096 28	0.40540 83180 98	0.85947 47501 67
65	1.24322 67115 48	0.92066 81318 94	0.39034 62449 09	0.85729 16382 93
66	1.26235 32763 41	0.92693 69753 58	0.37521 70621 31	0.85517 67018 00
67	1.28147 98411 34	0.93294 29010 62	0.36002 43649 50	0.85313 20385 52
68	1.30060 64059 27	0.93868 65892 20	0.34477 16450 34	0.85115 96607 51
69	1.31973 29707 20	0.94416 87335 49	0.32946 22931 22	0.84926 14946 26
70	1.33885 95355 13	0.94939 00358 23	0.31409 96018 47	0.84743 93802 12
71	1.35798 61003 06	0.95435 12006 34	0.29868 67687 86	0.84569 50711 87
72	1.37711 26650 99	0.95905 29303 85	0.28322 68997 10	0.84403 02347 81
73	1.39623 92298 92	0.96349 59205 01	0.26772 30120 44	0.84244 64517 28
74	1.41536 57946 85	0.96768 08548 78	0.25217 80385 03	0.84094 52162 78
75	1.43449 23594 79	0.97160 84015 65	0.23659 48308 98	0.83952 79362 34
76	1.45361 89242 72	0.97527 92086 85	0.22097 61641 16	0.83819 59330 41
77	1.47274 54890 65	0.97869 39005 88	0.20532 47402 33	0.83695 04418 85
78	1.49187 20538 58	0.98185 30742 60	0.18964 31927 77	0.83579 26118 23
79	1.51099 86186 51	0.98475 72959 61	0.17393 40911 12	0.83472 35059 30
80	1.53012 51834 44	0.98740 70981 21	0.15819 99449 46	0.83374 41014 49
81	1.54925 17482 37	0.98980 29764 70	0.14244 32089 33	0.83285 52899 57
82	1.56837 83130 30	0.99194 53874 28	0.12666 62873 85	0.83205 78775 22
83	1.58750 48778 23	0.99383 47457 33	0.11087 15390 64	0.83135 25848 65
84	1.60663 14426 16	0.99547 14223 20	0.09506 12820 48	0.83074 00475 13
85	1.62575 80074 09	0.99685 57424 53	0.07923 77986 77	0.83022 08159 37
86	1.64488 45722 02	0.99798 79841 00	0.06340 33405 45	0.82979 53556 90
87	1.66401 11369 95	0.99886 83765 63	0.04756 01335 47	0.82946 40475 11
88	1.68313 77017 88	0.99949 70993 51	0.03171 03829 76	0.82922 71874 31
89	1.70226 42665 81	0.99987 42813 11	0.01585 62786 37	0.82908 49868 41
90	1.72139 08313 74	1.00000 00000 00	0.00000 00000 00	0.82903 75725 55

q = 0.02341 90910 88188 44   D(90) = 1.09827 95402 37323
q'= 0.07215 43668 98737 07   1/D(90) = 0.91051 50040 25217

r	φ	E(φ,k)	A(r)	D(r)
45	0.83220 21110 31	0.80531 22872 80	0.70633 15752 77	1.04913 85077 88
46	0.84958 86962 29	0.82111 71961 78	0.71857 87056 10	1.05085 34625 70
47	0.86691 85615 41	0.83681 91532 13	0.73060 78435 18	1.05256 63310 14
48	0.88419 19947 08	0.85241 90144 75	0.74241 52716 43	1.05427 50262 36
49	0.90140 93499 86	0.86791 77507 19	0.75399 73378 60	1.05597 74664 26
50	0.91857 10470 80	0.88331 64439 17	0.76535 04565 37	1.05767 15773 84
51	0.93567 75700 11	0.89861 62837 59	0.77647 11097 90	1.05935 52950 47
52	0.95272 94659 27	0.91381 85641 20	0.78735 58487 17	1.06102 65680 04
53	0.96972 73438 59	0.92892 46794 94	0.79800 12946 13	1.06268 33599 95
54	0.98667 18734 38	0.94393 61214 23	0.80840 41401 79	1.06432 36523 96
55	1.00356 37835 53	0.95885 44749 17	0.81856 11506 98	1.06594 54466 71
56	1.02040 38609 76	0.97368 14148 84	0.82846 91652 09	1.06754 67668 16
57	1.03719 29489 53	0.98841 87025 82	0.83812 50976 49	1.06912 56617 61
58	1.05393 19457 48	1.00306 81820 86	0.84752 59379 81	1.07068 02077 49
59	1.07062 18031 71	1.01763 17768 06	0.85666 87532 99	1.07220 85106 82
60	1.08726 35250 67	1.03211 14860 28	0.86555 06889 11	1.07370 87084 30
61	1.10385 81657 87	1.04650 93815 24	0.87416 89693 98	1.07517 89730 94
62	1.12040 68286 30	1.06082 76042 01	0.88252 08996 58	1.07661 75132 43
63	1.13691 06642 75	1.07506 83608 15	0.89060 38659 07	1.07802 25760 89
64	1.15337 08691 89	1.08923 39207 55	0.89841 53366 78	1.07939 24496 29
65	1.16978 86840 22	1.10332 66128 88	0.90595 28637 73	1.08072 54647 28
66	1.18616 53919 93	1.11734 88224 82	0.91321 40832 04	1.08201 99971 54
67	1.20250 23172 62	1.13130 29881 98	0.92019 67160 94	1.08327 44695 61
68	1.21880 08232 93	1.14519 15991 61	0.92689 85695 58	1.08448 73534 06
69	1.23506 23112 19	1.15901 71921 13	0.93331 75375 52	1.08565 71708 17
70	1.25128 82181 88	1.17278 23486 38	0.93945 16016 89	1.08678 24963 89
71	1.26748 00157 15	1.18648 96924 70	0.94529 88320 30	1.08786 19589 29
72	1.28363 92080 34	1.20014 18868 77	0.95085 73878 36	1.08889 42431 20
73	1.29976 73304 37	1.21374 16321 28	0.95612 55182 97	1.08987 80911 27
74	1.31586 59476 23	1.22729 16630 33	0.96110 15632 20	1.09081 23041 33
75	1.33193 66520 48	1.24079 47465 57	0.96578 39536 87	1.09169 57437 95
76	1.34798 10622 62	1.25425 36795 13	0.97017 12126 81	1.09252 73336 36
77	1.36400 08212 70	1.26767 12863 20	0.97426 19556 73	1.09330 60603 57
78	1.37999 75948 76	1.28105 04168 35	0.97805 48911 73	1.09403 09750 67
79	1.39597 30700 39	1.29439 39442 42	0.98154 88212 55	1.09470 11944 47
80	1.41192 89532 29	1.30770 47630 10	0.98474 26420 32	1.09531 59018 22
81	1.42786 69687 89	1.32098 57869 07	0.98763 53441 03	1.09587 43481 57
82	1.44378 88572 97	1.33423 99470 66	0.99022 60129 61	1.09637 58529 74
83	1.45969 63739 30	1.34747 01901 00	0.99251 38293 62	1.09681 98051 76
84	1.47559 12868 39	1.36067 94762 70	0.99449 80696 61	1.09720 56637 94
85	1.49147 53755 11	1.37387 07776 84	0.99617 81060 98	1.09753 29586 49
86	1.50735 04291 55	1.38704 70765 35	0.99755 34070 62	1.09780 12909 22
87	1.52321 82450 69	1.40021 13633 77	0.99862 35372 99	1.09801 03336 43
88	1.53908 06270 25	1.41336 66354 17	0.99938 81580 96	1.09815 98320 85
89	1.55493 93836 48	1.42651 58948 34	0.99984 70274 17	1.09824 96040 80
90	1.57079 63267 95	1.43966 21471 15	1.00000 00000 00	1.09827 95402 37

K = 1.73124 51756 57058   E = 1.43229 09693 06756
K' = 2.03471 53121 85791   E' = 1.25867 96247 79997

r	u=(r/90)K=F(φ,k)	sn u	cn u	dn u
0	0.00000 00000 00	0.00000 00000 00	1.00000 00000 00	1.00000 00000 00
1	0.01923 60575 07	0.01923 44810 43	0.99981 50002 57	0.99993 91407 26
2	0.03847 21150 15	0.03845 95063 10	0.99926 01595 05	0.99975 66603 60
3	0.05770 81725 22	0.05766 56350 55	0.99833 59527 40	0.99945 28510 21
4	0.07694 42300 29	0.07684 34565 33	0.99704 31701 73	0.99902 81987 22
5	0.09618 02875 37	0.09598 36048 58	0.99538 29150 63	0.99848 33821 09
6	0.11541 63450 44	0.11507 67736 84	0.99335 66007 02	0.99781 92706 96
7	0.13465 24025 51	0.13411 37306 53	0.99096 59465 64	0.99703 69226 06
8	0.15388 84600 58	0.15308 53315 68	0.98821 29736 34	0.99613 75818 45
9	0.17312 45175 66	0.17198 25342 22	0.98509 99989 45	0.99512 26751 04
10	0.19236 05750 73	0.19079 64118 38	0.98162 96293 56	0.99399 38081 09
11	0.21159 66325 80	0.20951 81660 73	0.97780 47545 83	0.99275 27615 45
12	0.23083 26900 88	0.22813 91395 47	0.97362 85395 40	0.99140 14865 65
13	0.25006 87475 95	0.24665 08278 36	0.96910 44160 09	0.98994 20999 07
14	0.26930 48051 02	0.26504 48909 09	0.96423 60736 89	0.98837 68786 41
15	0.28854 08626 10	0.28331 31639 60	0.95902 74506 64	0.98670 82545 70
16	0.30777 69201 17	0.30144 76676 08	0.95348 27233 33	0.98493 88083 20
17	0.32701 29776 24	0.31944 06174 34	0.94760 62958 49	0.98307 12631 25
18	0.34624 90351 31	0.33728 44328 35	0.94140 27891 22	0.98110 84783 55
19	0.36548 50926 39	0.35497 17451 59	0.93487 70294 21	0.97905 34428 03
20	0.38472 11501 46	0.37249 54051 29	0.92803 40366 38	0.97690 92677 63
21	0.40395 72076 53	0.38984 84895 09	0.92087 90122 64	0.97467 91799 25
22	0.42319 32651 61	0.40702 43070 39	0.91341 73271 18	0.97236 65141 27
23	0.44242 93226 68	0.42401 64035 99	0.90565 45088 94	0.96997 47059 70
24	0.46166 53801 75	0.44081 85666 25	0.89759 62295 59	0.96750 72843 55
25	0.48090 14376 83	0.45742 48287 68	0.88924 82926 76	0.96496 78639 37
26	0.50013 74951 90	0.47382 94707 95	0.88061 66206 73	0.96236 01375 58
27	0.51937 35526 97	0.49002 70237 58	0.87170 72421 33	0.95968 78686 49
28	0.53860 96102 04	0.50601 22704 24	0.86252 62791 24	0.95695 48836 65
29	0.55784 56677 12	0.52178 02459 91	0.85307 99346 45	0.95416 50645 44
30	0.57708 17252 19	0.53732 62381 06	0.84337 44801 94	0.95132 23412 39
31	0.59631 77827 26	0.55264 57862 05	0.83341 62435 36	0.94843 06843 27
32	0.61555 38402 34	0.56773 46801 92	0.82321 15966 79	0.94549 40977 35
33	0.63478 98977 41	0.58258 89584 92	0.81276 69441 14	0.94251 66115 85
34	0.65402 59552 48	0.59720 49054 91	0.80208 87113 39	0.93950 22751 85
35	0.67326 20127 56	0.61157 90484 08	0.79118 33337 15	0.93645 51501 90
36	0.69249 80702 63	0.62570 81536 11	0.78005 72456 59	0.93337 93039 29
37	0.71173 41277 70	0.63958 92224 20	0.76871 68702 22	0.93027 88029 40
38	0.73097 01852 77	0.65321 94864 26	0.75716 86090 65	0.92715 77066 90
39	0.75020 62427 85	0.66659 64023 51	0.74541 88328 53	0.92402 00615 34
40	0.76944 23002 92	0.67971 76464 98	0.73347 38720 90	0.92086 98948 78
41	0.78867 83577 99	0.69258 11088 06	0.72134 00084 04	0.91771 12095 87
42	0.80791 44153 07	0.70518 48865 60	0.70902 34663 02	0.91454 79786 33
43	0.82715 04728 14	0.71752 72777 74	0.69653 04054 02	0.91138 41399 81
44	0.84638 65303 21	0.72960 67742 97	0.68386 69131 49	0.90822 35917 28
45	0.86562 25878 29	0.74142 20546 59	0.67103 89980 22	0.90507 01874 93

q = 0.02491 50625 23980 95   D(90) = 1.10488 66859 37276
q′= 0.06904 22996 09032 02   1/D(90) = 0.90507 01874 93209

r	ϕ	$E(\phi,k)$	$A(r)$	$D(r)$
0	0.00000 00000 00	0.00000 00000 00	0.00000 00000 00	1.00000 00000 00
1	0.01923 56672 56	0.01923 52770 18	0.01740 91114 82	1.00003 19450 92
2	0.03846 89937 51	0.03846 58729 44	0.03481 29990 82	1.00012 77414 54
3	0.05769 76424 74	0.05768 71158 85	0.05220 64402 93	1.00028 72723 95
4	0.07691 92838 99	0.07689 43523 19	0.06958 42153 56	1.00051 03435 88
5	0.09613 15997 02	0.09608 29561 97	0.08694 11086 37	1.00079 66833 04
6	0.11533 22864 55	0.11524 83379 41	0.10427 19100 01	1.00114 59427 46
7	0.13451 90592 72	0.13438 59533 23	0.12157 14161 89	1.00155 76964 73
8	0.15368 96554 17	0.15349 13121 70	0.13883 44321 94	1.00203 14429 17
9	0.17284 18378 42	0.17255 99868 86	0.15605 57726 40	1.00256 66049 95
10	0.19197 33986 74	0.19158 76207 47	0.17323 02631 61	1.00316 25308 09
11	0.21108 21626 17	0.21056 99359 54	0.19035 27417 81	1.00381 84944 44
12	0.23016 59902 75	0.22950 27414 03	0.20741 80602 96	1.00453 36968 47
13	0.24922 27813 86	0.24838 19401 66	0.22442 10856 57	1.00530 72668 02
14	0.26825 04779 54	0.26720 35366 46	0.24135 67013 55	1.00613 82619 93
15	0.28724 70672 86	0.28596 36433 86	0.25821 98088 09	1.00702 56701 47
16	0.30621 05849 05	0.30465 84875 31	0.27500 53287 50	1.00796 84102 69
17	0.32513 91173 60	0.32328 44169 00	0.29170 82026 16	1.00896 53339 58
18	0.34403 08049 02	0.34183 79056 72	0.30832 33939 40	1.01001 52268 06
19	0.36288 38440 41	0.36031 55596 76	0.32484 58897 45	1.01111 68098 74
20	0.38169 64899 70	0.37871 41212 57	0.34127 07019 38	1.01226 87412 52
21	0.40046 70588 52	0.39703 04737 30	0.35759 28687 06	1.01346 96176 91
22	0.41919 39299 70	0.41526 16454 07	0.37380 74559 18	1.01471 79763 12
23	0.43787 55477 38	0.43340 48131 90	0.38990 95585 19	1.01601 22963 90
24	0.45651 04235 66	0.45145 73057 42	0.40589 43019 34	1.01735 10012 02
25	0.47509 71375 84	0.46941 66062 24	0.42175 68434 69	1.01873 24599 48
26	0.49363 43402 19	0.48728 03546 07	0.43749 23737 15	1.02015 49897 38
27	0.51212 07536 21	0.50504 63495 65	0.45309 61179 49	1.02161 68576 42
28	0.53055 51729 55	0.52271 25499 49	0.46856 33375 40	1.02311 62827 98
29	0.54893 64675 37	0.54027 70758 60	0.48388 93313 52	1.02465 14385 81
30	0.56726 35818 30	0.55773 82093 26	0.49906 94371 46	1.02622 04548 29
31	0.58553 55362 95	0.57509 43945 89	0.51409 90329 87	1.02782 14201 21
32	0.60375 14281 05	0.59234 42380 27	0.52897 35386 44	1.02945 23841 01
33	0.62191 04317 15	0.60948 65077 15	0.54368 84169 89	1.03111 13598 60
34	0.64001 17993 02	0.62652 01326 43	0.55823 91754 00	1.03279 63263 49
35	0.65805 48610 61	0.64344 42016 13	0.57262 13671 55	1.03450 52308 45
36	0.67603 90253 85	0.66025 79618 16	0.58683 05928 26	1.03623 59914 49
37	0.69396 37789 09	0.67696 08171 28	0.60086 25016 73	1.03798 64996 24
38	0.71182 86864 33	0.69355 23261 27	0.61471 27930 25	1.03975 46227 61
39	0.72963 33907 29	0.71003 21998 51	0.62837 72176 69	1.04153 82067 76
40	0.74737 76122 33	0.72640 02993 26	0.64185 15792 22	1.04333 50787 40
41	0.76506 11486 23	0.74265 66328 71	0.65513 17355 06	1.04514 30495 17
42	0.78268 38742 99	0.75880 13532 06	0.66821 35999 13	1.04695 99164 37
43	0.80024 57397 55	0.77483 47543 78	0.68109 31427 59	1.04878 34659 78
44	0.81774 67708 62	0.79075 72685 27	0.69376 63926 42	1.05061 14764 62
45	0.83518 70680 53	0.80656 94625 09	0.70622 94377 76	1.05244 17207 62

K = 1.73124 51756 57058   E = 1.43229 09693 06756
K'= 2.03471 53121 85791   E'= 1.25867 96247 79997

r	u=(r/90)K=F(ϕ,k)	sn u	cn u	dn u
45	0.86562 25878 29	0.74142 20546 59	0.67103 89980 22	0.90507 01874 93
46	0.88485 86453 36	0.75297 19767 00	0.65805 25832 36	0.90192 77320 59
47	0.90409 47028 43	0.76425 55700 14	0.64491 35009 46	0.89879 99772 59
48	0.92333 07603 50	0.77527 20282 23	0.63162 74869 37	0.89569 06181 28
49	0.94256 68178 58	0.78602 07011 40	0.61820 01758 16	0.89260 32892 83
50	0.96180 28753 65	0.79650 10868 20	0.60463 70966 90	0.88954 15615 66
51	0.98103 89328 72	0.80671 28235 46	0.59094 36693 34	0.88650 89389 17
52	1.00027 49903 80	0.81665 56817 70	0.57712 52008 30	0.88350 88554 82
53	1.01951 10478 87	0.82632 95560 35	0.56318 68826 80	0.88054 46729 52
54	1.03874 71053 94	0.83573 44569 08	0.54913 37883 76	0.87761 96781 31
55	1.05798 31629 02	0.84487 05029 33	0.53497 08714 25	0.87473 70807 06
56	1.07721 92204 09	0.85373 79126 42	0.52070 29638 07	0.87190 00112 35
57	1.09645 52779 16	0.86233 69966 36	0.50633 47748 60	0.86911 15193 31
58	1.11569 13354 23	0.87066 81497 55	0.49187 08905 82	0.86637 45720 37
59	1.13492 73929 31	0.87873 18433 58	0.47731 57733 28	0.86369 20523 83
60	1.15416 34504 38	0.88652 86177 30	0.46267 37618 94	0.86106 67581 11
61	1.17339 95079 45	0.89405 90746 24	0.44794 90719 74	0.85850 14005 73
62	1.19263 55654 53	0.90132 38699 62	0.43314 57969 74	0.85599 86037 71
63	1.21187 16229 60	0.90832 37067 06	0.41826 79091 62	0.85356 09035 49
64	1.23110 76804 67	0.91505 93279 02	0.40331 92611 56	0.85119 07469 15
65	1.25034 37379 75	0.92153 15099 17	0.38830 35877 12	0.84889 04914 89
66	1.26957 97954 82	0.92774 10558 80	0.37322 45078 16	0.84666 24050 64
67	1.28881 58529 89	0.93368 87893 25	0.35808 55270 58	0.84450 86652 75
68	1.30805 19104 96	0.93937 55480 55	0.34289 00402 70	0.84243 13593 57
69	1.32728 79680 04	0.94480 21782 25	0.32764 13344 22	0.84043 24840 01
70	1.34652 40255 11	0.94996 95286 58	0.31234 25917 52	0.83851 39452 77
71	1.36576 00830 18	0.95487 84453 93	0.29699 68931 21	0.83667 75586 26
72	1.38499 61405 26	0.95952 97664 75	0.28160 72215 85	0.83492 50489 23
73	1.40423 21980 33	0.96392 43169 79	0.26617 64661 58	0.83325 80505 76
74	1.42346 82555 40	0.96806 29042 93	0.25070 74257 62	0.83167 81076 85
75	1.44270 43130 48	0.97194 63136 36	0.23520 28133 51	0.83018 66742 22
76	1.46194 03705 55	0.97557 53038 41	0.21966 52601 94	0.82878 51142 53
77	1.48117 64280 62	0.97895 06033 73	0.20409 73203 04	0.82747 47021 73
78	1.50041 24855 69	0.98207 29066 22	0.18850 14750 07	0.82625 66229 62
79	1.51964 85430 77	0.98494 28704 30	0.17288 01376 36	0.82513 19724 50
80	1.53888 46005 84	0.98756 11108 93	0.15723 56583 36	0.82410 17575 83
81	1.55812 06580 91	0.98992 82004 03	0.14157 03289 80	0.82316 68966 88
82	1.57735 67155 99	0.99204 46649 58	0.12588 63881 76	0.82232 82197 34
83	1.59659 27731 06	0.99391 09817 26	0.11018 60263 55	0.82158 64685 81
84	1.61582 88306 13	0.99552 75768 62	0.09447 13909 44	0.82094 22972 14
85	1.63506 48881 21	0.99689 48235 87	0.07874 45915 94	0.82039 62719 52
86	1.65430 09456 28	0.99801 30405 21	0.06300 77054 78	0.81994 88716 51
87	1.67353 70031 35	0.99888 24902 75	0.04726 27826 24	0.81960 04878 59
88	1.69277 30606 42	0.99950 33782 97	0.03151 18512 99	0.81935 14249 70
89	1.71200 91181 50	0.99987 58519 76	0.01575 69234 22	0.81920 19003 22
90	1.73124 51756 57	1.00000 00000 00	0.00000 00000 00	0.81915 20442 89

q = 0.02491 50625 23980 95
q′= 0.06904 22996 09032 02

D(90) = 1.10488 66859 37276
1/D(90) = 0.90507 01874 93209

r	ϕ	$E(\phi,k)$	A(r)	D(r)
45	0.83518 70680 53	0.80656 94625 09	0.70622 94377 76	1.05244 17207 62
46	0.85256 68054 27	0.82227 20343 89	0.71847 84273 27	1.05427 19690 12
47	0.86988 62297 69	0.83786 58098 33	0.73050 95727 37	1.05609 99913 32
48	0.88714 56594 94	0.85335 17384 05	0.74231 91490 32	1.05792 35605 35
49	0.90434 54835 19	0.86873 08897 89	0.75390 34961 22	1.05974 04548 48
50	0.92148 61600 71	0.88400 44499 55	0.76525 90200 91	1.06154 84606 14
51	0.93856 82154 23	0.89917 37172 83	0.77638 21944 68	1.06334 53749 94
52	0.95559 22425 88	0.91424 00986 52	0.78726 95614 85	1.06512 90086 46
53	0.97255 88999 41	0.92920 51055 19	0.79791 77333 24	1.06689 71883 96
54	0.98946 89098 10	0.94407 03499 95	0.80832 33933 43	1.06864 77598 88
55	1.00632 30570 07	0.95883 75409 26	0.81848 32972 86	1.07037 85902 02
56	1.02312 21873 30	0.97350 84800 05	0.82839 42744 77	1.07208 75704 63
57	1.03986 72060 18	0.98808 50579 01	0.83805 32289 94	1.07377 26184 02
58	1.05655 90761 85	1.00256 92504 41	0.84745 71408 21	1.07543 16808 98
59	1.07319 88172 09	1.01696 31148 35	0.85660 30669 83	1.07706 27364 83
60	1.08978 75031 10	1.03126 87859 61	0.86548 81426 56	1.07866 37977 98
61	1.10632 62608 96	1.04548 84727 11	0.87410 95822 58	1.08023 29140 21
62	1.12281 62688 93	1.05962 44544 10	0.88246 46805 13	1.08176 81732 43
63	1.13925 87550 52	1.07367 90773 10	0.89055 08134 92	1.08326 77047 98
64	1.15565 49952 56	1.08765 47511 68	0.89836 54396 26	1.08472 96815 44
65	1.17200 63115 94	1.10155 39459 00	0.90590 61007 02	1.08615 23220 89
66	1.18831 40706 47	1.11537 91883 29	0.91317 04228 17	1.08753 38929 62
67	1.20457 96817 52	1.12913 30590 24	0.92015 61173 17	1.08887 27107 26
68	1.22080 45952 63	1.14281 81892 25	0.92686 09817 02	1.09016 71440 32
69	1.23699 03008 18	1.15643 72578 63	0.93328 29004 98	1.09141 56156 06
70	1.25313 83255 89	1.16999 29886 78	0.93941 98461 06	1.09261 66041 71
71	1.26925 02325 43	1.18348 81474 22	0.94526 98796 13	1.09376 86463 03
72	1.28532 76186 95	1.19692 55391 59	0.95083 11515 72	1.09487 03382 13
73	1.30137 21133 73	1.21030 80056 58	0.95610 19027 53	1.09592 03374 61
74	1.31738 53764 74	1.22363 84228 72	0.96108 04648 56	1.09691 73645 90
75	1.33336 90967 30	1.23691 96985 04	0.96576 52611 94	1.09786 02046 87
76	1.34932 49899 78	1.25015 47696 62	0.97015 48073 32	1.09874 77088 64
77	1.36525 47974 29	1.26334 66005 92	0.97424 77117 04	1.09957 87956 59
78	1.38116 02839 51	1.27649 81804 91	0.97804 26761 80	1.10035 24523 52
79	1.39704 32363 45	1.28961 25213 93	0.98153 84966 06	1.10106 77362 04
80	1.41290 54616 39	1.30269 26561 30	0.98473 40633 03	1.10172 37756 03
81	1.42874 87853 77	1.31574 16363 55	0.98762 83615 23	1.10231 97711 28
82	1.44457 50499 17	1.32876 25306 26	0.99022 04718 80	1.10285 49965 23
83	1.46038 61127 35	1.34175 84225 50	0.99250 95707 24	1.10332 87995 81
84	1.47618 38447 33	1.35473 24089 80	0.99449 49304 93	1.10374 06029 44
85	1.49197 01285 47	1.36768 75982 53	0.99617 59200 12	1.10408 99048 02
86	1.50774 68568 69	1.38062 71084 73	0.99755 20047 62	1.10437 62795 08
87	1.52351 59307 58	1.39355 40658 28	0.99862 27471 01	1.10459 93780 93
88	1.53927 92579 70	1.40647 16029 38	0.99938 78064 51	1.10475 89286 96
89	1.55503 87512 77	1.41938 28572 26	0.99984 69394 39	1.10485 47368 94
90	1.57079 63267 95	1.43229 09693 07	1.00000 00000 00	1.10488 66859 37

141

K = 1.74149 92344 26774   E = 1.42476 03101 24890
K'= 2.01326 65652 05468   E'= 1.26814 65310 65206

r	u=(r/90)K=F(ϕ,k)	sn u	cn u	dn u
0	0.00000 00000 00	0.00000 00000 00	1.00000 00000 00	1.00000 00000 00
1	0.01934 99914 94	0.01934 83669 33	0.99981 28028 27	0.99993 53289 30
2	0.03869 99829 87	0.03868 69897 28	0.99925 13781 96	0.99974 14209 09
3	0.05804 99744 81	0.05800 61403 87	0.99831 62262 92	0.99941 85912 23
4	0.07739 99659 75	0.07729 61231 14	0.99700 81791 80	0.99896 73644 06
5	0.09674 99574 68	0.09654 72902 68	0.99532 83984 40	0.99838 84728 26
6	0.11609 99489 62	0.11575 00581 04	0.99327 83718 82	0.99768 28547 21
7	0.13544 99404 55	0.13489 49222 77	0.99085 99093 43	0.99685 16516 92
8	0.15479 99319 49	0.15397 24730 19	0.98807 51376 05	0.99589 62056 57
9	0.17414 99234 43	0.17297 34099 47	0.98492 64944 41	0.99481 80552 97
10	0.19349 99149 36	0.19188 85564 47	0.98141 67218 39	0.99361 89319 98
11	0.21284 99064 30	0.21070 88735 67	0.97754 88584 21	0.99230 07553 17
12	0.23219 98979 24	0.22942 54733 84	0.97332 62311 08	0.99086 56279 89
13	0.25154 98894 17	0.24802 96317 93	0.96875 24460 63	0.98931 58305 07
14	0.27089 98809 11	0.26651 28006 66	0.96383 13789 67	0.98765 38152 88
15	0.29024 98724 04	0.28486 66193 57	0.95856 71646 66	0.98588 22004 73
16	0.30959 98638 98	0.30308 29255 10	0.95296 41862 44	0.98400 37633 60
17	0.32894 98553 92	0.32115 37651 35	0.94702 70635 73	0.98202 14335 39
18	0.34829 98468 85	0.33907 14019 30	0.94076 06413 93	0.97993 82857 22
19	0.36764 98383 79	0.35682 83258 30	0.93416 99769 77	0.97775 75323 26
20	0.38699 98298 73	0.37441 72607 57	0.92726 03274 42	0.97548 25158 28
21	0.40634 98213 66	0.39183 11715 59	0.92003 71367 48	0.97311 67009 34
22	0.42569 98128 60	0.40906 32701 33	0.91250 60224 61	0.97066 36665 87
23	0.44504 98043 54	0.42610 70207 26	0.90467 27623 22	0.96812 70978 49
24	0.46439 97958 47	0.44295 61444 07	0.89654 32806 80	0.96551 07776 91
25	0.48374 97873 41	0.45960 46227 16	0.88812 36348 49	0.96281 85787 20
26	0.50309 97788 34	0.47604 67005 08	0.87942 00014 41	0.96005 44548 82
27	0.52244 97703 28	0.49227 68879 79	0.87043 86627 22	0.95722 24331 53
28	0.54179 97618 22	0.50828 99619 11	0.86118 59930 47	0.95432 66052 69
29	0.56114 97533 15	0.52408 09661 42	0.85166 84454 22	0.95137 11195 09
30	0.58049 97448 09	0.53964 52112 86	0.84189 25382 35	0.94836 01725 59
31	0.59984 97363 03	0.55497 82737 18	0.83186 48422 08	0.94529 80014 87
32	0.61919 97277 96	0.57007 59938 63	0.82159 19675 97	0.94218 88758 49
33	0.63854 97192 90	0.58493 44738 10	0.81108 05517 02	0.93903 70899 46
34	0.65789 97107 83	0.59955 00742 73	0.80033 72466 90	0.93584 69552 59
35	0.67724 97022 77	0.61391 94109 53	0.78936 87078 01	0.93262 27930 73
36	0.69659 96937 71	0.62803 93503 06	0.77818 15819 37	0.92936 89273 12
37	0.71594 96852 64	0.64190 70047 84	0.76678 24966 76	0.92608 96775 99
38	0.73529 96767 58	0.65551 97275 49	0.75517 80497 30	0.92278 93525 51
39	0.75464 96682 52	0.66887 51067 27	0.74337 47988 74	0.91947 22433 21
40	0.77399 96597 45	0.68197 09592 22	0.73137 92523 57	0.91614 26174 09
41	0.79334 96512 39	0.69480 53241 32	0.71919 78598 12	0.91280 47127 25
42	0.81269 96427 32	0.70737 64558 05	0.70683 70036 81	0.90946 27319 37
43	0.83204 96342 26	0.71968 28165 63	0.69430 29911 67	0.90612 08370 89
44	0.85139 96257 20	0.73172 30691 51	0.68160 20467 05	0.90278 31445 05
45	0.87074 96172 13	0.74349 60689 20	0.66874 03049 76	0.89945 37199 74

q = 0.02646 71830 76961 27   D(90) = 1.11178 59405 02842
q′= 0.06603 86859 10861 03   1/D(90) = 0.89945 37199 73934

r	ϕ	$E(\phi,k)$	A(r)	D(r)
0	0.00000 00000 00	0.00000 00000 00	0.00000 00000 00	1.00000 00000 00
1	0.01934 95743 43	0.01934 91572 08	0.01740 35531 13	1.00003 40459 63
2	0.03869 66465 95	0.03869 33107 20	0.03480 18941 94	1.00013 61423 81
3	0.05803 87187 34	0.05802 74669 15	0.05218 98125 50	1.00030 61648 94
4	0.07737 33008 66	0.07734 66522 86	0.06956 21001 79	1.00054 39064 00
5	0.09669 79152 60	0.09664 59234 01	0.08691 35531 05	1.00084 90773 13
6	0.11601 01003 50	0.11592 03767 58	0.10423 89727 31	1.00122 13059 10
7	0.13530 74146 99	0.13516 51584 82	0.12153 31671 75	1.00166 01387 88
8	0.15458 74409 02	0.15437 54738 46	0.13879 09526 26	1.00216 50414 11
9	0.17384 77894 31	0.17354 65965 75	0.15600 71546 87	1.00273 53987 65
10	0.19308 61024 02	0.19267 38778 95	0.17317 66097 26	1.00337 05161 07
11	0.21230 00572 62	0.21175 27553 05	0.19029 41662 28	1.00406 96198 06
12	0.23148 73703 81	0.23077 87610 34	0.20735 46861 51	1.00483 18582 88
13	0.25064 58005 48	0.24974 75301 70	0.22435 30462 79	1.00565 63030 74
14	0.26977 31523 51	0.26865 48084 14	0.24128 41395 86	1.00654 19499 07
15	0.28886 72794 46	0.28749 64594 59	0.25814 28765 90	1.00748 77199 77
16	0.30792 60877 01	0.30626 84719 59	0.27492 41867 25	1.00849 24612 32
17	0.31694 75382 09	0.32496 69660 73	0.29162 30197 04	1.00955 49497 84
18	0.34592 96501 66	0.34358 81995 72	0.30823 43468 87	1.01067 38913 95
19	0.36487 05036 11	0.36212 85734 90	0.32475 31626 60	1.01184 79230 55
20	0.38376 82420 10	0.38058 46373 19	0.34117 44858 03	1.01307 56146 43
21	0.40262 10747 04	0.39895 30937 27	0.35749 33608 78	1.01435 54706 62
22	0.42142 72791 93	0.41723 08027 97	0.37370 48595 99	1.01568 59320 69
23	0.44018 52032 69	0.43541 47858 01	0.38980 40822 29	1.01706 53781 63
24	0.45889 32669 93	0.45350 22284 75	0.40578 61589 56	1.01849 21285 67
25	0.47754 99645 05	0.47149 04838 35	0.42164 62512 91	1.01996 44452 68
26	0.49615 38656 79	0.48937 70745 04	0.43737 95534 56	1.02148 05347 38
27	0.51470 36176 20	0.50715 96945 88	0.45298 12937 77	1.02303 85501 13
28	0.53319 79459 95	0.52483 62110 77	0.46844 67360 86	1.02463 65934 45
29	0.55163 56562 05	0.54240 46648 13	0.48377 11811 13	1.02627 27180 14
30	0.57001 56344 01	0.55986 32710 09	0.49894 99678 90	1.02794 49306 94
31	0.58833 68483 46	0.57721 04193 59	0.51397 84751 49	1.02965 11943 86
32	0.60659 83481 15	0.59444 46737 27	0.52885 21227 24	1.03138 94304 95
33	0.62479 92666 50	0.61156 47714 60	0.54356 63729 52	1.03315 75214 60
34	0.64293 88201 68	0.62856 96223 15	0.55811 67320 76	1.03495 33133 39
35	0.66101 63084 19	0.64545 83070 44	0.57249 87516 45	1.03677 46289 84
36	0.67903 11148 07	0.66223 00756 33	0.58670 80299 11	1.03861 92179 16
37	0.69698 27063 71	0.67888 43452 41	0.60074 02132 33	1.04048 48646 13
38	0.71487 06336 43	0.69542 06978 30	0.61459 09974 66	1.04236 92856 62
39	0.73269 45303 63	0.71183 88775 35	0.62825 61293 59	1.04427 01853 18
40	0.75045 41130 90	0.72813 87877 79	0.64173 14079 40	1.04618 52477 43
41	0.76814 91806 80	0.74432 04881 57	0.65501 26859 05	1.04811 21398 28
42	0.78577 96136 61	0.76038 41911 16	0.66809 58709 95	1.05004 85140 34
43	0.80334 53734 98	0.77633 02584 42	0.68097 69273 71	1.05199 20112 49
44	0.82084 65017 56	0.79215 91975 93	0.69365 18769 84	1.05394 02636 69
45	0.83828 31191 72	0.80787 16578 75	0.70611 68009 34	1.05589 08976 76

K = 1.74149 92344 26774   E = 1.42476 03101 24890
K' = 2.01326 65652 05468   E' = 1.26814 65310 65206

r	u=(r/90)K=F(ϕ,k)	sn u	cn u	dn u
45	0.87074 96172 13	0.74349 60689 20	0.66874 03049 76	0.89945 37199 74
46	0.89009 96087 07	0.75500 08558 02	0.65572 38044 63	0.89613 65742 14
47	0.90944 96002 01	0.76623 66460 95	0.64255 84815 27	0.89283 56586 24
48	0.92879 95916 94	0.77720 28241 07	0.62925 01650 38	0.88955 48613 10
49	0.94814 95831 88	0.78789 89336 77	0.61580 45715 24	0.88629 80033 92
50	0.96749 95746 82	0.79832 46696 08	0.60222 73008 55	0.88306 88355 74
51	0.98684 95661 75	0.80847 98690 49	0.58852 38324 34	0.87987 10349 89
52	1.00619 95576 69	0.81836 45028 44	0.57469 95219 11	0.87670 82022 99
53	1.02554 95491 62	0.82797 86668 87	0.56075 95983 85	0.87358 38590 41
54	1.04489 95406 56	0.83732 25734 89	0.54670 91621 02	0.87050 14452 28
55	1.06424 95321 50	0.84639 65428 09	0.53255 31826 23	0.86746 43171 75
56	1.08359 95236 43	0.85520 09943 43	0.51829 64974 56	0.86447 57455 57
57	1.10294 95151 37	0.86373 64385 13	0.50394 38111 39	0.86153 89136 77
58	1.12229 95066 31	0.87200 34683 67	0.48949 96947 45	0.85865 69159 46
59	1.14164 94981 24	0.88000 27514 06	0.47496 85858 22	0.85583 27565 51
60	1.16099 94896 18	0.88773 50215 62	0.46035 47887 14	0.85306 93483 17
61	1.18034 94811 11	0.89520 10713 36	0.44566 24752 88	0.85036 95117 35
62	1.19969 94726 05	0.90240 17441 12	0.43089 56860 11	0.84773 59741 50
63	1.21904 94640 99	0.90933 79266 67	0.41605 83313 97	0.84517 13691 15
64	1.23839 94555 92	0.91601 05418 70	0.40115 41937 74	0.84267 82358 66
65	1.25774 94470 86	0.92242 05416 04	0.38618 69293 85	0.84025 90189 42
66	1.27709 94385 80	0.92856 88998 98	0.37116 00707 81	0.83791 60679 18
67	1.29644 94300 73	0.93445 66062 99	0.35607 70295 10	0.83565 16372 41
68	1.31579 94215 67	0.94008 46594 67	0.34094 10990 69	0.83346 78861 72
69	1.33514 94130 61	0.94545 40610 23	0.32575 54581 20	0.83136 68788 11
70	1.35449 94045 54	0.95056 58096 34	0.31052 31739 42	0.82935 05841 96
71	1.37384 93960 48	0.95542 08953 57	0.29524 72061 09	0.82742 08764 73
72	1.39319 93875 41	0.96002 02942 36	0.27993 04103 78	0.82557 95351 22
73	1.41254 93790 35	0.96436 49631 56	0.26457 55427 81	0.82382 82452 34
74	1.43189 93705 29	0.96845 58349 56	0.24918 52638 91	0.82216 85978 24
75	1.45124 93620 22	0.97229 38138 11	0.23376 21432 66	0.82060 20901 76
76	1.47059 93535 16	0.97587 97708 74	0.21830 86640 48	0.81913 01262 16
77	1.48994 93450 10	0.97921 45401 80	0.20282 72277 08	0.81775 40168 95
78	1.50929 93365 03	0.98229 89148 21	0.18732 01589 27	0.81647 49805 85
79	1.52864 93279 97	0.98513 36433 87	0.17178 97105 97	0.81529 41434 74
80	1.54799 93194 90	0.98771 94266 67	0.15623 80689 34	0.81421 25399 60
81	1.56734 93109 84	0.99005 69146 25	0.14066 73586 96	0.81323 11130 34
82	1.58669 93024 78	0.99214 67036 35	0.12507 96484 92	0.81235 07146 42
83	1.60604 92939 71	0.99398 93339 81	0.10947 69561 67	0.81157 21060 42
84	1.62539 92854 65	0.99558 52876 31	0.09386 12542 68	0.81089 59581 16
85	1.64474 92769 59	0.99693 49862 61	0.07823 44755 71	0.81032 28516 70
86	1.66409 92684 52	0.99803 87895 58	0.06259 85186 57	0.80985 32776 95
87	1.68344 92599 46	0.99889 69937 71	0.04695 52535 47	0.80948 76375 92
88	1.70279 92514 40	0.99950 98305 39	0.03130 65273 65	0.80922 62433 61
89	1.72214 92429 33	0.99987 74659 73	0.01565 41700 34	0.80906 93177 54
90	1.74149 92344 27	1.00000 00000 00	0.00000 00000 00	0.80901 69943 75

q = 0.02646 71830 76961 27   D(90) = 1.11178 59405 02842
q'= 0.06603 86859 10861 03   1/D(90) = 0.89945 37199 73934

r	ϕ	$E(\phi,k)$	A(r)	D(r)
45	0.83828 31191 72	0.80787 16578 75	0.70611 68009 34	1.05589 08976 76
46	0.85565 54246 28	0.82346 84264 98	0.71836 78408 21	1.05784 15367 31
47	0.87296 36940 47	0.83895 04245 32	0.73040 12000 94	1.05978 98042 73
48	0.89020 82792 04	0.85431 87027 67	0.74221 31453 80	1.06173 33266 09
49	0.90738 96064 70	0.86957 44375 14	0.75380 00078 07	1.06366 97358 12
50	0.92450 81754 74	0.88471 89263 49	0.76515 81843 21	1.06559 66726 00
51	0.94156 45577 18	0.89975 35838 28	0.77628 41389 81	1.06751 17892 18
52	0.95855 93951 19	0.91467 99371 82	0.78717 44042 45	1.06941 27522 90
53	0.97549 33985 06	0.92949 96220 07	0.79782 55822 42	1.07129 72456 71
54	0.99236 73460 65	0.94421 43779 68	0.80823 43460 28	1.07316 29732 63
55	1.00918 20817 38	0.95882 60445 25	0.81839 74408 27	1.07500 76618 18
56	1.02593 85135 89	0.97333 65566 96	0.82831 16852 50	1.07682 90637 02
57	1.04263 76121 24	0.98774 79408 61	0.83797 39725 01	1.07862 49596 43
58	1.05928 04085 91	1.00206 23106 37	0.84738 12715 59	1.08039 31614 28
59	1.07586 79932 40	1.01628 18627 99	0.85653 06283 47	1.08213 15145 72
60	1.09240 15135 74	1.03040 88732 93	0.86541 91668 68	1.08383 79009 46
61	1.10888 21725 64	1.04444 56933 24	0.87404 40903 30	1.08551 02413 56
62	1.12531 12268 59	1.05839 47455 26	0.88240 26822 38	1.08714 64980 82
63	1.14168 99849 76	1.07225 85202 35	0.89049 23074 73	1.08874 46773 54
64	1.15801 98054 79	1.08603 95718 53	0.89831 04133 31	1.09030 28317 88
65	1.17430 20951 49	1.09974 05153 19	0.90585 45305 48	1.09181 90627 60
66	1.19053 83071 52	1.11336 40226 78	0.91312 22742 92	1.09329 15227 18
67	1.20672 99391 98	1.12691 28197 62	0.92011 13451 25	1.09471 84174 33
68	1.22287 85317 00	1.14038 96829 78	0.92681 95299 42	1.09609 80081 91
69	1.23898 56659 31	1.15379 74362 03	0.93324 47028 73	1.09742 86139 08
70	1.25505 29621 84	1.16713 89477 91	0.93938 48261 57	1.09870 86131 84
71	1.27108 20779 35	1.18041 71276 84	0.94523 79509 85	1.09993 64462 74
72	1.28707 47060 10	1.19363 49246 33	0.95080 22183 07	1.10111 06169 94
73	1.30303 25727 51	1.20679 53235 26	0.95607 58596 09	1.10222 96945 44
74	1.31895 74361 98	1.21990 13428 16	0.96105 71976 52	1.10329 23152 53
75	1.33485 10842 71	1.23295 60320 49	0.96574 46471 74	1.10429 71842 38
76	1.35071 53329 54	1.24596 24694 93	0.97013 67155 67	1.10524 30769 90
77	1.36655 20245 02	1.25892 37598 56	0.97423 20035 01	1.10612 88408 58
78	1.38236 30256 36	1.27184 30320 95	0.97802 92055 25	1.10695 33964 63
79	1.39815 02257 64	1.28472 34373 12	0.98152 71106 16	1.10771 57390 08
80	1.41391 55351 94	1.29756 81467 28	0.98472 46027 08	1.10841 49395 05
81	1.42966 08833 67	1.31038 03497 32	0.98762 06611 58	1.10905 01459 11
82	1.44538 82170 87	1.32316 32519 98	0.99021 43611 94	1.10962 05841 60
83	1.46109 94987 66	1.33592 00736 76	0.99250 48743 12	1.11012 55591 15
84	1.47679 67046 74	1.34865 40476 24	0.99449 14686 28	1.11056 44554 09
85	1.49248 18231 87	1.36136 84177 10	0.99617 35092 03	1.11093 67381 98
86	1.50815 68530 51	1.37406 64371 49	0.99755 04583 10	1.11124 19538 14
87	1.52382 38016 48	1.38675 13668 86	0.99862 18756 73	1.11147 97303 18
88	1.53948 46832 59	1.39942 64740 08	0.99938 74186 58	1.11164 97779 51
89	1.55514 15173 40	1.41209 50301 82	0.99984 68424 17	1.11175 18894 91
90	1.57079 63267 95	1.42476 03101 25	1.00000 00000 00	1.11178 59405 03

ELLIPTIC FUNCTIONS TABLE $\theta = 37°$

K = 1.75216 52364 68845
K′= 1.99266 97557 34209

E = 1.41707 49233 71952
E′= 1.27757 39482 50391

r	u=(r/90)K=F(φ,k)	sn u	cn u	dn u
0	0.00000 00000 00	0.00000 00000 00	1.00000 00000 00	1.00000 00000 00
1	0.01946 85026 27	0.01946 68275 15	0.99981 05033 59	0.99993 13720 04
2	0.03893 70052 55	0.03892 36078 26	0.99924 21892 38	0.99972 56014 45
3	0.05840 55078 82	0.05836 03110 48	0.99829 55845 31	0.99938 30282 99
4	0.07787 40105 10	0.07776 69418 69	0.99697 15656 69	0.99890 42181 39
5	0.09734 25131 37	0.09713 35566 54	0.99527 13560 49	0.99828 99605 65
6	0.11681 10157 65	0.11645 02803 40	0.99319 65224 51	0.99754 12670 22
7	0.13627 95183 92	0.13570 73230 49	0.99074 89704 62	0.99665 93679 99
8	0.15574 80210 19	0.15489 49963 57	0.98793 09389 34	0.99564 57096 55
9	0.17521 65236 47	0.17400 37291 41	0.98474 49935 11	0.99450 19498 57
10	0.19468 50262 74	0.19302 40829 63	0.98119 40192 42	0.99322 99536 75
11	0.21415 35289 02	0.21194 67669 18	0.97728 12123 40	0.99183 17883 42
12	0.23362 20315 29	0.23076 26518 87	0.97301 00711 16	0.99030 97177 14
13	0.25309 05341 57	0.24946 27841 68	0.96838 43861 38	0.98866 61962 53
14	0.27255 90367 84	0.26803 83984 03	0.96340 82296 62	0.98690 38625 61
15	0.29202 75394 11	0.28648 09297 95	0.95808 59444 04	0.98502 55325 02
16	0.31149 60420 39	0.30478 20255 41	0.95242 21316 77	0.98303 41919 45
17	0.33096 45446 66	0.32293 35554 79	0.94642 16389 89	0.98093 29891 57
18	0.35043 30472 94	0.34092 76219 02	0.94008 95471 31	0.97872 52268 81
19	0.36990 15499 21	0.35875 65685 18	0.93343 11568 32	0.97641 43541 52
20	0.38937 00525 49	0.37641 29885 42	0.92645 19750 41	0.97400 39578 61
21	0.40883 85551 76	0.39388 97319 00	0.91915 77008 89	0.97149 77541 26
22	0.42830 70578 03	0.41117 99115 45	0.91155 42114 11	0.96889 95794 99
23	0.44777 55604 31	0.42827 69088 70	0.90364 75470 72	0.96621 33820 42
24	0.46724 40630 58	0.44517 43782 24	0.89544 38971 67	0.96344 32123 19
25	0.48671 25656 86	0.46186 62505 36	0.88694 95851 60	0.96059 32143 25
26	0.50618 10683 13	0.47834 67360 61	0.87817 10540 09	0.95766 76164 06
27	0.52564 95709 41	0.49461 03262 43	0.86911 48515 44	0.95467 07221 81
28	0.54511 80735 68	0.51065 17947 38	0.85978 76159 44	0.95160 69015 19
29	0.56458 65761 96	0.52646 61975 98	0.85019 60613 80	0.94848 05815 89
30	0.58405 50788 23	0.54204 88726 50	0.84034 69638 54	0.94529 62380 16
31	0.60352 35814 50	0.55739 54380 87	0.83024 71473 00	0.94205 83861 76
32	0.62299 20840 78	0.57250 17903 21	0.81990 34699 76	0.93877 15726 46
33	0.64246 05867 05	0.58736 41011 02	0.80932 28112 05	0.93544 03668 37
34	0.66192 90893 33	0.60197 88139 63	0.79851 20584 81	0.93206 93528 40
35	0.68139 75919 60	0.61634 26400 13	0.78747 80949 98	0.92866 31214 91
36	0.70086 60945 88	0.63045 25531 16	0.77622 77876 18	0.92522 62626 87
37	0.72033 45972 15	0.64430 57845 07	0.76476 79753 04	0.92176 33579 51
38	0.73980 30998 42	0.65789 98168 66	0.75310 54580 65	0.91827 89732 84
39	0.75927 16024 70	0.67123 23779 08	0.74124 69864 01	0.91477 76522 96
40	0.77874 01050 97	0.68430 14335 14	0.72919 92512 96	0.91126 39096 30
41	0.79820 86077 25	0.69710 51804 64	0.71696 88747 57	0.90774 22246 96
42	0.81767 71103 52	0.70964 20387 91	0.70456 24009 14	0.90421 70357 12
43	0.83714 56129 80	0.72191 06438 07	0.69198 62876 95	0.90069 27340 57
44	0.85661 41156 07	0.73390 98378 50	0.67924 68990 78	0.89717 36589 42
45	0.87608 26182 34	0.74563 86617 63	0.66635 04979 24	0.89366 40924 01

146

ELLIPTIC FUNCTIONS   TABLE $\theta = 37°$

q = 0.02807 67957 17219 06   D(90) = 1.11898 86765 09385
q'= 0.06313 88302 96461 25   1/D(90) = 0.89366 40924 01218

r	ϕ	$E(\phi,k)$	$A(r)$	$D(r)$
0	0.00000 00000 00	0.00000 00000 00	0.00000 00000 00	1.00000 00000 00
1	0.01946 80572 41	0.01946 76118 74	0.01739 74351 89	1.00003 62391 36
2	0.03893 34430 50	0.03892 98814 33	0.03478 96713 85	1.00014 49124 03
3	0.05839 34904 09	0.05838 14773 85	0.05217 15109 06	1.00032 58874 35
4	0.07784 55411 16	0.07781 70904 48	0.06953 77586 85	1.00057 89438 00
5	0.09728 69501 66	0.09723 14442 37	0.08688 32235 81	1.00090 37732 69
6	0.11671 50900 87	0.11661 93060 43	0.10420 27196 92	1.00129 99801 91
7	0.13612 73552 38	0.13597 54974 30	0.12149 10676 65	1.00176 70819 74
8	0.15552 11660 38	0.15529 49046 29	0.13874 30960 06	1.00230 45096 76
9	0.17489 39731 28	0.17457 24886 87	0.15595 36424 04	1.00291 16086 89
10	0.19424 32614 52	0.19380 32953 34	0.17311 75550 42	1.00358 76395 47
11	0.21356 65542 37	0.21298 24645 26	0.19022 96939 20	1.00433 17788 15
12	0.23286 14168 81	0.23210 52396 46	0.20728 49321 80	1.00514 31200 99
13	0.25212 54607 24	0.25116 69763 19	0.22427 81574 30	1.00602 06751 48
14	0.27135 63466 90	0.27016 31508 18	0.24120 42730 78	1.00696 33750 51
15	0.29055 17888 11	0.28908 93680 38	0.25805 81996 62	1.00797 00715 47
16	0.30970 95576 08	0.30794 13690 15	0.27483 48761 92	1.00903 95384 16
17	0.32882 74833 24	0.32671 50379 58	0.29152 92614 88	1.01017 04729 72
18	0.34790 34590 12	0.34540 64088 03	0.30813 63355 30	1.01136 14976 54
19	0.36693 54434 61	0.36401 16712 46	0.32465 11008 02	1.01261 11616 98
20	0.38592 14639 64	0.38252 71762 63	0.34106 85836 56	1.01391 79429 01
21	0.40485 96189 18	0.40094 94411 04	0.35738 38356 61	1.01528 02494 83
22	0.42374 80802 53	0.41927 51537 51	0.37359 19349 75	1.01669 64220 14
23	0.44258 50956 90	0.43750 11768 46	0.38968 79877 06	1.01816 47354 40
24	0.46136 89908 28	0.45562 45510 83	0.40566 71292 90	1.01968 34011 86
25	0.48009 81710 47	0.47364 24980 69	0.42152 45258 63	1.02125 05693 24
26	0.49877 11232 40	0.49155 24226 60	0.43725 53756 44	1.02286 43308 34
27	0.51738 64173 68	0.50935 19147 83	0.45285 49103 17	1.02452 27199 26
28	0.53594 27078 35	0.52703 87507 45	0.46831 83964 23	1.02622 37164 31
29	0.55443 87346 93	0.54461 08940 59	0.48364 11367 48	1.02796 52482 60
30	0.57287 33246 71	0.56206 64957 79	0.49881 84717 20	1.02974 51939 34
31	0.59124 53920 32	0.57940 38943 81	0.51384 57808 07	1.03156 13851 60
32	0.60955 39392 62	0.59662 16151 97	0.52871 84839 14	1.03341 16094 71
33	0.62779 80576 02	0.61371 83694 19	0.54343 20427 90	1.03529 36129 28
34	0.64597 69274 05	0.63069 30527 10	0.55798 19624 28	1.03720 51028 55
35	0.66408 98183 48	0.64754 47434 18	0.57236 37924 73	1.03914 37506 39
36	0.68213 60894 91	0.66427 27004 41	0.58657 31286 26	1.04110 71945 60
37	0.70011 51891 79	0.68087 63607 51	0.60060 56140 52	1.04309 30426 71
38	0.71802 66548 14	0.69735 53366 04	0.61445 69407 81	1.04509 88757 10
39	0.73587 01124 85	0.71370 94124 66	0.62812 28511 19	1.04712 22500 46
40	0.75364 52764 66	0.72993 85416 68	0.64159 91390 42	1.04916 07006 57
41	0.77135 19485 91	0.74604 28428 30	0.65488 16516 03	1.05121 17441 30
42	0.78899 00175 09	0.76202 25960 58	0.66796 62903 25	1.05327 28816 88
43	0.80655 94578 31	0.77787 82389 63	0.68084 90125 95	1.05534 16022 35
44	0.82406 03291 58	0.79361 03624 98	0.69352 58330 47	1.05741 53854 10
45	0.84149 27750 23	0.80921 97066 62	0.70599 28249 49	1.05949 17046 64

147

K = 1.75216 52364 68845
K' = 1.99266 97557 34209

E = 1.41707 49233 71952
E' = 1.27757 39482 50391

r	u=(r/90)K=F(φ,k)	sn u	cn u	dn u
45	0.87608 26182 34	0.74563 86617 63	0.66635 04979 24	0.89366 40924 01
46	0.89555 11208 62	0.75709 63461 85	0.65330 32393 87	0.89016 82545 93
47	0.91501 96234 89	0.76828 23026 43	0.64011 11649 13	0.88669 02994 21
48	0.93448 81261 17	0.77919 61145 24	0.62678 01968 08	0.88323 43104 64
49	0.95395 66287 44	0.78983 75279 36	0.61331 61333 80	0.87980 42972 11
50	0.97342 51313 72	0.80020 64424 92	0.59972 46446 45	0.87640 41915 93
51	0.99289 36339 99	0.81030 29020 67	0.58601 12685 80	0.87303 78448 17
52	1.01236 21366 26	0.82012 70855 32	0.57218 14079 27	0.86970 90244 71
53	1.03183 06392 54	0.82967 92975 20	0.55824 03275 18	0.86642 14119 15
54	1.05129 91418 81	0.83895 99592 25	0.54419 31521 23	0.86317 85999 33
55	1.07076 76445 09	0.84796 95992 81	0.53004 48647 94	0.85998 40906 41
56	1.09023 61471 36	0.85670 88447 31	0.51580 03056 99	0.85684 12936 38
57	1.10970 46497 64	0.86517 84121 11	0.50146 41714 19	0.85375 35243 94
58	1.12917 31523 91	0.87337 90986 72	0.48704 10147 03	0.85072 40028 54
59	1.14864 16550 18	0.88131 17737 53	0.47253 52446 59	0.84775 58522 55
60	1.16811 01576 46	0.88897 73703 30	0.45795 11273 50	0.84485 20981 35
61	1.18757 86602 73	0.89637 68767 48	0.44329 27868 04	0.84201 56675 32
62	1.20704 71629 01	0.90351 13286 50	0.42856 42063 93	0.83924 93883 48
63	1.22651 56655 28	0.91038 18011 28	0.41376 92305 80	0.83655 59888 78
64	1.24598 41681 56	0.91698 94010 88	0.39891 15670 08	0.83393 80974 84
65	1.26545 26707 83	0.92333 52598 51	0.38399 47889 18	0.83139 82423 96
66	1.28492 11734 10	0.92942 05260 02	0.36902 23378 68	0.82893 88516 48
67	1.30438 96760 38	0.93524 63584 82	0.35399 75267 51	0.82656 22531 11
68	1.32385 81786 65	0.94081 39199 34	0.33892 35430 86	0.82427 06746 35
69	1.34332 66812 93	0.94612 43703 19	0.32380 34525 58	0.82206 62442 66
70	1.36279 51839 20	0.95117 88607 88	0.30864 02028 11	0.81995 09905 49
71	1.38226 36865 48	0.95597 85278 28	0.29343 66274 55	0.81792 68428 93
72	1.40173 21891 75	0.96052 44876 81	0.27819 54502 95	0.81599 56319 84
73	1.42120 06918 03	0.96481 78310 35	0.26291 92897 40	0.81415 90902 49
74	1.44066 91944 30	0.96885 96179 87	0.24761 06634 09	0.81241 88523 56
75	1.46013 76970 57	0.97265 08732 93	0.23227 19928 94	0.81077 64557 32
76	1.47960 61996 85	0.97619 25818 82	0.21690 56086 84	0.80923 33411 03
77	1.49907 47023 12	0.97948 56846 61	0.20151 37552 25	0.80779 08530 44
78	1.51854 32049 40	0.98253 10745 84	0.18609 85961 19	0.80645 02405 27
79	1.53801 17075 67	0.98532 95930 09	0.17066 22194 30	0.80521 26574 63
80	1.55748 02101 95	0.98788 20263 24	0.15520 66431 13	0.80407 91632 21
81	1.57694 87128 22	0.99018 91028 49	0.13973 38205 24	0.80305 07231 91
82	1.59641 72154 49	0.99225 14900 17	0.12424 56460 36	0.80212 82091 64
83	1.61588 57180 77	0.99406 97918 19	0.10874 39607 16	0.80131 23998 93
84	1.63535 42207 04	0.99564 45465 32	0.09323 05580 82	0.80060 39814 59
85	1.65482 27233 32	0.99697 62247 09	0.07770 71899 20	0.80000 35476 62
86	1.67429 12259 59	0.99806 52274 42	0.06217 55721 49	0.79951 16003 57
87	1.69375 97285 87	0.99891 18848 96	0.04663 73907 31	0.79912 85497 48
88	1.71322 82312 14	0.99951 64551 09	0.03109 43076 22	0.79885 47146 26
89	1.73269 67338 41	0.99987 91230 59	0.01554 79667 48	0.79869 03225 64
90	1.75216 52364 69	1.00000 00000 00	0.00000 00000 00	0.79863 55100 47

q = 0.02807 67957 17219 06

q′ = 0.06313 88302 96461 25

D(90) = 1.11898 86765 09385

1/D(90) = 0.89366 40924 01218

r	ϕ	$E(\phi, k)$	A(r)	D(r)
45	0.84149 27750 23	0.80921 97066 62	0.70599 28249 49	1.05949 17046 64
46	0.85885 70217 27	0.82470 71560 77	0.71824 61215 78	1.06156 80303 33
47	0.87615 33770 95	0.84007 37354 58	0.73028 19175 80	1.06364 18327 23
48	0.89338 22291 41	0.85532 06050 19	0.74209 64703 40	1.06571 05851 90
49	0.91054 40446 69	0.87044 90558 02	0.75368 61013 20	1.06777 17672 19
50	0.92763 93677 88	0.88546 05049 78	0.76504 71974 09	1.06982 28674 96
51	0.94466 88183 78	0.90035 64911 20	0.77617 62122 40	1.07186 13869 68
52	0.96163 30904 86	0.91513 86694 75	0.78706 96675 15	1.07388 48418 86
53	0.97853 29506 71	0.92980 88072 44	0.79772 41542 97	1.07589 07668 36
54	0.99536 92363 07	0.94436 87788 86	0.80813 63343 06	1.07787 67177 39
55	1.01214 28538 33	0.95882 05614 72	0.81830 29411 83	1.07984 02748 33
56	1.01885 47769 71	0.97316 62300 78	0.82822 07817 48	1.08177 90456 17
57	1.04550 60449 10	0.98740 79532 56	0.83788 67372 37	1.08369 06677 75
58	1.06209 77604 56	1.00154 79885 71	0.84729 77645 19	1.08557 28120 47
59	1.07863 10881 67	1.01558 86782 28	0.85645 08972 93	1.08742 31850 74
60	1.09510 72524 53	1.02953 24447 87	0.86534 32472 66	1.08923 95321 89
61	1.11152 75356 69	1.04338 17869 89	0.87397 20053 07	1.09101 96401 68
62	1.12789 32761 93	1.05713 92756 74	0.88233 44425 75	1.09276 13399 28
63	1.14420 58664 88	1.07080 75498 27	0.89042 79116 32	1.09446 25091 68
64	1.16046 67511 60	1.08438 93127 31	0.89824 98475 17	1.09612 10749 61
65	1.17667 74250 10	1.09788 73282 42	0.90579 77688 06	1.09773 50162 77
66	1.19283 94310 88	1.11130 44171 94	0.91306 92786 34	1.09930 23664 48
67	1.20895 43587 35	1.12464 34539 16	0.92006 20656 96	1.10082 12155 67
68	1.22502 38416 40	1.13790 73628 90	0.92677 39052 13	1.10228 97128 16
69	1.24104 95558 94	1.15109 91155 26	0.93320 26598 73	1.10370 60687 21
70	1.25703 32180 46	1.16422 17270 60	0.93934 62807 30	1.10506 85573 36
71	1.27297 65831 76	1.17727 82535 91	0.94520 28080 85	1.10637 55183 44
72	1.28888 14429 60	1.19027 17892 22	0.95077 03723 15	1.10762 53590 89
73	1.30474 96237 63	1.20320 54633 39	0.95604 71946 88	1.10881 65565 07
74	1.32058 29847 21	1.21608 24379 93	0.96103 15881 24	1.10994 76589 93
75	1.33638 34158 48	1.22890 59054 06	0.96572 19579 29	1.11101 72881 67
76	1.35215 28361 49	1.24167 90855 84	0.97011 68024 93	1.11202 41405 53
77	1.36789 31917 40	1.25440 52240 33	0.97421 47139 45	1.11296 69891 71
78	1.38360 64539 81	1.26708 75895 84	0.97801 43787 70	1.11384 46850 35
79	1.39929 46176 23	1.27972 94722 98	0.98151 45783 92	1.11465 61585 51
80	1.41495 96989 61	1.29233 41814 84	0.98471 41897 08	1.11540 04208 20
81	1.43060 37339 97	1.30490 50437 79	0.98761 21855 91	1.11607 65648 49
82	1.44622 87766 17	1.31744 54013 21	0.99020 76353 42	1.11668 37666 55
83	1.46183 68967 73	1.32995 86099 90	0.99249 97051 09	1.11722 12862 67
84	1.47743 01786 75	1.34244 80377 08	0.99448 76582 56	1.11768 84686 33
85	1.49301 07189 92	1.35491 70628 10	0.99617 08556 96	1.11808 47444 16
86	1.50858 06250 57	1.36736 90724 57	0.99754 87561 75	1.11840 96306 89
87	1.52414 20130 82	1.37980 74610 95	0.99862 09165 18	1.11866 27315 24
88	1.53969 70063 72	1.39223 56289 55	0.99938 69918 25	1.11884 37384 77
89	1.55524 77335 53	1.40465 69805 79	0.99984 67356 27	1.11895 24309 58
90	1.57079 63267 95	1.41707 49233 72	1.00000 00000 00	1.11898 86765 09

K = 1.76325 61840 59342

K' = 1.97288 22662 74650

E = 1.40923 97160 46096

E' = 1.28695 37387 83001

r	u=(r/90)K=F(φ,k)	sn u	cn u	dn u
0	0.00000 00000 00	0.00000 00000 00	1.00000 00000 00	1.00000 00000 00
1	0.01959 17353 78	0.01959 00071 34	0.99980 80973 97	0.99992 72657 53
2	0.03918 34707 57	0.03916 96485 27	0.99923 25748 46	0.99970 91852 26
3	0.05877 52061 35	0.05872 85770 27	0.99827 39875 61	0.99934 61247 06
4	0.07836 69415 14	0.07825 64825 89	0.99693 32590 16	0.99883 86935 00
5	0.09795 86768 92	0.09774 31106 27	0.99521 16781 49	0.99818 77421 94
6	0.11755 04122 71	0.11717 82801 34	0.99311 08954 52	0.99739 43602 14
7	0.13714 21476 49	0.13655 19014 93	0.99063 29179 87	0.99645 98727 26
8	0.15673 38830 27	0.15585 39938 97	0.98778 01033 56	0.99538 58368 76
9	0.17632 56184 06	0.17507 47023 25	0.98455 51526 48	0.99417 40373 93
10	0.19591 73537 84	0.19420 43139 79	0.98096 11024 05	0.99282 64815 84
11	0.21550 90891 63	0.21323 32741 50	0.97700 13156 57	0.99134 53937 40
12	0.23510 08245 41	0.23215 22014 26	0.97267 94720 63	0.98973 32089 92
13	0.25469 25599 20	0.25095 19021 94	0.96799 95572 24	0.98799 25666 37
14	0.27428 42952 98	0.26962 33843 99	0.96296 58512 04	0.98612 63029 77
15	0.29387 60306 77	0.28815 78704 93	0.95758 29163 44	0.98413 74437 02
16	0.31346 77660 55	0.30654 68095 37	0.95185 55844 05	0.98202 91958 63
17	0.33305 95014 33	0.32478 18884 42	0.94578 89431 26	0.97980 49394 64
18	0.35265 12368 12	0.34285 50422 82	0.93938 83222 51	0.97746 82187 18
19	0.37224 29721 90	0.36075 84636 85	0.93265 92790 94	0.97502 27330 12
20	0.39183 47075 69	0.37848 46112 72	0.92560 75837 15	0.97247 23276 17
21	0.41142 64429 47	0.39602 62171 19	0.91823 92037 78	0.96982 09841 92
22	0.43101 81783 26	0.41337 62932 58	0.91056 02891 47	0.96707 28111 09
23	0.45060 99137 04	0.43052 81371 89	0.90257 71563 08	0.96423 20336 67
24	0.47020 16490 82	0.44747 53364 21	0.89429 62726 61	0.96130 29842 06
25	0.48979 33844 61	0.46421 17720 42	0.88572 42407 76	0.95829 00921 83
26	0.50938 51198 39	0.48073 16213 38	0.87686 77826 48	0.95519 78742 38
27	0.52897 68552 18	0.49702 93594 62	0.86773 37240 38	0.95203 09242 96
28	0.54856 85905 96	0.51309 97601 89	0.85832 89789 43	0.94879 39037 29
29	0.56816 03259 75	0.52893 78957 77	0.84866 05342 60	0.94549 15316 24
30	0.58775 20613 53	0.54453 91359 56	0.83873 54346 94	0.94212 85751 83
31	0.60734 37967 32	0.55989 91460 83	0.82856 07679 68	0.93870 98402 90
32	0.62693 55321 10	0.57501 38844 95	0.81814 36503 68	0.93524 01622 64
33	0.64652 72674 88	0.58987 95991 00	0.80749 12126 86	0.93172 43968 43
34	0.66611 90028 67	0.60449 28232 37	0.79661 05865 82	0.92816 74113 95
35	0.68571 07382 45	0.61885 03708 54	0.78550 88914 16	0.92457 40764 06
36	0.70530 24736 24	0.63294 93310 43	0.77419 32215 75	0.92094 92572 45
37	0.72489 42090 02	0.64678 70619 75	0.76267 06343 25	0.91729 78062 31
38	0.74448 59443 81	0.66036 11842 83	0.75094 81382 18	0.91362 45550 13
39	0.76407 76797 59	0.67366 95739 31	0.73903 26820 64	0.90993 43072 82
40	0.78366 94151 37	0.68671 03546 24	0.72693 11445 06	0.90623 18318 10
41	0.80326 11505 16	0.69948 18897 90	0.71465 03241 84	0.90252 18558 45
42	0.82285 28858 94	0.71198 27741 97	0.70219 69305 30	0.89880 90588 46
43	0.84244 46212 73	0.72421 18252 36	0.68957 75751 78	0.89509 80665 79
44	0.86203 63566 51	0.73616 80739 10	0.67679 87640 03	0.89139 34455 63
45	0.88162 80920 30	0.74785 07555 90	0.66386 68897 93	0.88769 96978 75

q = 0.02974 53239 19583 19   D(90) = 1.12650 70861 17339
q′= 0.06033 83890 33716 41   1/D(90) = 0.88769 96978 74637

r	φ	E(φ,k)	A(r)	D(r)
0	0.00000 00000 00	0.00000 00000 00	0.00000 00000 00	1.00000 00000 00
1	0.01959 12603 55	0.01959 07853 53	0.01739 07134 23	1.00003 85282 94
2	0.03917 96715 28	0.03917 58729 63	0.03477 62421 83	1.00015 40662 51
3	0.05876 23891 24	0.05874 95771 42	0.05215 14028 86	1.00034 64731 49
4	0.07833 65783 05	0.07830 62362 61	0.06951 10146 80	1.00061 55146 45
5	0.09789 94185 40	0.09784 02246 61	0.08684 99005 26	1.00096 08630 54
6	0.11744 81083 05	0.11734 59644 18	0.10416 28884 70	1.00138 20977 55
7	0.13697 98697 35	0.13681 79369 18	0.12144 48129 22	1.00187 87056 98
8	0.15649 19532 07	0.15625 06941 99	0.13869 05159 25	1.00245 00820 27
9	0.17598 16418 42	0.17563 88700 15	0.15589 48484 44	1.00309 55308 21
10	0.19544 62559 14	0.19497 71905 76	0.17305 26716 44	1.00381 42659 38
11	0.21488 31571 62	0.21426 04849 34	0.19015 88581 76	1.00460 54119 70
12	0.23428 97529 77	0.23348 36949 76	0.20720 82934 70	1.00546 80053 13
13	0.25366 35004 68	0.25264 18849 76	0.22419 58770 27	1.00640 09953 35
14	0.27300 19103 99	0.27173 02506 98	0.24111 65237 18	1.00740 32456 55
15	0.29230 25509 64	0.29074 41280 08	0.25796 51650 91	1.00847 35355 31
16	0.31156 30514 31	0.30967 90009 66	0.27473 67506 76	1.00961 05613 38
17	0.33078 11056 04	0.32853 05093 86	0.29142 62493 01	1.01081 29381 61
18	0.34995 44751 32	0.34729 44558 49	0.30802 86504 11	1.01207 92014 77
19	0.36908 09926 38	0.36596 68121 32	0.32453 89653 95	1.01340 78089 38
20	0.38815 85646 63	0.38454 37250 71	0.34095 22289 18	1.01479 71422 47
21	0.40718 51744 38	0.40302 15218 25	0.35726 35002 53	1.01624 55091 33
22	0.42615 88844 57	0.42139 67145 56	0.37346 78646 33	1.01775 11454 03
23	0.44507 78388 68	0.43966 60045 00	0.38956 04345 93	1.01931 22170 95
24	0.46394 02656 63	0.45782 62854 63	0.40553 63513 31	1.02092 68227 08
25	0.48274 44786 79	0.47587 46467 08	0.42139 07860 65	1.02259 29955 17
26	0.50148 88794 05	0.49380 83752 77	0.43711 89414 07	1.02430 87059 69
27	0.52017 19585 93	0.51162 49577 30	0.45271 60527 30	1.02607 18641 48
28	0.53879 22976 73	0.52932 20813 35	0.46817 73895 51	1.02788 03223 27
29	0.55734 85699 80	0.54689 76347 07	0.48349 82569 15	1.02973 18775 77
30	0.57583 95417 94	0.56434 97079 29	0.49867 39967 85	1.03162 42744 51
31	0.59426 40731 83	0.58167 65921 61	0.51369 99894 35	1.03355 52077 29
32	0.61262 11186 78	0.59887 67787 63	0.52857 16548 51	1.03552 23252 27
33	0.63090 97277 52	0.61594 89579 65	0.54328 44541 33	1.03752 32306 59
34	0.64912 90451 43	0.63289 20170 92	0.55783 38909 03	1.03955 54865 54
35	0.66727 83109 92	0.64970 50383 74	0.57221 55127 15	1.04161 66172 28
36	0.68535 68608 22	0.66638 72963 74	0.58642 49124 64	1.04370 41117 94
37	0.70336 41253 65	0.68293 82550 59	0.60045 77298 07	1.04581 54272 23
38	0.72129 96302 26	0.69935 75645 29	0.61430 96525 73	1.04794 79914 40
39	0.73916 29954 09	0.71564 50574 50	0.62797 64181 84	1.05009 92064 55
40	0.75695 39347 01	0.73180 07452 06	0.64145 38150 67	1.05226 64515 32
41	0.77467 22549 18	0.74782 48138 00	0.65473 76840 77	1.05444 70863 75
42	0.79231 78550 35	0.76371 76195 39	0.66782 39199 03	1.05663 84543 46
43	0.80989 07251 90	0.77947 96845 13	0.68070 84724 86	1.05883 78857 06
44	0.82739 09455 74	0.79511 16919 16	0.69338 73484 27	1.06104 27008 58
45	0.84481 86852 21	0.81061 44812 20	0.70585 66123 88	1.06325 02136 20

ELLIPTIC FUNCTIONS   TABLE $\theta = 38°$

K = 1.76325 61840 59342
K'= 1.97288 22662 74650

E = 1.40923 97160 46096
E'= 1.28695 37387 83001

r	u=(r/90)K=F(ϕ,k)	sn u	cn u	dn u
45	0.88162 80920 30	0.74785 07555 90	0.66386 68897 93	0.88769 96978 75
46	0.90121 98274 08	0.75925 93005 61	0.65078 82255 48	0.88402 12563 03
47	0.92081 15627 87	0.77039 33244 03	0.63756 89184 05	0.88036 24798 55
48	0.94040 32981 65	0.78125 26182 50	0.62421 49841 82	0.87672 76496 06
49	0.95999 50335 43	0.79183 71389 63	0.61073 23025 34	0.87312 09648 87
50	0.97958 67689 22	0.80214 69992 44	0.59712 66127 08	0.86954 65398 00
51	0.99917 85043 00	0.81218 24577 34	0.58340 35098 88	0.86600 84000 58
52	1.01877 02396 79	0.82194 39091 22	0.56956 84421 18	0.86251 04801 34
53	1.03836 19750 57	0.83143 18743 00	0.55562 67077 80	0.85905 66207 12
54	1.05795 37104 36	0.84064 69905 75	0.54158 34536 23	0.85565 05664 21
55	1.07754 54458 14	0.84959 00019 92	0.52744 36733 10	0.85229 59638 56
56	1.09713 71811 92	0.85826 17497 68	0.51321 22064 84	0.84899 63598 51
57	1.11672 89165 71	0.86666 31628 64	0.49889 37383 19	0.84575 52000 10
58	1.13632 06519 49	0.87479 52487 28	0.48449 27995 37	0.84257 58274 74
59	1.15591 23873 28	0.88265 90842 09	0.47001 37668 87	0.83946 14819 03
60	1.17550 41227 06	0.89025 58066 78	0.45546 08640 44	0.83641 52986 80
61	1.19509 58580 85	0.89758 66053 53	0.44083 81629 26	0.83344 03082 95
62	1.21468 75934 63	0.90465 27128 49	0.42614 95853 98	0.83053 94359 19
63	1.23427 93288 42	0.91145 53969 76	0.41139 89053 49	0.82771 55011 42
64	1.25387 10642 20	0.91799 59527 73	0.39658 97511 19	0.82497 12178 59
65	1.27346 27995 98	0.92427 56948 04	0.38172 56082 52	0.82230 91942 98
66	1.29305 45349 77	0.93029 59497 20	0.36680 98225 71	0.81973 19331 71
67	1.31264 62703 55	0.93605 80490 93	0.35184 56035 37	0.81724 18319 37
68	1.33223 80057 34	0.94156 33225 20	0.33683 60278 89	0.81484 11831 61
69	1.35182 97411 12	0.94681 30910 19	0.32178 40435 37	0.81253 21749 60
70	1.37142 14764 91	0.95180 86606 98	0.30669 24736 95	0.81031 68915 23
71	1.39101 32118 69	0.95655 13167 19	0.29156 40212 41	0.80819 73136 90
72	1.41060 49472 47	0.96104 23175 53	0.27640 12732 82	0.80617 53195 83
73	1.43019 66826 26	0.96528 28895 14	0.26120 67059 07	0.80425 26852 72
74	1.44978 84180 04	0.96927 42215 96	0.24598 26891 26	0.80243 10854 77
75	1.46938 01533 83	0.97301 74605 91	0.23073 14919 66	0.80071 20942 81
76	1.48897 18887 61	0.97651 37065 07	0.21545 52877 14	0.79909 71858 55
77	1.50856 36241 40	0.97976 40082 64	0.20015 61593 12	0.79758 77351 88
78	1.52815 53595 18	0.98276 93596 88	0.18483 61048 56	0.79618 50187 98
79	1.54774 70948 97	0.98553 06957 86	0.16949 70432 29	0.79489 02154 41
80	1.56733 88302 75	0.98804 88893 09	0.15414 08198 22	0.79370 44067 86
81	1.58693 05656 53	0.99032 47475 96	0.13876 92123 58	0.79262 85780 64
82	1.60652 23010 32	0.99235 90097 04	0.12338 39367 95	0.79166 36186 82
83	1.62611 40364 10	0.99415 23438 13	0.10798 66532 98	0.79081 03227 99
84	1.64570 57717 89	0.99570 53449 14	0.09257 89722 89	0.79006 93898 43
85	1.66529 75071 67	0.99701 85327 69	0.07716 24605 37	0.78944 14249 92
86	1.68488 92425 46	0.99809 23501 50	0.06173 86473 12	0.78892 69395 90
87	1.70448 09779 24	0.99892 71613 52	0.04630 90305 72	0.78852 63515 07
88	1.72407 27133 02	0.99952 32509 74	0.03087 50831 84	0.78823 99854 40
89	1.74366 44486 81	0.99988 08229 75	0.01543 82591 75	0.78806 80731 44
90	1.76325 61840 59	1.00000 00000 00	0.00000 00000 00	0.78801 07536 07

152

q = 0.02974 53239 19583 19   D(90) = 1.12650 70861 17339
q'= 0.06033 83890 33716 41   1/D(90) = 0.88769 96978 74637

r	ϕ	$E(\phi,k)$	A(r)	D(r)
45	0.84481 86852 21	0.81061 44812 20	0.70585 66123 88	1.06325 02136 20
46	0.86217 42007 00	0.82598 90432 24	0.71811 23884 95	1.06545 77344 93
47	0.88517 86361 45	0.84123 65150 25	0.73015 08617 32	1.06766 25739 37
48	0.89667 00145 85	0.85635 81749 01	0.74196 82793 23	1.06986 20456 51
49	0.91381 12507 53	0.87135 54371 53	0.75356 09521 13	1.07205 34698 43
50	0.93088 21350 73	0.88622 98469 26	0.76492 52559 37	1.07423 41764 98
51	0.94788 33391 51	0.90098 30750 06	0.77605 76329 80	1.07640 15086 30
52	0.96481 56125 71	0.91561 69126 43	0.78695 45931 21	1.07855 28255 20
53	0.98167 97810 88	0.93013 32663 95	0.79761 27152 67	1.08068 55059 32
54	0.99847 67447 64	0.94453 41530 12	0.80802 86486 81	1.08279 69513 13
55	1.01520 74760 67	0.95882 16943 91	0.81819 91142 79	1.08488 45889 53
56	1.03187 30179 34	0.97299 81125 91	0.82812 09059 29	1.08694 58751 27
57	1.04847 44818 02	0.98706 57249 42	0.83779 08917 15	1.08897 82981 91
58	1.06501 30456 11	1.00102 69392 46	0.84720 60151 99	1.09097 93816 45
59	1.08148 99517 85	1.01488 42490 80	0.85636 32966 53	1.09294 66871 52
60	1.09790 65052 01	1.02864 02292 25	0.86525 98342 73	1.09487 78175 09
61	1.11426 40711 35	1.04229 75312 06	0.87389 28053 69	1.09677 04195 72
62	1.13056 40732 05	1.05585 88789 65	0.88225 94675 39	1.09862 21871 23
63	1.14680 79913 05	1.06932 70646 67	0.89035 71598 08	1.10043 08636 78
64	1.16299 73595 32	1.08270 49446 49	0.89818 33037 49	1.10219 42452 47
65	1.18771 49662 77	1.09599 54354 96	0.90573 54045 77	1.10391 01830 11
66	1.19521 88413 71	1.10920 15102 82	0.91301 10522 07	1.10557 65859 50
67	1.21125 42755 81	1.12232 61949 35	0.92000 79222 95	1.10719 14233 89
68	1.22724 17969 93	1.13537 25647 60	0.92672 37772 38	1.10875 27274 72
69	1.24318 31797 41	1.14834 37411 04	0.93315 64671 49	1.11025 85955 67
70	1.25908 02398 09	1.16124 28881 62	0.93930 39307 96	1.11170 71925 83
71	1.27493 48329 99	1.17407 32099 32	0.94516 41965 12	1.11309 67532 05
72	1.29074 88529 16	1.18683 79473 02	0.95073 53830 61	1.11442 55840 55
73	1.30652 42289 58	1.19954 03752 75	0.95601 57004 82	1.11569 20657 47
74	1.32226 29243 26	1.21218 38003 34	0.96100 34508 84	1.11689 46548 70
75	1.33796 69340 46	1.22477 15579 28	0.96569 70292 09	1.11803 18858 67
76	1.35363 82830 00	1.23730 70100 83	0.97009 49239 58	1.11910 23728 22
77	1.36927 90239 81	1.24979 35431 34	0.97419 57178 73	1.12010 48111 51
78	1.38489 12357 55	1.26223 45655 71	0.97799 80885 84	1.12103 79791 95
79	1.40047 70211 38	1.27463 35059 88	0.98150 08092 11	1.12190 07397 06
80	1.41603 85050 86	1.28699 38111 37	0.98470 27489 24	1.12269 20412 39
81	1.43157 78328 04	1.29931 89440 71	0.98760 28734 68	1.12341 09194 30
82	1.44709 71678 58	1.31161 23823 83	0.99020 02456 34	1.12405 64981 76
83	1.46259 86903 04	1.32387 76165 14	0.99249 40256 94	1.12462 79907 01
84	1.47808 45948 31	1.33611 81481 43	0.99448 34717 91	1.12512 47005 17
85	1.49355 70889 04	1.34833 74886 38	0.99616 79402 82	1.12554 60222 73
86	1.50901 83909 28	1.36053 91575 63	0.99754 68860 37	1.12589 14424 96
87	1.52447 07284 07	1.37272 66812 35	0.99861 98626 93	1.12616 05402 12
88	1.53991 63361 19	1.38490 35913 26	0.99938 65228 63	1.12635 29874 65
89	1.55535 74542 95	1.39707 34234 96	0.99984 66182 97	1.12646 85497 13
90	1.57079 63267 95	1.40923 97160 46	1.00000 00000 00	1.12650 70861 17

K = 1.77478 59091 05608
K′= 1.95386 48092 51663

E = 1.40125 97507 85523
E′= 1.29627 80079 94134

r	u=(r/90)K=F(ϕ,k)	sn u	cn u	dn u
0	0.00000 00000 00	0.00000 00000 00	1.00000 00000 00	1.00000 00000 00
1	0.01971 98434 35	0.01971 80593 40	0.99980 55801 68	0.99992 30056 83
2	0.03943 96868 69	0.03942 54181 11	0.99922 25159 63	0.99969 21543 08
3	0.05915 95303 04	0.05911 13956 97	0.99825 13926 36	0.99930 78402 10
4	0.07887 93737 38	0.07876 53513 05	0.99689 31835 63	0.99877 07193 15
5	0.09859 92171 73	0.09837 67036 60	0.99514 92471 87	0.99808 17072 00
6	0.11831 90606 07	0.11793 49504 31	0.99302 13227 65	0.99724 19763 86
7	0.13803 89040 42	0.13742 96873 31	0.99051 15249 41	0.99625 29528 93
8	0.15775 87474 76	0.15685 06267 69	0.98762 23371 73	0.99511 63120 63
9	0.17747 85909 11	0.17618 76160 21	0.98435 66040 62	0.99383 39736 79
10	0.19719 84343 45	0.19543 06548 08	0.98071 75226 14	0.99240 80964 13
11	0.21691 82777 80	0.21456 99122 35	0.97670 86324 81	0.99084 10716 19
12	0.23663 81212 14	0.23359 57430 06	0.97233 38052 59	0.98913 55165 20
13	0.25635 79646 49	0.25249 87028 74	0.96759 72328 64	0.98729 42668 20
14	0.27607 78080 83	0.27126 95632 54	0.96250 34150 86	0.98532 03687 70
15	0.29579 76515 18	0.28989 93249 56	0.95705 71463 56	0.98321 70707 46
16	0.31551 74949 52	0.30837 92309 89	0.95126 35018 20	0.98098 78143 77
17	0.33523 73383 87	0.32670 07784 09	0.94512 78227 77	0.97863 62252 54
18	0.35495 71818 21	0.34485 57291 63	0.93865 57015 56	0.97616 61032 92
19	0.37467 70252 56	0.36283 61199 15	0.93185 29659 15	0.97358 14127 64
20	0.39439 68686 90	0.38063 42708 27	0.92472 56630 33	0.97088 62720 81
21	0.41411 67121 25	0.39824 27932 89	0.91728 00431 68	0.96808 49433 43
22	0.43383 65555 59	0.41565 45965 81	0.90952 25430 64	0.96518 18217 19
23	0.45355 63989 94	0.43286 28934 77	0.90145 97691 80	0.96218 14247 12
24	0.47327 62424 28	0.44986 12047 79	0.89309 84808 15	0.95908 83813 28
25	0.49299 60858 63	0.46664 33628 11	0.88444 55731 95	0.95590 74212 29
26	0.51271 59292 97	0.48320 35138 70	0.87550 80606 05	0.95264 33638 85
27	0.53243 57727 32	0.49953 61196 64	0.86629 30596 23	0.94930 11077 76
28	0.55215 56161 66	0.51563 59577 60	0.85680 77725 29	0.94588 56196 96
29	0.57187 54596 01	0.53149 81210 66	0.84705 94709 37	0.94240 19241 76
30	0.59159 53030 35	0.54711 80163 89	0.83705 54797 28	0.93885 50930 79
31	0.61131 51464 70	0.56249 13620 92	0.82680 31613 22	0.93525 02353 91
32	0.63103 49899 04	0.57761 41849 04	0.81630 99003 43	0.93159 24872 44
33	0.65075 48333 39	0.59248 28159 10	0.80558 30887 32	0.92788 70021 95
34	0.67047 46767 73	0.60709 38857 81	0.79463 01113 39	0.92413 89417 91
35	0.69019 45202 08	0.62144 43192 77	0.78345 83320 37	0.92035 34664 40
36	0.70991 43636 42	0.63553 13290 70	0.77207 50803 97	0.91653 57266 07
37	0.72963 42070 77	0.64935 24089 58	0.76048 76389 40	0.91269 08543 62
38	0.74935 40505 11	0.66290 53264 81	0.74870 32310 09	0.90882 39552 80
39	0.76907 38939 46	0.67618 81150 27	0.73672 90092 68	0.90494 01007 17
40	0.78879 37373 80	0.68919 90654 53	0.72457 20448 51	0.90104 43204 71
41	0.80851 35808 15	0.70193 67172 81	0.71223 93171 77	0.89714 15958 24
42	0.82823 34242 49	0.71439 98495 18	0.69973 77044 36	0.89323 68529 85
43	0.84795 32676 84	0.72658 74711 39	0.68707 39747 54	0.88933 49569 32
44	0.86767 31111 18	0.73849 88112 97	0.67425 47780 42	0.88544 07056 43
45	0.88739 29545 53	0.75013 33092 89	0.66128 66385 27	0.88155 88247 29

ELLIPTIC FUNCTIONS TABLE $\theta = 39°$

q = 0.03147 42771 20285 85

q'= 0.05763 33361 79494 01

D(90) = 1.13435 42506 17137

1/D(90) = 0.88155 88247 28657

r	ϕ	$E(\phi,k)$	A(r)	D(r)
0	0.00000 00000 00	0.00000 00000 00	0.00000 00000 00	1.00000 00000 00
1	0.01971 93373 00	0.01971 88311 90	0.01738 33404 70	1.00004 09173 87
2	0.03943 56388 34	0.03943 15915 47	0.03476 15119 93	1.00016 36197 17
3	0.05914 58740 21	0.05913 22234 11	0.05212 93468 50	1.00036 79575 51
4	0.07884 70226 39	0.07881 46954 10	0.06948 16797 81	1.00065 36820 27
5	0.09853 60799 64	0.09847 30154 70	0.08681 33492 14	1.00102 04451 63
6	0.11821 00618 68	0.11810 12436 61	0.10411 91984 96	1.00146 78002 81
7	0.13786 60098 48	0.13769 35048 26	0.12139 40771 31	1.00199 52025 47
8	0.15750 09959 89	0.15724 40009 50	0.13863 28420 12	1.00260 20096 37
9	0.17711 21278 31	0.17674 70232 08	0.15583 03586 66	1.00328 74825 16
10	0.19669 65531 38	0.19619 69636 59	0.17298 15024 97	1.00405 07863 41
11	0.21625 14645 48	0.21558 83265 32	0.19008 11600 33	1.00489 09914 72
12	0.23577 41040 93	0.23491 57390 63	0.20712 42301 82	1.00580 70746 06
13	0.25526 17675 86	0.25417 39618 54	0.22410 56254 90	1.00679 79200 21
14	0.27471 18088 45	0.27335 78987 11	0.24102 02734 03	1.00786 23209 34
15	0.29412 16437 71	0.29246 26059 29	0.25786 31175 44	1.00899 89809 68
16	0.31348 87542 40	0.31148 33010 09	0.27462 91189 82	1.01020 65157 31
17	0.33281 06918 26	0.33041 53707 57	0.29131 32575 23	1.01148 34545 00
18	0.35208 50813 37	0.34925 43787 83	0.30791 05329 97	1.01282 82420 09
19	0.37130 96241 47	0.36799 60723 47	0.32441 59665 57	1.01423 92403 44
20	0.39048 21013 46	0.38663 63885 63	0.34082 46019 85	1.01571 47309 34
21	0.40960 03766 70	0.40517 14599 45	0.35713 15070 09	1.01725 29166 44
22	0.42866 23992 34	0.42359 76192 89	0.37333 17746 19	1.01885 19239 60
23	0.44766 62060 48	0.44191 14038 97	0.38942 05244 01	1.02050 98052 71
24	0.46660 99243 23	0.46010 95591 38	0.40539 29038 71	1.02222 45412 38
25	0.48549 17735 66	0.47818 90413 58	0.42124 40898 27	1.02399 40432 53
26	0.50431 00674 53	0.49614 70201 46	0.43696 92896 94	1.02581 61559 78
27	0.52306 32154 98	0.51398 08799 72	0.45256 37428 92	1.02768 86599 72
28	0.54174 97245 01	0.53168 82212 07	0.46802 27222 05	1.02960 92743 92
29	0.56036 81997 96	0.54926 68605 48	0.48334 15351 55	1.03157 56597 66
30	0.57891 73462 80	0.56671 48308 68	0.49851 55253 86	1.03358 54208 44
31	0.59739 59692 51	0.58403 03805 17	0.51354 00740 60	1.03563 61095 14
32	0.61580 29750 40	0.60121 19720 86	0.52841 06012 50	1.03772 52277 81
33	0.63413 73714 48	0.61825 82806 80	0.54312 25673 45	1.03985 02308 08
34	0.65239 82679 97	0.63516 81917 12	0.55767 14744 62	1.04200 85300 15
35	0.67058 48759 99	0.65194 07982 54	0.57205 28678 61	1.04419 74962 31
36	0.68869 65084 43	0.66857 53979 77	0.58626 23373 62	1.04641 44628 96
37	0.70673 25797 17	0.68507 14897 02	0.60029 55187 72	1.04865 67293 06
38	0.72469 26051 66	0.70142 87696 05	0.61414 80953 12	1.05092 15639 04
39	0.74257 62004 88	0.71764 71270 97	0.62781 57990 47	1.05320 62076 03
40	0.76038 30809 93	0.73372 66404 17	0.64129 44123 20	1.05550 78771 54
41	0.77811 30607 07	0.74966 75719 62	0.65457 97691 82	1.05782 37685 24
42	0.79576 60513 57	0.76547 03634 00	0.66766 77568 31	1.06015 10603 24
43	0.81334 20612 16	0.78113 56305 71	0.68055 43170 41	1.06248 69172 34
44	0.83084 11938 47	0.79666 41582 34	0.69323 54475 98	1.06482 84934 67
45	0.84826 36467 19	0.81205 68946 64	0.70570 72037 25	1.06717 29362 28

K = 1.77478 59091 05608   E = 1.40125 97507 85523
K'= 1.95386 48092 51663   E'= 1.29627 80079 94134

r	u=(r/90)K=F(ϕ,k)	sn u	cn u	dn u
45	0.88739 29545 53	0.75013 33092 89	0.66128 66385 27	0.88155 88247 29
46	0.90711 27979 87	0.76149 06043 34	0.64817 59479 58	0.87769 39624 58
47	0.92683 26414 22	0.77257 05251 98	0.63492 89594 88	0.87385 06851 66
48	0.94655 24848 56	0.78337 30797 12	0.62155 17822 21	0.87003 34730 48
49	0.96627 23282 91	0.79389 84442 28	0.60805 03764 10	0.86624 67163 21
50	0.98599 21717 25	0.80414 69530 29	0.59443 05492 95	0.86249 47117 48
51	1.00571 20151 60	0.81411 90877 54	0.58069 79515 68	0.85878 16595 16
52	1.02543 18585 94	0.82381 54668 56	0.56685 80744 49	0.85511 16604 51
53	1.04515 17020 29	0.83323 68351 29	0.55291 62473 50	0.85148 87135 59
54	1.06487 15454 63	0.84238 40533 26	0.53887 76361 13	0.84791 67138 79
55	1.08459 13888 98	0.85125 80879 04	0.52474 72418 01	0.84439 94506 41
56	1.10431 12323 32	0.85986 00009 20	0.51052 99000 23	0.84094 06056 96
57	1.12403 10757 67	0.86819 09400 89	0.49623 02807 64	0.83754 37522 22
58	1.14375 09192 01	0.87625 21290 38	0.48185 28887 09	0.83421 23536 83
59	1.16347 07626 36	0.88404 48577 66	0.46740 20640 28	0.83094 97630 14
60	1.18319 06060 70	0.89157 04733 34	0.45288 19836 11	0.82775 92220 42
61	1.20291 04495 05	0.89883 03707 86	0.43829 66627 21	0.82464 38610 96
62	1.22263 02929 39	0.90582 59843 34	0.42364 99570 46	0.82160 66988 17
63	1.24235 01363 74	0.91255 87787 97	0.40894 55651 31	0.81865 06421 31
64	1.26206 99798 08	0.91903 02413 22	0.39418 70311 62	0.81577 84863 87
65	1.28178 98232 43	0.92524 18733 79	0.37937 77480 91	0.81299 29156 29
66	1.30150 96666 77	0.93119 51830 54	0.36452 09610 68	0.81029 65029 99
67	1.32122 95101 12	0.93689 16776 28	0.34961 97711 69	0.80769 17112 49
68	1.34094 93535 46	0.94233 28564 59	0.33467 71394 00	0.80518 08933 50
69	1.36066 91969 81	0.94752 02041 67	0.31969 58909 56	0.80276 62931 86
70	1.38038 90404 15	0.95245 51841 18	0.30467 87197 13	0.80045 00463 18
71	1.40010 88838 50	0.95713 92322 19	0.28962 81929 44	0.79823 41807 97
72	1.41982 87272 84	0.96157 37510 15	0.27454 67562 34	0.79612 06180 35
73	1.43954 85707 19	0.96576 01040 99	0.25943 67385 89	0.79411 11736 95
74	1.45926 84141 54	0.96969 96108 19	0.24430 03577 09	0.79220 75586 13
75	1.47898 82575 88	0.97339 35412 95	0.22913 97254 19	0.79041 13797 24
76	1.49870 81010 23	0.97684 31117 36	0.21395 68532 54	0.78872 41409 89
77	1.51842 79444 57	0.98004 94800 61	0.19875 36581 61	0.78714 72443 16
78	1.53814 77878 92	0.98301 37418 17	0.18353 19683 28	0.78568 19904 63
79	1.55786 76313 26	0.98573 69263 93	0.16829 35291 24	0.78432 95799 07
80	1.57758 74747 61	0.98821 99935 28	0.15304 00091 23	0.78309 11136 92
81	1.59730 73181 95	0.99046 38301 09	0.13777 30062 32	0.78196 75942 25
82	1.61702 71616 30	0.99246 92472 64	0.12249 40538 79	0.78095 99260 27
83	1.63674 70050 64	0.99423 69777 32	0.10720 46272 82	0.78006 89164 34
84	1.65646 68484 99	0.99576 76735 23	0.09190 61497 74	0.77929 52762 31
85	1.67618 66919 33	0.99706 19038 59	0.07659 99991 77	0.77863 96202 34
86	1.69590 65353 68	0.99812 01533 88	0.06128 75142 27	0.77810 24677 91
87	1.71562 63788 02	0.99894 28206 89	0.04597 00010 28	0.77768 42432 20
88	1.73534 62222 37	0.99953 02170 34	0.03064 87395 46	0.77738 52761 65
89	1.75506 60656 71	0.99988 25654 43	0.01532 49901 21	0.77720 58018 87
90	1.77478 59091 06	1.00000 00000 00	0.00000 00000 00	0.77714 59614 57

$q = 0.03147\ 42771\ 20285\ 85$
$q' = 0.05763\ 33361\ 79494\ 01$

$D(90) = 1.13435\ 42506\ 17137$
$1/D(90) = 0.88155\ 88247\ 28657$

r	ϕ	$E(\phi,k)$	$A(r)$	$D(r)$
45	0.84826 36467 19	0.81205 68946 64	0.70570 72037 25	1.06717 29362 28
46	0.86560 97097 37	0.82731 49461 44	0.71796 56995 16	1.06951 73891 93
47	0.88287 97636 68	0.84243 95713 70	0.73000 71093 48	1.07185 89959 90
48	0.90007 42784 84	0.85743 21757 96	0.74182 76693 06	1.07419 49036 74
49	0.91719 38116 23	0.87229 43059 44	0.75342 36785 87	1.07652 22662 10
50	0.93423 90061 84	0.88702 76437 00	0.76479 15009 05	1.07883 82479 35
51	0.95121 05890 47	0.90163 40006 24	0.77592 75658 82	1.08114 00270 18
52	0.96810 93689 47	0.91611 53122 80	0.78682 83704 32	1.08342 47988 95
53	0.98493 62344 83	0.93047 36326 23	0.79749 04801 28	1.08568 97796 89
54	1.00169 21520 95	0.94471 11284 46	0.80791 05305 69	1.08793 22096 03
55	1.01837 81639 91	0.95883 00739 04	0.81808 52287 15	1.09014 93562 84
56	1.03499 53860 45	0.97283 28451 43	0.82801 13542 22	1.09233 85181 49
57	1.05154 50056 67	0.98672 19150 27	0.83768 57607 53	1.09449 70276 87
58	1.06802 82796 49	1.00049 98479 89	0.84710 53772 74	1.09662 22547 00
59	1.08444 65319 96	1.01416 92950 09	0.85626 72093 25	1.09871 16095 18
60	1.10080 11517 34	1.02773 29887 35	0.86516 83402 84	1.10076 25461 52
61	1.11709 35907 20	1.04119 37387 42	0.87380 59325 92	1.10277 25653 99
62	1.13332 53614 40	1.05455 44269 50	0.88217 72289 66	1.10473 92178 88
63	1.14949 80348 05	1.06781 80031 97	0.89027 95535 87	1.10666 01070 67
64	1.16561 32379 50	1.08098 74809 66	0.89811 03132 57	1.10853 28921 29
65	1.18167 26520 35	1.09406 59332 91	0.90566 69985 33	1.11035 52908 58
66	1.19767 80100 55	1.10705 64888 11	0.91294 71848 32	1.11212 50824 20
67	1.21363 10946 58	1.11996 23280 02	0.91994 85335 06	1.11384 01100 69
68	1.22953 37359 74	1.13278 66795 72	0.92666 87928 85	1.11549 82837 73
69	1.24538 78094 55	1.14553 28170 21	0.93310 57992 92	1.11709 75827 71
70	1.26119 52337 33	1.15820 40553 62	0.93925 74780 16	1.11863 60580 29
71	1.27695 79684 94	1.17080 37480 05	0.94512 18442 62	1.12011 18346 23
72	1.29267 80123 60	1.18333 52838 03	0.95069 70040 59	1.12152 31140 25
73	1.30835 74008 02	1.19580 20842 41	0.95598 11551 26	1.12286 81762 94
74	1.32399 82040 58	1.20820 76007 84	0.96097 25877 16	1.12414 53821 77
75	1.33960 25250 79	1.22055 53123 62	0.96566 96854 01	1.12535 31751 09
76	1.35517 24974 89	1.23284 87230 01	0.97007 09258 35	1.12649 00831 07
77	1.37071 02835 58	1.24509 13595 78	0.97417 48814 66	1.12755 47205 71
78	1.38621 80722 06	1.25728 67697 06	0.97798 02202 08	1.12854 57899 72
79	1.40169 80770 13	1.26943 85197 38	0.98148 57060 74	1.12946 20834 37
80	1.41715 25342 49	1.28155 01928 86	0.98469 01997 59	1.13030 24842 17
81	1.43258 37009 25	1.29362 53874 32	0.98759 26591 88	1.13106 59680 58
82	1.44799 38528 51	1.30566 77150 54	0.99019 21400 11	1.13175 16044 42
83	1.46338 52827 16	1.31768 07992 25	0.99248 77960 58	1.13235 85577 28
84	1.47876 02981 75	1.32966 82736 97	0.99447 88797 42	1.13288 60881 71
85	1.49412 12199 53	1.34163 37810 61	0.99616 47424 23	1.13333 35528 21
86	1.50947 03799 59	1.35358 09713 62	0.99754 48347 19	1.13370 04063 13
87	1.52481 01194 02	1.36551 35007 79	0.99861 87067 73	1.13398 62015 25
88	1.54014 27869 28	1.37743 50303 36	0.99938 60084 68	1.13419 05901 32
89	1.55547 07367 51	1.38934 92246 65	0.99984 64896 01	1.13431 33230 25
90	1.57079 63267 95	1.40125 97507 86	1.00000 00000 00	1.13435 42506 17

K = 1.78676 91348 85021   E = 1.39314 02485 23812
K' = 1.93558 10960 04722   E' = 1.30553 90942 97794

r	u=(r/90)K=F(φ,k)	sn u	cn u	dn u
0	0.00000 00000 00	0.00000 00000 00	1.00000 00000 00	1.00000 00000 00
1	0.01985 29903 88	0.01985 11475 77	0.99980 29465 55	0.99991 85869 71
2	0.03970 59807 75	0.03969 12425 80	0.99921 19921 53	0.99967 44894 43
3	0.05955 89711 63	0.05950 92538 52	0.99822 77539 25	0.99926 81316 61
4	0.07941 19615 50	0.07929 41929 76	0.99685 12581 93	0.99870 02192 52
5	0.09926 49519 38	0.09903 51354 03	0.99508 39371 41	0.99797 17370 74
6	0.11911 79423 26	0.11872 12412 95	0.99292 76241 83	0.99708 39462 12
7	0.13897 09327 13	0.13834 17759 80	0.99038 45480 51	0.99603 83801 49
8	0.15882 39231 01	0.15788 61299 49	0.98745 73256 45	0.99483 68401 29
9	0.17867 69134 89	0.17734 38382 92	0.98414 89536 75	0.99348 13897 47
10	0.19852 99038 76	0.19670 45994 89	0.98046 27991 62	0.99197 43487 84
11	0.21838 28942 64	0.21595 82934 98	0.97640 25888 28	0.99031 82863 34
12	0.23823 58846 51	0.23509 49990 47	0.97197 23974 59	0.98851 60132 53
13	0.25808 88750 39	0.25410 50100 76	0.96717 66352 92	0.98657 05739 79
14	0.27794 18654 27	0.27297 88512 61	0.96202 00344 92	0.98448 52377 57
15	0.29779 48558 14	0.29170 72925 67	0.95650 76348 17	0.98226 34893 31
16	0.31764 78462 02	0.31028 13627 95	0.95064 47685 13	0.97990 90191 36
17	0.33750 08365 89	0.32869 23620 54	0.94443 70445 55	0.97742 57130 58
18	0.35735 38269 77	0.34693 18731 56	0.93789 03322 82	0.97481 76418 00
19	0.37720 68173 65	0.36499 17718 84	0.93101 07445 44	0.97208 90499 12
20	0.39705 98077 52	0.38286 42361 25	0.92380 46204 13	0.96924 43445 45
21	0.41691 27981 40	0.40054 17538 46	0.91627 85075 65	0.96628 80839 77
22	0.43676 57885 27	0.41801 71299 21	0.90843 91444 08	0.96322 49659 57
23	0.45661 87789 15	0.43528 34917 87	0.90029 34420 39	0.96005 98159 40
24	0.47647 17693 03	0.45233 42939 61	0.89184 84661 12	0.95679 75752 44
25	0.49632 47596 90	0.46916 33214 13	0.88311 14187 02	0.95344 32891 89
26	0.51617 77500 78	0.48576 46918 15	0.87408 96202 25	0.95000 20952 71
27	0.53603 07404 66	0.50213 28567 06	0.86479 04915 16	0.94647 92114 07
28	0.55588 37308 53	0.51826 26015 77	0.85522 15360 99	0.94287 99243 01
29	0.57573 67212 41	0.53414 90449 30	0.84539 03227 51	0.93920 95779 76
30	0.59558 97116 28	0.54978 76363 41	0.83530 44683 98	0.93547 35625 03
31	0.61544 27020 16	0.56517 41535 70	0.82497 16214 12	0.93167 73029 75
32	0.63529 56924 04	0.58030 46987 58	0.81439 94453 58	0.92782 62487 49
33	0.65514 86827 91	0.59517 56937 63	0.80359 56032 44	0.92392 58629 91
34	0.67500 16731 79	0.60978 38746 92	0.79256 77423 20	0.91998 16125 53
35	0.69485 46635 66	0.62412 62856 62	0.78132 34794 54	0.91599 89582 08
36	0.71470 76539 54	0.63820 02718 66	0.76987 03871 37	0.91198 33452 53
37	0.73456 06443 42	0.65200 34719 74	0.75821 59801 36	0.90794 01945 17
38	0.75441 36347 29	0.66553 38099 50	0.74636 77028 20	0.90387 48937 71
39	0.77426 66251 17	0.67878 94863 20	0.73433 29171 85	0.89979 27895 68
40	0.79411 96155 04	0.69176 89689 49	0.72211 88915 96	0.89569 91795 07
41	0.81397 26058 92	0.70447 09833 95	0.70973 27902 49	0.89159 93049 44
42	0.83382 55962 80	0.71689 45028 78	0.69718 16633 73	0.88749 83441 36
43	0.85367 85866 67	0.72903 87379 23	0.68447 24381 65	0.88340 14058 42
44	0.87353 15770 55	0.74090 31257 27	0.67161 19104 72	0.87931 35233 50
45	0.89338 45674 43	0.75248 73193 06	0.65860 67371 99	0.87523 96489 64

158

q = 0.03326 52566 95577 34   D(90) = 1.14254 42176 70493
q'= 0.05501 99336 98829 42   1/D(90) = 0.87523 96489 64201

r	ϕ	$E(\phi,k)$	A(r)	D(r)
0	0.00000 00000 00	0.00000 00000 00	0.00000 00000 00	1.00000 00000 00
1	0.01985 24515 92	0.01985 19128 23	0.01737 52656 76	1.00004 34106 52
2	0.03970 16715 37	0.03969 73631 41	0.03474 53796 17	1.00017 35897 43
3	0.05954 44338 06	0.05952 99028 34	0.05210 51912 73	1.00039 03787 38
4	0.07937 75235 87	0.07934 31124 91	0.06944 95524 57	1.00069 35136 31
5	0.09919 77428 54	0.09913 06156 11	0.08677 33185 37	1.00108 26252 60
6	0.11900 19158 82	0.11888 60926 23	0.10407 13496 19	1.00155 72397 60
7	0.13878 68946 91	0.13860 32946 55	0.12133 85117 36	1.00211 67791 35
8	0.15854 95644 14	0.15827 60570 15	0.13856 96780 45	1.00276 05619 67
9	0.17828 68485 56	0.17789 83123 05	0.15575 97300 23	1.00348 78042 41
10	0.19799 57141 46	0.19746 41031 43	0.17290 35586 66	1.00429 76202 97
11	0.21767 31767 51	0.21696 75944 12	0.18999 60657 01	1.00518 90239 11
12	0.23731 63053 60	0.23640 30850 21	0.20703 21647 97	1.00616 09294 94
13	0.25692 22270 94	0.25576 50191 12	0.22400 67827 86	1.00721 21534 09
14	0.27648 81317 65	0.27504 79966 87	0.24091 48608 88	1.00834 14154 14
15	0.29601 12762 43	0.29424 67836 20	0.25775 13559 47	1.00954 73402 19
16	0.31548 89886 38	0.31335 63210 16	0.27451 12416 73	1.01082 84591 57
17	0.33491 86722 85	0.33237 17338 99	0.29118 95098 93	1.01218 32119 74
18	0.35429 78095 17	0.35128 83392 06	0.30778 11718 10	1.01360 99487 22
19	0.37362 39652 29	0.37010 16530 61	0.32428 12592 71	1.01510 69317 72
20	0.39289 47902 12	0.38880 73973 39	0.34068 48260 47	1.01667 23379 23
21	0.41210 80242 74	0.40740 15054 81	0.35698 69491 19	1.01830 42606 24
22	0.43126 14991 22	0.42588 01275 83	0.37318 27299 76	1.02000 07122 90
23	0.45035 31410 16	0.44423 96347 47	0.38926 72959 25	1.02175 96267 24
24	0.46938 09731 81	0.46247 66226 97	0.40523 58014 05	1.02357 88616 29
25	0.48834 31179 98	0.48058 79146 81	0.42108 34293 19	1.02545 62012 15
26	0.50723 77989 47	0.49857 05636 49	0.43680 53923 68	1.02738 93588 94
27	0.52606 33423 18	0.51642 18537 55	0.45239 69344 05	1.02937 59800 68
28	0.54481 81786 96	0.53413 93011 63	0.46785 33317 88	1.03141 36449 86
29	0.56350 08442 09	0.55172 06542 17	0.48316 98947 53	1.03349 98716 97
30	0.58210 99815 59	0.56916 38929 73	0.49834 19687 87	1.03563 21190 66
31	0.60064 43408 18	0.58646 72281 29	0.51336 49360 23	1.03780 77898 70
32	0.61910 27800 23	0.60362 90993 83	0.52823 42166 29	1.04002 42339 54
33	0.63748 42655 53	0.62064 81732 54	0.54294 52702 17	1.04227 87514 66
34	0.65578 78722 97	0.63752 33403 85	0.55749 35972 55	1.04456 85961 35
35	0.67401 27836 34	0.65425 37123 72	0.57187 47404 90	1.04689 09786 20
36	0.69215 82912 18	0.67083 86181 58	0.58608 42863 75	1.04924 30699 02
37	0.71022 37945 79	0.68727 76000 08	0.60011 78665 00	1.05162 20047 34
38	0.72820 88005 54	0.70357 04091 23	0.61397 11590 40	1.05402 48851 22
39	0.74611 29225 46	0.71971 70009 15	0.62763 98901 95	1.05644 87838 64
40	0.76393 58796 29	0.73571 75299 74	0.64111 98356 40	1.05889 07481 03
41	0.78167 74955 05	0.75157 23447 84	0.65440 68219 80	1.06134 78029 34
42	0.79933 76973 17	0.76728 19821 92	0.66749 67282 04	1.06381 69550 21
43	0.81691 65143 32	0.78284 71616 90	0.68038 54871 44	1.06629 51962 44
44	0.83441 40765 00	0.79826 87795 30	0.69306 90869 31	1.06877 95073 64
45	0.85183 06129 05	0.81354 79027 02	0.70554 35724 54	1.07126 68617 00

ELLIPTIC FUNCTIONS TABLE $\theta = 40°$

K = 1.78676 91348 85021

K' = 1.93558 10960 04722

E = 1.39314 02485 23812

E' = 1.30553 90942 97794

r	u=(r/90)K=F(ϕ,k)	sn u	cn u	dn u
45	0.89338 45674 43	0.75248 73193 06	0.65860 67371 99	0.87523 96489 64
46	0.91323 75578 30	0.76379 11764 54	0.64546 34294 61	0.87118 46489 07
47	0.93309 05482 18	0.77481 47485 83	0.63218 83464 43	0.86715 32986 63
48	0.95294 35386 05	0.78555 82694 65	0.61878 76899 84	0.86315 02787 36
49	0.97279 65289 93	0.79602 21439 32	0.60526 74998 47	0.85918 01708 14
50	0.99264 95193 81	0.80620 69365 67	0.59163 36496 78	0.85524 74543 30
51	1.01250 25097 68	0.81611 33604 30	0.57789 18436 24	0.85135 65034 09
52	1.03235 55001 56	0.82574 22658 42	0.56404 76135 95	0.84751 15841 78
53	1.05220 84905 43	0.83509 46292 66	0.55010 63171 52	0.84371 68524 37
54	1.07206 14809 31	0.84417 15423 25	0.53607 31359 89	0.83997 63516 58
55	1.09191 44713 19	0.85297 42009 55	0.52195 30750 03	0.83629 40113 13
56	1.11176 74617 06	0.86150 38947 57	0.50775 09619 07	0.83267 36455 01
57	1.13162 04520 94	0.86976 19965 34	0.49347 14473 85	0.82911 89518 60
58	1.15147 34424 81	0.87774 99520 59	0.47911 90057 39	0.82563 35107 48
59	1.17132 64328 69	0.88546 92700 77	0.46469 79360 29	0.82222 07846 78
60	1.19117 94232 57	0.89292 15125 69	0.45021 23636 59	0.81888 41179 75
61	1.21103 24136 44	0.90010 82852 80	0.43566 62424 03	0.81562 67366 54
62	1.23088 54040 32	0.90703 12285 33	0.42106 33568 30	0.81245 17484 94
63	1.25073 83944 20	0.91369 20083 33	0.40640 73251 17	0.80936 21432 85
64	1.27059 13848 07	0.92009 23077 71	0.39170 16022 18	0.80636 07932 36
65	1.29044 43751 95	0.92623 38187 45	0.37694 94833 71	0.80345 04535 36
66	1.31029 73655 82	0.93211 82339 80	0.36215 41079 19	0.80063 37630 23
67	1.33015 03559 70	0.93774 72393 81	0.34731 84634 21	0.79791 32449 87
68	1.35000 33463 58	0.94312 25066 98	0.33244 53900 40	0.79529 13080 46
69	1.36985 63367 45	0.94824 56865 18	0.31753 75851 77	0.79277 02471 15
70	1.38970 93271 33	0.95311 84015 80	0.30259 76083 36	0.79035 22444 37
71	1.40956 23175 20	0.95774 22404 14	0.28762 78862 12	0.78803 93706 61
72	1.42941 53079 08	0.96211 87513 09	0.27263 07179 68	0.78583 35859 67
73	1.44926 82982 96	0.96624 94365 94	0.25760 82806 94	0.78373 67412 02
74	1.46912 12886 83	0.97013 57472 47	0.24256 26350 31	0.78175 05790 43
75	1.48897 42790 71	0.97377 90778 20	0.22749 57309 48	0.77987 67351 53
76	1.50882 72694 58	0.97718 07616 78	0.21240 94136 48	0.77811 67393 27
77	1.52868 02598 46	0.98034 20665 50	0.19730 54296 08	0.77647 20166 24
78	1.54853 32502 34	0.98326 41903 91	0.18218 54327 20	0.77494 38884 64
79	1.56838 62406 21	0.98594 82575 47	0.16705 09905 37	0.77353 35736 91
80	1.58823 92310 09	0.98839 53152 25	0.15190 35906 11	0.77224 21895 87
81	1.60809 22213 97	0.99060 63302 56	0.13674 46469 02	0.77107 07528 34
82	1.62794 52117 84	0.99258 21861 57	0.12157 55062 69	0.77002 01804 14
83	1.64779 82021 72	0.99432 36804 82	0.10639 74550 10	0.76909 12904 42
84	1.66765 11925 59	0.99583 15224 66	0.09121 17254 71	0.76828 48029 29
85	1.68750 41829 47	0.99710 63309 45	0.07601 95026 88	0.76760 13404 60
86	1.70735 71733 35	0.99814 86325 69	0.06082 19310 76	0.76704 14288 01
87	1.72721 01637 22	0.99895 88602 87	0.04562 01211 50	0.76660 54974 11
88	1.74706 31541 10	0.99953 73521 13	0.03041 51562 73	0.76629 38798 66
89	1.76691 61444 97	0.99988 43501 68	0.01520 80994 29	0.76610 68141 95
90	1.78676 91348 85	1.00000 00000 00	0.00000 00000 00	0.76604 44431 19

160

q = 0.03326 52566 95577 34   D(90) = 1.14254 42176 70493
q' = 0.05501 99336 98829 42   1/D(90) = 0.87523 96489 64201

r	φ	E(φ,k)	A(r)	D(r)
45	0.85183 06129 05	0.81354 79027 02	0.70554 35724 54	1.07126 68617 00
46	0.86916 64501 00	0.82868 57628 17	0.71780 50468 13	1.07375 42288 18
47	0.88642 20103 54	0.84368 37499 04	0.72984 96727 77	1.07623 85782 21
48	0.90359 78098 08	0.85854 34061 81	0.74167 36742 26	1.07871 68830 42
49	0.92069 44565 51	0.87326 64197 85	0.75327 33376 01	1.08118 61237 31
50	0.93771 26486 20	0.88785 46185 24	0.76464 50133 41	1.08364 32917 38
51	0.95465 31719 45	0.90230 99636 47	0.77578 51173 11	1.08608 53931 76
52	0.97151 68982 24	0.91663 45436 75	0.78669 01322 24	1.08850 94524 68
53	0.98830 47827 61	0.93083 05682 91	0.79735 66090 52	1.09091 25159 79
54	1.00501 78622 54	0.94490 03623 23	0.80778 11684 26	1.09329 16556 12
55	1.02165 72525 44	0.95884 63598 38	0.81796 05020 24	1.09564 39723 77
56	1.03822 41463 42	0.97267 10983 42	0.82789 13739 37	1.09796 65999 27
57	1.05471 98109 26	0.98637 72131 29	0.83757 06220 33	1.10025 67080 51
58	1.07114 55858 21	0.99996 74317 64	0.84699 51592 91	1.10251 15061 22
59	1.08750 28804 61	1.01344 45687 23	0.85616 19751 23	1.10472 82465 05
60	1.10379 31718 52	1.02681 15202 05	0.86506 81366 73	1.10690 42279 01
61	1.12001 80022 17	1.04007 12591 03	0.87371 07900 97	1.10903 67986 46
62	1.13617 89766 53	1.05322 68301 66	0.88208 71618 18	1.11112 33599 38
63	1.15227 77607 85	1.06628 13453 29	0.89019 45597 57	1.11316 13690 14
64	1.16831 60784 23	1.07923 79792 44	0.89803 03745 40	1.11514 83422 44
65	1.18429 57092 40	1.09209 99649 84	0.90559 20806 71	1.11708 18581 65
66	1.20021 84864 50	1.10487 05899 48	0.91287 72376 89	1.11895 95604 31
67	1.21608 62945 05	1.11755 31919 48	0.91988 34912 80	1.12077 91606 89
68	1.23190 10668 17	1.13015 11554 89	0.92660 85743 68	1.12253 84413 68
69	1.24766 47834 82	1.14266 79082 30	0.93305 03081 71	1.12423 52583 87
70	1.26337 94690 38	1.15510 69176 36	0.93920 66032 20	1.12586 75437 68
71	1.27904 71902 37	1.16747 16878 04	0.94507 54603 41	1.12743 33081 60
72	1.29467 00538 43	1.17976 57564 70	0.95065 49716 12	1.12893 06432 67
73	1.31025 02044 46	1.19199 26921 86	0.95594 33212 65	1.13035 77241 73
74	1.32578 98223 06	1.20415 60916 59	0.96093 87865 62	1.13171 28115 71
75	1.34129 11212 16	1.21625 95772 57	0.96563 97386 29	1.13299 42538 84
76	1.35675 63463 90	1.22830 67946 67	0.97004 46432 37	1.13420 04892 82
77	1.37218 77723 70	1.24030 14106 92	0.97415 20615 59	1.13533 00475 85
78	1.38758 77009 61	1.25224 71111 97	0.97796 06508 70	1.13638 15520 60
79	1.40295 84591 79	1.26414 75991 81	0.98146 91652 08	1.13735 37210 97
80	1.41830 23972 32	1.27600 65929 72	0.98467 64559 88	1.13824 53697 77
81	1.43362 18865 06	1.28782 78245 41	0.98758 14725 69	1.13905 54113 16
82	1.44891 93175 81	1.29961 50379 13	0.99018 32627 82	1.13978 28583 91
83	1.46419 70982 61	1.31137 19876 86	0.99248 09733 98	1.14042 68243 46
84	1.47945 76516 14	1.32310 24376 32	0.99447 38505 58	1.14098 65242 72
85	1.49470 34140 36	1.33481 01593 72	0.99616 12401 47	1.14146 12759 69
86	1.50993 68333 20	1.34649 89311 32	0.99754 25881 29	1.14185 05007 74
87	1.52516 03667 42	1.35817 25365 48	0.99861 74408 16	1.14215 37242 70
88	1.54037 64791 51	1.36983 47635 23	0.99938 54451 06	1.14237 05768 63
89	1.55558 76410 68	1.38148 94031 27	0.99984 63486 53	1.14250 07942 37
90	1.57079 63267 95	1.39314 02485 24	1.00000 00000 00	1.14254 42176 70

K = 1.79922 15440 49811   E = 1.38488 65913 75413
K'= 1.91799 75464 36423   E'= 1.31472 95602 64623

r	u=(r/90)K=F(ϕ,k)	sn u	cn u	dn u
0	0.00000 00000 00	0.00000 00000 00	1.00000 00000 00	1.00000 00000 00
1	0.01999 13504 89	0.01998 94459 37	0.99980 01910 64	0.99991 40044 41
2	0.03998 27009 79	0.03996 74691 60	0.99920 09814 89	0.99965 61699 72
3	0.05997 40514 68	0.05992 26699 46	0.99820 30222 49	0.99922 69527 37
4	0.07996 54019 58	0.07984 36944 43	0.99680 73958 68	0.99862 71113 73
5	0.09995 67524 47	0.09971 92573 42	0.99501 56128 00	0.99785 77046 17
6	0.11994 81029 37	0.11953 81642 26	0.99282 96063 74	0.99692 00879 72
7	0.13993 94534 26	0.13928 93335 01	0.99025 17263 67	0.99581 59094 57
8	0.15993 08039 16	0.15896 18178 10	0.98728 47312 09	0.99454 71044 69
9	0.17992 21544 05	0.17854 48248 33	0.98393 17788 98	0.99311 58897 77
10	0.19991 35048 94	0.19802 77373 73	0.98019 64166 59	0.99152 47566 92
11	0.21990 48553 84	0.21740 01326 71	0.97608 25694 14	0.98977 64634 53
12	0.23989 62058 73	0.23665 18008 34	0.97159 45271 37	0.98787 40268 69
13	0.25988 75563 63	0.25577 27623 35	0.96673 69311 49	0.98582 07132 61
14	0.27987 89068 52	0.27475 32844 96	0.96151 47594 60	0.98362 00287 72
15	0.29987 02573 42	0.29358 38969 18	0.95593 33112 05	0.98127 57090 73
16	0.31986 16078 31	0.31225 54057 78	0.94999 81902 94	0.97879 17085 48
17	0.33985 29583 21	0.33075 89069 79	0.94371 52883 44	0.97617 21889 95
18	0.35984 43088 10	0.34908 57980 94	0.93709 07669 85	0.97342 15079 12
19	0.37983 56592 99	0.36722 77890 93	0.93013 10396 49	0.97054 42064 34
20	0.39982 70097 89	0.38517 69118 20	0.92284 27529 11	0.96754 49969 64
21	0.41981 83602 78	0.40292 55282 15	0.91523 27675 04	0.96442 87505 76
22	0.43980 97107 68	0.42046 63372 74	0.90730 81390 68	0.96120 04842 49
23	0.45980 10612 57	0.43779 23807 55	0.89907 60987 55	0.95786 53479 74
24	0.47979 24117 47	0.45489 70476 25	0.89054 40337 58	0.95442 86118 14
25	0.49978 37622 36	0.47177 40772 82	0.88171 94678 61	0.95089 56529 61
26	0.51977 51127 26	0.48841 75615 63	0.87261 00420 90	0.94727 19428 43
27	0.53976 64632 15	0.50482 19455 77	0.86322 34955 47	0.94356 30343 43
28	0.55975 78137 04	0.52098 20273 79	0.85356 76464 98	0.93977 45491 69
29	0.57974 91641 94	0.53689 29565 47	0.84365 03737 99	0.93591 21654 21
30	0.59974 05146 83	0.55255 02316 90	0.83347 95987 06	0.93198 16054 13
31	0.61973 18651 73	0.56794 96969 41	0.82306 32671 58	0.92798 86237 65
32	0.63972 32156 62	0.58308 75374 81	0.81240 93325 62	0.92393 89958 30
33	0.65971 45661 52	0.59796 02741 54	0.80152 57391 59	0.91983 85064 62
34	0.67970 59166 41	0.61256 47572 24	0.79042 04059 91	0.91569 29391 76
35	0.69969 72671 30	0.62689 81593 43	0.77910 12115 33	0.91150 80657 13
36	0.71968 86176 20	0.64095 79677 65	0.76757 59790 14	0.90728 96360 35
37	0.73967 99681 09	0.65474 19759 00	0.75585 24624 52	0.90304 33687 76
38	0.75967 13185 99	0.66824 82742 40	0.74393 83334 49	0.89877 49421 55
39	0.77966 26690 88	0.68147 52407 35	0.73184 11687 42	0.89448 99853 67
40	0.79965 40195 78	0.69442 15306 70	0.71956 84385 39	0.89019 40704 58
41	0.81964 53700 67	0.70708 60661 12	0.70712 74956 54	0.88589 27047 05
42	0.83963 67205 57	0.71946 80249 71	0.69452 55654 36	0.88159 13234 72
43	0.85962 80710 46	0.73156 68297 54	0.68176 97364 98	0.87729 52835 79
44	0.87961 94215 35	0.74338 21360 41	0.66886 69522 52	0.87300 98571 53
45	0.89961 07720 25	0.75491 38207 62	0.65582 40032 38	0.86874 02259 73

q = 0.03511 99625 22096 26   D(90) = 1.15109 20872 58361
q'= 0.05249 47051 04843 90   1/D(90) = 0.86874 02259 72513

r	ϕ	$E(\phi,k)$	A(r)	D(r)
0	0.00000 00000 00	0.00000 00000 00	0.00000 00000 00	1.00000 00000 00
1	0.01999 07774 00	0.01999 02043 40	0.01736 64348 19	1.00004 60126 37
2	0.03997 81174 79	0.03997 35349 25	0.03472 77367 27	1.00018 39945 18
3	0.05995 85890 01	0.05994 31337 07	0.05207 87739 48	1.00041 37776 20
4	0.07992 87728 72	0.07989 21739 70	0.06941 44169 71	1.00073 50821 34
5	0.09988 52681 71	0.09981 38758 37	0.08672 95396 87	1.00114 75168 01
6	0.11982 46981 16	0.11970 15215 48	0.10401 90205 29	1.00165 05793 90
7	0.13974 37159 52	0.13954 84704 77	0.12127 77436 12	1.00224 36573 10
8	0.15963 90107 56	0.15934 81738 12	0.13850 05998 75	1.00292 60283 53
9	0.17950 73131 15	0.17909 41888 25	0.15568 24882 37	1.00369 68615 72
10	0.19934 54006 93	0.19878 01926 94	0.17281 83167 51	1.00455 52182 92
11	0.21915 01036 37	0.21839 99958 04	0.18990 30037 63	1.00550 00532 52
12	0.23891 83098 34	0.23794 75544 85	0.20693 14790 86	1.00653 02158 73
13	0.25864 69699 93	0.25741 69831 41	0.22389 86851 75	1.00764 44516 63
14	0.27833 31025 33	0.27680 25657 16	0.24079 95783 14	1.00884 14037 35
15	0.29797 37982 77	0.29609 87664 71	0.25762 91298 06	1.01011 96144 63
16	0.31756 62249 37	0.31530 02400 35	0.27438 23271 86	1.01147 75272 52
17	0.33710 76313 68	0.33440 18407 02	0.29105 41754 27	1.01291 34884 30
18	0.35659 53516 01	0.35339 86309 44	0.30763 96981 69	1.01442 57492 64
19	0.37602 68086 36	0.37228 58891 34	0.32413 39389 56	1.01601 24680 80
20	0.39539 95179 90	0.39105 91164 60	0.34053 19624 81	1.01767 17125 07
21	0.41471 10909 92	0.40971 40430 23	0.35682 88558 47	1.01940 14618 30
22	0.43395 92378 33	0.42824 66331 12	0.37301 97298 37	1.02119 96094 40
23	0.45314 17703 50	0.44665 30896 65	0.38909 97202 02	1.02306 39654 04
24	0.47225 66045 56	0.46492 98579 26	0.40506 39889 51	1.02499 22591 27
25	0.49130 17629 14	0.48307 36282 92	0.42090 77256 65	1.02698 21421 11
26	0.51027 53763 46	0.50108 13383 87	0.43662 61488 16	1.02903 11908 19
27	0.52917 56859 91	0.51895 01743 65	0.45221 45071 01	1.03113 69096 14
28	0.54800 10447 08	0.53667 75714 73	0.46766 80807 91	1.03329 67338 07
29	0.56674 99183 24	0.55426 12139 05	0.48298 21830 89	1.03550 80327 67
30	0.58542 08866 42	0.57169 90339 59	0.49815 21614 98	1.03776 81131 30
31	0.60401 26442 03	0.58898 92105 48	0.51317 33992 11	1.04007 42220 74
32	0.62252 40008 17	0.60613 01670 88	0.52804 13165 02	1.04242 35506 67
33	0.64095 38818 66	0.62312 05687 96	0.54275 13721 31	1.04481 32372 89
34	0.65930 13283 83	0.63995 93194 47	0.55729 90647 65	1.04724 03711 15
35	0.67756 54969 19	0.65664 55576 17	0.57167 99344 03	1.04970 19956 56
36	0.69574 56592 10	0.67317 86524 56	0.58588 95638 12	1.05219 51123 61
37	0.71384 12016 43	0.68955 81990 34	0.59992 35799 76	1.05471 66842 64
38	0.73185 16245 40	0.70578 40132 89	0.61377 76555 47	1.05726 36396 86
39	0.74977 65412 62	0.72185 61266 35	0.62744 75103 12	1.05983 28759 70
40	0.76761 56771 46	0.73777 47802 50	0.64092 89126 55	1.06242 12632 64
41	0.78536 88682 87	0.75354 04190 99	0.65421 76810 36	1.06502 56483 29
42	0.80303 60601 72	0.76915 36857 20	0.66730 96854 69	1.06764 28583 81
43	0.82061 73061 71	0.78461 54138 19	0.68020 08490 04	1.07026 97049 55
44	0.83811 27659 11	0.79992 66216 99	0.69288 71492 17	1.07290 29877 88
45	0.85552 27035 19	0.81508 85055 76	0.70536 46196 89	1.07553 94987 17

K = 1.79922 15440 49811   E = 1.38488 65913 75413
K′= 1.91799 75464 36423   E′= 1.31472 95602 64623

r	u=(r/90)K=F(ϕ,k)	sn u	cn u	dn u
45	0.89961 07720 25	0.75491 38207 62	0.65582 40032 38	0.86874 02259 73
46	0.91960 21225 14	0.76616 19703 05	0.64264 75202 31	0.86449 14762 86
47	0.93959 34730 04	0.77712 68685 23	0.62934 39681 29	0.86026 85941 09
48	0.95958 48234 93	0.78780 89846 67	0.61591 96406 01	0.85607 64609 73
49	0.97957 61739 83	0.79820 89613 10	0.60238 06554 70	0.85191 98501 29
50	0.99956 75244 72	0.80832 76022 82	0.58873 29508 27	0.84780 34231 73
51	1.01955 88749 62	0.81816 58606 74	0.57498 22818 38	0.84373 17270 95
52	1.03955 02254 51	0.82772 48269 35	0.56113 42182 36	0.83970 91917 28
53	1.05954 15759 40	0.83700 57170 97	0.54719 41424 64	0.83574 01275 71
54	1.07953 29264 30	0.84600 98611 60	0.53316 72484 50	0.83182 87239 80
55	1.09952 42769 19	0.85473 86916 69	0.51905 85409 80	0.82797 90477 03
56	1.11951 56274 09	0.86319 37324 99	0.50487 28356 47	0.82419 50417 37
57	1.13950 69778 98	0.87137 65878 77	0.49061 47593 58	0.82048 05244 84
58	1.15949 83283 88	0.87928 89316 60	0.47628 87513 48	0.81683 91891 99
59	1.17948 96788 77	0.88693 24968 86	0.46189 90646 97	0.81327 46036 92
60	1.19948 10293 67	0.89430 90656 14	0.44744 97683 10	0.80979 02102 79
61	1.21947 23798 56	0.90142 04590 65	0.43294 47493 39	0.80638 93259 50
62	1.23946 37303 45	0.90826 85280 77	0.41838 77160 05	0.80307 51427 46
63	1.25945 50808 35	0.91485 51438 83	0.40378 22008 35	0.79985 07283 07
64	1.27944 64313 24	0.92118 21892 15	0.38913 15642 21	0.79671 90265 95
65	1.29943 77818 14	0.92725 15497 53	0.37443 89983 45	0.79368 28587 58
66	1.31942 91323 03	0.93306 51059 01	0.35970 75314 05	0.79074 49241 15
67	1.33942 04827 93	0.93862 47249 22	0.34494 00321 28	0.78790 78012 57
68	1.35941 18332 82	0.94393 22534 01	0.33013 92145 57	0.78517 39492 33
69	1.37940 31837 72	0.94898 95100 67	0.31530 76430 77	0.78254 57088 17
70	1.39939 45342 61	0.95379 82789 51	0.30044 77376 70	0.78002 53038 27
71	1.41938 58847 50	0.95836 03028 92	0.28556 17793 76	0.77761 48424 97
72	1.43937 72352 40	0.96267 72773 85	0.27065 19159 48	0.77531 63188 69
73	1.45936 85857 29	0.96675 08447 62	0.25572 01676 66	0.77313 16142 08
74	1.47935 99362 19	0.97058 25887 14	0.24076 84333 24	0.77106 24984 17
75	1.49935 12867 08	0.97417 40291 40	0.22579 84963 40	0.76911 06314 41
76	1.51934 26371 98	0.97752 66173 26	0.21081 20310 10	0.76727 75646 56
77	1.53933 39876 87	0.98064 17314 48	0.19581 06088 64	0.76556 47422 20
78	1.55932 53381 77	0.98352 06723 84	0.18079 57051 29	0.76397 35023 86
79	1.57931 66886 66	0.98616 46598 56	0.16576 87052 86	0.76250 50787 63
80	1.59930 80391 55	0.98857 48288 62	0.15073 09116 96	0.76116 06015 17
81	1.61929 93896 45	0.99075 22264 29	0.13568 35503 16	0.75994 10985 08
82	1.63929 07401 34	0.99269 78086 53	0.12062 77774 60	0.75884 74963 44
83	1.65928 20906 24	0.99441 24380 45	0.10556 46866 23	0.75788 06213 63
84	1.67927 34411 13	0.99589 68811 57	0.09049 53153 54	0.75704 12005 22
85	1.69926 47916 03	0.99715 18065 11	0.07542 06521 64	0.75632 98621 94
86	1.71925 61420 92	0.99817 77827 94	0.06034 16434 73	0.75574 71368 72
87	1.73924 74925 81	0.99897 52773 53	0.04525 92005 82	0.75529 34577 63
88	1.75923 88430 71	0.99954 46549 56	0.03017 42066 71	0.75496 91612 91
89	1.77923 01935 60	0.99988 61768 35	0.01508 75238 12	0.75477 44874 77
90	1.79922 15440 50	1.00000 00000 00	0.00000 00000 00	0.75470 95802 23

q = 0.03511 99625 22096 26
q' = 0.05249 47051 04843 90

D(90) = 1.15109 20872 58361
1/D(90) = 0.86874 02259 72513

r	ϕ	$E(\phi,k)$	A(r)	D(r)
45	0.85552 27035 19	0.81508 85055 76	0.70536 46196 89	1.07553 94987 17
46	0.87284 74857 66	0.83010 24327 91	0.71762 93515 04	1.07817 60255 89
47	0.89008 75801 13	0.84496 99349 71	0.72967 74947 29	1.08080 93561 73
48	0.90724 35526 55	0.85969 27011 67	0.74150 52599 01	1.08343 62820 74
49	0.92431 60660 04	0.87427 25709 79	0.75310 89195 11	1.08605 36026 43
50	0.94130 58770 83	0.88871 15277 17	0.76448 48094 77	1.08865 81288 76
51	0.95821 38348 65	0.90301 16916 14	0.77562 93306 21	1.09124 66873 01
52	0.97504 08780 57	0.91717 53131 09	0.78653 89501 24	1.09381 61238 45
53	0.99178 80327 34	0.93120 47662 28	0.79721 02029 90	1.09636 33076 81
54	1.00845 64099 38	0.94510 25420 83	0.80763 96934 84	1.09888 51350 39
55	1.02504 72032 36	0.95887 12425 01	0.81782 40965 65	1.10137 85329 95
56	1.04156 16862 60	0.97251 35737 98	0.82776 01593 07	1.10384 04632 15
57	1.05800 12102 24	0.98603 23407 19	0.83744 47023 01	1.10626 79256 55
58	1.07436 72014 26	0.99943 04405 51	0.84687 46210 44	1.10865 79622 28
59	1.09066 11587 45	1.01271 08574 22	0.85604 68873 07	1.11100 76604 03
60	1.10688 46511 30	1.02587 66567 84	0.86495 85504 82	1.11331 41567 59
61	1.12303 93150 92	1.03893 09801 08	0.87360 67389 15	1.11557 46404 78
62	1.13912 68522 07	1.05187 70397 73	0.88198 86612 10	1.11778 63567 72
63	1.15514 90266 15	1.06471 81141 77	0.89010 16075 04	1.11994 66102 42
64	1.17110 76625 49	1.07745 75430 44	0.89794 29507 32	1.12205 27681 70
65	1.18700 46418 64	1.09009 87229 63	0.90551 01478 45	1.12410 22637 22
66	1.20284 19015 95	1.10264 51031 28	0.91280 07410 13	1.12609 25990 89
67	1.21862 14315 30	1.11510 01812 98	0.91981 23587 92	1.12802 13485 28
68	1.23434 52718 12	1.12746 74999 68	0.92654 27172 58	1.12988 61613 20
69	1.25001 55105 57	1.13975 06427 47	0.93298 96211 08	1.13168 47646 46
70	1.26563 42815 07	1.15195 32309 46	0.93915 09647 30	1.13341 49663 50
71	1.28120 37617 02	1.16407 89203 63	0.94502 47332 31	1.13507 46576 24
72	1.29672 61691 85	1.17613 13982 67	0.95060 90034 27	1.13666 18155 71
73	1.31220 37607 34	1.18811 43805 68	0.95590 19448 01	1.13817 45056 83
74	1.32763 88296 17	1.20003 16091 80	0.96090 18204 12	1.13961 08841 95
75	1.34303 37033 89	1.21188 68495 48	0.96560 69877 66	1.14096 92003 39
76	1.35839 07416 96	1.22368 38883 54	0.97001 58996 45	1.14224 77984 79
77	1.37371 23341 30	1.23542 65313 80	0.97412 71048 90	1.14344 51201 33
78	1.38900 08980 88	1.24711 86015 27	0.97793 92491 40	1.14455 97058 74
79	1.40425 88766 75	1.25876 39369 69	0.98145 10755 24	1.14559 01971 10
80	1.41948 87366 22	1.27036 63894 55	0.98466 14253 06	1.14653 53377 48
81	1.43469 29662 26	1.28192 98227 28	0.98756 92384 81	1.14739 39757 19
82	1.44987 40733 23	1.29345 81110 57	0.99017 35543 25	1.14816 50643 94
83	1.46503 45832 66	1.30495 51378 83	0.99247 35118 92	1.14884 76638 51
84	1.48017 70369 33	1.31642 47945 56	0.99446 83504 60	1.14944 09420 31
85	1.49530 39887 51	1.32787 09791 59	0.99615 74099 32	1.14994 41757 51
86	1.51041 80047 26	1.33929 75954 01	0.99754 01311 76	1.15035 67515 85
87	1.52552 16604 98	1.35070 85515 87	0.99861 60563 20	1.15067 81666 16
88	1.54061 75393 98	1.36210 77596 30	0.99938 48289 92	1.15090 80290 46
89	1.55570 82305 20	1.37349 91341 12	0.99984 61945 07	1.15104 60586 78
90	1.57079 63267 95	1.38488 65913 75	1.00000 00000 00	1.15109 20872 58

K = 1.81215 98536 62126
K' = 1.90108 30334 63664

E = 1.37650 43257 72082
E' = 1.32384 21844 81263

r	u=(r/90)K=F(ϕ,k)	sn u	cn u	dn u
0	0.00000 00000 00	0.00000 00000 00	1.00000 00000 00	1.00000 00000 00
1	0.02013 51094 85	0.02013 31399 91	0.99979 73077 95	0.99990 92525 30
2	0.04027 02189 70	0.04025 44679 60	0.99918 94604 17	0.99963 71736 91
3	0.06040 53284 55	0.06035 21965 64	0.99817 71447 84	0.99918 42536 67
4	0.08054 04379 41	0.08041 45876 97	0.99676 15031 12	0.99855 13076 48
5	0.10067 55474 26	0.10042 99768 20	0.99494 41289 62	0.99773 94731 79
6	0.12081 06569 11	0.12038 67969 25	0.99272 70617 48	0.99675 02064 57
7	0.14094 57663 96	0.14027 36020 53	0.99011 27797 21	0.99558 52776 25
8	0.16108 08758 81	0.16007 90902 20	0.98710 41914 99	0.99424 67650 65
9	0.18121 59853 66	0.17979 21256 79	0.98370 46261 68	0.99273 70487 47
10	0.20135 10948 51	0.19940 17603 95	0.97991 78220 40	0.99105 88026 61
11	0.22148 62043 36	0.21889 72546 54	0.97574 79141 18	0.98921 49863 90
12	0.24162 13138 22	0.23826 80967 16	0.97119 94203 49	0.98720 88358 53
13	0.26175 64233 07	0.25750 40214 27	0.96627 72267 57	0.98504 38533 01
14	0.28189 15327 92	0.27659 50277 20	0.96098 65715 19	0.98272 37965 97
15	0.30202 66422 77	0.29553 13949 58	0.95533 30281 08	0.98025 26678 64
16	0.32216 17517 62	0.31430 36980 30	0.94932 24875 69	0.97763 47015 44
17	0.34229 68612 47	0.33290 28211 94	0.94296 11400 48	0.97487 43519 54
18	0.36243 19707 32	0.35131 99705 91	0.93625 54556 66	0.97197 62803 91
19	0.38256 70802 18	0.36954 66854 35	0.92921 21648 38	0.96894 53418 59
20	0.40270 21897 03	0.38757 48478 32	0.92183 82381 57	0.96578 65714 96
21	0.42283 72991 88	0.40539 66912 34	0.91414 08659 15	0.96250 51707 52
22	0.44297 24086 73	0.42300 48075 20	0.90612 74374 03	0.95910 64933 98
23	0.46310 75181 58	0.44039 21527 04	0.89780 55200 52	0.95559 60314 34
24	0.48324 26276 43	0.45755 20512 95	0.88918 28385 41	0.95197 94009 52
25	0.50337 77371 28	0.47447 81993 18	0.88026 72539 47	0.94826 23280 20
26	0.52351 28466 14	0.49116 46660 26	0.87106 67430 50	0.94445 06346 55
27	0.54364 79560 99	0.50760 58943 51	0.86158 93778 48	0.94055 02249 26
28	0.56378 30655 84	0.52379 67001 07	0.85184 33054 01	0.93656 70712 64
29	0.58391 81750 69	0.53973 22700 20	0.84183 67280 53	0.93250 72010 03
30	0.60405 32845 54	0.55540 81586 10	0.83157 78841 15	0.92837 66832 26
31	0.62418 83940 39	0.57082 02840 00	0.82107 50290 77	0.92418 16159 37
32	0.64432 35035 24	0.58596 49226 95	0.81033 64174 04	0.91992 81136 16
33	0.66445 86130 09	0.60083 87033 99	0.79937 02849 73	0.91562 22951 78
34	0.68459 37224 95	0.61543 85999 32	0.78818 48322 03	0.91127 02723 78
35	0.70472 88319 80	0.62976 19233 11	0.77678 82079 09	0.90687 81386 84
36	0.72486 39414 65	0.64380 63130 70	0.76518 84939 ·36	0.90245 19586 46
37	0.74499 90509 50	0.65756 97278 62	0.75339 36905 76	0.89799 77577 70
38	0.76513 41604 35	0.67105 04354 48	0.74141 17028 25	0.89352 15129 26
39	0.78526 92699 20	0.68424 70021 02	0.72925 03274 69	0.88902 91432 94
40	0.80540 43794 05	0.69715 82815 27	0.71691 72410 38	0.88452 65018 51
41	0.82553 94888 91	0.70978 34033 26	0.70441 99886 17	0.88001 93674 19
42	0.84567 45983 76	0.72212 17611 12	0.69176 59735 26	0.87551 34372 57
43	0.86580 97078 61	0.73417 30002 99	0.67896 24478 80	0.87101 43202 12
44	0.88594 48173 46	0.74593 70056 52	0.66601 65039 99	0.86652 75304 06
45	0.90607 99268 31	0.75741 38886 35	0.65293 50666 82	0.86205 84814 72

q = 0.03704 02001 87132 72
q' = 0.05005 44121 29953 00

D(90) = 1.16001 41075 03170
1/D(90) = 0.86205 84814 71759

r	ϕ	$E(\phi,k)$	A(r)	D(r)
0	0.00000 00000 00	0.00000 00000 00	0.00000 00000 00	1.00000 00000 00
1	0.02013 45003 78	0.02013 38913 05	0.01735 67898 13	1.00004 87282 31
2	0.04026 53474 34	0.04026 04769 59	0.03470 84672 74	1.00019 48535 94
3	0.06038 88944 29	0.06037 24684 47	0.05204 99211 13	1.00043 81981 64
4	0.08050 15077 68	0.08046 26114 48	0.06937 60422 14	1.00077 84656 44
5	0.10059 95735 23	0.10052 37027 32	0.08668 17247 03	1.00121 52417 22
6	0.12067 95038 85	0.12054 86068 29	0.10396 18670 27	1.00174 79945 74
7	0.14073 77435 35	0.14053 02723 87	0.12121 13730 47	1.00237 60755 10
8	0.16077 07759 09	0.16046 17481 48	0.13842 51531 28	1.00309 87197 66
9	0.18077 51293 40	0.18033 61984 72	0.15559 81252 39	1.00391 50474 29
10	0.20074 73830 56	0.20014 69183 48	0.17272 52160 59	1.00482 40645 09
11	0.22068 41730 16	0.21988 73478 23	0.18980 13620 88	1.00582 46641 48
12	0.24058 21975 68	0.23955 10858 01	0.20682 15107 70	1.00691 56279 62
13	0.26043 82229 15	0.25913 19031 41	0.22378 06216 25	1.00809 56275 26
14	0.28024 90883 69	0.27862 37550 34	0.24067 36673 85	1.00936 32259 87
15	0.30001 17113 88	0.29802 07925 93	0.25749 56351 53	1.01071 68798 11
16	0.31972 30923 71	0.31731 73736 27	0.27424 15275 56	1.01215 49406 56
17	0.33938 03192 12	0.33650 80725 81	0.29090 63639 28	1.01367 56573 85
18	0.35898 05716 00	0.35558 76895 93	0.30748 51814 94	1.01527 71781 84
19	0.37852 11250 53	0.37455 12586 72	0.32397 30365 71	1.01695 75528 21
20	0.39799 93546 80	0.39339 40549 75	0.34036 50057 83	1.01871 47350 17
21	0.41741 27386 73	0.41211 16011 66	0.35665 61872 86	1.02054 65849 28
22	0.43675 88615 10	0.43069 96728 81	0.37284 17020 17	1.02245 08717 55
23	0.45603 54168 85	0.44915 43032 76	0.38891 66949 46	1.02442 52764 52
24	0.47524 02103 47	0.46747 17866 81	0.40487 63363 52	1.02646 73945 47
25	0.49437 11616 55	0.48564 86813 76	0.42071 58231 10	1.02857 47390 70
26	0.51342 63068 55	0.50368 18115 03	0.43643 03799 92	1.03074 47435 71
27	0.53240 38000 66	0.52156 82681 36	0.45201 52609 91	1.03297 47652 49
28	0.55130 19150 00	0.53930 54095 39	0.46746 57506 48	1.03526 20881 62
29	0.57011 90461 98	0.55689 08606 48	0.48277 71654 05	1.03760 39265 35
30	0.58885 37100 04	0.57432 25117 96	0.49794 48549 71	1.03999 74281 45
31	0.60750 45452 77	0.59159 85167 39	0.51296 42036 96	1.04243 96777 94
32	0.62607 03138 47	0.60871 72900 00	0.52783 06319 68	1.04492 77008 57
33	0.64454 99007 21	0.62567 75035 86	0.54253 95976 19	1.04745 84669 00
34	0.66294 23140 62	0.64247 80831 25	0.55708 65973 46	1.05002 88933 69
35	0.68124 66849 25	0.65911 82034 44	0.57146 71681 48	1.05263 58493 40
36	0.69946 22667 86	0.67559 72836 64	0.58567 68887 69	1.05527 61593 34
37	0.71758 84348 53	0.69191 49818 31	0.59971 13811 58	1.05794 66071 76
38	0.73562 46851 86	0.70807 11891 41	0.61356 63119 39	1.06064 39399 19
39	0.75357 06336 23	0.72406 60238 06	0.62723 73938 91	1.06336 48717 96
40	0.77142 60145 33	0.73989 98245 92	0.64072 03874 37	1.06610 60882 24
41	0.78919 06794 00	0.75557 31440 96	0.65401 11021 41	1.06886 42498 43
42	0.80686 45952 59	0.77108 67417 75	0.66710 53982 15	1.07163 59965 78
43	0.82444 78429 79	0.78644 15767 97	0.67999 91880 25	1.07441 79517 34
44	0.84194 06154 20	0.80163 88007 33	0.69268 84376 16	1.07720 67261 05
45	0.85934 32154 67	0.81667 97501 47	0.70516 91682 24	1.07999 89221 10

ELLIPTIC FUNCTIONS   TABLE $\theta = 42°$

K = 1.81215 98536 62126

K′= 1.90108 30334 63664

E = 1.37650 43257 72082

E′= 1.32384 21844 81263

r	u=(r/90)K=F(ϕ,k)	sn u	cn u	dn u
45	0.90607 99268 31	0.75741 38886 35	0.65293 50666 82	0.86205 84814 72
46	0.92621 50363 16	0.76860 39746 34	0.63972 48863 20	0.85761 24813 13
47	0.94635 01458 01	0.77950 77900 84	0.62639 25328 40	0.85319 47273 80
48	0.96648 52552 86	0.79012 60495 70	0.61294 43904 55	0.84881 03024 50
49	0.98662 03647 72	0.80045 96429 31	0.59938 66532 04	0.84446 41708 93
50	1.00675 54742 57	0.81050 96224 23	0.58572 53212 55	0.84016 11754 11
51	1.02689 05837 42	0.82027 71899 77	0.57196 61979 55	0.83590 60342 21
52	1.04702 56932 27	0.82976 36845 88	0.55811 48875 80	0.83170 33386 73
53	1.06716 08027 12	0.83897 05698 67	0.54417 67937 87	0.82755 75512 83
54	1.08729 59121 97	0.84789 94217 97	0.53015 71187 07	0.82347 30041 39
55	1.10743 10216 82	0.85655 19167 07	0.51606 08626 76	0.81945 38976 93
56	1.12756 61311 68	0.86492 98194 99	0.50189 28245 57	0.81550 42998 80
57	1.14770 12406 53	0.87303 49721 52	0.48765 76026 26	0.81162 81455 69
58	1.16783 63501 38	0.88086 92825 12	0.47335 95960 02	0.80782 92363 04
59	1.18797 14596 23	0.88843 47133 92	0.45900 30065 70	0.80411 12403 26
60	1.20810 65691 08	0.89573 32720 01	0.44459 18413 90	0.80047 76928 43
61	1.22824 16785 93	0.90276 69997 05	0.43012 99155 41	0.79693 19965 34
62	1.24837 67880 78	0.90953 79621 36	0.41562 08553 88	0.79347 74222 57
63	1.26851 18975 63	0.91604 82396 52	0.40106 81022 36	0.79011 71099 45
64	1.28864 70070 49	0.92229 99181 61	0.38647 49163 39	0.78685 40696 67
65	1.30878 21165 34	0.92829 50803 13	0.37184 43812 49	0.78369 11828 28
66	1.32891 72260 19	0.93403 57970 47	0.35717 94084 69	0.78063 12035 05
67	1.34905 23355 04	0.93952 41195 23	0.34248 27423 90	0.77767 67598 77
68	1.36918 74449 89	0.94476 20714 08	0.32775 69654 93	0.77483 03557 46
69	1.38932 25544 74	0.94975 16415 43	0.31300 45037 80	0.77209 43721 24
70	1.40945 76639 59	0.95449 47769 65	0.29822 76324 32	0.76947 10688 78
71	1.42959 27734 45	0.95899 33762 99	0.28342 84816 59	0.76696 25864 05
72	1.44972 78829 30	0.96324 92835 00	0.26860 90427 30	0.76457 09473 27
73	1.46986 29924 15	0.96726 42819 64	0.25377 11741 63	0.76229 80581 94
74	1.48999 81019 00	0.97104 00889 72	0.23891 66080 65	0.76014 57111 78
75	1.51013 32113 85	0.97457 83504 88	0.22404 69565 95	0.75811 55857 47
76	1.53026 83208 70	0.97788 06362 96	0.20916 37185 49	0.75620 92503 01
77	1.55040 34303 55	0.98094 84354 62	0.19426 82860 48	0.75442 81637 69
78	1.57053 85398 41	0.98378 31521 33	0.17936 19513 12	0.75277 36771 47
79	1.59067 36493 26	0.98638 61016 49	0.16444 59135 23	0.75124 70349 74
80	1.61080 87588 11	0.98875 85069 71	0.14952 12857 50	0.74984 93767 29
81	1.63094 38682 96	0.99090 14954 26	0.13458 91019 47	0.74858 17381 51
82	1.65107 89777 81	0.99281 60957 45	0.11965 03239 88	0.74744 50524 65
83	1.67121 40872 66	0.99450 32354 06	0.10470 58487 70	0.74644 01515 16
84	1.69134 91967 51	0.99596 37382 73	0.08975 65153 35	0.74556 77667 92
85	1.71148 43062 36	0.99719 83225 16	0.07480 31120 37	0.74482 85303 48
86	1.73161 94157 22	0.99820 75988 26	0.05984 63837 39	0.74422 29756 10
87	1.75175 45252 07	0.99899 20689 01	0.04488 70390 20	0.74375 15380 67
88	1.77188 96346 92	0.99955 21242 25	0.02992 57574 19	0.74341 45558 37
89	1.79202 47441 77	0.99988 80451 06	0.01496 31966 77	0.74321 22701 11
90	1.81215 98536 62	1.00000 00000 00	0.00000 00000 00	0.74314 48254 77

q = 0.03704 02001 87132 72   D(90) = 1.16001 41075 03170
q'= 0.05005 44121 29953 00   1/D(90) = 0.86205 84814 71759

r	ϕ	$E(\phi,k)$	A(r)	D(r)
45	0.85934 32154 67	0.81667 97501 47	0.70516 91682 24	1.07999 89221 10
46	0.87665 60539 55	0.83156 59390 99	0.71743 74578 05	1.08279 11379 22
47	0.89387 96474 87	0.84629 90516 15	0.72948 94425 55	1.08557 99716 22
48	0.91101 46161 72	0.86088 09341 48	0.74132 13184 39	1.08836 20253 37
49	0.92806 16812 72	0.87531 35880 62	0.75292 93427 07	1.09113 39093 82
50	0.94502 16627 91	0.88959 91621 69	0.76430 98354 24	1.09389 22463 93
51	0.96189 54769 89	0.90373 99453 38	0.77545 91809 76	1.09663 36754 41
52	0.97868 41338 46	0.91773 83592 22	0.78637 38295 86	1.09935 48561 28
53	0.99538 87345 35	0.93159 69510 90	0.79705 02988 13	1.10205 24726 61
54	1.01201 04687 12	0.94531 83868 20	0.80748 51750 47	1.10472 32378 91
55	1.02855 06119 76	0.95890 54440 53	0.81767 51149 90	1.10736 38973 22
56	1.04501 05231 59	0.97236 10055 14	0.82761 68471 28	1.10997 12330 78
57	1.06139 16416 64	0.98568 80525 46	0.83730 71731 84	1.11254 20678 30
58	1.07769 54847 80	0.99888 96588 31	0.84674 29695 59	1.11507 32686 65
59	1.09392 36449 97	1.01196 89843 38	0.85592 11887 56	1.11756 17509 11
60	1.11007 77873 27	1.02492 92694 90	0.86483 88607 82	1.12000 44818 95
61	1.12615 96466 29	1.03777 38295 63	0.87349 30945 29	1.12239 84846 49
62	1.14217 10249 45	1.05050 60493 21	0.88188 10791 36	1.12474 08415 32
63	1.15811 37888 58	1.06312 93778 85	0.89000 00853 23	1.12702 86977 97
64	1.17398 98668 64	1.07564 73238 53	0.89784 74666 98	1.12925 92650 68
65	1.18980 12467 70	1.08806 34506 54	0.90542 06610 41	1.13142 98247 47
66	1.20554 99731 15	1.10038 13721 45	0.91271 71915 53	1.13353 77313 26
67	1.22123 81446 22	1.11260 47484 49	0.91973 46680 79	1.13558 04156 19
68	1.23686 79116 80	1.12473 72820 31	0.92647 07882 94	1.13755 53878 97
69	1.25244 14738 50	1.13678 27140 05	0.93292 33388 53	1.13946 02409 21
70	1.26796 10774 15	1.14874 48206 68	0.93909 01965 12	1.14129 26528 89
71	1.28342 90129 54	1.16062 74102 62	0.94496 93292 06	1.14305 03902 62
72	1.29884 76129 56	1.17243 43199 51	0.95055 87970 87	1.14473 13104 93
73	1.31421 92494 61	1.18416 94130 03	0.95585 67535 27	1.14633 33646 43
74	1.32954 63317 48	1.19583 65761 79	0.96086 14460 69	1.14785 45998 82
75	1.34483 13040 40	1.20743 97173 19	0.96557 12173 49	1.14929 31618 72
76	1.36007 66432 57	1.21898 27631 02	0.96998 45059 59	1.15064 72970 30
77	1.37528 48567 94	1.23046 96569 96	0.97409 98472 72	1.15191 53546 74
78	1.39045 84803 34	1.24190 43573 62	0.97791 58742 17	1.15309 57890 30
79	1.40560 00756 85	1.25329 08357 28	0.98143 13180 10	1.15418 71611 27
80	1.42071 22286 58	1.26463 30751 95	0.98464 50088 27	1.15518 81405 51
81	1.43579 75469 57	1.27593 50689 92	0.98755 58764 35	1.15609 75070 69
82	1.45085 86581 10	1.28720 08191 47	0.99016 29507 68	1.15691 41521 19
83	1.46589 82074 11	1.29843 43352 83	0.99246 53624 50	1.15763 70801 64
84	1.48091 88558 92	1.30963 96335 05	0.99446 23432 65	1.15826 54099 12
85	1.49592 32783 11	1.32082 07353 89	0.99615 32265 79	1.15879 83753 83
86	1.51091 41611 58	1.33198 16670 49	0.99753 74476 97	1.15923 53268 53
87	1.52589 42006 78	1.34312 64582 76	0.99861 45441 76	1.15957 57316 43
88	1.54086 61009 01	1.35425 91417 27	0.99938 41560 74	1.15981 91747 73
89	1.55583 25716 91	1.36538 37521 73	0.99984 60261 49	1.15996 53594 64
90	1.57079 63267 95	1.37650 43257 72	1.00000 00000 00	1.16001 41075 03

K = 1.82560 18981 35889

K' = 1.88480 86573 80404

E = 1.36799 91658 73159

E' = 1.33286 99541 17179

r	u=(r/90)K=F(φ,k)	sn u	cn u	dn u
0	0.00000 00000 00	0.00000 00000 00	1.00000 00000 00	1.00000 00000 00
1	0.02028 44655 35	0.02028 24277 14	0.99979 42904 05	0.99990 43252 55
2	0.04056 89310 70	0.04055 26338 06	0.99917 74036 13	0.99961 74767 22
3	0.06085 33966 05	0.06079 84231 49	0.99815 00647 41	0.99913 99809 18
4	0.08113 78621 39	0.08100 76534 78	0.99671 34794 30	0.99847 27133 97
5	0.10142 23276 74	0.10116 82614 88	0.99486 93295 44	0.99761 68958 00
6	0.12170 67932 09	0.12126 82885 52	0.99261 97671 78	0.99657 40917 62
7	0.14199 12587 44	0.14129 59059 20	0.98996 74070 24	0.99534 62016 79
8	0.16227 57242 79	0.16123 94392 89	0.98691 53171 46	0.99393 54563 95
9	0.18256 01898 14	0.18108 73926 16	0.98346 70082 09	0.99234 44098 27
10	0.20284 46553 48	0.20082 84710 76	0.97962 64212 47	0.99057 59305 88
11	0.22312 91208 83	0.22045 16030 67	0.97539 79140 36	0.98863 31926 57
12	0.24341 35864 18	0.23994 59611 45	0.97078 62461 58	0.98651 96651 44
13	0.26369 80519 53	0.25930 09818 27	0.96579 65628 56	0.98423 91012 33
14	0.28398 25174 88	0.27850 63841 72	0.96043 43777 56	0.98179 55263 41
15	0.30426 69830 23	0.29755 21870 72	0.95470 55545 92	0.97919 32255 93
16	0.32455 14485 57	0.31642 87251 97	0.94861 62880 06	0.97643 67306 57
17	0.34483 59140 92	0.33512 66635 41	0.94217 30835 59	0.97353 08060 41
18	0.36512 03796 27	0.35363 70105 38	0.93538 27370 54	0.97048 04349 03
19	0.38540 48451 62	0.37195 11297 03	0.92825 23132 82	0.96729 08044 72
20	0.40568 93106 97	0.39006 07498 01	0.92078 91243 19	0.96396 72911 41
21	0.42597 37762 32	0.40795 79735 11	0.91300 07074 74	0.96051 54453 25
22	0.44625 82417 67	0.42563 52845 98	0.90489 48030 05	0.95694 09761 47
23	0.46654 27073 01	0.44308 55536 04	0.89647 93317 13	0.95324 97360 32
24	0.48682 71728 36	0.46030 20420 63	0.88776 23725 26	0.94944 77052 79
25	0.50711 16383 71	0.47727 84052 79	0.87875 21401 71	0.94554 09766 90
26	0.52739 61039 06	0.49400 86936 91	0.86945 69630 28	0.94153 57403 08
27	0.54768 05694 41	0.51048 73528 68	0.85988 52612 77	0.93743 82683 38
28	0.56796 50349 76	0.52670 92221 87	0.85004 55254 06	0.93325 49003 10
29	0.58824 95005 10	0.54266 95322 30	0.83994 62951 82	0.92899 20285 38
30	0.60853 39660 45	0.55836 39009 83	0.82959 61391 42	0.92465 60839 18
31	0.62881 84315 80	0.57378 83288 69	0.81900 36347 01	0.92025 35221 36
32	0.64910 28971 15	0.58893 91927 10	0.80817 73489 09	0.91579 08102 98
33	0.66938 73626 50	0.60381 32386 63	0.79712 58199 40	0.91127 44140 42
34	0.68967 18281 85	0.61840 75742 17	0.78585 75393 49	0.90671 07851 62
35	0.70995 62937 20	0.63271 96593 16	0.77438 09351 44	0.90210 63497 57
36	0.73024 07592 54	0.64674 72966 83	0.76270 43557 19	0.89746 74969 52
37	0.75052 52247 89	0.66048 86214 23	0.75083 60546 55	0.89280 05681 95
38	0.77080 96903 24	0.67394 20899 77	0.73878 41764 40	0.88811 18471 45
39	0.79109 41558 59	0.68710 64684 94	0.72655 67431 07	0.88340 75501 76
40	0.81137 86213 94	0.69998 08207 12	0.71416 16418 12	0.87869 38174 83
41	0.83166 30869 29	0.71256 44953 97	0.70160 66133 52	0.87397 67048 09
42	0.85194 75524 63	0.72485 71134 28	0.68889 92416 26	0.86926 21757 89
43	0.87223 20179 98	0.73685 85545 80	0.67604 69440 38	0.86455 60949 01
44	0.89251 64835 33	0.74856 89440 79	0.66305 69628 33	0.85986 42210 18
45	0.91280 09490 68	0.75998 86389 94	0.64993 63573 46	0.85519 22015 66

q = 0.03902 78889 26606 97   D(90) = 1.16932 77817 18452
q'= 0.04769 60340 17055 65   1/D(90) = 0.85519 22015 65923

r	ϕ	$E(\phi,k)$	A(r)	D(r)
0	0.00000 00000 00	0.00000 00000 00	0.00000 00000 00	1.00000 00000 00
1	0.02028 38185 92	0.02028 31716 85	0.01734 62683 84	1.00005 15626 95
2	0.04056 37569 49	0.04055 85840 16	0.03468 74468 45	1.00020 61880 03
3	0.06083 59419 63	0.06081 84963 30	0.05201 84464 78	1.00046 36876 70
4	0.08109 65147 47	0.08105 52052 59	0.06933 41804 19	1.00082 37481 98
5	0.10134 16376 91	0.10126 10631 59	0.08662 95648 64	1.00128 59312 16
6	0.12156 75014 44	0.12142 84962 69	0.10389 95200 95	1.00184 96740 24
7	0.14177 03317 94	0.14155 00225 27	0.12113 89715 15	1.00251 42902 69
8	0.16194 63964 44	0.16161 82689 55	0.13834 28506 78	1.00327 89707 80
9	0.18209 20116 36	0.18162 59885 38	0.15550 60963 33	1.00414 27845 53
10	0.20220 35486 26	0.20156 60765 15	0.17262 36554 78	1.00510 46798 83
11	0.22227 74399 69	0.22143 15860 30	0.18969 04844 17	1.00616 34856 39
12	0.24231 01856 16	0.24121 57430 58	0.20670 15498 28	1.00731 79126 87
13	0.26229 83587 87	0.26091 19605 59	0.22365 18298 43	1.00856 65554 59
14	0.28223 86116 15	0.28051 38518 14	0.24053 63151 44	1.00990 78936 59
15	0.30212 76805 41	0.30001 52428 82	0.25735 00100 59	1.01134 02941 13
16	0.32196 23914 53	0.31941 01841 41	0.27408 79336 87	1.01286 20127 48
17	0.34173 96645 45	0.33869 29608 96	0.29074 51210 26	1.01447 11967 19
18	0.36145 65188 98	0.35785 81030 09	0.30731 66241 20	1.01616 58866 55
19	0.38111 00767 70	0.37690 03935 36	0.32379 75132 19	1.01794 40190 44
20	0.40069 75675 82	0.39581 48763 67	0.34018 28779 60	1.01980 34287 39
21	0.42021 63316 03	0.41459 68628 50	0.35646 78285 62	1.02174 18515 91
22	0.43966 38233 26	0.43324 19374 17	0.37264 74970 33	1.02375 69272 02
23	0.45903 76145 28	0.45174 59621 90	0.38871 70384 04	1.02584 62017 92
24	0.47833 53970 24	0.47010 50806 15	0.40467 16319 74	1.02800 71311 86
25	0.49755 49851 03	0.48831 57201 13	0.42050 64825 73	1.03023 70839 04
26	0.51669 43176 53	0.50637 45937 84	0.43621 68218 50	1.03253 33443 65
27	0.53575 14599 86	0.52427 87011 89	0.45179 79095 69	1.03489 31161 82
28	0.55472 46053 46	0.54202 53282 50	0.46724 50349 34	1.03731 35255 72
29	0.57361 20761 35	0.55961 20462 87	0.48255 35179 22	1.03979 16248 45
30	0.59241 23248 30	0.57703 67102 53	0.49771 87106 42	1.04232 43959 92
31	0.61112 39346 33	0.59429 74561 89	0.51273 59987 11	1.04490 87543 53
32	0.62974 56198 32	0.61139 26979 63	0.52760 08026 41	1.04754 15523 74
33	0.64827 62259 06	0.62832 11233 30	0.54230 85792 50	1.05021 95834 36
34	0.66671 47293 64	0.64508 16893 57	0.55685 48230 90	1.05293 95857 53
35	0.68506 02373 45	0.66167 36172 77	0.57123 50678 83	1.05569 82463 44
36	0.70331 19869 83	0.67809 63868 17	0.58544 48879 85	1.05849 22050 66
37	0.72146 93445 44	0.69434 97300 41	0.59947 98998 55	1.06131 80587 00
38	0.73953 18043 60	0.71043 36247 76	0.61333 57635 39	1.06417 23650 96
39	0.75749 89875 54	0.72634 82876 61	0.62700 81841 75	1.06705 16473 64
40	0.77537 06405 89	0.74209 41668 68	0.64049 29134 98	1.06995 23981 04
41	0.79314 66336 34	0.75767 19345 53	0.65378 57513 70	1.07287 10836 79
42	0.81082 69587 74	0.77308 24790 75	0.66688 25473 07	1.07580 41485 18
43	0.82841 17280 71	0.78832 68970 31	0.67977 92020 24	1.07874 80194 42
44	0.84590 11714 80	0.80340 64851 56	0.69247 16689 87	1.08169 91100 21
45	0.86329 56346 54	0.81832 27321 27	0.70495 59559 64	1.08465 38249 41

171

ELLIPTIC FUNCTIONS   TABLE $\theta = 43°$

K = 1.82560 18981 35889   E = 1.36799 91658 73159
K'= 1.88480 86573 80404   E'= 1.33286 99541 17179

r	u=(r/90)K=F(ϕ,k)	sn u	cn u	dn u
45	0.91280 09490 68	0.75998 86389 94	0.64993 63573 46	0.85519 22015 66
46	0.93308 54146 03	0.77111 82145 10	0.63669 19971 63	0.85054 55672 44
47	0.95336 98801 38	0.78195 84501 52	0.62333 05561 55	0.84592 97273 28
48	0.97365 43456 72	0.79251 03160 04	0.60985 85073 82	0.84134 99655 10
49	0.99393 88112 07	0.80277 49589 79	0.59628 21188 30	0.83681 14362 72
50	1.01422 32767 42	0.81275 36891 72	0.58260 74499 49	0.83231 91617 69
51	1.03450 77422 77	0.82244 79663 57	0.56884 03489 86	0.82787 80291 99
52	1.05479 22078 12	0.83185 93866 47	0.55498 64510 49	0.82349 27886 28
53	1.07507 66733 47	0.84098 96693 65	0.54105 11768 96	0.81916 80512 68
54	1.09536 11388 82	0.84984 06441 56	0.52703 97324 11	0.81490 82881 58
55	1.11564 56044 16	0.85841 42383 58	0.51295 71087 18	0.81071 78292 41
56	1.13593 00699 51	0.86671 24646 67	0.49880 80829 24	0.80660 08627 97
57	1.15621 45354 86	0.87473 74091 24	0.48459 72194 30	0.80256 14352 27
58	1.17649 90010 21	0.88249 12194 16	0.47032 88718 05	0.79860 34511 33
59	1.19678 34665 56	0.88997 60935 45	0.45600 71851 61	0.79473 06736 97
60	1.21706 79320 91	0.89719 42688 43	0.44163 60990 17	0.79094 67253 17
61	1.23735 23976 25	0.90414 80113 71	0.42721 93506 09	0.78725 50884 75
62	1.25763 68631 60	0.91083 96056 89	0.41276 04786 16	0.78365 91068 27
63	1.27792 13286 95	0.91727 13450 26	0.39826 28272 81	0.78016 19864 70
64	1.29820 57942 30	0.92344 55218 28	0.38372 95508 77	0.77676 67973 82
65	1.31849 02597 65	0.92936 44187 13	0.36916 36185 09	0.77347 64750 01
66	1.33877 47253 00	0.93503 02998 15	0.35456 78192 21	0.77029 38219 27
67	1.35905 91908 34	0.94044 54025 28	0.33994 47673 71	0.76722 15097 21
68	1.37934 36563 69	0.94561 19296 39	0.32529 69082 63	0.76426 20807 85
69	1.39962 81219 04	0.95053 20418 51	0.31062 65240 03	0.76141 79503 09
70	1.41991 25874 39	0.95520 78507 04	0.29593 57395 68	0.75869 14082 47
71	1.44019 70529 74	0.95964 14118 59	0.28122 65290 56	0.75608 46213 34
72	1.46048 15185 09	0.96383 47187 77	0.26650 07221 01	0.75359 96351 04
73	1.48076 59840 44	0.96778 96967 54	0.25176 00104 40	0.75123 83759 00
74	1.50105 04495 78	0.97150 81973 29	0.23700 59546 16	0.74900 26528 67
75	1.52133 49151 13	0.97499 19930 40	0.22223 99907 93	0.74689 41599 11
76	1.54161 93806 48	0.97824 27725 41	0.20746 34376 75	0.74491 44776 05
77	1.56190 38461 83	0.98126 21360 46	0.19267 75035 20	0.74306 50750 44
78	1.58218 83117 18	0.98405 15911 22	0.17788 32932 30	0.74134 73116 24
79	1.60247 27772 53	0.98661 25488 00	0.16308 18155 09	0.73976 24387 40
80	1.62275 72427 87	0.98894 63200 11	0.14827 39900 87	0.73831 16013 98
81	1.64304 17083 22	0.99105 41123 32	0.13346 06549 85	0.73699 58397 27
82	1.66332 61738 57	0.99293 70270 44	0.11864 25738 34	0.73581 60903 85
83	1.68361 06393 92	0.99459 60564 82	0.10382 04432 23	0.73477 31878 47
84	1.70389 51049 27	0.99603 20816 92	0.08899 49000 83	0.73386 78655 86
85	1.72417 95704 62	0.99724 58703 66	0.07416 65290 92	0.73310 07571 12
86	1.74446 40359 97	0.99823 80750 69	0.05933 58701 10	0.73247 23968 98
87	1.76474 85015 31	0.99900 92317 43	0.04450 34256 18	0.73198 32211 57
88	1.78503 29670 66	0.99955 97584 89	0.02966 96681 83	0.73163 35684 90
89	1.80531 74326 01	0.99988 99546 22	0.01483 50479 26	0.73142 36803 93
90	1.82560 18981 36	1.00000 00000 00	0.00000 00000 00	0.73135 37016 19

q = 0.03902 78889 26606 97   D(90) = 1.16932 77817 18452
q′= 0.04769 60340 17055 65   1/D(90) = 0.85519 22015 65923

r	ϕ	$E(\phi, k)$	A(r)	D(r)
45	0.86329 56346 54	0.81832 27321 27	0.70495 59559 64	1.08465 38249 41
46	0.88059 55766 25	0.83307 73103 06	0.71722 81265 89	1.08760 85643 81
47	0.89780 15673 88	0.84767 20674 71	0.72928 43019 30	1.09055 97284 01
48	0.91491 42853 94	0.86210 90185 58	0.74112 06620 51	1.09350 37213 29
49	0.93193 45149 67	0.87639 03374 59	0.75273 34475 83	1.09643 69561 39
50	0.94886 31436 52	0.89051 83488 98	0.76411 89612 91	1.09935 58588 27
51	0.96570 11594 96	0.90449 55204 13	0.77527 35696 35	1.10225 68727 63
52	0.98244 96482 97	0.91832 44544 83	0.78619 37043 37	1.10513 64630 26
53	0.99910 97907 97	0.93200 78807 97	0.79687 58639 28	1.10799 11207 18
54	1.01568 28598 57	0.94554 86487 22	0.80731 66152 99	1.11081 73672 36
55	1.03217 02175 99	0.95894 97199 48	0.81751 25952 34	1.11361 17585 15
56	1.04857 33125 39	0.97221 41613 67	0.82746 05119 42	1.11637 08892 32
57	1.06489 36767 13	0.98534 51381 64	0.83715 71465 64	1.11909 13969 50
58	1.08113 29227 95	0.99834 59071 53	0.84659 93546 70	1.12176 99662 28
59	1.09729 27412 30	1.01121 98103 71	0.85578 40677 46	1.12440 33326 58
60	1.11337 48973 64	1.02397 02689 15	0.86470 82946 48	1.12698 82868 49
61	1.12938 12286 03	1.03660 07770 55	0.87336 91230 50	1.12952 16783 47
62	1.14531 36415 85	1.04911 48966 10	0.88176 37208 56	1.13200 04194 68
63	1.16117 41093 71	1.06151 62515 94	0.88988 93376 02	1.13442 14890 78
64	1.17696 46686 74	1.07380 85231 34	0.89774 33058 16	1.13678 19362 70
65	1.19268 74171 16	1.08599 54446 65	0.90532 30423 64	1.13907 88839 67
66	1.20834 45105 07	1.09808 07973 88	0.91262 60497 55	1.14130 95324 39
67	1.22393 81601 79	1.11006 84060 01	0.91964 99174 22	1.14347 11627 13
68	1.23947 06303 38	1.12196 21346 85	0.92639 23229 65	1.14556 11398 94
69	1.25494 42354 71	1.13376 58833 60	0.93285 10333 59	1.14757 69163 84
70	1.27036 13377 80	1.14548 35841 84	0.93902 39061 27	1.14951 60349 89
71	1.28572 43446 65	1.15711 91983 04	0.94490 88904 69	1.15137 61319 22
72	1.30103 57062 46	1.16867 67128 36	0.95050 40283 60	1.15315 49396 85
73	1.31629 79129 21	1.18016 01380 90	0.95580 74555 95	1.15485 02898 40
74	1.33151 34929 72	1.19157 35049 99	0.96081 74027 95	1.15646 01156 60
75	1.34668 50102 07	1.20292 08627 71	0.96553 21963 72	1.15798 24546 47
76	1.36181 50616 39	1.21420 62767 42	0.96995 02594 37	1.15941 54509 31
77	1.37690 62752 11	1.22543 38264 14	0.97407 01126 73	1.16075 73575 40
78	1.39196 13075 50	1.23660 76036 83	0.97789 03751 45	1.16200 65385 28
79	1.40698 28417 57	1.24773 17112 27	0.98140 97650 71	1.16316 14709 77
80	1.42197 35852 38	1.25881 02610 62	0.98462 71005 33	1.16422 07468 58
81	1.43693 62675 58	1.26984 73732 40	0.98754 13001 39	1.16518 30747 46
82	1.45187 36383 27	1.28084 71746 82	0.99015 13836 33	1.16604 72814 03
83	1.46678 84651 20	1.29181 37981 39	0.99245 64724 42	1.16681 23132 10
84	1.48168 35314 07	1.30275 13812 58	0.99445 57901 77	1.16747 72374 50
85	1.49656 16345 26	1.31366 40657 57	0.99614 86630 71	1.16804 12434 53
86	1.51142 55836 56	1.32455 59966 74	0.99753 45203 63	1.16850 36435 84
87	1.52627 81978 22	1.33543 13217 06	0.99861 28946 19	1.16886 38740 84
88	1.54112 23039 05	1.34629 41905 95	0.99938 34220 06	1.16912 14957 55
89	1.55596 07346 69	1.35714 87545 81	0.99984 58424 93	1.16927 61945 04
90	1.57079 63267 95	1.36799 91658 73	1.00000 00000 00	1.16932 77817 18

K = 1.83956 67210 93652
K' = 1.86914 75460 26462

E = 1.35937 69972 75008
E' = 1.34180 60581 29911

r	u=(r/90)K=F(ϕ,k)	sn u	cn u	dn u
0	0.00000 00000 00	0.00000 00000 00	1.00000 00000 00	1.00000 00000 00
1	0.02043 96302 34	0.02043 75204 97	0.99979 11320 65	0.99989 92161 73
2	0.04087 92604 69	0.04086 23882 66	0.99916 47838 20	0.99959 70533 49
3	0.06131 88907 03	0.06126 19790 30	0.99812 17209 97	0.99909 40768 48
4	0.08175 85209 37	0.08162 37252 69	0.99666 32166 75	0.99839 12266 78
5	0.10219 81511 72	0.10193 51442 35	0.99479 10465 87	0.99748 98142 69
6	0.12263 77814 06	0.12218 38655 40	0.99250 74825 92	0.99639 15179 27
7	0.14307 74116 41	0.14235 76581 75	0.98981 52843 63	0.99509 83770 43
8	0.16351 70418 75	0.16244 44568 27	0.98671 76893 35	0.99361 27850 93
9	0.18395 66721 09	0.18243 23873 67	0.98321 84009 87	0.99193 74814 70
10	0.20439 63023 44	0.20230 97913 93	0.97932 15755 34	0.99007 55422 17
11	0.22483 59325 78	0.22206 52497 13	0.97503 18071 07	0.98803 03696 96
12	0.24527 55628 12	0.24168 76046 58	0.97035 41115 26	0.98580 56812 84
13	0.26571 51930 47	0.26116 59811 43	0.96529 39087 62	0.98340 54971 47
14	0.28615 48232 81	0.28048 98063 85	0.95985 70042 01	0.98083 41271 76
15	0.30659 44535 16	0.29964 88281 98	0.95404 95688 17	0.97809 61571 68
16	0.32703 40837 50	0.31863 31318 17	0.94787 81183 83	0.97519 64343 27
17	0.34747 37139 84	0.33743 31551 83	0.94134 94918 38	0.97214 00521 69
18	0.36791 33442 19	0.35603 97026 61	0.93447 08289 34	0.96893 23349 30
19	0.38835 29744 53	0.37444 39571 52	0.92724 95472 92	0.96557 88215 51
20	0.40879 26046 87	0.39263 74905 85	0.91969 33189 86	0.96208 52493 26
21	0.42923 22349 22	0.41061 22727 79	0.91181 00467 99	0.95845 75373 20
22	0.44967 18651 56	0.42836 06786 83	0.90360 78402 48	0.95470 17696 13
23	0.47011 14953 91	0.44587 54940 00	0.89509 49915 24	0.95082 41784 79
24	0.49055 11256 25	0.46314 99192 13	0.88627 99514 45	0.94683 11275 66
25	0.51099 07558 59	0.48017 75720 69	0.87717 13055 51	0.94272 90951 57
26	0.53143 03860 94	0.49695 24885 21	0.86777 77504 37	0.93852 46575 97
27	0.55187 00163 28	0.51346 91222 17	0.85810 80704 26	0.93422 44729 35
28	0.57230 96465 62	0.52972 23425 56	0.84817 11146 91	0.92983 52648 72
29	0.59274 92767 97	0.54570 74313 98	0.83797 57748 99	0.92536 38070 51
30	0.61318 89070 31	0.56142 00784 70	0.82753 09634 64	0.92081 69077 68
31	0.63362 85372 66	0.57685 63755 64	0.81684 55924 91	0.91620 13951 35
32	0.65406 81675 00	0.59201 28095 78	0.80592 85534 68	0.91152 41027 58
33	0.67450 77977 34	0.60688 62544 93	0.79478 86977 73	0.90679 18559 55
34	0.69494 74279 69	0.62147 39623 58	0.78343 48180 36	0.90201 14585 58
35	0.71538 70582 03	0.63577 35533 68	0.77187 56304 21	0.89718 96803 32
36	0.73582 66884 37	0.64978 30051 16	0.76011 97578 42	0.89233 32450 23
37	0.75626 63186 72	0.66350 06411 01	0.74817 57141 60	0.88744 88190 61
38	0.77670 59489 06	0.67692 51185 73	0.73605 18893 70	0.88254 30009 42
39	0.79714 55791 41	0.69005 54158 03	0.72375 65358 05	0.87762 23112 78
40	0.81758 52093 75	0.70289 08188 44	0.71129 77553 64	0.87269 31835 39
41	0.83802 48396 09	0.71543 09078 74	0.69868 34877 53	0.86776 19554 78
42	0.85846 44698 44	0.72767 55431 90	0.68592 14997 67	0.86283 48612 38
43	0.87890 41000 78	0.73962 48509 26	0.67301 93755 70	0.85791 80241 37
44	0.89934 37303 12	0.75127 92085 61	0.65998 45079 88	0.85301 74501 12
45	0.91978 33605 47	0.76263 92302 93	0.64682 40907 84	0.84813 90218 23

q = 0.04108 50703 79885 46   D(90) = 1.17905 19882 58651
q′= 0.04541 67490 83529 43   1/D(90) = 0.84813 90218 22868

r	ϕ	$E(\phi,k)$	A(r)	D(r)
0	0.00000 00000 00	0.00000 00000 00	0.00000 00000 00	1.00000 00000 00
1	0.02043 89435 30	0.02043 82568 67	0.01733 48037 14	1.00005 45216 93
2	0.04087 37683 77	0.04086 82776 14	0.03466 45419 43	1.00021 80203 99
3	0.06130 03635 67	0.06128 18465 04	0.05198 41501 57	1.00049 02970 88
4	0.08171 46335 12	0.08167 07884 68	0.06928 85657 33	1.00087 10203 06
5	0.10211 25056 42	0.10202 69891 91	0.08657 27289 18	1.00135 97265 84
6	0.12248 99379 51	0.12234 24148 98	0.10383 15837 88	1.00195 58209 98
7	0.14284 29264 35	0.14260 91317 49	0.12106 00792 15	1.00265 85778 91
8	0.16316 75124 10	0.16281 93247 49	0.13825 31698 43	1.00346 71417 57
9	0.18345 97896 60	0.18296 53160 92	0.15540 58170 66	1.00438 05282 77
10	0.20371 59114 22	0.20303 95828 39	0.17251 29900 22	1.00539 76255 16
11	0.22393 20971 56	0.22303 47738 77	0.18956 96665 92	1.00651 71952 72
12	0.24410 46391 07	0.24294 37260 67	0.20657 08344 13	1.00773 78745 80
13	0.26422 99086 18	0.26275 94795 23	0.22351 14919 01	1.00905 81773 72
14	0.28430 43621 84	0.28247 52919 71	0.24038 66492 90	1.01047 64962 72
15	0.30432 45472 39	0.30208 46521 24	0.25719 13296 85	1.01199 11045 61
16	0.32428 71076 44	0.32158 12920 40	0.27392 05701 30	1.01360 01582 62
17	0.34418 87888 80	0.34095 91984 28	0.29056 94226 91	1.01530 16983 91
18	0.36402 64429 22	0.36021 26228 61	0.30713 29555 57	1.01709 36533 29
19	0.38379 70327 92	0.37933 60908 92	0.32360 62541 66	1.01897 38413 43
20	0.40349 76367 80	0.39832 44100 54	0.33998 44223 33	1.02093 99732 35
21	0.42312 54523 32	0.41717 26767 37	0.35626 25834 17	1.02298 96551 26
22	0.44267 77995 92	0.43587 62819 46	0.37243 58814 95	1.02512 03913 61
23	0.46215 21246 04	0.45443 09159 49	0.38849 94825 58	1.02732 95875 46
24	0.48154 60021 67	0.47283 25718 37	0.40444 85757 33	1.02961 45536 99
25	0.50085 71383 51	0.49107 75480 10	0.42027 83745 22	1.03197 25075 20
26	0.52008 33726 73	0.50916 24496 16	0.43598 41180 64	1.03440 05777 74
27	0.53922 26799 26	0.52708 41889 89	0.45156 10724 15	1.03689 58077 80
28	0.55827 31716 92	0.54483 99851 12	0.46700 45318 56	1.03945 51590 06
29	0.57723 30975 19	0.56242 73621 52	0.48230 98202 18	1.04207 55147 65
30	0.59610 08457 85	0.57984 41471 13	0.49747 22922 28	1.04475 36840 03
31	0.61487 49442 57	0.59708 84666 57	0.51248 73348 79	1.04748 64051 83
32	0.63355 40603 42	0.61415 87431 45	0.52735 03688 19	1.05027 03502 46
33	0.65213 70010 65	0.63105 36899 55	0.54205 68497 65	1.05310 21286 65
34	0.67062 27127 61	0.64777 23061 23	0.55660 22699 26	1.05597 82915 68
35	0.68901 02805 00	0.66431 38703 77	0.57098 21594 59	1.05889 53359 32
36	0.70729 89272 80	0.68067 79346 15	0.58519 20879 38	1.06184 97088 47
37	0.72548 80129 58	0.69686 43168 86	0.59922 76658 36	1.06483 78118 40
38	0.74357 70329 75	0.71287 30939 22	0.61308 45460 36	1.06785 60052 52
39	0.76156 56168 65	0.72870 45933 01	0.62675 84253 45	1.07090 06126 73
40	0.77945 35265 63	0.74435 93852 71	0.64024 50460 37	1.07396 79254 10
41	0.79724 06545 38	0.75983 82743 02	0.65354 01973 98	1.07705 42070 08
42	0.81492 70217 55	0.77514 22904 21	0.66663 97172 93	1.08015 56977 99
43	0.83251 27754 83	0.79027 26803 69	0.67953 94937 39	1.08326 86194 77
44	0.84999 81869 57	0.80523 08986 46	0.69223 54664 95	1.08638 91797 00
45	0.86738 36489 23	0.82001 85984 68	0.70472 36286 54	1.08951 35767 13

K = 1.83956 67210 93652 E = 1.35937 69972 75008
K' = 1.86914 75460 26462 E' = 1.34180 60581 29911

r	u=(r/90)K=F(ϕ,k)	sn u	cn u	dn u
45	0.91978 33605 47	0.76263 92302 93	0.64682 40907 84	0.84813 90218 23
46	0.94022 29907 81	0.77370 57523 28	0.63354 51119 01	0.84328 84933 88
47	0.96066 26210 16	0.78447 98181 59	0.62015 43476 44	0.83847 14857 37
48	0.98110 22512 50	0.79496 26638 67	0.60665 83577 75	0.83369 34825 58
49	1.00154 18814 84	0.80515 57035 23	0.59306 34814 97	0.82895 98268 25
50	1.02198 15117 19	0.81506 05147 15	0.57937 58342 84	0.82427 57178 66
51	1.04242 11419 53	0.82467 88242 56	0.56560 13055 36	0.81964 62089 61
52	1.06286 07721 87	0.83401 24941 04	0.55174 55570 08	0.81507 62054 32
53	1.08330 04024 22	0.84306 35075 40	0.53781 40219 95	0.81057 04632 07
54	1.10374 00326 56	0.85183 39556 24	0.52381 19052 17	0.80613 35878 17
55	1.12417 96628 91	0.86032 60239 63	0.50974 41833 83	0.80177 00338 15
56	1.14461 92931 25	0.86854 19798 19	0.49561 56063 84	0.79748 41045 69
57	1.16505 89233 59	0.87648 41595 72	0.48143 06990 83	0.79327 99524 11
58	1.18549 85535 94	0.88415 49565 50	0.46719 37636 66	0.78916 15791 20
59	1.20593 81838 28	0.89155 68092 65	0.45290 88825 07	0.78513 28366 86
60	1.22637 78140 62	0.89869 21900 35	0.43857 99215 30	0.78119 74283 60
61	1.24681 74442 97	0.90556 35940 30	0.42421 05340 12	0.77735 89099 31
62	1.26725 70745 31	0.91217 35287 25	0.40980 41648 08	0.77362 06912 28
63	1.28769 67047 66	0.91852 45037 84	0.39536 40549 53	0.76998 60378 08
64	1.30813 63350 00	0.92461 90213 68	0.38089 32466 26	0.76645 80728 02
65	1.32857 59652 34	0.93045 95668 65	0.36639 45884 28	0.76303 97789 08
66	1.34901 55954 69	0.93604 86000 53	0.35187 07409 53	0.75973 40004 95
67	1.36945 52257 03	0.94138 85466 76	0.33732 41826 29	0.75654 34458 02
68	1.38989 48559 37	0.94648 17904 49	0.32275 72157 97	0.75347 06892 08
69	1.41033 44861 72	0.95133 06654 65	0.30817 19730 05	0.75051 81735 54
70	1.43077 41164 06	0.95593 74490 25	0.29357 04234 94	0.74768 82124 97
71	1.45121 37466 41	0.96030 43548 56	0.27895 43798 64	0.74498 29928 78
72	1.47165 33768 75	0.96443 35267 24	0.26432 55048 80	0.74240 45770 86
73	1.49209 30071 09	0.96832 70324 45	0.24968 53184 22	0.73995 49054 01
74	1.51253 26373 44	0.97198 68582 55	0.23503 52045 54	0.73763 57983 05
75	1.53297 22675 78	0.97541 49035 60	0.22037 64186 86	0.73544 89587 42
76	1.55341 18978 12	0.97861 29760 44	0.20571 00948 38	0.73339 59743 12
77	1.57385 15280 47	0.98158 27871 24	0.19103 72529 70	0.73147 83193 97
78	1.59429 11582 81	0.98432 59477 48	0.17635 88063 85	0.72969 73571 93
79	1.61473 07885 16	0.98684 39645 30	0.16167 55691 83	0.72805 43416 50
80	1.63517 04187 50	0.98913 82362 01	0.14698 82637 66	0.72655 04193 03
81	1.65561 00489 84	0.99121 00503 85	0.13229 75283 78	0.72518 66309 89
82	1.67604 96792 19	0.99306 05806 80	0.11760 39246 81	0.72396 39134 39
83	1.69648 93094 53	0.99469 08840 35	0.10290 79453 56	0.72288 31007 40
84	1.71692 89396 87	0.99610 18984 36	0.08821 00217 24	0.72194 49256 61
85	1.73736 85699 22	0.99729 44408 62	0.07351 05313 88	0.72115 00208 31
86	1.75780 82001 56	0.99826 92055 41	0.05880 98058 85	0.72049 89197 79
87	1.77824 78303 91	0.99902 67624 70	0.04410 81383 48	0.71999 20578 13
88	1.79868 74606 25	0.99956 75562 19	0.02940 57911 82	0.71962 97727 45
89	1.81912 70908 59	0.99989 19049 98	0.01470 30037 39	0.71941 23054 64
90	1.83956 67210 94	1.00000 00000 00	0.00000 00000 00	0.71933 98003 39

ELLIPTIC FUNCTIONS   TABLE $\theta = 44°$

$q = 0.04108\ 50703\ 79885\ 46$ $D(90) = 1.17905\ 19882\ 58651$
$q' = 0.04541\ 67490\ 83529\ 43$ $1/D(90) = 0.84813\ 90218\ 22868$

r	ϕ	$E(\phi,k)$	$A(r)$	$D(r)$
45	0.86738 36489 23	0.82001 85984 68	0.70472 36286 54	1.08951 35767 13
46	0.88466 96730 61	0.83463 76226 99	0.71700 00282 48	1.09263 80039 74
47	0.90185 68873 10	0.84908 99947 86	0.72906 07698 55	1.09575 86547 94
48	0.91894 60331 00	0.86337 79097 50	0.74090 20162 16	1.09887 17269 76
49	0.93593 79625 15	0.87750 37252 41	0.75251 99898 52	1.10197 34274 47
50	0.95283 36353 85	0.89146 99527 28	0.76391 09746 76	1.10505 99768 77
51	0.96963 41163 19	0.90527 92488 16	0.77507 13176 20	1.10812 76142 95
52	0.98634 05717 10	0.91893 44067 44	0.78599 74302 41	1.11117 26016 61
53	1.00295 42666 83	0.93243 83480 74	0.79668 57903 38	1.11419 12284 36
54	1.01947 65620 42	0.94579 41146 01	0.80713 29435 54	1.11717 98160 94
55	1.03590 89111 80	0.95900 48604 92	0.81733 55049 72	1.12013 47226 17
56	1.05225 28569 98	0.97207 38446 85	0.82729 01607 04	1.12305 23469 32
57	1.06851 00288 09	0.98500 44235 48	0.83699 36694 63	1.12592 91333 03
58	1.08468 21392 61	0.99780 00438 19	0.84644 28641 24	1.12876 15756 71
59	1.10077 09812 62	1.01046 42358 36	0.85563 46532 67	1.13154 62219 28
60	1.11677 84249 33	1.02300 06070 49	0.86456 60227 05	1.13427 96781 30
61	1.13270 64145 78	1.03541 28358 53	0.87323 40369 88	1.13695 86126 40
62	1.14855 69656 85	1.04770 46656 98	0.88163 58408 85	1.13957 97601 90
63	1.16433 21619 63	1.05987 98995 30	0.88976 86608 46	1.14213 99258 70
64	1.18003 41524 05	1.07194 23945 14	0.89762 98064 31	1.14463 59890 23
65	1.19566 51484 03	1.08389 60570 77	0.90521 66717 14	1.14706 49070 60
66	1.21122 74208 97	1.09574 48382 38	0.91252 67366 59	1.14942 37191 70
67	1.22672 32975 70	1.10749 27292 48	0.91955 75684 56	1.15170 95499 35
68	1.24215 51600 87	1.11914 37575 08	0.92630 68228 32	1.15391 96128 43
69	1.25752 54413 86	1.13070 19827 79	0.93277 22453 15	1.15605 12136 90
70	1.27283 66230 09	1.14217 14936 68	0.93895 16724 70	1.15810 17538 68
71	1.28809 12324 92	1.15355 64043 83	0.94484 30330 87	1.16006 87335 44
72	1.30329 18407 89	1.16486 08517 45	0.95044 43493 30	1.16194 97547 06
73	1.31844 10597 60	1.17608 89924 56	0.95575 37378 43	1.16374 25240 97
74	1.33354 15396 93	1.18724 50006 05	0.96076 94108 06	1.16544 48560 17
75	1.34859 59668 82	1.19833 30654 05	0.96548 96769 53	1.16705 46749 90
76	1.36360 70612 47	1.20935 73891 43	0.96991 29425 28	1.16857 00183 01
77	1.37857 75739 96	1.22032 21853 47	0.97403 77122 03	1.16998 90383 95
78	1.39351 02853 34	1.23123 16771 42	0.97786 25899 39	1.17131 00051 35
79	1.40840 80022 08	1.24209 00957 88	0.98138 62797 90	1.17253 13079 12
80	1.42327 35560 97	1.25290 16793 95	0.98460 75866 58	1.17365 14576 19
81	1.43810 98008 29	1.26367 06717 88	0.98752 54169 95	1.17466 90884 66
82	1.45291 96104 42	1.27440 13215 27	0.99013 87794 38	1.17558 29596 51
83	1.46770 58770 67	1.28509 78810 48	0.99244 67853 94	1.17639 19568 79
84	1.48247 15088 48	1.29576 46059 38	0.99444 86495 67	1.17709 50937 19
85	1.49721 94278 80	1.30640 57542 99	0.99614 36904 18	1.17769 15128 13
86	1.51195 25681 74	1.31702 55862 25	0.99753 13305 75	1.17818 04869 23
87	1.52667 38736 42	1.32762 83633 37	0.99861 10971 70	1.17856 14198 20
88	1.54138 62960 96	1.33821 83484 08	0.99938 26221 25	1.17883 38470 14
89	1.55609 27932 60	1.34879 98050 19	0.99984 56423 70	1.17899 74363 18
90	1.57079 63267 95	1.35937 69972 75	1.00000 00000 00	1.17905 19882 59

ELLIPTIC FUNCTIONS   TABLE $\theta = 45°$

K = K′ = 1.85407 46773 01372   E = E′ = 1.35064 38810 47676

r	u=(r/90)K=F(φ,k)	sn u	cn u	dn u
0	0.00000 00000 00	0.00000 00000 00	1.00000 00000 00	1.00000 00000 00
1	0.02060 08297 48	0.02059 86442 85	0.99978 78254 18	0.99989 39183 37
2	0.04120 16594 96	0.04118 41819 10	0.99915 15716 65	0.99957 58758 49
3	0.06180 24892 43	0.06174 35367 72	0.99809 20476 92	0.99904 64793 16
4	0.08240 33189 91	0.08226 36937 24	0.99661 05983 26	0.99830 67376 05
5	0.10300 41487 39	0.10273 17286 47	0.99470 90991 49	0.99735 80580 54
6	0.12360 49784 87	0.12313 48380 57	0.99238 99493 93	0.99620 22414 29
7	0.14420 58082 35	0.14346 03680 70	0.98965 60628 79	0.99484 14755 11
8	0.16480 66379 82	0.16369 58426 07	0.98651 08570 68	0.99327 83273 37
9	0.18540 74677 30	0.18382 89906 71	0.98295 82403 08	0.99151 57341 64
10	0.20600 82974 78	0.20384 77725 82	0.97900 25973 48	0.98955 69932 08
11	0.22660 91272 26	0.22374 04050 46	0.97464 87732 25	0.98740 57502 24
12	0.24720 99569 74	0.24349 53849 30	0.96990 20556 31	0.98506 59870 07
13	0.26781 07867 21	0.26310 15116 61	0.96476 81558 60	0.98254 20078 96
14	0.28841 16164 69	0.28254 79081 39	0.95925 31884 78	0.97983 84253 55
15	0.30901 24462 17	0.30182 40400 97	0.95336 36498 31	0.97696 01447 40
16	0.32961 32759 65	0.32091 97338 34	0.94710 63955 21	0.97391 23483 24
17	0.35021 41057 12	0.33982 51922 68	0.94048 86169 96	0.97070 04787 01
18	0.37081 49354 60	0.35853 10092 70	0.93351 78173 94	0.96733 02216 39
19	0.39141 57652 08	0.37702 81822 39	0.92620 17867 60	0.96380 74885 05
20	0.41201 65949 56	0.39530 81229 14	0.91854 85768 09	0.96013 83983 46
21	0.43261 74247 04	0.41336 26664 08	0.91056 64753 44	0.95632 92597 27
22	0.45321 82544 51	0.43118 40784 73	0.90226 39804 80	0.95238 65524 23
23	0.47381 90841 99	0.44876 50610 18	0.89364 97748 05	0.94831 69090 58
24	0.49441 99139 47	0.46609 87558 96	0.88473 26996 06	0.94412 70967 81
25	0.51502 07436 95	0.48317 87470 16	0.87552 17292 75	0.93982 39990 64
26	0.53562 15734 43	0.49999 90608 08	0.86602 59460 26	0.93541 45977 03
27	0.55622 24031 90	0.51655 41651 14	0.85625 45150 26	0.93090 59551 06
28	0.57682 32329 38	0.53283 89665 52	0.84621 66600 37	0.92630 51969 31
29	0.59742 40626 86	0.54884 88064 35	0.83592 16396 74	0.92161 94951 48
30	0.61802 48924 34	0.56457 94553 18	0.82537 87243 64	0.91685 60515 79
31	0.63862 57221 82	0.58002 71062 40	0.81459 71740 84	0.91202 20819 77
32	0.65922 65519 29	0.59518 83667 73	0.80358 62169 42	0.90712 48006 91
33	0.67982 73816 77	0.61006 02499 27	0.79235 50286 71	0.90217 14059 59
34	0.70042 82114 25	0.62464 01640 40	0.78091 27130 92	0.89716 90658 59
35	0.72102 90411 73	0.63892 59017 15	0.76926 82835 77	0.89212 49049 65
36	0.74162 98709 21	0.65291 56279 05	0.75743 06455 62	0.88704 59917 16
37	0.76223 07006 68	0.66660 78672 40	0.74540 85801 31	0.88193 93265 22
38	0.78283 15304 16	0.68000 14906 82	0.73321 07286 92	0.87681 18306 31
39	0.80343 23601 64	0.69309 57015 99	0.72084 55787 65	0.87167 03357 42
40	0.82403 31899 12	0.70589 00213 41	0.70832 14508 76	0.86652 15743 91
41	0.84463 40196 60	0.71838 42744 10	0.69564 64865 72	0.86137 21710 97
42	0.86523 48494 07	0.73057 85732 96	0.68282 86375 37	0.85622 86342 56
43	0.88583 56791 55	0.74247 33030 64	0.66987 56558 02	0.85109 73487 91
44	0.90643 65089 03	0.75406 91057 64	0.65679 50850 40	0.84598 45695 20
45	0.92703 73386 51	0.76536 68647 30	0.64359 42529 06	0.84089 64152 54

178

q = q′ = 0.04321 39182 63772 25   D(90) = 1.18920 71150 02721
                                         1/D(90) = 0.84089 64152 53715

r	ϕ	$E(\phi,k)$	A(r)	D(r)
0	0.00000 00000 00	0.00000 00000 00	0.00000 00000 00	1.00000 00000 00
1	0.02060 01012 45	0.02059 93727 88	0.01732 23240 43	1.00005 76113 34
2	0.04119 58331 39	0.04119 00082 66	0.03463 96092 02	1.00023 03752 13
3	0.06178 28346 73	0.06176 31913 50	0.05194 68174 79	1.00051 80813 55
4	0.08235 67614 81	0.08231 02512 92	0.06923 89126 41	1.00092 03795 72
5	0.10291 32940 94	0.10282 25835 66	0.08651 08611 13	1.00143 67801 97
6	0.12344 81460 97	0.12329 16714 25	0.10375 76328 71	1.00206 66546 77
7	0.14395 70721 72	0.14370 91070 04	0.12097 42023 35	1.00280 92363 35
8	0.16443 58759 91	0.16406 66118 93	0.13815 55492 82	1.00366 36213 05
9	0.18488 04179 37	0.18435 60570 51	0.15529 66597 56	1.00462 87696 23
10	0.20528 66226 39	0.20456 94819 99	0.17239 25269 96	1.00570 35064 93
11	0.22565 04862 47	0.22469 91131 76	0.18943 81523 69	1.00688 65237 13
12	0.24596 80835 12	0.24473 73814 06	0.20642 85463 28	1.00817 63812 60
13	0.26623 55745 54	0.26467 69383 80	0.22335 87293 66	1.00957 15090 44
14	0.28644 92113 68	0.28451 06721 07	0.24022 37330 03	1.01107 02088 06
15	0.30660 53440 11	0.30423 17212 66	0.25701 86007 82	1.01267 06561 87
16	0.32670 04264 77	0.32383 34884 19	0.27373 83892 79	1.01437 09029 40
17	0.34673 10222 28	0.34330 96520 46	0.29037 81691 41	1.01616 88792 95
18	0.36669 38093 83	0.36265 41773 70	0.30693 30261 34	1.01806 23964 73
19	0.38658 55855 48	0.38186 13259 53	0.32339 80622 22	1.02004 91493 44
20	0.40640 32722 75	0.40092 56640 49	0.33976 83966 58	1.02212 67192 28
21	0.42614 39191 61	0.41984 20697 20	0.35603 91671 05	1.02429 25768 31
22	0.44580 47075 57	0.43860 57387 02	0.37220 55307 74	1.02654 40853 16
23	0.46538 29539 09	0.45721 21890 58	0.38826 26655 88	1.02887 85035 09
24	0.48487 61127 18	0.47565 72646 15	0.40420 57713 75	1.03129 29892 28
25	0.50428 17791 24	0.49393 71372 30	0.42003 00710 73	1.03378 46027 37
26	0.52359 76911 14	0.51204 83079 08	0.43573 08119 75	1.03635 03103 16
27	0.54282 17313 67	0.52998 76068 17	0.45130 32669 87	1.03898 69879 50
28	0.56195 19287 35	0.54775 21922 47	0.46674 27359 18	1.04169 14251 24
29	0.58098 64593 70	0.56533 95485 56	0.48204 45467 91	1.04446 03287 29
30	0.59992 36475 07	0.58274 74831 61	0.49720 40571 84	1.04729 03270 60
31	0.61876 19659 16	0.59997 41226 34	0.51221 66555 90	1.05017 79739 20
32	0.63750 00360 27	0.61701 79079 59	0.52707 77628 06	1.05311 97528 06
33	0.65613 66277 53	0.63387 75890 11	0.54178 28333 45	1.05611 20811 89
34	0.67467 06590 07	0.65055 22183 23	0.55632 73568 72	1.05915 13148 69
35	0.69310 11949 46	0.66704 11442 08	0.57070 68596 61	1.06223 37524 09
36	0.71142 74469 42	0.68334 40032 99	0.58491 69060 80	1.06535 56396 36
37	0.72964 87713 01	0.69946 07125 67	0.59895 31000 89	1.06851 31742 10
38	0.74776 46677 47	0.71539 14608 86	0.61281 10867 69	1.07170 25102 50
39	0.76577 47776 81	0.73113 67002 17	0.62648 65538 65	1.07491 97630 16
40	0.78367 88822 39	0.74669 71364 48	0.63997 52333 48	1.07816 10136 33
41	0.80147 69001 53	0.76207 37199 83	0.65327 29029 93	1.08142 23138 66
42	0.81916 88854 44	0.77726 76361 05	0.66637 53879 82	1.08469 96909 25
43	0.83675 50249 51	0.79228 02951 96	0.67927 85625 12	1.08798 91523 02
44	0.85423 56357 19	0.80711 33228 49	0.69197 83514 21	1.09128 66906 33
45	0.87161 11622 54	0.82176 85499 31	0.70447 07318 27	1.09458 82885 78

K = K′= 1.85407 46773 01372   E = E′= 1.35064 38810 47676

r	u=(r/90)K=F(φ,k)	sn u	cn u	dn u
45	0.92703 73386 51	0.76536 68647 30	0.64359 42529 06	0.84089 64152 54
46	0.94763 81683 98	0.77636 76888 49	0.63028 02644 16	0.83583 88635 71
47	0.96823 89981 46	0.78707 28968 36	0.61685 99963 25	0.83081 77462 79
48	0.98883 98278 94	0.79748 40016 07	0.60334 00924 70	0.82583 87455 13
49	1.00944 06576 42	0.80760 26947 63	0.58972 69600 51	0.82090 73904 56
50	1.03004 14873 90	0.81743 08312 79	0.57602 67668 04	0.81602 90546 53
51	1.05064 23171 37	0.82697 04143 96	0.56224 54390 34	0.81120 89538 81
52	1.07124 31468 85	0.83622 35807 93	0.54838 86604 64	0.80645 21445 58
53	1.09184 39766 33	0.84519 25860 60	0.53446 18718 57	0.80176 35226 39
54	1.11244 48063 81	0.85387 97904 92	0.52047 02713 80	0.79714 78229 88
55	1.13304 56361 29	0.86228 76452 57	0.50641 88156 44	0.79260 96191 81
56	1.15364 64658 76	0.87041 86789 41	0.49231 22214 11	0.78815 33237 10
57	1.17424 72956 24	0.87827 54845 00	0.47815 49678 99	0.78378 31885 56
58	1.19484 81253 72	0.88586 07066 30	0.46395 12996 53	0.77950 33061 03
59	1.21544 89551 20	0.89317 70295 72	0.44970 52299 50	0.77531 76103 52
60	1.23604 97848 68	0.90022 71653 69	0.43542 05446 82	0.77122 98784 19
61	1.25665 06146 15	0.90701 38425 61	0.42110 08066 99	0.76724 37322 66
62	1.27725 14443 63	0.91353 97953 51	0.40674 93605 53	0.76336 26406 60
63	1.29785 22741 11	0.91980 77532 22	0.39236 93376 32	0.75958 99213 11
64	1.31845 31038 59	0.92582 04310 19	0.37796 36616 24	0.75592 87431 72
65	1.33905 39336 07	0.93158 05194 88	0.36353 50543 09	0.75238 21288 78
66	1.35965 47633 54	0.93709 06762 69	0.34908 60416 15	0.74895 29572 85
67	1.38025 55931 02	0.94235 35173 42	0.33461 89599 43	0.74564 39660 97
68	1.40085 64228 50	0.94737 16089 17	0.32013 59627 06	0.74245 77545 62
69	1.42145 72525 98	0.95214 74597 61	0.30563 90270 75	0.73939 67861 95
70	1.44205 80823 46	0.95668 35139 51	0.29112 99609 02	0.73646 33915 32
71	1.46265 89120 93	0.96098 21440 55	0.27661 04097 96	0.73365 97708 77
72	1.48325 97418 41	0.96504 56447 15	0.26208 18643 41	0.73098 79970 34
73	1.50386 05715 89	0.96887 62266 35	0.24754 56674 26	0.72845 00180 05
74	1.52446 14013 37	0.97247 60109 58	0.23300 30216 80	0.72604 76596 31
75	1.54506 22310 84	0.97584 70240 21	0.21845 49969 89	0.72378 26281 80
76	1.56566 30608 32	0.97899 11924 82	0.20390 25380 97	0.72165 65128 38
77	1.58626 38905 80	0.98191 03388 01	0.18934 64722 54	0.71967 07881 23
78	1.60686 47203 28	0.98460 61770 72	0.17478 75169 20	0.71782 68161 86
79	1.62746 55500 76	0.98708 03091 89	0.16022 62875 19	0.71612 58490 00
80	1.64806 63798 23	0.98933 42213 41	0.14566 33052 08	0.71456 90304 25
81	1.66866 72095 71	0.99136 92808 28	0.13109 90046 88	0.71315 73981 35
82	1.68926 80393 19	0.99318 67331 82	0.11653 37420 28	0.71189 18854 12
83	1.70986 88690 67	0.99478 76995 89	0.10196 78025 00	0.71077 33227 78
84	1.73046 96988 15	0.99617 31746 05	0.08740 14084 38	0.70980 24394 85
85	1.75107 05285 62	0.99734 40241 61	0.07283 47270 90	0.70897 98648 31
86	1.77167 13583 10	0.99830 09838 40	0.05826 78784 85	0.70830 61293 20
87	1.79227 21880 58	0.99904 46574 38	0.04370 09432 99	0.70778 16656 45
88	1.81287 30178 06	0.99957 55157 81	0.02913 39707 27	0.70740 68094 99
89	1.83347 38475 54	0.99989 38958 25	0.01456 69863 47	0.70718 18002 08
90	1.85407 46773 01	1.00000 00000 00	0.00000 00000 00	0.70710 67811 87

ELLIPTIC FUNCTIONS   TABLE $\theta = 45°$

q = q' = 0.04321 39182 63772 25

D(90) = 1.18920 71150 02721
1/D(90) = 0.84089 64152 53715

r	ϕ	$E(\phi, k)$	A(r)	D(r)
45	0.87161 11622 54	0.82176 85499 31	0.70447 07318 27	1.09458 82885 78
46	0.88888 21736 71	0.83624 80026 36	0.71675 17347 77	1.09788 99237 19
47	0.90604 93607 31	0.85055 38925 85	0.72881 74469 04	1.10118 75734 51
48	0.92311 35328 02	0.86468 86070 03	0.74066 40120 91	1.10447 72198 95
49	0.94007 56147 38	0.87865 46990 10	0.75228 76331 41	1.10775 48547 83
50	0.95693 66436 98	0.89245 48780 68	0.76368 45734 54	1.11101 64843 53
51	0.97369 77659 19	0.90609 20006 14	0.77485 11586 97	1.11425 81342 09
52	0.99036 02334 51	0.91956 90609 03	0.78578 37784 82	1.11747 58541 71
53	1.00692 54008 55	0.93288 91820 81	0.79647 88880 40	1.12066 57230 89
54	1.02339 47218 97	0.94605 56075 31	0.80693 30098 83	1.12382 38536 26
55	1.03976 97462 22	0.95907 16924 81	0.81714 27354 73	1.12694 63969 97
56	1.05605 21160 36	0.97194 08959 24	0.82710 47268 69	1.13002 95476 67
57	1.07224 35627 90	0.98466 67728 26	0.83681 57183 69	1.13306 95479 88
58	1.08834 59038 85	0.99725 29666 72	0.84627 25181 43	1.13606 26927 87
59	1.10436 10393 95	1.00970 32023 25	0.85547 20098 41	1.13900 53338 87
60	1.12029 09488 16	1.02202 12792 30	0.86441 11541 88	1.14189 38845 58
61	1.13613 76878 57	1.03421 10649 47	0.87308 69905 65	1.14472 48238 95
62	1.15190 33852 61	1.04627 64890 30	0.88149 66385 58	1.14749 47011 16
63	1.16759 02396 69	1.05822 15372 46	0.88963 72994 86	1.15020 01397 74
64	1.18320 05165 35	1.07005 02461 33	0.89750 62579 06	1.15283 78418 77
65	1.19873 65450 85	1.08176 66978 93	0.90510 08830 86	1.15540 45919 22
66	1.21420 07153 25	1.09337 50156 18	0.91241 86304 45	1.15789 72608 14
67	1.22959 54751 13	1.10487 93588 45	0.91945 70429 63	1.16031 28096 93
68	1.24492 33272 73	1.11628 39194 27	0.92621 37525 55	1.16264 82936 42
69	1.26018 68267 74	1.12759 29177 18	0.93268 64814 06	1.16490 08652 86
70	1.27538 85779 61	1.13881 05990 60	0.93887 30432 66	1.16706 77782 72
71	1.29053 12318 43	1.14994 12305 64	0.94477 13447 06	1.16914 63906 22
72	1.30561 74834 39	1.16098 90981 74	0.95037 93863 26	1.17113 41679 64
73	1.32065 00691 81	1.17195 85040 02	0.95569 52639 23	1.17302 86866 24
74	1.33563 17643 67	1.18285 37639 27	0.96071 71696 04	1.17482 76365 95
75	1.35056 53806 74	1.19367 92054 35	0.96544 33928 59	1.17652 88243 54
76	1.36545 37637 18	1.20443 91657 02	0.96987 23215 73	1.17813 01755 47
77	1.38029 97906 69	1.21513 79898 95	0.97400 24429 89	1.17962 97375 24
78	1.39510 63679 13	1.22578 00296 87	0.97783 23446 23	1.18102 56817 23
79	1.40987 64287 57	1.23636 96419 67	0.98136 07151 14	1.18231 63059 11
80	1.42461 29311 84	1.24691 11877 29	0.98458 63450 18	1.18350 00362 60
81	1.43931 88556 44	1.25740 90311 35	0.98750 81275 51	1.18457 54292 75
82	1.45399 72028 87	1.26786 75387 32	0.99012 50592 62	1.18554 11735 56
83	1.46865 09918 26	1.27829 10788 11	0.99243 62406 50	1.18639 60914 03
84	1.48328 32574 39	1.28868 40208 89	0.99444 08767 23	1.18713 91402 58
85	1.49789 70486 96	1.29905 07353 11	0.99613 82774 84	1.18776 94139 77
86	1.51249 54265 11	1.30939 55929 45	0.99752 78583 62	1.18828 61439 38
87	1.52708 14617 18	1.31972 29649 69	0.99860 91405 73	1.18868 86999 85
88	1.54165 82330 65	1.33003 72227 19	0.99938 17514 21	1.18897 65911 93
89	1.55622 88252 20	1.34034 27376 01	0.99984 54245 28	1.18914 94664 74
90	1.57079 63267 95	1.35064 38810 48	1.00000 00000 00	1.18920 71150 03

K = 1.86914 75460 26462   E = 1.34180 60581 29911
K' = 1.83956 67210 93652   E' = 1.35937 69972 75008

r	u=(r/90)K=F(φ,k)	sn u	cn u	dn u
0	0.00000 00000 00	0.00000 00000 00	1.00000 00000 00	1.00000 00000 00
1	0.02076 83060 67	0.02076 60408 29	0.99978 43625 24	0.99988 84242 49
2	0.04153 66121 34	0.04151 84968 07	0.99913 77354 61	0.99955 39142 97
3	0.06230 49182 01	0.06224 38159 08	0.99806 09737 79	0.99899 71212 47
4	0.08307 32242 68	0.08292 85115 91	0.99655 54986 88	0.99821 91275 74
5	0.10384 15303 35	0.10355 91950 86	0.99462 32920 62	0.99722 14431 16
6	0.12460 98364 02	0.12412 26071 73	0.99226 68886 89	0.99600 59994 87
7	0.14537 81424 69	0.14460 56492 49	0.98948 93663 93	0.99457 51429 70
8	0.16614 64485 36	0.16499 54135 51	0.98629 43341 15	0.99293 16259 27
9	0.18691 47546 03	0.18527 92123 55	0.98268 59180 17	0.99107 85967 97
10	0.20768 30606 70	0.20544 46060 28	0.97866 87457 22	0.98901 95887 42
11	0.22845 13667 37	0.22547 94297 84	0.97424 79287 86	0.98675 85070 23
12	0.24921 96728 04	0.24537 18190 21	0.96942 90435 25	0.98429 96151 91
13	0.26998 79788 70	0.26511 02331 36	0.96421 81103 29	0.98164 75201 81
14	0.29075 62849 37	0.28468 34777 03	0.95862 15715 93	0.97880 71564 14
15	0.31152 45910 04	0.30408 07249 54	0.95264 62684 08	0.97578 37690 04
16	0.33229 28970 71	0.32329 15324 54	0.94629 94161 70	0.97258 28961 75
17	0.35306 12031 38	0.34230 58599 53	0.93958 85792 42	0.96921 03510 03
18	0.37382 95092 05	0.36111 40843 43	0.93252 16448 37	0.96567 22025 85
19	0.39459 78152 72	0.37970 70126 93	0.92510 67962 74	0.96197 47567 57
20	0.41536 61213 39	0.39807 58933 65	0.91735 24857 55	0.95812 45364 58
21	0.43613 44274 06	0.41621 24251 91	0.90926 74068 26	0.95412 82618 66
22	0.45690 27334 73	0.43410 87647 21	0.90086 04666 61	0.94999 28303 93
23	0.47767 10395 40	0.45175 75315 79	0.89214 07583 23	0.94572 52966 66
24	0.49843 93456 07	0.46915 18119 55	0.88311 75331 40	0.94133 28525 73
25	0.51920 76516 74	0.48628 51602 68	0.87380 01733 25	0.93682 28074 85
26	0.53997 59577 41	0.50315 15990 77	0.86419 81649 75	0.93220 25687 34
27	0.56074 42638 08	0.51974 56172 85	0.85432 10715 61	0.92747 96224 42
28	0.58151 25698 75	0.53606 21667 22	0.84417 85080 24	0.92266 15147 69
29	0.60228 08759 42	0.55209 66571 78	0.83378 01155 78	0.91775 58336 66
30	0.62304 91820 09	0.56784 49499 79	0.82313 55373 10	0.91277 01911 78
31	0.64381 74880 76	0.58330 33501 92	0.81225 43946 66	0.90771 22063 84
32	0.66458 57941 43	0.59846 85975 53	0.80114 62648 87	0.90258 94889 96
33	0.68535 41002 10	0.61333 78562 22	0.78982 06594 70	0.89740 96236 90
34	0.70612 24062 77	0.62790 87034 58	0.77828 70036 96	0.89218 01551 80
35	0.72689 07123 44	0.64217 91173 18	0.76655 46172 85	0.88690 85740 89
36	0.74765 90184 11	0.65614 74634 80	0.75463 26961 96	0.88160 23036 26
37	0.76842 73244 78	0.66981 24812 94	0.74253 02956 13	0.87626 86870 99
38	0.78919 56305 45	0.68317 32691 49	0.73025 63141 25	0.87091 49762 59
39	0.80996 39366 11	0.69622 92692 74	0.71781 94791 21	0.86554 83205 03
40	0.83073 22426 78	0.70898 02520 42	0.70522 83333 88	0.86017 57569 17
41	0.85150 05487 45	0.72142 62998 90	0.69249 12229 25	0.85480 42011 61
42	0.87226 88548 12	0.73356 77909 26	0.67961 62859 41	0.84944 04391 97
43	0.89303 71608 79	0.74540 53823 27	0.66661 14430 44	0.84409 11198 21
44	0.91380 54669 46	0.75693 99935 82	0.65348 43885 79	0.83876 27480 15
45	0.93457 37730 13	0.76817 27896 76	0.64024 25830 90	0.83346 16790 58

q = 0.04541 67490 83529 43   D(90) = 1.19981 52106 16088
q'= 0.04108 50703 79885 46   1/D(90) = 0.83346 16790 58490

r	ϕ	$E(\phi,k)$	$A(r)$	$D(r)$
0	0.00000 00000 00	0.00000 00000 00	0.00000 00000 00	1.00000 00000 00
1	0.02076 75336 04	0.02076 67611 92	0.01730 87522 27	1.00006 08382 15
2	0.04153 04342 33	0.04152 42579 86	0.03461 24944 99	1.00024 32788 20
3	0.06228 40779 35	0.06226 32502 12	0.05190 62176 71	1.00054 70997 91
4	0.08302 38587 62	0.08297 45460 28	0.06918 49142 09	1.00097 19313 81
5	0.10374 51976 96	0.10364 90257 67	0.08644 35790 10	1.00151 72565 77
6	0.12444 35514 64	0.12427 76654 11	0.10367 72102 11	1.00218 24117 21
7	0.14511 44212 32	0.14485 15595 55	0.12088 08100 21	1.00296 65873 19
8	0.16575 33611 25	0.16536 19437 74	0.13804 93855 46	1.00386 88290 19
9	0.18635 59865 61	0.18580 02162 54	0.15517 79496 38	1.00488 80387 72
10	0.20691 79823 64	0.20615 79585 96	0.17226 15217 45	1.00602 29761 64
11	0.22743 51106 20	0.22642 69557 07	0.18929 51287 78	1.00727 22599 16
12	0.24790 32182 67	0.24659 92146 61	0.20627 38059 98	1.00863 43695 66
13	0.26831 82443 83	0.26666 69824 81	0.22319 25979 11	1.01010 76473 11
14	0.28867 62271 52	0.28662 27627 51	0.24004 65591 86	1.01169 03000 17
15	0.30897 33104 95	0.30645 93310 05	0.25683 07555 89	1.01338 04013 96
16	0.32920 57503 38	0.32616 97488 40	0.27354 02649 41	1.01517 58943 44
17	0.34936 99205 14	0.34574 73767 14	0.29017 01780 93	1.01707 45934 36
18	0.36946 23182 76	0.36518 58853 98	0.30671 55999 27	1.01907 41875 82
19	0.38947 95694 12	0.38447 92660 52	0.32317 16503 82	1.02117 22428 26
20	0.40941 84329 62	0.40362 18389 34	0.33953 34654 97	1.02336 62053 05
21	0.42927 58055 18	0.42260 82607 27	0.35579 61984 92	1.02565 34043 49
22	0.44904 87251 14	0.44143 35304 83	0.37195 50208 61	1.02803 10557 22
23	0.46873 43746 99	0.46009 29942 34	0.38800 51235 05	1.03049 62650 02
24	0.48833 00851 94	0.47858 23482 58	0.40394 17178 87	1.03304 60310 99
25	0.50783 33381 38	0.49689 76410 57	0.41976 00372 08	1.03567 72498 96
26	0.52724 17679 24	0.51503 52740 84	0.43545 53376 30	1.03838 67180 22
27	0.54655 31636 32	0.53299 20012 63	0.45102 28995 07	1.04117 11367 43
28	0.56576 54704 73	0.55076 49273 47	0.46645 80286 61	1.04402 71159 66
29	0.58487 67908 45	0.56835 15051 95	0.48175 60576 74	1.04695 11783 65
30	0.60388 53850 14	0.58574 95320 06	0.49691 23472 24	1.04993 97636 00
31	0.62278 96714 37	0.60295 71445 86	0.51192 22874 36	1.05298 92326 47
32	0.64158 82267 37	0.61997 28137 27	0.52678 12992 69	1.05609 58722 23
33	0.66027 97853 45	0.63679 53377 46	0.54148 48359 29	1.05925 58992 96
34	0.67886 32388 22	0.65342 38352 77	0.55602 83843 11	1.06246 54656 90
35	0.69733 76348 84	0.66985 77373 80	0.57040 74664 68	1.06572 06627 58
36	0.71570 21761 34	0.68609 67790 40	0.58461 76411 06	1.06901 75261 41
37	0.73395 62185 37	0.70214 09901 33	0.59865 45051 03	1.07235 20405 88
38	0.75209 92696 31	0.71799 06859 25	0.61251 36950 59	1.07572 01448 43
39	0.77013 09865 19	0.73364 64571 81	0.62619 08888 58	1.07911 77365 82
40	0.78805 11736 32	0.74910 91599 50	0.63968 18072 69	1.08254 06774 09
41	0.80585 97803 08	0.76437 99050 86	0.65298 22155 51	1.08598 47978 92
42	0.82355 68981 73	0.77946 00475 81	0.66608 79250 91	1.08944 59026 39
43	0.84114 27583 77	0.79435 11757 61	0.67899 47950 56	1.09291 97754 04
44	0.85861 77286 72	0.80905 51004 02	0.69169 87340 60	1.09640 21842 22
45	0.87598 23103 61	0.82357 38438 35	0.70419 57018 47	1.09988 88865 65

K = 1.86914 75460 26462   E = 1.34180 60581 29911
K′= 1.83956 67210 93652   E′= 1.35937 69972 75008

r	u=(r/90)K=F(φ,k)	sn u	cn u	dn u
45	0.93457 37730 13	0.76817 27896 76	0.64024 25830 90	0.83346 16790 58
46	0.95534 20790 80	0.77910 51642 74	0.62689 32468 95	0.82819 41134 17
47	0.97611 03851 47	0.78973 87229 77	0.61344 33547 04	0.82296 60923 41
48	0.99687 86912 14	0.80007 52667 05	0.59989 96312 77	0.81778 34941 74
49	1.01764 69972 81	0.81011 67752 61	0.58626 85480 57	0.81265 20313 25
50	1.03841 53033 48	0.81986 53911 34	0.57255 63207 42	0.80757 72478 74
51	1.05918 36094 15	0.82932 34035 78	0.55876 89077 59	0.80256 45177 79
52	1.07995 19154 82	0.83849 32330 16	0.54491 20095 82	0.79761 90436 44
53	1.10072 02215 49	0.84737 74157 92	0.53099 10688 57	0.79274 58560 22
54	1.12148 85276 16	0.85597 85893 17	0.51701 12712 81	0.78794 98132 00
55	1.14225 68336 83	0.86429 94776 24	0.50297 75471 92	0.78323 56014 52
56	1.16302 51397 50	0.87234 28773 63	0.48889 45738 24	0.77860 77356 97
57	1.18379 34458 17	0.88011 16442 47	0.47476 67781 77	0.77407 05605 57
58	1.20456 17518 84	0.88760 86799 75	0.46059 83404 59	0.76962 82517 44
59	1.22533 00579 51	0.89483 69196 25	0.44639 31980 62	0.76528 48177 80
60	1.24609 83640 18	0.90179 93195 50	0.43215 50500 21	0.76104 41019 80
61	1.26686 66700 85	0.90849 88457 63	0.41788 73619 13	0.75690 97846 91
62	1.28763 49761 52	0.91493 84628 18	0.40359 33711 75	0.75288 53857 45
63	1.30840 32822 19	0.92112 11231 92	0.38927 60927 79	0.74897 42670 90
64	1.32917 15882 85	0.92704 97571 67	0.37493 83252 43	0.74517 96355 83
65	1.34993 98943 52	0.93272 72631 97	0.36058 26569 45	0.74150 45459 07
66	1.37070 82004 19	0.93815 64987 63	0.34621 14727 00	0.73795 19035 80
67	1.39147 65064 86	0.94334 02717 14	0.33182 69605 73	0.73452 44680 54
68	1.41224 48125 53	0.94828 13320 69	0.31743 11189 04	0.73122 48558 46
69	1.43301 31186 20	0.95298 23642 88	0.30302 57635 20	0.72805 55437 07
70	1.45378 14246 87	0.95744 59799 83	0.28861 25350 95	0.72501 88717 92
71	1.47454 97307 54	0.96167 47110 83	0.27419 29066 60	0.72211 70468 14
72	1.49531 80368 21	0.96567 10034 11	0.25976 81912 22	0.71935 21451 68
73	1.51608 63428 88	0.96943 72106 83	0.24533 95494 88	0.71672 61159 97
74	1.53685 46489 55	0.97297 55889 10	0.23090 79976 63	0.71424 07841 95
75	1.55762 29550 22	0.97628 82911 86	0.21647 44153 31	0.71189 78533 21
76	1.57839 12610 89	0.97937 73628 55	0.20203 95533 71	0.70969 89084 18
77	1.59915 95671 56	0.98224 47370 43	0.18760 40419 36	0.70764 54187 25
78	1.61992 78732 23	0.98489 22305 40	0.17316 83984 50	0.70573 87402 56
79	1.64069 61792 90	0.98732 15400 24	0.15873 30356 42	0.70398 01182 51
80	1.66146 44853 57	0.98953 42386 16	0.14429 82695 87	0.70237 06894 85
81	1.68223 27914 24	0.99153 17727 51	0.12986 43277 64	0.70091 14844 21
82	1.70300 10974 91	0.99331 54593 55	0.11543 13571 22	0.69960 34292 00
83	1.72376 94035 58	0.99488 64833 27	0.10099 94321 46	0.69844 73474 62
84	1.74453 77096 25	0.99624 58953 06	0.08656 85629 20	0.69744 39620 01
85	1.76530 60156 92	0.99739 46097 21	0.07213 87031 95	0.69659 38962 25
86	1.78607 43217 59	0.99833 34031 18	0.05770 97584 44	0.69589 76754 41
87	1.80684 26278 26	0.99906 29127 48	0.04328 15939 21	0.69535 57279 44
88	1.82761 09338 93	0.99958 36354 30	0.02885 40427 12	0.69496 83859 20
89	1.84837 92399 60	0.99989 59266 64	0.01442 69137 77	0.69473 58861 38
90	1.86914 75460 26	1.00000 00000 00	0.00000 00000 00	0.69465 83704 59

q = 0.04541 67490 83529 43   D(90) = 1.19981 52106 16088
q′ = 0.04108 50703 79885 46   1/D(90) = 0.83346 16790 58490

r	ϕ	$E(\phi, k)$	$A(r)$	$D(r)$
45	0.87598 23103 61	0.82357 38438 35	0.70419 57018 47	1.09988 88865 65
46	0.89323 71351 36	0.83790 96290 67	0.71648 17109 93	1.10337 56345 06
47	0.91038 29618 17	0.85206 48689 83	0.72855 28286 14	1.10685 81798 96
48	0.92742 06730 04	0.86604 21556 71	0.74040 51780 85	1.11033 22795 41
49	0.94435 12716 61	0.87984 42499 04	0.75203 49407 70	1.11379 37003 71
50	0.96117 58776 46	0.89347 40708 13	0.76343 83577 54	1.11723 82246 00
51	0.97789 57241 95	0.90693 46857 95	0.77461 17315 83	1.12066 16548 69
52	0.99451 21543 71	0.92022 93006 78	0.78555 14280 03	1.12405 98193 61
53	1.01102 66175 04	0.93336 12501 64	0.79625 38776 99	1.12742 85768 91
54	1.02744 06656 09	0.94633 39885 82	0.80671 55780 32	1.13076 38219 52
55	1.04375 59498 13	0.95915 10809 65	0.81693 30947 73	1.13406 14897 27
56	1.05997 42167 88	0.97181 61944 64	0.82690 30638 22	1.13731 75610 47
57	1.07609 73052 04	0.98433 30901 22	0.83662 21929 29	1.14052 80672 93
58	1.09212 71422 03	0.99670 56150 02	0.84608 72633 94	1.14368 90952 41
59	1.10806 57399 10	1.00893 76947 00	0.85529 51317 54	1.14679 67918 38
60	1.12391 51919 82	1.02103 33262 17	0.86424 27314 54	1.14984 73689 02
61	1.13967 76702 00	1.03299 65712 28	0.87292 70745 01	1.15283 71077 52
62	1.15535 54211 05	1.04483 15497 20	0.88134 52530 93	1.15576 23637 43
63	1.17095 07626 98	1.05654 24340 09	0.88949 44412 21	1.15861 95707 21
64	1.18646 60811 84	1.06813 34431 43	0.89737 18962 50	1.16140 52453 77
65	1.20190 38277 86	1.07960 88376 63	0.90497 49604 68	1.16411 59915 02
66	1.21726 65156 12	1.09097 29147 40	0.91230 10626 04	1.16674 85041 33
67	1.23255 67165 89	1.10223 00036 64	0.91934 77193 08	1.16929 95735 96
68	1.24777 70584 68	1.11338 44616 87	0.92611 25366 00	1.17176 60894 26
69	1.26293 02218 78	1.12444 06702 03	0.93259 32112 75	1.17414 50441 65
70	1.27801 89374 67	1.13540 30312 57	0.93878 75322 75	1.17643 35370 44
71	1.29304 59830 90	1.14627 59643 75	0.94469 33820 04	1.17862 87775 21
72	1.30801 41810 74	1.15706 39036 97	0.95030 87376 15	1.18072 80887 01
73	1.32292 63955 42	1.16777 12954 09	0.95563 16722 30	1.18272 89106 01
74	1.33778 55298 03	1.17840 25954 44	0.96066 03561 27	1.18462 88032 86
75	1.35259 45238 01	1.18896 22674 68	0.96539 30578 68	1.18642 54498 49
76	1.36735 63516 24	1.19945 47810 98	0.96982 81453 67	1.18811 66592 44
77	1.38207 40190 71	1.20988 46103 76	0.97396 40869 20	1.18970 03689 71
78	1.39675 05612 76	1.22025 62324 56	0.97779 94521 55	1.19117 46475 91
79	1.41138 90403 79	1.23057 41265 07	0.98133 29129 47	1.19253 76970 94
80	1.42599 25432 52	1.24084 27728 10	0.98456 32442 50	1.19378 78550 99
81	1.44056 41792 70	1.25106 66520 27	0.98748 93248 85	1.19492 35968 82
82	1.45510 70781 20	1.26125 02446 51	0.99011 01382 56	1.19594 35372 49
83	1.46962 43876 57	1.27139 80305 88	0.99242 47729 99	1.19684 64322 24
84	1.48411 92717 91	1.28151 44888 88	0.99443 24235 77	1.19763 11805 75
85	1.49859 49084 11	1.29160 40975 85	0.99613 23907 94	1.19829 68251 61
86	1.51305 44873 29	1.30167 13336 55	0.99752 40822 50	1.19884 25541 03
87	1.52750 12082 61	1.31172 06730 46	0.99860 70127 29	1.19926 77017 76
88	1.54193 82788 16	1.32175 65908 02	0.99938 08045 11	1.19957 17496 26
89	1.55636 89125 11	1.33178 35612 31	0.99984 51876 20	1.19975 43268 03
90	1.57079 63267 95	1.34180 60581 30	1.00000 00000 00	1.19981 52106 16

K = 1.88480 86573 80404   E = 1.33286 99541 17179
K'= 1.82560 18981 35889   E'= 1.36799 91658 73159

r	u=(r/90)K=F(φ,k)	sn u	cn u	dn u
0	0.00000 00000 00	0.00000 00000 00	1.00000 00000 00	1.00000 00000 00
1	0.02094 23184 15	0.02093 99690 94	0.99978 07348 09	0.99988 27258 02
2	0.04188 46368 31	0.04186 58493 21	0.99912 32409 77	0.99953 11363 45
3	0.06282 69552 46	0.06276 35870 95	0.99802 84225 09	0.99894 59301 43
4	0.08376 92736 61	0.08361 91991 93	0.99649 77819 98	0.99812 82684 03
5	0.10471 15920 77	0.10441 88074 47	0.99453 34145 47	0.99707 97705 73
6	0.12565 39104 92	0.12514 86728 49	0.99213 79993 15	0.99580 25081 60
7	0.14659 62289 07	0.14579 52288 89	0.98931 47887 47	0.99429 89968 50
8	0.16753 85473 23	0.16634 51139 43	0.98606 75955 87	0.99257 21870 03
9	0.18848 08657 38	0.18678 52025 46	0.98240 07777 43	0.99062 54525 79
10	0.20942 31841 53	0.20710 26353 77	0.97831 92211 24	0.98846 25785 82
11	0.23036 55025 69	0.22728 48478 26	0.97382 83205 72	0.98608 77471 05
12	0.25130 78209 84	0.24731 95969 92	0.96893 39590 21	0.98350 55220 73
13	0.27225 01393 99	0.26719 49870 02	0.96364 24850 12	0.98072 08327 95
14	0.29319 24578 15	0.28689 94925 34	0.95796 06887 47	0.97773 89564 28
15	0.31413 47762 30	0.30642 19804 52	0.95189 57768 03	0.97456 54994 78
16	0.33507 70946 45	0.32575 17294 94	0.94545 53457 10	0.97120 63784 47
17	0.35601 94130 61	0.34487 84479 22	0.93864 73545 26	0.96766 77997 59
18	0.37696 17314 76	0.36379 22891 17	0.93148 00966 09	0.96395 62390 86
19	0.39790 40498 91	0.38248 38650 75	0.92396 21707 39	0.96007 84202 01
20	0.41884 63683 07	0.40094 42577 98	0.91610 24517 70	0.95604 12934 77
21	0.43978 86867 22	0.41916 50285 75	0.90791 00609 75	0.95185 20141 64
22	0.46073 10051 37	0.43713 82251 72	0.89939 43362 58	0.94751 79205 51
23	0.48167 33235 53	0.45485 63869 67	0.89056 48023 78	0.94304 65121 47
24	0.50261 56419 68	0.47231 25480 61	0.88143 11413 52	0.93844 54279 71
25	0.52355 79603 83	0.48950 02384 29	0.87200 31631 70	0.93372 24250 77
26	0.54450 02787 99	0.50641 34831 76	0.86229 07769 76	0.92888 53573 97
27	0.56544 25972 14	0.52304 67999 62	0.85230 39628 26	0.92394 21550 12
28	0.58638 49156 29	0.53939 51947 00	0.84205 27441 52	0.91890 08039 19
29	0.60732 72340 45	0.55545 41555 96	0.83154 71610 38	0.91376 93263 87
30	0.62826 95524 60	0.57121 96456 47	0.82079 72444 07	0.90855 57619 70
31	0.64921 18708 75	0.58668 80936 88	0.80981 29912 05	0.90326 81492 29
32	0.67015 41892 91	0.60185 63841 01	0.79860 43406 57	0.89791 45082 37
33	0.69109 65077 06	0.61672 18452 92	0.78718 11516 67	0.89250 28238 96
34	0.71203 88261 21	0.63128 22370 50	0.77555 31814 03	0.88704 10301 12
35	0.73298 11445 37	0.64553 57368 95	0.76373 00651 35	0.88153 69948 68
36	0.75392 34629 52	0.65948 09255 34	0.75172 12973 29	0.87599 85061 98
37	0.77486 57813 68	0.67311 67715 30	0.73953 62140 46	0.87043 32591 02
38	0.79580 80997 83	0.68644 26152 96	0.72718 39766 56	0.86484 88433 92
39	0.81675 04181 98	0.69945 81525 16	0.71467 35568 63	0.85925 27324 90
40	0.83769 27366 14	0.71216 34171 00	0.70201 37230 46	0.85365 22731 50
41	0.85863 50550 29	0.72455 87637 70	0.68921 30279 13	0.84805 46761 33
42	0.87957 73734 44	0.73664 48503 72	0.67627 97974 36	0.84246 70077 78
43	0.90051 96918 60	0.74842 26200 05	0.66322 21210 61	0.83689 61824 86
44	0.92146 20102 75	0.75989 32830 47	0.65004 78431 46	0.83134 89560 74
45	0.94240 43286 90	0.77105 82991 64	0.63676 45556 17	0.82583 19199 83

ELLIPTIC FUNCTIONS   TABLE $\theta = 47°$

q = 0.04769 60340 17055 65

q′ = 0.03902 78889 26606 97

D(90) = 1.21090 01551 07606

1/D(90) = 0.82583 19199 82813

r	ϕ	$E(\phi,k)$	$A(r)$	$D(r)$
0	0.00000 00000 00	0.00000 00000 00	0.00000 00000 00	1.00000 00000 00
1	0.02094 14996 97	0.02094 06810 35	0.01729 40052 48	1.00006 42094 66
2	0.04187 80890 34	0.04187 15430 79	0.03458 30319 77	1.00025 67597 38
3	0.06280 48674 10	0.06278 27935 47	0.05186 21023 89	1.00057 74165 28
4	0.08371 69537 05	0.08366 46925 33	0.06912 62401 37	1.00102 57896 71
5	0.10460 94959 23	0.10450 75787 83	0.08637 04710 51	1.00160 13335 99
6	0.12547 76807 30	0.12530 18952 55	0.10358 98238 72	1.00230 33480 04
7	0.14631 67428 39	0.14603 82141 12	0.12077 93310 00	1.00313 09786 80
8	0.16712 19742 19	0.16670 72610 24	0.13793 40292 40	1.00408 32185 68
9	0.18788 87330 81	0.18729 99386 65	0.15504 89605 69	1.00515 89089 67
10	0.20861 24526 22	0.20780 73492 63	0.17211 91729 15	1.00635 67409 48
11	0.22928 86494 90	0.22822 08161 30	0.18913 97209 45	1.00767 52569 31
12	0.24991 29319 40	0.24853 19040 38	0.20610 56668 78	1.00911 28524 62
13	0.27048 10076 65	0.26873 24383 86	0.22301 20813 08	1.01066 77781 51
14	0.29098 86912 59	0.28881 45230 48	0.23985 40440 58	1.01233 81417 94
15	0.31143 19113 17	0.30877 05568 63	0.25662 66450 44	1.01412 19106 72
16	0.33180 67171 26	0.32859 32486 95	0.27332 49851 68	1.01601 69140 12
17	0.35210 92849 50	0.34827 56310 25	0.28994 41772 38	1.01802 08456 20
18	0.37233 59238 86	0.36781 10720 43	0.30647 93469 05	1.02013 12666 80
19	0.39248 30812 82	0.38719 32862 14	0.32292 56336 39	1.02234 56087 11
20	0.41254 73477 06	0.40641 63433 22	0.33927 81917 21	1.02466 11766 83
21	0.43252 54614 69	0.42547 46759 80	0.35553 21912 72	1.02707 51522 86
22	0.45241 43126 82	0.44436 30856 27	0.37168 28193 09	1.02958 45973 54
23	0.47221 09468 66	0.46307 67470 28	0.38772 52808 33	1.03218 64574 24
24	0.49191 25680 94	0.48161 12113 16	0.40365 47999 49	1.03487 75654 49
25	0.51151 65416 92	0.49996 24076 15	0.41946 66210 13	1.03765 46456 38
26	0.53102 03964 90	0.51812 66432 85	0.43515 60098 21	1.04051 43174 37
27	0.55042 18266 29	0.53610 06028 57	0.45071 82548 21	1.04345 30996 30
28	0.56971 86929 43	0.55388 13457 11	0.46614 86683 67	1.04646 74145 69
29	0.58890 90239 28	0.57146 63025 65	0.48144 25880 00	1.04955 35925 17
30	0.60799 10162 97	0.58885 32708 56	0.49659 53777 63	1.05270 78761 07
31	0.62696 30351 49	0.60604 04090 75	0.51160 24295 56	1.05592 64249 06
32	0.64582 36137 68	0.62302 62301 47	0.52645 91645 13	1.05920 53200 83
33	0.66457 14530 56	0.63980 95939 28	0.54116 10344 20	1.06254 05691 71
34	0.68320 54206 30	0.65638 96989 10	0.55570 35231 65	1.06592 81109 17
35	0.70172 45495 96	0.67276 60732 03	0.57008 21482 13	1.06936 38202 21
36	0.72012 80371 23	0.68893 85648 97	0.58429 24621 19	1.07284 35131 55
37	0.73841 52421 23	0.70490 73318 58	0.59833 00540 66	1.07636 29520 44
38	0.75658 56841 81	0.72067 28310 68	0.61219 05514 35	1.07991 78506 26
39	0.77463 90402 30	0.73623 58075 63	0.62586 96214 02	1.08350 38792 63
40	0.79257 51425 03	0.75159 72830 58	0.63936 29725 61	1.08711 66702 12
41	0.81039 39756 85	0.76675 85443 33	0.65266 63565 71	1.09075 18229 35
42	0.82809 56739 71	0.78172 11314 32	0.66577 55698 32	1.09440 49094 61
43	0.84568 05179 62	0.79648 68257 73	0.67868 64551 78	1.09807 14797 73
44	0.82824 23463 76	0.81105 76381 93	0.69139 49035 94	1.10174 70672 26
45	0.88050 14778 58	0.82543 57970 27	0.70389 68559 47	1.10542 71939 88

187

K = 1.88480 86573 80404   E = 1.33286 99541 17179
K'= 1.82560 18981 35889   E'= 1.36799 91658 73159

r	u=(r/90)K=F(ϕ,k)	sn u	cn u	dn u
45	0.94240 43286 90	0.77105 82991 64	0.63676 45556 17	0.82583 19199 83
46	0.96334 66471 06	0.78191 93593 70	0.62337 95917 76	0.82035 14962 99
47	0.98428 89655 21	0.79247 83682 14	0.60990 00212 44	0.81491 39335 74
48	1.00523 12839 36	0.80273 74261 45	0.59633 26459 84	0.80952 53033 84
49	1.02617 36023 52	0.81269 88121 27	0.58268 39973 49	0.80419 14976 19
50	1.04711 59207 67	0.82236 49665 40	0.56896 03341 26	0.79891 82264 41
51	1.06805 82391 82	0.83173 84744 21	0.55516 76415 00	0.79371 10168 82
52	1.08900 05575 98	0.84082 20490 92	0.54131 16309 12	0.78857 52120 42
53	1.10994 28760 13	0.84961 85161 96	0.52739 77407 39	0.78351 59708 47
54	1.13088 51944 28	0.85813 07981 81	0.51343 11377 52	0.77853 82683 16
55	1.15182 75128 44	0.86636 18992 53	0.49941 67193 06	0.77364 68963 11
56	1.17276 98312 59	0.87431 48908 29	0.48535 91161 96	0.76884 64647 19
57	1.19371 21496 74	0.88199 28974 91	0.47126 26961 43	0.76414 14030 33
58	1.21465 44680 90	0.88939 90834 66	0.45713 15678 55	0.75953 59622 84
59	1.23559 67865 05	0.89653 66396 42	0.44296 95856 15	0.75503 42172 97
60	1.25653 91049 20	0.90340 87711 11	0.42878 03543 53	0.75064 00692 28
61	1.27748 14233 36	0.91001 86852 69	0.41456 72351 51	0.74635 72483 43
62	1.29842 37417 51	0.91636 95804 39	0.40033 33511 54	0.74218 93170 12
63	1.31936 60601 66	0.92246 46350 45	0.38608 15938 26	0.73813 96728 82
64	1.34030 83785 82	0.92830 69973 16	0.37181 46295 33	0.73421 15521 91
65	1.36125 06969 97	0.93389 97755 12	0.35753 49064 06	0.73040 80332 08
66	1.38219 30154 12	0.93924 60286 77	0.34324 46614 51	0.72673 20397 49
67	1.40313 53338 28	0.94434 87578 90	0.32894 59278 84	0.72318 63447 65
68	1.42407 76522 43	0.94921 08980 22	0.31464 05426 45	0.71977 35739 56
69	1.44501 99706 58	0.95383 53099 70	0.30033 01540 89	0.71649 62094 05
70	1.46596 22890 74	0.95822 47733 65	0.28601 62298 02	0.71335 65931 89
71	1.48690 46074 89	0.96238 19797 41	0.27170 00645 39	0.71035 69309 68
72	1.50784 69259 04	0.96630 95261 38	0.25738 27882 64	0.70749 92955 17
73	1.52878 92443 20	0.97000 99091 44	0.24306 53742 56	0.70478 56301 84
74	1.54973 15627 35	0.97348 55193 41	0.22874 86472 83	0.70221 77522 69
75	1.57067 38811 50	0.97673 86361 54	0.21443 32918 29	0.69979 73562 86
76	1.59161 61995 66	0.97977 14230 86	0.20011 98603 41	0.69752 60171 22
77	1.61255 85179 81	0.98258 59233 22	0.18580 87815 20	0.69540 51930 55
78	1.63350 08363 96	0.98518 40556 81	0.17150 03686 04	0.69343 62286 29
79	1.65444 31548 12	0.98756 76109 26	0.15719 48276 81	0.69162 03573 82
80	1.67538 54732 27	0.98973 82483 88	0.14289 22659 82	0.68995 87043 96
81	1.69632 77916 42	0.99169 74929 17	0.12859 27001 87	0.68845 22886 90
82	1.71727 01100 58	0.99344 67321 36	0.11429 60647 09	0.68710 20254 17
83	1.73821 24284 73	0.99498 72139 88	0.10000 22199 78	0.68590 87278 81
84	1.75915 47468 88	0.99632 00445 72	0.08571 09607 05	0.68487 31093 50
85	1.78009 70653 04	0.99744 61862 52	0.07142 20241 35	0.68399 57846 81
86	1.80103 93837 19	0.99836 64560 39	0.05713 50982 88	0.68327 72717 22
87	1.82198 17021 34	0.99908 15242 28	0.04284 98301 85	0.68271 79925 19
88	1.84292 40205 50	0.99959 19132 95	0.02856 58340 61	0.68231 82743 02
89	1.86386 63389 65	0.99989 79970 44	0.01428 26995 74	0.68207 83502 54
90	1.88480 86573 80	1.00000 00000 00	0.00000 00000 00	0.68199 83600 62

q = 0.04769 60340 17055 65   D(90) = 1.21090 01551 07606
q'= 0.03902 78889 26606 97   1/D(90) = 0.82583 19199 82813

r	ϕ	$E(\phi,k)$	A(r)	D(r)
45	0.88050 14778 58	0.82543 57970 27	0.70389 68559 47	1.10542 71939 88
46	0.89773 88570 91	0.83962 37362 37	0.71618 83047 43	1.10910 73764 93
47	0.91486 19015 98	0.85362 40836 70	0.72826 52958 91	1.11278 31309 04
48	0.93187 15728 75	0.86743 96494 80	0.74012 39304 83	1.11644 99785 75
49	0.94876 89576 95	0.88107 34147 53	0.75176 03665 86	1.12010 34515 11
50	0.96555 52643 16	0.89452 85203 80	0.76317 08210 40	1.12373 90978 12
51	0.98223 18186 70	0.90780 82562 07	0.77435 15712 67	1.12735 24871 01
52	0.99880 00605 10	0.92091 60504 96	0.78529 89570 80	1.13093 92159 26
53	1.01526 15395 57	0.93385 54597 13	0.79600 93824 94	1.13449 49131 33
54	1.03161 79116 45	0.94663 01586 84	0.80647 93175 39	1.13801 52451 93
55	1.04787 09348 80	0.95924 39311 18	0.81670 53000 71	1.14149 59214 92
56	1.06402 24658 09	0.97170 06605 23	0.82668 39375 69	1.14493 26995 65
57	1.08007 44556 30	0.98400 43215 24	0.83641 19089 32	1.14832 13902 76
58	1.09602 89464 34	0.99615 89715 96	0.84588 59662 66	1.15165 78629 28
59	1.11188 80674 88	1.00816 87432 12	0.85510 29366 46	1.15493 80503 08
60	1.12765 40315 70	1.02003 78364 16	0.86405 97238 74	1.15815 79536 52
61	1.14332 91313 67	1.03177 05118 14	0.87275 33102 15	1.16131 36475 30
62	1.15891 57359 19	1.04337 10839 94	0.88118 07581 04	1.16440 12846 38
63	1.17441 62871 43	1.05484 39153 63	0.88933 92118 38	1.16741 71005 00
64	1.18983 32964 12	1.06619 34103 94	0.89722 58992 38	1.17035 74180 69
65	1.20516 93412 15	1.07742 40102 87	0.90483 81332 74	1.17321 86522 14
66	1.22042 70618 83	1.08854 01880 31	0.91217 33136 73	1.17599 73141 09
67	1.23560 91583 92	1.09954 64438 49	0.91922 89284 73	1.17869 00154 93
68	1.25071 83872 41	1.11044 73010 32	0.92600 25555 59	1.18129 34728 13
69	1.26575 75584 10	1.12124 73021 38	0.93249 18641 38	1.18380 45112 39
70	1.28072 95323 85	1.13195 10055 45	0.93869 46161 92	1.18622 00685 49
71	1.29563 72172 65	1.14256 29823 54	0.94460 86678 70	1.18853 71988 66
72	1.31048 35659 45	1.15308 78136 19	0.95023 19708 41	1.19075 30762 72
73	1.32527 15733 67	1.16353 00878 86	0.95556 25735 94	1.19286 49982 56
74	1.34000 42738 46	1.17389 43990 44	0.96059 86226 84	1.19487 03890 25
75	1.35468 47384 63	1.18418 53444 50	0.96533 83639 32	1.19676 68026 52
76	1.36931 60725 28	1.19440 75233 35	0.96978 01435 57	1.19855 19260 75
77	1.38390 14131 08	1.20456 55354 53	0.97392 24092 59	1.20022 35819 21
78	1.39844 39266 13	1.21466 39799 78	0.97776 37112 35	1.20177 97311 74
79	1.41294 68064 43	1.22470 74546 18	0.98130 27031 40	1.20321 84756 70
80	1.42741 32706 94	1.23470 05549 37	0.98453 81429 76	1.20453 80604 22
81	1.44184 65599 06	1.24464 78738 68	0.98746 88939 25	1.20573 68757 68
82	1.45624 99348 69	1.25455 40013 98	0.99009 39251 03	1.20681 34593 38
83	1.47062 66744 71	1.26442 35244 15	0.99241 23122 59	1.20776 64978 51
84	1.48498 00735 80	1.27426 10266 97	0.99442 32383 95	1.20859 48287 16
85	1.49931 34409 67	1.28407 10890 18	0.99612 59943 20	1.20929 74414 60
86	1.51363 00972 66	1.29385 82893 84	0.99751 99791 30	1.20987 34789 66
87	1.52793 33729 45	1.30362 72033 38	0.99860 47006 15	1.21032 22385 19
88	1.54222 66063 21	1.31338 24043 69	0.99937 97755 99	1.21064 31726 68
89	1.55651 31415 76	1.32312 84643 64	0.99984 49301 96	1.21083 58898 98
90	1.57079 63267 95	1.33286 99541 17	1.00000 00000 00	1.21090 01551 08

K = 1.90108 30334 63664   E = 1.32384 21844 81263
K'= 1.81215 98536 62126   E'= 1.37650 43257 72082

r	u=(r/90)K=F(φ,k)	sn u	cn u	dn u
0	0.00000 00000 00	0.00000 00000 00	1.00000 00000 00	1.00000 00000 00
1	0.02112 31448 16	0.02112 07068 16	0.99977 69329 92	0.99987 68142 23
2	0.04224 62896 33	0.04222 67932 26	0.99910 80511 81	0.99950 75069 79
3	0.06336 94344 49	0.06330 36767 54	0.99799 43108 60	0.99889 28275 34
4	0.08449 25792 65	0.08433 68505 60	0.99643 73014 08	0.99803 40213 59
5	0.10561 57240 81	0.10531 19207 20	0.99443 92386 44	0.99693 28251 97
6	0.12673 88688 98	0.12621 46428 54	0.99200 29556 05	0.99559 14602 10
7	0.14786 20137 14	0.14703 09578 99	0.98913 18908 11	0.99401 26232 54
8	0.16898 51585 30	0.16774 70268 35	0.98583 00740 94	0.99219 04763 57
9	0.19010 83033 46	0.18834 92641 76	0.98210 21101 11	0.99015 56344 59
10	0.21123 14481 63	0.20882 43700 37	0.97795 31596 55	0.98788 51515 31
11	0.23235 45929 79	0.22915 93606 38	0.97338 89188 97	0.98539 25051 47
12	0.25347 77377 95	0.24934 15970 66	0.96841 55967 21	0.98268 25796 33
13	0.27460 08826 11	0.26935 88121 96	0.96303 98902 91	0.97976 06479 21
14	0.29572 40274 28	0.28919 91356 27	0.95726 89590 46	0.97663 23522 08
15	0.31684 71722 44	0.30885 11165 49	0.95111 03972 76	0.97330 36835 82
16	0.33797 03170 60	0.32830 37444 54	0.94457 22054 87	0.96978 09607 28
17	0.35909 34618 76	0.34754 64676 30	0.93766 27607 18	0.96607 08078 66
18	0.38021 66066 93	0.36656 92093 98	0.93039 07860 26	0.96218 01320 61
19	0.40133 97515 09	0.38536 23820 44	0.92276 53193 01	0.95811 61000 36
20	0.42246 28963 25	0.40391 68984 67	0.91479 56816 32	0.95388 61146 44
21	0.44358 60411 42	0.42222 41815 23	0.90649 14453 75	0.94949 77911 20
22	0.46470 91859 58	0.44027 61710 93	0.89786 24021 35	0.94495 89332 60
23	0.48583 23307 74	0.45806 53289 33	0.88891 85308 17	0.94027 75096 47
24	0.50695 54755 90	0.47558 46413 22	0.87966 99659 18	0.93546 16300 55
25	0.52807 86204 07	0.49282 76196 09	0.87012 69662 24	0.93051 95221 41
26	0.54920 17652 23	0.50978 82987 08	0.86029 98840 52	0.92545 95085 43
27	0.57032 49100 39	0.52646 12336 48	0.85019 91351 83	0.92028 99844 76
28	0.59144 80548 55	0.54284 14942 59	0.83983 51696 08	0.91501 93959 31
29	0.61257 11996 72	0.55892 46581 10	0.82921 84432 08	0.90965 62185 51
30	0.63369 43444 88	0.57470 68018 05	0.81835 93904 63	0.90420 89372 75
31	0.65481 74893 04	0.59018 44907 49	0.80726 83982 91	0.89868 60267 93
32	0.67594 06341 20	0.60535 47675 13	0.79595 57810 89	0.89309 59329 01
33	0.69706 37789 37	0.62021 51389 14	0.78443 17570 46	0.88744 70547 73
34	0.71818 69237 53	0.63476 35619 30	0.77270 64257 83	0.88174 77282 16
35	0.73931 00685 69	0.64899 84285 89	0.76078 97473 60	0.87600 62099 20
36	0.76043 32133 85	0.66291 85499 40	0.74869 15226 89	0.87023 06627 40
37	0.78155 63582 02	0.67652 31392 31	0.73642 13753 59	0.86442 91420 10
38	0.80267 95030 18	0.68981 17944 22	0.72398 87349 10	0.85860 95829 10
39	0.82380 26478 34	0.70278 44801 37	0.71140 28215 28	0.85277 97888 76
40	0.84492 57926 51	0.71544 15091 76	0.69867 26321 74	0.84694 74210 49
41	0.86604 89374 67	0.72778 35236 80	0.68580 69281 22	0.84111 99887 54
42	0.88717 20822 83	0.73981 14760 73	0.67281 42238 92	0.83530 48409 78
43	0.90829 52270 99	0.75152 66098 54	0.65970 27775 30	0.82950 91588 44
44	0.92941 83719 16	0.76293 04403 45	0.64648 05822 26	0.82373 99490 28
45	0.95054 15167 32	0.77402 47354 64	0.63315 53592 04	0.81800 40381 07

ELLIPTIC FUNCTIONS   TABLE $\theta = 48°$

q = 0.05005 44121 29953 00   D(90) = 1.22248 78526 45010
q'= 0.03704 02001 87132 72   1/D(90) = 0.81800 40381 06694

r	ϕ	$E(\phi,k)$	A(r)	D(r)
0	0.00000 00000 00	0.00000 00000 00	0.00000 00000 00	1.00000 00000 00
1	0.02112 22774 01	0.02112 14100 49	0.01727 79936 71	1.00006 77328 10
2	0.04223 93524 20	0.04223 24172 58	0.03455 10429 52	1.00027 08488 44
3	0.06334 60332 36	0.06332 26475 73	0.05181 42040 84	1.00060 91010 07
4	0.08443 71491 01	0.08438 17843 51	0.06906 25345 78	1.00108 20778 09
5	0.10550 75607 72	0.10539 95966 61	0.08629 10938 50	1.00168 92038 61
6	0.12655 21708 26	0.12636 59671 10	0.10349 49438 71	1.00242 97405 73
7	0.14756 59337 95	0.14727 09190 33	0.12066 91498 19	1.00330 27870 48
8	0.16854 38661 12	0.16810 46429 13	0.13780 87807 43	1.00430 72811 73
9	0.18948 10558 09	0.18885 75218 79	0.15490 89102 46	1.00544 20009 05
10	0.21037 26719 37	0.20952 01561 58	0.17196 46171 75	1.00670 55657 52
11	0.23121 39736 85	0.23008 33863 68	0.18897 09863 34	1.00809 64384 47
12	0.25200 03191 47	0.25053 83155 25	0.20592 31092 09	1.00961 29268 05
13	0.27272 71737 29	0.27087 63296 82	0.22281 60847 25	1.01125 31857 77
14	0.29339 01181 49	0.29108 91171 14	0.23964 50200 11	1.01301 52196 87
15	0.31398 48560 32	0.31116 86859 56	0.25640 50312 05	1.01489 68846 45
16	0.33450 72210 49	0.33110 73802 66	0.27309 12442 70	1.01689 58911 51
17	0.35495 31836 09	0.35089 78944 40	0.28969 87958 53	1.01900 98068 63
18	0.37531 88570 72	0.37053 32859 55	0.30622 28341 56	1.02123 60595 51
19	0.39560 05034 82	0.39000 69864 31	0.32265 85198 53	1.02357 19402 12
20	0.41579 45388 00	0.40931 28109 82	0.33900 10270 32	1.02601 46063 55
21	0.43589 75376 47	0.42844 49658 87	0.35524 55441 66	1.02856 10854 48
22	0.45590 62375 31	0.44739 80545 78	0.37138 72751 25	1.03120 82785 22
23	0.47581 75425 87	0.46616 70819 83	0.38742 14402 20	1.03395 29639 28
24	0.49562 85268 00	0.48474 74572 70	0.40334 32772 81	1.03679 18012 47
25	0.51533 64367 48	0.50313 49950 21	0.41914 80427 76	1.03972 13353 43
26	0.53493 86938 45	0.52132 59149 19	0.43483 10129 63	1.04273 80005 53
27	0.55443 28961 09	0.53931 68399 89	0.45038 74850 78	1.04583 81250 15
28	0.57381 68194 68	0.55710 47934 88	0.46581 27785 69	1.04901 79351 24
29	0.59308 84186 04	0.57468 71945 02	0.48110 22363 56	1.05227 35601 15
30	0.61224 58273 66	0.59206 18523 48	0.49625 12261 42	1.05560 10367 61
31	0.63128 73587 54	0.60922 69598 64	0.51125 51417 50	1.05899 63141 85
32	0.65021 15045 12	0.62618 10856 69	0.52610 94045 07	1.06245 52587 81
33	0.66901 69343 18	0.64292 31654 97	0.54080 94646 59	1.06597 36592 36
34	0.68770 24946 30	0.65945 24926 90	0.55535 08028 27	1.06954 72316 48
35	0.70626 72071 75	0.67576 87079 43	0.56972 89314 96	1.07317 16247 27
36	0.72471 02671 20	0.69187 17884 01	0.58393 93965 42	1.07684 24250 89
37	0.74303 10409 47	0.70776 20361 86	0.59797 77787 95	1.08055 51626 21
38	0.76122 90640 42	0.72344 00664 59	0.61183 96956 27	1.08430 53159 12
39	0.77930 40380 37	0.73890 67950 88	0.62552 08025 86	1.08808 83177 57
40	0.79725 58279 09	0.75416 34260 16	0.63901 67950 49	1.09189 95607 12
41	0.81508 44588 79	0.76921 14384 08	0.65232 34099 10	1.09573 44026 96
42	0.83279 01131 05	0.78405 25736 52	0.66543 64272 95	1.09958 81726 44
43	0.85037 31262 22	0.79868 88222 76	0.67835 16723 07	1.10345 61761 92
44	0.86783 39837 18	0.81312 24108 71	0.69106 50167 88	1.10733 37013 91
45	0.88517 33171 93	0.82735 57890 61	0.70357 23811 12	1.11121 60244 47

191

K = 1.90108 30334 63664
K′= 1.81215 98536 62126

E = 1.32384 21844 81263
E′= 1.37650 43257 72082

r	u=(r/90)K=F(ϕ,k)	sn u	cn u	dn u
45	0.95054 15167 32	0.77402 47354 64	0.63315 53592 04	0.81800 40381 07
46	0.97166 46615 48	0.78481 14966 25	0.61973 45518 57	0.81230 80677 93
47	0.99278 78063 64	0.79529 29398 02	0.60622 53210 65	0.80665 84910 18
48	1.01391 09511 81	0.80547 14768 61	0.59263 45416 56	0.80106 15688 22
49	1.03503 40959 97	0.81534 96971 80	0.57896 87999 44	0.79552 33680 16
50	1.05615 72408 13	0.82493 03496 41	0.56523 43923 02	0.79004 97595 59
51	1.07728 03856 29	0.83421 63250 20	0.55143 73246 97	0.78464 64176 18
52	1.09840 35304 46	0.84321 06388 28	0.53758 33131 40	0.77931 88192 60
53	1.11952 66752 62	0.85191 64146 25	0.52367 77849 91	0.77407 22447 22
54	1.14064 98200 78	0.86033 68678 49	0.50972 58810 57	0.76891 17782 31
55	1.16177 29648 94	0.86847 52901 81	0.49573 24584 35	0.76384 23093 14
56	1.18289 61097 11	0.87633 50344 51	0.48170 20940 31	0.75886 85345 56
57	1.20401 92545 27	0.88391 95001 29	0.46763 90887 12	0.75399 49597 67
58	1.22514 23993 43	0.89123 21193 80	0.45354 74720 31	0.74922 59025 13
59	1.24626 55441 60	0.89827 63437 10	0.43943 10074 76	0.74456 54949 66
60	1.26738 86889 76	0.90505 56312 01	0.42529 31981 95	0.74001 76870 35
61	1.28851 18337 92	0.91157 34343 34	0.41113 72931 48	0.73558 62497 42
62	1.30963 49786 08	0.91783 31883 93	0.39696 62936 39	0.73127 47788 02
63	1.33075 81234 25	0.92383 83004 53	0.38278 29601 95	0.72708 66983 73
64	1.35188 12682 41	0.92959 21389 43	0.36858 98197 39	0.72302 52649 43
65	1.37300 44130 57	0.93509 80237 60	0.35438 91730 29	0.71909 35713 19
66	1.39412 75578 73	0.94035 92169 43	0.34018 31023 30	0.71529 45506 91
67	1.41525 07026 90	0.94537 89138 81	0.32597 34792 72	0.71163 09807 41
68	1.43637 38475 06	0.95016 02350 46	0.31176 19728 86	0.70810 54877 70
69	1.45749 69923 22	0.95470 62182 26	0.29755 00577 71	0.70472 05508 18
70	1.47862 01371 38	0.95901 98112 62	0.28333 90223 85	0.70147 85057 53
71	1.49974 32819 55	0.96310 38652 48	0.26912 99774 16	0.69838 15493 06
72	1.52086 64267 71	0.96696 11281 96	0.25492 38642 37	0.69543 17430 41
73	1.54198 95715 87	0.97059 42391 42	0.24072 14634 06	0.69263 10172 20
74	1.56311 27164 03	0.97400 57226 71	0.22652 34032 14	0.68998 11745 70
75	1.58423 58612 20	0.97719 79838 56	0.21233 01682 48	0.68748 38939 23
76	1.60535 90060 36	0.98017 33035 79	0.19814 21079 72	0.68514 07337 12
77	1.62648 21508 52	0.98293 38342 33	0.18395 94453 15	0.68295 31353 18
78	1.64760 52956 69	0.98548 15957 79	0.16978 22852 39	0.68092 24262 51
79	1.66872 84404 85	0.98781 84721 45	0.15561 06233 15	0.67904 98231 56
80	1.68985 15853 01	0.98994 62079 56	0.14144 43542 64	0.67733 64346 27
81	1.71097 47301 17	0.99186 64055 75	0.12728 32804 86	0.67578 32638 35
82	1.73209 78749 34	0.99358 05224 51	0.11312 71205 60	0.67439 12109 45
83	1.75322 10197 50	0.99508 98687 51	0.09897 55177 26	0.67316 10753 27
84	1.77434 41645 66	0.99639 56052 78	0.08482 80483 31	0.67209 35575 50
85	1.79546 73093 82	0.99749 87416 50	0.07068 42302 58	0.67118 92611 48
86	1.81659 04541 99	0.99840 01347 48	0.05654 35313 28	0.67044 86941 71
87	1.83771 35990 15	0.99910 04874 11	0.04240 53776 78	0.66987 22704 92
88	1.85883 67438 31	0.99960 03473 75	0.02826 91621 21	0.66946 03108 90
89	1.87995 98886 47	0.99990 01064 64	0.01413 42524 97	0.66921 30438 88
90	1.90108 30334 64	1.00000 00000 00	0.00000 00000 00	0.66913 06063 59

q = 0.05005 44121 29953 00
q' = 0.03704 02001 87132 72

D(90) = 1.22248 78526 45010
1/D(90) = 0.81800 40381 06694

r	ϕ	$E(\phi,k)$	A(r)	D(r)
45	0.88517 33171 93	0.82735 57890 61	0.70357 23811 12	1.11121 60244 47
46	0.90239 19005 00	0.84139 16165 90	0.71586 97359 94	1.11509 84154 70
47	0.91949 06458 00	0.85523 27505 77	0.72795 31043 16	1.11897 61442 41
48	0.93647 05995 35	0.86888 22329 90	0.73981 85629 78	1.12284 44859 73
49	0.95333 29383 56	0.88234 32783 72	0.75146 22447 51	1.12669 87270 69
50	0.97007 89649 94	0.89561 92618 79	0.76288 03401 52	1.13053 41708 71
51	0.98671 01041 19	0.90871 37076 45	0.77406 90993 24	1.13434 61433 80
52	1.00322 78981 72	0.92163 02775 10	0.78502 48339 23	1.13812 99989 64
53	1.01963 40032 12	0.93437 27601 49	0.79574 39190 08	1.14188 11260 16
54	1.03593 01847 56	0.94694 50606 02	0.80622 27949 36	1.14559 49525 89
55	1.05211 83136 60	0.95935 11902 43	0.81645 79692 50	1.14926 69519 66
56	1.06820 03620 21	0.97159 52571 94	0.82644 60185 72	1.15289 26481 92
57	1.08417 83991 21	0.98368 14571 88	0.83618 35904 79	1.15646 76215 34
58	1.10005 45874 29	0.99561 40649 07	0.84566 74053 75	1.15998 75138 79
59	1.11583 11786 50	1.00739 74257 80	0.85489 42583 48	1.16344 80340 54
60	1.13151 05098 41	1.01903 59482 54	0.86386 10210 16	1.16684 49630 70
61	1.14709 49996 02	1.03053 40965 37	0.87256 46433 48	1.17017 41592 77
62	1.16258 71443 27	1.04189 63838 04	0.88100 21554 67	1.17343 15634 18
63	1.17798 95145 46	1.05312 73658 68	0.88917 06694 29	1.17661 32036 01
64	1.19330 47513 40	1.06423 16353 06	0.89706 73809 73	1.17971 52001 41
65	1.20853 55628 42	1.07521 38160 29	0.90468 95712 41	1.18273 37703 16
66	1.22368 47208 21	1.08607 85582 87	0.91203 46084 67	1.18566 52329 82
67	1.23875 50573 53	1.09683 05341 07	0.91909 99496 28	1.18850 60130 80
68	1.25374 94615 86	1.10747 44331 28	0.92588 31420 55	1.19125 26460 09
69	1.26867 08765 75	1.11801 49588 54	0.93238 18250 04	1.19390 17818 61
70	1.28352 22962 27	1.12845 68252 72	0.93859 37311 85	1.19645 01895 24
71	1.29830 67623 08	1.13880 47538 53	0.94451 66882 37	1.19889 47606 32
72	1.31302 73615 55	1.14906 34708 97	0.95014 86201 63	1.20123 25133 73
73	1.32768 72228 57	1.15923 77052 23	0.95548 75487 02	1.20346 05961 33
74	1.34228 95145 22	1.16933 21861 74	0.96053 15946 54	1.20557 62909 96
75	1.35683 74416 23	1.17935 16419 27	0.96527 89791 49	1.20757 70170 62
76	1.37133 42434 19	1.18930 07980 92	0.96972 80248 47	1.20946 03336 13
77	1.38578 31908 44	1.19918 43765 77	0.97387 71570 88	1.21122 39431 02
78	1.40018 75840 71	1.20900 70947 08	0.97772 49049 69	1.21286 56939 64
79	1.41455 07501 38	1.21877 36645 85	0.98126 99023 64	1.21438 35832 52
80	1.42887 60406 37	1.22848 87926 52	0.98451 08888 70	1.21577 57590 94
81	1.44316 68294 59	1.23815 71794 68	0.98744 67106 83	1.21704 05229 56
82	1.45742 65105 92	1.24778 35196 68	0.99007 63214 11	1.21817 63317 29
83	1.47165 84959 72	1.25737 25020 81	0.99239 87828 08	1.21918 17996 16
84	1.48586 62133 72	1.26692 88100 02	0.99441 32654 35	1.22005 56998 28
85	1.50005 31043 37	1.27645 71215 95	0.99611 90492 45	1.22079 69660 95
86	1.51422 26221 46	1.28596 21104 17	0.99751 55241 00	1.22140 46939 65
87	1.52837 82298 17	1.29544 84460 29	0.99860 21902 00	1.22187 81419 15
88	1.54252 33981 23	1.30492 07947 01	0.99937 86584 41	1.22221 67322 62
89	1.55666 16036 38	1.31438 38201 74	0.99984 46506 94	1.22242 00518 67
90	1.57079 63267 95	1.32384 21844 81	1.00000 00000 00	1.22248 78526 45

K = 1.91799 75464 36423

K′ = 1.79922 15440 49811

E = 1.31472 95602 64623

E′ = 1.38488 65913 75413

r	u=(r/90)K=F(ϕ,k)	sn u	cn u	dn u
0	0.00000 00000 00	0.00000 00000 00	1.00000 00000 00	1.00000 00000 00
1	0.02131 10838 49	0.02130 85522 66	0.99977 29470 24	0.99987 06799 99
2	0.04262 21676 99	0.04260 19232 02	0.99909 21259 52	0.99948 29882 39
3	0.06393 32515 48	0.06386 49722 70	0.99795 85488 97	0.99883 77283 53
4	0.08524 43353 97	0.08508 26402 76	0.99637 38978 53	0.99793 62360 63
5	0.10655 54192 46	0.10623 99894 40	0.99434 05174 51	0.99678 03737 16
6	0.12786 65030 96	0.12732 22427 43	0.99186 14048 86	0.99537 25226 86
7	0.14917 75869 45	0.14831 48223 38	0.98894 01971 17	0.99371 55737 17
8	0.17048 86707 94	0.16920 33867 91	0.98558 11554 10	0.99181 29152 68
9	0.19179 97546 44	0.18997 38669 52	0.98178 91473 61	0.98966 84199 52
10	0.21311 08384 93	0.21061 25002 63	0.97756 96265 40	0.98728 64291 77
11	0.23442 19223 42	0.23110 58633 25	0.97292 86098 87	0.98467 17360 98
12	0.25573 30061 92	0.25144 09025 56	0.96787 26530 50	0.98182 95670 13
13	0.27704 40900 41	0.27160 49627 99	0.96240 88238 29	0.97876 55613 31
14	0.29835 51738 90	0.29158 58137 60	0.95654 46739 25	0.97548 57502 58
15	0.31966 62577 39	0.31137 16741 57	0.95028 82091 94	0.97199 65343 53
16	0.34097 73415 89	0.33095 12335 12	0.94364 78585 98	0.96830 46601 08
17	0.36228 84254 38	0.35031 36714 95	0.93663 24420 84	0.96441 71957 09
18	0.38359 95092 87	0.36944 86748 04	0.92925 11375 76	0.96034 15061 30
19	0.40491 05931 37	0.38834 64515 31	0.92151 34473 16	0.95608 52277 34
20	0.42622 16769 86	0.40699 77430 18	0.91342 91637 44	0.95165 62425 22
21	0.44753 27608 35	0.42539 38332 17	0.90500 83351 33	0.94706 26521 97
22	0.46884 38446 84	0.44352 65555 80	0.89626 12311 68	0.94231 27521 78
23	0.49015 49285 34	0.46138 82975 26	0.88719 83086 70	0.93741 50057 28
24	0.51146 60123 83	0.47897 20025 49	0.87783 01776 39	0.93237 80183 08
25	0.53277 70962 32	0.49627 11700 47	0.86816 75678 00	0.92721 05123 11
26	0.55408 81800 82	0.51327 98529 55	0.85822 12957 92	0.92192 13022 79
27	0.57539 92639 31	0.52999 26532 83	0.84800 22331 73	0.91651 92707 23
28	0.59671 03477 80	0.54640 47156 81	0.83752 12753 60	0.91101 33446 43
29	0.61802 14316 30	0.56251 17191 34	0.82678 93116 37	0.90541 24728 49
30	0.63933 25154 79	0.57830 98669 22	0.81581 71963 26	0.89972 56041 52
31	0.66064 35993 28	0.59379 58749 74	0.80461 57212 38	0.89396 16665 06
32	0.68195 46831 77	0.60896 69587 54	0.79319 55894 64	0.88812 95471 53
33	0.70326 57670 27	0.62382 08188 05	0.78156 73905 85	0.88223 80738 29
34	0.72457 68508 76	0.63835 56251 00	0.76974 15773 52	0.87629 59970 68
35	0.74588 79347 25	0.65257 00003 34	0.75772 84438 79	0.87031 19736 31
36	0.76719 90185 75	0.66646 30022 94	0.74553 81053 80	0.86429 45510 84
37	0.78851 01024 24	0.68003 41054 27	0.73318 04794 57	0.85825 21535 34
38	0.80982 11862 73	0.69328 31817 65	0.72066 52689 58	0.85219 30685 35
39	0.83113 22701 22	0.70621 04813 02	0.70800 19463 95	0.84612 54351 43
40	0.85244 33539 72	0.71881 66119 66	0.69519 97399 04	0.84005 72331 25
41	0.87375 44378 21	0.73110 25192 81	0.68226 76207 33	0.83399 62732 91
42	0.89506 55216 70	0.74306 94658 55	0.66921 42922 22	0.82795 01889 34
43	0.91637 66055 20	0.75471 90107 62	0.65604 81802 39	0.82192 64283 40
44	0.93768 76893 69	0.76605 29889 49	0.64277 74250 26	0.81593 22483 40
45	0.95899 87732 18	0.77707 34907 27	0.62940 98744 13	0.80997 47088 59

194

ELLIPTIC FUNCTIONS TABLE $\theta = 49°$

q = 0.05249 47051 04843 90   D(90) = 1.23460 64501 31302
q′= 0.03511 99625 22096 26   1/D(90) = 0.80997 47088 58559

r	ϕ	$E(\phi,k)$	$A(r)$	$D(r)$
0	0.00000 00000 00	0.00000 00000 00	0.00000 00000 00	1.00000 00000 00
1	0.02131 01651 36	0.02130 92464 94	0.01726 06210 25	1.00007 14166 20
2	0.04261 48202 79	0.04260 74751 39	0.03451 63346 90	1.00028 55796 20
3	0.06390 84668 61	0.06388 36994 63	0.05176 22341 68	1.00064 22285 27
4	0.08518 56291 19	0.08512 69955 69	0.06899 34137 05	1.00114 09295 73
5	0.10644 08653 77	0.10632 65329 64	0.08620 49691 59	1.00178 10762 12
6	0.12766 87791 95	0.12747 16048 57	0.10339 19985 53	1.00256 18898 63
7	0.14886 40303 28	0.14855 16577 41	0.12054 96026 30	1.00348 24208 44
8	0.17002 13454 63	0.16955 63201 00	0.13767 28854 24	1.00454 15495 29
9	0.19113 55286 82	0.19047 54300 93	0.15475 69548 52	1.00573 79876 95
10	0.21220 14716 22	0.21129 90620 52	0.17179 69233 09	1.00707 02800 86
11	0.23321 41632 84	0.23201 75516 80	0.18878 79082 94	1.00853 68061 75
12	0.25416 86994 68	0.25262 15198 10	0.20572 50330 52	1.01013 57821 19
13	0.27506 02917 88	0.27310 18946 31	0.22260 34272 42	1.01186 52629 26
14	0.29588 42762 57	0.29344 99322 72	0.23941 82276 25	1.01372 31448 05
15	0.31663 61213 94	0.31365 72356 84	0.25616 45787 86	1.01570 71677 15
16	0.33731 14358 48	0.33371 57717 36	0.27283 76338 83	1.01781 49180 98
17	0.35790 59755 17	0.35361 78864 85	0.28943 25554 25	1.02004 38318 06
18	0.37841 56501 36	0.37335 63185 94	0.30594 45160 83	1.02239 11972 04
19	0.39883 65293 33	0.39292 42108 62	0.32236 86995 40	1.02485 41584 56
20	0.41916 48481 38	0.41231 51198 76	0.33870 03013 72	1.02742 97189 82
21	0.43939 70119 43	0.43152 30237 90	0.35493 45299 64	1.03011 47450 92
22	0.45952 96009 05	0.45054 23282 58	0.37106 66074 73	1.03290 59697 79
23	0.47955 93738 01	0.46936 78705 46	0.38709 17708 20	1.03579 99966 84
24	0.49948 32713 30	0.48799 49218 87	0.40300 52727 31	1.03879 33042 07
25	0.51929 84188 70	0.50641 91881 30	0.41880 23828 12	1.04188 22497 82
26	0.53900 21287 13	0.52463 68087 43	0.43447 83886 74	1.04506 30742 89
27	0.55859 19017 61	0.54264 43542 67	0.45002 85970 88	1.04833 19066 16
28	0.57806 54287 28	0.56043 88222 84	0.46544 83351 99	1.05168 47683 55
29	0.59742 05908 46	0.57801 76320 05	0.48073 29517 67	1.05511 75786 26
30	0.61665 54600 92	0.59537 86175 63	0.49587 78184 61	1.05862 61590 31
31	0.63576 82989 65	0.61252 00201 23	0.51087 83311 97	1.06220 62387 27
32	0.65475 75598 30	0.62944 04788 91	0.52572 99115 09	1.06585 34596 09
33	0.67362 18838 47	0.64613 90211 55	0.54042 80079 71	1.06956 33815 99
34	0.69236 00995 14	0.66261 50514 31	0.55496 80976 62	1.07333 14880 45
35	0.71097 12208 37	0.67886 83398 46	0.56934 56876 63	1.07715 31912 02
36	0.72945 44451 76	0.69489 90098 41	0.58355 63166 07	1.08102 38378 09
37	0.74780 91707 52	0.71070 75253 09	0.59759 55562 56	1.08493 87147 44
38	0.76603 48938 84	0.72629 46772 61	0.61145 90131 29	1.08889 30547 51
39	0.78413 14059 44	0.74166 15701 17	0.62514 23301 54	1.09288 20422 41
40	0.80209 85900 76	0.75680 96077 12	0.63864 11883 69	1.09690 08191 44
41	0.81993 65176 99	0.77174 04791 07	0.65195 13086 47	1.10094 44908 19
42	0.83764 54248 11	0.78645 61442 92	0.66506 84534 60	1.10500 81320 14
43	0.85522 57081 24	0.80095 88198 45	0.67798 84286 71	1.10908 67928 53
44	0.87267 79210 53	0.81525 09646 36	0.69070 70853 54	1.11317 55048 70
45	0.89000 27695 74	0.82933 52656 37	0.70322 03216 48	1.11726 92870 50

195

K = 1.91799 75464 36423   E = 1.31472 95602 64623
K' = 1.79922 15440 49811   E' = 1.38488 65913 75413

r	u=(r/90)K=F(φ,k)	sn u	cn u	dn u
45	0.95899 87732 18	0.77707 34907 27	0.62940 98744 13	0.80997 47088 59
46	0.98030 98570 68	0.78778 28414 47	0.61595 30783 44	0.80406 06684 26
47	1.00162 09409 17	0.79818 35814 23	0.60241 42846 47	0.79819 67805 99
48	1.02293 20247 66	0.80827 84461 75	0.58880 04360 12	0.79238 94912 51
49	1.04424 31086 15	0.81807 03470 54	0.57511 81680 94	0.78664 50366 76
50	1.06555 41924 65	0.82756 23522 90	0.56137 38086 80	0.78096 94424 63
51	1.08686 52763 14	0.83675 76685 30	0.54757 33778 74	0.77536 85230 84
52	1.10817 63601 63	0.84565 96228 80	0.53372 25892 08	0.76984 78821 45
53	1.12948 74440 13	0.85427 16455 04	0.51982 68516 42	0.76441 29132 55
54	1.15079 85278 62	0.86259 72528 06	0.50589 12723 61	0.75906 88014 50
55	1.17210 96117 11	0.87064 00312 03	0.49192 06603 37	0.75382 05251 31
56	1.19342 06955 60	0.87840 36215 24	0.47791 95305 63	0.74867 28584 69
57	1.21473 17794 10	0.88589 17040 31	0.46389 21089 33	0.74363 03742 18
58	1.23604 28632 59	0.89310 79840 85	0.44984 23376 73	0.73869 74468 91
59	1.25735 39471 08	0.90005 61784 52	0.43577 38813 08	0.73387 82562 73
60	1.27866 50309 58	0.90674 00022 41	0.42169 01330 78	0.72917 67911 94
61	1.29997 61148 07	0.91316 31564 95	0.40759 42217 69	0.72459 68535 49
62	1.32128 71986 56	0.91932 93163 99	0.39348 90189 19	0.72014 20625 16
63	1.34259 82825 05	0.92524 21201 18	0.37937 71463 32	0.71581 58589 22
64	1.36390 93663 55	0.93090 51582 50	0.36526 09838 79	0.71162 15097 41
65	1.38522 04502 04	0.93632 19638 61	0.35114 26775 41	0.70756 21126 81
66	1.40653 15340 53	0.94149 60031 26	0.33702 41476 48	0.70364 06008 17
67	1.42784 26179 03	0.94643 06665 12	0.32290 70972 97	0.69985 97472 64
68	1.44915 37017 52	0.95112 92605 31	0.30879 30209 08	0.69622 21698 41
69	1.47046 47856 01	0.95559 50000 08	0.29468 32128 92	0.69273 03357 06
70	1.49177 58694 51	0.95983 10008 70	0.28057 87764 05	0.68938 65659 43
71	1.51308 69533 00	0.96384 02734 24	0.26648 06321 79	0.68619 30400 76
72	1.53439 80371 49	0.96762 57161 06	0.25238 95273 78	0.68315 18004 82
73	1.55570 91209 98	0.97119 01096 86	0.23830 60445 06	0.68026 47566 94
74	1.57702 02048 48	0.97453 61119 02	0.22423 06103 09	0.67753 36895 70
75	1.59833 12886 97	0.97766 62525 10	0.21016 35046 87	0.67496 02553 14
76	1.61964 23725 46	0.98058 29287 33	0.19610 48695 91	0.67254 59893 36
77	1.64095 34563 96	0.98328 84010 75	0.18205 47179 05	0.67029 23099 36
78	1.66226 45402 45	0.98578 47895 07	0.16801 29422 88	0.66820 05217 94
79	1.68357 56240 94	0.98807 40699 87	0.15397 93240 01	0.66627 18192 67
80	1.70488 67079 43	0.99015 80713 05	0.13995 35416 80	0.66450 72894 78
81	1.72619 77917 93	0.99203 84722 47	0.12593 51800 80	0.66290 79151 80
82	1.74750 88756 42	0.99371 67990 42	0.11192 37387 73	0.66147 45774 03
83	1.76881 99594 91	0.99519 44231 07	0.09791 86408 08	0.66020 80578 61
84	1.79013 10433 41	0.99647 25590 48	0.08391 92413 28	0.65910 90411 26
85	1.81144 21271 90	0.99755 22629 36	0.06992 48361 52	0.65817 81165 54
86	1.83275 32110 39	0.99843 44308 25	0.05593 46703 19	0.65741 57799 68
87	1.85406 42948 89	0.99911 97975 10	0.04194 79466 03	0.65682 24350 84
88	1.87537 53787 38	0.99960 89355 28	0.02796 38340 00	0.65639 83946 81
89	1.89668 64625 87	0.99990 22543 85	0.01398 14761 93	0.65614 38815 18
90	1.91799 75464 36	1.00000 00000 00	0.00000 00000 00	0.65605 90289 91

q = 0.05249 47051 04843 90   D(90) = 1.23460 64501 31302
q'= 0.03511 99625 22096 26   1/D(90) = 0.80997 47088 58559

r	ϕ	$E(\phi,k)$	A(r)	D(r)
45	0.89000 27695 74	0.82933 52656 37	0.70322 03216 48	1.11726 92870 50
46	0.90720 11079 78	0.84321 46238 97	0.71552 40846 22	1.12136 31519 01
47	0.92427 39345 42	0.85689 21407 39	0.72761 43721 79	1.12545 21115 28
48	0.94122 23871 25	0.87037 11042 42	0.73948 72349 65	1.12953 11837 13
49	0.95804 77387 29	0.88365 49760 31	0.75113 87783 10	1.13359 53979 82
50	0.97475 13930 11	0.89674 73784 40	0.76256 51641 69	1.13763 98016 69
51	0.99133 48797 91	0.90965 20820 69	0.77376 26130 87	1.14165 94659 54
52	1.00779 98505 53	0.92237 29937 62	0.78472 74061 69	1.14564 94918 75
53	1.02414 80739 63	0.93491 41450 50	0.79545 58870 57	1.14960 50163 02
54	1.04038 14314 03	0.94727 96810 57	0.80594 44639 11	1.15352 12178 75
55	1.05650 19125 48	0.95947 38499 08	0.81618 96113 89	1.15739 33228 85
56	1.07251 16109 88	0.97150 09926 32	0.82618 78726 29	1.16121 66111 05
57	1.08841 27199 04	0.98336 55335 86	0.83593 58612 22	1.16498 64215 51
58	1.10420 75278 08	0.99507 19713 96	0.84543 02631 77	1.16869 81581 78
59	1.11989 84143 60	1.00662 48704 18	0.85466 78388 77	1.17234 72954 90
60	1.13548 78462 48	1.01802 88527 27	0.86364 54250 18	1.17592 93840 76
61	1.15097 83731 73	1.02928 85906 17	0.87235 99365 27	1.17944 00560 43
62	1.16637 26239 00	1.04040 87996 23	0.88080 83684 70	1.18287 50303 56
63	1.18167 33024 15	1.05139 42320 43	0.88898 77979 17	1.18623 01180 75
64	1.19688 31841 73	1.06224 96709 58	0.89689 53858 01	1.18950 12274 77
65	1.21200 51124 39	1.07297 99247 44	0.90452 83787 28	1.19268 43690 59
66	1.22704 19947 29	1.08358 98220 48	0.91188 41107 63	1.19577 56604 19
67	1.24199 67993 57	1.09408 42072 26	0.91896 00051 78	1.19877 13310 12
68	1.25687 25520 68	1.10446 79362 34	0.92575 35761 55	1.20166 77267 56
69	1.27167 23327 86	1.11474 58729 32	0.93226 24304 52	1.20446 13145 12
70	1.28639 92724 44	1.12492 28858 15	0.93848 42690 16	1.20714 86864 08
71	1.30105 65499 28	1.13500 38451 29	0.94441 68885 54	1.20972 65640 09
72	1.31564 73890 99	1.14499 36203 70	0.95005 81830 49	1.21219 18023 35
73	1.33017 50559 22	1.15489 70781 34	0.95540 61452 17	1.21454 13937 14
74	1.34464 28556 78	1.16471 90803 17	0.96045 88679 12	1.21677 24714 65
75	1.35905 41302 65	1.17446 44826 31	0.96521 45454 73	1.21888 23134 09
76	1.37341 22555 80	1.18413 81334 26	0.96967 14749 98	1.22086 83452 08
77	1.38772 06389 92	1.19374 48727 89	0.97382 80575 66	1.22272 81435 18
78	1.40198 27168 74	1.20328 95319 24	0.97768 27993 80	1.22445 94389 62
79	1.41620 19522 24	1.21277 69327 61	0.98123 43128 51	1.22606 01189 06
80	1.43038 18323 45	1.22221 18878 07	0.98448 13176 03	1.22752 82300 58
81	1.44452 58665 91	1.23159 92002 03	0.98742 26414 07	1.22886 19808 52
82	1.45863 75841 71	1.24094 36639 68	0.99005 72210 42	1.23005 97436 56
83	1.47272 05320 06	1.25025 00644 25	0.99238 41030 74	1.23112 00567 60
84	1.48677 82726 40	1.25952 31787 75	0.99440 24445 65	1.23204 16261 73
85	1.50081 43821 86	1.26876 77768 16	0.99611 15136 93	1.23282 33272 06
86	1.51483 24483 19	1.27798 86217 76	0.99751 06902 99	1.23346 42058 57
87	1.52883 60682 95	1.28719 04712 53	0.99859 94663 46	1.23396 34799 77
88	1.54282 88470 04	1.29637 80782 38	0.99937 74463 01	1.23432 05402 29
89	1.55681 43950 41	1.30555 61922 07	0.99984 43474 28	1.23453 49508 40
90	1.57079 63267 95	1.31472 95602 65	1.00000 00000 00	1.23460 64501 31

K = 1.93558 10960 04722   E = 1.30553 90942 97794
K′ = 1.78676 91348 85021   E′ = 1.39314 02485 23812

r	u=(r/90)K=F(φ,k)	sn u	cn u	dn u
0	0.00000 00000 00	0.00000 00000 00	1.00000 00000 00	1.00000 00000 00
1	0.02150 64566 22	0.02150 38262 11	0.99976 87659 95	0.99986 43127 98
2	0.04301 29132 45	0.04299 18787 47	0.99907 54217 58	0.99945 75389 06
3	0.06451 93698 67	0.06444 84278 25	0.99792 10390 36	0.99878 05402 36
4	0.08602 58264 89	0.08585 78311 85	0.99630 73987 60	0.99783 47492 49
5	0.10753 22831 11	0.10720 45771 75	0.99423 69831 35	0.99662 21628 95
6	0.12903 87397 34	0.12847 33270 49	0.99171 29646 41	0.99514 53341 95
7	0.15054 51963 56	0.14964 89562 15	0.98873 91920 54	0.99340 73615 44
8	0.17205 16529 78	0.17071 65941 86	0.98532 01735 83	0.99141 18758 04
9	0.19355 81096 00	0.19166 16630 28	0.98146 10572 64	0.98916 30253 00
10	0.21506 45662 23	0.21246 99140 59	0.97716 76087 65	0.98666 54588 30
11	0.23657 10228 45	0.23312 74626 33	0.97244 61867 71	0.98392 43068 31
12	0.25807 74794 67	0.25362 08208 14	0.96730 37161 36	0.98094 51608 25
13	0.27958 39360 90	0.27393 69277 87	0.96174 76590 01	0.97773 40513 19
14	0.30109 03927 12	0.29406 31778 72	0.95578 59841 09	0.97429 74243 16
15	0.32259 68493 34	0.31398 74460 28	0.94942 71345 06	0.97064 21165 93
16	0.34410 33059 56	0.33369 81107 51	0.94267 99938 90	0.96677 53299 47
17	0.36560 97625 79	0.35318 40743 02	0.93555 38518 22	0.96270 46045 65
18	0.38711 62192 01	0.37243 47802 24	0.92805 83680 35	0.95843 77917 04
19	0.40862 26758 23	0.39144 02281 08	0.92020 35360 83	0.95398 30258 65
20	0.43012 91324 45	0.41019 09856 32	0.91199 96465 50	0.94934 86966 27
21	0.45163 55890 68	0.42867 81978 68	0.90345 72500 53	0.94454 34203 28
22	0.47314 20456 90	0.44689 35939 11	0.89458 71202 52	0.93957 60117 37
23	0.49464 85023 12	0.46482 94908 85	0.88540 02170 79	0.93445 54559 03
24	0.51615 49589 35	0.48247 87953 97	0.87590 76503 79	0.92919 08803 14
25	0.53766 14155 57	0.49983 50025 33	0.86612 06441 61	0.92379 15275 13
26	0.55916 78721 79	0.51689 21924 98	0.85605 05016 26	0.91826 67283 07
27	0.58067 43288 01	0.53364 50250 20	0.84570 85711 23	0.91262 58756 93
28	0.60218 07854 24	0.55008 87316 39	0.83510 62131 99	0.90687 83995 98
29	0.62368 72420 46	0.56621 91060 20	0.82425 47688 54	0.90103 37425 49
30	0.64519 36986 68	0.58203 24924 34	0.81316 55291 21	0.89510 13363 45
31	0.66670 01552 91	0.59752 57725 48	0.80184 97060 80	0.88909 05798 19
32	0.68820 66119 13	0.61269 63506 82	0.79031 84053 66	0.88301 08177 39
33	0.70971 30685 35	0.62754 21376 78	0.77858 26002 67	0.87687 13209 11
34	0.73121 95251 57	0.64206 15335 40	0.76665 31074 41	0.87068 12675 17
35	0.75272 59817 80	0.65625 34089 97	0.75454 05643 04	0.86444 97257 17
36	0.77423 24384 02	0.67011 70861 31	0.74225 54081 15	0.85818 56375 33
37	0.79573 88950 24	0.68365 23182 27	0.72980 78567 56	0.85189 78040 33
38	0.81724 53516 46	0.69685 92689 79	0.71720 78912 27	0.84559 48717 88
39	0.83875 18082 69	0.70973 84911 87	0.70446 52398 29	0.83928 53206 27
40	0.86025 82648 91	0.72229 09050 90	0.69158 93640 19	0.83297 74526 43
41	0.88176 47215 13	0.73451 77764 33	0.67858 94459 12	0.82667 93824 37
42	0.90327 11781 36	0.74642 06944 15	0.66547 43773 80	0.82039 90285 74
43	0.92477 76347 58	0.75800 15495 94	0.65225 27507 13	0.81414 41062 02
44	0.94628 40913 80	0.76926 25118 85	0.63893 28507 82	0.80792 21208 02
45	0.96779 05480 02	0.78020 60087 10	0.62552 26486 49	0.80174 03630 14

q = 0.05501 99336 98829 42   D(90) = 1.24728 65856 97294
q'= 0.03326 52566 95577 34   1/D(90) = 0.80174 03630 14448

r	ϕ	$E(\phi,k)$	$A(r)$	$D(r)$
0	0.00000 00000 00	0.00000 00000 00	0.00000 00000 00	1.00000 00000 00
1	0.02150 54838 37	0.02150 45111 30	0.01724 17831 24	1.00007 52699 89
2	0.04300 51334 34	0.04299 73561 56	0.03447 86990 40	1.00030 09884 32
3	0.06449 31269 20	0.06446 69031 80	0.05170 58809 68	1.00067 68808 78
4	0.08596 36671 03	0.08590 15885 11	0.06891 84629 88	1.00120 24902 69
5	0.10741 09936 81	0.10728 99502 55	0.08611 15804 71	1.00187 71775 03
6	0.12882 93952 97	0.12862 06613 04	0.10328 03705 33	1.00270 01222 00
7	0.15021 32213 86	0.14988 25615 18	0.12041 99724 80	1.00367 03236 95
8	0.17155 68937 68	0.17106 46889 26	0.13752 55282 84	1.00478 66022 51
9	0.19285 49179 44	0.19215 63097 71	0.15459 21830 67	1.00604 76004 79
10	0.21410 18940 45	0.21314 69472 27	0.17161 50856 01	1.00745 17849 83
11	0.23529 25273 95	0.23402 64086 53	0.18858 93888 40	1.00899 74482 16
12	0.25642 16386 53	0.25478 48112 36	0.20551 02504 65	1.01068 27105 37
13	0.27748 41734 92	0.27541 26059 08	0.22237 28334 61	1.01250 55224 93
14	0.29847 52117 91	0.29590 05994 40	0.23917 23067 18	1.01446 36672 90
15	0.31938 99763 08	0.31623 99746 13	0.25590 38456 70	1.01655 47634 79
16	0.34022 38408 08	0.33642 23084 12	0.27256 26329 61	1.01877 62678 36
17	0.36097 23376 28	0.35643 95881 81	0.28914 38591 45	1.02112 54784 37
18	0.38163 11646 61	0.37628 42257 09	0.30564 27234 26	1.02359 95379 27
19	0.40219 61917 51	0.39594 90692 30	0.32205 44344 35	1.02619 54369 82
20	0.42266 34664 78	0.41542 74133 38	0.33837 42110 50	1.02891 00179 47
21	0.44302 92193 42	0.43471 30068 26	0.35459 72832 48	1.03173 99786 59
22	0.46328 98783 35	0.45380 00584 95	0.37071 88930 13	1.03468 18764 48
23	0.48344 20229 03	0.47268 32409 53	0.38673 42952 82	1.03773 21323 04
24	0.50348 24873 11	0.49135 76924 96	0.40263 87589 28	1.04088 70352 10
25	0.52340 82634 11	0.50981 90171 07	0.41842 75678 09	1.04414 27466 44
26	0.54321 65528 23	0.52806 32826 73	0.43409 60218 42	1.04749 53052 22
27	0.56290 47585 56	0.54608 70175 13	0.44963 94381 42	1.05094 06315 05
28	0.58247 04860 71	0.56388 72053 00	0.46505 31521 97	1.05447 45329 43
29	0.60191 15438 11	0.58146 12784 93	0.48033 25191 02	1.05809 27089 55
30	0.62122 59432 20	0.59880 71103 81	0.49547 29148 30	1.06179 07561 48
31	0.64041 18982 70	0.61592 30058 68	0.51046 97375 62	1.06556 41736 60
32	0.65946 78245 26	0.63280 76910 87	0.52531 84090 59	1.06940 83686 15
33	0.67839 23377 62	0.64946 03019 96	0.54001 43760 85	1.07331 86617 03
34	0.69718 42521 74	0.66588 03720 44	0.55455 31118 76	1.07729 02928 57
35	0.71584 25781 93	0.68206 78190 40	0.56893 01176 57	1.08131 84270 34
36	0.73436 65199 45	0.69802 29313 38	0.58314 09242 03	1.08539 81600 88
37	0.75275 54723 79	0.71374 63534 49	0.59718 10934 51	1.08952 45247 24
38	0.77100 90180 83	0.72923 90711 90	0.61104 62201 44	1.09369 24965 40
39	0.78912 69238 32	0.74450 23964 80	0.62473 19335 32	1.09789 70001 31
40	0.80710 91368 78	0.75953 79518 67	0.63823 38991 05	1.10213 29152 58
41	0.82495 57810 23	0.77434 76549 14	0.65154 78203 63	1.10639 50830 78
42	0.84266 71524 90	0.78893 37024 95	0.66466 94406 36	1.11067 83124 20
43	0.86024 37156 28	0.80329 85551 18	0.67759 45449 25	1.11497 73860 99
44	0.87768 60984 69	0.81744 49213 33	0.69031 89617 85	1.11928 70672 68
45	0.89499 50881 56	0.83137 57423 06	0.70283 85652 43	1.12360 21057 93

K = 1.93558 10960 04722   E = 1.30553 90942 97794
K' = 1.78676 91348 85021   E' = 1.39314 02485 23812

r	$u=(r/90)K=F(\phi,k)$	sn u	cn u	dn u
45	0.96779 05480 02	0.78020 60087 10	0.62552 26486 49	0.80174 03630 14
46	0.98929 70046 25	0.79083 47034 08	0.61202 97965 67	0.79560 59045 00
47	1.01080 34612 47	0.80115 14739 76	0.59846 16242 88	0.78952 55947 81
48	1.03230 99178 69	0.81115 93922 01	0.58482 51366 38	0.78350 60590 02
49	1.05381 63744 91	0.82086 17032 54	0.57112 70122 57	0.77755 36965 64
50	1.07532 28311 14	0.83026 18057 97	0.55737 36034 61	0.77167 46805 66
51	1.09682 92877 36	0.83936 32326 40	0.54357 09371 30	0.76587 49580 01
52	1.11833 57443 58	0.84816 96320 02	0.52972 47165 74	0.76016 02506 50
53	1.13984 22009 81	0.85668 47493 93	0.51584 03242 85	0.75453 60566 06
54	1.16134 86576 03	0.86491 24101 49	0.50192 28255 12	0.74900 76523 93
55	1.18285 51142 25	0.87285 65026 48	0.48797 69725 97	0.74358 00955 96
56	1.20436 15708 47	0.88052 09621 96	0.47400 72100 01	0.73825 82279 73
57	1.22586 80274 70	0.88790 97556 27	0.46001 76799 45	0.73304 66789 80
58	1.24737 44840 92	0.89502 68665 90	0.44601 22286 24	0.72794 98696 66
59	1.26888 09407 14	0.90187 62815 40	0.43199 44129 21	0.72297 20168 86
60	1.29038 73973 36	0.90846 19764 30	0.41796 75075 66	0.71811 71377 88
61	1.31189 38539 59	0.91478 79040 82	0.40393 45126 94	0.71338 90545 19
62	1.33340 03105 81	0.92085 79822 49	0.38989 81617 41	0.70879 13991 24
63	1.35490 67672 03	0.92667 60823 33	0.37586 09296 43	0.70432 76185 86
64	1.37641 32238 26	0.93224 60187 62	0.36182 50412 86	0.70000 09799 68
65	1.39791 96804 48	0.93757 15389 96	0.34779 24801 73	0.69581 45756 30
66	1.41942 61370 70	0.94265 63141 50	0.33376 49972 55	0.69177 13284 80
67	1.44093 25936 92	0.94750 39302 15	0.31974 41199 26	0.68787 39972 31
68	1.46243 90503 15	0.95211 78798 50	0.30573 11611 04	0.68412 51816 32
69	1.48394 55069 37	0.95650 15547 29	0.29172 72284 17	0.68052 73276 52
70	1.50545 19635 59	0.96065 82384 22	0.27773 32334 33	0.67708 27325 83
71	1.52695 84201 82	0.96459 10997 72	0.26374 99009 30	0.67379 35500 52
72	1.54846 48768 04	0.96830 31867 77	0.24977 77781 89	0.67066 17949 02
73	1.56997 13334 26	0.97179 74209 18	0.23581 72442 76	0.66768 93479 46
74	1.59147 77900 48	0.97507 65919 33	0.22186 85193 16	0.66487 79605 51
75	1.61298 42466 71	0.97814 33530 20	0.20793 16737 38	0.66222 92590 63
76	1.63449 07032 93	0.98100 02164 18	0.19400 66374 85	0.65974 47490 31
77	1.65599 71599 15	0.98364 95493 88	0.18009 32091 70	0.65742 58192 39
78	1.67750 36165 37	0.98609 35705 34	0.16619 10651 97	0.65527 37455 23
79	1.69901 00731 60	0.98833 43464 74	0.15229 97688 11	0.65328 96943 64
80	1.72051 65297 82	0.99037 37888 26	0.13841 87790 97	0.65147 47262 45
81	1.74202 29864 04	0.99221 36515 02	0.12454 74599 18	0.64982 97987 75
82	1.76352 94430 27	0.99385 55282 92	0.11068 50888 00	0.64835 57695 58
83	1.78503 58996 49	0.99530 08507 17	0.09683 08657 46	0.64705 33988 06
84	1.80654 23562 71	0.99655 08861 51	0.08298 39220 11	0.64592 33516 95
85	1.82804 88128 93	0.99760 67361 85	0.06914 33288 11	0.64496 62004 50
86	1.84955 52695 16	0.99846 93352 38	0.05530 81059 98	0.64418 24261 69
87	1.87106 17261 38	0.99913 94493 94	0.04147 72306 84	0.64357 24203 59
88	1.89256 81827 60	0.99961 76754 57	0.02764 96458 33	0.64313 64862 09
89	1.91407 46393 82	0.99990 44402 30	0.01382 42688 26	0.64287 48395 74
90	1.93558 10960 05	1.00000 00000 00	0.00000 00000 00	0.64278 76096 87

$q = 0.05501\ 99336\ 98829\ 42$
$q' = 0.03326\ 52566\ 95577\ 34$

$D(90) = 1.24728\ 65856\ 97294$
$1/D(90) = 0.80174\ 03630\ 14448$

r	ϕ	$E(\phi,k)$	$A(r)$	$D(r)$
45	0.89499 50881 56	0.83137 57423 06	0.70283 85652 43	1.12360 21057 93
46	0.91217 16262 81	0.84509 41766 19	0.71514 92767 33	1.12791 72446 47
47	0.92921 68041 39	0.85860 35853 69	0.72724 70670 66	1.13222 72263 16
48	0.94613 18579 25	0.87190 75175 91	0.73912 79584 28	1.13652 67992 02
49	0.96291 81638 89	0.88500 96960 94	0.75078 80263 86	1.14081 07240 24
50	0.97957 72334 80	0.89791 40037 03	0.76222 34019 28	1.14507 37802 12
51	0.99611 07084 72	0.91062 44699 91	0.77343 02735 05	1.14931 07722 63
52	1.01252 03561 16	0.92314 52584 85	0.78440 48890 95	1.15351 65360 90
53	1.02880 80643 11	0.93548 06544 15	0.79514 35582 72	1.15768 59453 14
54	1.03497 58368 11	0.94763 50529 89	0.80564 26542 83	1.16181 39175 26
55	1.06102 57884 92	0.95961 29482 29	0.81589 86161 27	1.16589 54204 92
56	1.07696 01406 71	0.97141 89223 85	0.82590 79506 35	1.16992 54782 96
57	1.09278 12165 08	0.98305 76359 09	0.83566 72345 44	1.17389 91774 19
58	1.10849 14364 75	0.99453 38180 18	0.84517 31165 69	1.17781 16727 43
59	1.12409 33139 23	1.00585 22578 39	0.85442 23194 58	1.18165 81934 73
60	1.13958 94507 38	1.01701 77961 19	0.86341 16420 39	1.18543 40489 66
61	1.15498 25330 92	1.02803 53175 18	0.87213 79612 45	1.18913 46344 70
62	1.17027 53273 08	1.03890 97434 55	0.88059 82341 21	1.19275 54367 56
63	1.18547 06758 19	1.04964 60255 15	0.88878 94998 06	1.19629 20396 36
64	1.20057 14932 49	1.06024 91393 90	0.89670 88814 86	1.19974 01293 69
65	1.21558 07625 96	1.07072 40793 51	0.90435 35883 20	1.20309 54999 41
66	1.23050 15315 32	1.08107 58532 24	0.91172 09173 21	1.20635 40582 12
67	1.24533 69088 16	1.09130 94778 75	0.91880 82552 11	1.20951 18289 31
68	1.26009 00608 17	1.10142 99751 51	0.92561 30802 29	1.21256 49596 01
69	1.27476 42081 54	1.11144 23683 04	0.93213 29638 89	1.21550 97252 02
70	1.28936 26224 41	1.12135 16788 34	0.93836 55726 99	1.21834 25327 52
71	1.30388 86231 47	1.13116 29237 65	0.94430 86698 23	1.22105 99257 10
72	1.31834 55745 55	1.14088 11133 18	0.94996 01166 90	1.22365 85882 14
73	1.33273 68828 30	1.15051 12489 60	0.95531 78745 45	1.22613 53491 47
74	1.34706 59931 89	1.16005 83218 21	0.96038 00059 40	1.22848 71860 22
75	1.36133 63871 60	1.16952 73114 41	0.96514 46761 59	1.23071 12286 90
76	1.37555 15799 44	1.17892 31848 46	0.96961 01545 83	1.23280 47628 61
77	1.38971 51178 56	1.18825 08959 14	0.97377 48159 83	1.23476 52334 33
78	1.40383 05758 58	1.19751 53850 24	0.97763 71417 36	1.23659 02476 24
79	1.41790 15551 72	1.20672 15789 62	0.98119 57209 79	1.23827 75779 14
80	1.43193 16809 56	1.21587 43910 67	0.98444 92516 78	1.23982 51647 73
81	1.44592 46000 67	1.22497 87215 95	0.98739 65416 24	1.24123 11191 91
82	1.45988 39788 76	1.23403 94582 81	0.99003 65093 44	1.24249 37249 95
83	1.47381 35011 46	1.24306 14770 85	0.99236 81849 39	1.24361 14409 58
84	1.48771 68659 63	1.25204 96430 98	0.99439 07108 32	1.24458 29026 90
85	1.50159 77857 16	1.26100 88115 89	0.99610 33424 32	1.24540 69243 11
86	1.51545 99841 18	1.26994 38291 80	0.99750 54487 12	1.24608 24999 12
87	1.52930 71942 62	1.27885 95351 24	0.99859 65127 05	1.24660 88047 84
88	1.54314 31567 11	1.28776 07626 75	0.99937 61319 04	1.24698 51964 35
89	1.55697 16176 04	1.29665 23405 25	0.99984 40185 78	1.24721 12153 79
90	1.57079 63267 95	1.30553 90942 98	1.00000 00000 00	1.24728 65856 97

ELLIPTIC FUNCTIONS   TABLE $\theta = 51°$

K = 1.95386 48092 51663   E = 1.29627 80079 94134
K'= 1.77478 59091 05608   E'= 1.40125 97507 85523

r	u=(r/90)K=F(φ,k)	sn u	cn u	dn u
0	0.00000 00000 00	0.00000 00000 00	1.00000 00000 00	1.00000 00000 00
1	0.02170 96089 92	0.02170 68741 35	0.99976 43780 49	0.99985 77013 86
2	0.04341 92179 83	0.04339 73485 97	0.99905 78912 83	0.99943 11141 44
3	0.06512 88269 75	0.06505 50709 68	0.99788 16752 21	0.99872 11627 20
4	0.08683 84359 67	0.08666 37830 46	0.99623 76165 90	0.99772 93833 54
5	0.10854 80449 58	0.10820 73672 06	0.99412 83446 73	0.99645 79173 61
6	0.13025 76539 50	0.12966 98918 80	0.99155 72192 97	0.99490 95018 08
7	0.15196 72629 42	0.15103 56558 79	0.98852 83155 55	0.99308 74576 59
8	0.17367 68719 33	0.17228 92312 74	0.98504 64053 98	0.99099 56754 81
9	0.19538 64809 25	0.19341 55046 05	0.98111 69362 41	0.98863 85988 42
10	0.21709 60899 17	0.21439 97161 64	0.97674 60067 53	0.98602 12055 21
11	0.23880 56989 09	0.23522 74971 49	0.97194 03400 34	0.98314 89866 80
12	0.26051 53079 00	0.25588 49044 88	0.96670 72543 72	0.98002 79241 78
13	0.28222 49168 92	0.27635 84531 70	0.96105 46318 30	0.97666 44661 81
14	0.30393 45258 84	0.29663 51459 25	0.95499 08848 79	0.97306 55012 64
15	0.32564 41348 75	0.31670 25001 38	0.94852 49213 42	0.96923 83312 04
16	0.34735 37438 67	0.33654 85719 05	0.94166 61078 90	0.96519 06426 46
17	0.36906 33528 59	0.35616 19771 55	0.93442 42323 64	0.96093 04778 55
18	0.39077 29618 50	0.37553 19097 93	0.92680 94651 69	0.95646 62047 57
19	0.41248 25708 42	0.39464 81568 46	0.91883 23200 12	0.95180 64864 57
20	0.43419 21798 34	0.41350 11106 21	0.91050 36142 24	0.94696 02504 47
21	0.45590 17888 25	0.43208 17778 99	0.90183 44289 32	0.94193 66576 90
22	0.47761 13978 17	0.45038 17862 08	0.89283 60693 05	0.93674 50717 57
23	0.49932 10068 09	0.46839 33872 66	0.88352 00251 07	0.93139 50282 12
24	0.52103 06158 00	0.48610 94576 55	0.87389 79317 85	0.92589 62044 01
25	0.54274 02247 92	0.50352 34968 61	0.86398 15322 73	0.92025 83897 97
26	0.56444 98337 84	0.52062 96227 74	0.85378 26397 22	0.91449 14570 68
27	0.58615 94427 75	0.53742 25648 06	0.84331 31013 08	0.90860 53339 66
28	0.60786 90517 67	0.55389 76547 52	0.83258 47632 89	0.90260 99761 98
29	0.62957 86607 59	0.57005 08155 61	0.82160 94374 33	0.89651 53413 42
30	0.65128 82697 51	0.58587 85481 71	0.81039 88689 49	0.89033 13639 36
31	0.67299 78787 42	0.60137 79165 75	0.79896 47060 14	0.88406 79317 94
32	0.69470 74877 34	0.61654 65312 88	0.78731 84709 86	0.87773 48636 24
33	0.71641 70967 26	0.63138 25313 86	0.77547 15333 66	0.87134 18880 04
34	0.73812 67057 17	0.64588 45652 77	0.76343 50845 60	0.86489 86237 41
35	0.75983 63147 09	0.66005 17703 88	0.75122 01144 86	0.85841 45616 45
36	0.78154 59237 01	0.67388 37519 16	0.73883 73900 28	0.85189 90477 46
37	0.80325 55326 92	0.68738 05608 20	0.72629 74353 58	0.84536 12679 29
38	0.82496 51416 84	0.70054 26711 83	0.71361 05141 12	0.83881 02340 12
39	0.84667 47506 76	0.71337 09571 26	0.70078 66134 06	0.83225 47712 18
40	0.86838 43596 67	0.72586 66693 81	0.68783 54296 50	0.82570 35070 53
41	0.89009 39686 59	0.73803 14116 77	0.67476 63561 40	0.81916 48615 20
42	0.91180 35776 51	0.74986 71170 58	0.66158 84723 57	0.81264 70386 57
43	0.93351 31866 42	0.76137 60242 42	0.64831 05349 37	0.80615 80193 44
44	0.95522 27956 34	0.77256 06541 34	0.63494 09702 36	0.79970 55553 26
45	0.97693 24046 26	0.78342 37865 91	0.62148 78684 28	0.79329 71644 03

202

q = 0.05763 33361 79494 01   D(90) = 1.26056 16720 59622
q'= 0.03147 42771 20285 85   1/D(90) = 0.79329 71644 02998

r	ϕ	$E(\phi, k)$	$A(r)$	$D(r)$
0	0.00000 00000 00	0.00000 00000 00	0.00000 00000 00	1.00000 00000 00
1	0.02170 85791 68	0.02170 75494 32	0.01722 13672 94	1.00007 93028 12
2	0.04341 09820 75	0.04340 27489 79	0.03443 79108 96	1.00031 71148 52
3	0.06510 10458 50	0.06507 32860 47	0.05164 48074 24	1.00071 31470 46
4	0.08677 26343 40	0.08670 69224 03	0.06883 72341 28	1.00126 69179 97
5	0.10841 96513 28	0.10829 15307 77	0.08601 03692 05	1.00197 77545 56
6	0.13003 60535 68	0.12981 51307 75	0.10315 93921 32	1.00284 47926 45
7	0.15161 58636 00	0.15126 59239 06	0.12027 94840 13	1.00386 69782 95
8	0.17315 31822 67	0.17263 23274 86	0.13736 58279 32	1.00504 30689 17
9	0.19464 22009 12	0.19390 30072 47	0.15441 36093 31	1.00637 16348 06
10	0.21607 72131 81	0.21506 69084 62	0.17141 80164 09	1.00785 10608 66
11	0.23745 26263 98	0.23611 32854 12	0.18837 42405 42	1.00947 95485 60
12	0.25876 29724 66	0.25703 17290 53	0.20527 74767 30	1.01125 51180 82
13	0.28000 29182 58	0.27781 21927 55	0.22212 29240 77	1.01317 56107 49
14	0.30116 72754 65	0.29844 50159 88	0.23890 57862 93	1.01523 86916 09
15	0.32225 10098 62	0.31892 09458 69	0.25562 12722 45	1.01744 18522 61
16	0.34324 92499 70	0.33923 11564 93	0.27226 45965 32	1.01978 24138 87
17	0.36415 72951 00	0.35936 72660 02	0.28883 09801 03	1.02225 75304 89
18	0.38497 06227 46	0.37932 13513 43	0.30531 56509 15	1.02486 41923 29
19	0.40568 48953 28	0.39908 59607 20	0.32171 38446 40	1.02759 92295 67
20	0.42629 59662 61	0.41865 41237 26	0.33802 08054 07	1.03045 93160 95
21	0.44679 98853 66	0.43801 93591 88	0.35423 17865 97	1.03344 09735 60
22	0.46719 29035 98	0.45717 56807 70	0.37034 20516 82	1.03654 05755 70
23	0.48747 14771 13	0.47611 76003 70	0.38634 68751 20	1.03975 43520 82
24	0.50763 22706 75	0.49484 01294 07	0.40224 15432 90	1.04307 83939 63
25	0.52767 21604 10	0.51333 87780 56	0.41802 13554 90	1.04650 86577 27
26	0.54758 82359 22	0.53160 95525 43	0.43368 16249 81	1.05004 09704 22
27	0.56737 78017 96	0.54964 89506 03	0.44921 76800 84	1.05367 10346 92
28	0.58703 83784 97	0.56745 39552 06	0.46462 48653 35	1.05739 44339 76
29	0.60656 77026 90	0.58502 20266 78	0.47989 85426 89	1.06120 66378 62
30	0.62596 37270 09	0.60235 10933 40	0.49503 40927 88	1.06510 30075 76
31	0.64522 46192 98	0.61943 95408 01	0.51002 69162 68	1.06907 88016 09
32	0.66434 87613 50	0.63628 62000 25	0.52487 24351 37	1.07312 91814 62
33	0.68333 47471 77	0.65289 03343 17	0.53956 60941 98	1.07724 92175 16
34	0.70218 13808 38	0.66925 16253 53	0.55410 33625 23	1.08143 38950 13
35	0.72088 76738 55	0.68537 01583 90	0.56847 97349 91	1.08567 81201 45
36	0.73945 28422 47	0.70124 64067 82	0.58269 07338 65	1.08997 67262 31
37	0.75787 63032 23	0.71688 12159 24	0.59673 19104 29	1.09432 44800 00
38	0.77615 76715 45	0.73227 57867 57	0.61059 88466 70	1.09871 60879 38
39	0.79429 67556 18	0.74743 16589 34	0.62428 71570 14	1.10314 62027 29
40	0.81229 35533 08	0.76235 06937 72	0.63779 24900 98	1.10760 94297 47
41	0.83014 82475 48	0.77703 50570 76	0.65111 05306 00	1.11210 03336 21
42	0.84786 12017 33	0.79148 72019 61	0.66423 70011 01	1.11661 34448 42
43	0.86543 29549 56	0.80570 98517 25	0.67716 76639 95	1.12114 32664 17
44	0.88286 42170 94	0.81970 59828 90	0.68989 83234 34	1.12568 42805 61
45	0.90015 58637 79	0.83347 88084 72	0.70242 48273 12	1.13023 09554 13

203

K = 1.95386 48092 51663   E = 1.29627 80079 94134
K'= 1.77478 59091 05608   E'= 1.40125 97507 85523

r	u=(r/90)K=F(φ,k)	sn u	cn u	dn u
45	0.97693 24046 26	0.78342 37865 91	0.62148 78684 28	0.79329 71644 03
46	0.99864 20136 18	0.79396 84375 17	0.60795 89790 66	0.78694 01267 24
47	1.02035 16226 09	0.80419 78363 80	0.59436 17080 21	0.78064 14821 28
48	1.04206 12316 01	0.81411 54042 11	0.58070 31157 37	0.77440 80284 72
49	1.06377 08405 93	0.82372 47321 47	0.56698 99167 09	0.76824 63208 72
50	1.08548 04495 84	0.83302 95605 80	0.55322 84801 06	0.76216 26717 99
51	1.10719 00585 76	0.84203 37589 41	0.53942 48314 67	0.75616 31519 74
52	1.12889 96675 68	0.85074 13061 70	0.52558 46553 85	0.75025 35919 72
53	1.15060 92765 59	0.85915 62718 94	0.51171 32990 90	0.74443 95845 00
54	1.17231 88855 51	0.86728 27983 35	0.49781 57768 82	0.73872 64872 70
55	1.19402 84945 43	0.87512 50829 74	0.48389 67753 03	0.73311 94264 04
56	1.21573 81035 34	0.88268 73619 69	0.46996 06590 14	0.72762 33003 22
57	1.23744 77125 26	0.88997 38943 36	0.45601 14772 67	0.72224 27840 48
58	1.25915 73215 18	0.89698 89469 08	0.44205 29709 49	0.71698 23338 81
59	1.28086 69305 09	0.90373 67800 38	0.42808 85800 93	0.71184 61923 77
60	1.30257 65395 01	0.91022 16340 73	0.41412 14518 29	0.70683 83935 93
61	1.32428 61484 93	0.91644 77165 58	0.40015 44487 01	0.70196 27685 43
62	1.34599 57574 84	0.92241 91901 75	0.38619 01573 02	0.69722 29508 26
63	1.36770 53664 76	0.92814 01613 91	0.37223 08971 77	0.69262 23823 74
64	1.38941 49754 68	0.93361 46697 97	0.35827 87299 59	0.68816 43192 90
65	1.41112 45844 60	0.93884 66781 20	0.34433 54686 69	0.68385 18377 30
66	1.43283 41934 51	0.94384 00628 83	0.33040 26871 81	0.67968 78398 02
67	1.45454 38024 43	0.94859 86056 88	0.31648 17297 82	0.67567 50594 40
68	1.47625 34114 35	0.95312 59850 99	0.30257 37208 17	0.67181 60682 39
69	1.49796 30204 26	0.95742 57691 00	0.28867 95743 78	0.66811 32811 98
70	1.51967 26294 18	0.96150 14081 05	0.27480 00040 26	0.66456 89623 75
71	1.54138 22384 10	0.96535 62284 84	0.26093 55325 13	0.66118 52304 06
72	1.56309 18474 01	0.96899 34265 95	0.24708 65014 85	0.65796 40638 84
73	1.58480 14563 93	0.97241 60632 82	0.23325 30811 60	0.65490 73065 66
74	1.60651 10653 85	0.97562 70588 25	0.21943 52799 54	0.65201 66724 00
75	1.62822 06743 76	0.97862 91883 06	0.20563 29540 59	0.64929 37503 49
76	1.64993 02833 68	0.98142 50773 85	0.19184 58169 47	0.64674 00090 05
77	1.67163 98923 60	0.98401 71984 42	0.17807 34488 06	0.64435 68009 70
78	1.69334 95013 51	0.98640 78670 84	0.16431 53059 04	0.64214 53670 08
79	1.71505 91103 43	0.98859 92389 78	0.15057 07298 66	0.64010 68399 36
80	1.73676 87193 35	0.99059 33070 04	0.13683 89568 72	0.63824 22482 66
81	1.75847 83283 26	0.99239 18987 07	0.12311 91267 83	0.63655 25195 83
82	1.78018 79373 18	0.99399 66740 22	0.10941 02921 76	0.63503 84836 39
83	1.80189 75463 10	0.99540 91232 66	0.09571 14273 14	0.63370 08751 81
84	1.82360 71553 02	0.99663 05653 88	0.08202 14370 42	0.63254 03364 89
85	1.84531 67642 93	0.99766 21464 42	0.06833 91656 16	0.63155 74196 22
86	1.86702 63732 85	0.99850 48382 97	0.05466 34054 75	0.63075 25883 77
87	1.88873 59822 77	0.99915 94375 58	0.04099 29059 58	0.63012 62199 51
88	1.91044 55912 68	0.99962 65646 97	0.02732 63819 82	0.62967 86063 03
89	1.93215 52002 60	0.99990 66633 81	0.01366 25226 77	0.62940 99552 14
90	1.95386 48092 52	1.00000 00000 00	0.00000 00000 00	0.62932 03910 50

ELLIPTIC FUNCTIONS TABLE $\theta = 51°$

q = 0.05763 33361 79494 01   D(90) = 1.26056 16720 59622
q'= 0.03147 42771 20285 85   1/D(90) = 0.79329 71644 02998

r	ϕ	$E(\phi,k)$	A(r)	D(r)
45	0.90015 58637 79	0.83347 88084 72	0.70242 48273 12	1.13023 09554 13
46	0.91730 89312 78	0.84703 17615 45	0.71474 30692 79	1.13477 77517 72
47	0.93432 46113 03	0.86036 84791 74	0.72684 89907 92	1.13931 91298 44
48	0.95120 42457 73	0.87349 27867 59	0.73873 85831 86	1.14384 95559 96
49	0.96794 93215 51	0.88640 86828 56	0.75040 78897 79	1.14836 35094 96
50	0.98456 14651 75	0.89912 03244 88	0.76185 30079 94	1.15285 54892 49
51	1.00104 24375 99	0.91163 20130 16	0.77307 00915 02	1.15732 00205 04
52	1.01739 41289 57	0.92394 81805 73	0.78405 53523 77	1.16175 16615 35
53	1.03361 85533 77	0.93607 33770 95	0.79480 50632 73	1.16614 50102 81
54	1.04971 78438 48	0.94801 22579 72	0.80531 55596 00	1.17049 47109 45
55	1.06569 42471 49	0.95976 95723 20	0.81558 32417 10	1.17479 54605 29
56	1.08155 01188 68	0.97135 01518 93	0.82560 45770 85	1.17904 20153 17
57	1.09728 79185 03	0.98275 89006 41	0.83537 61025 24	1.18322 91972 80
58	1.11291 02046 60	0.99400 07849 03	0.84489 44263 20	1.18735 19004 07
59	1.12841 96303 62	1.00508 08242 46	0.85415 62304 34	1.19140 50969 47
60	1.14381 89384 63	1.01600 40829 31	0.86315 82726 54	1.19538 38435 59
61	1.15911 09571 81	1.02677 56620 15	0.87189 73887 33	1.19928 32873 58
62	1.17429 85957 48	1.03740 06920 53	0.88037 04945 15	1.20309 86718 59
63	1.18938 48401 93	1.04788 43264 12	0.88857 45880 25	1.20682 53427 93
64	1.20437 27492 37	1.05823 17351 67	0.89650 67515 43	1.21045 87538 07
65	1.21926 54503 28	1.06844 80995 58	0.90416 41536 40	1.21399 44720 38
66	1.23406 61357 96	1.07853 86070 11	0.91154 40511 74	1.21742 81835 36
67	1.24877 80591 36	1.08850 84466 75	0.91864 37912 57	1.22075 56985 53
68	1.26340 45314 26	1.09836 28054 82	0.92546 08131 67	1.22397 29566 81
69	1.27794 89178 61	1.10810 68646 85	0.93199 26502 26	1.22707 60318 27
70	1.29241 46344 16	1.11774 57968 72	0.93823 69316 16	1.23006 11370 26
71	1.30680 51446 30	1.12728 47634 19	0.94419 13841 45	1.23292 46290 90
72	1.32112 39565 06	1.13672 89123 75	0.94985 38339 64	1.23566 30130 72
73	1.33537 46195 29	1.14608 33767 36	0.95522 22082 06	1.23827 29465 62
74	1.34956 07217 95	1.15535 32731 11	0.96029 45365 80	1.24075 12437 79
75	1.36368 58872 41	1.16454 37007 31	0.96506 89528 86	1.24309 48794 90
76	1.37775 37729 87	1.17365 97408 04	0.96954 36964 63	1.24530 09927 21
77	1.39176 80667 68	1.18270 64561 71	0.97371 71135 67	1.24736 68902 68
78	1.40573 24844 62	1.19168 88912 63	0.97758 76586 70	1.24929 00500 08
79	1.41965 07677 07	1.20061 20723 20	0.98115 38956 85	1.25106 81239 96
80	1.43352 66815 92	1.20948 10078 60	0.98441 44991 03	1.25269 89413 46
81	1.44736 40124 37	1.21830 06893 71	0.98736 82550 60	1.25418 05109 04
82	1.46116 65656 28	1.22707 60922 23	0.99001 40623 06	1.25551 10236 88
83	1.47493 81635 32	1.23581 21767 46	0.99235 09330 95	1.25668 88551 18
84	1.48868 26434 57	1.24451 38894 95	0.99437 79939 82	1.25771 25670 08
85	1.50240 38556 73	1.25318 61646 48	0.99609 44865 36	1.25858 09093 34
86	1.51615 41428 41	1.26183 39255 41	0.99749 97679 55	1.25929 28217 73
87	1.52979 19312 75	1.27046 20863 06	0.99859 33115 90	1.25984 74350 02
88	1.54346 65427 60	1.27907 55536 06	0.99937 47073 78	1.26024 40717 73
89	1.55713 33790 30	1.28767 92284 39	0.99984 36621 75	1.26048 22477 41
90	1.57079 63267 95	1.29627 80079 94	1.00000 00000 00	1.26056 16720 60

205

ELLIPTIC FUNCTIONS   TABLE $\theta = 52°$

K = 1.97288 22662 74650

K′= 1.76325 61840 59342

E = 1.28695 37387 83001

E′= 1.40923 97160 46096

r	u=(r/90)K=F(ϕ,k)	sn u	cn u	dn u
0	0.00000 00000 00	0.00000 00000 00	1.00000 00000 00	1.00000 00000 00
1	0.02192 09140 70	0.02191 80687 41	0.99975 97702 76	0.99985 08335 16
2	0.04384 18281 39	0.04381 90757 07	0.99903 94830 06	0.99940 36650 96
3	0.06576 27422 09	0.06568 60100 29	0.99784 03419 82	0.99865 94863 41
4	0.08768 36562 79	0.08750 19623 15	0.99616 43471 79	0.99761 99449 19
5	0.10960 45703 49	0.10925 01745 71	0.99401 42852 88	0.99628 73371 23
6	0.13152 54844 18	0.13091 40891 22	0.99139 37165 77	0.99466 45975 32
7	0.15344 63984 88	0.15247 73962 64	0.98830 69582 01	0.99275 52858 75
8	0.17536 73125 58	0.17392 40803 09	0.98475 90640 80	0.99056 35711 99
9	0.19728 82266 27	0.19523 84637 74	0.98075 58015 44	0.98809 42134 94
10	0.21920 91406 97	0.21640 52494 41	0.97630 36249 11	0.98535 25429 00
11	0.24113 00547 67	0.23740 95600 55	0.97140 96462 33	0.98234 44366 94
12	0.26305 09688 37	0.25823 69754 47	0.96608 16034 44	0.97907 62942 23
13	0.28497 18829 06	0.27887 35668 97	0.96032 78261 54	0.97555 50099 95
14	0.30689 27969 76	0.29930 59285 78	0.95415 71993 75	0.97178 79451 34
15	0.32881 37110 46	0.31952 12059 52	0.94757 91254 28	0.96778 28974 18
16	0.35073 46251 15	0.33950 71210 16	0.94060 34843 54	0.96354 80701 21
17	0.37265 55391 85	0.35925 19943 28	0.93324 05930 79	0.95909 20398 97
18	0.39457 64532 55	0.37874 47637 70	0.92550 11636 49	0.95442 37239 17
19	0.41649 73673 25	0.39797 50000 31	0.91739 62608 11	0.94955 23465 00
20	0.43841 82813 94	0.41693 29188 22	0.90893 72592 22	0.94448 74054 48
21	0.46033 91954 64	0.43560 93898 71	0.90013 58005 63	0.93923 86383 09
22	0.48226 01095 34	0.45399 59427 47	0.89100 37508 16	0.93381 59887 71
23	0.50418 10236 04	0.47208 47696 04	0.88155 31579 59	0.92822 95733 77
24	0.52610 19376 73	0.48986 87249 54	0.87179 62103 10	0.92248 96487 63
25	0.54802 28517 43	0.50734 13225 92	0.86174 51957 46	0.91660 65795 72
26	0.56994 37658 13	0.52449 67298 00	0.85141 24619 88	0.91059 08072 14
27	0.59186 46798 82	0.54132 97590 13	0.84081 03781 51	0.90445 28196 16
28	0.61378 55939 52	0.55783 58570 73	0.82995 12977 06	0.89820 31220 85
29	0.63570 65080 22	0.57401 10922 86	0.81884 75230 05	0.89185 22093 96
30	0.65762 74220 92	0.58985 21394 29	0.80751 12715 07	0.88541 05392 13
31	0.67954 83361 61	0.60535 62629 16	0.79595 46437 76	0.87888 85069 13
32	0.70146 92502 31	0.62052 12982 99	0.78418 95933 75	0.87229 64218 77
33	0.72339 01643 01	0.63534 56322 99	0.77222 78986 92	0.86564 44853 17
34	0.74531 10783 70	0.64982 81815 52	0.76008 11367 61	0.85894 27696 49
35	0.76723 19924 40	0.66396 83702 55	0.74776 06591 02	0.85220 11994 64
36	0.78915 29065 10	0.67776 61068 91	0.73527 75695 95	0.84542 95340 77
37	0.81107 38205 80	0.69122 17602 15	0.72264 27043 88	0.83863 73516 72
38	0.83299 47346 49	0.70433 61346 54	0.70986 66138 23	0.83183 40350 29
39	0.85491 56487 19	0.71711 04453 01	0.69695 95463 44	0.82502 87587 90
40	0.87683 65627 89	0.72954 62926 27	0.68393 14343 66	0.81823 04782 58
41	0.89875 74768 58	0.74164 56370 88	0.67079 18820 23	0.81144 79196 63
42	0.92067 83909 28	0.75341 07737 18	0.65755 01547 76	0.80468 95718 65
43	0.94259 93049 98	0.76484 43068 67	0.64421 51707 72	0.79796 36794 27
44	0.96452 02190 68	0.77594 91251 73	0.63079 54939 15	0.79127 82370 05
45	0.98644 11331 37	0.78672 83768 71	0.61729 93285 48	0.78464 09849 90

q = 0.06033 83890 33716 41   D(90) = 1.27446 82206 64111
q′= 0.02974 53239 19583 19   1/D(90) = 0.78464 09849 89733

r	ϕ	$E(\phi,k)$	A(r)	D(r)
0	0.00000 00000 00	0.00000 00000 00	0.00000 00000 00	1.00000 00000 00
1	0.02191 98240 34	0.02191 87340 96	0.01719 92515 09	1.00008 35258 76
2	0.04383 31107 55	0.04382 43964 91	0.03439 37264 62	1.00033 40020 08
3	0.06573 33373 55	0.06570 39561 58	0.05157 86484 93	1.00075 11240 34
4	0.08761 40099 61	0.08754 44631 51	0.06874 92416 12	1.00133 43850 89
5	0.10946 86779 45	0.10933 30884 96	0.08590 07304 05	1.00208 30764 19
6	0.13129 09480 35	0.13105 71633 17	0.10302 83402 43	1.00299 62882 36
7	0.15307 44981 64	0.15270 42169 37	0.12012 72975 02	1.00407 29108 11
8	0.17481 30910 08	0.17426 20137 40	0.13719 28298 00	1.00531 16358 16
9	0.19650 05871 46	0.19571 85885 64	0.15422 01662 61	1.00671 09578 99
10	0.21813 09577 86	0.21706 22804 20	0.17120 45377 88	1.00826 91765 00
11	0.23969 82970 24	0.23828 17643 67	0.18814 11773 80	1.00998 43979 03
12	0.26119 68335 55	0.25936 60813 49	0.20502 53204 63	1.01185 45375 20
13	0.28262 09418 37	0.28030 46658 81	0.22185 22052 65	1.01387 73224 04
14	0.30396 51526 26	0.30108 73714 32	0.23861 70732 18	1.01605 02939 91
15	0.32522 41628 83	0.32170 44934 22	0.25531 51694 04	1.01837 08110 71
16	0.34639 28450 07	0.34214 67897 45	0.27194 17430 37	1.02083 60529 70
17	0.36746 62553 71	0.36240 54987 64	0.28849 20479 91	1.02344 30229 60
18	0.38843 96421 49	0.38247 23547 51	0.30496 13433 75	1.02618 85518 71
19	0.40930 84524 16	0.40233 96007 48	0.32134 48941 49	1.02906 93019 24
20	0.43006 83385 11	0.42199 99988 81	0.33763 79717 98	1.03208 17707 59
21	0.45071 51636 64	0.44144 68381 32	0.35383 58550 53	1.03522 22956 67
22	0.47124 50068 78	0.46067 39396 41	0.36993 38306 67	1.03848 70580 15
23	0.49165 41670 91	0.47967 56595 99	0.38592 71942 45	1.04187 20878 61
24	0.51193 91665 94	0.49844 68898 02	0.40181 12511 28	1.04537 32687 57
25	0.53209 67537 60	0.51698 30559 99	0.41758 13173 43	1.04898 63427 22
26	0.55212 39050 58	0.53528 01141 00	0.43323 27206 05	1.05270 69153 95
27	0.57201 78264 08	0.55333 45444 11	0.44876 08013 75	1.05653 04613 51
28	0.59177 59538 77	0.57114 33439 90	0.46416 09139 91	1.06045 23295 78
29	0.61139 59537 53	0.58870 40172 88	0.47942 84278 43	1.06446 77491 09
30	0.63087 57220 20	0.60601 45652 07	0.49455 87286 28	1.06857 18347 96
31	0.65021 33832 64	0.62307 34727 25	0.50954 72196 45	1.07275 95932 31
32	0.66940 72890 47	0.63987 96952 33	0.52438 93231 72	1.07702 59287 96
33	0.68845 60157 76	0.65643 26437 47	0.53908 04818 84	1.08136 56498 36
34	0.70735 83621 04	0.67273 21691 28	0.55361 61603 50	1.08577 34749 61
35	0.72611 33458 89	0.68877 85454 66	0.56799 18465 70	1.09024 40394 44
36	0.74472 02007 70	0.70457 24527 71	0.58220 30535 89	1.09477 19017 36
37	0.76317 83723 57	0.72011 49591 06	0.59624 53211 55	1.09935 15500 66
38	0.78148 75141 07	0.73540 75022 94	0.61011 42174 36	1.10397 74091 38
39	0.79964 74828 96	0.75045 18713 36	0.62380 53407 99	1.10864 38468 99
40	0.81765 83343 33	0.76525 01876 48	0.63731 43216 31	1.11334 51813 83
41	0.83552 03178 40	0.77980 48862 34	0.65063 68242 15	1.11807 56876 19
42	0.85323 38715 38	0.79411 86969 05	0.66376 85486 62	1.12282 96045 89
43	0.87079 96169 66	0.80819 46256 29	0.67670 52328 75	1.12760 11422 37
44	0.88821 83536 62	0.82203 59361 21	0.68944 26545 72	1.13238 44885 15
45	0.91979 30572 25	0.83564 61317 29	0.70197 66333 41	1.13717 38164 57

K = 1.97288 22662 74650   E = 1.28695 37387 83001
K'= 1.76325 61840 59342   E'= 1.40923 97160 46096

r	u=(r/90)K=F(ϕ,k)	sn u	cn u	dn u
45	0.98644 11331 37	0.78672 83768 71	0.61729 93285 48	0.78464 09849 90
46	1.00836 20472 07	0.79718 54455 42	0.60373 45156 74	0.77805 94063 29
47	1.03028 29612 77	0.80732 39263 65	0.59010 85306 26	0.77154 07244 69
48	1.05220 38753 46	0.81714 76029 59	0.57642 84821 01	0.76509 19023 33
49	1.07412 47894 16	0.82666 04248 64	0.56270 11124 61	0.75871 96422 68
50	1.09604 57034 86	0.83586 64857 14	0.54893 27992 20	0.75243 03868 96
51	1.11796 66175 56	0.84477 00021 59	0.53512 95576 32	0.74623 03207 81
52	1.13988 75316 25	0.85337 52935 44	0.52129 70442 73	0.74012 53728 51
53	1.16180 84456 95	0.86168 67623 98	0.50744 05615 52	0.73412 12194 97
54	1.18372 93597 65	0.86970 88757 35	0.49356 50630 54	0.72822 32882 93
55	1.20565 02738 35	0.87744 61471 92	0.47967 51596 43	0.72243 67622 49
56	1.22757 11879 04	0.88490 31199 97	0.46577 51262 36	0.71676 65845 50
57	1.24949 21019 74	0.89208 43507 82	0.45186 89091 86	0.71121 74637 15
58	1.27141 30160 44	0.89899 43942 30	0.43796 01341 93	0.70579 38791 04
59	1.29333 39301 13	0.90563 77885 42	0.42405 21146 80	0.70050 00867 38
60	1.31525 48441 83	0.91201 90417 25	0.41014 78605 71	0.69534 01253 53
61	1.33717 57582 53	0.91814 26186 75	0.39625 00874 11	0.69031 78226 61
62	1.35909 66723 23	0.92401 29290 35	0.38236 12257 75	0.68543 68017 52
63	1.38101 75863 92	0.92963 43158 16	0.36848 34309 13	0.68070 04876 02
64	1.40293 85004 62	0.93501 10447 45	0.35461 85925 82	0.67611 21136 39
65	1.42485 94145 32	0.94014 72943 26	0.34076 83450 26	0.67167 47283 37
66	1.44678 03286 01	0.94504 71465 77	0.32693 40770 66	0.66739 12017 89
67	1.46870 12426 71	0.94971 45784 23	0.31311 69422 62	0.66326 42322 37
68	1.49062 21567 41	0.95415 34537 11	0.29931 78691 14	0.65929 63525 24
69	1.51254 30708 11	0.95836 75158 25	0.28553 75712 79	0.65548 99364 38
70	1.53446 39848 80	0.96236 03808 58	0.27177 65577 74	0.65184 72049 22
71	1.55638 48989 50	0.96613 55313 29	0.25803 51431 54	0.64837 02321 36
72	1.57830 58130 20	0.96969 63104 09	0.24431 34576 30	0.64506 09513 34
73	1.60022 67270 89	0.97304 59166 15	0.23061 14571 29	0.64192 11605 51
74	1.62214 76411 59	0.97618 73989 71	0.21692 89332 72	0.63895 25280 75
75	1.64406 85552 29	0.97912 36525 84	0.20326 55232 69	0.63615 65976 92
76	1.66598 94692 99	0.98185 74146 26	0.18962 07197 10	0.63353 47936 84
77	1.68791 03833 68	0.98439 12606 82	0.17599 38802 69	0.63108 84255 81
78	1.70983 12974 38	0.98672 76014 58	0.16238 42372 91	0.62881 86926 37
79	1.73175 22115 08	0.98886 86798 10	0.14879 09072 83	0.62672 66880 42
80	1.75367 31255 77	0.99081 65680 86	0.13521 29002 96	0.62481 34028 39
81	1.77559 40396 47	0.99257 31657 48	0.12164 91292 08	0.62307 97295 62
82	1.79751 49537 17	0.99414 01972 70	0.10809 84189 11	0.62152 64655 66
83	1.81943 58677 87	0.99551 92102 86	0.09455 95153 95	0.62015 43160 59
84	1.84135 67818 56	0.99671 15739 69	0.08103 10947 53	0.61896 38968 28
85	1.86327 76959 26	0.99771 84776 41	0.06751 17721 06	0.61795 57366 49
86	1.88519 86099 96	0.99854 09295 92	0.05400 01104 50	0.61713 02793 83
87	1.90711 95240 65	0.99917 97560 93	0.04049 46294 46	0.61648 78857 57
88	1.92904 04381 35	0.99963 56006 05	0.02699 38141 51	0.61602 88348 22
89	1.95096 13522 05	0.99990 89231 75	0.01349 61237 07	0.61575 33250 84
90	1.97288 22662 75	1.00000 00000 00	0.00000 00000 00	0.61566 14753 26

208

q = 0.06033 83890 33716 41   D(90) = 1.27446 82206 64111
q' = 0.02974 53239 19583 19   1/D(90) = 0.78464 09849 89733

r	ϕ	$E(\phi,k)$	$A(r)$	$D(r)$
45	0.91979 30572 25	0.83564 61317 29	0.70197 66333 41	1.13717 38164 57
46	0.92261 88557 44	0.84902 89377 06	0.71430 30327 35	1.14196 32912 71
47	0.93960 30600 55	0.86218 82839 28	0.72641 77624 09	1.14674 70774 52
48	0.95644 51221 15	0.87512 82881 13	0.73831 67802 85	1.15151 93458 90
49	0.97314 66472 49	0.88785 32395 89	0.74999 60947 42	1.15627 42809 77
50	0.98970 93848 53	0.90036 75836 57	0.76145 17668 47	1.16100 60876 96
51	1.00613 52227 23	0.91267 59065 78	0.77267 99125 92	1.16570 89986 94
52	1.02242 61814 17	0.92478 29212 22	0.78367 67051 61	1.17037 72813 19
53	1.03858 44086 85	0.93669 34533 86	0.79443 83772 13	1.17500 52446 16
54	1.05461 21739 77	0.94841 24288 10	0.80496 12231 69	1.17958 72462 83
55	1.07051 18630 30	0.95994 48609 00	0.81524 16015 17	1.18411 76995 56
56	1.08628 59725 61	0.97129 58391 56	0.82527 59371 14	1.18859 10800 43
57	1.10193 71050 61	0.98247 05183 18	0.83506 07234 91	1.19300 19324 75
58	1.11746 79637 19	0.99347 41082 14	0.84459 25251 56	1.19734 48773 77
59	1.13288 13474 52	1.00431 18643 22	0.85386 79798 87	1.20161 46176 51
60	1.14818 01460 84	1.01498 90790 15	0.86288 38010 12	1.20580 59450 55
61	1.16336 73356 44	1.02551 10734 95	0.87163 67796 77	1.20991 37465 85
62	1.17844 59738 16	1.03588 31903 90	0.88012 37870 88	1.21393 30107 27
63	1.19341 91955 22	1.04611 07870 06	0.88834 17767 37	1.21785 88336 06
64	1.20829 02086 48	1.05619 92292 03	0.89628 77865 88	1.22168 64249 85
65	1.22306 22899 24	1.06615 38858 86	0.90395 89412 44	1.22541 11141 45
66	1.23773 87809 37	1.07598 01240 86	0.91135 24540 62	1.22902 83556 05
67	1.25232 30842 93	1.08568 33046 08	0.91846 56292 44	1.23253 37347 01
68	1.26681 86599 21	1.09526 87782 17	0.92529 58638 66	1.23592 29730 00
69	1.28122 90215 20	1.10474 18823 48	0.93184 06498 71	1.23919 19335 48
70	1.29555 77331 36	1.11410 79383 12	0.93809 75760 07	1.24233 66259 51
71	1.30980 84058 80	1.12337 22489 67	0.94406 43297 01	1.24535 32112 73
72	1.32398 46947 77	1.13254 00968 42	0.94973 86988 80	1.24823 80067 50
73	1.33809 02957 38	1.14161 67426 71	0.95511 85737 30	1.25098 74903 12
74	1.35212 89426 56	1.15060 74243 36	0.96020 19483 78	1.25359 83049 14
75	1.36610 44046 22	1.15951 73561 75	0.96498 69225 16	1.25606 72626 56
76	1.38002 04832 47	1.16835 17286 36	0.96947 17029 38	1.25839 13487 05
77	1.39388 10100 99	1.17711 57082 62	0.97365 46050 11	1.26056 77250 01
78	1.40768 98442 36	1.18581 44379 74	0.97753 40540 59	1.26259 37337 46
79	1.42145 08698 33	1.19445 30376 31	0.98110 85866 68	1.26446 69006 70
80	1.43516 79939 05	1.20303 66048 50	0.98437 68519 03	1.26618 49380 77
81	1.44884 51441 02	1.21157 02160 53	0.98733 76124 38	1.26774 57476 60
82	1.46248 62665 93	1.22005 89277 40	0.98998 97455 95	1.26914 74230 79
83	1.47609 53240 10	1.22850 77779 38	0.99233 22442 96	1.27038 82523 09
84	1.48967 62934 57	1.23692 17878 34	0.99436 42179 08	1.27146 67197 48
85	1.50323 31645 81	1.24530 59635 49	0.99608 48930 06	1.27238 15080 79
86	1.51676 99376 86	1.25366 52980 56	0.99749 36140 30	1.27313 14998 93
87	1.53029 06218 90	1.26200 47731 94	0.99858 98438 44	1.27371 57790 65
88	1.54379 92333 23	1.27032 93617 91	0.99937 31641 99	1.27413 36318 80
89	1.55729 97933 45	1.27864 40298 47	0.99984 32760 87	1.27438 45479 15
90	1.57079 63267 95	1.28695 37387 83	1.00000 00000 00	1.27446 82206 64

K = 1.99266 97557 34209   E = 1.27757 39482 50391
K' = 1.75216 52364 68845   E' = 1.41707 49233 71952

r	u=(r/90)K=F(ϕ,k)	sn u	cn u	dn u
0	0.00000 00000 00	0.00000 00000 00	1.00000 00000 00	1.00000 00000 00
1	0.02214 07750 64	0.02213 78127 85	0.99975 49285 93	0.99984 36958 17
2	0.04428 15501 27	0.04425 78628 91	0.99902 01407 24	0.99937 51384 19
3	0.06642 23251 91	0.06634 24425 11	0.99779 69133 65	0.99859 53915 88
4	0.08856 31002 55	0.08837 39532 11	0.99608 73678 52	0.99750 62227 58
5	0.11070 38753 19	0.11033 49597 03	0.99389 44595 21	0.99611 00947 45
6	0.13284 46503 82	0.13220 82425 18	0.99122 19633 41	0.99441 01542 93
7	0.15498 54254 46	0.15397 68492 49	0.98807 44556 44	0.99241 02175 08
8	0.17712 62005 10	0.17562 41440 29	0.98445 72921 33	0.99011 47523 25
9	0.19926 69755 73	0.19713 38549 34	0.98037 65823 60	0.98752 88581 51
10	0.22140 77506 37	0.21849 01190 33	0.97583 91608 69	0.98465 82428 70
11	0.24354 85257 01	0.23967 75248 19	0.97085 25552 82	0.98150 91973 89
12	0.26568 93007 65	0.26068 11517 81	0.96542 49515 66	0.97808 85679 50
13	0.28783 00758 28	0.28148 66069 38	0.95956 51567 84	0.97440 37264 38
14	0.30997 08508 92	0.30208 00581 41	0.95328 25596 19	0.97046 25389 03
15	0.33211 16259 56	0.32244 82640 16	0.94658 70889 85	0.96627 33325 76
16	0.35425 24010 19	0.34257 86004 38	0.93948 91710 51	0.96184 48616 01
17	0.37639 31760 83	0.36245 90834 74	0.93199 96849 82	0.95718 62717 61
18	0.39853 39511 47	0.38207 83887 38	0.92412 99177 38	0.95230 70644 52
19	0.42067 47262 11	0.40142 58671 62	0.91589 15182 34	0.94721 70601 40
20	0.44281 55012 74	0.42049 15572 04	0.90729 64511 78	0.94192 63615 77
21	0.46495 62763 38	0.43926 61935 33	0.89835 69508 94	0.93644 53169 96
22	0.48709 70514 02	0.45774 12122 88	0.88908 54754 03	0.93078 44835 18
23	0.50923 78264 65	0.47590 87529 95	0.87949 46610 54	0.92495 45910 01
24	0.53137 86015 29	0.49376 16572 70	0.86959 72779 45	0.91896 65065 15
25	0.55351 93765 93	0.51129 34644 67	0.85940 61863 83	0.91283 11996 54
26	0.57566 01516 57	0.52849 84044 13	0.84893 42945 91	0.90655 97088 35
27	0.59780 09267 20	0.54537 13874 20	0.83819 45178 68	0.90016 31087 66
28	0.61994 17017 84	0.56190 79917 55	0.82719 97393 63	0.89365 24791 89
29	0.64208 24768 48	0.57810 44487 72	0.81596 27726 25	0.88703 88750 51
30	0.66422 32519 11	0.59395 76259 06	0.80449 63260 50	0.88033 32981 77
31	0.68636 40269 75	0.60946 50077 35	0.79281 29693 36	0.87354 66705 50
32	0.70850 48020 39	0.62462 46753 26	0.78092 51020 26	0.86668 98092 47
33	0.73064 55771 03	0.63943 52840 75	0.76884 49242 08	0.85977 34030 97
34	0.75278 63521 66	0.65389 60402 39	0.75658 44094 08	0.85280 79910 78
35	0.77492 71272 30	0.66800 66763 76	0.74415 52797 08	0.84580 39424 88
36	0.79706 79022 94	0.68176 74258 84	0.73156 89830 79	0.83877 14388 76
37	0.81920 86773 57	0.69517 89968 25	0.71883 66729 47	0.83172 04577 37
38	0.84134 94524 21	0.70824 25452 26	0.70596 91899 31	0.82466 07579 43
39	0.86349 02274 85	0.72095 96480 24	0.69297 70457 39	0.81760 18668 79
40	0.88563 10025 49	0.73333 22758 07	0.67987 04091 66	0.81055 30692 37
41	0.90777 17776 12	0.74536 27655 26	0.66665 90941 16	0.80352 33974 20
42	0.92991 25526 76	0.75705 37932 90	0.65335 25495 97	0.79652 16235 01
43	0.95205 33277 40	0.76840 83473 95	0.63995 98515 95	0.78955 62526 61
44	0.97419 41028 03	0.77942 97016 88	0.62648 96967 44	0.78263 55180 44
45	0.99633 48778 67	0.79012 13893 73	0.61295 03977 12	0.77576 73769 58

q = 0.06313 88302 96461 25
q'= 0.02807 67957 17219 06

D(90) = 1.28904 62137 26445
1/D(90) = 0.77576 73769 57841

r	ϕ	$E(\phi,k)$	A(r)	D(r)
0	0.00000 00000 00	0.00000 00000 00	0.00000 00000 00	1.00000 00000 00
1	0.02213 96214 11	0.02213 84678 67	0.01717 53034 08	1.00008 79509 59
2	0.04427 23240 52	0.04426 31014 36	0.03434 58813 02	1.00035 16970 07
3	0.06639 12048 67	0.06636 01107 79	0.05150 70082 21	1.00079 09177 78
4	0.08848 93921 56	0.08841 57944 02	0.06865 39588 12	1.00140 50797 61
5	0.11056 00610 66	0.11041 65827 41	0.08578 20078 92	1.00219 34369 38
6	0.13259 64488 70	0.13234 90807 75	0.10288 64305 25	1.00315 50316 84
7	0.15459 18699 50	0.15420 01095 02	0.11996 25021 10	1.00428 86959 19
8	0.17653 97304 32	0.17595 67460 10	0.13700 54984 91	1.00559 30525 14
9	0.19843 35423 96	0.19760 63618 97	0.15401 06960 84	1.00706 65169 50
10	0.22026 69376 08	0.21913 66598 11	0.17097 33720 41	1.00870 72992 25
11	0.24203 36807 13	0.24053 57079 12	0.18788 88044 27	1.01051 34060 11
12	0.26372 76818 44	0.26179 19720 57	0.20475 22724 46	1.01248 26430 50
13	0.28534 30085 89	0.28289 43455 61	0.22155 90566 90	1.01461 26178 04
14	0.30687 38972 87	0.30383 21763 92	0.23830 44394 35	1.01690 07423 34
15	0.32831 47636 04	0.32459 52916 90	0.25498 37049 81	1.01934 42364 17
16	0.34966 02123 69	0.34517 40195 30	0.27159 21400 23	1.02194 01308 99
17	0.37090 50466 34	0.36555 92078 68	0.28812 50340 91	1.02468 52712 73
18	0.39204 42759 51	0.38574 22406 41	0.30457 76800 22	1.02757 63214 83
19	0.41307 31238 39	0.40571 50510 21	0.32094 53744 94	1.03060 97679 46
20	0.43398 70344 45	0.42547 01318 23	0.33722 34186 15	1.03378 19237 94
21	0.45478 16783 82	0.44500 05431 37	0.35340 71185 67	1.03708 89333 16
22	0.47545 29577 60	0.46429 99172 14	0.36949 17863 11	1.04052 67766 17
23	0.49599 70104 13	0.48336 24607 22	0.38547 27403 52	1.04409 12744 69
24	0.51641 02133 24	0.50218 29544 41	0.40134 53065 67	1.04777 80933 57
25	0.53668 91852 81	0.52075 67505 36	0.41710 48190 99	1.05158 27507 13
26	0.55683 07887 68	0.53907 97675 36	0.43274 66213 12	1.05550 06203 36
27	0.57683 21311 31	0.55714 84831 42	0.44826 60668 18	1.05952 69379 78
28	0.59669 05650 31	0.57495 99250 42	0.46365 85205 67	1.06365 68071 09
29	0.61640 36882 19	0.59251 16598 68	0.47891 93600 05	1.06788 52048 37
30	0.63596 93426 78	0.60980 17804 84	0.49404 39763 00	1.07220 69879 86
31	0.65538 56131 42	0.62682 88917 42	0.50902 77756 40	1.07661 68993 18
32	0.67465 08250 48	0.64359 20949 05	0.52386 61805 92	1.08110 95739 04
33	0.69376 35419 55	0.66009 09708 84	0.53855 46315 35	1.08567 95456 16
34	0.71272 25624 61	0.67632 55624 73	0.55308 85881 56	1.09032 12537 54
35	0.73152 69166 60	0.69229 63557 23	0.56746 35310 15	1.09502 90497 85
36	0.75017 58621 83	0.70800 42606 44	0.58167 49631 72	1.09979 72041 91
37	0.76866 88798 61	0.72345 05913 57	0.59571 84118 84	1.10461 99134 24
38	0.78700 56690 36	0.73863 70458 68	0.60958 94303 61	1.10949 13069 41
39	0.80518 61425 80	0.75356 56855 82	0.62328 35995 79	1.11440 54543 38
40	0.82321 04216 42	0.76823 89147 07	0.63679 65301 64	1.11935 63725 51
41	0.84107 88301 64	0.78265 94596 51	0.65012 38643 19	1.12433 80331 23
42	0.85879 18892 03	0.79683 03485 39	0.66326 12778 21	1.12934 43695 35
43	0.87635 03110 94	0.81075 48909 47	0.67620 44820 58	1.13436 92845 82
44	0.89375 49934 78	0.82443 66579 47	0.68894 92261 21	1.13940 66577 89
45	0.91100 70132 40	0.83787 94625 49	0.70149 12989 49	1.14445 03528 62

211

K = 1.99266 97557 34209   E = 1.27757 39482 50391
K'= 1.75216 52364 68845   E'= 1.41707 49233 71952

r	u=(r/90)K=F(ϕ,k)	sn u	cn u	dn u
45	0.99633 48778 67	0.79012 13893 73	0.61295 03977 12	0.77576 73769 58
46	1.01847 56529 31	0.80048 71773 65	0.59934 98801 83	0.76895 95083 24
47	1.04061 64279 95	0.81053 10412 50	0.58569 56813 65	0.76221 93113 21
48	1.06275 72030 58	0.82025 71409 49	0.57199 49499 09	0.75555 39051 24
49	1.08489 79781 22	0.82966 97971 17	0.55825 44471 40	0.74897 01296 61
50	1.10703 87531 86	0.83877 34683 50	0.54448 05495 07	0.74247 45473 09
51	1.12917 95282 49	0.84757 27292 36	0.53067 92521 44	0.73607 34454 40
52	1.15132 03033 13	0.85607 22492 62	0.51685 61734 60	0.72977 28397 47
53	1.17346 10783 77	0.86427 67726 35	0.50301 65606 45	0.72357 84782 66
54	1.19560 18534 41	0.87219 10989 96	0.48916 52960 22	0.71749 58460 18
55	1.21774 26285 04	0.87982 00650 60	0.47530 69041 35	0.71153 01701 97
56	1.23988 34035 68	0.88716 85271 76	0.46144 55595 07	0.70568 64258 40
57	1.26202 41786 32	0.89424 13447 99	0.44758 50949 84	0.69996 93419 04
58	1.28416 49536 95	0.90104 33648 74	0.43372 90105 78	0.69438 34076 87
59	1.30630 57287 59	0.90757 94071 05	0.41988 04827 56	0.68893 28795 37
60	1.32844 65038 23	0.91385 42501 08	0.40604 23740 94	0.68362 17877 92
61	1.35058 72788 87	0.91987 26184 11	0.39221 72432 43	0.67845 39438 79
62	1.37272 80539 50	0.92563 91702 89	0.37840 73551 43	0.67343 29475 57
63	1.39486 88290 14	0.93115 84863 96	0.36461 46914 38	0.66856 21942 20
64	1.41700 96040 78	0.93643 50591 77	0.35084 09610 40	0.66384 48822 37
65	1.43915 03791 41	0.94147 32830 22	0.33708 76108 01	0.65928 40202 88
66	1.46129 11542 05	0.94627 74451 30	0.32335 58362 52	0.65488 24346 54
67	1.48343 19292 69	0.95085 17170 58	0.30964 65923 72	0.65064 27764 21
68	1.50557 27043 33	0.95520 01469 15	0.29596 06043 60	0.64656 75285 83
69	1.52771 34793 96	0.95932 66521 70	0.28229 83783 81	0.64265 90130 03
70	1.54985 42544 60	0.96323 50130 41	0.26866 02122 59	0.63891 93972 07
71	1.57199 50295 24	0.96692 88664 40	0.25504 62060 98	0.63535 07009 92
72	1.59413 58045 87	0.97041 17004 22	0.24145 62728 22	0.63195 48028 33
73	1.61627 65796 51	0.97368 68491 30	0.22789 01486 03	0.62873 34460 46
74	1.63841 73547 15	0.97675 74881 96	0.21434 74031 88	0.62568 82447 24
75	1.66055 81297 79	0.97962 66305 53	0.20082 74500 93	0.62282 06894 08
76	1.68269 89048 42	0.98229 71226 65	0.18732 95566 77	0.62013 21524 81
77	1.70483 96799 06	0.98477 16411 06	0.17385 28540 84	0.61762 38932 83
78	1.72698 04549 70	0.98705 26895 01	0.16039 63470 54	0.61529 70629 37
79	1.74912 12300 33	0.98914 25957 74	0.14695 89235 96	0.61315 27088 62
80	1.77126 20050 97	0.99104 35097 00	0.13353 93645 43	0.61119 17789 85
81	1.79340 27801 61	0.99275 74007 25	0.12013 63529 70	0.60941 51256 29
82	1.81554 35552 25	0.99428 60560 57	0.10674 84835 03	0.60782 35090 82
83	1.83768 43302 88	0.99563 10789 75	0.09337 42715 07	0.60641 76008 42
84	1.85982 51053 52	0.99679 38873 73	0.08001 21621 73	0.60519 79865 19
85	1.88196 58804 16	0.99777 57125 09	0.06666 05395 11	0.60416 51684 15
86	1.90410 66554 79	0.99857 75979 40	0.05331 77352 53	0.60331 95677 60
87	1.92624 74305 43	0.99920 03986 50	0.03998 20376 82	0.60266 15266 02
88	1.94838 82056 07	0.99964 47803 42	0.02665 17004 04	0.60219 13093 66
89	1.97052 89806 70	0.99991 12188 99	0.01332 49510 60	0.60190 91040 63
90	1.99266 97557 34	1.00000 00000 00	0.00000 00000 00	0.60181 50231 52

ELLIPTIC FUNCTIONS TABLE $\theta = 53°$

q = 0.06313 88302 96461 25
q'= 0.02807 67957 17219 06

D(90) = 1.28904 62137 26445
1/D(90) = 0.77576 73769 57841

r	ϕ	$E(\phi,k)$	A(r)	D(r)
45	0.91100 70132 40	0.83787 94625 49	0.70149 12989 49	1.14445 03528 62
46	0.92810 76203 64	0.85108 73406 18	0.71382 65315 07	1.14949 42251 61
47	0.94505 82317 57	0.86406 45323 26	0.72595 07990 15	1.15453 21291 80
48	0.96186 04250 50	0.87681 54641 99	0.73786 00232 09	1.15955 79260 39
49	0.97851 59324 05	0.88934 47318 17	0.74955 01746 43	1.16456 54909 68
50	0.99502 66343 46	0.90165 70831 91	0.76101 72750 09	1.16954 87207 77
51	1.01139 45536 47	0.91375 74028 66	0.77225 73995 03	1.17450 15413 00
52	1.02762 18492 72	0.92565 06967 68	0.78326 66791 96	1.17941 79148 15
53	1.04371 08104 06	0.93734 20778 13	0.79404 13034 37	1.18429 18474 10
54	1.05966 38505 82	0.94883 67523 04	0.80457 75222 64	1.18911 73963 11
55	1.07548 35019 09	0.96014 00071 04	0.81487 16488 30	1.19388 86771 43
56	1.09117 24094 27	0.97125 71976 04	0.82492 00618 37	1.19859 98711 24
57	1.10673 33255 94	0.98219 37364 80	0.83471 92079 63	1.20324 52321 81
58	1.12216 91049 04	0.99295 50832 23	0.84426 56043 02	1.20781 90939 87
59	1.13748 26986 57	1.00354 67344 46	0.85355 58407 85	1.21231 58768 87
60	1.15267 71498 75	1.01397 42149 43	0.86258 65826 00	1.21673 00947 39
61	1.16775 55883 79	1.02424 30694 94	0.87135 45725 85	1.22105 63616 33
62	1.18272 12260 23	1.03435 88553 85	0.87985 66336 13	1.22528 93984 88
63	1.19757 73520 84	1.04432 71356 33	0.88808 96709 46	1.22942 40395 25
64	1.21232 73288 23	1.05415 34728 89	0.89605 06745 65	1.23345 52386 04
65	1.22697 45872 01	1.06384 34239 93	0.90373 67214 56	1.23737 80754 13
66	1.24152 26227 59	1.07340 25351 58	0.91114 49778 74	1.24118 77615 05
67	1.25597 49916 66	1.08283 63377 56	0.91827 27015 49	1.24487 96461 79
68	1.27033 53069 09	1.09215 03446 86	0.92511 72438 58	1.24844 92221 86
69	1.28460 72346 58	1.10135 00472 79	0.93167 60519 40	1.25189 21312 74
70	1.29879 44907 69	1.11044 09127 38	0.93794 66707 50	1.25520 41695 31
71	1.31290 08374 39	1.11942 83820 61	0.94392 67450 71	1.25838 12925 65
72	1.32693 00800 11	1.12831 78684 36	0.94961 40214 42	1.26141 96204 66
73	1.34088 60639 11	1.13711 47560 79	0.95500 63500 32	1.26431 54425 81
74	1.35477 26717 22	1.14582 43994 77	0.96010 16864 42	1.26706 52220 81
75	1.36859 38203 86	1.15445 21230 23	0.96489 80934 24	1.26966 56003 09
76	1.38235 34585 30	1.16300 32210 13	0.96939 37425 31	1.27211 34009 12
77	1.39605 55639 05	1.17148 29579 78	0.97358 69156 79	1.27440 56337 57
78	1.40970 41409 38	1.17989 65693 21	0.97747 60066 28	1.27653 94986 04
79	1.42330 32183 87	1.18824 92622 51	0.98105 95223 72	1.27851 23885 63
80	1.43685 68470 92	1.19654 62169 72	0.98433 60844 38	1.28032 18932 98
81	1.45036 90978 16	1.20479 25881 17	0.98730 44300 96	1.28196 58019 99
82	1.46384 40591 68	1.21299 35063 96	0.98996 34134 66	1.28344 21061 04
83	1.47728 58355 99	1.22115 40804 44	0.99231 20065 29	1.28474 90017 77
84	1.49069 85454 75	1.22927 93988 44	0.99434 93000 41	1.28588 48921 29
85	1.50408 63192 00	1.23737 45322 98	0.99607 45043 41	1.28684 83891 86
86	1.51745 32973 98	1.24544 45359 39	0.99748 69500 52	1.28763 83155 99
87	1.53080 36291 39	1.25349 44517 53	0.99858 60886 83	1.28825 37060 99
88	1.54414 14702 06	1.26152 93110 96	0.99937 14931 17	1.28869 38086 83
89	1.55747 09813 87	1.26955 41372 85	0.99984 28579 98	1.28895 80855 42
90	1.57079 63267 95	1.27757 39482 50	1.00000 00000 00	1.28904 62137 26

ELLIPTIC FUNCTIONS TABLE $\theta = 54°$

K = 2.01326 65652 05468
K′ = 1.74149 92344 26774

E = 1.26814 65310 65206
E′ = 1.42476 03101 24890

r	u=(r/90)K=F(φ,k)	sn u	cn u	dn u
0	0.00000 00000 00	0.00000 00000 00	1.00000 00000 00	1.00000 00000 00
1	0.02236 96285 02	0.02236 65422 99	0.99974 98376 02	0.99983 62736 62
2	0.04473 92570 05	0.04471 45792 35	0.99899 98030 05	0.99934 54757 50
3	0.06710 88855 07	0.06702 56646 33	0.99775 12517 06	0.99852 87477 24
4	0.08947 85140 09	0.08928 14702 86	0.99600 64352 52	0.99738 79858 63
5	0.11184 81425 11	0.11146 38439 16	0.99376 84898 91	0.99592 58321 06
6	0.13421 77710 14	0.13355 48659 16	0.99104 14208 25	0.99414 56613 29
7	0.15658 73995 16	0.15553 69045 02	0.98783 00822 20	0.99205 15652 07
8	0.17895 70280 18	0.17739 26688 98	0.98414 01531 39	0.98964 83327 72
9	0.20132 66565 21	0.19910 52602 21	0.97997 81096 29	0.98694 14278 74
10	0.22369 62850 23	0.22065 82197 52	0.97535 11931 89	0.98393 69637 24
11	0.24606 59135 25	0.24203 55742 90	0.97026 73759 22	0.98064 16747 44
12	0.26843 55420 27	0.26322 18783 66	0.96473 53226 40	0.97706 28859 73
13	0.29080 51705 30	0.28420 22530 68	0.95876 43502 71	0.97320 84802 91
14	0.31317 47990 32	0.30496 24213 08	0.95236 43848 81	0.96908 68637 15
15	0.33554 44275 34	0.32548 87393 82	0.94554 59166 72	0.96470 69290 69
16	0.35791 40560 37	0.34576 82247 13	0.93831 99533 10	0.96007 80183 02
17	0.38028 36845 39	0.36578 85796 98	0.93069 79719 34	0.95520 98837 47
18	0.40265 33130 41	0.38553 82116 38	0.92269 18702 18	0.95011 26486 17
19	0.42502 29415 43	0.40500 62487 32	0.91431 39168 19	0.94479 67670 07
20	0.44739 25700 46	0.42418 25521 82	0.90557 67015 69	0.93927 29836 96
21	0.46976 21985 48	0.44305 77244 69	0.89649 30857 45	0.93355 22940 10
22	0.49213 18270 50	0.46162 31138 95	0.88707 61527 16	0.92764 59039 98
23	0.51450 14555 53	0.47987 08155 17	0.87733 91592 85	0.92156 51911 69
24	0.53687 10840 55	0.49779 36686 10	0.86729 54879 92	0.91532 16660 09
25	0.55924 07125 57	0.51538 52508 45	0.85695 86006 40	0.90892 69344 90
26	0.58161 03410 59	0.53263 98693 50	0.84634 19932 74	0.90239 26617 57
27	0.60397 99695 62	0.54955 25488 63	0.83545 91528 24	0.89573 05371 53
28	0.62634 95980 64	0.56611 90172 04	0.82432 35155 93	0.88895 22407 46
29	0.64871 92265 66	0.58233 56882 60	0.81294 84277 48	0.88206 94114 70
30	0.67108 88550 68	0.59819 96427 50	0.80134 71079 46	0.87509 36169 95
31	0.69345 84835 71	0.61370 86069 70	0.78953 26122 03	0.86803 63254 01
32	0.71582 81120 73	0.62886 09297 72	0.77751 78010 86	0.86090 88787 41
33	0.73819 77405 75	0.64365 55580 10	0.76531 53092 96	0.85372 24685 16
34	0.76056 73690 78	0.65809 20106 65	0.75293 75176 59	0.84648 81131 14
35	0.78293 69975 80	0.67217 03518 97	0.74039 65275 65	0.83921 66372 05
36	0.80530 66260 82	0.68589 11632 15	0.72770 41378 36	0.83191 86531 01
37	0.82767 62545 84	0.69925 55149 90	0.71487 18240 04	0.82460 45440 59
38	0.85004 58830 87	0.71226 49375 04	0.70191 07199 65	0.81728 44494 92
39	0.87241 55115 89	0.72492 13917 08	0.68883 16019 49	0.80996 82520 47
40	0.89478 51400 91	0.73722 72398 80	0.67564 48747 52	0.80266 55664 95
41	0.91715 47685 94	0.74918 52163 32	0.66236 05601 41	0.79538 57303 68
42	0.93952 43970 96	0.76079 83983 13	0.64898 82873 55	0.78813 77962 80
43	0.96189 40255 98	0.77207 01772 52	0.63553 72856 08	0.78093 05258 38
44	0.98426 36541 00	0.78300 42304 51	0.62201 63784 79	0.77377 23850 80
45	1.00663 32826 03	0.79360 44933 35	0.60843 39801 15	0.76667 15413 35

214

ELLIPTIC FUNCTIONS TABLE $\theta = 54°$

q = 0.06603 86859 10861 03   D(90) = 1.30433 95327 53677

q'= 0.02646 71830 76961 27   1/D(90) = 0.76667 15413 34666

r	ϕ	$E(\phi,k)$	$A(r)$	$D(r)$
0	0.00000 00000 00	0.00000 00000 00	0.00000 00000 00	1.00000 00000 00
1	0.02236 84075 75	0.02236 71867 68	0.01714 93791 89	1.00009 25909 55
2	0.04472 94929 98	0.04471 97328 26	0.03429 40881 17	1.00037 02514 00
3	0.06707 59511 51	0.06704 30458 78	0.05142 94564 26	1.00083 26442 19
4	0.08940 05109 11	0.08932 26301 25	0.06855 08135 77	1.00147 92079 97
5	0.11169 59519 29	0.11154 41336 87	0.08565 34887 61	1.00230 91577 00
6	0.13395 51211 85	0.13369 33950 45	0.10273 28108 34	1.00332 14856 15
7	0.15617 09492 00	0.15575 64881 94	0.11978 41082 63	1.00451 49625 63
8	0.17833 64658 67	0.17771 97662 14	0.13680 27090 92	1.00588 81393 76
9	0.20044 48157 96	0.19956 99029 83	0.15378 39409 38	1.00743 93486 38
10	0.22248 92731 39	0.22129 39327 76	0.17072 31310 09	1.00916 67066 87
11	0.24446 32557 98	0.24287 92875 24	0.18761 56061 59	1.01106 81158 86
12	0.26636 03389 88	0.26431 38315 24	0.20445 66929 77	1.01314 12671 38
13	0.28817 42680 84	0.28558 58934 25	0.22124 17179 17	1.01538 36426 66
14	0.30989 89707 16	0.30668 42953 46	0.23796 60074 72	1.01779 25190 44
15	0.33152 85680 68	0.32759 83789 94	0.25462 48883 88	1.02036 49704 68
16	0.35305 73853 47	0.34831 80287 18	0.27121 36879 41	1.02309 78722 79
17	0.37447 99613 98	0.36883 36914 16	0.28772 77342 54	1.02598 79047 26
18	0.39579 10574 48	0.38913 63932 85	0.30416 23566 77	1.02903 15569 59
19	0.41698 56649 49	0.40921 77534 01	0.32051 28862 23	1.03222 51312 60
20	0.43805 90125 34	0.42906 99941 69	0.33677 46560 69	1.03556 47474 91
21	0.45900 65720 71	0.44868 59486 89	0.35294 30021 13	1.03904 63477 78
22	0.47982 40638 18	0.46805 90651 20	0.36901 32636 04	1.04266 57013 93
23	0.50050 74607 01	0.48718 34081 34	0.38498 07838 39	1.04641 84098 62
24	0.52105 29917 11	0.50605 36575 94	0.40084 09109 26	1.05029 99122 62
25	0.54145 71444 67	0.52466 51045 81	0.41658 89986 17	1.05430 54907 29
26	0.56171 66669 31	0.54301 36449 26	0.43222 04072 24	1.05843 02761 51
27	0.58182 85683 49	0.56109 57704 09	0.44773 05045 92	1.06266 92540 44
28	0.60179 01194 10	0.57890 85578 11	0.46311 46671 61	1.06701 72706 09
29	0.62159 88516 77	0.59644 96559 82	0.47836 82810 98	1.07146 90389 59
30	0.64125 25563 31	0.61371 72711 29	0.49348 67435 00	1.07601 91455 11
31	0.66074 92822 55	0.63071 01505 02	0.50846 54636 80	1.08066 20565 29
32	0.68008 73335 06	0.64742 75646 79	0.52329 98645 21	1.08539 21248 17
33	0.69926 52662 17	0.66386 92886 33	0.53798 53839 18	1.09020 35965 60
34	0.71828 18849 78	0.68003 55817 64	0.55251 74762 76	1.09509 06182 80
35	0.73713 62387 24	0.69592 71670 93	0.56689 16141 01	1.10004 72439 34
36	0.75582 76161 90	0.71154 52097 73	0.58110 32896 49	1.10506 74421 15
37	0.77435 55409 76	0.72689 12951 01	0.59514 80166 59	1.11014 51033 65
38	0.79271 97662 47	0.74196 74061 91	0.60902 13321 44	1.11527 40475 88
39	0.81092 02691 33	0.75677 59014 44	0.62271 87982 61	1.12044 80315 41
40	0.82895 72448 61	0.77131 94919 79	0.63623 60042 45	1.12566 07564 21
41	0.84683 11006 50	0.78560 12191 31	0.64956 85684 00	1.13090 58755 14
42	0.86454 24494 21	0.79962 44321 66	0.66271 21401 61	1.13617 70019 03
43	0.88209 21033 56	0.81339 27662 89	0.67566 24022 14	1.14146 77162 36
44	0.89948 10673 31	0.82691 01210 74	0.68841 50726 65	1.14677 15745 34
45	0.91671 05322 68	0.84018 06393 86	0.70096 59072 76	1.15208 21160 30

215

K = 2.01326 65652 05468   E = 1.26814 65310 65206
K' = 1.74149 92344 26774   E' = 1.42476 03101 24890

r	u=(r/90)K=F(φ,k)	sn u	cn u	dn u
45	1.00663 32826 03	0.79360 44933 35	0.60843 39801 15	0.76667 15413 35
46	1.02900 29111 05	0.80387 51323 68	0.59479 80931 04	0.75963 58614 32
47	1.05137 25396 07	0.81382 05187 01	0.58111 63079 28	0.75267 29111 55
48	1.07374 21681 10	0.82344 52026 27	0.56739 58038 89	0.74578 99558 51
49	1.09611 17966 12	0.83275 38889 01	0.55364 33513 73	0.73899 39621 12
50	1.11848 14251 14	0.84175 14129 86	0.53986 53153 67	0.73229 16004 23
51	1.14085 10536 16	0.85044 27182 28	0.52606 76601 10	0.72568 92486 92
52	1.16322 06821 19	0.85883 28340 29	0.51225 59547 66	0.71919 29965 85
53	1.18559 03106 21	0.86692 68550 06	0.49843 53800 34	0.71280 86505 56
54	1.20795 99391 23	0.87472 99211 57	0.48461 07355 72	0.70654 17395 10
55	1.23032 95676 26	0.88224 71990 44	0.47078 64481 69	0.70039 75210 15
56	1.25269 91961 28	0.88948 38639 72	0.45696 65805 44	0.69438 09879 74
57	1.27506 88246 30	0.89644 50831 74	0.44315 48407 20	0.68849 68757 05
58	1.29743 84531 32	0.90313 59999 72	0.42935 45918 63	0.68274 96693 41
59	1.31980 80816 35	0.90956 17189 04	0.41556 88625 30	0.67714 36114 97
60	1.34217 77101 37	0.91572 72917 82	0.40180 03572 50	0.67168 27101 44
61	1.36454 73386 39	0.92163 77046 71	0.38805 14673 70	0.66637 07466 21
62	1.38691 69671 42	0.92729 78657 46	0.37432 42821 18	0.66121 12837 46
63	1.40928 65956 44	0.93271 25939 90	0.36062 05998 16	0.65620 76739 74
64	1.43165 62241 46	0.93788 66087 25	0.34694 19391 96	0.65136 30675 45
65	1.45402 58526 48	0.94282 45199 06	0.33328 95507 88	0.64668 04206 02
66	1.47639 54811 51	0.94753 08191 65	0.31966 44283 20	0.64216 25032 17
67	1.49876 51096 53	0.95200 98715 67	0.30606 73201 09	0.63781 19073 13
68	1.52113 47381 55	0.95626 59080 29	0.29249 87404 09	0.63363 10544 35
69	1.54350 43666 58	0.96030 30183 71	0.27895 89806 89	0.62962 22033 45
70	1.56587 39951 60	0.96412 51449 67	0.26544 81208 13	0.62578 74574 22
71	1.58824 36236 62	0.96773 60769 50	0.25196 60401 10	0.62212 87718 36
72	1.61061 32521 64	0.97113 94449 50	0.23851 24283 17	0.61864 79604 79
73	1.63298 28806 67	0.97433 87163 07	0.22508 67963 80	0.61534 67026 39
74	1.65535 25091 69	0.97733 71907 52	0.21168 84871 06	0.61222 65493 93
75	1.67772 21376 71	0.98013 79965 05	0.19831 66856 50	0.60928 89297 06
76	1.70009 17661 74	0.98274 40867 69	0.18497 04298 55	0.60653 51562 39
77	1.72246 13946 76	0.98515 82365 84	0.17164 86204 19	0.60396 64308 28
78	1.74483 10231 78	0.98738 30400 18	0.15835 00308 99	0.60158 38496 49
79	1.76720 06516 80	0.98942 09076 68	0.14507 33175 65	0.59938 84080 50
80	1.78957 02801 83	0.99127 40644 46	0.13181 70290 87	0.59738 10050 47
81	1.81193 99086 85	0.99294 45476 21	0.11857 96160 81	0.59556 24474 68
82	1.83430 95371 87	0.99443 42051 11	0.10535 94405 10	0.59393 34537 62
83	1.85667 91656 89	0.99574 46939 91	0.09215 47849 52	0.59249 46574 43
84	1.87904 87941 92	0.99687 74792 01	0.07896 38617 47	0.59124 66101 86
85	1.90141 84226 94	0.99783 38324 54	0.06578 48220 28	0.59018 97845 64
86	1.92378 80511 96	0.99861 48313 09	0.05261 57646 58	0.58932 45764 17
87	1.94615 76796 99	0.99922 13584 04	0.03945 47450 80	0.58865 13068 68
88	1.96852 73082 01	0.99965 41008 55	0.02629 97840 83	0.58817 02239 67
89	1.99089 69367 03	0.99991 35497 86	0.01314 88765 26	0.58788 15039 78
90	2.01326 65652 05	1.00000 00000 00	0.00000 00000 00	0.58778 52522 92

ELLIPTIC FUNCTIONS   TABLE $\theta = 54°$

q = 0.06603 86859 10861 03   D(90) = 1.30433 95327 53677
q'= 0.02646 71830 76961 27   1/D(90) = 0.76667 15413 34666

r	ϕ	$E(\phi,k)$	A(r)	D(r)
45	0.91671 05322 68	0.84018 06393 86	0.70096 59072 76	1.15208 21160 30
46	0.93378 18684 29	0.85320 86868 82	0.71331 07017 34	1.15739 28710 38
47	0.95069 66186 89	0.86599 88321 51	0.72544 52939 85	1.16269 73688 31
48	0.96744 67798 02	0.87855 58275 59	0.73736 55665 98	1.16798 91455 28
49	0.98406 33557 01	0.89088 45908 44	0.74906 74491 72	1.17326 17519 72
50	1.00051 92308 42	0.90299 01874 97	0.76054 69207 85	1.17850 87616 02
51	1.01682 62836 15	0.91487 78139 70	0.77180 00124 67	1.18372 37782 91
52	1.03298 68198 51	0.92655 27817 18	0.78282 28097 01	1.18890 04441 57
53	1.04900 32784 27	0.93802 05021 14	0.79361 14549 52	1.19403 24473 32
54	1.06487 82249 90	0.94928 64722 29	0.80416 21502 15	1.19911 35296 73
55	1.08061 43458 23	0.96035 62614 81	0.81447 11595 66	1.20413 74944 13
56	1.09621 44418 44	0.97123 54991 66	0.82453 48117 39	1.20909 82137 45
57	1.11168 14227 66	0.98192 98628 49	0.83434 95026 97	1.21398 96363 18
58	1.12701 83014 18	0.99244 50676 13	0.84391 16982 05	1.21880 57946 48
59	1.14222 81882 31	1.00278 68561 43	0.85321 79363 99	1.22354 08124 27
60	1.15731 42859 04	1.01296 09896 36	0.86226 48303 50	1.22818 89117 23
61	1.17227 98842 41	1.02297 32395 17	0.87104 90706 03	1.23274 44200 65
62	1.18712 83551 77	1.03282 93799 17	0.87956 74277 07	1.23720 17774 01
63	1.20186 31479 75	1.04253 51809 24	0.88781 67547 16	1.24155 55429 17
64	1.21648 77846 15	1.05209 64025 41	0.89579 39896 60	1.24580 04017 18
65	1.23100 58553 61	1.06151 87893 53	0.90349 61579 83	1.24993 11713 55
66	1.24542 10145 08	1.07080 80658 58	0.91092 03749 43	1.25394 28081 89
67	1.25973 69763 13	1.07996 99324 34	0.91806 38479 69	1.25783 04135 92
68	1.27395 75110 88	1.08901 00619 19	0.92492 38789 61	1.26158 92399 67
69	1.28808 64414 81	1.09793 40967 65	0.93149 78665 51	1.26521 46965 85
70	1.30212 76389 18	1.10674 76467 40	0.93778 33082 94	1.26870 23552 39
71	1.31608 50202 06	1.11545 62871 45	0.94377 78028 00	1.27204 79556 86
72	1.32996 25442 92	1.12406 55575 23	0.94947 90518 05	1.27524 74108 94
73	1.34376 42091 85	1.13258 09608 21	0.95488 48621 58	1.27829 68120 79
74	1.35749 40490 13	1.14100 79629 80	0.95999 31477 48	1.28119 24335 11
75	1.37115 61312 22	1.14935 19929 29	0.96480 19313 41	1.28393 07371 13
76	1.38475 45539 14	1.15761 84429 48	0.96930 93463 36	1.28650 83768 15
77	1.39829 34433 04	1.16581 26693 78	0.97351 36384 37	1.28892 22026 83
78	1.41177 69513 02	1.17393 99936 49	0.97741 31672 32	1.29116 92647 99
79	1.42520 92532 01	1.18200 57036 06	0.98100 64076 79	1.29324 68169 04
80	1.43859 45454 76	1.19001 50550 95	0.98429 19514 94	1.29515 23197 81
81	1.45193 70436 72	1.19797 32738 03	0.98726 85084 44	1.29688 34443 89
82	1.46524 09803 88	1.20588 55573 17	0.98993 49075 27	1.29843 80747 40
83	1.47851 06033 39	1.21375 70773 82	0.99229 00980 60	1.29981 43105 06
84	1.49175 01734 89	1.22159 29823 34	0.99433 31506 48	1.30101 04693 68
85	1.50496 39632 56	1.22939 83996 92	0.99606 32580 51	1.30202 50890 91
86	1.51815 62547 65	1.23717 84388 86	0.99747 97359 36	1.30285 69293 31
87	1.53133 13381 56	1.24493 81940 95	0.99858 20235 18	1.30350 49731 64
88	1.54449 35099 35	1.25268 27471 88	0.99936 96840 81	1.30396 84283 46
89	1.55764 70713 48	1.26041 71707 32	0.99984 24053 94	1.30424 67282 87
90	1.57079 63267 95	1.26814 65310 65	1.00000 00000 00	1.30433 95327 54

ELLIPTIC FUNCTIONS   TABLE $\theta = 55°$

K = 2.03471 53121 85791

K'= 1.73124 51756 57058

E = 1.25867 96247 79997

E'= 1.43229 09693 06756

r	u=(r/90)K=F(φ,k)	sn u	cn u	dn u
0	0.00000 00000 00	0.00000 00000 00	1.00000 00000 00	1.00000 00000 00
1	0.02260 79479 13	0.02260 47302 60	0.99974 44804 40	0.99982 85510 09
2	0.04521 58958 26	0.04519 01674 00	0.99897 84025 55	0.99931 46131 01
3	0.06782 38437 40	0.06773 70821 95	0.99770 32062 17	0.99845 94114 09
4	0.09043 17916 53	0.09022 63727 53	0.99592 12828 63	0.99726 49809 97
5	0.11303 97395 66	0.11263 91270 40	0.99363 59630 47	0.99573 41566 76
6	0.13564 76874 79	0.13495 66840 51	0.99085 14991 81	0.99387 05589 03
7	0.15825 56353 92	0.15716 06932 05	0.98757 30436 33	0.99167 85758 57
8	0.18086 35833 05	0.17923 31715 54	0.98380 66223 68	0.98916 33419 04
9	0.20347 15312 19	0.20115 65584 35	0.97955 91043 93	0.98633 07126 05
10	0.22607 94791 32	0.22291 37672 06	0.97483 81672 82	0.98318 72365 36
11	0.24868 74270 45	0.24448 82337 69	0.96965 22590 85	0.97974 01241 41
12	0.27129 53749 58	0.26586 39615 80	0.96401 05569 61	0.97599 72139 24
13	0.29390 33228 71	0.28702 55629 29	0.95792 29229 04	0.97196 69362 47
14	0.31651 12707 84	0.30795 82962 76	0.95139 98569 24	0.96765 82750 66
15	0.33911 92186 98	0.32864 80994 99	0.94445 24480 86	0.96308 07279 13
16	0.36172 71666 11	0.34908 16189 30	0.93709 23238 00	0.95824 42644 43
17	0.38433 51145 24	0.36924 62341 14	0.92933 15977 59	0.95315 92838 96
18	0.40694 30624 37	0.38913 00782 58	0.92118 28169 23	0.94783 65717 67
19	0.42955 10103 50	0.40872 20543 83	0.91265 89079 50	0.94228 72560 36
20	0.45215 89582 64	0.42801 18472 15	0.90377 31234 35	0.93652 27632 47
21	0.47476 69061 77	0.44698 99309 20	0.89453 89883 37	0.93055 47747 41
22	0.49737 48540 90	0.46564 75727 70	0.88497 02469 43	0.92439 51833 31
23	0.51998 28020 03	0.48397 68329 08	0.87508 08106 73	0.91805 60506 82
24	0.54259 07499 16	0.50197 05603 81	0.86488 47070 63	0.91154 95656 39
25	0.56519 86978 29	0.51962 23856 22	0.85439 60301 64	0.90488 80037 41
26	0.58780 66457 43	0.53692 67096 16	0.84362 88926 42	0.89808 36881 06
27	0.61041 45936 56	0.55387 86899 65	0.83259 73797 72	0.89114 89518 90
28	0.63302 25415 69	0.57047 42241 04	0.82131 55055 35	0.88409 61024 59
29	0.65563 04894 82	0.58670 99299 25	0.80979 71709 80	0.87693 73874 17
30	0.67823 84373 95	0.60258 31240 48	0.79805 61249 76	0.86968 49625 95
31	0.70084 63853 08	0.61809 17980 28	0.78610 59274 74	0.86235 08620 90
32	0.72345 43332 22	0.63323 45927 37	0.77395 99153 45	0.85494 69704 20
33	0.74606 22811 35	0.64801 07711 85	0.76163 11708 62	0.84748 49968 32
34	0.76867 02290 48	0.66242 01900 41	0.74913 24928 39	0.83997 64517 92
35	0.79127 81769 61	0.67646 32700 83	0.73647 63704 48	0.83243 26256 57
36	0.81388 61248 74	0.69014 09658 32	0.72367 49596 89	0.82486 45695 19
37	0.83649 40727 87	0.70345 47345 69	0.71074 00624 79	0.81728 30781 83
38	0.85910 20207 01	0.71640 65049 79	0.69768 31083 12	0.80969 86752 52
39	0.88170 99686 14	0.72899 86455 89	0.68451 51384 23	0.80212 16002 38
40	0.90431 79165 27	0.74123 39332 08	0.67124 67923 66	0.79456 17976 60
41	0.92692 58644 40	0.75311 55215 25	0.65788 82969 30	0.78702 89080 24
42	0.94953 38123 53	0.76464 69100 31	0.64444 94572 74	0.77953 22606 22
43	0.97214 17602 67	0.77583 19133 87	0.63093 96501 81	0.77208 08680 51
44	0.99474 97081 80	0.78667 46313 90	0.61736 78193 17	0.76468 34223 42
45	1.01735 76560 93	0.79717 94196 16	0.60374 24723 67	0.75734 82926 31

218

q = 0.06904 22996 09032 02   D(90) = 1.32039 64539 56575
q′= 0.02491 50625 23980 95   1/D(90) = 0.75734 82926 30970

r	ϕ	$E(\phi, k)$	$A(r)$	$D(r)$
0	0.00000 00000 00	0.00000 00000 00	0.00000 00000 00	1.00000 00000 00
1	0.02260 66557 74	0.02260 53637 67	0.01712 13223 49	1.00009 74600 00
2	0.04520 55624 11	0.04519 52332 46	0.03423 80342 32	1.00038 97217 30
3	0.06778 89892 56	0.06775 41670 00	0.05134 55249 28	1.00087 64305 20
4	0.09034 92425 21	0.09026 68289 28	0.06843 91832 16	1.00155 69957 24
5	0.11287 86834 92	0.11271 80399 93	0.08551 43971 33	1.00243 05914 31
6	0.13536 97464 52	0.13509 28288 53	0.10256 65537 51	1.00349 61574 54
7	0.15781 49562 55	0.15737 64810 33	0.11959 10389 67	1.00475 24006 02
8	0.18020 69454 37	0.17955 45863 19	0.13658 32373 21	1.00619 77962 29
9	0.20253 84708 18	0.20161 30840 46	0.15353 85318 37	1.00783 05900 67
10	0.22480 24294 86	0.22353 83060 30	0.17045 23038 98	1.00964 88003 27
11	0.24699 18741 27	0.24531 70168 42	0.18731 99331 59	1.01165 02200 76
12	0.26910 00276 01	0.26693 64512 43	0.20413 67974 92	1.01383 24198 89
13	0.29112 02967 43	0.28838 43485 45	0.22089 82729 83	1.01619 27507 64
14	0.31304 62853 14	0.30964 89837 75	0.23759 97339 76	1.01872 83473 01
15	0.33487 18060 65	0.33071 91954 76	0.25423 65531 61	1.02143 61311 43
16	0.35659 08918 83	0.35158 44100 90	0.27080 41017 27	1.02431 28146 75
17	0.37819 78059 85	0.37223 46628 36	0.28729 77495 68	1.02735 49049 73
18	0.39968 70511 43	0.39266 06150 74	0.30371 28655 50	1.03055 87080 00
19	0.42105 33779 19	0.41285 35681 65	0.32004 48178 47	1.03392 03330 51
20	0.44229 17919 15	0.43280 54738 53	0.33628 89743 40	1.03743 56974 27
21	0.46339 75600 27	0.45250 89412 57	0.35244 07030 90	1.04110 05313 50
22	0.48436 62157 12	0.47195 72405 48	0.36849 53728 82	1.04491 03830 99
23	0.50519 35632 88	0.49114 43034 52	0.38444 83538 43	1.04886 06243 69
24	0.52587 56812 76	0.51006 47207 06	0.40029 50181 42	1.05294 64558 44
25	0.54640 89248 20	0.52871 37366 33	0.41603 07407 58	1.05716 29129 80
26	0.56678 99271 96	0.54708 72410 12	0.43165 09003 41	1.06150 48719 88
27	0.58701 56004 64	0.56518 17584 44	0.44715 08801 47	1.06596 70560 11
28	0.60708 31352 86	0.58299 44353 94	0.46252 60690 52	1.07054 40414 91
29	0.62698 99999 55	0.60052 30251 35	0.47777 18626 63	1.07523 02647 08
30	0.64673 39386 77	0.61776 58708 02	0.49288 36644 94	1.08002 00285 06
31	0.66631 29691 56	0.63472 18867 64	0.50785 68872 44	1.08490 75091 66
32	0.69445 20257 82	0.65139 05385 43	0.52268 69541 44	1.08988 67634 47
33	0.70496 97246 54	0.66777 18214 76	0.53736 93003 97	1.09495 17357 74
34	0.72404 48219 47	0.68386 62383 42	0.55189 93746 99	1.10009 62655 57
35	0.74294 97465 77	0.69967 47761 49	0.56627 26408 39	1.10531 40946 50
36	0.76168 38262 99	0.71519 88822 75	0.58048 45793 85	1.11059 88749 30
37	0.78024 66358 44	0.73044 04401 50	0.59453 06894 44	1.11594 41759 84
38	0.79863 79909 52	0.74540 17446 53	0.60840 64905 08	1.12134 34929 03
39	0.81685 79420 92	0.76008 54773 96	0.62210 75243 69	1.12679 02541 75
40	0.83490 67679 10	0.77449 46820 25	0.63562 93571 10	1.13227 78296 54
41	0.85278 49684 56	0.78863 27397 14	0.64896 75811 73	1.13779 95386 12
42	0.87049 32582 28	0.80250 33449 39	0.66211 78174 89	1.14334 86578 51
43	0.88803 25590 66	0.81611 04816 90	0.67507 57176 81	1.14891 84298 78
44	0.90540 39929 51	0.82945 84001 86	0.68783 69663 24	1.15450 20711 17
45	0.92260 88747 24	0.84255 15942 14	0.70039 72832 74	1.16009 27801 69

K = 2.03471 53121 85791   E = 1.25867 96247 79997
K' = 1.73124 51756 57058   E' = 1.43229 09693 06756

r	u=(r/90)K=F(ϕ,k)	sn u	cn u	dn u
45	1.01735 76560 93	0.79717 94196 16	0.60374 24723 67	0.75734 82926 31
46	1.03996 56040 06	0.80735 08608 64	0.59007 16799 35	0.75008 35242 30
47	1.06257 35519 19	0.81719 37374 56	0.57636 30760 74	0.74289 68390 31
48	1.08518 14998 32	0.82671 30044 88	0.56262 38603 29	0.73579 56371 08
49	1.10778 94477 46	0.83591 37640 60	0.54886 08011 64	0.72878 69994 40
50	1.13039 73956 59	0.84480 12405 62	0.53508 02406 61	0.72187 76916 29
51	1.15300 53435 72	0.85338 07570 06	0.52128 81003 54	0.71507 41685 31
52	1.17561 32914 85	0.86165 77124 76	0.50748 98881 08	0.70838 25796 96
53	1.19822 12393 98	0.86963 75606 59	0.49369 07059 00	0.70180 87755 17
54	1.22082 91873 11	0.87732 57895 07	0.47989 52584 33	0.69535 83140 15
55	1.24343 71352 25	0.88472 79019 93	0.46610 78624 48	0.68903 64681 45
56	1.26604 50831 38	0.89184 93979 69	0.45233 24566 54	0.68284 82335 75
57	1.28865 30310 51	0.89869 57571 03	0.43857 26121 91	0.67679 83368 38
58	1.31126 09789 64	0.90527 24228 79	0.42483 15435 26	0.67089 12437 80
59	1.33386 89268 77	0.91158 47876 22	0.41111 21197 14	0.66513 11682 59
60	1.35647 68747 91	0.91763 81785 37	0.39741 68759 52	0.65952 20810 07
61	1.37908 48227 04	0.92343 78447 08	0.38374 80253 52	0.65406 77186 09
62	1.40169 27706 17	0.92898 89450 38	0.37010 74708 76	0.64877 15925 40
63	1.42430 07185 30	0.93429 65370 79	0.35649 68173 81	0.64363 69982 09
64	1.44690 86664 43	0.93936 55667 23	0.34291 73837 16	0.63866 70239 62
65	1.46951 66143 56	0.94420 08587 05	0.32937 02148 35	0.63386 45600 12
66	1.49212 45622 70	0.94880 71078 79	0.31585 60938 75	0.62923 23072 40
67	1.51473 25101 83	0.95318 88712 28	0.30237 55541 83	0.62477 27858 50
68	1.53734 04580 96	0.95735 05605 62	0.28892 88912 37	0.62048 83438 32
69	1.55994 84060 09	0.96129 64358 67	0.27551 61744 60	0.61638 11652 15
70	1.58255 63539 22	0.96503 05992 58	0.26213 72588 86	0.61245 32780 84
71	1.60516 43018 35	0.96855 69895 00	0.24879 17966 73	0.60870 65623 32
72	1.62777 22497 49	0.97187 93770 60	0.23547 92484 41	0.60514 27571 33
73	1.65038 01976 62	0.97500 13596 47	0.22219 88944 32	0.60176 34681 23
74	1.67298 81455 75	0.97792 63582 07	0.20894 98454 74	0.59857 01742 60
75	1.69559 60934 88	0.98065 76133 37	0.19573 10537 54	0.59556 42343 65
76	1.71820 40414 01	0.98319 81820 84	0.18254 13233 93	0.59274 68933 31
77	1.74081 19893 15	0.98555 09351 00	0.16937 93208 26	0.59011 92879 73
78	1.76341 99372 28	0.98771 85541 19	0.15624 35849 83	0.58768 24525 40
79	1.78602 78851 41	0.98970 35297 34	0.14313 25372 92	0.58543 73238 55
80	1.80863 58330 54	0.99150 81594 39	0.13004 44914 83	0.58338 47460 96
81	1.83124 37809 67	0.99313 45459 22	0.11697 76632 33	0.58152 54751 99
82	1.85385 17288 80	0.99458 45955 78	0.10393 01796 38	0.57986 01828 97
83	1.87645 96767 94	0.99586 00172 24	0.09090 00885 34	0.57838 94603 70
84	1.89906 76247 07	0.99696 23210 04	0.07788 53676 73	0.57711 38215 27
85	1.92167 55726 20	0.99789 28174 60	0.06488 39337 77	0.57603 37058 89
86	1.94428 35205 33	0.99865 26167 48	0.05189 36514 72	0.57514 94811 12
87	1.96689 14684 46	0.99924 26280 09	0.03891 23421 25	0.57446 14450 99
88	1.98949 94163 59	0.99966 35588 61	0.02593 77925 99	0.57396 98277 51
89	2.01210 73642 73	0.99991 59150 14	0.01296 77639 37	0.57367 47923 15
90	2.03471 53121 86	1.00000 00000 00	0.00000 00000 00	0.57357 64363 51

q = 0.06904 22996 09032 02   D(90) = 1.32039 64539 56575
q′= 0.02491 50625 23980 95   1/D(90) = 0.75734 82926 30970

r	ϕ	$E(\phi,k)$	A(r)	D(r)
45	0.92260 88747 24	0.84255 15942 14	0.70039 72832 74	1.16009 27801 69
46	0.93964 87047 78	0.85539 47791 59	0.71275 24260 42	1.16568 37460 83
47	0.95652 51617 32	0.86799 28707 85	0.72489 81922 34	1.17126 81566 60
48	0.97324 00951 42	0.88035 09648 45	0.73683 04220 27	1.17683 92067 51
49	0.98979 55182 50	0.89247 43175 56	0.74854 50007 06	1.18239 01065 56
50	1.00619 36008 14	0.90436 83269 64	0.76003 78612 23	1.18791 40899 03
51	1.02243 66620 23	0.91603 85152 56	0.77130 49868 10	1.19340 44225 18
52	1.03852 71635 36	0.92749 05120 16	0.78234 24136 14	1.19885 44102 37
53	1.05446 77026 48	0.93873 00384 37	0.79314 62333 62	1.20425 74071 97
54	1.07026 10056 00	0.94976 28925 19	0.80371 25960 46	1.20960 68239 55
55	1.08590 99210 52	0.96059 49352 19	0.81403 77126 33	1.21489 61355 54
56	1.10141 74137 24	0.97123 20775 66	0.82411 78577 79	1.22011 88895 03
57	1.11678 65582 23	0.98168 02687 31	0.83394 93725 55	1.22526 87136 85
58	1.13202 05330 48	0.99194 54850 22	0.84352 86671 74	1.23033 93241 61
59	1.14712 26147 95	1.00203 37197 98	0.85285 22237 16	1.23532 45328 73
60	1.16209 61725 66	1.01195 09742 65	0.86191 65988 46	1.24021 82552 36
61	1.17694 46625 66	1.02170 32491 42	0.87071 84265 13	1.24501 45176 00
62	1.19167 16229 15	1.03129 65371 62	0.87925 44206 34	1.24970 74645 86
63	1.20628 06686 62	1.04073 68163 69	0.88752 13777 58	1.25429 13662 79
64	1.22077 54870 00	1.05003 00442 01	0.89551 61796 89	1.25876 06252 67
65	1.23515 98326 87	1.05918 21523 02	0.90323 57960 87	1.26310 97835 21
66	1.24943 75236 67	1.06819 90420 48	0.91067 72870 15	1.26733 35291 10
67	1.26361 24368 86	1.07708 65807 42	0.91783 78054 56	1.27142 67027 37
68	1.27768 85043 03	1.08585 05984 50	0.92471 45997 64	1.27538 43040 88
69	1.29166 97090 95	1.09449 68854 42	0.93130 50160 72	1.27920 14979 89
70	1.30556 00820 34	1.10303 11902 05	0.93760 65006 26	1.28287 36203 66
71	1.31936 36980 55	1.11145 92179 91	0.94361 66020 70	1.28639 61839 88
72	1.33308 46729 89	1.11978 66298 76	0.94933 29736 40	1.28976 48840 03
73	1.34672 71604 64	1.12801 90422 85	0.95475 33753 03	1.29297 56032 44
74	1.36029 53489 62	1.13616 20269 64	0.95987 56758 02	1.29602 44173 11
75	1.37379 34590 33	1.14422 11113 65	0.96469 78546 22	1.29890 75994 09
76	1.38722 57406 46	1.15220 17794 09	0.96921 80038 66	1.30162 16249 54
77	1.40059 64706 84	1.16010 94726 03	0.97343 43300 46	1.30416 31759 21
78	1.41390 99505 60	1.16794 95914 87	0.97734 51557 63	1.30652 91449 46
79	1.42717.05039 59	1.17572 74973 74	0.98094 89213 00	1.30871 66391 58
80	1.44038 24746 92	1.18344 85143 71	0.98424 41861 09	1.31072 29837 63
81	1.45355 02246 43	1.19111 79316 37	0.98722 96301 86	1.31254 57253 41
82	1.46667 81318 37	1.19874 10058 81	0.98990 40553 42	1.31418 26348 84
83	1.47977 05885 61	1.20632 29640 43	0.99226 63863 60	1.31563 17105 52
84	1.49283 19995 90	1.21386 90061 73	0.99431 56720 36	1.31689 11801 47
85	1.50586 67804 73	1.22138 43084 47	0.99605 10861 04	1.31795 95033 05
86	1.51887 93558 76	1.22887 40263 38	0.99747 19280 42	1.31883 53734 02
87	1.53187 41579 87	1.23634 32978 86	0.99857 76237 57	1.31951 77191 71
88	1.54485 56249 58	1.24379 72470 76	0.99936 77261 46	1.32000 57060 25
89	1.55782 81993 81	1.25124 09872 83	0.99984 19155 37	1.32029 87370 93
90	1.57079 63267 95	1.25867 96247 80	1.00000 00000 00	1.32039 64539 57

K = 2.05706 23227 97365

K' = 1.72139 08313 74249

E = 1.24918 16206 07472

E' = 1.43966 21471 15459

r	u=(r/90)K=F(ϕ,k)	sn u	cn u	dn u
0	0.00000 00000 00	0.00000 00000 00	1.00000 00000 00	1.00000 00000 00
1	0.02285 62480 31	0.02285 28907 93	0.99973 88385 89	0.99982 05102 32
2	0.04571 24960 62	0.04568 56519 86	0.99895 58654 93	0.99928 24801 48
3	0.06856 87440 93	0.06847 82230 14	0.99765 26113 70	0.99838 72251 35
4	0.09142 49921 24	0.09121 06808 66	0.99583 16181 44	0.99713 69299 11
5	0.11428 12401 55	0.11386 33075 93	0.99349 64253 50	0.99553 46372 27
6	0.13713 74881 86	0.13641 66563 02	0.99065 15511 94	0.99358 42321 97
7	0.15999 37362 18	0.15885 16151 69	0.98730 24685 26	0.99129 04224 17
8	0.18284 99842 49	0.18114 94690 18	0.98345 55759 54	0.98865 87140 58
9	0.20570 62322 80	0.20329 19580 50	0.97911 81643 66	0.98569 53841 76
10	0.22856 24803 11	0.22526 13333 34	0.97429 83791 96	0.98240 74494 82
11	0.25141 87283 42	0.24704 04087 21	0.96900 51787 58	0.97880 26318 74
12	0.27427 49763 73	0.26861 26088 66	0.96324 82890 50	0.97488 93210 52
13	0.29713 12244 04	0.28996 20131 11	0.95703 81554 32	0.97067 65345 33
14	0.31998 74724 35	0.31107 33950 02	0.95038 58915 84	0.96617 38754 38
15	0.34284 37204 66	0.33193 22572 98	0.94330 32262 03	0.96139 14883 98
16	0.36569 99684 97	0.35252 48623 24	0.93580 24478 72	0.95634 00139 61
17	0.38855 62165 28	0.37283 82576 27	0.92789 63485 49	0.95103 05418 53
18	0.41141 24645 59	0.39286 02968 93	0.91959 81661 17	0.94547 45634 76
19	0.43426 87125 91	0.41257 96561 58	0.91092 15264 36	0.93968 39239 92
20	0.45712 49606 22	0.43198 58453 72	0.90188 03853 05	0.93367 07743 42
21	0.47998 12086 53	0.45106 92154 21	0.89248 89707 44	0.92744 75235 41
22	0.50283 74566 84	0.46982 09607 39	0.88276 17259 77	0.92102 67915 45
23	0.52569 37047 15	0.48823 31177 06	0.87271 32534 66	0.91442 13630 11
24	0.54854 99527 46	0.50629 85590 05	0.86235 82603 24	0.90764 41421 97
25	0.57140 62007 77	0.52401 09841 79	0.85171 15054 17	0.90070 81092 58
26	0.59426 24488 08	0.54136 49066 43	0.84078 77483 97	0.89362 62781 68
27	0.61711 86968 39	0.55835 56373 95	0.82960 17009 32	0.88641 16564 41
28	0.63997 49448 70	0.57497 92657 20	0.81816 79803 03	0.87907 72068 37
29	0.66283 11929 01	0.59123 26371 66	0.80650 10655 60	0.87163 58111 83
30	0.68568 74409 32	0.60711 33290 83	0.79461 52563 66	0.86410 02364 20
31	0.70854 36889 64	0.62261 96240 10	0.78252 46346 27	0.85648 31029 65
32	0.73139 99369 95	0.63775 04812 18	0.77024 30289 89	0.84879 68554 53
33	0.75425 61850 26	0.65250 55066 72	0.75778 39822 55	0.84105 37358 91
34	0.77711 24330 57	0.66688 49217 08	0.74516 07217 23	0.83326 57592 34
35	0.79996 86810 88	0.68088 95306 81	0.73238 61324 53	0.82544 46913 88
36	0.82282 49291 19	0.69452 06878 49	0.71947 27334 30	0.81760 20296 14
37	0.84568 11771 50	0.70778 02637 32	0.70643 26565 72	0.80974 89852 71
38	0.86853 74251 81	0.72067 06111 70	0.69327 76285 12	0.80189 64688 70
39	0.89139 36732 12	0.73319 45313 05	0.68001 89550 78	0.79405 50773 49
40	0.91424 99212 43	0.74535 52396 66	0.66666 75083 60	0.78623 50834 80
41	0.93710 61692 74	0.75715 63325 56	0.65323 37162 69	0.77844 64273 38
42	0.95996 24173 05	0.76860 17538 84	0.63972 75544 53	0.77069 87097 14
43	0.98281 86653 37	0.77969 57626 02	0.62615 85404 52	0.76300 11873 64
44	1.00567 49133 68	0.79044 29008 60	0.61253 57299 62	0.75536 27699 94
45	1.02853 11613 99	0.80084 79630 11	0.59886 77150 60	0.74779 20188 60

q = 0.07215 43668 98737 07   D(90) = 1.33727 02232 42633
q'= 0.02341 90910 88188 44   1/D(90) = 0.74779 20188 60022

r	φ	E(φ,k)	A(r)	D(r)
0	0.00000 00000 00	0.00000 00000 00	0.00000 00000 00	1.00000 00000 00
1	0.02285 48804 32	0.02285 35129 80	0.01709 09622 45	1.00010 25736 41
2	0.04570 15592 85	0.04569 06272 18	0.03417 73787 25	1.00041 01701 56
3	0.06853 18550 43	0.06849 50016 99	0.05125 47032 48	1.00092 24164 76
4	0.09133 76262 02	0.09125 04104 45	0.06831 83887 80	1.00163 86913 13
5	0.11411 07910 30	0.11394 07989 74	0.08536 38870 33	1.00255 81259 03
6	0.13684 33469 97	0.13655 03395 15	0.10238 66480 68	1.00367 96050 51
7	0.15952 73898 14	0.15906 34845 86	0.11938 21199 28	1.00500 17684 57
8	0.18215 51319 67	0.18146 50185 51	0.13634 57482 81	1.00652 30123 51
9	0.20471 89206 58	0.20374 01068 24	0.15327 29761 07	1.00824 14914 09
10	0.22721 12550 73	0.22587 43423 94	0.17015 92434 10	1.01015 51209 62
11	0.24962 48029 03	0.24785 37893 91	0.18699 99869 77	1.01226 15794 94
12	0.27195 24160 36	0.26966 50234 29	0.20379 06401 72	1.01455 83114 18
13	0.29418 71453 73	0.29129 51685 32	0.22052 66327 88	1.01704 25301 42
14	0.31632 22546 95	0.31273 19304 51	0.23720 33909 45	1.01971 12214 02
15	0.33835 12335 47	0.33396 36262 40	0.25381 63370 50	1.02256 11468 79
16	0.36026 78090 99	0.35497 92100 00	0.27036 08898 08	1.02558 88480 77
17	0.38206 59569 47	0.37576 82947 33	0.28683 24643 13	1.02879 06504 72
18	0.40373 99108 39	0.39632 11702 81	0.30322 64721 91	1.03216 26679 20
19	0.42528 41713 05	0.41662 88173 77	0.31953 83218 28	1.03570 08073 17
20	0.44669 35132 00	0.43668 29178 56	0.33576 34186 59	1.03940 07735 14
21	0.46796 29921 39	0.45647 58611 21	0.35189 71655 50	1.04325 80744 74
22	0.48908 79498 66	0.47600 07469 73	0.36793 49632 47	1.04726 80266 67
23	0.51006 40185 34	0.49525 13849 51	0.38387 22109 12	1.05142 57606 99
24	0.53088 71239 60	0.51422 22903 55	0.39970 43067 50	1.05572 62271 66
25	0.55155 34878 52	0.53290 86771 33	0.41542 66487 12	1.06016 42027 29
26	0.57205 96290 60	0.55130 64478 50	0.43103 46352 96	1.06473 42963 94
27	0.59240 23638 86	0.56941 21809 43	0.44652 36664 32	1.06943 09560 09
28	0.61257 88054 96	0.58722 31155 07	0.46188 91444 60	1.07424 84749 46
29	0.63258 63624 76	0.60473 71338 43	0.47712 64752 01	1.07918 09989 80
30	0.65242 27365 93	0.62195 27420 12	0.49223 10691 20	1.08422 25333 49
31	0.67208 59198 00	0.63886 90486 32	0.50719 83425 79	1.08936 69499 85
32	0.69157 41905 53	0.65548 57421 71	0.52202 37191 88	1.09460 79949 06
33	0.71088 61094 77	0.67180 30669 68	0.53670 26312 45	1.09993 92957 78
34	0.73002 05144 52	0.68782 17982 07	0.55123 05212 68	1.10535 43696 07
35	0.74897 65151 69	0.70354 32160 78	0.56560 28436 19	1.11084 66305 79
36	0.76775 34872 10	0.71896 90793 40	0.57981 50662 19	1.11640 93980 32
37	0.78635 10657 03	0.73410 15984 75	0.59386 26723 49	1.12203 59045 34
38	0.80476 91386 13	0.74894 34086 34	0.60774 11625 42	1.12771 93040 90
39	0.82300 78397 18	0.76349 75425 62	0.62144 60565 55	1.13345 26804 28
40	0.84106 75413 17	0.77776 74036 39	0.63497 28954 26	1.13922 90553 96
41	0.85894 88467 16	0.79175 67392 19	0.64831 72436 11	1.14504 13974 22
42	0.87665 25825 49	0.80546 96143 74	0.66147 46912 03	1.15088 26300 54
43	0.89417 97909 63	0.81891 03861 89	0.67444 08562 13	1.15674 56405 59
44	0.91153 17217 16	0.83208 36786 99	0.68721 13869 36	1.16262 32885 67
45	0.92870 98242 32	0.84499 43585 68	0.69978 19643 75	1.16850 84147 59

K = 2.05706 23227 97365   E = 1.24918 16206 07472
K'= 1.72139 08313 74249   E'= 1.43966 21471 15459

r	u=(r/90)K=F(ϕ,k)	sn u	cn u	dn u
45	1.02853 11613 99	0.80084 79630 11	0.59886 77150 60	0.74779 20188 60
46	1.05138 74094 30	0.81091 59655 39	0.58516 26242 62	0.74029 71468 60
47	1.07424 36574 61	0.82065 21180 07	0.57142 81242 73	0.73288 60200 11
48	1.09709 99054 92	0.83006 17950 82	0.55767 14232 81	0.72556 61601 90
49	1.11995 61535 23	0.83915 05096 93	0.54389 92756 78	0.71834 47490 19
50	1.14281 24015 54	0.84792 38873 56	0.53011 79880 46	0.71122 86327 85
51	1.16566 86495 85	0.85638 76417 09	0.51633 34263 13	0.70422 43282 89
52	1.18852 48976 16	0.86454 75512 43	0.50255 10239 17	0.69733 80295 07
53	1.21138 11456 47	0.87240 94372 73	0.48877 57908 87	0.69057 56149 65
54	1.23423 73936 78	0.87997 91431 17	0.47501 23237 12	0.68394 26557 38
55	1.25709 36417 10	0.88726 25144 89	0.46126 48158 94	0.67744 44239 63
56	1.27994 98897 41	0.89426 53810 82	0.44753 70690 78	0.67108 59017 96
57	1.30280 61377 72	0.90099 35393 16	0.43383 25046 73	0.66487 17907 17
58	1.32566 23858 03	0.90745 27362 35	0.42015 41758 68	0.65880 65211 11
59	1.34851 86338 34	0.91364 86545 01	0.40650 47799 58	0.65289 42620 53
60	1.37137 48818 65	0.91958 68984 58	0.39288 66709 17	0.64713 89312 28
61	1.39423 11298 96	0.92527 29812 29	0.37930 18721 37	0.64154 42049 26
62	1.41708 73779 27	0.93071 23127 97	0.36575 20892 73	0.63611 35280 51
63	1.43994 36259 58	0.93591 01890 24	0.35223 87231 43	0.63085 01241 02
64	1.46279 98739 89	0.94087 17815 70	0.33876 28826 27	0.62575 70050 62
65	1.48565 61220 20	0.94560 21286 61	0.32532 53975 20	0.62083 69811 74
66	1.50851 23700 51	0.95010 61266 56	0.31192 68313 11	0.61609 26705 45
67	1.53136 86180 82	0.95438 85223 67	0.29856 74938 32	0.61152 65085 55
68	1.55422 48661 14	0.95845 39060 98	0.28524 74537 75	0.60714 07570 38
69	1.57708 11141 45	0.96230 67053 29	0.27196 65510 29	0.60293 75132 04
70	1.59993 73621 76	0.96595 11790 34	0.25872 44088 29	0.59891 87182 87
71	1.62279 36102 07	0.96939 14125 58	0.24552 04457 05	0.59508 61658 84
72	1.64564 98582 38	0.97263 13130 37	0.23235 38872 06	0.59144 15099 81
73	1.66850 61062 69	0.97567 46052 98	0.21922 37773 99	0.58798 62726 40
74	1.69136 23543 00	0.97852 48282 10	0.20612 89901 40	0.58472 18513 37
75	1.71421 86023 31	0.98118 53314 56	0.19306 82401 02	0.58164 95259 41
76	1.73707 48503 62	0.98365 92726 68	0.18004 00935 75	0.57877 04653 24
77	1.75993 10983 93	0.98594 96149 17	0.16704 29790 35	0.57608 57335 85
78	1.78278 73464 24	0.98805 91245 07	0.15407 51974 79	0.57359 62959 03
79	1.80564 35944 55	0.98999 03690 51	0.14113 49325 48	0.57130 30239 82
80	1.82849 98424 87	0.99174 57158 03	0.12822 02604 36	0.56920 67011 16
81	1.85135 60905 18	0.99332 73302 12	0.11532 91595 95	0.56730 80268 49
82	1.87421 23385 49	0.99473 71746 89	0.10245 95202 59	0.56560 76212 34
83	1.89706 85865 80	0.99597 70075 45	0.08960 91537 84	0.56410 60286 93
84	1.91992 48346 11	0.99704 83821 02	0.07677 58018 37	0.56280 37214 66
85	1.94278 10826 42	0.99795 26459 45	0.06395 71454 28	0.56170 11026 64
86	1.96563 73306 73	0.99869 09403 04	0.05115 08138 26	0.56079 85089 08
87	1.98849 35787 04	0.99926 41995 54	0.03835 43933 53	0.56009 62125 64
88	2.01134 98267 35	0.99967 31508 24	0.02556 54360 89	0.55959 44235 78
89	2.03420 60747 66	0.99991 83136 95	0.01278 14684 98	0.55929 32908 94
90	2.05706 23227 97	1.00000 00000 00	0.00000 00000 00	0.55919 29034 71

q = 0.07215 43668 98737 07   D(90) = 1.33727 02232 42633
q'= 0.02341 90910 88188 44   1/D(90) = 0.74779 20188 60022

r	φ	E(φ,k)	A(r)	D(r)
45	0.92870 98242 32	0.84499 43585 68	0.69978 19643 75	1.16850 84147 59
46	0.94571 57396 26	0.85764 75115 94	0.71214 83047 34	1.17439 38495 77
47	0.96255 12927 63	0.87004 84201 00	0.72430 61619 67	1.18027 24219 63
48	0.97921 84843 57	0.88220 25412 79	0.73625 13303 87	1.18613 69680 93
49	0.99571 94831 45	0.89411 54865 24	0.74797 96473 20	1.19198 03401 17
50	1.01205 66181 67	0.90579 30017 92	0.75948 69958 12	1.19779 54148 77
51	1.02823 23711 68	0.91724 09490 07	0.77076 93073 75	1.20357 51026 08
52	1.04424 93691 37	0.92846 52885 44	0.78182 25647 67	1.20931 23556 00
53	1.06011 03770 17	0.93947 20627 75	0.79264 28048 09	1.21500 01768 12
54	1.07581 82905 80	0.95026 73806 94	0.80322 61212 29	1.22063 16284 33
55	1.09137 61295 02	0.96085 74036 04	0.81356 86675 19	1.22619 98403 73
56	1.10678 70306 27	0.97124 83318 67	0.82366 66598 16	1.23169 80186 77
57	1.12205 42414 46	0.98144 63926 78	0.83351 63797 94	1.23711 94538 53
58	1.13718 11137 94	0.99145 78288 62	0.84311 41775 52	1.24245 75290 96
59	1.15217 10977 61	1.00128 88886 58	0.85245 64745 11	1.24770 57284 09
60	1.16702 77358 35	1.01094 58164 55	0.86153 97662 95	1.25285 76445 99
61	1.18175 46572 71	1.02043 48444 60	0.87036 06256 09	1.25790 69871 51
62	1.19635 55726 84	1.02976 21852 64	0.87891 57050 89	1.26284 75899 54
63	1.21083 42688 81	1.03893 40252 51	0.88720 17401 34	1.26767 34188 87
64	1.22519 46039 08	1.04795 65188 42	0.89521 55517 07	1.27237 85792 40
65	1.23944 05023 28	1.05683 57835 14	0.90295 40490 95	1.27695 73229 72
66	1.25357 59507 26	1.06557 78955 64	0.91041 42326 38	1.28140 40557 85
67	1.26760 49934 18	1.07418 88865 85	0.91759 31963 97	1.28571 33440 24
68	1.28153 17283 85	1.08267 47406 04	0.92448 81307 81	1.28987 99213 70
69	1.29536 03034 04	1.09104 13918 57	0.93109 63251 08	1.29389 86953 34
70	1.30909 49123 90	1.09929 47231 52	0.93741 51701 03	1.29776 47535 45
71	1.32273 97919 25	1.10744 05647 95	0.94344 21603 33	1.30147 33698 08
72	1.33629 92179 75	1.11548 46940 35	0.94917 48965 54	1.30502 00099 43
73	1.34977 75027 86	1.12343 28349 97	0.95461 10879 94	1.30840 03373 88
74	1.36317 89919 57	1.13129 06590 68	0.95974 85545 41	1.31161 02185 52
75	1.37650 80616 71	1.13906 37857 05	0.96458 52288 41	1.31464 57279 32
76	1.38976 91160 83	1.14675 77836 34	0.96911 91583 10	1.31750 31529 64
77	1.40296 65848 56	1.15437 81724 04	0.97334 85070 43	1.32017 89986 15
78	1.41610 49208 32	1.16193 04242 78	0.97727 15576 15	1.32266 99917 10
79	1.42918 85978 34	1.16941 99664 23	0.98088 67127 87	1.32497 30849 82
80	1.44222 21085 92	1.17685 21833 73	0.98419 24970 90	1.32708 54608 45
81	1.45520 99627 73	1.18423 24197 50	0.98718 75583 06	1.32900 45348 86
82	1.46815 66851 14	1.19156 59832 06	0.98987 06688 22	1.33072 79590 62
83	1.48106 68136 56	1.19885 81475 60	0.99224 07268 71	1.33225 36246 13
84	1.49394 48980 52	1.20611 41561 29	0.99429 67576 45	1.33357 96646 73
85	1.50679 54979 51	1.21333 92251 99	0.99603 79142 91	1.33470 44565 83
86	1.51962 31814 52	1.22053 85476 47	0.99746 34787 66	1.33562 66239 08
87	1.53243 25236 12	1.22771 72966 63	0.99857 28625 76	1.33634 50381 36
88	1.54522 81049 94	1.23488 06295 81	0.99936 56073 76	1.33685 88200 81
89	1.55801 45102 62	1.24203 36917 73	0.99984 13854 41	1.33716 73409 75
90	1.57079 63267 95	1.24918 16206 07	1.00000 00000 00	1.33727 02232 43

K = 2.08035 80666 91578   E = 1.23966 11752 88672
K′= 1.71192 46951 55678   E′= 1.44686 92406 95183

r	u=(r/90)K=F(ϕ,k)	sn u	cn u	dn u
0	0.00000 00000 00	0.00000 00000 00	1.00000 00000 00	1.00000 00000 00
1	0.02311 50896 30	0.02311 15839 94	0.99973 28916 69	0.99981 21319 06
2	0.04623 01792 60	0.04620 21491 28	0.99893 21105 14	0.99924 89994 20
3	0.06934 52688 90	0.06925 07511 94	0.99759 92850 13	0.99831 20153 91
4	0.09246 03585 20	0.09223 65947 22	0.99573 71192 21	0.99700 35261 32
5	0.11557 54481 50	0.11513 91059 23	0.99334 93777 56	0.99532 67988 54
6	0.13869 05377 79	0.13793 80039 45	0.99044 08650 03	0.99328 60042 58
7	0.16180 56274 09	0.16061 33699 26	0.98701 73987 33	0.99088 61944 51
8	0.18492 07170 39	0.18314 57133 21	0.98308 57784 00	0.98813 32764 14
9	0.20803 58066 69	0.20551 60350 56	0.97865 37484 40	0.98503 39812 79
10	0.23115 08962 99	0.22770 58870 81	0.97372 99569 12	0.98159 58297 17
11	0.25426 59859 29	0.24969 74279 33	0.96832 39099 00	0.97782 70937 72
12	0.27738 10755 59	0.27147 34739 87	0.96244 59220 76	0.97373 67554 94
13	0.30049 61651 89	0.29301 75461 05	0.95610 70639 18	0.96933 44627 64
14	0.32361 12548 19	0.31431 39114 65	0.94931 91060 23	0.96463 04827 04
15	0.34672 63444 49	0.33534 76203 75	0.94209 44610 33	0.95963 56530 81
16	0.36984 14340 79	0.35610 45379 88	0.93444 61236 61	0.95436 13321 35
17	0.39295 65237 08	0.37657 13708 13	0.92638 76093 10	0.94881 93472 33
18	0.41607 16133 38	0.39673 56880 38	0.91793 28917 94	0.94302 19427 72
19	0.43918 67029 68	0.41658 59376 84	0.90909 63406 17	0.93698 17277 30
20	0.46230 17925 98	0.43611 14576 94	0.89989 26583 03	0.93071 16232 56
21	0.48541 68822 28	0.45530 24820 56	0.89033 68181 95	0.92422 48106 65
22	0.50853 19718 58	0.47415 01421 60	0.88044 40031 54	0.91753 46801 99
23	0.53164 70614 88	0.49264 64635 72	0.87022 95455 40	0.91065 47808 59
24	0.55476 21511 18	0.51078 43584 67	0.85970 88688 30	0.90359 87716 27
25	0.57787 72407 48	0.52855 76139 92	0.84889 74311 96	0.89638 03743 28
26	0.60099 23303 78	0.54596 08768 22	0.83781 06713 21	0.88901 33283 82
27	0.62410 74200 07	0.56298 96342 33	0.82646 39567 13	0.88151 13476 45
28	0.64722 25096 37	0.57964 01919 97	0.81487 25347 08	0.87388 80795 24
29	0.67033 75992 67	0.59590 96494 12	0.80305 14863 56	0.86615 70664 99
30	0.69345 26888 97	0.61179 58718 08	0.79101 56833 08	0.85833 17101 74
31	0.71656 77785 27	0.62729 74608 47	0.77877 97478 20	0.85042 52379 35
32	0.73968 28681 57	0.64241 37229 40	0.76635 80159 29	0.84245 06722 83
33	0.76279 79577 87	0.65714 46360 90	0.75376 45038 46	0.83442 08028 51
34	0.78591 30474 17	0.67149 08154 87	0.74101 28775 64	0.82634 81611 31
35	0.80902 81370 47	0.68545 34781 17	0.72811 64256 75	0.81824 49978 76
36	0.83214 32266 77	0.69903 44066 90	0.71508 80353 24	0.81012 32631 46
37	0.85525 83163 07	0.71223 59131 40	0.70194 01712 64	0.80199 45889 39
38	0.87837 34059 36	0.72506 08019 38	0.68868 48578 95	0.79387 02743 29
39	0.90148 84955 66	0.73751 23334 52	0.67533 36642 03	0.78576 12730 28
40	0.92460 35851 96	0.74959 41875 57	0.66189 76914 75	0.77767 81832 65
41	0.94771 86748 26	0.76131 04276 85	0.64838 75636 51	0.76963 12398 75
42	0.97083 37644 56	0.77266 54654 83	0.63481 34201 87	0.76163 03084 84
43	0.99394 88540 86	0.78366 40262 30	0.62118 49112 72	0.75368 48816 49
44	1.01706 39437 16	0.79431 11151 42	0.60751 11952 56	0.74580 40768 51
45	1.04017 90333 46	0.80461 19846 76	0.59380 09381 22	0.73799 66361 81

q = 0.07537 99738 58803 37   D(90) = 1.35501 97263 42264
q′= 0.02197 80013 16900 53   1/D(90) = 0.73799 66361 81377

r	φ	E(φ,k)	A(r)	D(r)
0	0.00000 00000 00	0.00000 00000 00	0.00000 00000 00	1.00000 00000 00
1	0.02311 36419 79	0.02311 21944 92	0.01705 81124 52	1.00010 79490 06
2	0.04621 86024 19	0.04620 70307 95	0.03411 17491 41	1.00043 16651 81
3	0.06930 62215 71	0.06926 72138 11	0.05115 64336 96	1.00097 07561 53
4	0.09236 78831 52	0.09227 55741 40	0.06818 76885 27	1.00172 45684 90
5	0.11539 50357 89	0.11521 51297 44	0.08520 10342 38	1.00269 21884 79
6	0.13837 92141 09	0.13806 91461 92	0.10219 19890 47	1.00387 24432 14
7	0.16131 20593 80	0.16082 11950 56	0.11915 60682 30	1.00526 39020 00
8	0.18418 53395 83	0.18345 52100 31	0.13608 87835 99	1.00686 48780 59
9	0.20699 09688 32	0.20595 55404 03	0.15298 56430 00	1.00867 34305 43
10	0.22972 10260 23	0.22830 70014 89	0.16984 21498 64	1.01068 73668 50
11	0.25236 77726 56	0.25049 49217 52	0.18665 38027 92	1.01290 42452 46
12	0.27492 36697 27	0.27250 51862 98	0.20341 60951 91	1.01532 13777 81
13	0.29738 13936 36	0.29432 42765 26	0.22012 45149 61	1.01793 58334 97
14	0.31973 38510 46	0.31593 93057 40	0.23677 45442 47	1.02074 44419 36
15	0.34197 41926 33	0.33733 80505 77	0.25336 16592 43	1.02374 37969 26
16	0.36409 58257 03	0.35850 89781 53	0.26988 13300 71	1.02693 02606 59
17	0.38609 24256 30	0.37944 12688 69	0.28632 90207 30	1.03029 99680 38
18	0.40795 79461 02	0.40012 48348 77	0.30270 01891 13	1.03384 88313 07
19	0.42968 66281 48	0.42055 03342 22	0.31899 02871 13	1.03757 25449 41
20	0.45127 30079 66	0.44070 91807 49	0.33519 47608 05	1.04146 65908 07
21	0.47271 19235 34	0.46059 35498 70	0.35130 90507 11	1.04552 62435 76
22	0.49399 85200 28	0.48019 63803 42	0.36732 85921 59	1.04974 65763 85
23	0.51512 82540 74	0.49951 13722 22	0.38324 88157 34	1.05412 24667 51
24	0.53609 68968 43	0.51853 29812 07	0.39906 51478 11	1.05864 86027 14
25	0.55690 05360 55	0.53725 64095 64	0.41477 30112 01	1.06331 94892 17
26	0.57753 55768 98	0.55567 75939 11	0.43036 78258 79	1.06812 94547 04
27	0.59799 87419 31	0.57379 31900 85	0.44584 50098 20	1.07307 26579 37
28	0.61828 70700 23	0.59160 05553 63	0.46119 99799 35	1.07814 30950 24
29	0.63839 79143 59	0.60909 77283 27	0.47642 81531 01	1.08333 46066 38
30	0.65832 89396 01	0.62628 34066 13	0.49152 49473 06	1.08864 08854 33
31	0.67807 81182 37	0.64315 69228 57	0.50648 57828 82	1.09405 54836 46
32	0.69764 37261 96	0.65971 82190 76	0.52130 60838 52	1.09957 18208 66
33	0.71702 43377 84	0.67596 78197 75	0.53598 12793 74	1.10518 31919 72
34	0.73621 88200 01	0.69190 68040 17	0.55050 68052 85	1.11088 27752 25
35	0.75522 63263 12	0.70753 67767 19	0.56487 81057 52	1.11666 36405 08
36	0.77404 62899 19	0.72285 98394 03	0.57909 06350 17	1.12251 87577 02
37	0.79267 84166 06	0.73787 85606 20	0.59313 98592 42	1.12844 10051 85
38	0.81112 26772 11	0.75259 59462 64	0.60702 12584 48	1.13442 31784 53
39	0.82937 92997 78	0.76701 54099 50	0.62073 03285 55	1.14045 79988 44
40	0.84744 87614 61	0.78114 07436 60	0.63426 25835 07	1.14653 81223 59
41	0.86533 17802 01	0.79497 60887 82	0.64761 35574 86	1.15265 61485 67
42	0.88302 93062 64	0.80852 59077 18	0.66077 88072 14	1.15880 46295 88
43	0.90054 25136 52	0.82179 49561 60	0.67375 39143 44	1.16497 60791 34
44	0.91787 27914 59	0.83478 82561 70	0.68653 44879 15	1.17116 29816 13
45	0.93502 17351 87	0.84751 10701 37	0.69911 61668 97	1.17735 78012 64

K = 2.08035 80666 91578   E = 1.23966 11752 88672
K' = 1.71192 46951 55678   E' = 1.44686 92406 95183

r	u=(r/90)K=F(φ,k)	sn u	cn u	dn u
45	1.04017 90333 46	0.80461 19846 76	0.59380 09381 22	0.73799 66361 81
46	1.06329 41229 76	0.81457 21029 32	0.58006 23148 63	0.73027 09276 07
47	1.08640 92126 06	0.82419 71232 24	0.56630 30125 91	0.72263 49476 77
48	1.10952 43022 36	0.83349 28548 88	0.55253 02352 37	0.71509 63255 38
49	1.13263 93918 65	0.84246 52353 72	0.53875 07096 89	0.70766 23281 34
50	1.15575 44814 95	0.85112 03036 41	0.52497 06932 11	0.70033 98664 58
51	1.17886 95711 25	0.85946 41749 15	0.51119 59820 25	0.69313 55027 41
52	1.20198 46607 55	0.86750 30167 57	0.49743 19208 87	0.68605 54584 63
53	1.22509 97503 85	0.87524 30265 05	0.48368 34135 61	0.67910 56230 63
54	1.24821 48400 15	0.88269 04100 33	0.46995 49340 47	0.67229 15632 61
55	1.27132 99296 45	0.88985 13618 35	0.45625 05384 55	0.66561 85328 70
56	1.29444 50192 75	0.89673 20463 93	0.44257 38774 17	0.65909 14830 25
57	1.31756 01089 05	0.90333 85808 10	0.42892 82089 36	0.65271 50727 24
58	1.34067 51985 35	0.90967 70186 59	0.41531 64115 76	0.64649 36796 11
59	1.36379 02881 64	0.91575 33350 15	0.40174 09979 19	0.64043 14109 23
60	1.38690 53777 94	0.92157 34126 24	0.38820 41281 92	0.63453 21145 19
61	1.41002 04674 24	0.92714 30291 52	0.37470 76240 15	0.62879 93899 49
62	1.43313 55570 54	0.93246 78454 84	0.36125 29821 86	0.62323 65994 87
63	1.45625 06466 84	0.93755 33949 97	0.34784 13884 65	0.61784 68790 79
64	1.47936 57363 14	0.94240 50737 76	0.33447 37312 87	0.61263 31491 64
65	1.50248 08259 44	0.94702 81317 04	0.32115 06153 85	0.60759 81253 19
66	1.52559 59155 74	0.95142 76643 85	0.30787 23752 53	0.60274 43286 96
67	1.54871 10052 04	0.95560 86058 42	0.29463 90884 48	0.59807 40962 03
68	1.57182 60948 34	0.95957 57219 37	0.28145 05886 82	0.59358 95904 20
69	1.59494 11844 64	0.96333 36044 66	0.26830 64786 90	0.58929 28092 06
70	1.61805 62740 93	0.96688 66658 77	0.25520 61428 51	0.58518 55949 86
71	1.64117 13637 23	0.97023 91345 66	0.24214 87595 61	0.58126 96436 83
72	1.66428 64533 53	0.97339 50506 98	0.22913 33133 28	0.57754 65133 02
73	1.68740 15429 83	0.97635 82625 21	0.21615 86066 01	0.57401 76321 27
74	1.71051 66326 13	0.97913 24231 15	0.20322 32713 16	0.57068 43065 37
75	1.73363 17222 43	0.98172 09875 52	0.19032 57801 74	0.56754 77284 18
76	1.75674 68118 73	0.98412 72104 13	0.17746 44576 36	0.56460 89821 76
77	1.77986 19015 03	0.98635 41436 38	0.16463 74906 53	0.56186 90513 30
78	1.80297 69911 33	0.98840 46346 68	0.15184 29391 41	0.55932 88246 97
79	1.82609 20807 63	0.99028 13248 55	0.13907 87461 93	0.55698 91021 47
80	1.84920 71703 93	0.99198 66481 02	0.12634 27480 56	0.55485 05999 38
81	1.87232 22600 22	0.99352 28297 09	0.11363 26838 88	0.55291 39556 26
82	1.89543 73496 52	0.99489 18854 02	0.10094 62052 86	0.55117 97325 47
83	1.91855 24392 82	0.99609 56205 26	0.08828 08856 33	0.54964 84238 71
84	1.94166 75289 12	0.99713 56293 73	0.07563 42292 54	0.54832 04562 24
85	1.96478 26185 42	0.99801 32946 28	0.06300 36804 14	0.54719 61928 91
86	1.98789 77081 72	0.99872 97869 29	0.05038 66321 69	0.54627 59365 84
87	2.01101 27978 02	0.99928 60645 10	0.03778 04350 97	0.54555 99317 83
88	2.03412 78874 32	0.99968 28729 31	0.02518 24059 18	0.54504 83666 54
89	2.05724 29770 62	0.99992 07448 74	0.01258 98360 33	0.54474 13745 39
90	2.08035 80666 92	1.00000 00000 00	0.00000 00000 00	0.54463 90350 15

q = 0.07537 99738 58803 37   D(90) = 1.35501 97263 42264
q′ = 0.02197 80013 16900 53   1/D(90) = 0.73799 66361 81377

r	ϕ	$E(\phi,k)$	A(r)	D(r)
45	0.93502 17351 87	0.84751 10701 37	0.69911 61668 97	1.17735 78012 64
46	0.95199 11380 86	0.85996 88757 11	0.71149 46228 00	1.18355 29913 31
47	0.96878 29825 35	0.87216 73417 69	0.72366 55623 51	1.18974 10032 51
48	0.98539 94314 95	0.88411 23054 69	0.73562 47302 37	1.19591 42958 59
49	1.00184 28200 81	0.89580 97504 40	0.74736 79118 97	1.20206 53445 82
50	1.01811 56472 55	0.90726 57861 29	0.75889 09363 78	1.20818 66506 25
51	1.03422 05676 86	0.91848 66283 27	0.77018 96792 29	1.21427 07501 27
52	1.05016 03837 69	0.92947 85808 94	0.78126 00654 45	1.22031 02232 88
53	1.06593 80378 59	0.94024 80186 61	0.79209 80724 41	1.22629 77034 40
54	1.08155 66046 95	0.95080 13715 30	0.80269 97330 60	1.23222 58860 67
55	1.09701 92840 57	0.96114 51097 39	0.81306 11386 08	1.23808 75377 48
56	1.11232 93936 48	0.97128 57302 77	0.82317 84419 06	1.24387 55050 29
57	1.12749 03622 20	0.98122 97444 32	0.83304 78603 55	1.24958 27231 88
58	1.14250 57229 47	0.99098 36664 29	0.84266 56790 11	1.25520 22249 11
59	1.15737 91070 44	1.00055 40031 42	0.85202 82536 55	1.26072 71488 50
60	1.17211 42376 47	1.00994 72448 30	0.86113 20138 68	1.26615 07480 49
61	1.18671 49239 46	1.01916 98568 61	0.86997 34660 81	1.27146 63982 45
62	1.20118 50555 69	1.02822 82723 99	0.87854 91966 20	1.27666 76060 18
63	1.21552 85972 27	1.03712 88859 84	0.88685 58747 20	1.28174 80167 85
64	1.22974 95836 08	1.04587 80479 93	0.89489 02555 03	1.28670 14226 27
65	1.24385 21145 19	1.05448 20599 22	0.90264 91829 37	1.29152 17699 46
66	1.25784 03502 68	1.06294 71704 43	0.91012 95927 28	1.29620 31669 24
67	1.27171 85072 94	1.07127 95722 08	0.91732 85151 84	1.30073 98908 01
68	1.28549 08540 18	1.07948 53993 46	0.92424 30780 09	1.30512 63949 34
69	1.29916 17069 29	1.08757 07256 15	0.93087 05090 45	1.30935 73156 57
70	1.31273 54268 81	1.09554 15631 69	0.93720 81389 36	1.31342 74789 01
71	1.32621 64156 08	1.10340 38619 00	0.94325 34037 31	1.31733 19065 99
72	1.33960 91124 31	1.11116 35093 13	0.94900 38473 99	1.32106 58228 42
73	1.35291 79911 76	1.11882 63309 06	0.95445 71242 63	1.32462 46597 90
74	1.36614 75572 54	1.12639 80910 07	0.95961 10013 42	1.32800 40633 29
75	1.37930 23449 40	1.13388 44940 42	0.96446 33606 01	1.33119 98984 63
76	1.39238 69148 04	1.14129 11861 99	0.96901 22010 96	1.33420 82544 39
77	1.40540 58513 01	1.14862 37574 55	0.97325 56410 22	1.33702 54495 96
78	1.41836 37605 17	1.15588 77439 37	0.97719 19196 42	1.33964 80359 31
79	1.43126 52680 43	1.16308 86305 83	0.98081 93991 11	1.34207 28033 71
80	1.44411 50169 84	1.17023 18540 85	0.98413 65661 75	1.34429 67837 64
81	1.45691 76660 81	1.17732 28060 80	0.98714 20337 52	1.34631 72545 59
82	1.46967 78879 47	1.18436 68365 66	0.98983 45423 91	1.34813 17421 87
83	1.48240 03674 00	1.19136 92575 14	0.99221 29615 92	1.34973 80251 30
84	1.49508 97998 78	1.19833 53466 68	0.99427 62910 09	1.35113 41366 86
85	1.50775 08899 46	1.20527 03514 89	0.99602 36615 05	1.35231 83674 09
86	1.52038 83498 61	1.21217 94932 40	0.99745 43360 81	1.35328 92672 32
87	1.53300 68981 98	1.21906 79711 80	0.99856 77106 57	1.35404 56472 72
88	1.54561 12585 32	1.22594 09668 58	0.99936 33147 24	1.35458 65813 06
89	1.55820 61581 49	1.23280 36484 71	0.99984 08118 41	1.35491 14069 21
90	1.57079 63267 95	1.23966 11752 89	1.00000 00000 00	1.35501 97263 42

K = 2.10465 76584 91159   E = 1.23012 72241 85949
K′= 1.70283 59363 12341   E′= 1.45390 77960 65210

r	u=(r/90)K=F(φ,k)	sn u	cn u	dn u
0	0.00000 00000 00	0.00000 00000 00	1.00000 00000 00	1.00000 00000 00
1	0.02338 50850 94	0.02338 14214 92	0.99972 66171 95	0.99980 33945 79
2	0.04677 01701 89	0.04674 08775 58	0.99890 70479 10	0.99921 40853 43
3	0.07015 52552 83	0.07005 64835 85	0.99754 30261 94	0.99823 35905 44
4	0.09354 03403 77	0.09330 65159 41	0.99563 74310 38	0.99686 44312 16
5	0.11692 54254 72	0.11646 94908 77	0.99319 42698 66	0.99511 01172 00
6	0.14031 05105 66	0.13952 42415 43	0.99021 86556 62	0.99297 51277 80
7	0.16369 55956 60	0.16244 99925 25	0.98671 67779 71	0.99046 48871 45
8	0.18708 06807 55	0.18522 64313 55	0.98269 58680 73	0.98758 57349 09
9	0.21046 57658 49	0.20783 37764 74	0.97816 41586 96	0.98434 48920 15
10	0.23385 08509 43	0.23025 28411 74	0.97313 08386 50	0.98075 04223 39
11	0.25723 59360 38	0.25246 50931 05	0.96760 60028 56	0.97681 11904 05
12	0.28062 10211 32	0.27445 27089 83	0.96160 05982 38	0.97253 68155 95
13	0.30400 61062 27	0.29619 86241 84	0.95512 63660 02	0.96793 76233 11
14	0.32739 11913 21	0.31768 65769 97	0.94819 57808 36	0.96302 45935 30
15	0.35077 62764 15	0.33890 11473 32	0.94082 19875 92	0.95780 93072 35
16	0.37416 13615 10	0.35982 77897 83	0.93301 87359 85	0.95230 38911 79
17	0.39754 64466 04	0.38045 28609 72	0.92480 03138 94	0.94652 09614 63
18	0.42093 15316 98	0.40076 36411 81	0.91618 14797 89	0.94047 35663 96
19	0.44431 66167 93	0.42074 83503 18	0.90717 73948 38	0.93417 51290 72
20	0.46770 17018 87	0.44039 61583 44	0.89780 35551 92	0.92763 93901 29
21	0.49108 67869 81	0.45969 71903 03	0.88807 57249 40	0.92088 03510 67
22	0.51447 18720 76	0.47864 25261 52	0.87800 98701 94	0.91391 22185 44
23	0.53785 69571 70	0.49722 41956 60	0.86762 20947 22	0.90674 93499 85
24	0.56124 20422 64	0.51543 51686 15	0.85692 85775 11	0.89940 62008 37
25	0.58462 71273 59	0.53326 93406 69	0.84594 55126 08	0.89189 72737 67
26	0.60801 22124 53	0.55072 15151 35	0.83468 90515 44	0.88423 70700 49
27	0.63139 72975 47	0.56778 73810 80	0.82317 52485 87	0.87644 00433 64
28	0.65478 23826 42	0.58446 34880 78	0.81142 00090 61	0.86852 05562 01
29	0.67816 74677 36	0.60074 72179 72	0.79943 90408 90	0.86049 28389 99
30	0.70155 25528 30	0.61663 67540 25	0.78724 78095 14	0.85237 09521 54
31	0.72493 76379 25	0.63213 10478 13	0.77486 14962 63	0.84416 87509 58
32	0.74832 27230 19	0.64722 97842 18	0.76229 49602 49	0.83589 98535 32
33	0.77170 78081 13	0.66193 33448 82	0.74956 27038 04	0.82757 76117 65
34	0.79509 28932 08	0.67624 27704 30	0.73667 88414 51	0.81921 50852 45
35	0.81847 79783 02	0.69015 97218 16	0.72365 70723 65	0.81082 50181 61
36	0.84186 30633 96	0.70368 64410 60	0.71051 06562 67	0.80241 98191 07
37	0.86524 81484 91	0.71682 57116 89	0.69725 23926 54	0.79401 15437 19
38	0.88863 32335 85	0.72958 08191 20	0.68389 46032 63	0.78561 18800 51
39	0.91201 83186 80	0.74195 55112 44	0.67044 91176 33	0.77723 21365 73
40	0.93540 34037 74	0.75395 39594 21	0.65692 72616 30	0.76888 32326 86
41	0.95878 84888 68	0.76558 07200 81	0.64333 98487 89	0.76057 56916 00
42	0.98217 35739 63	0.77684 06971 15	0.62969 71742 87	0.75231 96354 64
43	1.00555 86590 57	0.78773 91051 98	0.61600 90114 12	0.74412 47825 76
44	1.02894 37441 51	0.79828 14341 87	0.60228 46103 24	0.73600 04465 48
45	1.05232 88292 46	0.80847 34146 90	0.58853 26989 55	0.72795 55372 64

q = 0.07872 46415 92072 55   D(90) = 1.37371 02732 38087
q' = 0.02059 05967 10436 76   1/D(90) = 0.72795 55372 63922

r	ϕ	$E(\phi,k)$	A(r)	D(r)
0	0.00000 00000 00	0.00000 00000 00	0.00000 00000 00	1.00000 00000 00
1	0.02338 35524 18	0.02338 20199 22	0.01702 25688 74	1.00011 36050 24
2	0.04675 79135 19	0.04674 56626 31	0.03404 07377 24	1.00045 42824 97
3	0.07011 39156 81	0.07007 26199 07	0.05105 01057 18	1.00102 16197 86
4	0.09344 24385 29	0.09334 47209 76	0.06804 62704 04	1.00181 49297 15
5	0.11673 44322 40	0.11654 39998 85	0.08502 48269 22	1.00283 32513 83
6	0.13998 09404 46	0.13965 27612 78	0.10198 13672 30	1.00407 53513 06
7	0.16317 31226 28	0.16265 36440 84	0.11891 14793 52	1.00553 97248 84
8	0.18630 22758 78	0.18552 96826 28	0.13581 07466 56	1.00722 45981 97
9	0.20935 98559 17	0.20826 43647 51	0.15267 47471 76	1.00912 79301 09
10	0.23233 74972 63	0.23084 16865 19	0.16949 90529 67	1.01124 74147 04
11	0.25522 70324 55	0.25324 62031 80	0.18627 92295 11	1.01358 04840 30
12	0.27802 05102 49	0.27546 30760 54	0.20301 08351 77	1.01612 43111 58
13	0.30071 02127 03	0.29747 81151 07	0.21968 94207 37	1.01887 58135 50
14	0.32328 86710 95	0.31927 78169 87	0.23631 05289 51	1.02183 16567 33
15	0.34574 86805 99	0.34084 93983 85	0.25286 96942 13	1.02498 82582 76
16	0.36808 33137 05	0.36218 08246 09	0.26936 24422 76	1.02834 17920 62
17	0.39028 59323 21	0.38326 08333 25	0.28578 42900 52	1.03188 81928 54
18	0.41235 01985 48	0.40407 89534 61	0.30213 07454 99	1.03562 31611 48
19	0.43427 00841 16	0.42462 55193 34	0.31839 73075 85	1.03954 21683 06
20	0.45603 98784 80	0.44489 16800 76	0.33457 94663 54	1.04364 04619 71
21	0.47765 41955 82	0.46486 94045 10	0.35067 27030 77	1.04791 30717 43
22	0.49910 79792 94	0.48455 14816 39	0.36667 24905 05	1.05235 48151 27
23	0.52039 65075 82	0.50393 15169 55	0.38257 42932 18	1.05696 03037 36
24	0.54151 53954 07	0.52300 39248 02	0.39837 35680 79	1.06172 39497 40
25	0.56246 05964 21	0.54176 39170 56	0.41406 57647 98	1.06663 99725 61
26	0.58322 84034 99	0.56020 74883 90	0.42964 63265 93	1.07170 24058 07
27	0.60381 54481 59	0.57833 13984 30	0.44511 06909 68	1.07690 51044 22
28	0.62421 86989 38	0.59613 31510 88	0.46045 42906 02	1.08224 17520 67
29	0.64443 54587 73	0.61361 09713 99	0.47567 25543 42	1.08770 58687 07
30	0.66446 33614 63	0.63076 37801 59	0.49076 09083 19	1.09329 08183 95
31	0.68430 03672 78	0.64759 11666 84	0.50571 47771 65	1.09898 98172 59
32	0.70394 47577 83	0.66409 33599 79	0.52052 95853 55	1.10479 59416 62
33	0.72339 51299 44	0.68027 11986 36	0.53520 07586 56	1.11070 21365 45
34	0.74265 03895 91	0.69612 60997 27	0.54972 37256 82	1.11670 12239 29
35	0.76170 97443 10	0.71166 00269 69	0.56409 39195 74	1.12278 59115 74
36	0.78057 26958 22	0.72687 54584 28	0.57830 67797 78	1.12894 88017 81
37	0.79923 90319 28	0.74177 53539 92	0.59235 77539 37	1.13518 24003 33
38	0.81770 88180 80	0.75636 31228 45	0.60624 22998 87	1.14147 91255 50
39	0.83598 23886 40	0.77064 25911 40	0.61995 58877 62	1.14783 13174 67
40	0.85406 03378 83	0.78461 79700 71	0.63349 40021 92	1.15423 12471 09
41	0.87194 35108 16	0.79829 38244 95	0.64685 21446 05	1.16067 11258 56
42	0.88963 29938 52	0.81167 50422 76	0.66002 58356 30	1.16714 31148 93
43	0.90713 01053 89	0.82476 68044 59	0.67301 06175 75	1.17363 93347 24
44	0.92443 63863 60	0.83757 45564 05	0.68580 20570 13	1.18015 18747 41
45	0.94155 35907 71	0.85010 39799 76	0.69839 57474 37	1.18667 28028 49

ELLIPTIC FUNCTIONS TABLE $\theta = 58°$

K = 2.10465 76584 91159   E = 1.23012 72241 85949
K′= 1.70283 59363 12341   E′= 1.45390 77960 65210

r	u=(r/90)K=F(ϕ,k)	sn u	cn u	dn u
45	1.05232 88292 46	0.80847 34146 90	0.58853 26989 55	0.72795 55372 64
46	1.07571 39143 40	0.81832 09849 24	0.57476 14858 65	0.71999 85634 77
47	1.09909 89994 34	0.82783 02588 98	0.56097 86648 81	0.71213 76369 15
48	1.12248 40845 29	0.83700 74960 22	0.54719 14213 54	0.70438 04777 30
49	1.14586 91696 23	0.84585 90721 40	0.53340 64398 55	0.69673 44211 57
50	1.16925 42547 17	0.85439 14520 49	0.51962 99131 75	0.68920 64252 49
51	1.19263 93398 12	0.86261 11634 92	0.50586 75524 48	0.68180 30795 40
52	1.21602 44249 06	0.87052 47726 38	0.49212 45982 70	0.67453 06145 31
53	1.23940 95100 00	0.87813 88610 40	0.47840 58326 69	0.66739 49118 56
54	1.26279 45950 95	0.88546 00040 38	0.46471 55917 86	0.66040 15150 36
55	1.28617 96801 89	0.89249 47506 01	0.45105 77791 71	0.65355 56406 92
56	1.30956 47652 83	0.89924 96045 53	0.43743 58795 43	0.64686 21901 35
57	1.33294 98503 78	0.90573 10071 56	0.42385 29729 47	0.64032 57612 33
58	1.35633 49354 72	0.91194 53209 95	0.41031 17491 81	0.63395 06604 70
59	1.37972 00205 66	0.91789 88151 17	0.39681 45224 23	0.62774 09151 10
60	1.40310 51056 61	0.92359 76513 81	0.38336 32459 75	0.62170 02854 15
61	1.42649 01907 55	0.92904 78719 38	0.36995 95270 41	0.61583 22768 26
62	1.44987 52758 49	0.93425 53878 17	0.35660 46414 93	0.61014 01520 67
63	1.47326 03609 44	0.93922 59685 30	0.34329 95485 56	0.60462 69431 04
64	1.49664 54460 38	0.94396 52326 48	0.33004 49053 57	0.59929 54629 28
65	1.52003 05311 33	0.94847 86392 90	0.31684 10813 19	0.59414 83170 98
66	1.54341 56162 27	0.95277 14804 65	0.30368 81723 28	0.58918 79150 27
67	1.56680 07013 21	0.95684 88742 08	0.29058 60146 77	0.58441 64809 63
68	1.59018 57864 16	0.96071 57584 49	0.27753 41987 37	0.57983 60646 47
69	1.61357 08715 10	0.96437 68855 65	0.26453 20823 42	0.57544 85516 16
70	1.63695 59566 04	0.96783 68175 67	0.25157 88038 80	0.57125 56731 33
71	1.66034 10416 99	0.97109 99218 52	0.23867 32950 69	0.56725 90157 26
72	1.68372 61267 93	0.97417 03674 88	0.22581 42934 09	0.56346 00303 17
73	1.70711 12118 87	0.97705 21219 77	0.21300 03543 19	0.55986 00409 38
74	1.73049 62969 82	0.97974 89484 48	0.20022 98629 45	0.55646 02530 16
75	1.75388 13820 76	0.98226 44032 44	0.18750 10456 52	0.55326 17612 19
76	1.77726 64671 70	0.98460 18338 54	0.17481 19812 00	0.55026 55568 65
77	1.80065 15522 65	0.98676 43771 66	0.16216 06116 08	0.54747 25348 73
78	1.82403 66373 59	0.98875 49579 80	0.14954 47527 32	0.54488 35002 80
79	1.84742 17224 53	0.99057 62877 83	0.13696 21045 47	0.54249 91742 91
80	1.87080 68075 48	0.99223 08637 19	0.12441 02611 67	0.54032 01998 83
81	1.89419 18926 42	0.99372 09677 53	0.11188 67206 05	0.53834 71469 52
82	1.91757 69777 36	0.99504 86659 91	0.09938 88943 01	0.53658 05170 14
83	1.94096 20628 31	0.99621 58081 29	0.08691 41164 23	0.53502 07474 40
84	1.96434 71479 25	0.99722 40270 27	0.07445 96529 69	0.53366 82152 53
85	1.98773 22330 19	0.99807 47383 63	0.06202 27106 98	0.53252 32404 68
86	2.01111 73181 14	0.99876 91403 76	0.04960 04458 85	0.53158 60889 80
87	2.03450 24032 08	0.99930 82136 72	0.03718 99729 56	0.53085 69750 14
88	2.05788 74883 02	0.99969 27210 72	0.02478 83729 91	0.53033 60631 18
89	2.08127 25733 97	0.99992 32075 18	0.01239 27021 46	0.53002 34697 20
90	2.10465 76584 91	1.00000 00000 00	0.00000 00000 00	0.52991 92642 33

232

ELLIPTIC FUNCTIONS TABLE $\theta = 58°$

q = 0.07872 46415 92072 55
q′ = 0.02059 05967 10436 76

D(90) = 1.37371 02732 38087
1/D(90) = 0.72795 55372 63922

r	ϕ	$E(\phi,k)$	$A(r)$	$D(r)$
45	0.94155 35907 71	0.85010 39799 76	0.69839 57474 37	1.18667 28028 49
46	0.95848 36762 91	0.86236 09668 53	0.71078 73120 01	1.19319 41751 13
47	0.97522 87949 13	0.87435 15930 46	0.72297 24063 38	1.19970 80454 34
48	0.99179 12837 37	0.88608 20946 56	0.73494 67214 37	1.20620 64752 34
49	1.00817 36558 80	0.89755 88449 13	0.74670 59866 02	1.21268 15431 42
50	1.02437 85915 73	0.90878 83325 29	0.75824 59724 51	1.21912 53546 61
51	1.04040 89294 30	0.91977 71413 63	0.76956 24939 87	1.22553 00518 13
52	1.05626 76579 47	0.93053 19314 14	0.78065 14137 01	1.23188 78227 54
53	1.07195 79072 23	0.94105 94211 30	0.79150 86447 31	1.23819 09113 28
54	1.08748 29409 21	0.95136 63710 19	0.80213 01540 45	1.24443 16265 68
55	1.10284 61484 98	0.96145 95685 39	0.81251 19656 62	1.25060 23521 23
56	1.11805 10376 91	0.97134 58142 47	0.82265 01638 91	1.25669 55556 01
57	1.13310 12272 83	0.98103 19091 65	0.83254 08965 90	1.26270 37978 16
58	1.14800 04401 50	0.99052 46433 30	0.84218 03784 33	1.26861 97419 28
59	1.16275 24965 84	0.99983 07854 93	0.85156 48941 79	1.27443 61624 58
60	1.17736 13079 11	1.00895 70739 15	0.86069 08019 44	1.28014 59541 87
61	1.19183 08703 89	1.01791 02082 18	0.86955 45364 49	1.28574 21408 97
62	1.20616 52593 86	1.02669 68422 49	0.87815 26122 68	1.29121 78839 68
63	1.22036 86238 50	1.03532 35779 02	0.88648 16270 37	1.29656 64908 13
64	1.23444 51810 50	1.04379 69598 56	0.89453 82646 40	1.30178 14231 30
65	1.24839 92115 87	1.05212 34711 69	0.90231 92983 57	1.30685 63049 79
66	1.26223 50546 79	1.06030 95297 05	0.90982 15939 60	1.31178 49306 59
67	1.27595 71037 02	1.06836 14853 08	0.91704 21127 66	1.31656 12723 75
68	1.28956 98019 86	1.07628 56177 18	0.92397 79146 28	1.32117 94876 97
69	1.30307 76388 54	1.08408 81351 53	0.93062 61608 62	1.32563 39267 94
70	1.31648 51459 00	1.09177 51735 21	0.93698 41171 00	1.32991 91394 24
71	1.32979 68934 92	1.09935 27962 33	0.94304 91560 68	1.33402 98816 93
72	1.34301 74874 98	1.10682 69945 49	0.94881 87602 84	1.33796 11225 54
73	1.35615 15662 15	1.11420 36884 41	0.95429 05246 55	1.34170 80500 46
74	1.36920 37974 99	1.12148 87279 26	0.95946 21589 90	1.34526 60772 70
75	1.38217 88760 87	1.12868 78948 29	0.96433 14904 10	1.34863 08480 77
76	1.39508 15210 92	1.13580 69049 41	0.96889 64656 39	1.35179 82424 86
77	1.40791 64736 67	1.14285 14105 51	0.97315 51532 03	1.35476 43817 96
78	1.42068 84948 31	1.14982 70033 04	0.97710 57454 94	1.35752 56334 16
79	1.43340 23634 37	1.15673 92173 67	0.98074 65607 26	1.36007 86153 75
80	1.44606 28742 80	1.16359 35328 66	0.98407 60447 53	1.36242 02005 35
81	1.45867 48363 24	1.17039 53795 73	0.98709 27727 71	1.36454 75204 78
82	1.47124 50710 53	1.17715 01408 17	0.98979 54508 69	1.36645 79690 78
83	1.48377 24109 23	1.18386 31575 89	0.99218 29174 59	1.36814 92057 47
84	1.49626 76979 02	1.19053 97328 28	0.99425 41445 54	1.36961 91583 50
85	1.50873 37821 04	1.19718 51358 48	0.99600 82389 05	1.37086 60257 83
86	1.52117 55204 90	1.20380 46069 12	0.99744 44429 97	1.37188 82802 22
87	1.53359 77756 27	1.21040 33619 02	0.99855 21358 87	1.37268 46690 22
88	1.54600 54145 10	1.21698 65970 90	0.99936 08338 98	1.37325 42162 81
89	1.55840 33074 17	1.22355 94939 76	0.99984 01911 62	1.37359 62240 58
90	1.57079 63267 95	1.23012 72241 86	1.00000 00000 00	1.37371 02732 38

K = 2.13002 14383 99325   E = 1.22058 89957 54247
K'= 1.69411 43573 05914   E'= 1.46077 35062 13127

r	u=(r/90)K=F(ϕ,k)	sn u	cn u	dn u
0	0.00000 00000 00	0.00000 00000 00	1.00000 00000 00	1.00000 00000 00
1	0.02366 69048 71	0.02366 30728 88	0.99971 99902 88	0.99979 42744 88
2	0.04733 38097 42	0.04730 31714 23	0.99888 05784 34	0.99917 76431 36
3	0.07100 07146 13	0.07089 74088 24	0.99748 36126 08	0.99815 17383 57
4	0.09466 76194 84	0.09442 30727 35	0.99553 21608 74	0.99671 92703 81
5	0.11833 45243 56	0.11785 77106 53	0.99303 04930 06	0.99488 40117 03
6	0.14200 14292 27	0.14117 92132 51	0.98998 40552 99	0.99265 07755 27
7	0.16566 83340 98	0.16436 58949 20	0.98639 94386 59	0.99002 53884 73
8	0.18933 52389 69	0.18739 65709 30	0.98228 43403 03	0.98701 46578 01
9	0.21300 21438 40	0.21025 06306 22	0.97764 75194 69	0.98362 63335 37
10	0.23666 90487 11	0.23290 81061 16	0.97249 87476 11	0.97986 90658 55
11	0.26033 59535 82	0.25534 97360 68	0.96684 87535 75	0.97575 23581 87
12	0.28400 28584 53	0.27755 70240 87	0.96070 91643 05	0.97128 65165 11
13	0.30766 97633 24	0.29951 22914 70	0.95409 24416 74	0.96648 25953 20
14	0.33133 66681 95	0.32119 87239 93	0.94701 18160 33	0.96135 23407 95
15	0.35500 35730 67	0.34260 04125 86	0.93948 12171 07	0.95590 81317 17
16	0.37867 04779 38	0.36370 23877 41	0.93151 52028 56	0.95016 29186 37
17	0.40233 73828 09	0.38449 06476 31	0.92312 88869 30	0.94413 01618 58
18	0.42600 42876 80	0.40495 21799 39	0.91433 78653 22	0.93782 37687 41
19	0.44967 11925 51	0.42507 49774 77	0.90515 81428 25	0.93125 80308 46
20	0.47333 80974 22	0.44484 80477 38	0.89560 60598 41	0.92444 75613 93
21	0.49700 50022 93	0.46426 14165 78	0.88569 82200 94	0.91740 72334 99
22	0.52067 19071 64	0.48330 61262 48	0.87545 14197 43	0.91015 21196 35
23	0.54433 88120 35	0.50197 42280 91	0.86488 25783 50	0.90269 74326 67
24	0.56800 57169 06	0.52025 87701 89	0.85400 86721 11	0.89505 84688 64
25	0.59167 26217 78	0.53815 37803 46	0.84284 66697 44	0.88725 05531 76
26	0.61533 95266 49	0.55565 42447 48	0.83141 34713 21	0.87928 89870 48
27	0.63900 64315 20	0.57275 60827 15	0.81972 58503 38	0.87118 89990 29
28	0.66267 33363 91	0.58945 61179 40	0.80780 03992 47	0.86296 56983 31
29	0.68634 02412 62	0.60575 20466 17	0.79565 34786 07	0.85463 40315 26
30	0.71000 71461 33	0.62164 24028 77	0.78330 11700 14	0.84620 87424 58
31	0.73367 40510 04	0.63712 65219 38	0.77075 92328 63	0.83770 43354 73
32	0.75734 09558 75	0.65220 45013 48	0.75804 30650 18	0.82913 50419 85
33	0.78100 78607 46	0.66687 71607 23	0.74516 76673 78	0.82051 47903 91
34	0.80467 47656 18	0.68114 60003 44	0.73214 76123 13	0.81185 71793 12
35	0.82834 16704 89	0.69501 31589 44	0.71899 70159 15	0.80317 54540 97
36	0.85200 85753 60	0.70848 13710 36	0.70572 95139 75	0.79448 24865 30
37	0.87567 54802 31	0.72155 39240 69	0.69235 82415 64	0.78579 07576 25
38	0.89934 23851 02	0.73423 46157 00	0.67889 58160 93	0.77711 23434 04
39	0.92300 92899 73	0.74652 77114 34	0.66535 43236 97	0.76845 89035 16
40	0.94667 61948 44	0.75843 79028 63	0.65174 53087 67	0.75984 16725 66
41	0.97034 30997 15	0.76997 02667 12	0.63807 97664 70	0.75127 14539 85
42	0.99401 00045 86	0.78113 02248 61	0.62436 81380 47	0.74275 86162 91
43	1.01767 69094 57	0.79192 35055 12	0.61062 03087 17	0.73431 30915 69
44	1.04134 38143 29	0.80235 61056 25	0.59684 56079 81	0.72594 43760 00
45	1.06501 07192 00	0.81243 42547 36	0.58305 28121 28	0.71766 15322 77

234

q = 0.08219 43773 66407 71   D(90) = 1.39341 45206 68691
q'= 0.01925 57475 39635 14   1/D(90) = 0.71766 15322 76918

r	ϕ	$E(\phi,k)$	A(r)	D(r)
0	0.00000 00000 00	0.00000 00000 00	0.00000 00000 00	1.00000 00000 00
1	0.02366 52817 66	0.02366 36588 60	0.01698 41075 70	1.00011 95626 68
2	0.04732 08300 61	0.04730 78567 85	0.03396 38970 68	1.00047 81059 77
3	0.07095 69371 96	0.07091 32083 42	0.05093 50493 93	1.00107 51960 08
4	0.09456 39468 94	0.09446 04785 01	0.06789 32433 96	1.00191 01101 35
5	0.11813 22796 29	0.11793 06562 99	0.08483 41548 67	1.00298 18378 84
6	0.14165 24575 21	0.14130 50267 13	0.10175 34555 50	1.00428 90821 27
7	0.16511 51286 55	0.16456 52401 46	0.11864 68121 82	1.00583 02606 22
8	0.18851 10906 88	0.18769 33790 24	0.13550 98855 62	1.00760 35078 92
9	0.21183 13136 19	0.21067 20209 97	0.15233 83296 66	1.00960 66774 36
10	0.23506 69616 09	0.23348 42982 91	0.16912 77908 02	1.01183 73442 76
11	0.25820 94137 33	0.25611 39528 41	0.18587 39068 20	1.01429 28078 38
12	0.28125 02835 83	0.27854 53868 38	0.20257 23063 81	1.01697 00951 56
13	0.30418 14376 30	0.30076 37084 21	0.21921 86082 89	1.01986 59644 06
14	0.32699 50122 69	0.32275 47722 86	0.23580 84208 91	1.02297 69087 54
15	0.34968 34294 97	0.34450 52150 56	0.25233 73415 58	1.02629 91605 29
16	0.37223 94111 62	0.36600 24852 96	0.26880 09562 37	1.02982 86957 02
17	0.39465 59917 71	0.38723 48681 48	0.28519 48391 02	1.03356 12386 73
18	0.41692 65298 06	0.40819 15045 83	0.30151 45522 78	1.03749 22673 60
19	0.43904 47175 65	0.42886 24053 54	0.31775 56456 79	1.04161 70185 84
20	0.46100 45895 11	0.44923 84597 52	0.33391 36569 29	1.04593 04937 49
21	0.48280 05291 54	0.46931 14393 54	0.34998 41113 93	1.05042 74647 95
22	0.50442 72744 81	0.48907 39969 46	0.36596 25223 17	1.05510 24804 40
23	0.52587 99219 74	0.50851 96608 85	0.38184 43910 72	1.05994 98726 85
24	0.54715 39292 52	0.52764 28251 57	0.39762 52075 17	1.06496 37635 84
25	0.56824 51163 97	0.54643 87354 55	0.41330 04504 71	1.07013 80722 71
26	0.58914 96660 06	0.56490 34715 75	0.42886 55883 08	1.07546 65222 33
27	0.60986 41220 44	0.58303 39264 85	0.44431 60796 69	1.08094 26488 20
28	0.63038 53875 68	0.60082 77824 04	0.45964 73743 02	1.08655 98069 92
29	0.65071 07213 80	0.61828 34842 44	0.47485 49140 10	1.09231 11792 82
30	0.67083 77336 96	0.63540 02107 68	0.48993 41337 41	1.09818 97839 77
31	0.69076 43809 10	0.65217 78438 16	0.50488 04627 91	1.10418 84834 96
32	0.71048 89595 23	0.66861 69359 32	0.51968 93261 28	1.11029 99929 73
33	0.73001 00993 18	0.68471 86767 23	0.53435 61458 54	1.11651 68890 09
34	0.74932 67558 68	0.70048 48582 79	0.54887 63427 77	1.12283 16186 13
35	0.76843 82024 44	0.71591 78399 28	0.56324 53381 13	1.12923 65082 97
36	0.78734 40214 14	0.73102 05126 38	0.57745 85553 05	1.13572 37733 29
37	0.80604 40951 84	0.74579 62633 05	0.59151 14219 63	1.14228 55271 26
38	0.82453 85967 81	0.76024 89391 75	0.60539 93719 25	1.14891 37907 78
39	0.84282 79801 28	0.77438 28126 35	0.61911 78474 26	1.15560 05026 95
40	0.86091 29700 79	0.78820 25465 43	0.63266 23013 84	1.16233 75283 60
41	0.87879 45522 85	0.80171 31603 06	0.64602 81997 96	1.16911 66701 81
42	0.89647 39629 38	0.81491 99968 34	0.65921 10242 30	1.17592 96774 24
43	0.91395 26784 58	0.82782 86905 28	0.67220 62744 35	1.18276 82562 31
44	0.93123 24051 64	0.84044 51363 98	0.68500 94710 33	1.18962 40796 83
45	0.94831 50689 88	0.85277 54604 22	0.69761 61583 12	1.19648 87979 27

K = 2.13002 14383 99325   E = 1.22058 89957 54247
K' = 1.69411 43573 05914   E' = 1.46077 35062 13127

r	u=(r/90)K=F(φ,k)	sn u	cn u	dn u
45	1.06501 07192 00	0.81243 42547 36	0.58305 28121 28	0.71766 15322 77
46	1.08867 76240 71	0.82216 43802 37	0.56925 01487 66	0.70947 31937 29
47	1.11234 45289 42	0.83155 30741 97	0.55544 53031 52	0.70138 75699 94
48	1.13601 14338 13	0.84060 70617 73	0.54164 54261 75	0.69341 24540 78
49	1.15967 83386 84	0.84933 31712 34	0.52785 71437 82	0.68555 52306 40
50	1.18334 52435 55	0.85773 83056 22	0.51408 65676 80	0.67782 28853 53
51	1.20701 21484 26	0.86582 94160 59	0.50033 93071 57	0.67022 20151 97
52	1.23067 90532 97	0.87361 34766 82	0.48662 04818 55	0.66275 88395 45
53	1.25434 59581 68	0.88109 74611 82	0.47293 47353 48	0.65543 92119 18
54	1.27801 28630 40	0.88828 83209 39	0.45928 62493 95	0.64826 86322 76
55	1.30167 97679 11	0.89519 29646 85	0.44567 87587 24	0.64125 22597 44
56	1.32534 66727 82	0.90181 82396 73	0.43211 55662 47	0.63439 49256 53
57	1.34901 35776 53	0.90817 09142 90	0.41859 95585 73	0.62770 11468 18
58	1.37268 04825 24	0.91425 76620 61	0.40513 32217 46	0.62117 51389 46
59	1.39634 73873 95	0.92008 50469 84	0.39171 86570 94	0.61482 08300 96
60	1.42001 42922 66	0.92565 95101 33	0.37835 75971 23	0.60864 18741 25
61	1.44368 11971 37	0.93098 73574 62	0.36505 14213 73	0.60264 16640 47
62	1.46734 81020 08	0.93607 47487 51	0.35180 11721 84	0.59682 33452 45
63	1.49101 50068 80	0.94092 76876 22	0.33860 75703 02	0.59118 98284 81
64	1.51468 19117 51	0.94555 20125 55	0.32547 10302 82	0.58574 38026 59
65	1.53834 88166 22	0.94995 33888 46	0.31239 16756 58	0.58048 77473 07
66	1.56201 57214 93	0.95413 73014 38	0.29936 93538 18	0.57542 39447 21
67	1.58568 26263 64	0.95810 90485 59	0.28640 36505 86	0.57055 44917 62
68	1.60934 95312 35	0.96187 37361 11	0.27349 39044 64	0.56588 13112 65
69	1.63301 64361 06	0.96543 62727 39	0.26063 92205 31	0.56140 61630 47
70	1.65668 33409 77	0.96880 13655 33	0.24783 84839 80	0.55713 06544 79
71	1.68035 02458 48	0.97197 35163 01	0.23509 03732 80	0.55305 62506 31
72	1.70401 71507 19	0.97495 70183 64	0.22239 33729 75	0.54918 42839 53
73	1.72768 40555 91	0.97775 59538 12	0.20974 57860 97	0.54551 59634 95
74	1.75135 09604 62	0.98037 41911 89	0.19714 57462 17	0.54205 23836 58
75	1.77501 78653 33	0.98281 53835 44	0.18459 12291 22	0.53879 45324 67
76	1.79868 47702 04	0.98508 29668 23	0.17208 00641 44	0.53574 32993 65
77	1.82235 16750 75	0.98718 01585 40	0.15960 99451 32	0.53289 94825 20
78	1.84601 85799 46	0.98910 99567 16	0.14717 84411 02	0.53026 37956 51
79	1.86968 54848 17	0.99087 51390 28	0.13478 30065 59	0.52783 68743 75
80	1.89335 23896 88	0.99247 82621 47	0.12242 09915 23	0.52561 92820 61
81	1.91701 92945 59	0.99392 16612 40	0.11008 96512 75	0.52361 15152 16
82	1.94068 61994 30	0.99520 74495 94	0.09778 61558 32	0.52181 40083 73
83	1.96435 31043 02	0.99633 75183 55	0.08550 75991 85	0.52022 71385 23
84	1.98802 00091 73	0.99731 35363 47	0.07325 10083 13	0.51885 12290 60
85	2.01168 69140 44	0.99813 69499 61	0.06101 33520 03	0.51768 65532 58
86	2.03535 38189 15	0.99880 89830 89	0.04879 15494 90	0.51673 33372 75
87	2.05902 07237 86	0.99933 06370 94	0.03658 24789 50	0.51599 17626 93
88	2.08268 76286 57	0.99970 26908 04	0.02438 29858 63	0.51546 19685 98
89	2.10635 45335 28	0.99992 57005 15	0.01218 98912 78	0.51514 40531 84
90	2.13002 14383 99	1.00000 00000 00	0.00000 00000 00	0.51503 80749 10

q = 0.08219 43773 66407 71   D(90) = 1.39341 45206 68691
q'= 0.01925 57475 39635 14   1/D(90) = 0.71766 15322 76918

r	ϕ	$E(\phi,k)$	A(r)	D(r)
45	0.94831 50689 88	0.85277 54604 22	0.69761 61583 12	1.19648 87979 27
46	0.96520 28052 52	0.86482 59912 13	0.71002 19071 07	1.20335 40483 35
47	0.98189 79485 80	0.87660 32330 61	0.72222 23177 61	1.21021 14656 85
48	0.99840 30229 46	0.88811 38403 91	0.73421 30231 68	1.21705 26923 58
49	1.01472 07319 10	0.89936 45936 69	0.74598 96918 86	1.22386 93885 37
50	1.03085 39490 63	0.91036 23767 76	0.75754 80313 13	1.23065 32423 90
51	1.04680 57087 06	0.92111 41558 47	0.76888 37909 34	1.23739 59802 27
52	1.06257 91967 79	0.93162 69595 82	0.77999 27656 11	1.24408 93766 28
53	1.07817 77420 61	0.94190 78609 98	0.79087 07989 24	1.25072 52645 08
54	1.09360 48076 58	0.95196 39606 15	0.80151 37865 61	1.25729 55451 33
55	1.10886 39827 84	0.96180 23710 34	0.81191 76797 28	1.26379 21980 52
56	1.12395 89748 50	0.97143 02028 80	0.82207 84885 97	1.27020 72909 45
57	1.13889 36018 58	0.98085 45520 54	0.83199 22857 71	1.27653 29893 70
58	1.15367 17851 23	0.99008 24882 71	0.84165 52097 63	1.28276 15664 01
59	1.16829 75423 02	0.99912 10448 10	0.85106 34684 75	1.28888 54121 38
60	1.18277 49807 43	1.00797 72094 46	0.86021 33426 86	1.29489 70430 82
61	1.19710 82911 58	1.01665 79164 98	0.86910 11895 17	1.30078 91113 64
62	1.21130 17416 08	1.02517 00399 44	0.87772 34458 93	1.30655 44138 12
63	1.22535 96717 88	1.03352 03875 47	0.88607 66319 71	1.31218 59008 45
64	1.23928 64876 36	1.04171 56959 39	0.89415 73545 39	1.31767 66851 89
65	1.25308 66562 23	1.04976 26266 06	0.90196 23103 81	1.32302 00503 91
66	1.26676 47009 49	1.05766 77627 23	0.90948 82895 85	1.32820 94591 38
67	1.28032 51970 08	1.06543 76067 81	0.91673 21788 09	1.33323 85613 49
68	1.29377 27671 40	1.07307 85789 67	0.92369 09644 76	1.33810 12020 50
69	1.30711 20776 42	1.08059 70162 31	0.93036 17359 06	1.34279 14290 07
70	1.32034 78346 38	1.08799 91720 05	0.93674 16883 74	1.34730 35001 12
71	1.33348 47805 87	1.09529 12165 17	0.94282 81260 77	1.35163 18905 17
72	1.34652 76910 35	1.10247 92376 67	0.94861 84650 26	1.35577 12994 98
73	1.35948 13715 85	1.10956 92424 18	0.95411 02358 30	1.35971 66570 46
74	1.37235 06550 82	1.11656 71586 48	0.95930 10863 84	1.36346 31301 75
75	1.38514 03989 96	1.12347 88374 55	0.96418 87844 49	1.36700 61289 36
76	1.39785 54830 00	1.13031 00558 46	0.96877 12201 18	1.37034 13121 36
77	1.41050 08067 22	1.13706 65197 96	0.97304 64081 59	1.37346 45927 44
78	1.42308 12876 68	1.14375 38676 35	0.97701 24902 41	1.37637 21429 88
79	1.43560 18593 02	1.15037 76737 41	0.98066 77370 19	1.37906 03991 28
80	1.44806 74692 62	1.15694 34524 98	0.98401 05500 95	1.38152 60658 98
81	1.46048 30777 19	1.16345 66625 01	0.98703 94638 34	1.38376 61206 25
82	1.47285 36558 52	1.16992 27109 78	0.98975 31470 37	1.38577 78169 98
83	1.48518 41844 35	1.17634 69584 04	0.99215 04044 64	1.38755 86884 96
84	1.49747 96525 22	1.18273 47232 90	0.99423 01782 16	1.38910 65514 74
85	1.50974 50562 24	1.18909 12871 13	0.99599 15489 50	1.39041 95078 89
86	1.52198 53975 52	1.19542 18993 79	0.99743 37369 45	1.39149 59476 70
87	1.53420 56833 41	1.20173 17827 92	0.99855 61030 06	1.39233 45507 33
88	1.54641 09242 16	1.20802 61385 08	0.99935 81492 09	1.39293 42886 30
89	1.55860 61336 07	1.21431 01514 64	0.99983 95194 78	1.39329 44258 37
90	1.57079 63267 95	1.22058 89957 54	1.00000 00000 00	1.39341 45206 69

K = 2.15651 56474 99643

K' = 1.68575 03548 12596

E = 1.21105 60275 68459

E' = 1.46746 22093 39427

r	u=(r/90)K=F(ϕ,k)	sn u	cn u	dn u
0	0.00000 00000 00	0.00000 00000 00	1.00000 00000 00	1.00000 00000 00
1	0.02396 12849 72	0.02395 72732 47	0.99971 29833 40	0.99978 47452 30
2	0.04792 25699 44	0.04789 04951 78	0.99885 25919 63	0.99913 95675 05
3	0.07188 38549 17	0.07177 57094 86	0.99742 07976 21	0.99806 62230 76
4	0.09584 51398 89	0.09558 91490 73	0.99542 08730 88	0.99656 76273 76
5	0.11980 64248 61	0.11930 73286 54	0.99285 73720 98	0.99464 78376 78
6	0.14376 77098 33	0.14290 71349 93	0.98973 61015 79	0.99231 20290 90
7	0.16772 89948 06	0.16636 59140 35	0.98606 40864 81	0.98956 64641 58
8	0.19169 02797 78	0.18966 15542 30	0.98184 95275 99	0.98641 84564 04
9	0.21565 15647 50	0.21277 25654 36	0.97710 17528 37	0.98287 63282 06
10	0.23961 28497 22	0.23567 81527 92	0.97183 11624 44	0.97894 93634 62
11	0.26357 41346 94	0.25835 82850 75	0.96604 91687 97	0.97464 77555 51
12	0.28753 54196 67	0.28079 37570 93	0.95976 81313 62	0.96998 25511 23
13	0.31149 67046 39	0.30296 62457 58	0.95300 12874 76	0.96496 55902 93
14	0.33545 79896 11	0.32485 83595 58	0.94576 26796 53	0.95960 94438 20
15	0.35941 92745 83	0.34645 36812 36	0.93806 70800 95	0.95392 73478 98
16	0.38338 05595 55	0.36773 68035 50	0.92992 99131 20	0.94793 31371 39
17	0.40734 18445 28	0.38869 33580 75	0.92136 71762 05	0.94164 11763 73
18	0.43130 31295 00	0.40931 00370 96	0.91239 53603 19	0.93506 62918 47
19	0.45526 44144 72	0.42957 46086 79	0.90303 13702 07	0.92822 37023 93
20	0.47922 56994 44	0.44947 59251 10	0.89329 24452 53	0.92112 89511 03
21	0.50318 69844 17	0.46900 39249 22	0.88319 60815 17	0.91379 78380 39
22	0.52714 82693 89	0.48814 96288 14	0.87275 99554 80	0.90624 63544 30
23	0.55110 95543 61	0.50690 51297 70	0.86200 18500 06	0.89849 06187 93
24	0.57507 08393 33	0.52526 35777 80	0.85093 95829 66	0.89054 68153 85
25	0.59903 21243 05	0.54321 91595 42	0.83959 09389 14	0.88243 11352 90
26	0.62299 34092 78	0.56076 70735 85	0.82797 36041 58	0.87415 97204 67
27	0.64695 46942 50	0.57790 35012 61	0.81610 51055 05	0.86574 86109 85
28	0.67091 59792 22	0.59462 55740 53	0.80400 27529 07	0.85721 36956 51
29	0.69487 72641 94	0.61093 13376 69	0.79168 35861 97	0.84857 06661 74
30	0.71883 85491 67	0.62681 97133 70	0.77916 43260 13	0.83983 49749 79
31	0.74279 98341 39	0.64229 04569 89	0.76646 13290 06	0.83102 17967 33
32	0.76676 11191 11	0.65734 41160 76	0.75359 05473 53	0.82214 59936 02
33	0.79072 24040 83	0.67198 19855 92	0.74056 74925 62	0.81322 20842 30
34	0.81468 36890 55	0.68620 60625 50	0.72740 72035 11	0.80426 42164 05
35	0.83864 49740 28	0.70001 89999 82	0.71412 42186 51	0.79528 61433 14
36	0.86260 62590 00	0.71342 40605 91	0.70073 25522 41	0.78630 12033 10
37	0.88656 75439 72	0.72642 50704 03	0.68724 56744 79	0.77732 23030 49
38	0.91052 88289 44	0.73902 63727 27	0.67367 64953 70	0.76836 19038 64
39	0.93449 01139 17	0.75123 27826 87	0.66003 73521 37	0.75943 20112 18
40	0.95845 13988 89	0.76304 95425 64	0.64633 99999 95	0.75054 41670 52
41	0.98241 26838 61	0.77448 22781 64	0.63259 56060 62	0.74170 94448 68
42	1.00637 39688 33	0.78553 69564 02	0.61881 47462 10	0.73293 84473 44
43	1.03033 52538 05	0.79621 98442 31	0.60500 74046 26	0.72424 13062 92
44	1.05429 65387 78	0.80653 74690 89	0.59118 29758 67	0.71562 76847 75
45	1.07825 78237 50	0.81649 65809 28	0.57735 02691 90	0.70710 67811 87

ELLIPTIC FUNCTIONS   TABLE $\theta = 60°$

q = 0.08579 57337 02194 77
q′= 0.01797 23870 08967 24

D(90) = 1.41421 35623 73095
1/D(90) = 0.70710 67811 86548

r	ϕ	$E(\phi,k)$	A(r)	D(r)
0	0.00000 00000 00	0.00000 00000 00	0.00000 00000 00	1.00000 00000 00
1	0.02395 95655 56	0.02395 78463 61	0.01694 24822 34	1.00012 58452 48
2	0.04790 88202 36	0.04789 50776 26	0.03388 07350 82	1.00050 32288 33
3	0.07183 74812 47	0.07179 11614 01	0.05081 05278 94	1.00113 16944 57
4	0.09573 53217 94	0.09562 57300 01	0.06772 76275 00	1.00201 04822 25
5	0.11959 21986 60	0.11937 86610 71	0.08462 77969 70	1.00313 85295 37
6	0.14339 80792 93	0.14303 01561 63	0.10150 67943 92	1.00451 44723 48
7	0.16714 30682 38	0.16656 08166 21	0.11836 03716 85	1.00613 66467 78
8	0.19081 74327 68	0.18995 17161 86	0.13518 42734 43	1.00800 30910 80
9	0.21441 16275 76	0.21318 44697 61	0.15197 42358 25	1.01011 15479 54
10	0.23791 63183 85	0.23624 12978 35	0.16872 59854 95	1.01245 94672 23
11	0.26132 24043 80	0.25910 50861 41	0.18543 52386 21	1.01504 40088 43
12	0.28462 10393 30	0.28175 94401 40	0.20209 76999 36	1.01786 20462 67
13	0.30780 36513 23	0.30418 87340 60	0.21870 90618 65	1.02091 01701 41
14	0.33086 19610 40	0.32637 81542 15	0.23526 50037 40	1.02418 46923 49
15	0.35378 79984 67	0.34831 37364 55	0.25176 11910 84	1.02768 16503 71
16	0.37657 41180 59	0.36998 23976 30	0.26819 32749 93	1.03139 68119 91
17	0.39921 30122 54	0.39137 19610 57	0.28455 68916 08	1.03532 56803 04
18	0.42169 77233 53	0.41247 11759 92	0.30084 76616 83	1.03946 34990 61
19	0.44402 16537 57	0.43326 97312 29	0.31706 11902 66	1.04380 52583 10
20	0.46617 85745 46	0.45375 82629 58	0.33319 30664 75	1.04834 57003 47
21	0.48816 26324 49	0.47392 83570 96	0.34923 88634 04	1.05307 93259 68
22	0.50996 83552 01	0.49377 25463 32	0.36519 41381 26	1.05800 04010 09
23	0.53159 06553 58	0.51328 43021 84	0.38105 44318 36	1.06310 29631 72
24	0.55302 48326 07	0.53245 80223 89	0.39681 52701 04	1.06838 08291 24
25	0.57426 65746 25	0.55128 90139 66	0.41247 21632 59	1.07382 76018 72
26	0.59531 19565 69	0.56977 34723 44	0.42802 06069 06	1.07943 66783 92
27	0.61615 74392 58	0.58790 84569 32	0.44345 60825 72	1.08520 12575 13
28	0.63679 98661 36	0.60569 18635 16	0.45877 40584 78	1.09111 43480 47
29	0.65723 64590 91	0.62312 23939 08	0.47396 99904 63	1.09716 87771 46
30	0.67746 48132 15	0.64019 95232 21	0.48903 93230 23	1.10335 71988 91
31	0.69748 28906 08	0.65692 34651 73	0.50397 74905 06	1.10967 21030 95
32	0.71728 90132 95	0.67329 51357 99	0.51877 99184 26	1.11610 58243 05
33	0.73688 18553 61	0.68931 61159 37	0.53344 20249 28	1.12265 05510 09
34	0.75626 04343 83	0.70498 86128 34	0.54795 92223 79	1.12929 83350 16
35	0.77542 41022 54	0.72031 54212 05	0.56232 69190 96	1.13604 11010 18
36	0.79437 25354 80	0.73529 98840 51	0.57654 05212 13	1.14287 06563 14
37	0.81310 57250 26	0.74994 58535 17	0.59059 54346 70	1.14977 87006 76
38	0.83162 39658 08	0.76425 76520 57	0.60448 70673 39	1.15675 68363 70
39	0.84992 78458 89	0.77824 00341 31	0.61821 08312 72	1.16379 65782 90
40	0.86801 82354 54	0.79189 81486 54	0.63176 21450 74	1.17088 93642 16
41	0.88589 62756 46	0.80523 75023 69	0.64513 64363 99	1.17802 65651 78
42	0.90356 33673 04	0.81826 39243 21	0.65832 91445 58	1.18519 94959 02
43	0.92102 11596 78	0.83098 35315 57	0.67133 57232 40	1.19239 94253 47
44	0.93827 15391 64	0.84340 26961 70	0.68415 16433 44	1.19961 75873 02
45	0.95531 66181 25	0.85552 80137 84	0.69677 23959 14	1.20684 51910 34

239

ELLIPTIC FUNCTIONS TABLE $\theta = 60°$

K = 2.15651 56474 99643
K′ = 1.68575 03548 12596

E = 1.21105 60275 68459
E′ = 1.46746 22093 39427

r	u=(r/90)K=F(φ,k)	sn u	cn u	dn u
45	1.07825 78237 50	0.81649 65809 28	0.57735 02691 90	0.70710 67811 87
46	1.10221 91087 22	0.82610 41159 31	0.56351 75149 37	0.69868 73351 01
47	1.12618 03936 94	0.83536 71619 81	0.54969 23727 73	0.69037 76347 14
48	1.15014 16786 67	0.84429 29258 96	0.53588 19415 52	0.68218 55256 90
49	1.17410 29636 39	0.85288 87024 95	0.52209 27706 41	0.67411 84212 49
50	1.19806 42486 11	0.86116 18454 57	0.50833 08724 93	0.66618 33133 21
51	1.22202 55335 83	0.86911 97400 00	0.49460 17362 92	0.65838 67846 16
52	1.24598 68185 55	0.87676 97773 42	0.48091 03425 16	0.65073 50214 60
53	1.26994 81035 28	0.88411 93309 17	0.46726 11782 48	0.64323 38272 54
54	1.29390 93885 00	0.89117 57343 00	0.45365 82530 89	0.63588 86364 35
55	1.31787 06734 72	0.89794 62607 95	0.44010 51155 40	0.62870 45288 08
56	1.34183 19584 44	0.90443 81046 35	0.42660 48697 39	0.62168 62441 49
57	1.36579 32434 16	0.91065 83637 15	0.41316 01924 14	0.61483 81969 65
58	1.38975 45283 89	0.91661 40238 09	0.39977 33499 84	0.60816 44913 33
59	1.41371 58133 61	0.92231 19441 86	0.38644 62156 79	0.60166 89357 19
60	1.43767 70983 33	0.92775 88445 66	0.37318 02866 30	0.59535 50577 15
61	1.46163 83833 05	0.93296 12933 32	0.35997 67008 35	0.58922 61186 15
62	1.48559 96682 78	0.93792 56969 25	0.34683 62539 41	0.58328 51277 77
63	1.50956 09532 50	0.94265 82903 50	0.33375 94157 98	0.57753 48567 19
64	1.53352 22382 22	0.94716 51287 20	0.32074 63467 23	0.57197 78528 95
65	1.55748 35231 94	0.95145 20797 57	0.30779 69134 46	0.56661 64531 19
66	1.58144 48081 66	0.95552 48171 85	0.29491 07046 96	0.56145 27965 98
67	1.60540 60931 39	0.95938 88149 47	0.28208 70464 13	0.55648 88375 48
68	1.62936 73781 11	0.96304 93421 73	0.26932 50165 52	0.55172 63573 60
69	1.65332 86630 83	0.96651 14588 28	0.25662 34594 78	0.54716 69763 11
70	1.67728 99480 55	0.96978 00119 99	0.24398 09999 30	0.54281 21647 91
71	1.70125 12330 27	0.97285 96327 37	0.23139 60565 61	0.53866 32540 32
72	1.72521 25180 00	0.97575 47334 07	0.21886 68550 37	0.53472 14463 40
73	1.74917 38029 72	0.97846 95055 01	0.20639 14407 25	0.53098 78248 16
74	1.77313 50879 44	0.98100 79178 44	0.19396 76909 38	0.52746 33625 63
75	1.79709 63729 16	0.98337 37151 59	0.18159 33267 87	0.52414 89313 64
76	1.82105 76578 89	0.98557 04169 48	0.16926 59246 17	0.52104 53098 60
77	1.84501 89428 61	0.98760 13166 31	0.15698 29270 63	0.51815 31911 91
78	1.86898 02278 33	0.98946 94809 21	0.14474 16537 38	0.51547 31901 32
79	1.89294 15128 05	0.99117 77493 92	0.13253 93115 63	0.51300 58497 06
80	1.91690 27977 77	0.99272 87342 08	0.12037 30047 68	0.51075 16472 88
81	1.94086 40827 50	0.99412 48199 77	0.10823 97445 79	0.50871 10002 05
82	1.96482 53677 22	0.99536 81637 08	0.09613 64586 19	0.50688 42708 22
83	1.98878 66526 94	0.99646 06948 56	0.08406 00000 41	0.50527 17711 34
84	2.01274 79376 66	0.99740 41154 04	0.07200 71564 21	0.50387 37668 62
85	2.03670 92226 39	0.99819 98999 93	0.05997 46584 34	0.50269 04810 52
86	2.06067 05076 11	0.99884 92960 67	0.04795 91883 42	0.50172 20971 91
87	2.08463 17925 83	0.99935 33240 18	0.03595 73883 11	0.50096 87618 31
88	2.10859 30775 55	0.99971 27773 23	0.02396 58686 01	0.50043 05867 38
89	2.13255 43625 27	0.99992 82226 60	0.01198 12156 37	0.50010 76505 57
90	2.15651 56475 00	1.00000 00000 00	0.00000 00000 00	0.50000 00000 00

240

q = 0.08579 57337 02194 77   D(90) = 1.41421 35623 73095
q' = 0.01797 23870 08967 24   1/D(90) = 0.70710 67811 86548

r	ϕ	$E(\phi,k)$	$A(r)$	$D(r)$
45	0.95531 66181 25	0.85552 80137 84	0.69677 23959 14	1.20684 51910 34
46	0.97215 87238 15	0.86736 62735 49	0.70919 34951 64	1.21407 34319 87
47	0.98880 03874 77	0.87892 44297 03	0.72141 04816 07	1.22129 35024 98
48	1.00524 43336 31	0.89020 95747 38	0.73341 89252 65	1.22849 66025 39
49	1.02149 34695 83	0.90122 89141 97	0.74521 44289 56	1.23567 39504 49
50	1.03755 08752 02	0.91198 97431 01	0.75679 26316 62	1.24281 67936 68
51	1.05341 97929 62	0.92249 94240 13	0.76814 92119 61	1.24991 64194 35
52	1.06910 36182 96	0.93276 53667 12	0.77927 98915 21	1.25696 41654 55
53	1.08460 58902 50	0.94279 50094 57	0.79018 04386 48	1.26395 14305 13
54	1.09993 02824 82	0.95259 58018 16	0.80084 66718 80	1.27086 96850 28
55	1.11508 05945 84	0.96217 51890 03	0.81127 44636 20	1.27771 04815 20
56	1.13006 07437 68	0.97154 05976 85	0.82145 97438 03	1.28446 54649 97
57	1.14487 47568 88	0.98069 94232 15	0.83139 85035 84	1.29112 63832 34
58	1.15952 67628 28	0.98965 90182 17	0.84108 67990 43	1.29768 50969 36
59	1.17402 09852 38	0.99842 66824 83	0.85052 07548 99	1.30413 35897 69
60	1.18836 17356 30	1.00700 96541 18	0.85969 65682 25	1.31046 39782 53
61	1.20255 34068 25	1.01541 51018 57	0.86861 05121 54	1.31666 85215 00
62	1.21660 04667 37	1.02365 01185 17	0.87725 89395 66	1.32273 96307 78
63	1.23050 74525 15	1.03172 17155 01	0.88563 82867 57	1.32866 98789 05
64	1.24427 89650 03	1.03963 68183 00	0.89374 50770 69	1.33445 20094 43
65	1.25791 96635 37	1.04740 22629 35	0.90157 59244 88	1.34007 89456 95
66	1.27143 42610 53	1.05502 47932 78	0.90912 75371 83	1.34554 37994 80
67	1.28482 75195 02	1.06251 10591 89	0.91639 67210 01	1.35083 98796 84
68	1.29810 42455 67	1.06986 76154 20	0.92338 03828 83	1.35596 07005 76
69	1.31126 92866 64	1.07710 09212 27	0.93007 55342 22	1.36089 99898 69
70	1.32432 75272 14	1.08421 73406 45	0.93647 92941 33	1.36565 16965 27
71	1.33728 38851 81	1.09122 31433 64	0.94258 88926 41	1.37020 99982 97
72	1.35014 33088 65	1.09812 45061 72	0.94840 16737 65	1.37456 93089 62
73	1.36291 07739 26	1.10492 75149 12	0.95391 50985 15	1.37872 42853 12
74	1.37559 12806 42	1.11163 81669 12	0.95912 67477 67	1.38266 98338 05
75	1.38818 98513 75	1.11826 23738 50	0.96403 43250 31	1.38640 11169 25
76	1.40071 15282 46	1.12480 59650 12	0.96863 56590 96	1.38991 35592 29
77	1.41316 13709 95	1.13127 46909 12	0.97292 87065 42	1.39320 28530 58
78	1.42554 44550 16	1.13767 42272 36	0.97691 15541 29	1.39626 49639 31
79	1.43786 58695 62	1.14401 01790 81	0.98058 24210 35	1.39909 61355 85
80	1.45013 07160 99	1.15028 80854 59	0.98393 96609 59	1.40169 28946 80
81	1.46234 41068 04	1.15651 34240 40	0.98698 17640 67	1.40405 20551 45
82	1.47451 11631 83	1.16269 16161 02	0.98970 73587 95	1.40617 07221 72
83	1.48663 70148 12	1.16882 80316 72	0.99211 52134 80	1.40804 62958 38
84	1.49867 83168 14	1.17492 79948 27	0.99420 42378 41	1.40967 64743 69
85	1.51078 56556 35	1.18099 67891 45	0.99597 34842 86	1.41105 92570 20
86	1.52281 87343 73	1.18703 96632 65	0.99742 21490 60	1.41219 29465 89
87	1.53483 11855 52	1.19306 18365 61	0.99854 95732 10	1.41307 61515 43
88	1.54682 81634 16	1.19906 85048 99	0.99935 52433 87	1.41370 77877 63
89	1.55881 48244 89	1.20506 48464 51	0.99983 87924 68	1.41408 70799 05
90	1.57079 63267 95	1.21105 60275 68	1.00000 00000 00	1.41421 35623 73

K = 2.18421 32169 49248
K′= 1.67773 48840 80745

E = 1.20153 81841 13662
E′= 1.47396 98872 41625

r	u=(r/90)K=F(φ,k)	sn u	cn u	dn u
0	0.00000 00000 00	0.00000 00000 00	1.00000 00000 00	1.00000 00000 00
1	0.02426 90357 44	0.02426 48318 47	0.99970 55656 22	0.99977 47773 82
2	0.04853 80714 88	0.04850 44609 96	0.99882 29659 27	0.99909 97411 07
3	0.07280 71072 32	0.07269 37879 54	0.99735 43067 50	0.99797 67820 00
4	0.09707 61429 76	0.09680 79187 34	0.99530 30829 20	0.99640 90384 35
5	0.12134 51787 19	0.12082 22653 59	0.99267 41561 02	0.99440 08769 80
6	0.14561 42144 63	0.14471 26437 03	0.98947 37241 34	0.99195 78656 37
7	0.16988 32502 07	0.16845 53678 44	0.98570 92822 15	0.98908 67399 51
8	0.19415 22859 51	0.19202 73401 61	0.98138 95763 82	0.98579 53623 99
9	0.21842 13216 95	0.21540 61364 42	0.97652 45498 11	0.98209 26755 12
10	0.24269 03574 39	0.23857 00854 00	0.97112 52825 21	0.97798 86492 42
11	0.26695 93931 83	0.26149 83419 83	0.96520 39251 58	0.97349 42231 59
12	0.29122 84289 27	0.28417 09540 54	0.95877 36275 43	0.96862 12440 99
13	0.31549 74646 70	0.30656 89220 07	0.95184 84627 60	0.96338 23999 02
14	0.33976 65004 14	0.32867 42510 51	0.94444 33475 31	0.95779 11499 30
15	0.36403 55361 58	0.35046 99959 43	0.93657 39596 76	0.95186 16530 48
16	0.38830 45719 02	0.37194 02980 68	0.92825 66534 50	0.94560 86937 53
17	0.41257 36076 46	0.39307 04148 27	0.91950 83735 28	0.93904 76071 47
18	0.43684 26433 90	0.41384 67414 16	0.91034 65684 12	0.93219 42034 02
19	0.46111 16791 34	0.43425 68251 08	0.90078 91039 79	0.92506 46923 69
20	0.48538 07148 78	0.45428 93722 90	0.89085 41778 68	0.91767 56089 37
21	0.50964 97506 21	0.47393 42485 02	0.88056 02353 60	0.91004 37397 03
22	0.53391 87863 65	0.49318 24718 40	0.86992 58873 43	0.90218 60514 78
23	0.55818 78221 09	0.51202 62001 09	0.85896 98309 03	0.89411 96221 08
24	0.58245 68578 53	0.53045 87121 53	0.84771 07730 24	0.88586 15740 18
25	0.60672 58935 97	0.54847 43838 34	0.83616 73578 16	0.87742 90108 59
26	0.63099 49293 41	0.56606 86591 52	0.82435 80976 29	0.86883 89575 59
27	0.65526 39650 85	0.58323 80170 02	0.81230 13083 36	0.86010 83040 41
28	0.67953 30008 29	0.59997 99341 01	0.80001 50490 31	0.85125 37527 99
29	0.70380 20365 73	0.61629 28445 85	0.78751 70663 00	0.84229 17704 89
30	0.72807 10723 16	0.63217 60967 99	0.77482 47431 75	0.83323 85436 38
31	0.75234 01080 60	0.64762 99077 74	0.76195 50528 45	0.82410 99385 00
32	0.77660 91438 04	0.66265 53158 75	0.74892 45171 19	0.81492 14650 91
33	0.80087 81795 48	0.67725 41320 93	0.73574 91695 97	0.80568 82453 50
34	0.82514 72152 92	0.69142 88903 97	0.72244 45234 93	0.79642 49853 68
35	0.84941 62510 36	0.70518 27975 80	0.70902 55439 67	0.78714 59515 75
36	0.87368 52867 80	0.71851 96829 63	0.69550 66248 39	0.77786 49507 61
37	0.89795 43225 24	0.73144 39483 11	0.68190 15694 94	0.76859 53137 69
38	0.92222 33582 67	0.74396 05182 74	0.66822 35757 96	0.75934 98826 96
39	0.94649 23940 11	0.75607 47916 37	0.65448 52247 77	0.75014 10014 08
40	0.97076 14297 55	0.76779 25936 30	0.64069 84728 93	0.74098 05091 64
41	0.99503 04654 99	0.77912 01295 11	0.62687 46475 90	0.73187 97371 45
42	1.01929 95012 43	0.79006 39396 10	0.61302 44459 46	0.72284 95076 71
43	1.04356 85369 87	0.80063 08559 92	0.59915 79361 35	0.71390 01358 87
44	1.06783 75727 31	0.81082 79608 55	0.58528 45614 71	0.70504 14336 99
45	1.09210 66084 75	0.82066 25467 78	0.57141 31467 82	0.69628 27157 46

ELLIPTIC FUNCTIONS TABLE $\theta = 61°$

q = 0.08953 58769 52552 59   D(90) = 1.43619 82243 50425
q′= 0.01673 95077 33022 71   1/D(90) = 0.69628 27157 45793

r	ϕ	$E(\phi,k)$	A(r)	D(r)
0	0.00000 00000 00	0.00000 00000 00	0.00000 00000 00	1.00000 00000 00
1	0.02426 72135 95	0.02426 53916 92	0.01689 74212 69	1.00013 24787 50
2	0.04852 35004 28	0.04850 89372 41	0.03379 07091 47	1.00052 97549 87
3	0.07275 79643 64	0.07270 88811 73	0.05067 57287 27	1.00119 13488 65
4	0.09695 97703 22	0.09684 36485 62	0.06754 83420 74	1.00211 64612 65
5	0.12111 81743 39	0.12089 19333 37	0.08440 44067 29	1.00330 39747 39
6	0.14522 25530 65	0.14483 27842 64	0.10123 97742 44	1.00475 24548 19
7	0.16926 24325 23	0.16864 56878 84	0.11805 02887 43	1.00646 01517 11
8	0.19322 75159 62	0.19231 06477 22	0.13483 17855 22	1.00842 50023 48
9	0.21710 77106 57	0.21580 82591 56	0.15158 00896 99	1.01064 46328 24
10	0.24089 31534 86	0.23911 97793 74	0.16829 10149 24	1.01311 63611 84
11	0.26457 42351 75	0.26222 71919 45	0.18496 03621 38	1.01583 72005 85
12	0.28814 16230 84	0.28511 32655 58	0.20158 39184 19	1.01880 38628 15
13	0.31158 62824 26	0.30776 16066 29	0.21815 74558 89	1.02201 27621 70
14	0.33489 94958 42	0.33015 67054 77	0.23467 67307 16	1.02546 00196 81
15	0.35807 28812 54	0.35228 39759 22	0.25113 74822 02	1.02914 14676 93
16	0.38109 84079 49	0.37412 97881 95	0.26753 54319 65	1.03305 26547 82
17	0.40396 84108 52	0.39568 14951 29	0.28386 62832 27	1.03718 88510 19
18	0.42667 56029 75	0.41692 74517 12	0.30012 57202 12	1.04154 50535 53
19	0.44921 30860 30	0.43785 70281 03	0.31630 94076 51	1.04611 59925 37
20	0.47157 43592 19	0.45846 06163 12	0.33241 29904 14	1.05089 61373 60
21	0.49375 33262 32	0.47872 96307 88	0.34843 20932 59	1.05587 97032 01
22	0.51574 43004 81	0.49865 65032 15	0.36436 23207 13	1.06106 06578 85
23	0.53754 20086 33	0.51823 46718 57	0.38019 92570 83	1.06643 27290 39
24	0.55914 15924 89	0.53745 85658 39	0.39593 84666 05	1.07198 94115 45
25	0.58053 86092 92	0.55632 35847 58	0.41157 54937 27	1.07772 39752 65
26	0.60172 90305 35	0.57482 60740 70	0.42710 58635 40	1.08362 94730 48
27	0.62270 92393 65	0.59296 32966 90	0.44252 50823 48	1.08969 87490 04
28	0.64347 60266 55	0.61073 34012 52	0.45782 86383 88	1.09592 44470 31
29	0.66402 65858 65	0.62813 53874 99	0.47301 20026 94	1.10229 90195 88
30	0.68435 85067 72	0.64516 90692 31	0.48807 06301 14	1.10881 47367 11
31	0.70446 97681 73	0.66183 50352 68	0.50299 99604 73	1.11546 36952 51
32	0.72435 87296 70	0.67813 46088 39	0.51779 54198 88	1.12223 78283 31
33	0.74402 41226 31	0.69406 98058 11	0.53245 24222 30	1.12912 89150 12
34	0.76346 50404 23	0.70964 32921 42	0.54696 63707 38	1.13612 85901 48
35	0.78268 09280 25	0.72485 83409 16	0.56133 26597 82	1.14322 83544 30
36	0.80167 15711 08	0.73971 87892 87	0.57554 66767 67	1.15041 95846 04
37	0.82043 70846 74	0.75422 89956 58	0.58960 38041 86	1.15769 35438 41
38	0.83897 79013 45	0.76839 37973 45	0.60349 94218 11	1.16504 13922 67
39	0.85729 47593 77	0.78221 84690 06	0.61722 89090 33	1.17245 41976 22
40	0.87538 86904 86	0.79570 86820 22	0.63078 76473 24	1.17992 29460 47
41	0.89326 10075 56	0.80887 04650 52	0.64417 10228 40	1.18743 85529 76
42	0.91091 32922 92	0.82171 01659 04	0.65737 44291 54	1.19499 18741 39
43	0.92834 73828 83	0.83423 44148 76	0.67039 32701 07	1.20257 37166 36
44	0.94556 53617 44	0.84645 00896 62	0.68322 29627 78	1.21017 48500 92
45	0.96256 95433 66	0.85836 42819 34	0.69585 89405 79	1.21778 60178 71

243

K = 2.18421 32169 49248   E = 1.20153 81841 13662
K' = 1.67773 48840 80745   E' = 1.47396 98872 41625

r	u=(r/90)K=F(φ,k)	sn u	cn u	dn u
45	1.09210 66084 75	0.82066 25467 78	0.57141 31467 82	0.69628 27157 46
46	1.11637 56442 19	0.83014 20788 85	0.55755 19068 79	0.68763 28072 00
47	1.14064 46799 62	0.83927 41589 70	0.54370 84568 82	0.67910 00531 81
48	1.16491 37157 06	0.84806 64916 29	0.52988 98241 86	0.67069 23295 95
49	1.18918 27514 50	0.85652 68523 98	0.51610 24618 44	0.66241 70552 09
50	1.21345 17871 94	0.86466 30578 93	0.50235 22631 73	0.65428 12047 69
51	1.23772 08229 38	0.87248 29379 38	0.48864 45773 84	0.64629 13230 13
52	1.26198 98586 82	0.87999 43096 36	0.47498 42260 62	0.63845 35393 95
53	1.28625 88944 26	0.88720 49533 46	0.46137 55203 29	0.63077 35833 95
54	1.31052 79301 70	0.89412 25905 07	0.44782 22785 28	0.62325 68002 61
55	1.33479 69659 13	0.90075 48632 47	0.43432 78443 02	0.61590 81670 64
56	1.35906 60016 57	0.90710 93157 12	0.42089 51049 24	0.60873 23089 47
57	1.38333 50374 01	0.91319 33770 21	0.40752 65097 70	0.60173 35154 69
58	1.40760 40731 45	0.91901 43458 00	0.39422 40888 30	0.59491 57569 34
59	1.43187 31088 89	0.92457 93761 84	0.38098 94711 61	0.58828 27006 41
60	1.45614 21446 33	0.92989 54652 19	0.36782 39032 01	0.58183 77269 61
61	1.48041 11803 77	0.93496 94415 78	0.35472 82668 69	0.57558 39451 75
62	1.50468 02161 21	0.93980 79555 02	0.34170 30974 03	0.56952 42090 30
63	1.52894 92518 64	0.94441 74698 92	0.32874 86008 53	0.56366 11319 39
64	1.55321 82876 08	0.94880 42524 53	0.31586 46712 25	0.55799 71017 97
65	1.57748 73233 52	0.95297 43688 30	0.30305 09071 97	0.55253 42953 64
66	1.60175 63590 96	0.95693 36766 46	0.29030 66284 15	0.54727 46921 93
67	1.62602 53948 40	0.96068 78203 59	0.27763 08913 18	0.54222 00880 72
68	1.65029 44305 84	0.96424 22268 86	0.26502 25044 97	0.53737 21079 50
69	1.67456 34663 28	0.96760 21019 02	0.25248 00435 56	0.53273 22183 49
70	1.69883 25020 72	0.97077 24267 61	0.24000 18654 92	0.52830 17392 25
71	1.72310 15378 16	0.97375 79559 67	0.22758 61225 78	0.52408 18552 97
72	1.74737 05735 59	0.97656 32151 43	0.21523 07757 48	0.52007 36268 01
73	1.77163 96093 03	0.97919 24994 31	0.20293 36075 11	0.51627 79997 06
74	1.79590 86450 47	0.98164 98722 80	0.19069 22343 79	0.51269 58153 51
75	1.82017 76807 91	0.98393 91645 60	0.17850 41188 46	0.50932 78195 36
76	1.84444 67165 35	0.98606 39739 68	0.16636 65809 07	0.50617 46710 46
77	1.86871 57522 79	0.98802 76646 71	0.15427 68091 60	0.50323 69496 22
78	1.89298 47880 23	0.98983 33671 53	0.14223 18714 97	0.50051 51633 83
79	1.91725 38237 67	0.99148 39782 26	0.13022 87254 06	0.49800 97556 95
80	1.94152 28595 10	0.99298 21611 68	0.11826 42279 07	0.49572 11115 10
81	1.96579 18952 54	0.99433 03459 64	0.10633 51451 56	0.49364 95631 57
82	1.99006 09309 98	0.99553 07296 16	0.09443 81617 23	0.49179 53956 15
83	2.01432 99667 42	0.99658 52764 98	0.08256 98895 90	0.49015 88512 55
84	2.03859 90024 86	0.99749 57187 31	0.07072 68768 85	0.48874 01340 73
85	2.06286 80382 30	0.99826 35565 62	0.05890 56163 79	0.48753 94133 99
86	2.08713 70739 74	0.99889 00587 29	0.04710 25537 78	0.48655 68271 12
87	2.11140 61097 18	0.99937 62627 93	0.03531 40958 47	0.48579 24843 45
88	2.13567 51454 61	0.99972 29754 27	0.02353 66183 66	0.48524 64676 94
89	2.15994 41812 05	0.99993 07726 49	0.01176 64739 89	0.48491 88349 36
90	2.18421 32169 49	1.00000 00000 00	0.00000 00000 00	0.48480 96202 46

q = 0.08953 58769 52552 59
q' = 0.01673 95077 33022 71

D(90) = 1.43619 82243 50425
1/D(90) = 0.69628 27157 45793

r	ϕ	$E(\phi,k)$	A(r)	D(r)
45	0.96256 95433 66	0.85836 42819 34	0.69585 89405 79	1.21778 60178 71
46	0.97936 24623 40	0.86998 42656 50	0.70829 66564 39	1.22539 79483 33
47	0.99594 68615 88	0.88131 74671 43	0.72053 15861 09	1.23300 13661 19
48	1.01232 56808 48	0.89237 14370 20	0.73255 92315 54	1.24058 70034 65
49	1.02850 20454 20	0.90315 38238 77	0.74437 51244 32	1.24814 56115 09
50	1.04447 92552 39	0.91367 23498 39	0.75597 48296 63	1.25566 79715 93
51	1.06026 07742 62	0.92393 47878 99	0.76735 39490 71	1.26314 49065 45
52	1.07585 02202 10	0.93394 89410 28	0.77850 81250 91	1.27056 72919 18
53	1.09125 13546 77	0.94372 26230 32	0.78943 30445 38	1.27792 60671 77
54	1.10646 80736 09	0.95326 36410 94	0.80012 44424 36	1.28521 22468 30
55	1.12150 43981 77	0.96257 97799 61	0.81057 81058 79	1.29241 69314 65
56	1.13636 44660 37	0.97167 87877 08	0.82078 98779 36	1.29953 13187 05
57	1.15105 25229 88	0.98056 83630 31	0.83075 56615 88	1.30654 67140 53
58	1.16557 29150 24	0.98925 61439 80	0.84047 14236 75	1.31345 45416 15
59	1.17993 00807 86	0.99774 96980 90	0.84993 31988 62	1.32024 63546 83
60	1.19412 85444 03	1.00605 65138 21	0.85913 70936 00	1.32691 38461 84
61	1.20817 29087 21	1.01418 39932 50	0.86807 92900 91	1.33344 88589 49
62	1.22206 78489 13	1.02213 94459 24	0.87675 60502 26	1.33984 33958 25
63	1.23581 81064 63	1.02993 00838 36	0.88516 37195 08	1.34608 96295 81
64	1.24942 84835 13	1.03756 30174 26	0.89329 87309 36	1.35217 99126 31
65	1.26290 38375 68	1.04504 52525 50	0.90115 76088 53	1.35810 67865 26
66	1.27624 90765 39	1.05238 36883 63	0.90873 69727 35	1.36386 29912 35
67	1.28946 91541 23	1.05958 51160 27	0.91603 35409 32	1.36944 14741 74
68	1.30256 90655 01	1.06665 62182 13	0.92304 41343 35	1.37483 53989 96
69	1.31555 38433 40	1.07360 35693 16	0.92976 56799 63	1.38003 81541 12
70	1.32842 85540 99	1.08043 36363 35	0.93619 52144 73	1.38504 33609 42
71	1.34119 82946 06	1.08715 27803 68	0.94232 98875 76	1.38984 48818 77
72	1.35386 81889 12	1.09376 72586 68	0.94816 69653 49	1.39443 68279 54
73	1.36644 33853 88	1.10028 32272 15	0.95370 38334 41	1.39881 35662 19
74	1.37892 90540 78	1.10670 67437 55	0.95893 80001 65	1.40296 97267 73
75	1.39133 03842 65	1.11304 37712 67	0.96386 70994 64	1.40690 02095 06
76	1.40365 25822 60	1.11930 01818 26	0.96848 88937 47	1.41060 01904 78
77	1.41590 08693 88	1.12548 17608 05	0.97280 12765 93	1.41406 51279 78
78	1.42808 04801 60	1.13159 42114 09	0.97680 22753 06	1.41729 07682 13
79	1.44019 66606 18	1.13764 31594 83	0.98049 00533 26	1.42027 31506 56
80	1.45225 46668 45	1.14363 41585 83	0.98386 29124 82	1.42300 86130 14
81	1.46425 97636 15	1.14957 26952 70	0.98691 92950 87	1.42549 37958 35
82	1.47621 72231 84	1.15546 41946 12	0.98965 77858 68	1.42772 56467 26
83	1.48813 23241 96	1.16131 40258 60	0.99207 71137 21	1.42970 14241 98
84	1.50001 03507 07	1.16712 75082 79	0.99417 61533 03	1.43141 87011 07
85	1.51185 65912 93	1.17290 99171 19	0.99595 39264 38	1.43287 53677 15
86	1.52367 63382 53	1.17866 64896 95	0.99740 96033 42	1.43406 96343 43
87	1.53547 48868 77	1.18440 24315 69	0.99854 25036 71	1.43500 00336 24
88	1.54725 75347 81	1.19012 29228 05	0.99935 20973 74	1.43566 54223 51
89	1.55902 95812 77	1.19583 31242 93	0.99983 80053 65	1.43606 49829 19
90	1.57079 63267 95	1.20153 81841 14	1.00000 00000 00	1.43619 82243 50

K = 2.21319 46949 79374   E = 1.19204 56765 79886
K' = 1.67005 94262 69580   E' = 1.48029 26638 27039

r	u=(r/90)K=F(φ,k)	sn u	cn u	dn u
0	0.00000 00000 00	0.00000 00000 00	1.00000 00000 00	1.00000 00000 00
1	0.02459 10521 66	0.02458 66424 65	0.99969 77028 14	0.99976 43380 40
2	0.04918 21043 33	0.04914 68492 15	0.99879 15634 47	0.99905 80327 29
3	0.07377 31564 99	0.07365 42968 02	0.99728 38335 01	0.99788 31214 08
4	0.09836 42086 66	0.09808 28852 88	0.99517 82491 66	0.99624 29851 07
5	0.12295 52608 32	0.12240 68474 64	0.99248 00066 97	0.99414 23269 44
6	0.14754 63129 99	0.14660 08550 80	0.98919 57285 04	0.99158 71422 27
7	0.17213 73651 65	0.17064 01211 42	0.98533 34202 47	0.98858 46806 44
8	0.19672 84173 32	0.19450 04974 24	0.98090 24194 60	0.98514 34009 73
9	0.22131 94694 98	0.21815 85663 93	0.97591 33362 70	0.98127 29188 49
10	0.24591 05216 64	0.24159 17268 31	0.97037 79869 34	0.97698 39481 77
11	0.27050 15738 31	0.26477 82725 45	0.96430 93209 07	0.97228 82368 70
12	0.29509 26259 97	0.28769 74636 30	0.95772 13422 60	0.96719 84976 05
13	0.31968 36781 64	0.31032 95898 62	0.95062 90263 06	0.96172 83343 58
14	0.34427 47303 30	0.33265 60259 23	0.94304 82322 86	0.95589 21654 82
15	0.36886 57824 97	0.35465 92782 28	0.93499 56130 20	0.94970 51441 16
16	0.39345 68346 63	0.37632 30232 70	0.92648 85224 10	0.94318 30767 09
17	0.41804 78868 29	0.39763 21374 61	0.91754 49216 57	0.93634 23404 34
18	0.44263 89389 96	0.41857 27185 75	0.90818 32850 61	0.92919 98002 27
19	0.46722 99911 62	0.43913 20989 74	0.89842 25062 02	0.92177 27261 99
20	0.49182 10433 29	0.45929 88508 79	0.88828 18052 74	0.91407 87120 66
21	0.51641 20954 95	0.47906 27840 28	0.87778 06382 91	0.90613 55952 50
22	0.54100 31476 62	0.49841 49361 23	0.86693 86088 12	0.89796 13792 14
23	0.56559 41998 28	0.51734 75565 29	0.85577 53827 69	0.88957 41585 57
24	0.59018 52519 95	0.53585 40837 19	0.84431 06069 23	0.88099 20473 18
25	0.61477 63041 61	0.55392 91170 07	0.83256 38313 86	0.87223 31108 86
26	0.63936 73563 27	0.57156 83831 37	0.82055 44365 85	0.86331 53018 46
27	0.66395 84084 94	0.58876 86982 83	0.80830 15649 64	0.85425 64000 19
28	0.68854 94606 60	0.60552 79260 73	0.79582 40576 57	0.84507 39569 00
29	0.71314 05128 27	0.62184 49321 93	0.78314 03962 93	0.83578 52446 47
30	0.73773 15649 93	0.63771 95361 49	0.77026 86500 27	0.82640 72096 85
31	0.76232 26171 60	0.65315 24607 51	0.75722 64278 37	0.81695 64309 83
32	0.78691 36693 26	0.66814 52798 44	0.74403 08360 70	0.80744 90829 60
33	0.81150 47214 92	0.68270 03647 88	0.73069 84411 63	0.79790 09029 86
34	0.83609 57736 59	0.69682 08301 82	0.71724 52374 36	0.78832 71633 58
35	0.86068 68258 25	0.71051 04792 52	0.70368 66197 91	0.77874 26476 26
36	0.88527 78779 92	0.72377 37493 32	0.69003 73611 46	0.76916 16310 99
37	0.90986 89301 58	0.73661 56577 91	0.67631 15943 83	0.75959 78653 55
38	0.93445 99823 25	0.74904 17487 49	0.66252 27985 74	0.75006 45665 21
39	0.95905 10344 91	0.76105 80408 74	0.64868 37892 39	0.74057 44071 28
40	0.98364 20866 58	0.77267 09765 14	0.63480 67123 57	0.73113 95112 86
41	1.00823 31388 24	0.78388 73723 93	0.62090 30418 70	0.72177 14529 37
42	1.03282 41909 90	0.79471 43720 44	0.60698 35803 93	0.71248 12569 54
43	1.05741 52431 57	0.80515 94001 45	0.59305 84628 51	0.70327 94028 11
44	1.08200 62953 23	0.81523 01188 66	0.57913 71627 63	0.69417 58306 11
45	1.10659 73474 90	0.82493 43863 30	0.56522 85009 19	0.68517 99492 00

246

q = 0.09342 26672 88483 19   D(90) = 1.45947 06123 07597
q'= 0.01555 61584 97708 09   1/D(90) = 0.68517 99492 00129

r	ϕ	$E(\phi,k)$	A(r)	D(r)
0	0.00000 00000 00	0.00000 00000 00	0.00000 00000 00	1.00000 00000 00
1	0.02458 91202 55	0.02458 71886 07	0.01684 86243 60	1.00013 94922 45
2	0.04916 66557 39	0.04915 12158 78	0.03369 32192 72	1.00055 78006 98
3	0.07372 10551 16	0.07366 90199 33	0.05052 97534 98	1.00125 44207 08
4	0.09824 08337 09	0.09811 77370 49	0.06735 41922 19	1.00222 85118 44
5	0.12271 46062 92	0.12247 47984 28	0.08416 24952 72	1.00347 88988 83
6	0.14713 11192 50	0.14671 80243 87	0.10095 06154 11	1.00500 40731 82
7	0.17147 92819 09	0.17082 57150 78	0.11771 44965 97	1.00680 21944 45
8	0.19574 81968 39	0.19477 67369 74	0.13445 00723 39	1.00887 10928 77
9	0.21992 71889 58	0.21855 06044 39	0.15115 32640 84	1.01120 82717 30
10	0.24400 58332 73	0.24212 75557 35	0.16781 99796 65	1.01381 09102 20
11	0.26797 39811 05	0.26548 86229 24	0.18444 61118 24	1.01667 58668 43
12	0.29182 17846 82	0.28861 56952 15	0.20102 75368 01	1.01979 96830 54
13	0.31553 97199 61	0.31149 15753 60	0.21756 01130 18	1.02317 85873 24
14	0.33911 86076 07	0.33410 00288 58	0.23403 96798 47	1.02680 84995 71
15	0.36254 96320 52	0.35642 58257 40	0.25046 20564 80	1.03068 50359 51
16	0.38582 43585 56	0.37845 47748 91	0.26682 30409 02	1.03480 35140 11
17	0.40893 47482 68	0.40017 37508 61	0.28311 84089 80	1.03915 89581 97
18	0.43187 31712 32	0.42157 07132 87	0.29934 39136 66	1.04374 61057 08
19	0.45463 24173 72	0.44263 47190 64	0.31549 52843 28	1.04855 94126 99
20	0.47720 57054 44	0.46335 59275 11	0.33156 82262 09	1.05359 30608 15
21	0.49958 66900 13	0.48372 55988 30	0.34755 84200 23	1.05884 09640 55
22	0.52176 94664 80	0.50373 60862 19	0.36346 15216 87	1.06429 67759 61
23	0.54374 85742 44	0.52338 08220 39	0.37927 31622 03	1.06995 38971 18
24	0.56551 89980 50	0.54265 42984 79	0.39498 89476 85	1.07580 54829 63
25	0.58707 61676 24	0.56155 20432 07	0.41060 44595 37	1.08184 44518 93
26	0.60841 59556 78	0.58007 05904 85	0.42611 52547 89	1.08806 34936 58
27	0.62953 46743 94	0.59820 74482 70	0.44151 68665 90	1.09445 50780 39
28	0.65042 90704 77	0.61596 10618 22	0.45680 48048 60	1.10101 14637 93
29	0.67109 63189 10	0.63333 07743 14	0.47197 45571 03	1.10772 47078 62
30	0.69153 40155 00	0.65031 67849 70	0.48702 15893 88	1.11458 66748 31
31	0.71174 01683 47	0.66692 01052 09	0.50194 13474 85	1.12158 90466 28
32	0.73171 31883 44	0.68314 25132 77	0.51672 92581 77	1.12872 33324 53
33	0.75145 18788 16	0.69898 65078 08	0.53138 07307 21	1.13598 08789 24
34	0.77095 54244 23	0.71445 52607 42	0.54589 11584 89	1.14335 28804 32
35	0.79022 33794 20	0.72955 25699 90	0.56025 59207 58	1.15083 03896 92
36	0.80925 56553 93	0.74428 28122 09	0.57447 03846 67	1.15840 43284 75
37	0.82805 25085 61	0.75865 08960 18	0.58852 99073 32	1.16606 54985 14
38	0.84661 45267 44	0.77266 22159 43	0.60242 98381 15	1.17380 45925 66
39	0.86494 26160 93	0.78632 26073 59	0.61616 55210 46	1.18161 22056 23
40	0.88303 79876 49	0.79963 83026 61	0.62973 22974 01	1.18947 88462 53
41	0.90090 21438 37	0.81261 58888 53	0.64312 55084 12	1.19739 49480 62
42	0.91853 68649 40	0.82526 22667 22	0.65634 04981 34	1.20535 08812 62
43	0.93594 41956 38	0.83758 46117 43	0.66937 26164 38	1.21333 69643 32
44	0.95312 64316 68	0.84959 03368 12	0.68221 72221 35	1.22134 34757 55
45	0.97008 61066 51	0.86128 70568 97	0.69486 96862 34	1.22936 06658 26

K = 2.21319 46949 79374   E = 1.19204 56765 79886
K' = 1.67005 94262 69580   E' = 1.48029 26638 27039

r	u=(r/90)K=F(φ,k)	sn u	cn u	dn u
45	1.10659 73474 90	0.82493 43863 30	0.56522 85009 19	0.68517 99492 00
46	1.13118 83996 56	0.83428 02172 37	0.55134 06561 52	0.67630 06461 53
47	1.15577 94518 23	0.84327 57457 13	0.53748 11779 88	0.66754 62993 93
48	1.18037 05039 89	0.85192 91903 74	0.52365 70008 97	0.65892 47902 37
49	1.20496 15561 55	0.86024 88216 22	0.50987 44599 38	0.65044 35176 47
50	1.22955 26083 22	0.86824 29311 48	0.49613 93075 66	0.64210 94135 10
51	1.25414 36604 88	0.87591 98035 94	0.48245 67313 98	0.63392 89587 48
52	1.27873 47126 55	0.88328 76903 48	0.46883 13727 56	0.62590 82000 95
53	1.30332 57648 21	0.89035 47853 79	0.45526 73458 00	0.61805 27673 90
54	1.32791 68169 88	0.89712 92030 78	0.44176 82571 04	0.61036 78912 26
55	1.35250 78691 54	0.90361 89579 92	0.42833 72255 10	0.60285 84208 37
56	1.37709 89213 20	0.90983 19463 98	0.41497 69021 45	0.59552 88420 94
57	1.40168 99734 87	0.91577 59296 03	0.40168 94904 77	0.58838 32955 06
58	1.42628 10256 53	0.92145 85188 98	0.38847 67662 95	0.58142 55941 25
59	1.45087 20778 20	0.92688 71620 55	0.37534 00975 34	0.57465 92412 78
60	1.47546 31299 86	0.93206 91312 94	0.36228 04638 51	0.56808 74480 33
61	1.50005 41821 53	0.93701 15125 98	0.34929 84758 91	0.56171 31503 49
62	1.52464 52343 19	0.94172 11963 04	0.33639 43941 75	0.55553 90258 48
63	1.54923 62864 86	0.94620 48688 73	0.32356 81475 68	0.54956 75101 48
64	1.57382 73386 52	0.95046 90057 39	0.31081 93512 80	0.54380 08127 30
65	1.59841 83908 18	0.95451 98651 54	0.29814 73243 66	0.53824 09323 00
66	1.62300 94429 85	0.95836 34829 54	0.28555 11067 04	0.53288 96716 10
67	1.64760 04951 51	0.96200 56681 47	0.27302 94754 30	0.52774 86517 23
68	1.67219 15473 18	0.96545 19992 50	0.26058 09608 23	0.52281 93257 00
69	1.69678 25994 84	0.96870 78213 16	0.24820 38616 18	0.51810 29917 01
70	1.72137 36516 51	0.97177 82435 46	0.23589 62597 66	0.51360 08054 76
71	1.74596 47038 17	0.97466 81374 56	0.22365 60346 33	0.50931 37922 64
72	1.77055 57559 83	0.97738 21355 10	0.21148 08766 44	0.50524 28580 71
73	1.79514 68081 50	0.97992 46301 64	0.19936 83003 82	0.50138 88003 49
74	1.81973 78603 16	0.98229 97732 76	0.18731 56571 72	0.49775 23180 59
75	1.84432 89124 83	0.98451 14758 13	0.17532 01471 40	0.49433 40211 38
76	1.86891 99646 49	0.98656 34078 20	0.16337 88307 93	0.49113 44393 64
77	1.89351 10168 16	0.98845 89986 02	0.15148 86401 14	0.48815 40306 28
78	1.91810 20689 82	0.99020 14370 70	0.13964 63892 31	0.48539 31886 25
79	1.94269 31211 49	0.99179 36722 25	0.12784 87846 40	0.48285 22499 64
80	1.96728 41733 15	0.99323 84137 37	0.11609 24350 53	0.48053 15007 09
81	1.99187 52254 81	0.99453 81325 87	0.10437 38608 62	0.47843 11823 63
82	2.01646 62776 48	0.99569 50617 45	0.09268 95032 73	0.47655 14972 97
83	2.04105 73298 14	0.99671 11968 66	0.08103 57331 19	0.47489 26136 31
84	2.06564 83819 81	0.99758 82969 62	0.06940 88594 02	0.47345 46695 83
85	2.09023 94341 47	0.99832 78850 51	0.05780 51375 71	0.47223 77772 90
86	2.11483 04863 14	0.99893 12487 45	0.04622 07775 88	0.47124 20260 96
87	2.13942 15384 80	0.99939 94407 83	0.03465 19518 01	0.47046 74853 34
88	2.16401 25906 46	0.99973 32794 75	0.02309 48026 55	0.46991 42065 88
89	2.18860 36428 13	0.99993 33490 68	0.01154 54502 85	0.46958 22254 54
90	2.21319 46949 79	1.00000 00000 00	0.00000 00000 00	0.46947 15627 86

q = 0.09342 26672 88483 19   D(90) = 1.45947 06123 07597
q'= 0.01555 61584 97708 09   1/D(90) = 0.68517 99492 00129

r	ϕ	$E(\phi,k)$	$A(r)$	$D(r)$
45	0.97008 61066 51	0.86128 70568 97	0.69486 96862 34	1.22936 06658 26
46	0.98682 59791 51	0.87268 25556 61	0.70732 53953 08	1.23737 87685 03
47	1.00334 90199 95	0.88378 47540 98	0.71957 97549 86	1.24538 80132 95
48	1.01965 83998 98	0.89460 16812 03	0.73162 81935 39	1.25337 86371 81
49	1.03575 74774 25	0.90514 14466 62	0.74346 61655 72	1.26134 08965 22
50	1.05164 97873 11	0.91541 22155 62	0.75508 91558 08	1.26926 50789 76
51	1.06733 90291 79	0.92542 21850 88	0.76649 26829 54	1.27714 15153 88
52	1.08282 90566 46	0.93517 95631 51	0.77767 23036 46	1.28496 05916 39
53	1.09812 38668 67	0.94469 25489 27	0.78862 36164 55	1.29271 27604 50
54	1.11322 75904 94	0.95396 93152 09	0.79934 22659 61	1.30038 85531 13
55	1.12814 44820 78	0.96301 79925 45	0.80982 39468 76	1.30797 85911 47
56	1.14287 89109 15	0.97184 66550 61	0.82006 44081 99	1.31547 35978 49
57	1.15743 53523 28	0.98046 33079 09	0.83005 94574 21	1.32286 44097 46
58	1.17181 83793 97	0.98887 58762 64	0.83980 49647 37	1.33014 19879 10
59	1.18603 26551 27	0.99709 21957 78	0.84929 68672 79	1.33729 74291 39
60	1.20008 29250 41	1.00512 00044 22	0.85853 11733 60	1.34432 19769 86
61	1.21397 40102 11	1.01296 69356 36	0.86750 39666 99	1.35120 70326 08
62	1.22771 08006 96	1.02064 05126 99	0.87621 14106 43	1.35794 41654 50
63	1.24129 82493 91	1.02814 81442 48	0.88464 97523 62	1.36452 51237 13
64	1.25474 13662 75	1.03549 71208 67	0.89281 53270 07	1.37094 18446 24
65	1.26804 52130 35	1.04269 46126 73	0.90070 45618 31	1.37718 64644 77
66	1.28121 48980 73	1.04974 76678 22	0.90831 39802 51	1.38325 13284 40
67	1.29425 55718 56	1.05666 32118 79	0.91564 02058 51	1.38912 90001 04
68	1.30717 24226 24	1.06344 80479 71	0.92267 99663 15	1.39481 22707 78
69	1.31997 06724 18	1.07010 88576 70	0.92943 00972 78	1.40029 41685 02
70	1.33265 55734 25	1.07665 22025 41	0.93588 75460 85	1.40556 79667 75
71	1.34523 24046 27	1.08308 45263 07	0.94204 93754 59	1.41062 71929 79
72	1.35770 64687 28	1.08941 21575 66	0.94791 27670 52	1.41546 56365 00
73	1.37008 30893 54	1.09564 13130 19	0.95347 50248 88	1.42007 73565 20
74	1.38236 76085 12	1.10177 81011 63	0.95873 35786 81	1.42445 66894 79
75	1.39456 53842 84	1.10782 85264 01	0.96368 59870 20	1.42859 82561 93
76	1.40668 17887 46	1.11379 84935 27	0.96832 99404 16	1.43249 69686 22
77	1.41872 22061 04	1.11969 38125 59	0.97266 32642 05	1.43614 80362 73
78	1.43069 20310 19	1.12552 02038 68	0.97668 39212 91	1.43954 69722 36
79	1.44259 66671 15	1.13128 33035 94	0.98039 00147 38	1.44268 95988 35
80	1.45444 15256 63	1.13698 86692 90	0.98377 97901 92	1.44557 20529 01
81	1.46623 20244 05	1.14264 17857 97	0.98685 16381 27	1.44819 07906 42
82	1.47797 35865 34	1.14824 80713 02	0.98960 40959 26	1.45054 25921 19
83	1.48967 16397 86	1.15381 28835 63	0.99203 58497 65	1.45262 45653 11
84	1.50133 16156 57	1.15934 15262 84	0.99414 57363 20	1.45443 41497 67
85	1.51295 89487 14	1.16483 92556 11	0.99593 27442 84	1.45596 91198 48
86	1.52455 90759 93	1.17031 12867 38	0.99739 60156 81	1.45722 75875 33
87	1.53613 74364 78	1.17576 28006 01	0.99853 48469 93	1.45820 80048 10
88	1.54769 94706 35	1.18119 89506 45	0.99934 86900 78	1.45890 91656 35
89	1.55925 06199 98	1.18662 48696 46	0.99983 71528 92	1.45933 02074 57
90	1.57079 63267 95	1.19204 56765 80	1.00000 00000 00	1.45947 06123 08

K = 2.24354 93416 98626   E = 1.18258 90849 45384
K' = 1.66271 59584 91370   E' = 1.48642 68037 44253

r	u=(r/90)K=F(φ,k)	sn u	cn u	dn u
0	0.00000 00000 00	0.00000 00000 00	1.00000 00000 00	1.00000 00000 00
1	0.02492 83260 19	0.02492 36955 10	0.99968 93564 51	0.99975 33902 74
2	0.04985 66520 38	0.04981 96324 80	0.99875 82311 15	0.99901 42951 19
3	0.07478 49780 57	0.07466 01746 68	0.99720 90344 15	0.99778 49117 03
4	0.09971 33040 75	0.09941 79292 86	0.99504 57654 48	0.99606 88857 16
5	0.12464 16300 94	0.12406 58658 62	0.99227 39848 09	0.99387 12871 95
6	0.14956 99561 13	0.14857 74317 26	0.98890 07770 15	0.99119 85771 02
7	0.17449 82821 32	0.17292 66630 74	0.98493 47030 12	0.98805 85650 72
8	0.19942 66081 51	0.19708 82906 31	0.98038 57433 16	0.98446 03588 42
9	0.22435 49341 70	0.22103 78390 38	0.97526 52324 95	0.98041 43059 80
10	0.24928 32601 89	0.24475 17191 56	0.96958 57857 72	0.97593 19285 99
11	0.27421 15862 08	0.26820 73126 01	0.96336 12185 82	0.97102 58518 21
12	0.29913 99122 26	0.29138 30479 54	0.95660 64600 27	0.96570 97268 09
13	0.32406 82382 45	0.31425 84681 66	0.94933 74611 73	0.95999 81492 31
14	0.34899 65642 64	0.33681 42888 47	0.94157 10991 89	0.95390 65740 20
15	0.37392 48902 83	0.35903 24472 16	0.93332 50783 34	0.94745 12273 55
16	0.39885 32163 02	0.38089 61416 24	0.92461 78287 79	0.94064 90167 22
17	0.42378 15423 21	0.40238 98616 79	0.91546 84042 71	0.93351 74399 53
18	0.44870 98683 40	0.42349 94090 90	0.90589 63795 60	0.92607 44940 80
19	0.47363 81943 59	0.44421 19094 87	0.89592 17485 19	0.91833 85848 16
20	0.49856 65203 77	0.46451 58155 27	0.88556 48237 85	0.91032 84374 03
21	0.52349 48463 96	0.48440 09016 94	0.87484 61387 23	0.90206 30095 55
22	0.54842 31724 15	0.50385 82512 79	0.86378 63524 15	0.89356 14070 99
23	0.57335 14984 34	0.52288 02360 68	0.85240 61583 13	0.88484 28029 00
24	0.59827 98244 53	0.54146 04893 30	0.84072 61971 03	0.87592 63595 61
25	0.62320 81504 72	0.55959 38727 08	0.82876 69742 62	0.86683 11563 01
26	0.64813 64764 91	0.57727 64376 79	0.81654 87826 83	0.85757 61203 79
27	0.67306 48025 10	0.59450 53822 13	0.80409 16306 74	0.84817 99633 14
28	0.69799 31285 28	0.61127 90033 05	0.79141 51755 67	0.83866 11221 14
29	0.72292 14545 47	0.62759 66460 28	0.77853 86630 70	0.82903 77056 36
30	0.74784 97805 66	0.64345 86497 41	0.76548 08724 41	0.81932 74461 59
31	0.77277 81065 85	0.65886 62920 74	0.75226 00675 09	0.80954 76561 54
32	0.79770 64326 04	0.67382 17312 70	0.73889 39534 66	0.79971 51902 35
33	0.82263 47586 23	0.68832 79474 44	0.72539 96393 49	0.78984 64121 76
34	0.84756 30846 42	0.70238 86832 73	0.71179 36060 47	0.77995 71668 61
35	0.87249 14106 61	0.71600 83846 03	0.69809 16796 36	0.77006 27570 03
36	0.89741 97366 79	0.72919 21413 94	0.68430 90098 26	0.76017 79244 16
37	0.92234 80626 98	0.74194 56294 08	0.67046 00532 49	0.75031 68356 23
38	0.94727 63887 17	0.75427 50529 85	0.65655 85613 22	0.74049 30715 33
39	0.97220 47147 36	0.76618 70892 11	0.64261 75723 76	0.73071 96209 41
40	0.99713 30407 55	0.77768 88337 42	0.62864 94077 56	0.72100 88775 66
41	1.02206 13667 74	0.78878 77485 08	0.61466 56715 68	0.71137 26403 49
42	1.04698 96927 93	0.79949 16114 71	0.60067 72537 62	0.70182 21167 25
43	1.07191 80188 12	0.80980 84686 04	0.58669 43362 41	0.69236 79285 97
44	1.09684 63448 30	0.81974 65881 75	0.57272 64016 75	0.68302 01207 25
45	1.12177 46708 49	0.82931 44174 39	0.55878 22447 32	0.67378 81712 67

q = 0.09746 47524 70351 77   D(90) = 1.48414 59714 54717
q'= 0.01442 14412 80637 80   1/D(90) = 0.67378 81712 67162

r	ϕ	$E(\phi,k)$	A(r)	D(r)
0	0.00000 00000 00	0.00000 00000 00	0.00000 00000 00	1.00000 00000 00
1	0.02492 62766 26	0.02492 42275 37	0.01679 57584 62	1.00014 69183 76
2	0.04984 02642 18	0.04982 38860 92	0.03358 76000 73	1.00058 74965 02
3	0.07472 97102 95	0.07467 45160 16	0.05037 16058 90	1.00132 12035 75
4	0.09958 24352 46	0.09945 18753 03	0.06714 38527 97	1.00234 71556 10
5	0.12438 63681 51	0.12413 20458 62	0.08390 04114 42	1.00366 41164 69
6	0.14912 95818 96	0.14869 15367 84	0.10063 73442 03	1.00527 04992 99
7	0.17380 03273 32	0.17310 73836 69	0.11735 07031 93	1.00716 43683 80
8	0.19838 70662 86	0.19735 72431 52	0.13403 65283 11	1.00934 34413 78
9	0.22287 85032 07	0.22141 94818 27	0.15069 08453 52	1.01180 50920 03
10	0.24726 36152 73	0.24527 32588 82	0.16730 96641 80	1.01454 63530 73
11	0.27153 16807 94	0.26889 86018 10	0.18388 89769 77	1.01756 39199 71
12	0.29567 23057 53	0.29227 64747 08	0.20042 47565 77	1.02085 41544 96
13	0.31967 54483 84	0.31538 88387 45	0.21691 29548 89	1.02441 30891 19
14	0.34353 14416 54	0.33821 87045 12	0.23334 95014 23	1.02823 64316 06
15	0.36723 10135 95	0.36075 01760 60	0.24973 03019 17	1.03231 95700 41
16	0.39076 53054 10	0.38296 84865 55	0.26605 12370 91	1.03665 75782 17
17	0.41412 58873 25	0.40486 00255 64	0.28230 81615 10	1.04124 52214 02
18	0.43730 47721 68	0.42641 23580 90	0.29849 69025 88	1.04607 69624 70
19	0.46029 44266 86	0.44761 42355 77	0.31461 32597 22	1.05114 69683 96
20	0.48308 77806 14	0.46845 55991 67	0.33065 30035 66	1.05644 91170 98
21	0.50567 82335 51	0.48892 75755 71	0.34661 18754 59	1.06197 70046 28
22	0.52805 96597 00	0.50902 24659 90	0.36248 55870 01	1.06772 39527 05
23	0.55022 64105 39	0.52873 37285 55	0.37826 98197 91	1.07368 30165 70
24	0.57217 33155 22	0.54805 59548 21	0.39396 02253 23	1.07984 69931 76
25	0.59389 56809 05	0.56698 48408 44	0.40955 24250 47	1.08620 84296 81
26	0.61538 92867 97	0.58551 71534 39	0.42504 20106 11	1.09275 96322 54
27	0.63665 03825 73	0.60365 06921 91	0.44042 45442 58	1.09949 26751 67
28	0.65767 56807 48	0.62138 42478 05	0.45569 55594 15	1.10639 94101 85
29	0.67846 23494 58	0.63871 75573 85	0.47085 05614 44	1.11347 14762 22
30	0.69900 80036 64	0.65565 12572 04	0.48588 50285 87	1.12070 03092 70
31	0.71931 06952 13	0.67218 68335 24	0.50079 44130 73	1.12807 71525 73
32	0.73936 89018 93	0.68832 65719 74	0.51557 41424 22	1.13559 30670 54
33	0.75918 15155 92	0.70407 35060 06	0.53021 96209 13	1.14323 89419 69
34	0.77874 78297 07	0.71943 13648 71	0.54472 62312 44	1.15100 55057 81
35	0.79806 75259 06	0.73440 45215 49	0.55908 93363 60	1.15888 33372 42
36	0.81714 06603 71	0.74899 79410 28	0.57330 42814 66	1.16686 28766 74
37	0.83596 76496 30	0.76321 71292 78	0.58736 63962 00	1.17493 44374 25
38	0.85454 92560 75	0.77706 80832 34	0.60127 09969 96	1.18308 82175 05
39	0.87288 65732 76	0.79055 72420 58	0.61501 33895 98	1.19131 43113 68
40	0.89098 10111 80	0.80369 14399 29	0.62858 88717 46	1.19960 27218 41
41	0.90883 42812 69	0.81647 78605 43	0.64199 27360 22	1.20794 33721 85
42	0.92644 83817 73	0.82892 39935 07	0.65522 02728 51	1.21632 61182 67
43	0.94382 55829 90	0.84103 75927 39	0.66826 67736 47	1.22474 07608 31
44	0.96096 84127 89	0.85282 66369 99	0.68112 75341 09	1.23317 70578 57
45	0.97787 96423 56	0.86429 92926 03	0.69379 78576 52	1.24162 47369 94

K = 2.24354 93416 98626   E = 1.18258 90849 45384
K' = 1.66271 59584 91370   E' = 1.48642 68037 44253

r	u=(r/90)K=F(φ,k)	sn u	cn u	dn u
45	1.12177 46708 49	0.82931 44174 39	0.55878 22447 32	0.67378 81712 67
46	1.14670 29968 68	0.83852 05417 77	0.54486 99854 26	0.66468 10042 11
47	1.17163 13228 87	0.84737 36463 06	0.53099 70843 10	0.65570 70034 42
48	1.19655 96489 06	0.85588 24799 72	0.51717 03592 40	0.64687 40282 19
49	1.22148 79749 25	0.86405 58220 88	0.50339 60034 75	0.63818 94298 28
50	1.24641 63009 44	0.87190 24512 96	0.48967 96048 68	0.62966 00691 96
51	1.27134 46269 63	0.87943 11168 89	0.47602 61659 28	0.62129 23352 94
52	1.29627 29529 81	0.88665 05124 25	0.46244 01245 74	0.61309 21641 17
53	1.32120 12790 00	0.89356 92515 71	0.44892 53753 64	0.60506 50581 00
54	1.34612 96050 19	0.90019 58460 60	0.43548 52910 68	0.59721 61058 06
55	1.37105 79310 38	0.90653 86856 96	0.42212 27443 97	0.58955 00017 51
56	1.39598 62570 57	0.91260 60202 92	0.40884 01297 91	0.58207 10662 44
57	1.42091 45830 76	0.91840 59434 42	0.39563 93851 10	0.57478 32651 27
58	1.44584 29090 95	0.92394 63780 20	0.38252 20131 49	0.56769 02293 25
59	1.47077 12351 14	0.92923 50632 98	0.36948 91028 67	0.56079 52741 12
60	1.49569 95611 32	0.93427 95435 82	0.35654 13502 59	0.55410 14180 20
61	1.52062 78871 51	0.93908 71582 52	0.34367 90788 02	0.54761 14013 31
62	1.54555 62131 70	0.94366 50331 10	0.33090 22594 15	0.54132 77040 85
63	1.57048 45391 89	0.94802 00729 24	0.31821 05298 91	0.53525 25635 78
64	1.59541 28652 08	0.95215 89550 81	0.30560 32137 58	0.52938 79912 83
65	1.62034 11912 27	0.95608 81242 42	0.29307 93385 48	0.52373 57891 90
66	1.64526 95172 46	0.95981 37879 13	0.28063 76534 47	0.51829 75655 25
67	1.67019 78432 65	0.96334 19128 44	0.26827 66463 13	0.51307 47498 33
68	1.69512 61692 83	0.96667 82221 71	0.25599 45600 59	0.50806 86074 10
69	1.72005 44953 02	0.96982 81932 15	0.24378 94083 95	0.50328 02530 76
70	1.74498 28213 21	0.97279 70558 75	0.23165 89909 35	0.49871 06642 90
71	1.76991 11473 40	0.97558 97915 36	0.21960 09076 75	0.49436 06935 90
72	1.79483 94733 59	0.97821 11324 21	0.20761 25728 56	0.49023 10803 74
73	1.81976 77993 78	0.98066 55613 39	0.19569 12282 25	0.48632 24620 23
74	1.84469 61253 97	0.98295 73117 51	0.18383 39557 17	0.48263 53843 66
75	1.86962 44514 16	0.98509 03681 22	0.17203 76895 70	0.47917 03114 96
76	1.89455 27774 34	0.98706 84664 86	0.16029 92279 09	0.47592 76349 53
77	1.91948 11034 53	0.98889 50951 98	0.14861 52438 15	0.47290 76822 74
78	1.94440 94294 72	0.99057 34958 14	0.13698 22959 05	0.47011 07249 27
79	1.96933 77554 91	0.99210 66640 76	0.12539 68384 60	0.46753 69856 41
80	1.99426 60815 10	0.99349 73509 51	0.11385 52311 24	0.46518 66451 29
81	2.01919 44075 29	0.99474 80636 97	0.10235 37482 00	0.46305 98482 40
82	2.04412 27335 48	0.99586 10669 39	0.09088 85875 93	0.46115 67095 23
83	2.06905 10595 67	0.99683 83837 06	0.07945 58794 01	0.45947 73182 36
84	2.09397 93855 85	0.99768 17964 23	0.06805 16942 19	0.45802 17427 94
85	2.11890 77116 04	0.99839 28478 39	0.05667 20511 69	0.45679 00346 74
86	2.14383 60376 23	0.99897 28418 56	0.04531 29256 89	0.45578 22317 81
87	2.16876 43636 42	0.99942 28442 61	0.03397 02571 27	0.45499 83612 85
88	2.19369 26896 61	0.99974 36833 43	0.02263 09561 62	0.45443 84419 30
89	2.21862 10156 80	0.99993 59503 82	0.01131 79120 87	0.45410 24858 29
90	2.24354 93416 99	1.00000 00000 00	0.00000 00000 00	0.45399 04997 40

q = 0.09746 47524 70351 77   D(90) = 1.48414 59714 54717
q'= 0.01442 14412 80637 80   1/D(90) = 0.67378 81712 67162

r	ϕ	$E(\phi,k)$	A(r)	D(r)
45	0.97787 96423 56	0.86429 92926 03	0.69379 78576 52	1.24162 47369 94
46	0.99456 22722 13	0.87546 38783 83	0.70627 30589 74	1.25007 35080 42
47	1.01101 95185 82	0.88632 88329 07	0.71854 84677 43	1.25851 30754 82
48	1.02725 48001 07	0.89690 26839 74	0.73061 94324 00	1.26693 31510 30
49	1.04327 17249 83	0.90719 40203 52	0.74248 13240 80	1.27532 34661 98
50	1.05907 40785 14	0.91721 14657 42	0.75412 95406 28	1.28367 37848 53
51	1.07466 58111 09	0.92696 36549 26	0.76555 95107 08	1.29197 39157 59
52	1.09005 10267 61	0.93645 92120 19	0.77676 66980 02	1.30021 37250 75
53	1.10523 39719 92	0.94570 67307 87	0.78774 66054 81	1.30838 31488 10
54	1.12021 90252 90	0.95471 47569 40	0.79849 47797 39	1.31647 22052 04
55	1.13501 06870 41	0.96349 17723 18	0.80900 68153 98	1.32447 10070 27
56	1.14961 35699 50	0.97204 61808 96	0.81927 83595 40	1.33236 97737 85
57	1.16403 23899 65	0.98038 62965 11	0.82930 51161 94	1.34015 88438 05
58	1.17827 19576 76	0.98852 03322 21	0.83908 28508 44	1.34782 86861 90
59	1.19233 71702 15	0.99645 63912 08	0.84860 73949 50	1.35536 99126 37
60	1.20623 30036 20	1.00420 24591 28	0.85787 46504 85	1.36277 32890 84
61	1.22001 29870 38	1.01176 63978 25	0.86688 05944 65	1.37002 97471 87
62	1.23353 67891 75	1.01915 59403 14	0.87562 12834 59	1.37713 03956 05
63	1.24695 50257 04	1.02637 86869 49	0.88409 28580 89	1.38406 65310 78
64	1.26022 44397 52	1.03344 21026 86	0.89229 15474 81	1.39082 96492 84
65	1.27335 03033 10	1.04035 35153 68	0.90021 36736 85	1.39741 14554 64
66	1.28633 79308 44	1.04712 01149 54	0.90785 56560 26	1.40380 38747 94
67	1.29919 26746 52	1.05374 89536 05	0.91521 40153 99	1.40999 90624 96
68	1.31191 99205 91	1.06024 69465 68	0.92228 53784 93	1.41598 94136 72
69	1.32452 50841 58	1.06662 08737 96	0.92906 64819 12	1.42176 75728 44
70	1.33701 36069 00	1.07287 73822 17	0.93555 41762 21	1.42732 64431 98
71	1.34939 09531 50	1.07902 29886 25	0.94174 54298 77	1.43265 91955 08
72	1.36166 26070 58	1.08506 40831 09	0.94763 73330 43	1.43775 92767 27
73	1.37383 40699 12	1.09100 69329 85	0.95322 71012 91	1.44262 04182 51
74	1.38591 08577 27	1.09685 76871 78	0.95851 20791 58	1.44723 66438 15
75	1.39789 84990 87	1.10262 23810 08	0.96348 97435 74	1.45160 22770 47
76	1.40980 25332 21	1.10830 69413 40	0.96815 77071 34	1.45571 19486 26
77	1.42162 85083 05	1.11391 71920 60	0.97251 37212 17	1.45956 06030 79
78	1.43338 19799 63	1.11945 88598 43	0.97655 56789 37	1.46314 35051 72
79	1.44506 85099 66	1.12493 75801 74	0.98028 16179 28	1.46645 62459 05
80	1.45669 36651 00	1.13035 89036 07	0.98368 97229 46	1.46949 47480 99
81	1.46826 30161 96	1.13572 83022 17	0.98677 83282 92	1.47225 52715 61
82	1.47978 21373 08	1.14105 11762 32	0.98954 59200 36	1.47473 44178 28
83	1.49125 66050 19	1.14633 28608 21	0.99199 11380 55	1.47692 91344 81
84	1.50269 19978 72	1.15157 86330 14	0.99411 27778 68	1.47883 67190 16
85	1.51409 38958 92	1.15679 37187 35	0.99590 97922 58	1.48045 48222 79
86	1.52546 78802 15	1.16198 32999 33	0.99738 12926 99	1.48178 14514 49
87	1.53681 95327 82	1.16715 25217 97	0.99852 65505 56	1.48281 49725 70
88	1.54815 44361 02	1.17230 65000 24	0.99934 49980 82	1.48355 41126 27
89	1.55947 81730 65	1.17745 03281 58	0.99983 62291 88	1.48399 79611 67
90	1.57079 63267 95	1.18258 90849 45	1.00000 00000 00	1.48414 59714 55

K = 2.27537 64296 11676   E = 1.17317 93826 83722
K′= 1.65569 69263 10344   E′= 1.49236 87111 24151

r	u=(r/90)K=F(ϕ,k)	sn u	cn u	dn u
0	0.00000 00000 00	0.00000 00000 00	1.00000 00000 00	1.00000 00000 00
1	0.02528 19603 29	0.02527 70924 56	0.99968 04832 53	0.99974 18924 77
2	0.05056 39206 58	0.05052 50044 19	0.99872 27963 40	0.99896 83623 73
3	0.07584 58809 87	0.07571 46888 46	0.99712 95231 28	0.99768 17815 99
4	0.10112 78413 16	0.10081 73642 90	0.99490 49497 60	0.99588 60851 15
5	0.12640 98016 45	0.12580 46444 61	0.99205 50344 77	0.99358 67438 53
6	0.15169 17619 74	0.15064 86639 72	0.98858 73659 13	0.99079 07272 92
7	0.17697 37223 03	0.17532 21990 81	0.98451 11104 04	0.98750 64561 73
8	0.20225 56826 32	0.19979 87823 49	0.97983 69489 73	0.98374 37459 56
9	0.22753 76429 61	0.22405 28102 08	0.97457 70047 76	0.97951 37417 15
10	0.25281 96032 90	0.24805 96425 65	0.96874 47619 11	0.97482 88452 92
11	0.27810 15636 19	0.27179 56936 76	0.96235 49765 54	0.96970 26355 67
12	0.30338 35239 48	0.29523 85136 61	0.95542 35814 82	0.96414 97828 06
13	0.32866 54842 77	0.31836 68601 77	0.94796 75850 69	0.95818 59580 54
14	0.35394 74446 06	0.34116 07598 94	0.94000 49658 96	0.95182 77386 01
15	0.37922 94049 35	0.36360 15595 69	0.93155 45640 91	0.94509 25105 31
16	0.40451 13652 64	0.38567 19666 34	0.92263 59705 50	0.93799 83693 81
17	0.42979 33255 93	0.40735 60793 70	0.91326 94151 24	0.93056 40198 80
18	0.45507 52859 22	0.42863 94068 50	0.90347 56548 44	0.92280 86757 57
19	0.48035 72462 51	0.44950 88789 25	0.89327 58631 96	0.91475 19604 82
20	0.50563 92065 80	0.46995 28466 83	0.88269 15213 68	0.90641 38098 23
21	0.53092 11669 09	0.48996 10738 46	0.87174 43123 51	0.89781 43769 69
22	0.55620 31272 38	0.50952 47196 70	0.86045 60186 58	0.88897 39409 19
23	0.58148 50875 67	0.52863 63139 99	0.84884 84243 50	0.87991 28187 68
24	0.60676 70478 96	0.54728 97251 18	0.83694 32219 57	0.87065 12824 07
25	0.63204 90082 25	0.56548 01211 38	0.82476 19247 99	0.86120 94800 80
26	0.65733 09685 54	0.58320 39256 41	0.81232 57850 87	0.85160 73631 69
27	0.68261 29288 84	0.60045 87683 30	0.79965 57181 28	0.84186 46184 68
28	0.70789 48892 13	0.61724 34314 28	0.78677 22328 34	0.83200 06061 44
29	0.73317 68495 42	0.63355 77925 47	0.77369 53686 71	0.82203 43034 98
30	0.75845 88098 71	0.64940 27647 57	0.76044 46390 94	0.81198 42545 74
31	0.78374 07702 00	0.66478 02345 18	0.74703 89814 42	0.80186 85255 86
32	0.80902 27305 29	0.67969 29981 28	0.73349 67132 14	0.79170 46660 92
33	0.83430 46908 58	0.69414 46972 97	0.71983 54945 51	0.78150 96757 68
34	0.85958 66511 87	0.70813 97543 95	0.70607 22967 56	0.77129 99766 09
35	0.88486 86115 16	0.72168 33079 06	0.69222 33765 84	0.76109 13903 45
36	0.91015 05718 45	0.73478 11485 34	0.67830 42560 37	0.75089 91207 99
37	0.93543 25321 74	0.74743 96563 82	0.66432 97073 49	0.74073 77409 41
38	0.96071 44925 03	0.75966 57395 72	0.65031 37428 36	0.73062 11843 06
39	0.98599 64528 32	0.77146 67746 10	0.63626 96092 64	0.72056 27405 05
40	1.01127 84131 61	0.78285 05487 74	0.62220 97863 93	0.71057 50544 73
41	1.03656 03734 90	0.79382 52047 39	0.60814 59893 16	0.70067 01291 65
42	1.06184 23338 19	0.80439 91876 10	0.59408 91742 59	0.69085 93313 49
43	1.08712 42941 48	0.81458 11945 17	0.58004 95474 87	0.68115 34002 04
44	1.11240 62544 77	0.82438 01268 55	0.56603 65769 51	0.67156 24584 00
45	1.13768 82148 06	0.83380 50452 46	0.55205 90063 77	0.66209 60253 54

254

q = 0.10167 16783 93444 1   D(90) = 1.51035 49360 01753
q′= 0.01333 45085 07947 30   1/D(90) = 0.66209 60253 53632

r	ϕ	$E(\phi,k)$	A(r)	D(r)
0	0.00000 00000 00	0.00000 00000 00	0.00000 00000 00	1.00000 00000 00
1	0.02527 97849 52	0.02527 76099 11	0.01673 84530 58	1.00015 47939 36
2	0.05054 65256 55	0.05052 91414 20	0.03347 31112 95	1.00061 89895 39
3	0.07578 72178 85	0.07572 86364 11	0.05020 01774 79	1.00139 20284 05
4	0.10098 89371 88	0.10085 03761 65	0.06691 58495 56	1.00247 29805 82
5	0.12613 88780 80	0.12586 89981 58	0.08361 63182 72	1.00386 05456 40
6	0.15122 43924 22	0.15075 96094 19	0.10029 77648 19	1.00555 30541 79
7	0.17623 30267 34	0.17549 78954 07	0.11695 63585 27	1.00754 84697 55
8	0.20115 25581 88	0.20006 02234 14	0.13358 82546 03	1.00984 43912 42
9	0.22597 10290 63	0.22442 37396 09	0.15018 95919 38	1.01243 80556 06
10	0.25067 67794 54	0.24856 64589 17	0.16675 64909 81	1.01532 63411 11
11	0.27525 84780 56	0.27246 73470 71	0.18328 50516 95	1.01850 57709 28
12	0.29970 51508 42	0.29610 63942 51	0.19977 13516 08	1.02197 25171 72
13	0.32400 62075 29	0.31946 46798 90	0.21621 14439 58	1.02572 24053 43
14	0.34815 14656 84	0.34252 44283 20	0.23260 13559 54	1.02975 09191 67
15	0.37213 11724 12	0.36526 90550 78	0.24893 70871 46	1.03405 32058 49
16	0.39593 60235 54	0.38768 32038 03	0.26521 46079 30	1.03862 40817 12
17	0.41955 71803 51	0.40975 27737 83	0.28142 98581 81	1.04345 80382 31
18	0.44298 62835 83	0.43146 49383 10	0.29757 87460 26	1.04854 92484 52
19	0.46621 54651 76	0.45280 81541 16	0.31365 71467 73	1.05389 15737 85
20	0.48923 73573 27	0.47377 21622 44	0.32966 09019 85	1.05947 85711 67
21	0.51204 50991 95	0.49434 79807 98	0.34558 58187 26	1.06530 35006 00
22	0.53463 23412 29	0.51452 78900 78	0.36142 76689 64	1.07135 93330 28
23	0.55699 32472 31	0.53430 54106 64	0.37718 21891 51	1.07763 87585 75
24	0.57912 24942 63	0.55367 52750 66	0.39284 50799 84	1.08413 41951 19
25	0.60101 52704 92	0.57263 33935 66	0.40841 20063 41	1.09083 77971 95
26	0.62266 72711 36	0.59117 68149 29	0.42387 85974 04	1.09774 14652 21
27	0.64407 46926 12	0.60930 36826 48	0.43924 04469 76	1.10483 68550 37
28	0.66523 42250 56	0.62701 31873 84	0.45449 31139 78	1.11211 53877 46
29	0.68614 30433 37	0.64430 55162 70	0.46963 21231 55	1.11956 82598 44
30	0.70679 87967 33	0.66118 17997 18	0.48465 29659 60	1.12718 64536 33
31	0.72719 95973 99	0.67764 40563 31	0.49955 11016 49	1.13496 07479 04
32	0.74734 40077 83	0.69369 51365 16	0.51432 19585 61	1.14288 17288 77
33	0.76723 10271 33	0.70933 86653 41	0.52896 09356 03	1.15093 98013 88
34	0.78686 00772 35	0.72457 89851 33	0.54346 34039 28	1.15912 52003 09
35	0.80623 09875 06	0.73942 10982 90	0.55782 47088 02	1.16742 80021 91
36	0.82534 39795 93	0.75387 06107 21	0.57204 01716 73	1.17583 81371 13
37	0.84419 96515 70	0.76793 36762 86	0.58610 50924 24	1.18434 54007 29
38	0.86279 89618 75	0.78161 69425 73	0.60001 47518 17	1.19293 94664 96
39	0.88114 32130 81	0.79492 74982 85	0.61376 44141 15	1.20160 98980 66
40	0.89923 40355 94	0.80787 28224 81	0.62734 93298 93	1.21034 61618 38
41	0.91707 33713 87	0.82046 07358 90	0.64076 47390 20	1.21913 76396 43
42	0.93466 34578 31	0.83269 93544 20	0.65400 58738 04	1.22797 36415 55
43	0.95200 68117 21	0.84459 70450 35	0.66706 79623 15	1.23684 34188 17
44	0.96910 62135 37	0.85616 23840 53	0.67994 62318 56	1.24573 61768 50
45	0.98596 46920 25	0.86740 41179 47	0.69263 59125 94	1.25464 10883 50

255

K = 2.27537 64296 11676   E = 1.17317 93826 83722
K' = 1.65569 69263 10344   E' = 1.49236 87111 24151

r	u=(r/90)K=F(ϕ,k)	sn u	cn u	dn u
45	1.13768 82148 06	0.83380 50452 46	0.55205 90063 77	0.66209 60253 54
46	1.16297 01751 35	0.84286 51272 43	0.53812 48714 54	0.65276 30323 97
47	1.18825 21354 64	0.85156 96278 00	0.52424 15178 23	0.64357 18395 56
48	1.21353 40957 93	0.85992 78424 73	0.51041 56205 87	0.63453 02536 96
49	1.23881 60561 22	0.86794 90733 26	0.49665 32050 77	0.62564 55478 01
50	1.26409 80164 51	0.87564 25974 66	0.48295 96686 10	0.61692 44811 36
51	1.28937 99767 80	0.88301 76381 57	0.46933 98030 25	0.60837 33201 11
52	1.31466 19371 09	0.89008 33384 04	0.45579 78177 83	0.59999 78596 37
53	1.33994 38974 38	0.89684 87369 17	0.44233 73634 34	0.59180 34448 10
54	1.36522 58577 67	0.90332 27463 57	0.42896 15552 87	0.58379 49927 58
55	1.39050 78180 96	0.90951 41337 37	0.41567 29971 18	0.57597 70145 22
56	1.41578 97784 25	0.91543 15028 76	0.40247 38047 91	0.56835 36368 25
57	1.44107 17387 54	0.92108 32787 75	0.38936 56296 61	0.56092 86236 39
58	1.46635 36990 83	0.92647 76938 02	0.37634 96816 62	0.55370 53974 34
59	1.49163 56594 12	0.93162 27755 62	0.36342 67519 79	0.54668 70600 37
60	1.51691 76197 41	0.93652 63363 30	0.35059 72352 43	0.53987 64130 21
61	1.54219 95800 70	0.94119 59639 39	0.33786 11511 64	0.53327 59775 64
62	1.56748 15403 99	0.94563 90139 92	0.32521 81655 70	0.52688 80137 25
63	1.59276 35007 28	0.94986 26033 05	0.31266 76107 99	0.52071 45390 99
64	1.61804 54610 57	0.95387 36044 56	0.30020 85054 12	0.51475 73468 11
65	1.64332 74213 86	0.95767 86413 48	0.28783 95732 09	0.50901 80228 26
66	1.66860 93817 15	0.96128 40856 83	0.27555 92615 25	0.50349 79625 57
67	1.69389 13420 44	0.96469 60542 50	0.26336 57588 11	0.49819 83867 48
68	1.71917 33023 73	0.96792 04069 46	0.25125 70114 80	0.49312 03566 40
69	1.74445 52627 02	0.97096 27454 33	0.23923 07400 43	0.48826 47883 95
70	1.76973 72230 31	0.97382 84123 67	0.22728 44545 23	0.48363 24668 03
71	1.79501 91833 60	0.97652 24911 08	0.21541 54691 75	0.47922 40582 44
72	1.82030 11436 89	0.97904 98058 58	0.20362 09165 30	0.47504 01229 48
73	1.84558 31040 18	0.98141 49221 47	0.19189 77607 67	0.47108 11265 25
74	1.87086 50643 47	0.98362 21476 16	0.18024 28104 53	0.46734 74508 05
75	1.89614 70246 76	0.98567 55330 41	0.16865 27306 76	0.46383 94039 78
76	1.92142 89850 05	0.98757 88735 44	0.15712 40545 84	0.46055 72300 65
77	1.94671 09453 34	0.98933 57099 43	0.14565 31943 74	0.45750 11177 16
78	1.97199 29056 63	0.99094 93301 97	0.13423 64517 61	0.45467 12083 61
79	1.99727 48659 92	0.99242 27709 16	0.12287 00279 44	0.45206 76037 27
80	2.02255 68263 21	0.99375 88188 84	0.11155 00331 25	0.44969 03727 32
81	2.04783 87866 51	0.99496 00125 77	0.10027 24955 96	0.44753 95577 62
82	2.07312 07469 80	0.99602 86436 39	0.08903 33704 33	0.44561 51803 67
83	2.09840 27073 09	0.99696 67582 93	0.07782 85478 42	0.44391 72463 62
84	2.12368 46676 38	0.99777 61586 60	0.06665 38611 72	0.44244 57503 63
85	2.14896 66279 67	0.99845 84039 75	0.05550 50946 53	0.44120 06797 61
86	2.17424 85882 96	0.99901 48116 65	0.04437 79908 77	0.44018 20181 46
87	2.19953 05486 25	0.99944 64582 98	0.03326 82580 66	0.43938 97481 89
88	2.22481 25089 54	0.99975 41803 69	0.02217 15771 62	0.43882 38539 88
89	2.25009 44692 83	0.99993 85749 22	0.01108 36087 70	0.43848 43228 92
90	2.27537 64296 12	1.00000 00000 00	0.00000 00000 00	0.43837 11467 89

q = 0.10167 16783 93444 1   D(90) = 1.51035 49360 01753
q'= 0.01333 45085 07947 30   1/D(90) = 0.66209 60253 53632

r	ϕ	$E(\phi,k)$	A(r)	D(r)
45	0.98596 46920 25	0.86740 41179 47	0.69263 59125 94	1.25464 10883 50
46	1.00258 55091 34	0.87833 11266 74	0.70513 22413 28	1.26354 73064 44
47	1.01897 21453 54	0.88895 23895 41	0.71743 04653 97	1.27244 39778 93
48	1.03512 82855 03	0.89927 69536 04	0.72952 58467 24	1.28132 02563 27
49	1.05105 78049 79	0.90931 39045 44	0.74141 36659 73	1.29016 53154 95
50	1.06676 47565 20	0.91907 23399 98	0.75308 92268 19	1.29896 83625 13
51	1.08225 33574 77	0.92856 13452 58	0.76454 78603 31	1.30771 86510 91
52	1.09752 79776 20	0.93778 99712 83	0.77578 49294 33	1.31640 54947 33
53	1.11259 31274 96	0.94676 72149 22	0.78679 58334 67	1.32501 82798 80
54	1.12745 34473 30	0.95550 20012 66	0.79757 60128 15	1.33354 64789 85
55	1.14211 36964 82	0.96400 31680 30	0.80812 09535 95	1.34197 96635 09
56	1.15657 87434 56	0.97227 94518 64	0.81842 61924 09	1.35030 75168 11
57	1.17085 35564 58	0.98033 94764 90	0.82848 73211 30	1.35851 98469 22
58	1.18494 31944 91	0.98819 17425 52	0.83829 99917 23	1.36660 65991 87
59	1.19885 27989 89	0.99584 46190 90	0.84785 99210 91	1.37455 78687 53
60	1.21258 75859 71	1.00330 63365 26	0.85716 28959 24	1.38236 39128 93
61	1.22615 28386 96	1.01058 49810 48	0.86620 47775 53	1.39001 51631 44
62	1.23955 39008 24	1.01768 84903 26	0.87498 15067 87	1.39750 22372 51
63	1.25279 61700 50	1.02462 46504 20	0.88348 91087 29	1.40481 59508 86
64	1.26588 50922 03	1.03140 10938 30	0.89172 36975 58	1.41194 73291 48
65	1.27882 61557 92	1.03802 52985 67	0.89968 14812 58	1.41888 76178 07
66	1.29162 48869 77	1.04450 45881 84	0.90735 87662 97	1.42562 82942 91
67	1.30428 68449 60	1.05084 61326 64	0.91475 19622 35	1.43216 10783 95
68	1.31681 76177 54	1.05705 69501 14	0.92185 75862 50	1.43847 79427 02
69	1.32922 28183 42	1.06314 39091 74	0.92867 22675 76	1.44457 11226 91
70	1.34150 80811 79	1.06911 37320 85	0.93519 27518 40	1.45043 31265 32
71	1.35367 90590 38	1.07497 29983 49	0.94141 59052 87	1.45605 67445 48
72	1.36574 14201 72	1.08072 81489 27	0.94733 87188 82	1.46143 50583 26
73	1.37770 08457 79	1.08638 54909 17	0.95295 83122 82	1.46656 14494 73
74	1.38956 30277 47	1.09195 12026 65	0.95827 19376 67	1.47142 96080 01
75	1.40133 36666 66	1.09743 13392 64	0.96327 69834 22	1.47603 35403 27
76	1.41301 84700 87	1.10283 18383 97	0.96797 09776 53	1.48036 75768 78
77	1.42462 31510 12	1.10815 85264 84	0.97235 15915 44	1.48442 63792 95
78	1.43615 34266 00	1.11341 71251 06	0.97641 66425 33	1.48820 49472 19
79	1.44761 50170 69	1.11861 32576 64	0.98016 40973 02	1.49169 86246 54
80	1.45901 36447 78	1.12375 24562 47	0.98359 20745 81	1.49490 31058 91
81	1.47035 50334 82	1.12884 01686 92	0.98669 88477 54	1.49781 44409 97
82	1.48164 49077 34	1.13388 17657 94	0.98948 28472 51	1.50042 90408 51
83	1.49288 89924 21	1.13888 25486 60	0.99194 26627 45	1.50274 36817 18
84	1.50409 30124 30	1.14384 77561 84	0.99407 70451 17	1.50475 55093 66
85	1.51526 26923 98	1.14878 25726 17	0.99588 49082 16	1.50646 20427 11
86	1.52640 37566 13	1.15369 21352 28	0.99736 53303 82	1.50786 11769 82
87	1.53752 19289 13	1.15858 15420 29	0.99851 75557 47	1.50895 11864 15
88	1.54862 29327 18	1.16345 58595 65	0.99934 09953 02	1.50973 07264 53
89	1.55971 24910 82	1.16832 01307 41	0.99983 52277 30	1.51019 88354 72
90	1.57079 63267 95	1.17317 93826 84	1.00000 00000 00	1.51035 49360 02

K = 2.30878 67981 67196   E = 1.16382 79644 93139
K′= 1.64899 52184 78530   E′= 1.49811 49284 22116

r	u=(r/90)K=F(φ,k)	sn u	cn u	dn u
0	0.00000 00000 00	0.00000 00000 00	1.00000 00000 00	1.00000 00000 00
1	0.02565 31866 46	0.02564 80630 70	0.99967 10343 21	0.99972 97975 70
2	0.05130 63732 93	0.05126 54139 18	0.99868 50641 40	0.99892 00467 99
3	0.07695 95599 39	0.07682 14861 92	0.99704 48632 13	0.99757 33110 89
4	0.10261 27465 85	0.10228 60037 97	0.99475 50318 68	0.99569 38423 18
5	0.12826 59332 32	0.12762 91223 59	0.99182 19634 22	0.99328 75504 54
6	0.15391 91198 78	0.15282 15663 58	0.98825 37977 95	0.99036 19615 79
7	0.17957 23065 24	0.17783 47605 99	0.98406 03629 47	0.98692 61648 86
8	0.20522 54931 70	0.20264 09548 00	0.97925 31048 91	0.98299 07493 53
9	0.23087 86798 17	0.22721 33401 73	0.97384 50072 00	0.97856 77309 04
10	0.25653 18664 63	0.25152 61570 09	0.96785 05010 28	0.97367 04709 95
11	0.28218 50531 09	0.27555 47924 41	0.96128 53667 68	0.96831 35876 34
12	0.30783 82397 56	0.29927 58676 77	0.95416 66285 44	0.96251 28599 32
13	0.33349 14264 02	0.32266 73141 96	0.94651 24427 87	0.95628 51273 01
14	0.35914 46130 48	0.34570 84385 24	0.93834 19821 86	0.94964 81844 84
15	0.38479 77996 95	0.36837 99754 02	0.92967 53162 92	0.94262 06735 64
16	0.41045 09863 41	0.39066 41292 86	0.92053 32900 49	0.93522 19741 23
17	0.43610 41729 87	0.41254 46042 91	0.91093 74015 10	0.92747 20926 63
18	0.46175 73596 33	0.43400 66228 15	0.90090 96799 08	0.91939 15523 82
19	0.48741 05462 80	0.45503 69332 26	0.89047 25652 15	0.91100 12843 10
20	0.51306 37329 26	0.47562 38070 75	0.87964 87902 24	0.90232 25207 46
21	0.53871 69195 72	0.49575 70264 46	0.86846 12661 08	0.89337 66918 67
22	0.56437 01062 19	0.51542 78620 87	0.85693 29722 82	0.88418 53262 61
23	0.59002 32928 65	0.53462 90430 72	0.84508 68513 38	0.87476 99560 57
24	0.61567 64795 11	0.55335 47187 68	0.83294 57096 46	0.86515 20272 31
25	0.64132 96661 58	0.57160 04139 34	0.82053 21241 67	0.85535 28155 37
26	0.66698 28528 04	0.58936 29777 89	0.80786 83558 67	0.84539 33484 54
27	0.69263 60394 50	0.60664 05278 90	0.79497 62700 37	0.83529 43334 00
28	0.71828 92260 96	0.62343 23896 66	0.78187 72637 16	0.82507 60924 06
29	0.74394 24127 43	0.63973 90324 20	0.76859 22003 24	0.81475 85033 33
30	0.76959 55993 89	0.65556 20025 94	0.75514 13515 06	0.80436 09476 50
31	0.79524 87860 35	0.67090 38550 49	0.74154 43461 32	0.79390 22647 08
32	0.82090 19726 82	0.68576 80830 61	0.72782 01263 05	0.78340 07123 85
33	0.84655 51593 28	0.70015 90477 13	0.71398 69101 78	0.77287 39339 12
34	0.87220 83459 74	0.71408 19072 64	0.70006 21613 24	0.76233 89306 61
35	0.89786 15326 21	0.72754 25470 60	0.68606 25643 61	0.75181 20406 10
36	0.92351 47192 67	0.74054 75104 76	0.67200 40064 82	0.74130 89221 81
37	0.94916 79059 13	0.75310 39313 15	0.65790 15645 50	0.73084 45431 27
38	0.97482 10925 59	0.76521 94680 58	0.64376 94973 40	0.72043 31741 05
39	1.00047 42792 06	0.77690 22402 55	0.62962 12425 63	0.71008 83865 96
40	1.02612 74658 52	0.78816 07673 63	0.61546 94182 41	0.69982 30547 71
41	1.05178 06524 98	0.79900 39102 08	0.60132 58280 44	0.68964 93609 74
42	1.07743 38391 45	0.80944 08152 66	0.58720 14701 81	0.67957 88044 24
43	1.10308 70257 91	0.81948 08618 73	0.57310 65494 51	0.66962 22127 99
44	1.12874 02124 37	0.82913 36124 57	0.55905 04920 79	0.65978 97563 48
45	1.15439 33990 84	0.83840 87658 19	0.54504 19629 69	0.65009 09642 05

q = 0.10605 40201 85995 5   D(90) = 1.53824 62686 94483
q'= 0.01229 45605 27181 44   1/D(90) = 0.65009 09642 04779

r	ϕ	$E(\phi, k)$	A(r)	D(r)
0	0.00000 00000 00	0.00000 00000 00	0.00000 00000 00	1.00000 00000 00
1	0.02565 08758 84	0.02564 85654 97	0.01667 62945 21	1.00016 31605 74
2	0.05128 78959 87	0.05126 94306 57	0.03334 89265 64	1.00065 24463 66
3	0.07689 72484 21	0.07683 50276 67	0.05001 42308 85	1.00146 72698 13
4	0.10246 52087 66	0.10231 80524 16	0.06666 85367 23	1.00260 66523 94
5	0.12797 81830 22	0.12769 15930 29	0.08330 81650 70	1.00406 92257 49
6	0.15313 18614 21	0.15292 92544 72	0.09992 94259 70	1.00585 32332 53
7	0.17878 57002 71	0.17800 52780 39	0.11652 86158 76	1.00795 65320 33
8	0.20405 40791 79	0.20289 46545 94	0.13310 20150 49	1.01037 65954 28
9	0.22921 52206 94	0.22757 32305 64	0.14964 58850 35	1.01311 05158 92
10	0.25425 67848 46	0.25201 78057 90	0.16615 64662 14	1.01615 50083 40
11	0.27916 67907 43	0.27620 62224 73	0.18262 99754 46	1.01950 64139 23
12	0.30393 36475 95	0.30011 74445 91	0.19906 26038 03	1.02316 07042 45
13	0.32854 61832 16	0.32373 16273 19	0.21545 05144 24	1.02711 34860 00
14	0.35299 36698 87	0.34703 01761 05	0.23178 98404 83	1.03136 00060 40
15	0.37726 58474 83	0.36999 57952 35	0.24807 66832 78	1.03589 51568 60
16	0.40135 29438 03	0.39261 25258 40	0.26430 71104 74	1.04071 34824 98
17	0.42524 56920 72	0.41486 57734 33	0.28047 71544 75	1.04580 91848 46
18	0.44893 53456 08	0.43674 23252 08	0.29658 28109 61	1.05117 61303 57
19	0.47241 36896 74	0.45823 03574 22	0.31262 00375 82	1.05680 78571 58
20	0.49567 30505 71	0.47931 94333 29	0.32858 47528 23	1.06269 75825 47
21	0.51870 63020 33	0.50000 04921 54	0.34447 28350 45	1.06883 82108 74
22	0.54150 68690 14	0.52026 58297 60	0.36028 01217 05	1.07522 23417 91
23	0.56406 87289 90	0.54010 90716 37	0.37600 24087 72	1.08184 22788 83
24	0.58638 64108 82	0.55952 51389 40	0.39163 54503 27	1.08869 00386 36
25	0.60845 49917 64	0.57851 02083 30	0.40717 49583 69	1.09575 73597 72
26	0.63027 00914 71	0.59706 16663 56	0.42261 66028 17	1.10303 57129 15
27	0.65182 78653 05	0.61517 80591 72	0.43795 60117 23	1.11051 63105 88
28	0.67312 49949 68	0.63285 90383 25	0.45318 87716 92	1.11819 01175 25
29	0.69415 86779 07	0.65010 53033 75	0.46831 04285 11	1.12604 78613 02
30	0.71492 66152 38	0.66691 85420 60	0.48331 64879 96	1.13408 00432 54
31	0.73542 69984 12	0.68330 13686 88	0.49820 24170 48	1.14227 69496 88
32	0.75565 84947 86	0.69925 72613 99	0.51296 36449 29	1.15062 86633 61
33	0.77562 02322 72	0.71479 04989 00	0.52759 55647 47	1.15912 50752 27
34	0.79531 17832 06	0.72990 60972 23	0.54209 35351 59	1.16775 58964 30
35	0.81473 31475 94	0.74460 97470 03	0.55645 28822 88	1.17651 06705 34
36	0.83388 47358 77	0.75890 77517 25	0.57066 89018 46	1.18537 87859 76
37	0.85271 88699 75	0.77280 69673 35	0.58473 68614 70	1.19434 94887 27
38	0.87138 21723 17	0.78631 47435 61	0.59865 20032 58	1.20341 18951 47
39	0.88973 07342 47	0.79943 88672 24	0.61240 95465 14	1.21255 50050 26
40	0.90781 49117 78	0.81218 75077 98	0.62600 46906 80	1.22176 77147 85
41	0.92563 69009 31	0.82456 91654 14	0.63943 26184 73	1.23103 88308 25
42	0.94319 92014 58	0.83659 26214 46	0.65268 84991 92	1.24035 70830 21
43	0.96050 45994 62	0.84826 68918 17	0.66576 74922 23	1.24971 11383 29
44	0.97755 61503 43	0.85960 11830 88	0.67866 47507 07	1.25908 96144 91
45	0.99435 71621 45	0.87060 48513 76	0.69137 54253 76	1.26848 10938 41

K = 2.30878 67981 67196   E = 1.16382 79644 93139
K′= 1.64899 52184 78530   E′= 1.49811 49284 22116

r	u=(r/90)K=F(ϕ,k)	sn u	cn u	dn u
45	1.15439 33990 84	0.83840 87658 19	0.54504 19629 69	0.65009 09642 05
46	1.18004 65857 30	0.84731 61135 06	0.53108 88850 22	0.64053 47425 83
47	1.20569 97723 76	0.85586 54992 27	0.51719 84601 99	0.63112 93945 50
48	1.23135 29590 23	0.86406 67813 03	0.50337 71920 23	0.62188 26411 14
49	1.25700 61456 69	0.87192 97980 56	0.48963 09092 19	0.61280 16433 50
50	1.28265 93323 15	0.87946 43360 84	0.47596 47902 49	0.60389 30253 29
51	1.30831 25189 61	0.88668 01013 06	0.46238 33884 87	0.59516 28976 31
52	1.33396 57056 08	0.89358 66926 72	0.44889 06578 22	0.58661 68812 47
53	1.35961 88922 54	0.90019 35784 25	0.43548 99784 86	0.57826 01316 73
54	1.38527 20789 00	0.90651 00747 81	0.42218 41829 35	0.57009 73630 50
55	1.41092 52655 47	0.91254 53268 93	0.40897 55816 25	0.56213 28721 98
56	1.43657 84521 93	0.91830 82919 79	0.39586 59885 40	0.55437 05624 14
57	1.46223 16388 39	0.92380 77244 56	0.38285 67463 64	0.54681 39669 32
58	1.48788 48254 86	0.92905 21629 60	0.36994 87511 80	0.53946 62719 34
59	1.51353 80121 32	0.93404 99191 11	0.35714 24766 25	0.53233 03390 45
60	1.53919 11987 78	0.93880 90678 85	0.34443 79974 06	0.52540 87272 33
61	1.56484 43854 24	0.94333 74394 75	0.33183 50121 45	0.51870 37140 60
62	1.59049 75720 71	0.94764 26124 97	0.31933 28654 88	0.51221 73162 34
63	1.61615 07587 17	0.95173 19084 41	0.30693 05694 37	0.50595 13094 27
64	1.64180 39453 63	0.95561 23872 34	0.29462 68239 08	0.49990 72473 35
65	1.66745 71320 10	0.95929 08438 05	0.28242 00364 57	0.49408 64799 46
66	1.69311 03186 56	0.96277 38055 61	0.27030 83412 06	0.48849 01710 21
67	1.71876 35053 02	0.96606 75306 53	0.25828 96169 38	0.48311 93147 57
68	1.74441 66919 49	0.96917 80069 52	0.24636 15043 79	0.47797 47516 60
69	1.77006 98785 95	0.97211 09516 44	0.23452 14226 76	0.47305 71835 91
70	1.79572 30652 41	0.97487 18113 53	0.22276 65850 81	0.46836 71880 33
71	1.82137 62518 87	0.97746 57627 29	0.21109 40138 72	0.46390 52315 51
72	1.84702 94385 34	0.97989 77134 11	0.19950 05545 17	0.45967 16824 79
73	1.87268 26251 80	0.98217 23033 15	0.18798 28891 19	0.45566 68228 45
74	1.89833 58118 26	0.98429 39061 75	0.17653 75491 72	0.45189 08595 33
75	1.92398 89984 73	0.98626 66312 81	0.16516 09276 46	0.44834 39347 27
76	1.94964 21851 19	0.98809 43253 70	0.15384 92904 48	0.44502 61356 21
77	1.97529 53717 65	0.98978 05746 06	0.14259 87872 79	0.44193 75034 45
78	2.00094 85584 12	0.99132 87066 22	0.13140 54619 36	0.43907 80417 94
79	2.02660 17450 58	0.99274 17925 81	0.12026 52620 83	0.43644 77243 09
80	2.05225 49317 04	0.99402 26492 02	0.10917 40485 35	0.43404 65016 97
81	2.07790 81183 50	0.99517 38407 52	0.09812 76040 85	0.43187 43081 28
82	2.10356 13049 97	0.99619 76809 40	0.08712 16419 19	0.42993 10670 21
83	2.12921 44916 43	0.99709 62347 12	0.07615 18136 57	0.42821 66962 20
84	2.15486 76782 89	0.99787 13199 15	0.06521 37170 41	0.42673 11125 99
85	2.18052 08649 36	0.99852 45088 07	0.05430 29033 38	0.42547 42360 83
86	2.20617 40515 82	0.99905 71294 01	0.04341 48844 63	0.42444 59931 15
87	2.23182 72382 28	0.99947 02666 26	0.03254 51398 89	0.42364 63195 67
88	2.25748 04248 75	0.99976 47632 96	0.02168 91233 56	0.42307 51631 17
89	2.28313 36115 21	0.99994 12208 69	0.01084 22694 39	0.42273 24850 86
90	2.30878 67981 67	1.00000 00000 00	0.00000 00000 00	0.42261 82617 41

q = 0.10605 40201 85995 5
q' = 0.01229 45605 27181 44

D(90) = 1.53824 62686 94483
1/D(90) = 0.65009 09642 04779

r	ϕ	$E(\phi,k)$	A(r)	D(r)
45	0.99435 71621 45	0.87060 48513 76	0.69137 54253 76	1.26848 10938 41
46	1.01091 11793 28	0.88128 73641 17	0.70389 46685 53	1.27787 41371 69
47	1.02722 19670 50	0.89165 82646 66	0.71621 76382 98	1.28725 72976 47
48	1.04329 34959 53	0.90172 71396 94	0.72833 95026 99	1.29661 91347 85
49	1.05912 99275 19	0.91150 35893 32	0.74025 54443 00	1.30594 82284 17
50	1.07473 55999 97	0.92099 71999 82	0.75196 06646 44	1.31523 31926 77
51	1.09011 50149 27	0.93021 75197 28	0.76345 03889 40	1.32446 26899 73
52	1.10527 28242 73	0.93917 40362 30	0.77471 98708 32	1.33362 54449 21
53	1.12021 38181 74	0.94787 61570 12	0.78576 43972 52	1.34271 02582 32
54	1.13494 29133 11	0.95633 31920 27	0.79657 92933 75	1.35170 60205 31
55	1.14946 51418 94	0.96455 43383 79	0.80715 99276 24	1.36060 17260 92
56	1.16378 56412 60	0.97254 86670 90	0.81750 17167 54	1.36938 64864 68
57	1.17790 96440 86	0.98032 51117 93	0.82760 01309 71	1.37804 95440 08
58	1.19184 24691 83	0.98789 24592 22	0.83745 06990 98	1.38658 02852 22
59	1.20558 95128 90	0.99525 93413 92	0.84704 90137 58	1.39496 82540 05
60	1.21915 62410 26	1.00243 42293 42	0.85639 07365 79	1.40320 31646 81
61	1.23254 81814 03	1.00942 54283 33	0.86547 16033 88	1.41127 49148 53
62	1.24577 09168 70	1.01624 10743 98	0.87428 74294 05	1.41917 35980 56
63	1.25883 00788 77	1.02288 91321 20	0.88283 41144 06	1.42688 95161 72
64	1.27173 13415 40	1.02937 73935 60	0.89110 76478 56	1.43441 31916 16
65	1.28448 04161 81	1.03571 34782 17	0.89910 41139 85	1.44173 53792 52
66	1.29708 30463 26	1.04190 48339 48	0.90681 96968 16	1.44884 70780 45
67	1.30954 50031 48	1.04795 87387 51	0.91425 06851 05	1.45573 95424 15
68	1.32187 20813 20	1.05388 23033 29	0.92139 34772 16	1.46240 42932 87
69	1.33407 00952 66	1.05968 24743 76	0.92824 45858 80	1.46883 31288 22
70	1.34614 48757 89	1.06536 60384 89	0.93480 06428 62	1.47501 81348 05
71	1.35810 22670 57	1.07093 96266 67	0.94105 84035 03	1.48095 16946 86
72	1.36994 81239 21	1.07640 97193 20	0.94701 47511 27	1.48662 64992 59
73	1.38168 83095 49	1.08178 26517 40	0.95266 67013 19	1.49203 55559 49
74	1.39332 86933 57	1.08706 46199 81	0.95801 14060 43	1.49717 21977 23
75	1.40487 51492 14	1.09226 16871 01	0.96304 61575 99	1.50203 00915 81
76	1.41633 35539 16	1.09737 97897 31	0.96776 83924 15	1.50660 32466 43
77	1.42770 97858 85	1.10242 47449 17	0.97217 56946 52	1.51088 60217 94
78	1.43900 97241 00	1.10740 22572 19	0.97626 57996 28	1.51487 31328 96
79	1.45023 92472 34	1.11231 79260 22	0.98003 65970 31	1.51855 96595 54
80	1.46140 42329 75	1.11717 72530 35	0.98348 61339 44	1.52194 10514 10
81	1.47251 05575 21	1.12198 56499 58	0.98661 26176 43	1.52501 31339 77
82	1.48356 40952 32	1.12674 84462 82	0.98941 44181 81	1.52777 21139 89
83	1.49457 07184 20	1.13147 08972 16	0.99189 00707 47	1.53021 45842 75
84	1.50553 62972 71	1.13615 81917 13	0.99403 82777 86	1.53233 75281 23
85	1.51646 66998 66	1.14081 54605 83	0.99585 79108 93	1.53413 83231 66
86	1.52736 77923 11	1.14544 77846 74	0.99734 80124 53	1.53561 47447 40
87	1.53824 54389 39	1.15006 02031 20	0.99850 77970 43	1.53676 49687 56
88	1.54910 55025 86	1.15465 77216 27	0.99933 66525 80	1.53758 75740 35
89	1.55995 38449 18	1.15924 53207 99	0.99983 41412 21	1.53808 15441 42
90	1.57079 63267 95	1.16382 79644 93	1.00000 00000 00	1.53824 62686 94

K = 2.34390 47244 46913   E = 1.15454 66775 24465
K'= 1.64260 41437 12491   E'= 1.50366 21353 53715

r	u=(r/90)K=F(ϕ,k)	sn u	cn u	dn u
0	0.00000 00000 00	0.00000 00000 00	1.00000 00000 00	1.00000 00000 00
1	0.02604 33858 27	0.02603 79861 62	0.99966 09541 62	0.99971 70520 45
2	0.05208 67716 54	0.05204 36063 52	0.99864 48132 53	0.99886 91350 87
3	0.07813 01574 82	0.07798 46543 46	0.99695 45594 89	0.99745 90229 09
4	0.10417 35433 09	0.10382 92417 30	0.99459 51380 14	0.99549 13154 84
5	0.13021 69291 36	0.12954 59526 39	0.99157 34194 48	0.99297 24047 97
6	0.15626 03149 63	0.15510 39935 75	0.98789 81481 80	0.98991 04276 86
7	0.18230 37007 90	0.18047 33368 02	0.98357 98771 34	0.98631 52063 23
8	0.20834 70866 18	0.20562 48559 29	0.97863 08898 78	0.98219 81771 62
9	0.23439 04724 45	0.23053 04524 25	0.97306 51111 33	0.97757 23093 08
10	0.26043 38582 72	0.25516 31719 73	0.96689 80068 59	0.97245 20133 82
11	0.28647 72440 99	0.27949 73097 13	0.96014 64752 12	0.96685 30420 63
12	0.31252 06299 26	0.30350 85036 45	0.95282 87297 39	0.96079 23835 59
13	0.33856 40157 53	0.32717 38156 03	0.94496 41762 44	0.95428 81493 21
14	0.36460 74015 81	0.35047 17994 40	0.93657 32847 98	0.94735 94573 24
15	0.39065 07874 08	0.37338 25562 25	0.92767 74583 37	0.94002 63122 67
16	0.41669 41732 35	0.39588 77764 31	0.91829 88993 09	0.93230 94840 02
17	0.44273 75590 62	0.41797 07692 96	0.90846 04757 58	0.92423 03854 65
18	0.46878 09448 89	0.43961 64796 50	0.89818 55881 84	0.91581 09513 40
19	0.49482 43307 17	0.46081 14926 88	0.88749 80384 24	0.90707 35185 86
20	0.52086 77165 44	0.48154 40272 73	0.87642 19017 10	0.89804 07098 80
21	0.54691 11023 71	0.50180 39184 61	0.86498 14029 32	0.88873 53209 31
22	0.57295 44881 98	0.52158 25900 41	0.85320 07980 34	0.87918 02124 98
23	0.59899 78740 25	0.54087 30179 55	0.84110 42613 43	0.86939 82078 35
24	0.62504 12598 53	0.55966 96854 90	0.82871 57794 70	0.85941 19961 80
25	0.65108 46456 80	0.57796 85312 12	0.81605 90523 54	0.84924 40427 67
26	0.67712 80315 07	0.59576 68905 67	0.80315 74018 23	0.83891 65057 43
27	0.70317 14173 34	0.61306 34321 50	0.79003 36879 91	0.82845 11602 45
28	0.72921 48031 61	0.62985 80895 42	0.77671 02336 39	0.81786 93298 00
29	0.75525 81889 88	0.64615 19896 71	0.76320 87566 61	0.80719 18251 09
30	0.78130 15748 16	0.66194 73785 55	0.74955 03105 36	0.79643 88901 79
31	0.80734 49606 43	0.67724 75452 51	0.73575 52327 05	0.78563 01556 92
32	0.83338 83464 70	0.69205 67448 15	0.72184 31006 50	0.77478 45994 41
33	0.85943 17322 97	0.70638 01209 61	0.70783 26954 24	0.76392 05135 72
34	0.88547 51181 24	0.72022 36290 80	0.69374 19722 89	0.75305 54783 50
35	0.91151 85039 52	0.73359 39602 12	0.67958 80381 09	0.74220 63421 12
36	0.93756 18897 79	0.74649 84664 80	0.66538 71350 90	0.73138 92070 24
37	0.96360 52756 06	0.75894 50884 41	0.65115 46304 30	0.72061 94202 74
38	0.98964 86614 33	0.77094 22847 38	0.63690 50114 45	0.70991 15702 58
39	1.01569 20472 60	0.78249 89643 76	0.62265 18856 88	0.69927 94873 67
40	1.04173 54330 88	0.79362 44218 90	0.60840 79856 31	0.68873 62489 39
41	1.06777 88189 15	0.80432 82756 03	0.59418 51774 21	0.67829 41879 59
42	1.09382 22047 42	0.81462 04091 26	0.57999 44732 80	0.66796 49050 98
43	1.11986 55905 69	0.82451 09162 23	0.56584 60471 10	0.65775 92836 84
44	1.14590 89763 96	0.83401 00490 77	0.55174 92528 66	0.64768 75072 37
45	1.17195 23622 23	0.84312 81700 02	0.53771 26453 31	0.63775 90791 79

q = 0.11062 35386 78854 3   D(90) = 1.56799 02217 72521
q' = 0.01130 08432 78049 37   1/D(90) = 0.63775 90791 79434

r	φ	E(φ,k)	A(r)	D(r)
0	0.00000 00000 00	0.00000 00000 00	0.00000 00000 00	1.00000 00000 00
1	0.02604 09292 51	0.02603 84730 92	0.01660 88193 94	1.00017 20656 49
2	0.05206 71287 05	0.05204 74990 87	0.03321 41199 38	1.00068 80563 82
3	0.07806 39167 85	0.07799 77771 21	0.04981 23796 39	1.00154 73537 91
4	0.10401 67079 91	0.10386 02972 64	0.06640 00702 25	1.00274 89279 77
5	0.12991 10600 47	0.12960 64821 79	0.08297 36540 42	1.00429 13387 25
6	0.15573 27199 81	0.15520 83242 92	0.09952 95809 82	1.00617 27371 38
7	0.18146 76688 23	0.18063 85170 93	0.11606 42854 63	1.00839 08677 47
8	0.20710 21645 88	0.20587 05793 10	0.13257 41834 71	1.01094 30710 76
9	0.23262 27832 84	0.23087 89708 00	0.14905 56696 74	1.01382 62866 75
10	0.25801 64576 56	0.25563 91991 59	0.16550 51146 21	1.01703 70566 11
11	0.28327 05134 50	0.28012 79161 99	0.18191 88620 44	1.02057 15294 12
12	0.30837 27029 90	0.30432 30035 98	0.19829 32262 57	1.02442 54644 64
13	0.33331 12359 10	0.32820 36472 23	0.21462 44896 86	1.02859 42368 61
14	0.35807 48068 88	0.35175 03997 64	0.23090 89005 18	1.03307 28426 97
15	0.38265 26203 08	0.37494 52315 12	0.24714 26704 98	1.03785 59047 92
16	0.40703 44117 74	0.39777 15692 75	0.26332 19728 72	1.04293 76788 60
17	0.43121 04664 47	0.42021 43235 73	0.27944 29404 85	1.04831 20601 04
18	0.45517 16342 05	0.44225 99044 07	0.29550 16640 60	1.05397 25902 28
19	0.47890 93416 78	0.46389 62260 16	0.31149 41906 36	1.05991 24648 73
20	0.50241 56011 95	0.48511 27011 81	0.32741 65222 07	1.06612 45414 55
21	0.52568 30167 47	0.50590 02256 89	0.34326 46145 39	1.07260 13474 11
22	0.54870 47870 81	0.52625 11537 03	0.35903 43761 97	1.07933 50888 35
23	0.57147 47060 42	0.54615 92647 99	0.37472 16677 71	1.08631 76595 00
24	0.59398 71603 27	0.56561 97235 25	0.39032 23013 14	1.09354 06502 57
25	0.61623 71248 10	0.58462 90323 30	0.40583 20399 98	1.10099 53588 05
26	0.63822 01556 07	0.60318 49787 48	0.42124 65979 90	1.10867 27998 16
27	0.65993 23810 79	0.62128 65777 09	0.43656 16405 49	1.11656 37154 09
28	0.68137 04909 45	0.63893 40098 47	0.45177 27843 60	1.12465 85859 61
29	0.70253 17237 08	0.65612 85566 46	0.46687 55980 88	1.13294 76412 48
30	0.72341 38525 79	0.67287 25332 10	0.48186 56031 72	1.14142 08719 00
31	0.74401 51701 03	0.68916 92194 50	0.49673 82748 50	1.15006 80411 56
32	0.76433 44716 48	0.70502 27903 63	0.51148 90434 20	1.15887 86969 20
33	0.78437 10379 64	0.72043 82460 92	0.52611 32957 34	1.16784 21840 83
34	0.80412 46169 71	0.73542 13423 31	0.54060 63769 28	1.17694 76571 25
35	0.82359 54049 45	0.74997 85216 46	0.55496 35923 81	1.18618 40929 58
36	0.84278 40272 58	0.76411 68461 56	0.56918 02099 08	1.19554 03040 15
37	0.86169 15188 18	0.77784 39320 13	0.58325 14621 80	1.20500 49515 59
38	0.88031 93043 51	0.79116 78860 14	0.59717 25493 67	1.21456 65592 03
39	0.89866 91786 35	0.80409 72446 62	0.61093 86420 02	1.22421 35266 23
40	0.91674 32868 18	0.81664 09159 01	0.62454 48840 61	1.23393 41434 75
41	0.93454 41049 10	0.82880 81237 29	0.63798 63962 56	1.24371 66034 02
42	0.95207 44205 50	0.84060 83558 19	0.65125 82795 23	1.25354 90182 93
43	0.96933 73141 19	0.85205 13142 55	0.66435 56187 22	1.26341 94325 87
44	0.98633 61402 85	0.86314 68694 46	0.67727 34865 16	1.27331 58377 39
45	1.00307 45100 28	0.87390 50172 24	0.69000 69474 39	1.28322 61867 57

K = 2.34390 47244 46913   E = 1.15454 66775 24465
K′= 1.64260 41437 12491   E′= 1.50366 21353 53715

r	u=(r/90)K=F(ϕ,k)	sn u	cn u	dn u
45	1.17195 23622 23	0.84312 81700 02	0.53771 26453 31	0.63775 90791 79
46	1.19799 57480 51	0.85187 57065 74	0.52374 40028 76	0.62798 28443 99
47	1.22403 91338 78	0.86026 31101 47	0.50985 03518 88	0.61836 70123 18
48	1.25008 25197 05	0.86830 08176 84	0.49603 79925 06	0.60891 91811 90
49	1.27612 59055 32	0.87599 92168 12	0.48231 25253 86	0.59964 63633 27
50	1.30216 92913 59	0.88336 86139 91	0.46867 88792 08	0.59055 50110 11
51	1.32821 26771 87	0.89041 92056 77	0.45514 13386 64	0.58165 10428 57
52	1.35425 60630 14	0.89716 10523 45	0.44170 35727 22	0.57293 98704 24
53	1.38029 94488 41	0.90360 40552 21	0.42836 86629 40	0.56442 64248 68
54	1.40634 28346 68	0.90975 79355 83	0.41513 91316 71	0.55611 51835 02
55	1.43238 62204 95	0.91563 22164 75	0.40201 69699 82	0.54801 01960 85
56	1.45842 96063 23	0.92123 62066 72	0.38900 36651 71	0.54011 51107 31
57	1.48447 29921 50	0.92657 89867 51	0.37610 02277 47	0.53243 31993 31
58	1.51051 63779 77	0.93166 93971 08	0.36330 72177 83	0.52496 73823 78
59	1.53655 97638 04	0.93651 60277 69	0.35062 47705 62	0.51772 02531 35
60	1.56260 31496 31	0.94112 72098 57	0.33805 26214 45	0.51069 41010 68
61	1.58864 65354 58	0.94551 10085 60	0.32559 01299 05	0.50389 09345 01
62	1.61468 99212 86	0.94967 52174 69	0.31323 63026 95	0.49731 25024 45
63	1.64073 33071 13	0.95362 73541 55	0.30098 98161 18	0.49096 03155 79
64	1.66677 66929 40	0.95737 46568 64	0.28884 90373 79	0.48483 56663 52
65	1.69282 00787 67	0.96092 40821 93	0.27681 20450 07	0.47893 96481 96
66	1.71886 34645 94	0.96428 23036 61	0.26487 66483 59	0.47327 31738 49
67	1.74490 68504 22	0.96745 57110 45	0.25304 04061 92	0.46783 69927 73
68	1.77095 02362 49	0.97045 04104 00	0.24130 06443 32	0.46263 17076 91
69	1.79699 36220 76	0.97327 22246 54	0.22965 44724 51	0.45765 77902 29
70	1.82303 70079 03	0.97592 66947 13	0.21809 87999 67	0.45291 55956 98
71	1.84908 03937 30	0.97841 90809 67	0.20663 03511 09	0.44840 53770 09
72	1.87512 37795 58	0.98075 43651 55	0.19524 56791 57	0.44412 72977 58
73	1.90116 71653 85	0.98293 72524 91	0.18394 11799 06	0.44008 14444 89
74	1.92721 05512 12	0.98497 21740 12	0.17271 31043 75	0.43626 78381 54
75	1.95325 39370 39	0.98686 32890 71	0.16155 75708 04	0.43268 64448 03
76	1.97929 73228 66	0.98861 44879 41	0.15047 05759 73	0.42933 71855 12
77	2.00534 07086 93	0.99022 93944 61	0.13944 80058 83	0.42621 99455 85
78	2.03138 40945 21	0.99171 13687 02	0.12848 56458 38	0.42333 45830 33
79	2.05742 74803 48	0.99306 35095 94	0.11757 91899 66	0.42068 09363 79
80	2.08347 08661 75	0.99428 86574 91	0.10672 42502 22	0.41825 88317 77
81	2.10951 42520 02	0.99538 93966 39	0.09591 63649 11	0.41606 80894 94
82	2.13555 76378 29	0.99636 80557 20	0.08515 10067 70	0.41410 85297 58
83	2.16160 10236 57	0.99722 67190 33	0.07442 35906 58	0.41237 99779 91
84	2.18764 44094 84	0.99796 72105 17	0.06372 94808 80	0.41088 22694 46
85	2.21368 77953 11	0.99859 11135 67	0.05306 39982 00	0.40961 52532 65
86	2.23973 11811 38	0.99909 97636 49	0.04242 24265 72	0.40857 87959 67
87	2.26577 45669 65	0.99949 42514 85	0.03180 00196 41	0.40777 27843 79
88	2.29181 79527 93	0.99977 54242 02	0.02119 20070 38	0.40719 71280 21
89	2.31786 13386 20	0.99994 38862 40	0.01059 36005 21	0.40685 17609 49
90	2.34390 47244 47	1.00000 00000 00	0.00000 00000 00	0.40673 66430 76

q = 0.11062 35386 78854 3   D(90) = 1.56799 02217 72521
q′ = 0.01130 08432 78049 37   1/D(90) = 0.63775 90791 79434

r	φ	E(φ,k)	A(r)	D(r)
45	1.00307 45100 28	0.87390 50172 24	0.69000 69474 39	1.28322 61867 57
46	1.01955 62732 06	0.88433 58391 40	0.70255 10621 35	1.29313 84088 35
47	1.03578 55017 00	0.89444 94659 04	0.71490 08917 71	1.30304 04240 42
48	1.05176 64731 83	0.90425 60439 17	0.72705 15025 96	1.31292 01580 58
49	1.06750 36555 22	0.91376 57048 26	0.73899 79706 53	1.32276 55569 27
50	1.08300 16918 63	0.92298 85379 79	0.75073 53866 32	1.33256 46018 37
51	1.09826 53863 82	0.93193 45657 00	0.76225 88608 39	1.34230 53238 69
52	1.11329 96907 38	0.94061 37212 52	0.77356 35282 89	1.35197 58187 31
53	1.12810 96912 09	0.94903 58293 49	0.78464 45538 99	1.36156 42614 40
54	1.14270 05965 30	0.95721 05891 11	0.79549 71377 73	1.37105 89209 39
55	1.15707 77264 19	0.96514 75592 98	0.80611 65205 70	1.38044 81746 28
56	1.17124 65007 74	0.97285 61457 03	0.81649 79889 35	1.38972 05227 88
57	1.18521 24295 50	0.98034 55905 63	0.82663 68809 90	1.39886 46028 90
58	1.19898 11032 87	0.98762 49638 44	0.83652 85918 62	1.40786 92037 59
59	1.21255 81842 66	0.99470 31562 80	0.84616 85792 47	1.41672 32795 70
60	1.22594 93983 05	1.00158 88740 20	0.85555 23689 85	1.42541 59636 78
61	1.23916 05271 35	1.00829 06347 73	0.86467 55606 39	1.43393 65822 42
62	1.25219 74013 67	1.01481 67653 21	0.87353 38330 65	1.44227 46676 33
63	1.26506 58940 17	1.02117 54002 89	0.88212 29499 61	1.45041 99716 10
64	1.27777 19145 57	1.02737 44820 56	0.89043 87653 73	1.45836 24782 43
65	1.29032 14034 88	1.03342 17617 14	0.89847 72291 53	1.46609 24165 64
66	1.30272 03273 96	1.03932 48009 73	0.90623 43923 60	1.47360 02729 28
67	1.31497 46744 73	1.04509 09749 13	0.91370 64125 77	1.48087 68030 78
68	1.32709 04504 85	1.05072 74755 15	0.92088 95591 41	1.48791 30438 72
69	1.33907 36751 57	1.05624 13158 76	0.92778 02182 70	1.49470 03246 89
70	1.35093 03789 47	1.06163 93350 44	0.93437 48980 82	1.50123 02784 62
71	1.36266 66002 07	1.06692 82034 04	0.94067 02334 76	1.50749 48523 53
72	1.37428 83826 83	1.07211 44285 48	0.94666 29908 83	1.51348 63180 38
73	1.38580 17733 53	1.07720 43615 87	0.95235 00728 65	1.51919 72815 88
74	1.39721 28205 72	1.08220 42038 34	0.95772 85225 45	1.52462 06929 35
75	1.40852 75725 03	1.08712 00138 26	0.96279 55278 77	1.52974 98549 16
76	1.41975 20758 17	1.09195 77146 37	0.96754 84257 20	1.53457 84318 62
77	1.43089 23746 45	1.09672 31014 45	0.97198 47057 25	1.53910 04577 46
78	1.44195 45097 60	1.10142 18493 24	0.97610 20140 17	1.54331 03438 48
79	1.45294 45179 64	1.10605 95212 14	0.97989 81566 67	1.54720 28859 61
80	1.46386 84316 80	1.11064 15760 71	0.98337 11029 40	1.55077 32710 88
81	1.47473 22787 13	1.11517 33771 38	0.98651 89883 13	1.55401 70836 56
82	1.48554 20821 74	1.11966 02003 46	0.98934 01172 63	1.55693 03112 12
83	1.49630 38605 50	1.12410 72428 12	0.99183 29658 02	1.55950 93496 06
84	1.50702 36278 99	1.12851 96314 17	0.99399 61837 68	1.56175 10076 51
85	1.51770 73941 60	1.13290 24314 52	0.99582 85968 61	1.56365 25112 49
86	1.52836 11655 67	1.13726 06553 29	0.99732 92084 15	1.56521 15069 79
87	1.53899 09451 31	1.14159 92713 26	0.99849 72009 06	1.56642 60651 45
88	1.54960 27332 10	1.14592 32123 74	0.99933 19371 90	1.56729 46822 74
89	1.56020 25281 20	1.15023 73848 73	0.99983 29614 73	1.56781 62830 63
90	1.57079 63267 95	1.15454 66775 24	1.00000 00000 00	1.56799 02217 73

K = 2.38087 01906 04429   E = 1.14534 78566 80849
K'= 1.63651 74093 35819   E'= 1.50900 71479 16775

r	u=(r/90)K=F(φ,k)	sn u	cn u	dn u
0	0.00000 00000 00	0.00000 00000 00	1.00000 00000 00	1.00000 00000 00
1	0.02645 41132 29	0.02644 84147 24	0.99965 01794 92	0.99970 35947 92
2	0.05290 82264 58	0.05286 26735 58	0.99860 17913 78	0.99881 53836 29
3	0.07936 23396 87	0.07920 87959 22	0.99685 80473 91	0.99733 83720 85
4	0.10581 64529 16	0.10545 31499 28	0.99442 42722 15	0.99527 75435 20
5	0.13227 05661 45	0.13156 26219 85	0.99130 78616 13	0.99263 98205 88
6	0.15872 46793 74	0.15750 47807 82	0.98751 82246 58	0.98943 40121 24
7	0.18517 87926 03	0.18324 80339 75	0.98306 67108 82	0.98567 07461 80
8	0.21163 29058 32	0.20876 17759 83	0.97796 65233 99	0.98136 23901 56
9	0.23808 70190 60	0.23401 65254 91	0.97223 26191 80	0.97652 29591 35
10	0.26454 11322 89	0.25898 40514 24	0.96588 15978 72	0.97116 80136 84
11	0.29099 52455 18	0.28363 74863 64	0.95893 15806 30	0.96531 45484 89
12	0.31744 93587 47	0.30795 14265 75	0.95140 20805 48	0.95898 08732 73
13	0.34390 34719 76	0.33190 20180 46	0.94331 38663 33	0.95218 64875 14
14	0.37035 75852 05	0.35546 70281 50	0.93468 88208 91	0.94495 19504 94
15	0.39681 16984 34	0.37862 59027 54	0.92554 97964 80	0.93729 87482 26
16	0.42326 58116 63	0.40135 98088 23	0.91592 04680 87	0.92924 91587 42
17	0.44971 99248 92	0.42365 16627 29	0.90582 51865 94	0.92082 61172 21
18	0.47617 40381 21	0.44548 61446 94	0.89528 88332 19	0.91205 30823 13
19	0.50262 81513 50	0.46684 96999 37	0.88433 66766 50	0.90295 39049 54
20	0.52908 22645 79	0.48773 05272 33	0.87299 42341 19	0.89355 27008 25
21	0.55553 63778 08	0.50811 85557 17	0.86128 71375 66	0.88387 37275 33
22	0.58199 04910 37	0.52800 54108 74	0.84924 10058 92	0.87394 12673 98
23	0.60844 46042 66	0.54738 43707 10	0.83688 13241 45	0.86377 95166 54
24	0.63489 87174 95	0.56625 03131 57	0.82423 33303 44	0.85341 24816 95
25	0.66135 28307 23	0.58459 96558 13	0.81132 19104 79	0.84286 38828 76
26	0.68780 69439 52	0.60243 02890 92	0.79817 15021 12	0.83215 70662 33
27	0.71426 10571 81	0.61974 15038 97	0.78480 60068 24	0.82131 49233 89
28	0.74071 51704 10	0.63653 39148 55	0.77124 87116 61	0.81035 98197 48
29	0.76716 92836 39	0.65280 93801 58	0.75752 22195 93	0.79931 35310 10
30	0.79362 33968 68	0.66857 09189 82	0.74364 83888 85	0.78819 71879 08
31	0.82007 75100 97	0.68382 26273 90	0.72964 82812 08	0.77703 12290 16
32	0.84653 16233 26	0.69856 95935 77	0.71554 21182 08	0.76583 53613 55
33	0.87298 57365 55	0.71281 78132 32	0.70134 92461 95	0.75462 85284 94
34	0.89943 98497 84	0.72657 41057 08	0.68708 81085 53	0.74342 88857 84
35	0.92589 39630 13	0.73984 60316 26	0.67277 62254 17	0.73225 37822 97
36	0.95234 80762 42	0.75264 18124 58	0.65843 01801 55	0.72111 97490 39
37	0.97880 21894 71	0.76497 02525 50	0.64406 56121 19	0.71004 24929 71
38	1.00525 63027 00	0.77684 06639 76	0.62969 72151 70	0.69903 68963 49
39	1.03171 04159 29	0.78826 27945 53	0.61533 87414 45	0.68811 70209 07
40	1.05816 45291 58	0.79924 67592 53	0.60100 30098 29	0.67729 61164 01
41	1.08461 86423 86	0.80980 29752 20	0.58670 19186 30	0.66658 66330 26
42	1.11107 27556 15	0.81994 21005 18	0.57244 64619 49	0.65600 02372 57
43	1.13752 68688 44	0.82967 49766 86	0.55824 67492 62	0.64554 78306 62
44	1.16398 09820 73	0.83901 25751 48	0.54411 20277 51	0.63523 95712 59
45	1.19043 50953 02	0.84796 59474 65	0.53005 07069 52	0.62508 48970 25

266

q = 0.11539 33684 49986 6   D(90) = 1.59978 26931 32868
q'= 0.01035 26461 44729 26   1/D(90) = 0.62508 48970 25415

r	ϕ	$E(\phi,k)$	A(r)	D(r)
0	0.00000 00000 00	0.00000 00000 00	0.00000 00000 00	1.00000 00000 00
1	0.02645 14992 21	0.02644 88856 78	0.01653 55062 90	1.00018 15632 81
2	0.05288 73250 28	0.05286 64384 57	0.03306 76497 44	1.00072 60360 19
3	0.07929 18570 82	0.07922 14870 85	0.04959 30639 71	1.00163 27671 38
4	0.10564 95807 82	0.10548 31818 43	0.06610 83754 79	1.00290 06723 29
5	0.13194 51391 12	0.13162 11509 36	0.08261 02001 59	1.00452 82352 70
6	0.15816 33832 66	0.15760 56517 33	0.09909 51398 10	1.00651 35093 33
7	0.18428 94216 97	0.18340 77152 72	0.11555 97787 20	1.00885 41197 83
8	0.21030 86672 08	0.20899 92826 02	0.13200 06803 06	1.01154 72664 52
9	0.23620 68817 79	0.23435 33316 45	0.14841 43838 46	1.01458 97269 05
10	0.26197 02188 24	0.25944 39934 52	0.16479 74012 93	1.01797 78600 74
11	0.28758 52626 23	0.28424 66569 07	0.18114 62142 02	1.02170 76103 78
12	0.31303 90646 99	0.30873 80611 14	0.19745 72707 70	1.02577 45123 12
13	0.33831 91769 60	0.33289 63749 12	0.21372 69830 10	1.03017 36955 03
14	0.36341 36814 67	0.35670 12631 64	0.22995 17240 63	1.03489 98902 30
15	0.38831 12167 10	0.38013 39396 67	0.24612 78256 62	1.03994 74334 11
16	0.41300 10003 47	0.40317 72067 02	0.26225 15757 61	1.04531 02750 36
17	0.43747 28483 69	0.42581 54814 57	0.27831 92163 39	1.05098 19850 52
18	0.46171 71907 15	0.44803 48096 86	0.29432 69413 81	1.05695 57606 96
19	0.48572 50833 75	0.46982 28671 42	0.31027 08950 59	1.06322 44342 55
20	0.50948 82170 74	0.49116 89494 38	0.32614 71701 06	1.06978 04812 64
21	0.53299 89226 37	0.51206 39511 03	0.34195 18064 09	1.07661 60291 21
22	0.55625 01731 80	0.53250 03347 00	0.35768 07898 08	1.08372 28661 23
23	0.57923 55832 86	0.55247 20909 15	0.37333 00511 28	1.09109 24508 98
24	0.60194 94053 37	0.57197 46906 06	0.38889 54654 35	1.09871 59222 44
25	0.62438 65232 03	0.59100 50298 02	0.40437 28515 33	1.10658 41093 53
26	0.64654 24434 88	0.60956 13686 72	0.41975 79716 95	1.11468 75424 11
27	0.66841 32845 55	0.62764 32654 55	0.43504 65316 46	1.12301 64635 70
28	0.68999 57635 29	0.64525 15063 42	0.45023 41807 90	1.13156 08382 76
29	0.71128 71815 27	0.66238 80322 54	0.46531 65126 91	1.14031 03669 44
30	0.73228 54073 01	0.67905 58634 10	0.48028 90658 10	1.14925 44969 69
31	0.75298 88595 39	0.69525 90225 32	0.49514 73244 87	1.15838 24350 61
32	0.77339 64880 18	0.71100 24574 75	0.50988 67201 96	1.16768 31598 87
33	0.79350 77538 08	0.72629 19639 85	0.52450 26330 42	1.17714 54350 14
34	0.81332 26087 36	0.74113 41092 42	0.53899 03935 16	1.18675 78221 38
35	0.83284 14742 81	0.75553 61567 49	0.55334 52845 13	1.19650 86945 78
36	0.85206 52200 75	0.76950 59930 86	0.56756 25435 87	1.20638 62510 31
37	0.87099 51421 72	0.78305 20569 36	0.58163 73654 71	1.21637 85295 67
38	0.88963 29412 25	0.79618 32707 69	0.59556 49048 27	1.22647 34218 50
39	0.90798 07007 18	0.80890 89754 59	0.60934 02792 50	1.23665 86875 70
40	0.92604 08653 61	0.82123 88680 92	0.62295 85724 98	1.24692 19690 70
41	0.94381 62197 70	0.83318 29431 24	0.63641 48379 58	1.25725 08061 50
42	0.96130 98675 11	0.84475 14370 19	0.64970 41023 35	1.26763 26510 33
43	0.97852 52106 19	0.85595 47764 55	0.66282 13695 55	1.27805 48834 79
44	0.99546 59296 32	0.86680 35301 19	0.67576 16248 80	1.28850 48260 16
45	1.01213 59642 34	0.87730 83640 96	0.68851 98392 22	1.29896 97592 92

K = 2.38087 01906 04429   E = 1.14534 78566 80849
K'= 1.63651 74093 35819   E'= 1.50900 71479 16775

r	u=(r/90)K=F(ϕ,k)	sn u	cn u	dn u
45	1.19043 50953 02	0.84796 59474 65	0.53005 07069 52	0.62508 48970 25
46	1.21688 92085 31	0.85654 61793 77	0.51607 03853 11	0.61509 25511 69
47	1.24334 33217 60	0.86476 43485 84	0.50217 78782 64	0.60527 06088 23
48	1.26979 74349 89	0.87263 14861 45	0.48837 92475 00	0.59562 65048 36
49	1.29625 15482 18	0.88015 85413 84	0.47467 98310 75	0.58616 70623 60
50	1.32270 56614 47	0.88735 63501 63	0.46108 42741 04	0.57689 85219 72
51	1.34915 97746 76	0.89423 56063 71	0.44759 65597 48	0.56782 65710 89
52	1.37561 38879 05	0.90080 68364 62	0.43422 00402 83	0.55895 63734 48
53	1.40206 80011 34	0.90708 03768 71	0.42095 74680 37	0.55029 25984 81
54	1.42852 21143 63	0.91306 63541 42	0.40781 10260 08	0.54183 94503 96
55	1.45497 62275 92	0.91877 46675 84	0.39478 23580 22	0.53360 06968 29
56	1.48143 03408 21	0.92421 49742 78	0.38187 25982 85	0.52557 96969 43
57	1.50788 44540 49	0.92939 66762 62	0.36908 24002 20	0.51777 94288 65
58	1.53433 85672 78	0.93432 89097 31	0.35641 19645 03	0.51020 25163 71
59	1.56079 26805 07	0.93902 05360 62	0.34386 10662 08	0.50285 12547 48
60	1.58724 67937 36	0.94348 01345 32	0.33142 90810 18	0.49572 76357 79
61	1.61370 09069 65	0.94771 59965 45	0.31911 50104 46	0.48883 33718 01
62	1.64015 50201 94	0.95173 61212 47	0.30691 75060 41	0.48216 99188 03
63	1.66660 91334 23	0.95554 82123 54	0.29483 48925 53	0.47573 84985 50
64	1.69306 32466 52	0.95915 96761 00	0.28286 51900 52	0.46954 01197 01
65	1.71951 73598 81	0.96257 76201 39	0.27100 61350 01	0.46357 55979 44
66	1.74597 14731 10	0.96580 88533 07	0.25925 52002 84	0.45784 55751 12
67	1.77242 55863 39	0.96885 98861 28	0.24760 96142 14	0.45235 05373 26
68	1.79887 96995 68	0.97173 69319 57	0.23606 63785 26	0.44709 08321 48
69	1.82533 38127 97	0.97444 59086 59	0.22462 22853 98	0.44206 66847 74
70	1.85178 79260 26	0.97699 24407 51	0.21327 39335 11	0.43727 82132 81
71	1.87824 20392 55	0.97938 18619 07	0.20201 77431 99	0.43272 54429 55
72	1.90469 61524 84	0.98161 92177 63	0.19084 99707 07	0.42840 83197 20
73	1.93115 02657 12	0.98370 92689 42	0.17976 67216 09	0.42432 67226 92
74	1.95760 43789 41	0.98565 64942 47	0.16876 39634 18	0.42048 04758 91
75	1.98405 84921 70	0.98746 50939 54	0.15783 75374 32	0.41686 93591 33
76	2.01051 26053 99	0.98913 89931 54	0.14698 31698 61	0.41349 31181 26
77	2.03696 67186 28	0.99068 18451 04	0.13619 64822 64	0.41035 14738 06
78	2.06342 08318 57	0.99209 70345 32	0.12547 30013 70	0.40744 41309 30
79	2.08987 49450 86	0.99338 76808 66	0.11480 81682 83	0.40477 07859 59
80	2.11632 90583 15	0.99455 66413 46	0.10419 73471 61	0.40233 11342 46
81	2.14278 31715 44	0.99560 65139 94	0.09363 58333 77	0.40012 48765 68
82	2.16923 72847 73	0.99653 96404 10	0.08311 88612 21	0.39815 17249 98
83	2.19569 13980 02	0.99735 81083 66	0.07264 16111 93	0.39641 14081 74
84	2.22214 55112 31	0.99806 37541 84	0.06219 92169 09	0.39490 36759 42
85	2.24859 96244 60	0.99865 81648 78	0.05178 67716 86	0.39362 83034 24
86	2.27505 37376 89	0.99914 26800 39	0.04139 93348 31	0.39258 50945 13
87	2.30150 78509 18	0.99951 83934 49	0.03103 19376 88	0.39177 38847 98
88	2.32796 19641 47	0.99978 61544 25	0.02067 95894 75	0.39119 45439 50
89	2.35441 60773 75	0.99994 65688 63	0.01033 72829 56	0.39084 69775 69
90	2.38087 01906 04	1.00000 00000 00	0.00000 00000 00	0.39073 11284 89

q = 0.11539 33684 49986 6   D(90) = 1.59978 26931 32868
q'= 0.01035 26461 44729 26   1/D(90) = 0.62508 48970 25415

r	ϕ	$E(\phi,k)$	A(r)	D(r)
45	1.01213 59642 34	0.87730 83640 96	0.68851 98392 22	1.29896 97592 92
46	1.02853 94945 34	0.88748 00008 11	0.70109 09736 50	1.30943 69375 08
47	1.04468 09230 37	0.89732 91814 67	0.71346 99840 81	1.31989 36039 29
48	1.06056 48573 39	0.90686 66318 82	0.72565 18261 35	1.33032 70064 43
49	1.07619 60935 63	0.91610 30316 17	0.73763 14601 67	1.34072 44131 62
50	1.09157 96005 61	0.92504 89862 79	0.74940 38564 33	1.35107 31280 27
51	1.10672 05048 94	0.93371 50028 56	0.76096 40004 07	1.36136 05064 19
52	1.12162 40765 86	0.94211 14679 31	0.77230 68982 19	1.37157 39707 42
53	1.13629 57156 60	0.95024 86286 37	0.78342 75822 14	1.38170 10259 57
54	1.15074 09394 48	0.95813 65761 85	0.79432 11166 03	1.39172 92750 60
55	1.16496 53706 64	0.96578 52318 11	0.80498 26032 17	1.40164 64344 69
56	1.17897 47262 26	0.97320 43349 83	0.81540 71873 23	1.41144 03493 14
57	1.19277 48068 17	0.98040 34337 05	0.82559 00635 10	1.42109 90085 92
58	1.20637 14871 59	0.98739 18767 80	0.83552 64816 21	1.43061 05601 90
59	1.21977 07069 80	0.99417 88078 69	0.84521 17527 24	1.43996 33257 33
60	1.23297 84626 63	1.00077 31611 99	0.85464 12550 90	1.44914 58152 52
61	1.24600 07995 32	1.00718 36588 04	0.86381 04401 92	1.45814 67416 44
62	1.25884 38047 67	1.01341 88091 40	0.87271 48386 87	1.46695 50349 13
63	1.27151 36009 23	1.01948 69069 64	0.88135 00663 72	1.47555 98561 58
64	1.28401 63400 08	1.02539 60343 62	0.88971 18301 12	1.48395 06113 06
65	1.29635 81981 19	1.03115 40628 05	0.89779 59337 07	1.49211 69645 54
66	1.30854 53705 90	1.03676 86561 35	0.90559 82836 93	1.50004 88515 12
67	1.32058 40676 37	1.04224 72743 88	0.91311 48950 72	1.50773 64920 28
68	1.33248 05104 65	1.04759 71783 57	0.92034 18969 34	1.51517 04026 67
69	1.34424 09278 21	1.05282 54348 21	0.92727 55379 80	1.52234 14088 38
70	1.35587 15529 59	1.05793 89223 61	0.93391 21919 17	1.52924 06565 45
71	1.36737 86209 99	1.06294 43376 85	0.94024 83627 22	1.53585 96237 43
72	1.37876 83666 53	1.06784 82024 23	0.94628 06897 58	1.54219 01312 92
73	1.39004 70222 91	1.07265 68703 03	0.95200 59527 16	1.54822 43534 75
74	1.40122 08163 30	1.07737 65346 87	0.95742 10764 07	1.55395 48280 93
75	1.41229 59719 26	1.08201 32363 96	0.96252 31353 43	1.55937 44660 85
76	1.42327 87059 37	1.08657 28717 97	0.96730 93581 39	1.56447 65606 92
77	1.43417 52281 46	1.09106 12011 11	0.97177 71316 99	1.56925 47961 37
78	1.44499 17407 21	1.09548 38569 11	0.97592 40051 87	1.57370 32557 98
79	1.45573 44378 96	1.09984 63527 71	0.97974 76937 61	1.57781 64298 86
80	1.46640 95058 43	1.10415 40920 56	0.98324 60820 86	1.58158 92225 95
81	1.47702 31227 32	1.10841 23768 23	0.98641 72275 82	1.58501 69587 20
82	1.48758 14589 57	1.11262 64168 10	0.98925 93634 26	1.58809 53897 39
83	1.49809 06775 02	1.11680 13385 00	0.99177 09012 95	1.59082 06993 41
84	1.50855 69344 44	1.12094 21942 54	0.99395 04338 31	1.59318 95083 94
85	1.51898 63795 66	1.12505 39714 86	0.99579 67368 36	1.59519 88793 50
86	1.52938 51570 80	1.12914 16018 81	0.99730 87711 85	1.59684 63200 76
87	1.53975 94064 18	1.13320 99706 38	0.99848 56844 52	1.59812 97871 02
88	1.55011 52631 15	1.13726 39257 50	0.99932 68122 47	1.59904 76882 90
89	1.56045 88597 24	1.14130 82872 82	0.99983 16792 59	1.59959 88849 11
90	1.57079 63267 95	1.14534 78566 81	1.00000 00000 00	1.59978 26931 33

K = 2.41984 16537 39137   E = 1.13624 43646 84239
K'= 1.63072 91016 30788   E'= 1.51414 69174 93342

r	u=(r/90)K=F(ϕ,k)	sn u	cn u	dn u
0	0.00000 00000 00	0.00000 00000 00	1.00000 00000 00	1.00000 00000 00
1	0.02688 71294 86	0.02688 11066 41	0.99963 86377 62	0.99968 93556 40
2	0.05377 42589 72	0.05372 61148 71	0.99855 57093 03	0.99875 85127 40
3	0.08066 13884 58	0.08049 91190 96	0.99675 46798 61	0.99721 07330 21
4	0.10754 85179 44	0.10716 45971 64	0.99424 12932 05	0.99505 14233 89
5	0.13443 56474 30	0.13368 75966 51	0.99102 35246 96	0.99228 80924 71
6	0.16132 27769 16	0.16003 39147 43	0.98711 15165 63	0.98893 02906 74
7	0.18820 99064 02	0.18617 02697 75	0.98251 74963 59	0.98498 95346 72
8	0.21509 70358 88	0.21206 44626 30	0.97725 56797 94	0.98047 92174 26
9	0.24198 41653 74	0.23768 55264 29	0.97134 21593 48	0.97541 45050 43
10	0.26887 12948 60	0.26300 38631 01	0.96479 47802 48	0.96981 22219 38
11	0.29575 84243 46	0.28799 13657 08	0.95763 30055 28	0.96369 07258 96
12	0.32264 55538 32	0.31262 15256 17	0.94987 77719 90	0.95706 97747 13
13	0.34953 26833 18	0.33686 95238 69	0.94155 13389 55	0.94997 03861 85
14	0.37641 98128 04	0.36071 23063 65	0.93267 71317 22	0.94241 46931 96
15	0.40330 69422 90	0.38412 86427 19	0.92327 95816 23	0.93442 57956 86
16	0.43019 40717 76	0.40709 91688 74	0.91338 39645 53	0.92602 76112 09
17	0.45708 12012 62	0.42960 64138 11	0.90301 62397 28	0.91724 47257 40
18	0.48396 83307 48	0.45163 48108 79	0.89220 28903 80	0.90810 22462 93
19	0.51085 54602 34	0.47317 06944 33	0.88097 07679 20	0.89862 56567 66
20	0.53774 25897 20	0.49420 22826 77	0.86934 69409 83	0.88884 06783 52
21	0.56462 97192 06	0.51471 96476 76	0.85735 85506 05	0.87877 31356 43
22	0.59151 68486 92	0.53471 46736 62	0.84503 26726 06	0.86844 88294 39
23	0.61840 39781 78	0.55418 10047 86	0.83239 61880 82	0.85789 34171 08
24	0.64529 11076 64	0.57311 39835 62	0.81947 56627 54	0.84713 23011 54
25	0.67217 82371 50	0.59151 05812 34	0.80629 72356 94	0.83619 05265 37
26	0.69906 53666 36	0.60936 93213 36	0.79288 65178 67	0.82509 26870 81
27	0.72595 24961 22	0.62669 01976 64	0.77926 85006 80	0.81386 28412 07
28	0.75283 96256 08	0.64347 45878 75	0.76546 74746 58	0.80252 44370 60
29	0.77972 67550 94	0.65972 51638 41	0.75150 69581 81	0.79110 02470 00
30	0.80661 38845 80	0.67544 57998 51	0.73740 96361 35	0.77961 23112 96
31	0.83350 10140 66	0.69064 14796 63	0.72319 73081 87	0.76808 18907 72
32	0.86038 81435 52	0.70531 82033 35	0.70889 08463 53	0.75652 94280 89
33	0.88727 52730 38	0.71948 28946 57	0.69451 01614 06	0.74497 45172 37
34	0.91416 24025 24	0.73314 33099 44	0.68007 41776 34	0.73343 58808 10
35	0.94104 95320 10	0.74630 79488 42	0.66560 08154 26	0.72193 13545 36
36	0.96793 66614 96	0.75898 59677 01	0.65110 69810 97	0.71047 78785 62
37	0.99482 37909 82	0.77118 70960 02	0.63660 85633 73	0.69909 14949 17
38	1.02171 09204 68	0.78292 15562 23	0.62212 04359 30	0.68778 73506 22
39	1.04859 80499 54	0.79419 99874 59	0.60765 64653 81	0.67657 97058 69
40	1.07548 51794 40	0.80503 33730 34	0.59322 95241 31	0.66548 19467 26
41	1.10237 23089 26	0.81543 29722 67	0.57885 15075 04	0.65450 66018 34
42	1.12925 94384 12	0.82541 02565 11	0.56453 33545 92	0.64366 53625 67
43	1.15614 65678 98	0.83497 68495 07	0.55028 50722 91	0.63296 91061 73
44	1.18303 36973 84	0.84414 44720 58	0.53611 57620 27	0.62242 79214 12
45	1.20992 08268 70	0.85292 48909 76	0.52203 36486 79	0.61205 11362 75

q = 0.12037 82455 07893 9   D(90) = 1.63385 04100 90843
q'= 0.00944 92999 75082 239   1/D(90) = 0.61205 11362 75321

r	ϕ	$E(\phi,k)$	A(r)	D(r)
0	0.00000 00000 00	0.00000 00000 00	0.00000 00000 00	1.00000 00000 00
1	0.02688 43450 48	0.02688 15611 30	0.01645 57660 87	1.00019 17156 45
2	0.05375 19952 00	0.05372 97480 15	0.03290 83389 77	1.00076 66339 25
3	0.08058 63141 01	0.08051 13654 43	0.04935 45214 69	1.00172 40691 24
4	0.10737 07820 17	0.10719 35742 37	0.06579 11083 65	1.00306 28792 32
5	0.13408 90529 56	0.13374 40642 32	0.08221 48825 14	1.00478 14672 18
6	0.16072 50104 16	0.16013 12213 23	0.09862 26108 92	1.00687 77828 06
7	0.18726 28212 96	0.18632 42867 69	0.11501 10407 46	1.00934 93247 64
8	0.21368 69875 86	0.21229 35071 15	0.13137 68958 10	1.01219 31436 92
9	0.23998 23954 57	0.23801 02732 45	0.14771 68726 05	1.01540 58453 17
10	0.26613 43614 16	0.26344 72472 85	0.16402 76368 49	1.01898 35942 81
11	0.29212 86752 33	0.28857 84763 06	0.18030 58199 71	1.02292 21184 35
12	0.31795 16393 97	0.31337 94919 73	0.19654 80157 59	1.02721 67136 16
13	0.34359 01048 84	0.33782 73955 59	0.21275 07771 49	1.03186 22489 22
14	0.36903 15030 98	0.36190 09279 60	0.22891 06131 71	1.03685 31724 71
15	0.39426 38738 69	0.38558 05245 66	0.24502 39860 52	1.04218 35176 32
16	0.41927 58894 42	0.40884 83551 04	0.26108 73085 02	1.04784 69097 48
17	0.44405 68744 59	0.43168 83487 29	0.27709 69411 94	1.05383 65733 14
18	0.46859 68219 36	0.45408 62048 67	0.29304 91904 34	1.06014 53396 27
19	0.49288 64053 33	0.47602 93904 60	0.30894 03060 44	1.06676 56548 94
20	0.51691 69867 94	0.49750 71244 17	0.32476 64794 70	1.07368 95887 88
21	0.54068 06217 15	0.51851 03502 00	0.34052 38421 06	1.08090 88434 51
22	0.56417 00597 99	0.53903 16975 53	0.35620 84638 69	1.08841 47629 33
23	0.58737 87427 89	0.55906 54344 79	0.37181 63520 03	1.09619 83430 54
24	0.61030 07990 95	0.57860 74105 90	0.38734 34501 46	1.10425 02416 93
25	0.63293 10355 39	0.59765 49929 96	0.40278 56376 46	1.11256 07894 84
26	0.65526 49264 67	0.61620 69958 97	0.41813 87291 45	1.12112 00009 05
27	0.67729 86004 62	0.63426 36050 16	0.43339 84744 25	1.12991 75857 73
28	0.69902 88249 20	0.65182 62979 99	0.44856 05585 31	1.13894 29611 00
29	0.72045 29887 45	0.66889 77618 31	0.46362 06021 64	1.14818 52633 34
30	0.74156 90833 96	0.68548 18082 79	0.47857 41623 52	1.15763 33609 44
31	0.76237 56825 50	0.70158 32882 98	0.49341 67333 99	1.16727 58673 60
32	0.78287 19206 06	0.71720 80062 55	0.50814 37481 18	1.17710 11542 33
33	0.80305 74702 55	0.73236 26347 45	0.52275 05793 38	1.18709 73650 23
34	0.82293 25193 46	0.74705 46306 96	0.53723 25416 90	1.19725 24288 90
35	0.84249 77472 25	0.76129 21533 74	0.55158 48936 77	1.20755 40748 74
36	0.86175 43007 65	0.77508 39848 01	0.56580 28400 09	1.21798 98463 46
37	0.88070 37702 35	0.78843 94530 46	0.57988 15342 16	1.22854 71157 33
38	0.89934 81651 83	0.80136 83587 36	0.59381 60815 33	1.23921 30994 73
39	0.91768 98904 72	0.81388 09050 93	0.60760 15420 36	1.24997 48732 10
40	0.93573 17225 94	0.82598 76317 09	0.62123 29340 50	1.26081 93871 93
41	0.95347 67863 89	0.83769 93522 30	0.63470 52377 96	1.27173 34818 78
42	0.97092 85322 48	0.84902 70960 30	0.64801 33992 94	1.28270 39037 01
43	0.98809 07139 14	0.85998 20539 51	0.66115 23344 98	1.29371 73210 12
44	1.00496 73669 23	0.87057 55280 96	0.67411 69336 55	1.30476 03401 53
45	1.02156 27877 81	0.88081 88856 34	0.68690 20658 95	1.31581 95216 58

K = 2.41984 16537 39137   E = 1.13624 43646 84239
K′= 1.63072 91016 30788   E′= 1.51414 69174 93342

r	u=(r/90)K=F(φ,k)	sn u	cn u	dn u
45	1.20992 08268 70	0.85292 48909 76	0.52203 36486 79	0.61205 11362 75
46	1.23680 79563 56	0.86132 98722 38	0.50804 61112 85	0.60184 73473 46
47	1.26369 50858 42	0.86937 11382 20	0.49415 97151 03	0.59182 44504 55
48	1.29058 22153 28	0.87706 03288 95	0.48038 02446 80	0.58198 96722 76
49	1.31746 93448 14	0.88440 89668 19	0.46671 27375 70	0.57234 96025 34
50	1.34435 64743 00	0.89142 84257 44	0.45316 15184 18	0.56291 02265 79
51	1.37124 36037 86	0.89812 99026 71	0.43973 02331 31	0.55367 69580 38
52	1.39813 07332 72	0.90452 43931 38	0.42642 18829 02	0.54465 46713 56
53	1.42501 78627 57	0.91062 26695 68	0.41323 88578 89	0.53584 77340 09
54	1.45190 49922 43	0.91643 52624 39	0.40018 29703 50	0.52726 00382 35
55	1.47879 21217 29	0.92197 24441 16	0.38725 54871 02	0.51889 50321 41
56	1.50567 92512 15	0.92724 42151 09	0.37445 71611 64	0.51075 57500 49
57	1.53256 63807 01	0.93226 02925 83	0.36178 82624 87	0.50284 48420 02
58	1.55945 35101 87	0.93703 01009 23	0.34924 86076 76	0.49516 46023 37
59	1.58634 06396 73	0.94156 27641 73	0.33683 75886 43	0.48771 69972 58
60	1.61322 77691 59	0.94586 71001 60	0.32455 42001 49	0.48050 36913 71
61	1.64011 48986 45	0.94995 16161 58	0.31239 70661 80	0.47352 60731 32
62	1.66700 20281 31	0.95382 45059 08	0.30036 44651 58	0.46678 52791 98
63	1.69388 91576 17	0.95749 36478 54	0.28845 43539 62	0.46028 22176 53
64	1.72077 62871 03	0.96096 66044 57	0.27666 43907 67	0.45401 75901 22
65	1.74766 34165 89	0.96425 06224 43	0.26499 19567 06	0.44799 19127 61
66	1.77455 05460 75	0.96735 26338 65	0.25343 41763 72	0.44220 55361 43
67	1.80143 76755 61	0.97027 92578 70	0.24198 79371 95	0.43665 86640 55
68	1.82832 48050 47	0.97303 68030 45	0.23064 99076 97	0.43135 13712 23
69	1.85521 19345 33	0.97563 12702 69	0.21941 65546 94	0.42628 36199 95
70	1.88209 90640 19	0.97806 83559 57	0.20828 41594 46	0.42145 52760 01
71	1.90898 61935 05	0.98035 34556 21	0.19724 88328 28	0.41686 61228 35
72	1.93587 33229 91	0.98249 16676 76	0.18630 65295 37	0.41251 58757 68
73	1.96276 04524 77	0.98448 77974 07	0.17545 30614 04	0.40840 41945 44
74	1.98964 75819 63	0.98634 63610 56	0.16468 41098 35	0.40453 06952 86
75	2.01653 47114 49	0.98807 15899 39	0.15399 52374 46	0.40089 49615 32
76	2.04342 18409 35	0.98966 74345 75	0.14338 18989 31	0.39749 65544 58
77	2.07030 89704 21	0.99113 75687 58	0.13283 94512 05	0.39433 50222 95
78	2.09719 60999 07	0.99248 53935 29	0.12236 31628 89	0.39140 99089 88
79	2.12408 32293 93	0.99371 40410 25	0.11194 82231 61	0.38872 07621 18
80	2.15097 03588 79	0.99482 63781 62	0.10158 97500 39	0.38626 71401 14
81	2.17785 74883 65	0.99582 50101 12	0.09128 27981 33	0.38404 86187 97
82	2.20474 46178 51	0.99671 22835 71	0.08102 23659 19	0.38206 47972 52
83	2.23163 17473 37	0.99749 02897 69	0.07080 34025 75	0.38031 53030 87
84	2.25851 88768 23	0.99816 08672 24	0.06062 08144 28	0.37879 97970 62
85	2.28540 60063 09	0.99872 56042 03	0.05046 94710 57	0.37751 79771 46
86	2.31229 31357 95	0.99918 58408 88	0.04034 42110 98	0.37646 95819 84
87	2.33918 02652 81	0.99954 26712 28	0.03023 98477 87	0.37565 43938 12
88	2.36606 73947 67	0.99979 69444 71	0.02015 11742 96	0.37507 22408 24
89	2.39295 45242 53	0.99994 92663 62	0.01007 29688 97	0.37472 29990 02
90	2.41984 16537 39	1.00000 00000 00	0.00000 00000 00	0.37460 65934 16

q = 0.12037 82455 07893 9   D(90) = 1.63385 04100 90843
q'= 0.00944 92999 75082 239   1/D(90) = 0.61205 11362 75321

r	ϕ	$E(\phi,k)$	A(r)	D(r)
45	1.02156 27877 81	0.88081 88856 34	0.68690 20658 95	1.31581 95216 58
46	1.03788 15138 95	0.89072 35165 73	0.69950 25840 24	1.32688 13965 53
47	1.05392 83043 21	0.90030 07953 67	0.71191 33295 17	1.33793 24827 40
48	1.06970 81213 41	0.90956 20462 71	0.72412 91377 04	1.34895 93014 51
49	1.08522 61129 08	0.91851 85122 63	0.73614 48431 29	1.35994 83937 38
50	1.10048 75959 54	0.92718 13274 15	0.74795 52850 80	1.37088 63369 91
51	1.11549 80405 83	0.93556 14925 09	0.75955 53132 70	1.38175 97614 58
52	1.13026 30551 33	0.94366 98537 53	0.77093 97936 54	1.39255 53667 46
53	1.14478 83721 15	0.95151 70843 85	0.78210 36143 83	1.40325 99382 80
54	1.15907 98350 09	0.95911 36690 16	0.79304 16918 61	1.41386 03637 07
55	1.17314 33859 09	0.96646 98904 95	0.80374 89769 07	1.42434 36492 16
56	1.18698 50539 85	0.97359 58191 41	0.81422 04609 98	1.43469 69357 47
57	1.20061 09447 64	0.98050 13041 56	0.82445 11825 87	1.44490 75150 86
58	1.21402 72301 77	0.98719 59670 41	0.83443 62334 67	1.45496 28458 06
59	1.22724 01393 72	0.99368 91968 63	0.84417 07651 86	1.46485 05690 40
60	1.24025 59502 52	0.99999 01471 96	0.85364 99954 71	1.47455 85240 66
61	1.25308 09817 06	1.00610 77346 09	0.86286 92146 76	1.48407 47636 76
62	1.26572 15865 16	1.01205 06385 35	0.87182 37922 12	1.49338 75693 17
63	1.27818 41449 03	.1.01782 73023 98	0.88050 91829 57	1.50248 54659 74
64	1.29047 50586 79	1.02344 59358 74	0.88892 09336 29	1.51135 72367 78
65	1.30260 07459 82	1.02891 45181 59	0.89705 46891 02	1.51999 19373 15
66	1.31456 76365 60	1.03424 08021 45	0.90490 61986 58	1.52837 89096 25
67	1.32638 21675 70	1.03943 23193 98	0.91247 13221 40	1.53650 77958 57
68	1.33805 07798 76	1.04449 63858 38	0.91974 60360 24	1.54436 85515 65
69	1.34957 99148 05	1.04944 01080 56	0.92672 64393 58	1.55195 14586 38
70	1.36097 60113 36	1.05427 03901 70	0.93340 87595 78	1.55924 71378 21
71	1.37224 55037 01	1.05899 39411 54	0.93978 93581 82	1.56624 65608 31
72	1.38339 48193 65	1.06361 72825 93	0.94586 47362 38	1.57294 10620 34
73	1.39443 03773 64	1.06814 67567 76	0.95163 15397 22	1.57932 23496 77
74	1.40535 85869 74	1.07258 85351 10	0.95708 65646 70	1.58538 25166 50
75	1.41618 58466 85	1.07694 86267 78	0.96222 67621 34	1.59111 40507 65
76	1.42691 85434 70	1.08123 28876 23	0.96704 92429 16	1.59650 98445 37
77	1.43756 30523 08	1.08544 70292 13	0.97155 12820 90	1.60156 32044 47
78	1.44812 57359 55	1.08959 66280 53	0.97573 03232 81	1.60626 78596 83
79	1.45861 29449 35	1.09368 71349 24	0.97958 39826 98	1.61061 79703 36
80	1.46903 10177 42	1.09772 38843 21	0.98311 00529 21	1.61460 81350 37
81	1.47938 62812 14	1.10171 21039 71	0.98630 65064 05	1.61823 33980 37
82	1.48968 50510 36	1.10565 69244 12	0.98917 14987 22	1.62148 92557 03
83	1.49993 36326 86	1.10956 33886 30	0.99170 33715 19	1.62437 16624 25
84	1.51013 83217 64	1.11343 64617 17	0.99390 06551 80	1.62687 70359 34
85	1.52030 54054 42	1.11728 10405 74	0.99576 20711 92	1.62900 22620 06
86	1.53043 11632 61	1.12110 19636 26	0.99728 65342 14	1.63074 46985 59
87	1.54055 18683 14	1.12490 40205 47	0.99847 31538 28	1.63210 21791 32
88	1.55064 37884 53	1.12869 19620 08	0.99932 12359 85	1.63307 30157 31
89	1.56072 31875 48	1.13247 05094 20	0.99983 02841 28	1.63365 60010 56
90	1.57079 63267 95	1.13624 43646 84	1.00000 00000 00	1.63385 04100 91

K = 2.46099 94583 04126   E = 1.12724 96377 57702
K′= 1.62523 36677 58843   E′= 1.51907 85300 25531

r	u=(r/90)K=F(φ,k)	sn u	cn u	dn u
0	0.00000 00000 00	0.00000 00000 00	1.00000 00000 00	1.00000 00000 00
1	0.02734 44384 26	0.02733 80625 28	0.99962 62453 22	0.99967 42535 55
2	0.05468 88768 51	0.05463 79123 02	0.99850 62336 01	0.99869 81994 59
3	0.08203 33152 77	0.08186 15491 66	0.99664 37110 46	0.99707 53834 38
4	0.10937 77537 02	0.10897 13956 50	0.99404 48857 72	0.99481 16818 56
5	0.13672 21921 28	0.13593 05020 77	0.99071 83750 21	0.99191 52525 07
6	0.16406 66305 54	0.16270 27443 25	0.98667 51324 47	0.98839 64668 00
7	0.19141 10689 79	0.18925 30120 29	0.98192 83565 71	0.98426 78243 91
8	0.21875 55074 05	0.21554 73852 03	0.97649 33818 17	0.97954 38515 76
9	0.24609 99458 30	0.24155 32974 51	0.97038 75537 59	0.97424 09849 60
10	0.27344 43842 56	0.26723 96842 55	0.96363 00904 18	0.96837 74421 33
11	0.30078 88226 82	0.29257 71150 24	0.95624 19316 07	0.96197 30812 00
12	0.32813 32611 07	0.31753 79079 58	0.94824 55784 29	0.95504 92511 46
13	0.35547 76995 33	0.34209 62270 19	0.93966 49250 98	0.94762 86350 55
14	0.38282 21379 58	0.36622 81606 28	0.93052 50852 95	0.93973 50882 45
15	0.41016 65763 84	0.38991 17819 99	0.92085 22152 11	0.93139 34733 36
16	0.43751 10148 10	0.41312 71912 82	0.91067 33354 08	0.92262 94942 36
17	0.46485 54532 35	0.43585 65399 50	0.90001 61535 12	0.91346 95309 24
18	0.49219 98916 61	0.45808 40381 11	0.88890 88896 10	0.90394 04767 82
19	0.51954 43300 86	0.47979 59455 97	0.87738 01061 05	0.89406 95801 08
20	0.54688 87685 12	0.50098 05479 02	0.86545 85435 62	0.88388 42912 51
21	0.57423 32069 38	0.52162 81181 35	0.85317 29639 24	0.87341 21166 40
22	0.60157 76453 63	0.54173 08662 99	0.84055 20022 57	0.86268 04808 05
23	0.62892 20837 89	0.56128 28772 70	0.82762 40279 76	0.85171 65972 69
24	0.65626 65222 14	0.58028 00388 88	0.81441 70163 18	0.84054 73490 34
25	0.68361 09606 40	0.59871 99616 19	0.80095 84306 06	0.82919 91791 56
26	0.71095 53990 66	0.61660 18911 95	0.78727 51156 84	0.81769 79917 77
27	0.73829 98374 91	0.63392 66156 55	0.77339 32026 88	0.80606 90637 66
28	0.76564 42759 17	0.65069 63681 21	0.75933 80252 00	0.79433 69670 05
29	0.79298 87143 42	0.66691 47265 84	0.74513 40466 42	0.78252 55011 96
30	0.82033 31527 68	0.68258 65119 16	0.73080 47986 64	0.77065 76369 48
31	0.84767 75911 94	0.69771 76851 80	0.71637 28301 57	0.75875 54688 17
32	0.87502 20296 19	0.71231 52452 77	0.70185 96664 19	0.74684 01778 43
33	0.90236 64680 45	0.72638 71277 91	0.68728 57779 55	0.73493 20031 02
34	0.92971 09064 70	0.73994 21058 51	0.67267 05582 89	0.72305 02216 99
35	0.95705 53448 96	0.75298 96936 78	0.65803 23101 60	0.71121 31366 11
36	0.98439 97833 22	0.76554 00534 05	0.64338 82394 26	0.69943 80717 48
37	1.01174 42217 47	0.77760 39056 50	0.62875 44559 83	0.68774 13735 88
38	1.03908 86601 73	0.78919 24442 12	0.61414 59810 17	0.67613 84187 47
39	1.06643 30985 98	0.80031 72552 14	0.59957 67598 95	0.66464 36268 37
40	1.09377 75370 24	0.81099 02408 82	0.58505 96800 28	0.65327 04779 88
41	1.12112 19754 50	0.82122 35481 02	0.57060 65930 59	0.64203 15344 32
42	1.14846 64138 75	0.83102 95018 45	0.55622 83407 58	0.63093 84655 66
43	1.17581 08523 01	0.84042 05434 53	0.54193 47840 31	0.62000 20759 54
44	1.20315 52907 26	0.84940 91737 51	0.52773 48345 03	0.60923 23357 41
45	1.23049 97291 52	0.85800 79009 12	0.51363 64881 62	0.59863 84130 22

q = 0.12559 47852 09818 5   D(90) = 1.67045 74551 97628
q'= 0.00859 01752 53625 654   1/D(90) = 0.59863 84130 21834

r	ϕ	$E(\phi,k)$	A(r)	D(r)
0	0.00000 00000 00	0.00000 00000 00	0.00000 00000 00	1.00000 00000 00
1	0.02734 14689 47	0.02733 85000 49	0.01636 89299 52	1.00020 25945 86
2	0.05466 51339 94	0.05464 14096 85	0.03273 48513 72	1.00081 01374 24
3	0.08195 32559 66	0.08187 33372 07	0.04909 47512 37	1.00182 19060 16
4	0.10918 82246 04	0.10899 92859 98	0.06544 56075 54	1.00323 66970 82
5	0.13635 26216 57	0.13598 48462 42	0.08178 43849 20	1.00505 28278 83
6	0.16342 92823 86	0.16279 63797 92	0.09810 80301 23	1.00726 81380 69
7	0.19040 13549 64	0.18940 11961 14	0.11441 34678 14	1.00987 99920 60
8	0.21725 23573 17	0.21576 77174 21	0.13069 75962 51	1.01288 52819 45
9	0.24396 62309 83	0.24186 56312 95	0.14695 72831 43	1.01628 04309 08
10	0.27052 73916 09	0.26766 60293 75	0.16318 93616 04	1.02006 13971 74
11	0.29692 07757 52	0.29314 15309 00	0.17939 06262 34	1.02422 36784 70
12	0.32313 18837 12	0.31826 63902 02	0.19555 78293 31	1.02876 23170 06
13	0.34914 68181 67	0.34301 65875 15	0.21168 76772 66	1.03367 19049 60
14	0.37495 23184 54	0.36736 99027 21	0.22777 68270 22	1.03894 65904 75
15	0.40053 57903 69	0.39130 59719 62	0.24382 18829 14	1.04458 00841 57
16	0.42588 53314 41	0.41480 63272 85	0.25981 93935 02	1.05056 56660 69
17	0.45098 97516 80	0.43785 44197 16	0.27576 58487 08	1.05689 61932 20
18	0.47583 85898 24	0.46043 56263 98	0.29165 76771 56	1.06356 41075 38
19	0.50042 21252 04	0.48253 72426 09	0.30749 12437 32	1.07056 14443 26
20	0.52473 13853 44	0.50414 84596 35	0.32326 28473 91	1.07787 98411 91
21	0.54875 81494 74	0.52526 03296 08	0.33896 87192 05	1.08551 05474 37
22	0.57249 49481 56	0.54586 57185 23	0.35460 50206 76	1.09344 44339 22
23	0.59593 52592 57	0.56595 92487 18	0.37016 78423 06	1.10167 20033 62
24	0.61907 25005 29	0.58553 72321 53	0.38565 32024 49	1.11018 34010 80
25	0.64190 20190 43	0.60459 75958 16	0.40105 70464 36	1.11896 84261 87
26	0.66441 90777 88	0.62313 98006 13	0.41637 52459 92	1.12801 65431 87
27	0.68661 98397 00	0.64116 47550 36	0.43160 35989 39	1.13731 68939 96
28	0.70850 11494 21	0.65867 47248 78	0.44673 78291 99	1.14685 83103 66
29	0.73006 05130 85	0.67567 32401 81	0.46177 35870 92	1.15662 93266 94
30	0.75129 60763 94	0.69216 50005 42	0.47670 64499 43	1.16661 81932 20
31	0.77220 66012 91	0.70815 57798 03	0.49153 19229 82	1.17681 28895 88
32	0.79279 14414 63	0.72365 23310 66	0.50624 54405 63	1.18720 11387 60
33	0.81305 05169 60	0.73866 22928 69	0.52084 23676 74	1.19777 04212 76
34	0.83298 42881 41	0.75319 40972 70	0.53531 80017 58	1.20850 79898 39
35	0.85259 37291 88	0.76725 68804 68	0.54966 75748 41	1.21940 08842 13
36	0.87188 03013 84	0.78086 03965 13	0.56388 62559 50	1.23043 59464 22
37	0.89084 59263 51	0.79401 49345 57	0.57796 91538 37	1.24159 98362 23
38	0.90949 29594 13	0.80673 12399 96	0.59191 13199 89	1.25287 90468 58
39	0.92782 41632 39	0.81902 04397 89	0.60570 77519 32	1.26425 99210 41
40	0.94584 26819 04	0.83089 39721 63	0.61935 33968 12	1.27572 86671 92
41	0.96355 20154 88	0.84236 35208 14	0.63284 31552 54	1.28727 13758 73
42	0.98095 59953 09	0.85344 09537 01	0.64617 18854 87	1.29887 40364 26
43	0.99805 87598 87	0.86413 82664 23	0.65933 44077 31	1.31052 25537 89
44	1.01486 47317 10	0.87446 75301 61	0.67232 55088 32	1.32220 27654 69
45	1.03137 85948 47	0.88444 08441 06	0.68513 99471 39	1.33390 04586 50

K = 2.46099 94583 04126   E = 1.12724 96377 57702
K'= 1.62523 36677 58843   E'= 1.51907 85300 25531

r	u=(r/90)K=F(ϕ,k)	sn u	cn u	dn u
45	1.23049 97291 52	0.85800 79009 12	0.51363 64881 62	0.59863 84130 22
46	1.25784 41675 78	0.86622 91929 41	0.49964 68605 89	0.58822 87077 05
47	1.28518 86060 03	0.87408 54346 28	0.48577 22233 42	0.57801 08864 86
48	1.31253 30444 29	0.88158 88887 97	0.47201 80411 26	0.56799 19185 52
49	1.33987 74828 54	0.88875 16616 52	0.45838 90093 69	0.55817 81117 07
50	1.36722 19212 80	0.89558 56720 02	0.44488 90919 14	0.54857 51486 11
51	1.39456 63597 06	0.90210 26241 52	0.43152 15585 56	0.53918 81228 91
52	1.42191 07981 31	0.90831 39842 22	0.41828 90221 69	0.53002 15748 86
53	1.44925 52365 57	0.91423 09596 75	0.40519 34752 34	0.52107 95268 52
54	1.47659 96749 82	0.91986 44818 10	0.39223 63255 81	0.51236 55174 36
55	1.50394 41134 08	0.92522 51909 97	0.37941 84312 14	0.50388 26353 14
56	1.53128 85518 34	0.93032 34244 34	0.36674 01340 85	0.49563 35518 48
57	1.55863 29902 59	0.93516 92062 04	0.35420 12927 24	0.48762 05526 94
58	1.58597 74286 85	0.93977 22394 18	0.34180 13136 59	0.47984 55682 72
59	1.61332 18671 10	0.94414 19002 54	0.32953 91815 62	0.47231 02030 54
60	1.64066 63055 36	0.94828 72336 91	0.31741 34880 84	0.46501 57636 34
61	1.66801 07439 62	0.95221 69507 62	0.30542 24593 61	0.45796 32855 39
62	1.69535 51823 87	0.95593 94271 46	.0.29356 39821 71	0.45115 35587 93
63	1.72269 96208 13	0.95946 27029 53	0.28183 56287 65	0.44458 71522 11
64	1.75004 40592 38	0.96279 44835 40	0.27023 46803 53	0.43826 44364 42
65	1.77738 84976 64	0.96594 21412 14	0.25875 81492 97	0.43218 56057 67
66	1.80473 29360 90	0.96891 27177 12	0.24740 28000 18	0.42635 06986 93
67	1.83207 73745 15	0.97171 29273 16	0.23616 51686 57	0.42075 96173 35
68	1.85942 18129 41	0.97434 91605 06	0.22504 15815 37	0.41541 21456 54
69	1.88676 62513 66	0.97682 74880 43	0.21402 81724 51	0.41030 79665 58
70	1.91411 06897 92	0.97915 36653 93	0.20312 08988 45	0.40544 66779 11
71	1.94145 51282 18	0.98133 31374 04	0.19231 55569 20	0.40082 78074 98
72	1.96879 95666 43	0.98337 10431 63	0.18160 77957 27	0.39645 08269 63
73	1.99614 40050 69	0.98527 22209 59	0.17099 31302 91	0.39231 51647 79
74	2.02348 84434 95	0.98704 12132 90	0.16046 69538 16	0.38842 02182 83
75	2.05083 28819 20	0.98868 22718 57	0.15002 45490 43	0.38476 53648 05
76	2.07817 73203 46	0.99019 93624 96	0.13966 10987 84	0.38134 99719 53
77	2.10552 17587 71	0.99159 61699 95	0.12937 16957 14	0.37817 34070 59
78	2.13286 61971 97	0.99287 61027 68	0.11915 13514 53	0.37523 50458 53
79	2.16021 06356 23	0.99404 22973 32	0.10899 50050 00	0.37253 42803 75
80	2.18755 50740 48	0.99509 76225 72	0.09889 75305 67	0.37007 05261 74
81	2.21489 95124 74	0.99604 46837 49	0.08885 37448 64	0.36784 32288 09
82	2.24224 39508 99	0.99688 58262 41	0.07885 84138 84	0.36585 18696 93
83	2.26958 83893 25	0.99762 31389 85	0.06890 62592 37	0.36409 59713 04
84	2.29693 28277 51	0.99825 84576 02	0.05899 19640 83	0.36257 51017 76
85	2.32427 72661 76	0.99879 33671 92	0.04911 01787 04	0.36128 88789 03
86	2.35162 17046 02	0.99922 92047 85	0.03925 55257 75	0.36023 69735 71
87	2.37896 61430 27	0.99956 70614 29	0.02942 26053 60	0.35941 91126 35
88	2.40631 05814 53	0.99980 77839 14	0.01960 59997 00	0.35883 50812 48
89	2.43365 50198 79	0.99995 19761 24	0.00980 02778 19	0.35848 47246 70
90	2.46099 94583 04	1.00000 00000 00	0.00000 00000 00	0.35836 79495 45

q = 0.12559 47852 09818 5
q' = 0.00859 01752 53625 654

D(90) = 1.67045 74551 97628
1/D(90) = 0.59863 84130 21834

r	ϕ	$E(\phi,k)$	A(r)	D(r)
45	1.03137 85948 47	0.88444 08441 06	0.68513 99471 39	1.33390 04586 50
46	1.04760 52734 88	0.89407 02922 53	0.69777 24576 14	1.34560 13874 28
47	1.06354 99114 03	0.90336 79044 35	0.71021 77571 55	1.35729 12901 34
48	1.07921 78523 89	0.91234 56214 30	0.72247 05501 35	1.36895 59067 38
49	1.09461 46216 84	0.92101 52639 48	0.73452 55341 30	1.38058 09963 14
50	1.10974 59083 81	0.92938 85053 26	0.74637 74058 30	1.39215 23545 28
51	1.12461 75488 27	0.93747 68477 06	0.75802 08671 23	1.40365 58311 44
52	1.13923 55110 04	0.94529 16015 02	0.76945 06313 28	1.41507 73475 21
53	1.15360 58798 87	0.95284 38679 27	0.78066 14295 73	1.42640 29140 73
54	1.16773 48437 44	0.96014 45243 94	0.79164 80172 95	1.43761 86476 75
55	1.18162 86813 81	0.96720 42125 53	0.80240 51808 51	1.44871 07889 89
56	1.19529 37502 82	0.97403 33287 81	0.81292 77442 22	1.45966 57196 90
57	1.20873 64756 34	0.98064 20169 15	0.82321 05757 98	1.47046 99795 67
58	1.22196 33401 97	0.98704 01630 46	0.83324 85952 22	1.48111 02834 69
59	1.23498 08749 99	0.99323 73921 80	0.84303 67802 79	1.49157 35380 92
60	1.24779 56508 04	0.99924 30666 02	0.85257 01738 14	1.50184 68585 55
61	1.26041 42703 37	1.00506 62857 76	0.86184 38906 64	1.51191 75847 73
62	1.27284 33612 29	1.01071 58876 26	0.87085 31245 77	1.52177 32975 78
63	1.28508 95696 33	1.01620 04510 56	0.87959 31551 19	1.53140 18345 75
64	1.29715 95544 96	1.02152 82995 68	0.88805 93545 31	1.54079 13057 21
65	1.30905 99824 40	1.02670 75058 70	0.89624 71945 36	1.54993 01085 80
66	1.32079 75232 26	1.03174 58973 34	0.90415 22530 73	1.55880 69432 57
67	1.33237 88457 58	1.03665 10622 31	0.91177 02209 31	1.56741 08269 70
68	1.34381 06146 09	1.04143 03566 11	0.91909 69082 90	1.57573 11082 45
69	1.35509 94870 26	1.04609 09117 80	0.92612 82511 28	1.58375 74807 24
70	1.36625 21103 86	1.05063 96422 54	0.93286 03174 92	1.59147 99965 40
71	1.37727 51200 78	1.05508 32541 57	0.93928 93136 15	1.59888 90792 65
72	1.38817 51377 82	1.05942 82539 66	0.94541 15898 61	1.60597 55363 89
73	1.39895 87701 12	1.06368 09575 76	0.95122 36464 83	1.61273 05713 35
74	1.40963 26076 00	1.06784 74996 09	0.95672 21391 84	1.61914 57949 62
75	1.42020 32240 02	1.07193 38429 36	0.96190 38844 61	1.62521 32365 67
76	1.43067 71758 92	1.07594 57883 77	0.96676 58647 18	1.63092 53543 44
77	1.44106 10025 25	1.07988 89845 28	0.97130 52331 50	1.63627 50453 10
78	1.45136 12259 56	1.08376 89377 05	0.97551 93183 55	1.64125 56546 50
79	1.46158 43513 72	1.08759 10219 69	0.97940 56286 98	1.64586 09845 00
80	1.47173 68676 42	1.09136 04892 12	0.98296 18563 91	1.65008 53021 22
81	1.48182 52480 53	1.09508 24792 89	0.98618 58812 82	1.65392 33474 93
82	1.49185 59512 04	1.09876 20301 82	0.98907 57743 59	1.65737 03402 57
83	1.50183 54220 67	1.10240 40881 88	0.99162 98009 38	1.66042 19860 60
84	1.51177 00931 69	1.10601 35181 04	0.99384 64235 39	1.66307 44822 44
85	1.52166 63859 01	1.10959 51134 34	0.99572 43044 51	1.66532 45228 96
86	1.53153 07119 19	1.11315 36065 83	0.99726 23079 53	1.66716 93032 29
87	1.54136 94746 39	1.11669 36790 50	0.99845 95022 19	1.66860 65233 18
88	1.55118 90708 02	1.12021 99716 22	0.99931 51608 68	1.66963 43911 52
89	1.56099 58920 91	1.12373 70945 56	0.99982 87641 88	1.67025 16250 15
90	1.57079 63267 95	1.12724 96377 58	1.00000 00000 00	1.67045 74551 98

K = 2.50455 00790 01634   E = 1.11837 77379 69864
K'= 1.62002 58991 24204   E'= 1.52379 92052 59774

r	u=(r/90)K=F(φ,k)	sn u	cn u	dn u
0	0.00000 00000 00	0.00000 00000 00	1.00000 00000 00	1.00000 00000 00
1	0.02782 83342 11	0.02782 15727 66	0.99961 29051 23	0.99965 81943 63
2	0.05565 66684 22	0.05560 26239 93	0.99845 29774 63	0.99863 40684 97
3	0.08348 50026 33	0.08330 28671 91	0.99652 42758 30	0.99693 14841 72
4	0.11131 33368 45	0.11088 24830 71	0.99383 35247 66	0.99455 68399 88
5	0.13914 16710 56	0.13830 23459 56	0.99039 00550 30	0.99151 90155 06
6	0.16697 00052 67	0.16552 42417 60	0.98620 57216 37	0.98782 92943 05
7	0.19479 83394 78	0.19251 10749 55	0.98129 48007 71	0.98350 12672 15
8	0.22262 66736 89	0.21922 70622 54	0.97567 38672 20	0.97855 07172 65
9	0.25045 50079 00	0.24563 79109 22	0.96936 16542 44	0.97299 54881 49
10	0.27828 33421 11	0.27171 09800 10	0.96237 88980 14	0.96685 53382 09
11	0.30611 16763 22	0.29741 54230 59	0.95474 81689 57	0.96015 17821 48
12	0.33394 00105 34	0.32272 23112 26	0.94649 36924 44	0.95290 79227 38
13	0.36176 83447 45	0.34760 47361 10	0.93764 11613 37	0.94514 82749 15
14	0.38959 66789 56	0.37203 78918 92	0.92821 75429 26	0.93689 85846 09
15	0.41742 50131 67	0.39599 91367 79	0.91825 08827 50	0.92818 56446 86
16	0.44525 33473 78	0.41946 80340 09	0.90777 01077 06	0.91903 71102 28
17	0.47308 16815 89	0.44242 63730 39	0.89680 48307 41	0.90948 13153 37
18	0.50091 00158 00	0.46485 81717 14	0.88538 51592 33	0.89954 70934 21
19	0.52873 83500 11	0.48674 96605 38	0.87354 15090 12	0.88926 36028 01
20	0.55656 66842 23	0.50808 92502 76	0.86130 44257 14	0.87866 01592 46
21	0.58439 50184 34	0.52886 74843 31	0.84870 44149 87	0.86776 60768 31
22	0.61222 33526 45	0.54907 69774 21	0.83577 17827 65	0.85661 05183 00
23	0.64005 16868 56	0.56871 23421 69	0.82253 64866 47	0.84522 23558 66
24	0.66788 00210 67	0.58777 01052 51	0.80902 79991 28	0.83363 00431 93
25	0.69570 83552 78	0.60624 86147 77	0.79527 51832 43	0.82186 14990 55
26	0.72353 66894 89	0.62414 79405 16	0.78130 61809 24	0.80994 40029 71
27	0.75136 50237 00	0.64146 97685 76	0.76714 83142 15	0.79790 41029 39
28	0.77919 33579 12	0.65821 72920 36	0.75282 79992 57	0.78576 75352 09
29	0.80702 16921 23	0.67439 50989 58	0.73837 06728 34	0.77355 91558 72
30	0.83485 00263 34	0.69000 90591 09	0.72380 07311 05	0.76130 28839 29
31	0.86267 83605 45	0.70506 62105 79	0.70914 14800 31	0.74902 16553 79
32	0.89050 66947 56	0.71957 46474 00	0.69441 50969 12	0.73673 73877 65
33	0.91833 50289 67	0.73354 34091 10	0.67964 26023 66	0.72447 09545 65
34	0.94616 33631 78	0.74698 23730 98	0.66484 38420 27	0.71224 21687 36
35	0.97399 16973 90	0.75990 21504 39	0.65003 74771 95	0.70006 97746 97
36	1.00182 00316 01	0.77231 39858 19	0.63524 09836 49	0.68797 14480 15
37	1.02964 83658 12	0.78422 96620 07	0.62047 06578 30	0.67596 38020 30
38	1.05747 67000 23	0.79566 14092 52	0.60574 16295 97	0.66406 24006 92
39	1.08530 50342 34	0.80662 18198 84	0.59106 78807 78	0.65228 17768 69
40	1.11313 33684 45	0.81712 37682 82	0.57646 22687 64	0.64063 54554 13
41	1.14096 17026 56	0.82718 03363 19	0.56193 65544 32	0.62913 59803 24
42	1.16879 00368 67	0.83680 47443 12	0.54750 14336 95	0.61779 49453 47
43	1.19661 83710 79	0.84601 02874 31	0.53316 65720 58	0.60662 30274 24
44	1.22444 67052 90	0.85481 02774 98	0.51894 06415 80	0.59563 00224 19
45	1.25227 50395 01	0.86321 79900 13	0.50483 13596 81	0.58482 48826 15

278

ELLIPTIC FUNCTIONS   TABLE $\theta = 70°$

q = 0.13106 18244 99858 3   D(90) = 1.70991 35651 14649
q'= 0.00777 46804 16441 809   1/D(90) = 0.58482 48826 15017

r	ϕ	$E(\phi,k)$	A(r)	D(r)
0	0.00000 00000 00	0.00000 00000 00	0.00000 00000 00	1.00000 00000 00
1	0.02782 51631 84	0.02782 19928 08	0.01627 42345 82	1.00021 42836 51
2	0.05563 13145 85	0.05560 59815 31	0.03254 56619 21	1.00085 68806 43
3	0.08339 95141 68	0.08331 41831 74	0.04881 14697 52	1.00192 70293 67
4	0.11111 09647 69	0.11090 92541 91	0.06506 88357 82	1.00342 34613 90
5	0.13874 70819 60	0.13835 45034 71	0.08131 49227 20	1.00534 44028 28
6	0.16628 95620 69	0.16561 40973 77	0.09754 68733 60	1.00768 75762 69
7	0.19372 04477 76	0.19265 32544 60	0.11376 18057 33	1.01045 02032 37
8	0.22102 21907 62	0.21943 84276 81	0.12995 68083 44	1.01362 90072 11
9	0.24817 77109 18	0.24593 74721 98	0.14612 89355 16	1.01722 02171 76
10	0.27517 04516 88	0.27211 97971 08	0.16227 52028 53	1.02121 95717 27
11	0.30198 44311 79	0.29795 64997 79	0.17839 25828 33	1.02562 23237 01
12	0.32860 42887 11	0.32342 04818 01	0.19447 80005 64	1.03042 32453 52
13	0.35501 53265 81	0.34848 65458 54	0.21052 83296 98	1.03561 66340 57
14	0.38120 35468 46	0.37313 14731 51	0.22654 03885 33	1.04119 63185 49
15	0.40715 56830 28	0.39733 40814 43	0.24251 09363 07	1.04715 56656 75
16	0.43285 92266 73	0.42107 52638 26	0.25843 66697 07	1.05348 75876 74
17	0.45830 24487 92	0.44433 80089 31	0.27431 42195 99	1.06018 45499 75
18	0.48347 44162 46	0.46710 74032 57	0.29014 01479 98	1.06723 85794 93
19	0.50836 50031 97	0.48937 06166 93	0.30591 09452 79	1.07464 12734 44
20	0.53296 48978 09	0.51111 68723 94	0.32162 30276 58	1.08238 38086 45
21	0.55726 56043 85	0.53233 74023 56	0.33727 27349 37	1.09045 69513 13
22	0.58125 94412 24	0.55302 53901 36	0.35285 63285 30	1.09885 10673 39
23	0.60493 95344 39	0.57317 59022 26	0.36836 99897 82	1.10755 61330 49
24	0.62829 98080 72	0.59278 58096 36	0.38380 98185 80	1.11656 17464 23
25	0.65133 49707 95	0.61185 37012 43	0.39917 18322 75	1.12585 71387 75
26	0.67404 04995 46	0.63037 97904 55	0.41445 19649 12	1.13543 11868 84
27	0.69641 26204 28	0.64836 58166 59	0.42964 60667 78	1.14527 24255 63
28	0.71844 82872 08	0.66581 49429 03	0.44474 99042 77	1.15536 90606 57
29	0.74014 51577 50	0.68273 16511 37	0.45975 91601 23	1.16570 89824 56
30	0.76150 15686 99	0.69912 16362 48	0.47466 94338 67	1.17627 97795 20
31	0.78251 65087 45	0.71499 17000 48	0.48947 62427 59	1.18706 87528 88
32	0.80318 95907 46	0.73034 96462 05	0.50417 50229 34	1.19806 29306 78
33	0.82352 10230 12	0.74520 41770 45	0.51876 11309 36	1.20924 90830 48
34	0.84351 15799 98	0.75956 47929 83	0.53322 98455 79	1.22061 37375 08
35	0.86316 25726 61	0.77344 16952 84	0.54757 63701 23	1.23214 31945 79
36	0.88247 58187 06	0.78684 56926 75	0.56179 58347 95	1.24382 35437 65
37	0.90145 36129 16	0.79978 81122 82	0.57588 32996 25	1.25564 06798 39
38	0.92009 86977 57	0.81228 07152 31	0.58983 37576 02	1.26758 03194 14
39	0.93841 42344 21	0.82433 56171 67	0.60364 21381 44	1.27962 80177 94
40	0.95640 37744 38	0.83596 52138 64	0.61730 33108 85	1.29176 91860 70
41	0.97407 12319 99	0.84718 21120 29	0.63081 20897 47	1.30398 91084 64
42	0.99142 10970 79	0.85799 90653 11	0.64416 32373 19	1.31627 29598 84
43	1.00845 72094 47	0.86842 89155 04	0.65735 14695 16	1.32860 58236 78
44	1.02518 51336 50	0.87848 45388 51	0.67037 14605 05	1.34097 27095 69
45	1.04160 97350 14	0.88817 87973 22	0.68321 78479 08	1.35335 85717 42

K = 2.50455 00790 01634   E = 1.11837 77379 69864
K'= 1.62002 58991 24204   E'= 1.52379 92052 59774

r	u=(r/90)K=F(ϕ,k)	sn u	cn u	dn u
45	1.25227 50395 01	0.86321 79900 13	0.50483 13596 81	0.58482 48826 15
46	1.28010 33737 12	0.87124 66162 68	0.49084 55293 08	0.57421 57555 06
47	1.30793 17079 23	0.87890 92203 15	0.47698 90800 07	0.56381 00234 64
48	1.33576 00421 34	0.88621 87005 87	0.46326 71094 84	0.55361 43438 88
49	1.36358 83763 45	0.89318 77559 17	0.44968 39253 07	0.54363 46895 14
50	1.39141 67105 56	0.89982 88556 98	0.43624 30864 25	0.53387 63885 69
51	1.41924 50447 68	0.90615 42139 27	0.42294 74442 33	0.52434 41645 22
52	1.44707 33789 79	0.91217 57668 64	0.40979 91829 49	0.51504 21752 07
53	1.47490 17131 90	0.91790 51540 44	0.39679 98590 97	0.50597 40511 23
54	1.50273 00474 01	0.92335 37023 70	0.38395 04399 27	0.49714 29327 66
55	1.53055 83816 12	0.92853 24130 39	0.37125 13406 52	0.48855 15068 46
56	1.55838 67158 23	0.93345 19510 51	0.35870 24603 75	0.48020 20412 98
57	1.58621 50500 34	0.93812 26370 54	0.34630 32166 28	0.47209 64190 08
58	1.61404 33842 45	0.94255 44413 02	0.33405 25784 69	0.46423 61701 81
59	1.64187 17184 57	0.94675 69795 05	0.32194 90980 86	0.45662 25033 27
60	1.66970 00526 68	0.95073 95103 63	0.30999 09408 91	0.44925 63348 25
61	1.69752 83868 79	0.95451 09345 93	0.29817 59140 89	0.44213 83170 63
62	1.72535 67210 90	0.95807 97952 63	0.28650 14937 30	0.43526 88651 55
63	1.75318 50553 01	0.96145 42792 67	0.27496 48502 61	0.42864 81822 39
64	1.78101 33895 12	0.96464 22197 81	0.26356 28726 04	0.42227 62833 87
65	1.80884 17237 23	0.96765 10995 55	0.25229 21907 83	0.41615 30181 41
66	1.83667 00579 35	0.97048 80549 04	0.24114 91971 55	0.41027 80917 25
67	1.86449 83921 46	0.97315 98802 83	0.23013 00662 83	0.40465 10849 51
68	1.89232 67263 57	0.97567 30333 22	0.21923 07734 99	0.39927 14728 79
69	1.92015 50605 68	0.97803 36402 24	0.20844 71122 12	0.39413 86422 65
70	1.94798 33947 79	0.98024 75014 38	0.19777 47100 21	0.38925 19078 36
71	1.97581 17289 90	0.98232 00975 06	0.18720 90436 81	0.38461 05274 62
72	2.00364 00632 01	0.98425 65950 23	0.17674 54529 94	0.38021 37162 44
73	2.03146 83974 12	0.98606 18526 37	0.16637 91536 63	0.37606 06595 85
74	2.05929 67316 24	0.98774 04270 22	0.15610 52491 96	0.37215 05252 83
75	2.08712 50658 35	0.98929 65787 69	0.14591 87418 95	0.36848 24746 90
76	2.11495 34000 46	0.99073 42781 54	0.13581 45430 02	0.36505 56729 88
77	2.14278 17342 57	0.99205 72107 29	0.12578 74820 49	0.36186 92986 10
78	2.17061 00684 68	0.99326 87827 01	0.11583 23154 90	0.35892 25518 69
79	2.19843 84026 79	0.99437 21260 63	0.10594 37346 40	0.35621 46628 12
80	2.22626 67368 90	0.99537 01034 49	0.09611 63730 02	0.35374 48983 42
81	2.25409 50711 01	0.99626 53126 87	0.08634 48130 27	0.35151 25686 52
82	2.28192 34053 13	0.99706 00910 15	0.07662 35923 49	0.34951 70329 87
83	2.30975 17395 24	0.99775 65189 62	0.06694 72095 69	0.34775 77047 71
84	2.33758 00737 35	0.99835 64238 51	0.05731 01296 11	0.34623 40561 24
85	2.36540 84079 46	0.99886 13829 31	0.04770 67887 22	0.34494 56217 95
86	2.39323 67421 57	0.99927 27261 10	0.03813 15991 48	0.34389 20025 22
87	2.42106 50763 68	0.99959 15382 87	0.02857 89535 48	0.34307 28678 51
88	2.44889 34105 79	0.99981 86612 69	0.01904 32291 74	0.34248 79584 17
89	2.47672 17447 91	0.99995 46952 74	0.00951 87918 82	0.34213 70877 11
90	2.50455 00790 02	1.00000 00000 00	0.00000 00000 00	0.34202 01433 26

q = 0.13106 18244 99858 3   D(90) = 1.70991 35651 14649
q' = 0.00777 46804 16441 809   1/D(90) = 0.58482 48826 15017

r	ϕ	$E(\phi,k)$	A(r)	D(r)
45	1.04160 97350 14	0.88817 87973 22	0.68321 78479 08	1.35335 85717 42
46	1.05773 63566 99	0.89752 44947 26	0.69588 52382 45	1.36574 83270 76
47	1.07357 05578 61	0.90653 43374 45	0.70836 82126 27	1.37812 68734 83
48	1.08911 80929 10	0.91522 08996 01	0.72066 13326 70	1.39047 91083 40
49	1.10438 48919 05	0.92359 65924 17	0.73275 91466 28	1.40278 99469 96
50	1.11937 70420 53	0.93167 36375 54	0.74465 61957 22	1.41504 43413 19
51	1.13410 07703 32	0.93946 40441 50	0.75634 70206 61	1.42722 72982 74
52	1.14856 24272 03	0.94697 95893 49	0.76782 61683 27	1.43932 38984 92
53	1.16276 84714 12	0.95423 18020 54	0.77908 81986 18	1.45131 93148 21
54	1.17672 54558 29	0.96123 19496 60	0.79012 76914 27	1.46319 88308 24
55	1.19044 00143 23	0.96799 10275 42	0.80093 92537 47	1.47494 78592 06
56	1.20391 88496 23	0.97451 97510 62	0.81151 75268 76	1.48655 19601 42
57	1.21716 87221 37	0.98082 85498 71	0.82185 71937 11	1.49799 68594 80
58	1.23019 64396 90	0.98692 75643 01	0.83195 29861 13	1.50926 84667 92
59	1.24300 88481 43	0.99282 66436 40	0.84179 96923 21	1.52035 28932 65
60	1.25561 28228 56	0.99853 53461 12	0.85139 21644 00	1.53123 64693 72
61	1.26801 52609 54	1.00406 29403 77	0.86072 53257 05	1.54190 57623 35
62	1.28022 30743 55	1.00941 84083 81	0.86979 41783 38	1.55234 75933 33
63	1.29224 31835 23	1.01461 04494 19	0.87859 38105 88	1.56254 90544 34
64	1.30408 25119 04	1.01964 74852 57	0.88711 94043 26	1.57249 75252 25
65	1.31574 79810 08	1.02453 76661 84	0.89536 62423 44	1.58218 06891 29
66	1.32724 65061 04	1.02928 88778 75	0.90332 97156 12	1.59158 65493 56
67	1.33858 49924 83	1.03390 87489 68	0.91100 53304 42	1.60070 34444 97
68	1.34977 03322 54	1.03840 46592 36	0.91838 87155 43	1.60952 00637 13
69	1.36080 94016 54	1.04278 37482 81	0.92547 56289 32	1.61802 54615 07
70	1.37170 90588 12	1.04705 29246 69	0.93226 19647 07	1.62620 90720 50
71	1.38247 61419 66	1.05121 88754 24	0.93874 37596 50	1.63406 07230 45
72	1.39311 74680 71	1.05528 80758 32	0.94491 71996 44	1.64157 06491 09
73	1.40363 98318 00	1.05926 67994 86	0.95077 86258 94	1.64872 95046 34
74	1.41405 00048 85	1.06316 11285 38	0.95632 45409 30	1.65552 83761 33
75	1.42435 47357 83	1.06697 69640 97	0.96155 16143 82	1.66195 87940 32
76	1.43456 07496 46	1.07072 00367 53	0.96645 66885 08	1.66801 27438 96
77	1.44467 47485 54	1.07439 59171 86	0.97103 67834 58	1.67368 26770 70
78	1.45470 34120 14	1.07801 00268 36	0.97528 91022 74	1.67896 15207 19
79	1.46465 33976 72	1.08156 76486 15	0.97921 10355 95	1.68384 26872 47
80	1.47453 13422 46	1.08507 39376 36	0.98280 01660 68	1.68832 00830 86
81	1.48434 38626 41	1.08853 39319 51	0.98605 42724 52	1.69238 81168 33
82	1.49409 75572 37	1.09195 25632 85	0.98897 13333 92	1.69604 17067 28
83	1.50379 90073 23	1.09533 46677 56	0.99154 95308 74	1.69927 62874 54
84	1.51345 47786 73	1.09868 49965 81	0.99378 72533 39	1.70208 78162 61
85	1.52307 14232 35	1.10200 82267 50	0.99568 30984 42	1.70447 27783 81
86	1.53265 54809 18	1.10530 89716 92	0.99723 58754 66	1.70642 81917 48
87	1.54221 34814 75	1.10859 17919 04	0.99844 46073 74	1.70795 16110 06
88	1.55175 19464 46	1.11186 12055 68	0.99930 85324 93	1.70904 11307 94
89	1.56127 73911 62	1.11512 16991 49	0.99982 71058 26	1.70969 53883 02
90	1.57079 63267 95	1.11837 77379 70	1.00000 00000 00	1.70991 35651 15

K = 2.55073 14496 27254   E = 1.10964 34135 42761
K'= 1.61510 09160 67722   E'= 1.52830 62960 54359

r	u=(r/90)K=F(φ,k)	sn u	cn u	dn u
0	0.00000 00000 00	0.00000 00000 00	1.00000 00000 00	1.00000 00000 00
1	0.02834 14605 51	0.02833 42765 76	0.99959 85037 86	0.99964 10678 66
2	0.05668 29211 03	0.05662 55015 73	0.99839 54890 58	0.99856 56807 43
3	0.08502 43816 54	0.08483 08840 54	0.99639 53638 54	0.99677 80535 20
4	0.11336 58422 06	0.11290 81510 12	0.99360 54294 51	0.99428 51680 73
5	0.14170 73027 57	0.14081 57980 33	0.99003 58130 01	0.99109 67096 30
6	0.17004 87633 08	0.16851 33301 92	0.98569 93748 34	0.98722 49792 04
7	0.19839 02238 60	0.19596 14902 69	0.98061 15919 83	0.98268 47835 69
8	0.22673 16844 11	0.22312 24716 26	0.97479 04198 62	0.97749 33046 00
9	0.25507 31449 63	0.24996 01134 25	0.96825 61343 45	0.97166 99501 03
10	0.28341 46055 14	0.27644 00762 14	0.96103 11567 60	0.96523 61885 26
11	0.31175 60660 66	0.30252 99963 06	0.95313 98645 19	0.95821 53700 94
12	0.34009 75266 17	0.32819 96177 88	0.94460 83902 25	0.95063 25370 87
13	0.36843 89871 68	0.35342 09014 09	0.93546 44121 76	0.94251 42259 97
14	0.39678 04477 20	0.37816 81100 04	0.92573 69391 88	0.93388 82643 51
15	0.42512 19082 71	0.40241 78705 19	0.91545 60926 05	0.92478 35648 81
16	0.45346 33688 23	0.42614 92130 51	0.90465 28882 48	0.91522 99196 71
17	0.48180 48293 74	0.44934 35876 83	0.89335 90208 91	0.90525 77967 17
18	0.51014 62899 25	0.47198 48601 61	0.88160 66536 61	0.89489 81411 66
19	0.53848 77504 77	0.49405 92877 54	0.86942 82145 09	0.88418 21832 61
20	0.56682 92110 28	0.51555 54768 23	0.85685 62016 57	0.87314 12548 05
21	0.59517 06715 80	0.53646 43237 93	0.84392 29996 26	0.86180 66156 51
22	0.62351 21321 31	0.55677 89413 47	0.83066 07071 92	0.85020 92914 91
23	0.65185 35926 83	0.57649 45717 35	0.81710 09783 13	0.83837 99239 44
24	0.68019 50532 34	0.59560 84891 08	0.80327 48768 03	0.82634 86336 58
25	0.70853 65137 85	0.61411 98927 99	0.78921 27452 52	0.81414 48969 15
26	0.73687 79743 37	0.63202 97934 04	0.77494 40884 66	0.80179 74359 87
27	0.76521 94348 88	0.64934 08934 78	0.76049 74714 34	0.78933 41232 54
28	0.79356 08954 40	0.66605 74645 23	0.74590 04316 62	0.77678 18989 33
29	0.82190 23559 91	0.68218 52218 78	0.73117 94055 17	0.76416 67020 81
30	0.85024 38165 42	0.69773 11989 40	0.71635 96680 62	0.75151 34143 82
31	0.87858 52770 94	0.71270 36220 44	0.70146 52857 59	0.73884 58161 23
32	0.90692 67376 45	0.72711 17871 60	0.68651 90812 88	0.72618 65536 56
33	0.93526 81981 97	0.74096 59394 26	0.67154 26096 76	0.71355 71175 88
34	0.96360 96587 48	0.75427 71563 87	0.65655 61448 59	0.70097 78308 50
35	0.99195 11192 99	0.76705 72356 67	0.64157 86757 76	0.68846 78458 14
36	1.02029 25798 51	0.77931 85876 62	0.62662 79110 64	0.67604 51495 76
37	1.04863 40404 02	0.79107 41337 11	0.61172 02914 51	0.66372 65765 29
38	1.07697 55009 54	0.80233 72101 00	0.59687 10089 20	0.65152 78273 89
39	1.10531 69615 05	0.81312 14781 10	0.58209 40317 82	0.63946 34938 13
40	1.13365 84220 57	0.82344 08402 62	0.56740 21348 12	0.62754 70878 48
41	1.16199 98826 08	0.83330 93627 99	0.55280 69336 32	0.61579 10754 25
42	1.19034 13431 59	0.84274 12043 73	0.53831 89226 21	0.60420 69131 99
43	1.21868 28037 11	0.85175 05508 48	0.52394 75156 25	0.59280 50880 89
44	1.24702 42642 62	0.86035 15560 70	0.50970 10888 43	0.58159 51588 82
45	1.27536 57248 14	0.86855 82884 04	0.49558 70252 99	0.57058 57993 83

q = 0.13680 08474 28618 9   D(90) = 1.75258 48015 87998
q'= 0.00700 22602 97383 134   1/D(90) = 0.57058 57993 82667

r	ϕ	$E(\phi,k)$	A(r)	D(r)
0	0.00000 00000 00	0.00000 00000 00	0.00000 00000 00	1.00000 00000 00
1	0.02833 80692 20	0.02833 46786 19	0.01617 08038 61	1.00022 68806 75
2	0.05665 58064 36	0.05662 87151 10	0.03233 90202 19	1.00090 72548 51
3	0.08493 29594 04	0.08484 17139 77	0.04850 20559 71	1.00204 03192 70
4	0.11314 94346 66	0.11293 37698 32	0.06465 73068 32	1.00362 47361 16
5	0.14128 53751 30	0.14086 57045 84	0.08080 21517 87	1.00565 86344 37
6	0.16932 12354 98	0.16859 92954 19	0.09693 39476 10	1.00813 96121 38
7	0.19723 78548 95	0.19609 74907 78	0.11305 00234 52	1.01106 47385 34
8	0.22501 65260 79	0.22332 46118 39	0.12914 76755 20	1.01443 05574 75
9	0.25263 90606 84	0.25024 65373 06	0.14522 41618 76	1.01823 30910 32
10	0.28008 78499 96	0.27683 08696 43	0.16127 66973 65	1.02246 78437 46
11	0.30734 59208 54	0.30304 70812 50	0.17730 24486 85	1.02712 98074 34
12	0.33439 69863 10	0.32886 66395 11	0.19329 85296 31	1.03221 34665 57
13	0.36122 54908 01	0.35426 31099 68	0.20926 19965 15	1.03771 28041 37
14	0.38781 66496 26	0.37921 22373 34	0.22518 98437 87	1.04362 13082 29
15	0.41415 64826 22	0.40369 20043 73	0.24107 89998 69	1.04993 19789 37
16	0.44023 18419 99	0.42768 26690 65	0.25692 63232 22	1.05663 73359 77
17	0.46603 04343 76	0.45116 67807 84	0.27272 85986 49	1.06372 94267 72
18	0.49154 08370 99	0.47412 91764 79	0.28848 25338 61	1.07119 98350 89
19	0.51675 25090 32	0.49655 69581 32	0.30418 47563 18	1.07903 96901 98
20	0.54165 57960 10	0.51843 94529 23	0.31983 18103 40	1.08723 96765 53
21	0.56624 19312 34	0.53976 81577 24	0.33542 01545 28	1.09579 00439 97
22	0.59050 30309 06	0.56053 66696 34	0.35094 61594 78	1.10468 06184 66
23	0.61443 20854 39	0.58074 06043 38	0.36640 61058 16	1.11390 08132 01
24	0.63802 29465 98	0.60037 75041 09	0.38179 61825 58	1.12343 96404 56
25	0.66127 03109 54	0.61944 67372 66	0.39711 24858 03	1.13328 57236 83
26	0.68416 97000 40	0.63794 93908 41	0.41235 10177 57	1.14342 73102 02
27	0.70671 74375 83	0.65588 81581 71	0.42750 76861 17	1.15385 22843 34
28	0.72891 06242 26	0.67326 72230 09	0.44257 83037 97	1.16454 81809 93
29	0.75074 71100 97	0.69009 21416 65	0.45755 85890 10	1.17550 21997 21
30	0.77222 54656 07	0.70636 97245 43	0.47244 41657 13	1.18670 12191 58
31	0.79334 49508 35	0.72210 79183 21	0.48723 05644 11	1.19813 18119 40
32	0.81410 54838 23	0.73731 56898 76	0.50191 32233 24	1.20978 02599 92
33	0.83450 76081 05	0.75200 29129 14	0.51648 74899 17	1.22163 25702 36
34	0.85455 24597 59	0.76618 02581 35	0.53094 86227 91	1.23367 44906 66
35	0.87424 17342 57	0.77985 90876 22	0.54529 17939 37	1.24589 15267 96
36	0.89357 76533 39	0.79305 13540 00	0.55951 20913 49	1.25826 89584 56
37	0.91256 29321 57	0.80576 95048 17	0.57360 45219 83	1.27079 18569 31
38	0.93120 07468 55	0.81802 63924 70	0.58756 40150 75	1.28344 51024 05
39	0.94949 47027 78	0.82983 51898 88	0.60138 54257 98	1.29621 34017 17
40	0.96744 88034 47	0.84120 93121 09	0.61506 35392 54	1.30908 13063 93
41	0.98506 74204 27	0.85216 23437 97	0.62859 30747 99	1.32203 32309 43
42	1.00235 52641 92	0.86270 79726 72	0.64196 86906 86	1.33505 34714 03
43	1.01931 73560 77	0.87285 99287 69	0.65518 49890 18	1.34812 62240 91
44	1.03595 90013 78	0.88263 19293 87	0.66823 65210 03	1.36123 56045 78
45	1.05228 57636 59	0.89203 76295 43	0.68111 77924 97	1.37436 56668 29

K = 2.55073 14496 27254   E = 1.10964 34135 42761
K′= 1.61510 09160 67722   E′= 1.52830 62960 54359

r	u=(r/90)K=F(ϕ,k)	sn u	cn u	dn u
45	1.27536 57248 14	0.86855 82884 04	0.49558 70252 99	0.57058 57993 83
46	1.30370 71853 65	0.87638 46828 13	0.48161 17603 74	0.55978 48425 75
47	1.33204 86459 16	0.88384 44982 21	0.46778 08279 14	0.54919 93253 75
48	1.36039 01064 68	0.89095 12798 70	0.45409 89065 15	0.53883 55335 65
49	1.38873 15670 19	0.89771 83263 83	0.44056 98656 01	0.52869 90465 60
50	1.41707 30275 71	0.90415 86612 36	0.42719 68109 80	0.51879 47817 17
51	1.44541 44881 22	0.91028 50083 14	0.41398 21296 12	0.50912 70379 11
52	1.47375 59486 74	0.91610 97712 62	0.40092 75333 51	0.49969 95381 79
53	1.50209 74092 25	0.92164 50163 10	0.38803 41014 79	0.49051 54712 34
54	1.53043 88697 76	0.92690 24583 01	0.37530 23218 62	0.48157 75317 10
55	1.55878 03303 28	0.93189 34496 02	0.36273 21306 25	0.47288 79590 19
56	1.58712 17908 79	0.93662 89716 52	0.35032 29502 37	0.46444 85747 32
57	1.61546 32514 31	0.94111 96288 62	0.33807 37259 41	0.45626 08184 16
58	1.64380 47119 82	0.94537 56446 35	0.32598 29604 91	0.44832 57818 78
59	1.67214 61725 33	0.94940 68592 56	0.31404 87471 68	0.44064 42418 06
60	1.70048 76330 85	0.95322 27294 32	0.30226 88010 60	0.43321 66907 82
61	1.72882 90936 36	0.95683 23292 88	0.29064 04886 26	0.42604 33666 77
62	1.75717 05541 88	0.96024 43526 13	0.27916 08555 57	0.41912 42804 51
63	1.78551 20147 39	0.96346 71161 80	0.26782 66529 66	0.41245 92423 74
64	1.81385 34752 90	0.96650 85639 89	0.25663 43619 54	0.40604 78867 16
65	1.84219 49358 42	0.96937 62722 61	0.24558 02165 82	0.39988 96949 31
66	1.87053 63963 93	0.97207 74550 65	0.23466 02253 33	0.39398 40173 95
67	1.89887 78569 45	0.97461 89704 41	0.22387 01910 84	0.38833 00937 43
68	1.92721 93174 96	0.97700 73269 07	0.21320 57296 82	0.38292 70718 58
69	1.95556 07780 48	0.97924 86902 51	0.20266 22871 74	0.37777 40255 70
70	1.98390 22385 99	0.98134 88905 04	0.19223 51557 50	0.37286 99711 13
71	2.01224 36991 50	0.98331 34290 29	0.18191 94884 85	0.36821 38824 11
72	2.04058 51597 02	0.98514 74856 26	0.17171 03129 23	0.36380 47052 29
73	2.06892 66202 53	0.98685 59256 06	0.16160 25435 96	0.35964 13702 68
74	2.09726 80808 05	0.98844 33067 63	0.15159 09935 14	0.35572 28052 32
75	2.12560 95413 56	0.98991 38862 00	0.14167 03847 26	0.35204 79459 42
76	2.15395 10019 07	0.99127 16269 44	0.13183 53579 85	0.34861 57465 35
77	2.18229 24624 59	0.99252 02043 35	0.12208 04815 93	0.34542 51887 95
78	2.21063 39230 10	0.99366 30121 25	0.11240 02594 99	0.34247 52906 68
79	2.23897 53835 62	0.99470 31682 71	0.10278 91386 84	0.33976 51140 01
80	2.26731 68441 13	0.99564 35203 98	0.09324 15159 12	0.33729 37715 42
81	2.29565 83046 65	0.99648 66508 86	0.08375 17438 99	0.33506 04332 50
82	2.32399 97652 16	0.99723 48815 85	0.07431 41369 49	0.33306 43319 24
83	2.35234 12257 67	0.99789 02781 23	0.06492 29761 14	0.33130 47682 24
84	2.38068 26863 19	0.99845 46538 00	0.05557 25139 33	0.32978 11150 60
85	2.40902 41468 70	0.99892 95730 49	0.04625 69787 98	0.32849 28214 31
86	2.43736 56074 22	0.99931 63544 59	0.03697 05789 93	0.32743 94156 84
87	2.46570 70679 73	0.99961 60733 43	0.02770 75064 65	0.32662 05082 54
88	2.49404 85285 24	0.99982 95638 55	0.01846 19403 59	0.32603 57938 75
89	2.52238 99890 76	0.99995 74206 37	0.00922 80503 77	0.32568 50532 88
90	2.55073 14496 27	1.00000 00000 00	0.00000 00000 00	0.32556 81544 57

q = 0.13680 08474 28618 9
q'= 0.00700 22602 97383 134

D(90) = 1.75258 48015 87998
1/D(90) = 0.57058 57993 82667

r	ϕ	$E(\phi,k)$	A(r)	D(r)
45	1.05228 57636 59	0.89203 76295 43	0.68111 77924 97	1.37436 56668 29
46	1.06830 34402 90	0.90109 05777 23	0.69382 32698 25	1.38750 04225 08
47	1.08401 80392 53	0.90980 41766 84	0.70634 73858 61	1.40062 38604 10
48	1.09943 57572 16	0.91819 16490 41	0.71868 45463 67	1.41371 99660 15
49	1.11456 29588 81	0.92626 60073 68	0.73082 91365 57	1.42677 27411 21
50	1.11940 61575 92	0.93404 00285 35	0.74277 55278 89	1.43976 62235 41
51	1.14397 19971 93	0.94152 62319 82	0.75451 80850 56	1.45268 45068 45
52	1.15826 72351 04	0.94873 68616 48	0.76605 11731 65	1.46551 17601 02
53	1.17229 87265 94	0.95568 38712 80	0.77736 91650 95	1.47823 22476 21
54	1.18607 34102 07	0.96237 89128 35	0.78846 64489 94	1.49083 03486 46
55	1.19959 82943 20	0.96883 33277 13	0.79933 74359 22	1.50329 05769 80
56	1.21288 04447 67	0.97505 81405 70	0.80997 65676 03	1.51559 76005 31
57	1.22592 69735 15	0.98106 40554 57	0.82037 83242 82	1.52773 62607 21
58	1.23874 50283 21	0.98686 14540 58	0.83053 72326 50	1.53969 15917 56
59	1.25134 17833 47	0.99246 03958 14	0.84044 78738 39	1.55144 88397 23
60	1.26372 44306 68	0.99787 06197 25	0.85010 48914 45	1.56299 34814 82
61	1.27590 01726 43	1.00310 15476 36	0.85950 29995 75	1.57431 12433 25
62	1.28787 62150 95	1.00816 22888 47	0.86863 69908 94	1.58538 81193 83
63	1.29965 97612 51	1.01306 16458 63	0.87750 17446 44	1.59621 03897 51
64	1.31125 80064 13	1.01780 81211 59	0.88609 22346 32	1.60676 46382 88
65	1.32267 81332 97	1.02240 99248 07	0.89440 35371 43	1.61703 77700 98
66	1.33392 73080 17	1.02687 49828 53	0.90243 08387 83	1.62701 70286 26
67	1.34501 26766 57	1.03121 09463 26	0.91016 94442 11	1.63669 00123 76
68	1.35594 13624 13	1.03542 52007 83	0.91761 47837 55	1.64604 46912 03
69	1.36672 04632 36	1.03952 48763 03	0.92476 24208 89	1.65506 94221 67
70	1.37735 70499 76	1.04351 68578 44	0.93160 80595 41	1.66375 29649 12
71	1.38785 81649 69	1.04740 77958 95	0.93814 75512 33	1.67208 44965 58
72	1.39823 08210 38	1.05120 41173 68	0.94437 69020 15	1.68005 36260 73
73	1.40848 20008 83	1.05491 20366 66	0.95029 22791 94	1.68765 04080 98
74	1.41861 86568 30	1.05853 75668 85	0.95589 00178 22	1.69486 53562 24
75	1.42864 77109 06	1.06208 65311 13	0.96116 66269 39	1.70168 94556 68
76	1.43857 60552 11	1.06556 45737 86	0.96611 87955 51	1.70811 41753 54
77	1.44841 05525 77	1.06897 71720 78	0.97074 33983 29	1.71413 14793 62
78	1.45815 80374 69	1.07232 96473 00	0.97503 75010 13	1.71973 38377 32
79	1.46782 53171 26	1.07562 71762 87	0.97899 83655 01	1.72491 42366 15
80	1.47741 91729 05	1.07887 48027 60	0.98262 34546 25	1.72966 61877 24
81	1.48694 63618 09	1.08207 74486 57	0.98591 04365 85	1.73398 37371 12
82	1.49641 36182 00	1.08523 99254 16	0.98885 71890 42	1.73786 14732 19
83	1.50582 76556 42	1.08836 69452 15	0.99146 18028 52	1.74129 45342 06
84	1.51519 51688 97	1.09146 31321 56	0.99372 25854 29	1.74427 86145 47
85	1.52452 28360 21	1.09453 30334 04	0.99563 80637 46	1.74680 99708 75
86	1.53381 73205 73	1.09758 11302 82	0.99720 69869 36	1.74888 54270 66
87	1.54308 52739 01	1.10061 18493 13	0.99842 83285 16	1.75050 23785 58
88	1.55233 33375 04	1.10362 95732 29	0.99930 12882 09	1.75165 87958 95
89	1.56156 81454 41	1.10663 86519 53	0.99982 52933 69	1.75235 32274 86
90	1.57079 63267 95	1.10964 34135 43	1.00000 00000 00	1.75258 48015 88

10

285

K = 2.59981 97300 61099 E = 1.10106 21687 57941
K' = 1.61045 41537 89663 E' = 1.53259 72877 45636

r	u=(r/90)K=F(ϕ,k)	sn u	cn u	dn u
0	0.00000 00000 00	0.00000 00000 00	1.00000 00000 00	1.00000 00000 00
1	0.02888 68858 90	0.02887 92370 41	0.99958 29078 51	0.99962 27441 23
2	0.05777 37717 79	0.05771 26391 50	0.99833 32365 91	0.99849 25184 91
3	0.08666 06576 69	0.08645 46613 69	0.99625 57861 95	0.99661 39342 92
4	0.11554 75435 58	0.11506 03347 90	0.99335 85049 51	0.99399 46277 35
5	0.14443 44294 48	0.14348 55449 36	0.98965 24129 18	0.99064 51873 18
6	0.17332 13153 37	0.17168 72988 06	0.98515 14966 89	0.98657 90538 22
7	0.20220 82012 27	0.19962 39772 21	0.97987 25772 87	0.98181 23947 78
8	0.23109 50871 17	0.22725 55694 23	0.97383 51534 87	0.97636 39555 97
9	0.25998 19730 06	0.25454 38872 60	0.96706 12232 21	0.97025 48898 62
10	0.28886 88588 96	0.28145 27567 50	0.95957 50860 24	0.96350 85716 23
11	0.31775 57447 85	0.30794 81852 57	0.95140 31296 97	0.95615 03927 15
12	0.34664 26306 75	0.33399 85030 24	0.94257 36045 41	0.94820 75482 59
13	0.37552 95165 64	0.35957 44782 88	0.93311 63885 41	0.93970 88135 96
14	0.40441 64024 54	0.38464 94056 91	0.92306 27468 93	0.93068 43158 58
15	0.43330 32883 44	0.40919 91681 73	0.91244 50891 79	0.92116 53033 36
16	0.46219 01742 33	0.43320 22729 38	0.90129 67273 44	0.91118 39156 23
17	0.49107 70601 23	0.45663 98625 15	0.88965 16374 19	0.90077 29573 51
18	0.51996 39460 12	0.47949 57022 34	0.87754 42276 83	0.88996 56780 84
19	0.54885 08319 02	0.50175 61457 54	0.86500 91156 73	0.87879 55606 39
20	0.57773 77177 91	0.52341 00805 01	0.85208 09161 28	0.86729 61198 39
21	0.60662 46036 81	0.54444 88550 48	0.83879 40416 08	0.85550 07133 47
22	0.63551 14895 70	0.56486 61905 88	0.82518 25172 23	0.84344 23659 43
23	0.66439 83754 60	0.58465 80787 15	0.81127 98105 42	0.83115 36082 65
24	0.69328 52613 50	0.60382 26677 47	0.79711 86774 35	0.81866 63307 30
25	0.72217 21472 39	0.62236 01397 92	0.78273 10242 97	0.80601 16530 66
26	0.75105 90331 29	0.64027 25806 91	0.76814 77868 32	0.79321 98096 12
27	0.77994 59190 18	0.65756 38448 66	0.75339 88252 74	0.78032 00502 91
28	0.80883 28049 08	0.67423 94169 90	0.73851 28357 57	0.76734 05569 55
29	0.83771 96907 97	0.69030 62722 18	0.72351 72772 90	0.75430 83746 11
30	0.86660 65766 87	0.70577 27365 96	0.70843 83136 72	0.74124 93568 78
31	0.89549 34625 77	0.72064 83490 46	0.69330 07695 20	0.72818 81248 98
32	0.92438 03484 66	0.73494 37261 94	0.67812 80994 97	0.71514 80388 30
33	0.95326 72343 56	0.74867 04310 92	0.66294 23697 49	0.70215 11809 76
34	0.98215 41202 45	0.76184 08467 51	0.64776 42504 97	0.68921 83495 66
35	1.01104 10061 35	0.77446 80552 03	0.63261 30187 33	0.67636 90621 59
36	1.03992 78920 24	0.78656 57226 73	0.61750 65699 38	0.66362 15676 68
37	1.06881 47779 14	0.79814 79912 97	0.60246 14377 60	0.65099 28659 88
38	1.09770 16638 04	0.80922 93776 81	0.58749 28206 36	0.63849 87342 44
39	1.12658 85496 93	0.81982 46784 74	0.57261 46143 49	0.62615 37587 35
40	1.15547 54355 83	0.82994 88830 46	0.55783 94496 01	0.61397 13716 60
41	1.18436 23214 72	0.83961 70932 36	0.54317 87337 02	0.60196 38918 04
42	1.21324 92073 62	0.84884 44500 77	0.52864 26955 64	0.59014 25683 91
43	1.24213 60932 51	0.85764 60673 33	0.51424 04332 50	0.57851 76273 98
44	1.27102 29791 41	0.86603 69716 27	0.49997 99633 74	0.56709 83196 71
45	1.29990 98650 31	0.87403 20488 98	0.48586 82717 57	0.55589 29702 51

q = 0.14283 65198 36280 4   D(90) = 1.79890 74399 47867
q′ = 0.00627 23946 95993 661   1/D(90) = 0.55589 29702 51421

r	ϕ	$E(\phi,k)$	A(r)	D(r)
0	0.00000 00000 00	0.00000 00000 00	0.00000 00000 00	1.00000 00000 00
1	0.02888 32528 12	0.02887 96205 56	0.01605 76258 05	1.00024 05011 01
2	0.05774 47249 81	0.05771 57044 61	0.03211 29044 04	1.00096 17217 48
3	0.08656 27248 10	0.08646 49910 20	0.04816 34823 56	1.00216 28142 62
4	0.11531 57376 37	0.11508 47677 43	0.06420 69937 78	1.00384 23668 29
5	0.14398 25122 35	0.14353 31352 77	0.08024 10541 73	1.00599 84049 63
6	0.17254 21447 16	0.17176 92615 60	0.09626 32543 20	1.00862 83935 67
7	0.20097 41591 70	0.19975 36219 98	0.11227 11542 51	1.01172 92395 71
8	0.22925 85843 33	0.22744 82227 56	0.12826 22773 25	1.01529 72951 61
9	0.25737 60256 53	0.25481 68046 58	0.14423 41044 30	1.01932 83615 90
10	0.28530 77321 80	0.28182 50255 58	0.16018 40683 22	1.02381 76935 71
11	0.31303 56578 15	0.30844 06195 27	0.17610 95481 28	1.02876 00042 49
12	0.34054 25165 25	0.33463 35316 66	0.19200 78640 32	1.03414 94707 55
13	0.36781 18312 28	0.36037 60277 84	0.20787 62721 50	1.03997 97403 28
14	0.39482 79761 48	0.38564 27787 02	0.22371 19596 30	1.04624 39370 23
15	0.42157 62125 41	0.41041 09193 29	0.23951 20399 84	1.05293 46689 73
16	0.44804 27177 48	0.43466 00831 01	0.25527 35486 62	1.06004 40362 33
17	0.47421 46076 70	0.45837 24127 28	0.27099 34389 02	1.06756 36391 72
18	0.50007 99527 76	0.48153 25485 38	0.28666 85778 51	1.07548 45874 37
19	0.52562 77878 82	0.50412 75959 37	0.30229 57429 87	1.08379 75094 59
20	0.55084 81159 46	0.52614 70737 92	0.31787 16188 47	1.09249 25625 16
21	0.57573 19062 39	0.54758 28456 37	0.33339 27940 77	1.10155 94433 33
22	0.60027 10872 27	0.56842 90357 69	0.34885 57588 09	1.11098 73992 22
23	0.62445 85345 92	0.58868 19323 39	0.36425 69023 91	1.12076 52397 52
24	0.64828 80548 12	0.60833 98795 53	0.37959 25114 64	1.13088 13489 37
25	0.67175 43647 42	0.62740 31610 92	0.39485 87684 00	1.14132 36979 49
26	0.69485 30676 60	0.64587 38767 63	0.41005 17501 18	1.15207 98583 23
27	0.71758 06262 19	0.66375 58143 39	0.42516 74272 67	1.16313 70156 75
28	0.73993 43327 70	0.68105 43183 77	0.44020 16637 99	1.17448 19838 93
29	0.76191 22774 76	0.69777 61577 01	0.45515 02169 28	1.18610 12198 19
30	0.78351 33146 55	0.71392 93930 67	0.47000 87374 82	1.19798 08383 86
31	0.80473 70277 36	0.72952 32463 54	0.48477 27706 43	1.21010 66282 16
32	0.82558 36932 19	0.74456 79724 81	0.49943 77570 90	1.22246 40676 53
33	0.84605 42439 75	0.75907 47350 54	0.51399 90345 34	1.23503 83412 37
34	0.86615 02322 22	0.77305 54866 15	0.52845 18396 51	1.24781 43565 77
35	0.88587 37924 58	0.78652 28541 73	0.54279 13104 05	1.26077 67616 33
36	0.90522 76046 19	0.79949 00305 90	0.55701 24887 63	1.27390 99623 80
37	0.92421 48577 01	0.81197 06722 07	0.57111 03237 98	1.28719 81408 38
38	0.94283 92140 40	0.82397 88030 20	0.58507 96751 74	1.30062 52734 54
39	0.96110 47744 44	0.83552 87255 70	0.59891 53170 02	1.31417 51498 14
40	0.97901 60443 11	0.84663 49386 10	0.61261 19420 70	1.32783 13916 70
41	0.99657 79008 68	0.85731 20615 50	0.62616 41664 24	1.34157 74722 59
42	1.01379 55616 37	0.86757 47655 76	0.63956 65343 13	1.35539 67358 96
43	1.03067 45542 03	0.87743 77112 99	0.65281 35234 60	1.36927 24178 20
44	1.04722 06873 45	0.88691 54927 05	0.66589 95506 67	1.38318 76642 66
45	1.06344 00235 78	0.89602 25871 91	0.67881 89777 41	1.39712 55527 50

K = 2.59981 97300 61099   E = 1.10106 21687 57941
K' = 1.61045 41537 89663   E' = 1.53259 72877 45636

r	u=(r/90)K=F(ϕ,k)	sn u	cn u	dn u
45	1.29990 98650 31	0.87403 20488 98	0.48586 82717 57	0.55589 29702 51
46	1.32879 67509 20	0.88164 59968 77	0.47191 13647 61	0.54490 90283 92
47	1.35768 36368 10	0.88889 32832 74	0.45811 43208 31	0.53415 31177 96
48	1.38657 05226 99	0.89578 81093 13	0.44448 13418 05	0.52363 10866 67
49	1.41545 74085 89	0.90234 43782 88	0.43101 58036 23	0.51334 80572 21
50	1.44434 42944 78	0.90857 56687 52	0.41772 03061 28	0.50330 84743 66
51	1.47323 11803 68	0.91449 52120 16	0.40459 67216 87	0.49351 61532 84
52	1.50211 80662 58	0.92011 58735 75	0.39164 62424 11	0.48397 43257 14
53	1.53100 49521 47	0.92545 01381 45	0.37886 94258 01	0.47468 56847 75
54	1.55989 18380 37	0.93051 00979 58	0.36626 62386 83	0.46565 24281 76
55	1.58877 87239 26	0.93530 74440 07	0.35383 60993 25	0.45687 62997 36
56	1.61766 56098 16	0.93985 34599 44	0.34157 79176 56	0.44835 86291 19
57	1.64655 24957 05	0.94415 90183 29	0.32949 01335 52	0.44010 03697 60
58	1.67543 93815 95	0.94823 45789 65	0.31757 07531 48	0.43210 21349 38
59	1.70432 62674 84	0.95209 01890 79	0.30581 73831 86	0.42436 42320 01
60	1.73321 31533 74	0.95573 54850 95	0.29422 72634 04	0.41688 66947 51
61	1.76210 00392 64	0.95917 96957 89	0.28279 72969 93	0.40966 93140 05
62	1.79098 69251 53	0.96243 16466 31	0.27152 40791 57	0.40271 16663 84
63	1.81987 38110 43	0.96549 97651 20	0.26040 39238 44	0.39601 31413 51
64	1.84876 06969 32	0.96839 20869 40	0.24943 28886 75	0.38957 29665 73
65	1.87764 75828 22	0.97111 62627 99	0.23860 67981 60	0.38339 02316 42
66	1.90653 44687 11	0.97367 95657 94	0.22792 12652 56	0.37746 39102 35
67	1.93542 13546 01	0.97608 88991 82	0.21737 17113 48	0.37179 28807 65
68	1.96430 82404 91	0.97835 08044 44	0.20695 33847 10	0.36637 59455 92
69	1.99319 51263 80	0.98047 14695 40	0.19666 13775 45	0.36121 18488 67
70	2.02208 20122 70	0.98245 67372 52	0.18649 06416 65	0.35629 92930 63
71	2.05096 88981 59	0.98431 21135 53	0.17643 60028 82	0.35163 69542 77
72	2.07985 57840 49	0.98604 27759 11	0.16649 21742 14	0.34722 34963 49
73	2.10874 26699 38	0.98765 35814 70	0.15665 37679 39	0.34305 75838 82
74	2.13762 95558 28	0.98914 90750 56	0.14691 53066 08	0.33913 78942 02
75	2.16651 64417 18	0.99053 34969 46	0.13727 12330 69	0.33546 31283 39
76	2.19540 33276 07	0.99181 07903 66	0.12771 59195 76	0.33203 20210 73
77	2.22429 02134 97	0.99298 46086 80	0.11824 36760 48	0.32884 33500 93
78	2.25317 70993 86	0.99405 83222 22	0.10884 87575 53	0.32589 59443 45
79	2.28206 39852 76	0.99503 50247 67	0.09952 53710 68	0.32318 86915 80
80	2.31095 08711 65	0.99591 75395 89	0.09026 76815 87	0.32072 05451 78
81	2.33983 77570 55	0.99670 84251 02	0.08106 98176 32	0.31849 05302 76
82	2.36872 46429 45	0.99740 99800 63	0.07192 58762 22	0.31649 77492 29
83	2.39761 15288 34	0.99802 42483 17	0.06282 99273 61	0.31474 13864 59
84	2.42649 84147 24	0.99855 30230 68	0.05377 60180 94	0.31322 07127 02
85	2.45538 53006 13	0.99899 78506 81	0.04475 81761 87	0.31193 50886 99
86	2.48427 21865 03	0.99936 00339 82	0.03577 04134 78	0.31088 39683 36
87	2.51315 90723 92	0.99964 06350 70	0.02680 67289 51	0.31006 69012 76
88	2.54204 59582 82	0.99984 04776 23	0.01786 11115 83	0.30948 35350 81
89	2.57093 28441 72	0.99996 01486 94	0.00892 75429 98	0.30913 36168 49
90	2.59981 97300 61	1.00000 00000 00	0.00000 00000 00	0.30901 69943 75

q = 0.14283 65198 36280 4   D(90) = 1.79890 74399 47867
q'= 0.00627 23946 95993 661   1/D(90) = 0.55589 29702 51421

r	ϕ	$E(\phi,k)$	A(r)	D(r)
45	1.06344 00235 78	0.89602 25871 91	0.67881 89777 41	1.39712 55527 50
46	1.07933 88531 32	0.90477 33113 74	0.69156 61177 19	1.41106 91125 32
47	1.09492 36693 78	0.91318 17823 79	0.70413 52413 77	1.42500 13452 43
48	1.11020 11457 04	0.92126 18842 88	0.71652 05840 23	1.43890 52456 43
49	1.12517 81138 31	0.92902 72394 14	0.72871 63525 44	1.45276 38224 90
50	1.13986 15435 45	0.93649 11840 59	0.74071 67326 92	1.46656 01194 93
51	1.15425 85238 25	0.94366 67484 33	0.75251 58965 97	1.48027 72363 17
52	1.16837 62453 20	0.95056 66403 86	0.76410 80104 91	1.49389 83496 23
53	1.18222 19841 49	0.95720 32326 52	0.77548 72426 11	1.50740 67341 04
54	1.19580 30869 69	0.96358 85532 75	0.78664 77712 78	1.52078 57834 94
55	1.20912 69572 73	0.96973 42789 32	0.79758 37931 25	1.53401 90315 26
56	1.22220 10428 44	0.97565 17308 61	0.80828 95314 47	1.54709 01728 00
57	1.23503 28243 57	0.98135 18731 30	0.81875 92446 71	1.55998 30835 39
58	1.24762 98050 31	0.98684 53129 99	0.82898 72349 02	1.57268 18422 02
59	1.25999 95013 00	0.99214 23031 29	0.83896 78565 43	1.58517 07499 18
60	1.27214 94344 51	0.99725 27454 35	0.84869 55249 58	1.59743 43507 25
61	1.28408 71231 66	1.00218 61963 70	0.85816 47251 54	1.60945 74515 68
62	1.29582 00769 23	1.00695 18734 56	0.86737 00204 70	1.62122 51420 37
63	1.30735 57902 06	1.01155 86629 07	0.87630 60612 42	1.63272 28138 11
64	1.31870 17374 62	1.01601 51281 64	0.88496 75934 25	1.64393 61797 72
65	1.32986 53687 83	1.02032 95192 33	0.89334 94671 50	1.65485 12927 78
66	1.34085 41062 34	1.02450 97826 76	0.90144 66452 00	1.66545 45640 44
67	1.35167 53408 09	1.02856 35721 57	0.90925 42113 68	1.67573 27811 07
68	1.36233 64299 60	1.03249 82594 34	0.91676 73786 93	1.68567 31253 66
69	1.37284 46956 60	1.03632 09457 20	0.92398 14975 44	1.69526 31891 33
70	1.38320 74229 66	1.04003 84733 15	0.93089 20635 32	1.70449 09922 03
71	1.39343 18590 37	1.04365 74374 70	0.93749 47252 26	1.71334 49978 93
72	1.40352 52125 76	1.04718 41983 89	0.94378 52916 67	1.72181 41285 25
73	1.41349 46536 73	1.05062 48933 48	0.94975 97396 38	1.72988 77803 44
74	1.42334 73139 96	1.05398 54488 70	0.95541 42206 97	1.73755 58378 27
75	1.43309 02873 25	1.05727 15929 26	0.96074 50679 31	1.74480 86873 62
76	1.44273 06303 79	1.06048 88671 33	0.96574 88024 28	1.75163 72302 90
77	1.45227 53639 27	1.06364 26389 15	0.97042 21394 51	1.75803 28952 63
78	1.46173 14741 53	1.06673 81136 26	0.97476 19942 84	1.76398 76499 15
79	1.47110 59142 43	1.06978 03465 98	0.97876 54877 50	1.76949 40118 20
80	1.48040 56061 85	1.07277 42551 22	0.98242 99513 81	1.77454 50587 17
81	1.48963 74427 59	1.07572 46303 45	0.98575 29322 24	1.77913 44379 84
82	1.49880 82896 84	1.07863 61490 83	0.98873 21972 67	1.78325 63753 45
83	1.50792 49879 26	1.08151 33855 46	0.99136 57374 94	1.78690 56827 99
84	1.51699 43561 27	1.08436 08229 87	0.99365 17715 26	1.79007 77657 49
85	1.52602 31931 54	1.08718 28652 58	0.99558 87488 64	1.79276 86293 21
86	1.53501 82807 47	1.08998 38483 06	0.99717 53527 19	1.79497 48838 69
87	1.54398 63862 49	1.09276 80515 98	0.99841 05024 18	1.79669 37496 46
88	1.55293 42654 02	1.09553 97094 84	0.99929 33553 76	1.79792 30606 37
89	1.56186 86652 03	1.09830 30225 21	0.99982 33086 41	1.79866 12675 48
90	1.57079 63267 95	1.10106 21687 58	1.00000 00000 00	1.79890 74399 48

K = 2.65213 80046 30204   E = 1.09265 03455 37715
K′ = 1.60608 13494 10364   E′ = 1.53666 97975 68556

r	u=(r/90)K=F(ϕ,k)	sn u	cn u	dn u
0	0.00000 00000 00	0.00000 00000 00	1.00000 00000 00	1.00000 00000 00
1	0.02946 82000 51	0.02946 00375 17	0.99956 59588 99	0.99960 30686 26
2	0.05893 64001 03	0.05887 11647 77	0.99826 55888 88	0.99841 39662 23
3	0.08840 46001 54	0.08818 47953 09	0.99610 41320 45	0.99643 77509 42
4	0.11787 28002 06	0.11735 29856 59	0.99309 02661 68	0.99368 27966 58
5	0.14734 10002 57	0.14632 87456 38	0.98923 60174 40	0.99016 07095 06
6	0.17680 92003 09	0.17506 63353 53	0.98455 66404 36	0.98588 62132 22
7	0.20627 74003 60	0.20352 15451 15	0.97907 04676 75	0.98087 70053 78
8	0.23574 56004 12	0.23165 19547 03	0.97279 87314 35	0.97515 35871 16
9	0.26521 38004 63	0.25941 71689 41	0.96576 53609 75	0.96873 90693 93
10	0.29468 20005 14	0.28677 90270 84	0.95799 67586 71	0.96165 89590 84
11	0.32415 02005 66	0.31370 17840 39	0.94952 15588 34	0.95394 09285 44
12	0.35361 84006 17	0.34015 22620 78	0.94037 03731 00	0.94561 45723 62
13	0.38308 66006 69	0.36609 99722 54	0.93057 55263 90	0.93671 11551 19
14	0.41255 48007 20	0.39151 72053 29	0.92017 07873 71	0.92726 33539 08
15	0.44202 30007 72	0.41637 90925 43	0.90919 10972 36	0.91730 49992 78
16	0.47149 12008 23	0.44066 36370 91	0.89767 23004 22	0.90687 08180 62
17	0.50095 94008 75	0.46435 17175 84	0.88565 08806 39	0.89599 61812 92
18	0.53042 76009 26	0.48742 70651 89	0.87316 37052 25	0.88471 68601 21
19	0.55989 58009 77	0.50987 62164 54	0.86024 77805 23	0.87306 87923 08
20	0.58936 40010 29	0.53168 84440 67	0.84694 00205 72	0.86108 78614 50
21	0.61883 22010 80	0.55285 56679 85	0.83327 70309 91	0.84880 96907 88
22	0.64830 04011 32	0.57337 23494 98	0.81929 49095 60	0.83626 94529 92
23	0.67776 86011 83	0.59323 53708 22	0.80502 90645 72	0.82350 16969 80
24	0.70723 68012 35	0.61244 39028 13	0.79051 40516 82	0.81054 01924 48
25	0.73670 50012 86	0.63099 92633 57	0.77578 34296 00	0.79741 77924 48
26	0.76617 32013 38	0.64890 47688 56	0.76086 96346 65	0.78416 63140 54
27	0.79564 14013 89	0.66616 55811 17	0.74580 38740 42	0.77081 64368 65
28	0.82510 96014 41	0.68278 85517 72	0.73061 60370 32	0.75739 76188 58
29	0.85457 78014 92	0.69878 20661 80	0.71533 46237 85	0.74393 80289 13
30	0.88404 60015 43	0.71415 58885 35	0.69998 66904 96	0.73046 44951 35
31	0.91351 42015 95	0.72892 10097 34	0.68459 78100 82	0.71700 24680 01
32	0.94298 24016 46	0.74308 94993 14	0.66919 20471 80	0.70357 59972 50
33	0.97245 06016 98	0.75667 43625 74	0.65379 19462 82	0.69020 77213 45
34	1.00191 88017 49	0.76968 94037 93	0.63841 85317 56	0.67691 88683 55
35	1.03138 70018 01	0.78214 90962 79	0.62309 13185 00	0.66372 92670 23
36	1.06085 52018 52	0.79406 84597 81	0.60782 83320 00	0.65065 73668 63
37	1.09032 34019 04	0.80546 29456 57	0.59264 61365 55	0.63772 02661 03
38	1.11979 16019 55	0.81634 83300 36	0.57755 98705 31	0.62493 37463 79
39	1.14925 98020 06	0.82674 06150 82	0.56258 32875 00	0.61231 23130 96
40	1.17872 80020 58	0.83665 59383 47	0.54772 88022 63	0.59986 92404 78
41	1.20819 62021 09	0.84611 04901 32	0.53300 75407 43	0.58761 66203 80
42	1.23766 44021 61	0.85512 04386 38	0.51842 93929 02	0.57556 54139 95
43	1.26713 26022 12	0.86370 18626 92	0.50400 30678 30	0.56372 55057 02
44	1.29660 08022 64	0.87187 06917 18	0.48973 61503 14	0.55210 57583 37
45	1.32606 90023 15	0.87964 26526 03	0.47563 51582 06	0.54071 40692 85

q = 0.14919 73690 67429 2   D(90) = 1.84940 62884 70240
q'= 0.00558 45970 58516 804   1/D(90) = 0.54071 40692 84993

r	ϕ	$E(\phi,k)$	A(r)	D(r)
0	0.00000 00000 00	0.00000 00000 00	0.00000 00000 00	1.00000 00000 00
1	0.02946 43005 46	0.02946 04019 69	0.01593 35232 76	1.00025 52823 14
2	0.05890 52240 08	0.05887 40775 89	0.03186 49626 33	1.00102 08307 83
3	0.08829 94928 41	0.08819 46103 01	0.04779 22272 30	1.00229 57502 85
4	0.11762 40275 70	0.11737 61987 81	0.06371 32124 02	1.00407 85499 59
5	0.14685 60433 56	0.14637 39537 82	0.07962 57928 05	1.00636 71447 19
6	0.17597 31436 23	0.17514 41823 51	0.09552 78156 29	1.00915 88573 68
7	0.20495 34098 80	0.20364 46556 59	0.11141 70938 99	1.01245 04213 20
8	0.23377 54869 10	0.23183 48571 05	0.12729 13998 87	1.01623 79839 24
9	0.26241 86625 81	0.25967 62077 67	0.14314 84586 62	1.02051 71103 91
10	0.29086 29416 51	0.28713 22668 02	0.15898 59417 88	1.02528 27883 19
11	0.31908 91130 06	0.31416 89049 28	0.17480 14612 03	1.03052 94328 26
12	0.34707 88099 22	0.34075 44496 86	0.19059 25632 91	1.03625 08922 71
13	0.37481 45630 07	0.36685 98017 37	0.20635 67231 69	1.04244 04545 79
14	0.40227 98456 25	0.39245 85219 99	0.22209 13392 14	1.04909 08541 62
15	0.42945 91117 10	0.41752 68899 71	0.23779 37278 35	1.05619 42794 27
16	0.45633 78259 51	0.44204 39340 25	0.25346 11185 26	1.06374 23808 75
17	0.48290 24864 77	0.46599 14349 40	0.26909 06492 01	1.07172 62797 92
18	0.50914 06402 21	0.48935 39042 56	0.28467 93618 40	1.08013 65775 20
19	0.53504 08912 41	0.51211 85393 93	0.30022 41984 48	1.08896 33653 07
20	0.56059 29023 43	0.53427 51576 71	0.31572 19973 59	1.09819 62347 30
21	0.58578 73904 08	0.55581 61115 85	0.33116 94898 83	1.10782 42887 02
22	0.61061 61158 80	0.57673 61877 50	0.34656 32973 19	1.11783 61530 25
23	0.63507 18668 89	0.59703 24920 38	0.36189 99283 35	1.12821 99885 21
24	0.65914 84385 39	0.61670 43233 61	0.37717 57767 45	1.13896 35037 05
25	0.68284 06078 77	0.63575 30385 51	0.39238 71196 71	1.15005 39680 10
26	0.70614 41050 74	0.65418 19106 58	0.40753 01161 13	1.16147 82255 48
27	0.72905 55813 65	0.67199 59828 64	0.42260 08059 26	1.17322 27094 08
28	0.75157 25742 39	0.68920 19200 59	0.43759 51092 21	1.18527 34564 68
29	0.77369 34704 14	0.70580 78599 27	0.45250 88261 81	1.19761 61227 23
30	0.79541 74670 48	0.72182 32652 29	0.46733 76373 13	1.21023 59991 16
31	0.81674 45316 46	0.73725 87787 23	0.48207 71041 21	1.22311 80278 57
32	0.83767 53611 00	0.75212 60820 11	0.49672 26702 17	1.23624 68192 22
33	0.85821 13402 18	0.76643 77593 65	0.51126 96628 59	1.24960 66688 17
34	0.87835 45001 28	0.78020 71674 12	0.52571 32949 26	1.26318 15752 91
35	0.89810 74768 55	0.79344 83113 72	0.54004 86673 19	1.27695 52584 93
36	0.91747 34703 59	0.80617 57283 70	0.55427 07717 89	1.29091 11780 43
37	0.93645 62042 88	0.81840 43781 98	0.56837 44941 90	1.30503 25523 09
38	0.95505 98866 51	0.83014 95417 50	0.58235 46181 42	1.31930 23777 78
39	0.97328 91716 06	0.84142 67272 43	0.59620 58291 15	1.33370 34487 89
40	0.99114 91225 00	0.85225 15842 08	0.60992 27189 03	1.34821 83776 15
41	1.00864 51763 07	0.86263 98251 75	0.62349 97905 04	1.36282 96148 86
42	1.02578 31095 32	0.87260 71548 62	0.63693 14633 69	1.37751 94703 06
43	1.04256 90056 90	0.88216 92066 33	0.65021 20790 41	1.39227 01336 66
44	1.05900 92243 82	0.89134 14859 37	0.66333 59071 35	1.40706 36961 17
45	1.07511 03720 17	0.90013 93204 07	0.67629 71516 80	1.42188 21716 87

K = 2.65213 80046 30204   E = 1.09265 03455 37715
K'= 1.60608 13494 10364   E'= 1.53666 97975 68556

r	u=(r/90)K=F(ϕ,k)	sn u	cn u	dn u
45	1.32606 90023 15	0.87964 26526 03	0.47563 51582 06	0.54071 40692 85
46	1.35553 72023 67	0.88703 32231 08	0.46170 56000 34	0.52955 74268 30
47	1.38500 54024 18	0.89405 75913 84	0.44795 20323 52	0.51864 19662 86
48	1.41447 36024 69	0.90073 06212 21	0.43437 81163 85	0.50797 30255 04
49	1.44394 18025 21	0.90706 68225 80	0.42098 66736 30	0.49755 51993 98
50	1.47341 00025 72	0.91308 03270 16	0.40777 97400 75	0.48739 23931 99
51	1.50287 82026 24	0.91878 48675 72	0.39475 86188 05	0.47748 78741 94
52	1.53234 64026 75	0.92419 37627 42	0.38192 39307 89	0.46784 43217 65
53	1.56181 46027 27	0.92931 99041 28	0.36927 56636 88	0.45846 38755 63
54	1.59128 28027 78	0.93417 57474 15	0.35681 32185 64	0.44934 81817 21
55	1.62075 10028 30	0.93877 33063 13	0.34453 54544 21	0.44049 84370 12
56	1.65021 92028 81	0.94312 41491 43	0.33244 07305 13	0.43191 54309 19
57	1.67968 74029 32	0.94723 93977 40	0.32052 69464 02	0.42359 95855 75
58	1.70915 56029 84	0.95112 97284 10	0.30879 15797 66	0.41555 09935 89
59	1.73862 38030 35	0.95480 53746 46	0.29723 17219 75	0.40776 94537 62
60	1.76809 20030 87	0.95827 61313 63	0.28584 41114 65	0.40025 45047 30
61	1.79756 02031 38	0.96155 13604 40	0.27462 51649 71	0.39300 54565 83
62	1.82702 84031 90	0.96463 99973 29	0.26357 10066 63	0.38602 14205 10
63	1.85649 66032 41	0.96755 05585 68	0.25267 74952 68	0.37930 13365 31
64	1.88596 48032 93	0.97029 11500 13	0.24194 02492 47	0.37284 39993 95
65	1.91543 30033 44	0.97286 94756 34	0.23135 46701 04	0.36664 80827 14
66	1.94490 12033 95	0.97529 28467 31	0.22091 59639 22	0.36071 21614 04
67	1.97436 94034 47	0.97756 81914 49	0.21061 91612 05	0.35503 47325 27
68	2.00383 76034 98	0.97970 20644 83	0.20045 91351 08	0.34961 42345 95
69	2.03330 58035 50	0.98170 06568 54	0.19043 06181 57	0.34444 90654 33
70	2.06277 40036 01	0.98356 98056 93	0.18052 82175 40	0.33953 75986 72
71	2.09224 22036 53	0.98531 50039 28	0.17074 64290 51	0.33487 81989 44
72	2.12171 04037 04	0.98694 14098 26	0.16107 96497 74	0.33046 92358 67
73	2.15117 86037 56	0.98845 38563 13	0.15152 21895 98	0.32630 90968 77
74	2.18064 68038 07	0.98985 68600 33	0.14206 82816 34	0.32239 61989 95
75	2.21011 50038 59	0.99115 46300 86	0.13271 20916 09	0.31872 89995 72
76	2.23958 32039 10	0.99235 10764 16	0.12344 77263 31	0.31530 60060 99
77	2.26905 14039 61	0.99344 98178 06	0.11426 92412 72	0.31212 57851 21
78	2.29851 96040 13	0.99445 41894 60	0.10517 06473 61	0.30918 69703 24
79	2.32798 78040 64	0.99536 72501 33	0.09614 59170 37	0.30648 82698 44
80	2.35745 60041 16	0.99619 17888 06	0.08718 89896 47	0.30402 84728 39
81	2.38692 42041 67	0.99693 03308 68	0.07829 37762 23	0.30180 64553 81
82	2.41639 24042 19	0.99758 51438 05	0.06945 41637 27	0.29982 11856 94
83	2.44586 06042 70	0.99815 82423 76	0.06066 40187 98	0.29807 17287 89
84	2.47532 88043 22	0.99865 13932 66	0.05191 71910 72	0.29655 72505 24
85	2.50479 70043 73	0.99906 61192 09	0.04320 75161 15	0.29527 70211 10
86	2.53426 52044 24	0.99940 37025 77	0.03452 88180 36	0.29423 04181 03
87	2.56373 34044 76	0.99966 51884 20	0.02587 49118 15	0.29341 69289 01
88	2.59320 16045 27	0.99985 13869 60	0.01723 96054 01	0.29283 61527 52
89	2.62266 98045 79	0.99996 28755 37	0.00861 67016 29	0.29248 78023 08
90	2.65213 80046 30	1.00000 00000 00	0.00000 00000 00	0.29237 17047 23

ELLIPTIC FUNCTIONS TABLE $\theta = 73°$

$q = 0.14919\ 73690\ 67429\ 2$

$q' = 0.00558\ 45970\ 58516\ 804$

$D(90) = 1.84940\ 62884\ 70240$

$1/D(90) = 0.54071\ 40692\ 84993$

r	ϕ	$E(\phi,k)$	$A(r)$	$D(r)$
45	1.07511 03720 17	0.90013 93204 07	0.67629 71516 80	1.42188 21716 87
46	1.09087 92741 90	0.90857 78162 38	0.68908 99577 83	1.43670 75190 03
47	1.10632 29497 28	0.91667 18204 85	0.70170 84186 15	1.45152 16632 18
48	1.12144 85863 67	0.92443 58888 88	0.71414 65827 01	1.46630 65180 86
49	1.13626 35180 59	0.93188 42588 14	0.72639 84614 82	1.48104 40081 79
50	1.15077 52038 73	0.93903 08269 43	0.73845 80371 59	1.49571 60912 19
51	1.16499 12084 30	0.94588 91312 95	0.75031 92707 70	1.51030 47804 75
52	1.17891 91838 52	0.95247 23372 23	0.76197 61105 00	1.52479 21672 22
53	1.19256 68531 48	0.95879 32270 14	0.77342 25002 05	1.53916 04432 13
54	1.20594 19949 94	0.96486 41927 47	0.78465 23881 10	1.55339 19231 46
55	1.21905 24298 52	0.97069 72320 71	0.79565 97356 80	1.56746 90670 83
56	1.23190 60073 45	0.97630 39466 02	0.80643 85266 38	1.58137 45028 00
57	1.24451 05948 56	0.98169 55426 40	0.81698 27760 93	1.59509 10480 33
58	1.25687 40672 59	0.98688 28339 38	0.82728 65397 75	1.60860 17325 78
59	1.26900 42977 44	0.99187 62462 71	0.83734 39233 43	1.62188 98202 34
60	1.28090 91496 60	0.99668 58235 68	0.84714 90917 40	1.63493 88305 31
61	1.29259 64693 17	1.00132 12354 10	0.85669 62785 87	1.64773 25602 27
62	1.30407 40796 91	1.00579 17856 80	0.86597 97955 64	1.66025 51045 36
63	1.31534 97749 83	1.01010 64222 06	0.87499 40417 90	1.67249 08780 54
64	1.32643 13159 52	1.01427 37472 38	0.88373 35131 45	1.68442 46353 47
65	1.33732 64260 03	1.01830 20286 03	0.89219 28115 28	1.69604 14911 69
66	1.34804 27879 43	1.02219 92114 26	0.90036 66540 32	1.70732 69402 90
67	1.35858 80413 90	1.02597 29303 05	0.90824 98819 91	1.71826 68768 78
68	1.36896 97807 67	1.02963 05218 29	0.91583 74698 96	1.72884 76134 18
69	1.37919 55538 36	1.03317 90373 60	0.92312 45341 49	1.73905 58991 45
70	1.38927 28607 56	1.03662 52560 04	0.93010 63416 34	1.74887 89379 33
71	1.39920 91535 87	1.03997 56977 05	0.93677 83180 75	1.75830 44056 41
72	1.40901 18362 41	1.04323 66364 05	0.94313 60561 76	1.76732 04668 59
73	1.41868 82648 17	1.04641 41132 20	0.94917 53235 02	1.77591 57910 45
74	1.42824 57483 02	1.04951 39496 01	0.95489 20700 96	1.78407 95680 18
75	1.43769 15496 07	1.05254 17604 40	0.96028 24358 06	1.79180 15227 69
76	1.44703 28868 96	1.05550 29671 01	0.96534 27572 99	1.79907 19295 89
77	1.45627 69352 04	1.05840 28103 53	0.97006 95747 50	1.80588 16254 63
78	1.46543 08282 95	1.06124 63631 87	0.97445 96381 89	1.81222 20227 23
79	1.47450 16607 46	1.06403 85435 14	0.97850 99134 81	1.81808 51209 25
80	1.48349 64902 50	1.06678 41267 38	0.98221 75879 31	1.82346 35179 47
81	1.49242 23400 79	1.06948 77581 91	0.98558 00754 97	1.82835 04202 63
82	1.50128 62017 36	1.07215 39654 46	0.98859 50215 98	1.83273 96523 97
83	1.51009 50377 32	1.07478 71704 94	0.99126 03075 00	1.83662 56655 23
84	1.51885 57845 02	1.07739 17018 15	0.99357 40542 76	1.84000 35452 12
85	1.52757 53554 31	1.07997 18063 25	0.99553 46263 24	1.84286 90182 90
86	1.53626 06439 73	1.08253 16612 28	0.99714 06344 32	1.84521 84588 19
87	1.54491 85268 53	1.08507 53857 78	0.99839 09383 89	1.84704 88931 67
88	1.55355 58673 33	1.08760 70529 62	0.99928 46491 31	1.84835 80041 76
89	1.56217 95185 34	1.09013 07011 24	0.99982 11304 10	1.84914 41344 08
90	1.57079 63267 95	1.09265 03455 38	1.00000 00000 00	1.84940 62884 70

K = 2.70806 76145 90486   E = 1.08442 52193 72543
K'= 1.60197 85300 86952   E'= 1.54052 15741 27631

r	u=(r/90)K=F(ϕ,k)	sn u	cn u	dn u
0	0.00000 00000 00	0.00000 00000 00	1.00000 00000 00	1.00000 00000 00
1	0.03008 96401 62	0.03008 09072 49	0.99954 74671 17	0.99958 18559 24
2	0.06017 92803 24	0.06010 94898 54	0.99819 17898 03	0.99832 92852 55
3	0.09026 89204 86	0.09003 37861 78	0.99593 87116 42	0.99624 78530 43
4	0.12035 85606 48	0.11980 25552 61	0.99279 77375 85	0.99334 67693 46
5	0.15044 82008 11	0.14936 56239 34	0.98878 20338 11	0.98963 87930 37
6	0.18053 78409 73	0.17867 42184 34	0.98390 82902 73	0.98514 00997 55
7	0.21062 74811 35	0.20768 12759 69	0.97819 65485 59	0.97987 01165 58
8	0.24071 71212 97	0.23634 17321 48	0.97166 99983 25	0.97385 13263 70
9	0.27080 67614 59	0.26461 27807 78	0.96435 47460 60	0.96710 90458 73
10	0.30089 64016 21	0.29245 41031 83	0.95627 95603 44	0.95967 11808 22
11	0.33098 60417 83	0.31982 80648 61	0.94747 55980 64	0.95156 79630 86
12	0.36107 56819 45	0.34669 98780 21	0.93797 61162 10	0.94283 16738 39
13	0.39116 53221 08	0.37303 77292 45	0.92781 61739 05	0.93349 63574 13
14	0.42125 49622 70	0.39881 28721 93	0.91703 23292 96	0.92359 75302 15
15	0.45134 46024 32	0.42399 96859 32	0.90566 23357 13	0.91317 18889 82
16	0.48143 42425 94	0.44857 57000 38	0.89374 48412 92	0.90225 70223 81
17	0.51152 38827 56	0.47252 15881 50	0.88131 90958 63	0.89089 11296 30
18	0.54161 35229 18	0.49582 11320 93	0.86842 46685 64	0.87911 27494 50
19	0.57170 31630 80	0.51846 11590 42	0.85510 11791 39	0.86696 05022 00
20	0.60179 28032 42	0.54043 14544 67	0.84138 80454 48	0.85447 28476 22
21	0.63188 24434 04	0.56172 46537 93	0.82732 42492 04	0.84168 78601 40
22	0.66197 20835 67	0.58233 61158 12	0.81294 81214 82	0.82864 30231 92
23	0.69206 17237 29	0.60226 37808 88	0.79829 71490 81	0.81537 50436 25
24	0.72215 13638 91	0.62150 80170 20	0.78340 78023 48	0.80191 96867 72
25	0.75224 10040 53	0.64007 14566 46	0.76831 53847 13	0.78831 16324 05
26	0.78233 06442 15	0.65795 88270 01	0.75305 39037 62	0.77458 43514 38
27	0.81242 02843 77	0.67517 67766 11	0.73765 59633 90	0.76077 00029 14
28	0.84250 99245 39	0.69173 37003 01	0.72215 26762 87	0.74689 93505 77
29	0.87259 95647 01	0.70763 95648 59	0.70657 35957 74	0.73300 16980 64
30	0.90268 92048 63	0.72290 57372 62	0.69094 66658 39	0.71910 48416 34
31	0.93277 88450 26	0.73754 48170 76	0.67529 81880 65	0.70523 50391 61
32	0.96286 84851 88	0.75157 04744 52	0.65965 28040 82	0.69141 69940 87
33	0.99295 81253 50	0.76499 72948 28	0.64403 34920 69	0.67767 38529 06
34	1.02304 77655 12	0.77784 06312 79	0.62846 15758 60	0.66402 72148 04
35	1.05313 74056 74	0.79011 64651 83	0.61295 67451 67	0.65049 71520 19
36	1.08322 70458 36	0.80184 12757 18	0.59753 70855 07	0.63710 22395 56
37	1.11331 66859 98	0.81303 19184 84	0.58221 91164 22	0.62385 95929 22
38	1.14340 63261 60	0.82370 55134 30	0.56701 78367 08	0.61078 49126 19
39	1.17349 59663 23	0.83387 93420 75	0.55194 67753 87	0.59789 25342 04
40	1.20358 56064 85	0.84357 07539 36	0.53701 80472 80	0.58519 54828 06
41	1.23367 52466 47	0.85279 70819 41	0.52224 24121 36	0.57270 55310 93
42	1.26376 48868 09	0.86157 55665 56	0.50762 93363 40	0.56043 32597 63
43	1.29385 45269 71	0.86992 32882 58	0.49318 70563 45	0.54838 81197 22
44	1.32394 41671 33	0.87785 71079 44	0.47892 26430 57	0.53657 84952 24
45	1.35403 38072 95	0.88539 36148 48	0.46484 20664 99	0.52501 17673 13

q = 0.15591 66592 65792 2   D(90) = 1.90471 92125 20129
q' = 0.00493 84132 64213 395   1/D(90) = 0.52501 17673 12885

r	ϕ	$E(\phi,k)$	A(r)	D(r)
0	0.00000 00000 00	0.00000 00000 00	0.00000 00000 00	1.00000 00000 00
1	0.03008 54456 04	0.03008 12520 98	0.01579 71162 83	1.00027 13893 55
2	0.06014 57462 76	0.06011 22458 52	0.03159 24377 74	1.00108 52420 25
3	0.09015 58689 15	0.09004 30720 02	0.04738 41619 99	1.00244 06121 35
4	0.12009 10029 03	0.11982 45143 17	0.06317 04711 52	1.00433 59242 61
5	0.14992 66684 27	0.14940 83834 09	0.07894 95244 84	1.00676 89749 78
6	0.17963 88213 64	0.17874 78356 37	0.09471 94507 75	1.00973 69350 33
7	0.20920 39536 81	0.20779 76727 45	0.11047 83408 94	1.01323 63521 31
8	0.23859 91883 97	0.23651 46183 00	0.12622 42404 91	1.01726 31543 46
9	0.26780 23682 57	0.26485 75675 75	0.14195 51428 22	1.02181 26541 48
10	0.29679 21373 65	0.29278 78081 34	0.15766 89817 54	1.02687 95530 54
11	0.32554 80151 74	0.32026 92090 22	0.17336 36249 55	1.03245 79468 86
12	0.35405 04623 42	0.34726 83771 71	0.18903 68672 93	1.03854 13316 64
13	0.38228 09381 10	0.37375 47802 73	0.20468 64244 82	1.04512 26100 98
14	0.41022 19489 77	0.39970 08360 70	0.22030 99269 71	1.05219 40987 08
15	0.43785 70886 08	0.42508 19685 95	0.23590 49141 15	1.05974 75355 55
16	0.46517 10689 93	0.44987 66324 83	0.25146 88286 45	1.06777 40885 85
17	0.49214 97430 31	0.47406 63069 70	0.26699 90114 44	1.07626 43645 83
18	0.51878 01187 95	0.49763 54615 99	0.28249 26966 67	1.08520 84187 41
19	0.54505 03658 29	0.52057 14960 26	0.29794 70071 94	1.09459 57648 29
20	0.57094 98139 21	0.54286 46565 55	0.31335 89504 69	1.10441 53859 69
21	0.59646 89448 41	0.56450 79322 22	0.32872 54147 02	1.11465 57460 11
22	0.62159 93776 03	0.58549 69333 43	0.34404 31654 75	1.12530 48015 12
23	0.64633 38478 44	0.60582 97554 70	0.35930 88427 53	1.13635 00142 93
24	0.67066 61819 15	0.62550 68316 71	0.37451 89583 16	1.14777 83645 95
25	0.69459 12663 39	0.64453 07759 37	0.38966 98936 20	1.15957 63648 14
26	0.71810 50132 35	0.66290 62203 99	0.40475 78980 97	1.17173 00738 07
27	0.74120 43223 49	0.68063 96488 51	0.41977 90879 05	1.18422 51117 70
28	0.76388 70402 71	0.69773 92288 59	0.43472 94451 35	1.19704 66756 73
29	0.78615 19174 37	0.71421 46445 20	0.44960 48174 72	1.21017 95552 52
30	0.80799 85634 37	0.73007 69316 94	0.46440 09183 32	1.22360 81495 34
31	0.82942 74011 53	0.74533 83172 89	0.47911 33274 59	1.23731 64839 03
32	0.85043 96201 95	0.76001 20639 20	0.49373 74919 99	1.25128 82276 79
33	0.87103 71300 56	0.77411 23210 61	0.50826 87280 43	1.26550 67122 09
34	0.89122 25133 82	0.78765 39835 55	0.52270 22226 40	1.27995 49494 51
35	0.91099 89796 96	0.80065 25581 56	0.53703 30362 86	1.29461 56510 41
36	0.93037 03198 73	0.81312 40385 78	0.55125 61058 68	1.30947 12478 18
37	0.94934 08616 46	0.82508 47893 57	0.56536 62480 82	1.32450 39098 11
38	0.96791 54263 37	0.83655 14386 72	0.57935 81632 96	1.33969 55666 42
39	0.98609 92870 25	0.84754 07801 46	0.59322 64398 67	1.35502 79283 54
40	1.00389 81282 83	0.85806 96835 27	0.60696 55588 99	1.37048 25066 29
41	1.02131 80076 13	0.86815 50140 46	0.62056 98994 26	1.38604 06363 72
42	1.03836 53186 67	0.87781 35601 84	0.63403 37440 24	1.40168 34976 59
43	1.05504 67563 11	0.88706 19695 11	0.64735 12848 18	1.41739 21380 03
44	1.07136 92835 79	0.89591 66921 96	0.66051 66298 98	1.43314 74949 29
45	1.08734 01005 30	0.90439 39317 78	0.67352 38100 99	1.44893 04188 24

K = 2.70806 76145 90486   E = 1.08442 52193 72543
K′ = 1.60197 85300 86952   E′ = 1.54052 15741 27631

r	u=(r/90)K=F(φ,k)	sn u	cn u	dn u
45	1.35403 38072 95	0.88539 36148 48	0.46484 20664 99	0.52501 17673 13
46	1.38412 34474 57	0.89254 90814 85	0.45095 02601 62	0.51369 43770 02
47	1.41421 30876 19	0.89933 94251 41	0.43725 11845 46	0.50263 18877 16
48	1.44430 27277 82	0.90578 01754 21	0.42374 78894 50	0.49182 90465 73
49	1.47439 23679 44	0.91188 64473 67	0.41044 25746 79	0.48128 98441 73
50	1.50448 20081 06	0.91767 29196 62	0.39733 66488 49	0.47101 75726 16
51	1.53457 16482 68	0.92315 38174 69	0.38443 07860 88	0.46101 48815 19
52	1.56466 12884 30	0.92834 28994 29	0.37172 49804 35	0.45128 38318 73
53	1.59475 09285 92	0.93325 34484 16	0.35921 85978 20	0.44182 59476 08
54	1.62484 05687 54	0.93789 82656 27	0.34691 04255 19	0.43264 22647 79
55	1.65493 02089 16	0.94228 96676 25	0.33479 87190 64	0.42373 33783 27
56	1.68501 98490 79	0.94643 94859 86	0.32288 12465 40	0.41509 94863 94
57	1.71510 94892 41	0.95035 90692 00	0.31115 53303 25	0.40674 04321 93
58	1.74519 91294 03	0.95405 92865 42	0.29961 78862 53	0.39865 57434 58
59	1.77528 87695 65	0.95755 05336 04	0.28826 54602 88	0.39084 46695 23
60	1.80537 84097 27	0.96084 27392 44	0.27709 42627 38	0.38330 62160 88
61	1.83546 80498 89	0.96394 53737 15	0.26610 02001 01	0.37603 91777 33
62	1.86555 76900 51	0.96686 74577 49	0.25527 89046 25	0.36904 21682 71
63	1.89564 73302 13	0.96961 75724 12	0.24462 57616 64	0.36231 36490 15
64	1.92573 69703 75	0.97220 38695 52	0.23413 59349 37	0.35585 19550 59
65	1.95582 66105 38	0.97463 40826 78	0.22380 43897 76	0.34965 53196 56
66	1.98591 62507 00	0.97691 55381 40	0.21362 59144 85	0.34372 18967 98
67	2.01600 58908 62	0.97905 51664 81	0.20359 51398 89	0.33804 97820 88
68	2.04609 55310 24	0.98105 95138 44	0.19370 65571 86	0.33263 70319 94
69	2.07618 51711 86	0.98293 47533 49	0.18395 45342 18	0.32748 16815 95
70	2.10627 48113 48	0.98468 66963 53	0.17433 33302 21	0.32258 17608 88
71	2.13636 44515 10	0.98632 08035 07	0.16483 71091 99	0.31793 53097 60
72	2.16645 40916 72	0.98784 21955 62	0.15545 99519 73	0.31354 03917 07
73	2.19654 37318 35	0.98925 56638 52	0.14619 58670 28	0.30939 51063 71
74	2.22663 33719 97	0.99056 56804 23	0.13703 88002 26	0.30549 76009 94
75	2.25672 30121 59	0.99177 64077 50	0.12798 26434 73	0.30184 60808 34
76	2.28681 26523 21	0.99289 17080 17	0.11902 12424 36	0.29843 88186 41
77	2.31690 22924 83	0.99391 51519 31	0.11014 84033 57	0.29527 41632 34
78	2.34699 19326 45	0.99485 00270 37	0.10135 78990 73	0.29235 05472 56
79	2.37708 15728 07	0.99569 93455 22	0.09264 34742 81	0.28966 64941 55
80	2.40717 12129 69	0.99646 58514 85	0.08399 88501 38	0.28722 06244 44
81	2.43726 08531 31	0.99715 20276 60	0.07541 77282 49	0.28501 16612 94
82	2.46735 04932 94	0.99776 01015 82	0.06689 37941 09	0.28303 84354 91
83	2.49744 01334 56	0.99829 20511 90	0.05842 07200 46	0.28129 98898 11
84	2.52752 97736 18	0.99874 96098 44	0.04999 21677 47	0.27979 50828 37
85	2.55761 94137 80	0.99913 42707 75	0.04160 17903 91	0.27852 31922 56
86	2.58770 90539 42	0.99944 72909 38	0.03324 32344 59	0.27748 35176 63
87	2.61779 86941 04	0.99968 96942 86	0.02491 01412 67	0.27667 54828 88
88	2.64788 83342 66	0.99986 22744 47	0.01659 61482 72	0.27609 86378 82
89	2.67797 79744 28	0.99996 55968 07	0.00829 48901 94	0.27575 26601 58
90	2.70806 76145 90	1.00000 00000 00	0.00000 00000 00	0.27563 73558 17

q = 0.15591 66592 65792 2   D(90) = 1.90471 92125 20129
q' = 0.00493 84132 64213 395   1/D(90) = 0.52501 17673 12885

r	ϕ	$E(\phi,k)$	$A(r)$	$D(r)$
45	1.08734 01005 30	0.90439 39317 78	0.67352 38100 99	1.44893 04188 24
46	1.10296 66150 17	0.91250 96027 43	0.68636 67861 62	1.46472 16960 47
47	1.11825 64153 43	0.92027 92944 48	0.69903 94562 28	1.48050 20722 61
48	1.13321 72447 80	0.92771 82409 23	0.71153 56636 75	1.49625 22759 62
49	1.14785 69779 07	0.93484 12960 85	0.72384 92052 57	1.51195 30421 82
50	1.16218 35987 29	0.94166 29139 09	0.73597 38395 41	1.52758 51363 26
51	1.17620 51805 04	0.94819 71331 12	0.74790 32956 14	1.54312 93781 24
52	1.18992 98672 28	0.95445 75659 15	0.75963 12820 45	1.55856 66656 50
53	1.20336 58567 07	0.96045 73904 88	0.77115 14960 67	1.57387 79993 96
54	1.21652 13851 39	0.96620 93466 71	0.78245 76329 76	1.58904 45063 53
55	1.22940 47131 46	0.97172 57346 37	0.79354 33957 05	1.60404 74640 63
56	1.24202 41131 76	0.97701 84161 26	0.80440 25045 62	1.61886 83246 27
57	1.25438 78581 95	0.98209 88179 53	0.81502 87071 01	1.63348 87386 06
58	1.26650 42116 10	0.98697 79375 06	0.82541 57881 03	1.64789 05788 08
59	1.27838 14183 39	0.99166 63499 41	0.83555 75796 43	1.66205 59639 01
60	1.29002 76969 62	0.99617 42168 60	0.84544 79712 14	1.67596 72818 31
61	1.30145 12328 88	1.00051 12962 28	0.85508 09198 87	1.68960 72130 02
62	1.31266 01724 60	1.00468 69533 50	0.86445 04604 78	1.70295 87531 86
63	1.32366 26179 50	1.00871 01727 03	0.87355 07156 93	1.71600 52361 18
64	1.33446 67233 69	1.01258 95704 88	0.88237 59062 36	1.72873 03557 51
65	1.34508 01910 40	1.01633 34077 44	0.89092 03608 37	1.74111 81881 19
66	1.35551 12688 77	1.01994 96039 02	0.89917 85261 90	1.75315 32127 94
67	1.36576 77483 23	1.02344 57506 66	0.90714 49767 68	1.76482 03338 74
68	1.37585 74628 80	1.02682 91261 35	0.91481 44244 84	1.77610 49004 86
69	1.38578 81872 07	1.03010 67090 65	0.92218 17281 90	1.78699 27267 64
70	1.39556 76367 24	1.03328 51932 16	0.92924 19029 63	1.79747 01112 63
71	1.40520 34676 85	1.03637 10017 13	0.93599 01291 86	1.80752 38557 78
72	1.41470 32776 89	1.03937 03013 72	0.94242 17613 68	1.81714 12835 36
73	1.42407 46065 81	1.04228 90169 58	0.94853 23367 03	1.82631 02567 24
74	1.43332 49377 10	1.04513 28453 23	0.95431 75833 37	1.83501 91933 27
75	1.44246 16995 29	1.04790 72694 15	0.95977 34283 17	1.84325 70832 46
76	1.45149 22674 76	1.05061 75721 30	0.96489 60052 09	1.85101 35036 54
77	1.46042 39661 44	1.05326 88499 91	0.96968 16613 63	1.85827 86335 81
78	1.46926 40716 84	1.05586 60266 43	0.97412 69647 98	1.86504 32676 88
79	1.47801 98144 35	1.05841 38661 76	0.97822 87107 02	1.87129 88292 03
80	1.48669 83817 53	1.06091 69862 43	0.98198 39275 20	1.87703 73820 10
81	1.49530 69210 17	1.06337 98710 13	0.98538 98826 12	1.88225 16418 48
82	1.50385 25427 93	1.06580 68839 31	0.98844 40874 79	1.88693 49866 14
83	1.51234 23241 43	1.06820 22803 23	0.99114 43025 29	1.89108 14657 45
84	1.52078 33120 49	1.07057 02198 32	0.99348 85413 74	1.89468 58086 56
85	1.52918 25269 49	1.07291 47787 13	0.99547 50746 56	1.89774 34322 35
86	1.53754 69663 69	1.07523 99620 00	0.99710 24333 81	1.90025 04473 54
87	1.54588 36086 22	1.07754 97155 56	0.99836 94117 47	1.90220 36644 12
88	1.55419 94165 76	1.07984 79380 25	0.99927 50694 82	1.90360 05978 79
89	1.56250 13414 76	1.08213 84927 07	0.99981 87336 59	1.90443 94698 37
90	1.57079 63267 95	1.08442 52193 73	1.00000 00000 00	1.90471 92125 20

K = 2.76806 31453 68768   E = 1.07640 51130 76403
K'= 1.59814 20021 12540   E'= 1.54415 04969 14673

r	u=(r/90)K=F(ϕ,k)	sn u	cn u	dn u
0	0.00000 00000 00	0.00000 00000 00	1.00000 00000 00	1.00000 00000 00
1	0.03075 62571 71	0.03074 68874 80	0.99952 72026 86	0.99955 88810 90
2	0.06151 25143 42	0.06143 76388 57	0.99811 09239 62	0.99823 75797 77
3	0.09226 87715 12	0.09201 65268 73	0.99575 74799 03	0.99604 22395 64
4	0.12302 50286 83	0.12242 86356 44	0.99247 73192 24	0.99298 30242 43
5	0.15378 12858 54	0.15262 02507 31	0.98828 49078 41	0.98907 40064 55
6	0.18453 75430 25	0.18253 92309 13	0.98319 85705 73	0.98433 30148 83
7	0.21529 38001 95	0.21213 53563 42	0.97724 02931 67	0.97878 14431 31
8	0.24605 00573 66	0.24136 06483 06	0.97043 54885 56	0.97244 40240 92
9	0.27680 63145 37	0.27016 96565 91	0.96281 27318 73	0.96534 85741 58
10	0.30756 25717 08	0.29851 97111 66	0.95440 34692 13	0.95752 57120 99
11	0.33831 88288 78	0.32637 11357 93	0.94524 17054 49	0.94900 85577 40
12	0.36907 50860 49	0.35368 74220 03	0.93536 36766 08	0.93983 24157 38
13	0.39983 13432 20	0.38043 53627 29	0.92480 75122 88	0.93003 44497 90
14	0.43058 76003 91	0.40658 51457 22	0.91361 28935 60	0.91965 33524 75
15	0.46134 38575 61	0.43211 04076 08	0.90182 07114 71	0.90872 90157 36
16	0.49210 01147 32	0.45698 82501 75	0.88947 27310 05	0.89730 22066 36
17	0.52285 63719 03	0.48119 92210 39	0.87661 12648 55	0.88541 42526 33
18	0.55361 26290 74	0.50472 72613 51	0.86327 88608 84	0.87310 67400 99
19	0.58436 88862 45	0.52755 96236 11	0.84951 80065 99	0.86042 12293 05
20	0.61512 51434 15	0.54968 67629 31	0.83537 08533 69	0.84739 89885 02
21	0.64588 14005 86	0.57110 22052 65	0.82087 89625 40	0.83408 07491 81
22	0.67663 76577 57	0.59180 23962 34	0.80608 30750 07	0.82050 64840 28
23	0.70739 39149 28	0.61178 65341 38	0.79102 29052 61	0.80671 52085 42
24	0.73815 01720 98	0.63105 63907 00	0.77573 69604 17	0.79274 48068 12
25	0.76890 64292 69	0.64961 61229 03	0.76026 23842 23	0.77863 18814 63
26	0.79966 26864 40	0.66747 20790 96	0.74463 48256 88	0.76441 16274 04
27	0.83041 89436 11	0.68463 26022 98	0.72888 83315 51	0.75011 77286 44
28	0.86117 52007 81	0.70110 78333 41	0.71305 52615 53	0.73578 22771 59
29	0.89193 14579 52	0.71690 95162 02	0.69716 62252 14	0.72143 57125 69
30	0.92268 77151 23	0.73205 08075 69	0.68125 00386 33	0.70710 67811 87
31	0.95344 39722 94	0.74654 60923 81	0.66533 36996 95	0.69282 25128 78
32	0.98420 02294 64	0.76041 08067 73	0.64944 23800 02	0.67860 82141 16
33	1.01495 64866 35	0.77366 12695 79	0.63359 94317 81	0.66448 74755 30
34	1.04571 27438 06	0.78631 45232 88	0.61782 64080 36	0.65048 21922 89
35	1.07646 90009 77	0.79838 81850 70	0.60214 30942 40	0.63661 25956 63
36	1.10722 52581 48	0.80990 03083 00	0.58656 75499 17	0.62289 72941 70
37	1.13798 15153 18	0.82086 92547 95	0.57111 61585 29	0.60935 33227 98
38	1.16873 77724 89	0.83131 35777 89	0.55580 36842 12	0.59599 61988 64
39	1.19949 40296 60	0.84125 19155 63	0.54064 33339 65	0.58283 99831 82
40	1.23025 02868 31	0.85070 28954 74	0.52564 68240 48	0.56989 73453 41
41	1.26100 65440 01	0.85968 50480 66	0.51082 44494 27	0.55717 96319 66
42	1.29176 28011 72	0.86821 67308 34	0.49618 51552 60	0.54469 69369 79
43	1.32251 90583 43	0.87631 60611 79	0.48173 66094 87	0.53245 81729 83
44	1.35327 53155 14	0.88400 08580 08	0.46748 52757 48	0.52047 11429 93
45	1.38403 15726 84	0.89128 85914 45	0.45343 64859 16	0.50874 26118 41

q = 0.16303 35348 21580 5

q' = 0.00433 34205 09983 127

D(90) = 1.96563 05108 42837

1/D(90) = 0.50874 26118 40723

r	ϕ	$E(\phi,k)$	A(r)	D(r)
0	0.00000 00000 00	0.00000 00000 00	0.00000 00000 00	1.00000 00000 00
1	0.03075 17340 79	0.03074 72121 84	0.01564 67728 07	1.00028 90225 89
2	0.06147 63549 04	0.06144 02337 13	0.03129 20691 29	1.00115 57568 35
3	0.09214 68754 23	0.09202 52689 69	0.04693 44039 73	1.00259 92024 87
4	0.12273 65595 91	0.12244 93062 99	0.06257 22753 50	1.00461 76935 17
5	0.15321 90444 10	0.15266 04949 12	0.07820 41558 48	1.00720 88996 94
6	0.18356 84579 11	0.18260 85041 17	0.09382 84842 80	1.01036 98287 98
7	0.21375 95318 25	0.21224 48597 28	0.10944 36574 40	1.01409 68294 60
8	0.24376 77078 41	0.24152 32530 65	0.12504 80219 92	1.01838 55946 45
9	0.27356 92364 47	0.27039 98186 47	0.14063 98665 16	1.02323 11657 53
10	0.30314 12675 06	0.29883 33774 37	0.15621 74137 35	1.02862 79373 71
11	0.33246 19318 54	0.32678 56433 06	0.17177 88129 52	1.03456 96626 45
12	0.36151 04133 91	0.35422 13912 23	0.18732 21327 22	1.04104 94592 93
13	0.39026 70112 91	0.38110 85864 76	0.20284 53537 74	1.04805 98162 58
14	0.41871 31921 00	0.40741 84750 56	0.21834 63622 12	1.05559 26009 87
15	0.44683 16316 88	0.43312 56360 27	0.23382 29430 22	1.06363 90673 50
16	0.47460 62471 32	0.45820 79974 20	0.24927 27738 98	1.07218 98642 00
17	0.50202 22187 58	0.48264 68177 20	0.26469 34194 06	1.08123 50445 61
18	0.52906 60027 05	0.50642 66355 40	0.28008 23255 17	1.09076 40754 54
19	0.55572 53344 60	0.52953 51904 12	0.29543 68145 19	1.10076 58483 61
20	0.58198 92239 12	0.55196 33179 49	0.31075 40803 25	1.11122 86903 15
21	0.60784 79425 51	0.57370 48227 68	0.32603 11841 94	1.12214 03756 28
22	0.63329 30034 87	0.59475 63326 77	0.34126 50508 91	1.13348 81382 44
23	0.65831 71349 96	0.61511 71376 00	0.35645 24652 79	1.14525 86847 24
24	0.68291 42483 43	0.63478 90166 66	0.37159 00693 82	1.15743 82078 48
25	0.70707 94006 12	0.65377 60567 01	0.38667 43599 01	1.17001 24008 40
26	0.73080 87532 93	0.67208 44652 06	0.40170 16862 27	1.18296 64722 08
27	0.75409 95273 39	0.68972 23806 34	0.41666 82489 31	1.19628 51611 92
28	0.77694 99553 97	0.70669 96825 35	0.43157 00987 51	1.20995 27538 15
29	0.79935 92318 62	0.72302 78038 29	0.44640 31360 92	1.22395 30995 32
30	0.82132 74613 77	0.73871 95471 85	0.46116 31110 24	1.23826 96284 63
31	0.84285 56063 60	0.75378 89071 86	0.47584 56237 96	1.25288 53692 08
32	0.86394 54340 58	0.76825 08996 79	0.49044 61258 64	1.26778 29672 28
33	0.88459 94636 30	0.78212 13994 00	0.50495 99214 38	1.28294 47037 86
34	0.90482 09136 53	0.79541 69867 56	0.51938 21695 37	1.29835 25154 28
35	0.92461 36504 37	0.80815 48043 63	0.53370 78865 62	1.31398 80140 03
36	0.92652 88449 39	0.82035 24237 46	0.54793 19493 77	1.32983 25071 90
37	0.96293 13861 88	0.83202 77224 12	0.56204 90988 95	1.34586 70195 36
38	0.98146 69085 40	0.84319 87713 34	0.57605 39441 62	1.36207 23139 71
39	0.99959 46711 23	0.85388 37327 42	0.58994 09669 30	1.37842 89137 89
40	1.01732 10514 35	0.86410 07680 09	0.60370 45267 18	1.39491 71250 77
41	1.03465 27961 24	0.87386 79553 01	0.61733 88663 36	1.41151 70595 67
42	1.05159 69813 70	0.88320 32165 90	0.63083 81178 78	1.42820 86578 92
43	1.06816 09754 52	0.89212 42535 79	0.64419 63091 52	1.44497 17132 17
44	1.08435 24035 25	0.90064 84920 36	0.65740 73705 50	1.46178 58952 28
45	1.10017 91145 83	0.90879 30339 87	0.67046 51423 33	1.47863 07744 49

K = 2.76806 31453 68768   E = 1.07640 51130 76403
K'= 1.59814 20021 12540   E'= 1.54415 04969 14673

r	u=(r/90)K=F(φ,k)	sn u	cn u	dn u
45	1.38403 15726 84	0.89128 85914 45	0.45343 64859 16	0.50874 26118 41
46	1.41478 78298 55	0.89819 63400 70	0.43959 45116 64	0.49727 83766 92
47	1.44554 40870 26	0.90474 07551 06	0.42596 26345 70	0.48608 33361 85
48	1.47630 03441 97	0.91093 80309 94	0.41254 32143 29	0.47516 15577 98
49	1.50705 66013 67	0.91680 38817 66	0.39933 77547 64	0.46451 63431 21
50	1.53781 28585 38	0.92235 35226 91	0.38634 69673 49	0.45415 02907 82
51	1.56856 91157 09	0.92760 16566 56	0.37357 08320 63	0.44406 53568 23
52	1.59932 53728 80	0.93256 24647 79	0.36100 86554 15	0.43426 29124 08
53	1.63008 16300 50	0.93724 96007 83	0.34865 91255 53	0.42474 37987 44
54	1.66083 78872 21	0.94167 61886 86	0.33652 03644 08	0.41550 83791 90
55	1.69159 41443 92	0.94585 48233 93	0.32458 99768 38	0.40655 65885 22
56	1.72235 04015 63	0.94979 75737 99	0.31286 50968 16	0.39788 79793 64
57	1.75310 66587 34	0.95351 59880 56	0.30134 24306 69	0.38950 17658 48
58	1.78386 29159 04	0.95702 11006 78	0.29001 82974 52	0.38139 68645 22
59	1.81461 91730 75	0.96032 34411 82	0.27888 86665 25	0.37357 19326 26
60	1.84537 54302 46	0.96343 30440 02	0.26794 91924 31	0.36602 54037 84
61	1.87613 16874 17	0.96635 94594 33	0.25719 52471 65	0.35875 55212 38
62	1.90688 79445 87	0.96911 17653 80	0.24662 19499 60	0.35176 03687 08
63	1.93764 42017 58	0.97169 85797 26	0.23622 41946 92	0.34503 78990 12
64	1.96840 04589 29	0.97412 80731 39	0.22599 66750 26	0.33858 59605 27
65	1.99915 67161 00	0.97640 79821 58	0.21593 39074 29	0.33240 23216 42
66	2.02991 29732 70	0.97854 56224 39	0.20603 02521 61	0.32648 46932 82
67	2.06066 92304 41	0.98054 79020 17	0.19627 99323 67	0.32083 07496 40
68	2.09142 54876 12	0.98242 13345 02	0.18667 70513 87	0.31543 81472 18
69	2.12218 17447 83	0.98417 20521 02	0.17721 56084 02	0.31030 45422 84
70	2.15293 80019 53	0.98580 58183 98	0.16788 95125 17	0.30542 76068 47
71	2.18369 42591 24	0.98732 80408 07	0.15869 25954 02	0.30080 50432 60
72	2.21445 05162 95	0.98874 37826 74	0.14961 86225 81	0.29643 45975 31
73	2.24520 67734 66	0.99005 77749 32	0.14066 13034 78	0.29231 40714 45
74	2.27596 30306 37	0.99127 44273 08	0.13181 43003 09	0.28844 13335 76
75	2.30671 92878 07	0.99239 78390 20	0.12307 12359 12	0.28481 43292 67
76	2.33747 55449 78	0.99343 18089 54	0.11442 57006 03	0.28143 10896 67
77	2.36823 18021 49	0.99437 98452 81	0.10587 12581 31	0.27828 97398 70
78	2.39898 80593 20	0.99524 51745 06	0.09740 14508 27	0.27538 85062 57
79	2.42974 43164 90	0.99603 07499 23	0.08900 98039 96	0.27272 57230 63
80	2.46050 05736 61	0.99673 92594 82	0.08068 98296 43	0.27029 98382 52
81	2.49125 68308 32	0.99737 31330 29	0.07243 50295 91	0.26810 94187 44
82	2.52201 30880 03	0.99793 45489 45	0.06423 88980 47	0.26615 31550 30
83	2.55276 93451 73	0.99842 54401 49	0.05609 49236 89	0.26442 98652 36
84	2.58352 56023 44	0.99884 74994 82	0.04799 65913 21	0.26293 84986 48
85	2.61428 18595 15	0.99920 21844 59	0.03993 73831 48	0.26167 81387 57
86	2.64503 81166 86	0.99949 07213 86	0.03191 07797 39	0.26064 80058 41
87	2.67579 43738 56	0.99971 41088 50	0.02391 02607 03	0.25984 74590 95
88	2.70655 06310 27	0.99987 31205 69	0.01592 93051 52	0.25927 59983 65
89	2.73730 68881 98	0.99996 83076 17	0.00796 13919 78	0.25893 32654 62
90	2.76806 31453 69	1.00000 00000 00	0.00000 00000 00	0.25881 90451 03

q = 0.16303 35348 21580 5   D(90) = 1.96563 05108 42837
q'= 0.00433 34205 09983 127   1/D(90) = 0.50874 26118 40723

r	ϕ	$E(\phi,k)$	A(r)	D(r)
45	1.10017 91145 83	0.90879 30339 87	0.67046 51423 33	1.47863 07744 49
46	1.11564 91506 24	0.91657 46172 40	0.68336 33823 15	1.49548 58468 56
47	1.13077 07179 51	0.92400 95816 75	0.69609 57739 30	1.51233 05587 63
48	1.14555 21605 81	0.93111 38417 38	0.70865 59346 60	1.52914 43319 55
49	1.16000 19356 85	0.93790 28646 20	0.72103 74248 11	1.54590 65890 27
50	1.17412 85910 14	0.94439 16535 65	0.73323 37566 06	1.56259 67789 02
51	1.18794 07442 09	0.95059 47358 30	0.74523 84035 85	1.57919 44024 96
52	1.20144 70639 33	0.95652 61547 96	0.75704 48102 68	1.59567 90384 97
53	1.21465 62527 31	0.96219 94657 85	0.76864 64020 88	1.61203 03692 12
54	1.22757 70315 47	0.96762 77351 59	0.78003 65955 42	1.62822 82064 61
55	1.24021 81257 83	0.97282 35422 96	0.79120 88085 46	1.64425 25174 71
56	1.25258 82528 46	0.97779 89840 86	0.80215 64709 71	1.66008 34507 34
57	1.26469 61110 66	0.98256 56816 03	0.81287 30353 25	1.67570 13617 93
58	1.27655 03699 29	0.98713 47886 53	0.82335 19875 63	1.69108 68389 12
59	1.28815 96615 12	0.99151 70019 06	0.83358 68579 89	1.70622 07285 96
60	1.29953 25730 69	0.99572 25723 68	0.84357 12322 29	1.72108 41609 19
61	1.31067 76406 67	0.99976 13179 59	0.85329 87622 40	1.73565 85746 14
62	1.32160 33438 14	1.00364 26370 00	0.86276 31773 38	1.74992 57418 91
63	1.33231 81009 96	1.00737 55224 19	0.87195 82952 00	1.76386 77929 43
64	1.34283 02660 62	1.01096 85765 17	0.88087 80328 28	1.77746 72400 91
65	1.35314 81253 99	1.01443 00261 65	0.88951 64174 33	1.79070 70015 32
66	1.36327 98958 15	1.01776 77382 84	0.89786 75972 26	1.80357 04246 54
67	1.37323 37231 01	1.02098 92355 25	0.90592 58520 66	1.81604 13088 64
68	1.38301 76811 96	1.02410 17120 49	0.91368 56039 59	1.82810 39279 04
69	1.39263 97719 14	1.02711 20493 21	0.92114 14273 70	1.83974 30516 06
70	1.40210 79251 90	1.03002 68318 62	0.92828 80593 17	1.85094 39670 48
71	1.41142 99997 88	1.03285 23629 01	0.93512 04092 32	1.86169 24990 75
72	1.42061 37844 43	1.03559 46798 83	0.94163 35685 52	1.87197 50301 47
73	1.42966 69993 94	1.03825 95697 94	0.94782 28200 18	1.88177 85194 69
74	1.43859 72982 74	1.04085 25842 82	0.95368 36466 66	1.89109 05213 91
75	1.44741 22703 15	1.04337 90545 45	0.95921 17404 65	1.89989 92030 05
76	1.45611 94428 53	1.04584 41059 83	0.96440 30106 08	1.90819 33609 46
77	1.46472 62840 95	1.04825 26725 94	0.96925 35914 03	1.91596 24373 39
78	1.47324 02061 22	1.05060 95111 22	0.97375 98497 75	1.92319 65348 66
79	1.48166 85681 10	1.05291 92149 46	0.97791 83923 25	1.92988 64309 32
80	1.49001 86797 35	1.05518 62277 27	0.98172 60719 56	1.93602 35908 94
81	1.49829 78047 56	1.05741 48568 16	0.98517 99940 37	1.94160 01803 35
82	1.50651 31647 43	1.05960 92864 27	0.98827 75220 78	1.94660 90763 47
83	1.51467 19429 45	1.06177 35906 06	0.99101 62829 22	1.95104 38778 11
84	1.52278 12882 71	1.06391 17459 94	0.99339 41714 24	1.95489 89146 57
85	1.53084 83193 68	1.06602 76444 16	0.99540 93546 11	1.95816 92560 67
86	1.53888 01287 93	1.06812 51053 01	0.99706 02753 07	1.96085 07176 29
87	1.54688 37872 54	1.07020 78879 68	0.99834 56552 21	1.96293 98674 07
88	1.55486 63479 09	1.07227 97037 96	0.99926 44974 84	1.96443 40309 27
89	1.56283 48507 11	1.07434 42282 88	0.99981 60886 26	1.96533 12950 68
90	1.57079 63267 95	1.07640 51130 76	1.00000 00000 00	1.96563 05108 43

K = 2.83267 25829 18100   E = 1.06860 95329 78401
K′= 1.59456 83409 31825   E′= 1.54755 45758 69993

r	u=(r/90)K=F(φ,k)	sn u	cn u	dn u
0	0.00000 00000 00	0.00000 00000 00	1.00000 00000 00	1.00000 00000 00
1	0.03147 41398 10	0.03146 40548 31	0.99950 48840 57	0.99953 38680 70
2	0.06294 82796 20	0.06286 76926 83	0.99802 18701 09	0.99813 77505 48
3	0.09442 24194 31	0.09415 09594 19	0.99555 79324 38	0.99581 84556 96
4	0.12589 65592 41	0.12525 48190 69	0.99212 46042 21	0.99258 72427 29
5	0.15737 06990 51	0.15612 15943 28	0.98773 78436 53	0.98845 96919 82
6	0.18884 48388 61	0.18669 53853 28	0.98241 78505 59	0.98345 55270 53
7	0.22031 89786 71	0.21692 24603 65	0.97618 88373 62	0.97759 83926 98
8	0.25179 31184 82	0.24675 16130 46	0.96907 87591 62	0.97091 55930 74
9	0.28326 72582 92	0.27613 44811 45	0.96111 90084 08	0.96343 77956 44
10	0.31474 13981 02	0.30502 58234 91	0.95234 40801 54	0.95519 87065 81
11	0.34621 55379 12	0.33338 37521 76	0.94279 12143 13	0.94623 47238 70
12	0.37768 96777 22	0.36116 99184 89	0.93250 00214 36	0.93658 45744 54
13	0.40916 38175 33	0.38834 96519 47	0.92151 20985 82	0.92628 89417 93
14	0.44063 79573 43	0.41489 20528 29	0.90987 06416 29	0.91539 00899 99
15	0.47211 20971 53	0.44077 00395 02	0.89762 00600 91	0.90393 14904 25
16	0.50358 62369 63	0.46596 03526 45	0.88480 55999 84	0.89195 74561 02
17	0.53506 03767 73	0.49044 35191 64	0.87147 29797 93	0.87951 27889 02
18	0.56653 45165 84	0.51420 37791 67	0.85766 80438 79	0.86664 24436 64
19	0.59800 86563 94	0.53722 89797 66	0.84343 64370 24	0.85339 12128 56
20	0.62948 27962 04	0.55951 04398 29	0.82882 33030 76	0.83980 34346 43
21	0.66095 69360 14	0.58104 27899 10	0.81387 30099 30	0.82592 27265 53
22	0.69243 10758 24	0.60182 37916 86	0.79862 89024 08	0.81179 17462 26
23	0.72390 52156 35	0.62185 41411 56	0.78313 30839 18	0.79745 19801 40
24	0.75537 93554 45	0.64113 72597 21	0.76742 62272 02	0.78294 35605 63
25	0.78685 34952 55	0.65967 90770 31	0.75154 74138 92	0.76830 51105 25
26	0.81832 76350 65	0.67748 78092 13	0.73553 40021 83	0.75357 36160 71
27	0.84980 17748 75	0.69457 37357 73	0.71942 15214 84	0.73878 43247 43
28	0.88127 59146 86	0.71094 89781 01	0.70324 35926 03	0.72397 06688 70
29	0.91275 00544 96	0.72662 72821 32	0.68703 18717 94	0.70916 42120 33
30	0.94422 41943 06	0.74162 38073 63	0.67081 60167 68	0.69439 46168 87
31	0.97569 83341 16	0.75595 49240 32	0.65462 36726 79	0.67968 96323 98
32	1.00717 24739 26	0.76963 80199 27	0.63848 04760 39	0.66507 50985 09
33	1.03864 66137 37	0.78269 13179 49	0.62241 00744 74	0.65057 49662 15
34	1.07012 07535 47	0.79513 37052 56	0.60643 41602 90	0.63621 13310 76
35	1.10159 48933 57	0.80698 45745 18	0.59057 25158 60	0.62200 44782 33
36	1.13306 90331 67	0.81826 36776 00	0.57484 30689 51	0.60797 29371 11
37	1.16454 31729 77	0.82899 09917 17	0.55926 19561 99	0.59413 35440 73
38	1.19601 73127 88	0.83918 65979 85	0.54384 35931 05	0.58050 15114 24
39	1.22749 14525 98	0.84887 05720 82	0.52860 07490 10	0.56709 05013 06
40	1.25896 55924 08	0.85806 28866 37	0.51354 46256 91	0.55391 27031 39
41	1.29043 97322 18	0.86678 33248 62	0.49868 49383 54	0.54097 89134 25
42	1.32191 38720 28	0.87505 14048 40	0.48402 99979 21	0.52829 86168 62
43	1.35338 80118 39	0.88288 63138 67	0.46958 67936 67	0.51588 00678 35
44	1.38486 21516 49	0.89030 68521 69	0.45536 10753 90	0.50373 03714 97
45	1.41633 62914 59	0.89733 13853 27	0.44135 74344 08	0.49185 55637 58

ELLIPTIC FUNCTIONS TABLE $\theta = 76°$

q = 0.17059 45383 49476 6
q′= 0.00376 92262 86977 846

D(90) = 2.03311 71865 97651
1/D(90) = 0.49185 55637 57967

r	ϕ	$E(\phi,k)$	A(r)	D(r)
0	0.00000 00000 00	0.00000 00000 00	0.00000 00000 00	1.00000 00000 00
1	0.03146 92486 45	0.03146 43588 48	0.01548 05435 91	1.00030 84281 77
2	0.06290 91789 99	0.06287 01220 78	0.03095 99621 60	1.00123 33597 42
3	0.09429 06159 04	0.09415 91432 70	0.04643 71212 62	1.00277 37361 09
4	0.12558 46688 07	0.12527 41671 01	0.06191 08676 32	1.00492 77940 37
5	0.15676 28699 36	0.15615 92568 67	0.07738 00198 46	1.00769 30672 19
6	0.18779 73076 26	0.18676 02009 16	0.09284 33590 75	1.01106 63885 23
7	0.21866 07533 39	0.21702 48918 82	0.10829 96199 48	1.01504 38928 64
8	0.24932 67810 60	0.24690 36733 21	0.12374 74815 61	1.01962 10207 24
9	0.27976 98778 92	0.27634 96492 22	0.13918 55586 56	1.02479 25223 12
10	0.30996 55448 75	0.30531 89527 67	0.15461 23930 07	1.03055 24623 69
11	0.33989 03872 18	0.33377 09717 75	0.17002 64450 21	1.03689 42256 24
12	0.36952 21933 40	0.36166 85292 21	0.18542 60855 97	1.04381 05228 90
13	0.39884 00023 36	0.38897 80182 72	0.20080 95882 67	1.05129 33978 22
14	0.42782 41596 34	0.41566 94921 95	0.21617 51216 34	1.05933 42343 21
15	0.45645 63608 62	0.44171 67104 17	0.23152 07421 43	1.06792 37645 91
16	0.48471 96840 59	0.46709 71427 60	0.24684 43871 93	1.07705 20778 60
17	0.51259 86105 78	0.49179 19345 82	0.26214 38686 36	1.08670 86297 58
18	0.54007 90351 33	0.51578 58360 66	0.27741 68666 61	1.09688 22523 53
19	0.56714 82655 97	0.53906 70993 46	0.29266 09240 93	1.10756 11648 47
20	0.59379 50132 32	0.56162 73474 38	0.30787 34411 30	1.11873 29849 46
21	0.62000 93741 25	0.58346 14191 09	0.32305 16705 30	1.13038 47408 82
22	0.64578 28026 77	0.60456 71938 60	0.33819 27132 67	1.14250 28841 06
23	0.67110 80779 84	0.62494 54011 73	0.35329 35146 69	1.15507 33026 43
24	0.69597 92640 28	0.64459 94180 01	0.36835 08610 63	1.16808 13351 11
25	0.72039 16645 36	0.66353 50582 83	0.38336 13769 18	1.18151 17853 95
26	0.74434 17734 04	0.68176 03579 98	0.39832 15225 29	1.19534 89379 94
27	0.76782 72215 02	0.69928 53589 38	0.41322 75922 17	1.20957 65740 07
28	0.79084 67206 93	0.71612 18940 43	0.42807 57130 81	1.22417 79877 85
29	0.81340 00057 96	0.73228 33768 08	0.44286 18443 00	1.23913 60042 16
30	0.83548 77752 09	0.74778 45968 45	0.45758 17769 87	1.25443 29966 63
31	0.85711 16308 30	0.76264 15234 05	0.47223 11346 02	1.27005 09055 28
32	0.87827 40178 57	0.77687 11182 46	0.48680 53739 27	1.28597 12574 40
33	0.89897 81649 80	0.79049 11589 64	0.50129 97866 10	1.30217 51850 59
34	0.91922 80254 22	0.80352 00735 85	0.51570 95012 65	1.31864 34474 90
35	0.93902 82192 23	0.81597 67869 22	0.53002 94861 34	1.33535 64512 76
36	0.95838 39770 97	0.82788 05790 18	0.54425 45523 11	1.35229 42719 80
37	0.97730 10861 37	0.83925 09557 23	0.55837 93575 14	1.36943 66763 28
38	0.99578 58376 00	0.85010 75313 14	0.57239 84104 04	1.38676 31448 91
39	1.01384 49769 44	0.86046 99229 07	0.58630 60754 40	1.40425 28953 04
40	1.03148 56562 49	0.87035 76562 69	0.60009 65782 70	1.42188 49059 91
41	1.04871 53891 11	0.87979 00825 80	0.61376 40116 26	1.43963 79403 71
42	1.06554 20080 83	0.88878 63055 61	0.62730 23417 32	1.45749 05715 42
43	1.08197 36246 63	0.89736 51184 08	0.64070 54152 03	1.47542 12073 93
44	1.09801 85918 53	0.90554 49498 47	0.65396 69664 13	1.49340 81161 37
45	1.11368 54692 48	0.91334 38186 89	0.66708 06253 25	1.51142 94522 31

303

K = 2.83267 25829 18100   E = 1.06860 95329 78401
K'= 1.59456 83409 31825   E'= 1.54755 45758 69993

r	u=(r/90)K=F(ϕ,k)	sn u	cn u	dn u
45	1.41633 62914 59	0.89733 13853 27	0.44135 74344 08	0.49185 55637 58
46	1.44781 04312 69	0.90397 78047 08	0.42757 93828 00	0.48026 06896 24
47	1.47928 45710 79	0.91026 34952 30	0.41402 94304 18	0.46894 98794 07
48	1.51075 87108 90	0.91620 53097 85	0.40070 91592 70	0.45792 64224 40
49	1.54223 28507 00	0.92181 95496 70	0.38761 92949 87	0.44719 28380 13
50	1.57370 69905 10	0.92712 19504 10	0.37475 97751 46	0.43675 09432 96
51	1.60518 11303 20	0.93212 76723 77	0.36212 98142 78	0.42660 19181 11
52	1.63665 52701 30	0.93685 12956 51	0.34972 79654 77	0.41674 63664 41
53	1.66812 94099 41	0.94130 68186 07	0.33755 21785 50	0.40718 43746 46
54	1.69960 35497 51	0.94550 76597 36	0.32559 98547 01	0.39791 55663 56
55	1.73107 76895 61	0.94946 66622 63	0.31386 78977 71	0.38893 91540 83
56	1.76255 18293 71	0.95319 61011 51	0.30235 27621 01	0.38025 39876 03
57	1.79402 59691 81	0.95670 76921 12	0.29105 04970 85	0.37185 85991 82
58	1.82550 01089 92	0.96001 26022 92	0.27995 67885 25	0.36375 12457 50
59	1.85697 42488 02	0.96312 14623 20	0.26906 69968 95	0.35592 99481 24
60	1.88844 83886 12	0.96604 43794 56	0.25837 61926 37	0.34839 25274 14
61	1.91992 25284 22	0.96879 09515 69	0.24787 91886 35	0.34113 66387 29
62	1.95139 66682 32	0.97137 02817 55	0.23757 05699 86	0.33415 98023 26
63	1.98287 08080 43	0.97379 09933 78	0.22744 47212 32	0.32745 94323 37
64	2.01434 49478 53	0.97606 12453 74	0.21749 58511 75	0.32103 28632 01
65	2.04581 90876 63	0.97818 87476 69	0.20771 80154 30	0.31487 73739 57
66	2.07729 32274 73	0.98018 07765 68	0.19810 51368 50	0.30899 02105 15
67	2.10876 73672 83	0.98204 41900 23	0.18865 10239 63	0.30336 86060 41
68	2.14024 15070 94	0.98378 54426 58	0.17934 93875 47	0.29800 97995 87
69	2.17171 56469 04	0.98541 06004 90	0.17019 38554 79	0.29291 10530 83
70	2.20318 97867 14	0.98692 53552 51	0.16117 79859 76	0.28806 96668 05
71	2.23466 39265 24	0.98833 50382 78	0.15229 52793 49	0.28348 29934 45
72	2.26613 80663 34	0.98964 46338 96	0.14353 91883 81	0.27914 84508 61
73	2.29761 22061 45	0.99085 87922 65	0.13490 31274 34	0.27506 35336 43
74	2.32908 63459 55	0.99198 18416 57	0.12638 04803 86	0.27122 58235 46
75	2.36056 04857 65	0.99301 78001 31	0.11796 46075 06	0.26763 29989 19
76	2.39203 46255 75	0.99397 03865 82	0.10964 88513 33	0.26428 28431 76
77	2.42350 87653 85	0.99484 30311 58	0.10142 65416 71	0.26117 32524 10
78	2.45498 29051 96	0.99563 88850 20	0.09329 09997 64	0.25830 22422 09
79	2.48645 70450 06	0.99636 08294 32	0.08523 55417 25	0.25566 79537 29
80	2.51793 11848 16	0.99701 14841 99	0.07725 34813 09	0.25326 86591 10
81	2.54940 53246 26	0.99759 32154 14	0.06933 81320 74	0.25110 27662 54
82	2.58087 94644 36	0.99810 81425 36	0.06148 28090 06	0.24916 88230 42
83	2.61235 36042 47	0.99855 81447 89	0.05368 08296 76	0.24746 55210 22
84	2.64382 77440 57	0.99894 48668 85	0.04592 55149 58	0.24599 16986 02
85	2.67530 18838 67	0.99926 97240 62	0.03821 01893 99	0.24474 63437 93
86	2.70677 60236 77	0.99953 39064 53	0.03052 81812 60	0.24372 85965 26
87	2.73825 01634 87	0.99973 83827 78	0.02287 28222 95	0.24293 77505 67
88	2.76972 43032 98	0.99988 39033 60	0.01523 74473 14	0.24237 32550 61
89	2.80119 84431 08	0.99997 10024 70	0.00761 53935 66	0.24203 47157 09
90	2.83267 25829 18	1.00000 00000 00	0.00000 00000 00	0.24192 18956 00

q = 0.17059 45383 49476 6   D(90) = 2.03311 71865 97651
q'= 0.00376 92262 86977 846   1/D(90) = 0.49185 55637 57967

r	ϕ	$E(\phi,k)$	A(r)	D(r)
45	1.11368 54692 48	0.91334 38186 89	0.66708 06253 25	1.51142 94522 31
46	1.12898 29906 23	0.92077 92962 02	0.68003 99257 60	1.52946 32826 55
47	1.14392 00339 46	0.92786 84756 37	0.69283 83140 88	1.54748 76135 18
48	1.15850 55937 61	0.93462 79482 71	0.70546 91583 13	1.56548 04169 59
49	1.17274 87558 40	0.94107 37853 35	0.71792 57575 46	1.58341 96583 17
50	1.18665 86740 23	0.94722 15252 28	0.73020 13518 23	1.60128 33235 27
51	1.20024 45491 50	0.95308 61654 45	0.74228 91322 57	1.61904 94467 01
52	1.21351 56099 74	0.95868 21586 95	0.75418 22515 04	1.63669 61378 79
53	1.22648 10959 65	0.96402 34126 89	0.76587 38344 94	1.65420 16108 83
54	1.23915 02418 89	0.96912 32931 50	0.77735 69894 29	1.67154 42112 57
55	1.25153 22640 66	0.97399 46296 14	0.78862 48190 00	1.68870 24442 39
56	1.26363 63481 97	0.97864 97236 27	0.79967 04318 00	1.70565 50027 26
57	1.27547 16386 72	0.98310 03589 75	0.81048 69539 11	1.72238 07951 95
58	1.28704 72292 44	0.98735 78136 35	0.82106 75406 22	1.73885 89735 30
59	1.29837 21549 92	0.99143 28731 58	0.83140 53882 66	1.75506 89607 12
60	1.30945 53854 63	0.99533 58452 01	0.84149 37461 24	1.77099 04783 29
61	1.32030 58189 31	0.99907 65750 00	0.85132 59283 84	1.78660 35738 58
62	1.33093 22776 67	1.00266 44615 73	0.86089 53261 15	1.80188 86476 78
63	1.34134 35041 48	1.00610 84744 58	0.87019 54192 23	1.81682 64797 61
64	1.35154 81581 46	1.00941 71708 47	0.87921 97883 68	1.83139 82560 01
65	1.36155 48146 02	1.01259 87129 63	0.88796 21267 96	1.84558 55941 30
66	1.37137 19622 40	1.01566 08855 76	0.89641 62520 69	1.85937 05691 80
67	1.38100 80028 51	1.01861 11135 44	0.90457 61176 51	1.87273 57384 39
68	1.39047 12511 87	1.02145 64793 04	0.91243 58243 31	1.88566 41658 60
69	1.39976 99354 19	1.02420 37402 35	0.91998 96314 41	1.89813 94458 76
70	1.40891 21981 06	1.02685 93458 37	0.92723 19678 43	1.91014 57265 78
71	1.41790 60976 23	1.02942 94546 87	0.93415 74426 64	1.92166 77322 08
72	1.42675 96100 18	1.03191 99511 16	0.94076 08557 40	1.93269 07849 28
73	1.43548 06312 47	1.03433 64616 00	0.94703 72077 43	1.94320 08258 29
74	1.44407 69797 57	1.03668 43708 37	0.95298 17099 65	1.95318 44351 17
75	1.45255 63993 78	1.03896 88374 89	0.95858 97937 44	1.96262 88514 69
76	1.46092 65625 01	1.04119 48095 95	0.96385 71194 82	1.97152 19904 91
77	1.46919 50735 06	1.04336 70396 53	0.96877 95852 53	1.97985 24622 61
78	1.47736 94724 18	1.04549 00993 61	0.97335 33349 70	1.98760 95879 09
79	1.48545 72387 67	1.04756 83940 45	0.97757 47660 90	1.99478 34152 15
80	1.49346 57956 22	1.04960 61767 63	0.98144 05368 25	2.00136 47331 71
81	1.50140 25137 97	1.05160 75621 26	0.98494 75728 68	2.00734 50855 06
82	1.50927 47161 87	1.05357 65398 22	0.98809 30735 79	2.01271 67831 21
83	1.51708 96822 35	1.05551 69878 94	0.99087 45176 46	2.01747 29154 23
84	1.52485 46525 06	1.05743 26857 67	0.99328 96681 86	2.02160 73605 30
85	1.53257 68333 51	1.05932 73270 65	0.99533 65772 79	2.02511 47943 22
86	1.54026 34016 55	1.06120 45322 31	0.99701 35899 29	2.02799 06983 34
87	1.54792 15096 50	1.06306 78609 87	0.99831 93474 24	2.03023 13664 50
88	1.55555 82897 82	1.06492 08246 42	0.99925 27901 05	2.03183 39104 08
89	1.56318 08596 19	1.06676 68983 02	0.99981 31595 26	2.03279 62640 90
90	1.57079 63267 95	1.06860 95329 78	1.00000 00000 00	2.03311 71865 98

ELLIPTIC FUNCTIONS   TABLE $\theta = 77°$

K = 2.90256 49406 70027   E = 1.06105 93337 53857
K' = 1.59125 43820 13687   E' = 1.55073 19509 84013

r	u=(r/90)K=F(ϕ,k)	sn u	cn u	dn u
0	0.00000 00000 00	0.00000 00000 00	1.00000 00000 00	1.00000 00000 00
1	0.03225 07215 63	0.03223 98274 63	0.99948 01616 47	0.99950 64735 09
2	0.06450 14431 26	0.06441 43961 22	0.99792 32363 12	0.99802 84305 44
3	0.09675 21646 89	0.09645 89742 19	0.99533 69611 81	0.99557 34494 63
4	0.12900 28862 52	0.12830 98750 62	0.99173 41256 41	0.99215 40577 08
5	0.16125 36078 15	0.15990 49572 63	0.98713 24149 49	0.98778 75795 36
6	0.19350 43293 78	0.19118 40989 62	0.98155 41963 15	0.98249 59276 82
7	0.22575 50509 41	0.22208 96385 20	0.97502 62521 91	0.97630 53436 06
8	0.25800 57725 04	0.25256 67751 43	0.96757 94665 52	0.96924 60919 54
9	0.29025 64940 67	0.28256 39239 89	0.95924 84708 67	0.96135 21157 82
10	0.32250 72156 30	0.31203 30214 94	0.95007 12570 63	0.95266 06596 40
11	0.35475 79371 93	0.34092 97779 87	0.94008 87652 14	0.94321 18680 52
12	0.38700 86587 56	0.36921 38758 82	0.92934 44538 25	0.93304 83670 72
13	0.41925 93803 19	0.39684 91130 78	0.91788 38605 45	0.92221 48365 37
14	0.45151 01018 82	0.42380 34923 12	0.90575 41608 54	0.91075 75803 80
15	0.48376 08234 45	0.45004 92583 59	0.89300 37318 23	0.89872 41019 04
16	0.51601 15450 08	0.47556 28858 84	0.87968 17274 27	0.88616 26903 51
17	0.54826 22665 71	0.50032 50215 66	0.86583 76711 57	0.87312 20243 54
18	0.58051 29881 34	0.52432 03847 51	0.85152 10708 69	0.85965 07970 79
19	0.61276 37096 97	0.54753 76313 46	0.83678 10599 32	0.84579 73670 30
20	0.64501 44312 60	0.56996 91859 72	0.82166 60678 42	0.83160 94375 90
21	0.67726 51528 23	0.59161 10475 41	0.80622 35226 21	0.81713 37675 64
22	0.70951 58743 86	0.61246 25734 11	0.79049 95864 46	0.80241 59141 32
23	0.74176 65959 49	0.63252 62471 54	0.77453 89252 08	0.78750 00088 93
24	0.77401 73175 12	0.65180 74347 46	0.75838 45119 79	0.77242 85669 83
25	0.80626 80390 75	0.67031 41336 68	0.74207 74637 49	0.75724 23286 36
26	0.83851 87606 38	0.68805 67190 13	0.72565 69102 69	0.74198 01320 70
27	0.87076 94822 01	0.70504 76902 95	0.70915 98934 02	0.72667 88161 26
28	0.90302 02037 64	0.72130 14221 86	0.69262 12950 47	0.71137 31507 89
29	0.93527 09253 27	0.73683 39219 39	0.67607 37914 46	0.69609 57934 42
30	0.96752 16468 90	0.75166 25958 20	0.65954 78315 07	0.68087 72685 65
31	0.99977 23684 53	0.76580 60264 04	0.64307 16366 96	0.66574 59684 81
32	1.03202 30900 16	0.77928 37621 94	0.62667 12200 03	0.65072 81727 28
33	1.06427 38115 79	0.79211 61206 10	0.61037 04215 22	0.63584 80836 52
34	1.09652 45331 42	0.80432 40050 72	0.59419 09582 49	0.62112 78759 00
35	1.12877 52547 05	0.81592 87365 65	0.57815 24858 10	0.60658 77575 71
36	1.16102 59762 68	0.82695 18998 15	0.56227 26699 68	0.59224 60409 39
37	1.19327 66978 31	0.83741 52039 66	0.54656 72659 12	0.57811 92207 93
38	1.22552 74193 94	0.84734 03574 59	0.53105 02034 85	0.56422 20586 22
39	1.25777 81409 57	0.85674 89566 39	0.51573 36767 15	0.55056 76710 10
40	1.29002 88625 20	0.86566 23875 25	0.50062 82361 44	0.53716 76208 33
41	1.32227 95840 83	0.87410 17400 34	0.48574 28826 75	0.52403 20099 49
42	1.35453 03056 46	0.88208 77339 34	0.47108 51617 73	0.51116 95723 01
43	1.38678 10272 09	0.88964 06557 13	0.45666 12570 64	0.49858 77664 72
44	1.41903 17487 72	0.89678 03055 48	0.44247 60824 96	0.48629 28668 81
45	1.45128 24703 35	0.90352 59535 63	0.42853 33723 73	0.47429 00529 67

q = 0.17865 56628 04652 6   D(90) = 2.10841 44475 37723
q'= 0.00324 54674 43524 990   1/D(90) = 0.47429 00529 67448

r	ϕ	$E(\phi,k)$	A(r)	D(r)
0	0.00000 00000 00	0.00000 00000 00	0.00000 00000 00	1.00000 00000 00
1	0.03224 54151 24	0.03224 01102 57	0.01529 60741 79	1.00032 99126 45
2	0.06445 90243 57	0.06441 66557 81	0.03059 14127 14	1.00131 92767 29
3	0.09660 91850 79	0.09646 65854 65	0.04588 52695 27	1.00296 69710 11
4	0.12866 45792 17	0.12832 78666 53	0.06117 68777 08	1.00527 11278 25
5	0.16059 43705 52	0.15993 99726 58	0.07646 54391 73	1.00822 91346 66
6	0.19236 83562 06	0.19124 43449 05	0.09175 01144 25	1.01183 76364 33
7	0.22395 71105 72	0.22218 48224 31	0.10703 00124 33	1.01609 25383 02
8	0.25533 21200 96	0.25270 80323 32	0.12230 41806 72	1.02098 90092 51
9	0.28646 59075 73	0.28276 37358 55	0.13757 15953 49	1.02652 14862 23
10	0.31733 21447 75	0.31230 51260 09	0.15283 11518 48	1.03268 36789 51
11	0.34790 57525 02	0.34128 90737 93	0.16808 16554 16	1.03946 85754 30
12	0.37816 29874 04	0.36967 63214 23	0.18332 18121 29	1.04686 84480 44
13	0.40808 15151 24	0.39743 16221 52	0.19855 02201 59	1.05487 48603 66
14	0.43764 04696 03	0.42452 38274 57	0.21376 53613 72	1.06347 86746 11
15	0.46682 04985 87	0.45092 59233 91	0.22896 55932 82	1.07267 00597 74
16	0.49560 37956 01	0.47661 50188 76	0.24414 91413 89	1.08243 85004 32
17	0.52397 41188 54	0.50157 22894 29	0.25931 40919 17	1.09277 28062 37
18	0.55191 67976 81	0.52578 28805 01	0.27445 83849 93	1.10366 11220 86
19	0.57941 87273 14	0.54923 57749 97	0.28957 98082 68	1.11509 09389 84
20	0.60646 83528 38	0.57192 36298 78	0.30467 59910 14	1.12704 91056 04
21	0.63305 56433 08	0.59384 25868 73	0.31974 43987 18	1.13952 18405 39
22	0.65917 20570 55	0.61499 20623 33	0.33478 23281 84	1.15249 47452 57
23	0.68481 04992 33	0.63537 45211 21	0.34978 69031 59	1.16595 28177 65
24	0.70996 52726 71	0.65499 52392 37	0.36475 50705 13	1.17988 04669 71
25	0.73463 20231 08	0.67386 20595 33	0.37968 35969 73	1.19426 15277 56
26	0.75880 76798 13	0.69198 51445 43	0.39456 90664 21	1.20907 92767 61
27	0.78249 03925 97	0.70937 67299 90	0.40940 78777 91	1.22431 64488 76
28	0.80567 94661 43	0.72605 08821 41	0.42419 62435 39	1.23995 52544 33
29	0.82837 52925 07	0.74202 32616 92	0.43893 01887 32	1.25597 73971 14
30	0.85057 92826 02	0.75731 08964 46	0.45360 55507 26	1.27236 40925 48
31	0.87229 37973 67	0.77193 19645 87	0.46821 79794 71	1.28909 60876 19
32	0.89352 20792 68	0.78590 55899 84	0.48276 29384 22	1.30615 36804 49
33	0.91426 81846 97	0.79925 16505 40	0.49723 57060 67	1.32351 67410 75
34	0.93453 69177 40	0.81199 06002 90	0.51163 13780 74	1.34116 47327 98
35	0.95433 37657 43	0.82414 33056 31	0.52594 48700 50	1.35907 67341 91
36	0.97366 48370 04	0.83573 08958 19	0.54017 09209 12	1.37723 14617 65
37	0.99253 68008 79	0.84677 46276 04	0.55430 40968 60	1.39560 72932 69
38	1.01095 68305 12	0.85729 57637 40	0.56833 87959 54	1.41418 22916 10
39	1.02893 25483 46	0.86731 54648 99	0.58226 92532 73	1.43293 42293 85
40	1.04647 19745 43	0.87685 46944 27	0.59608 95466 63	1.45184 06139 89
41	1.06358 34783 66	0.88593 41352 81	0.60979 36030 42	1.47087 87132 95
42	1.08027 57325 64	0.89457 41184 16	0.62337 52052 66	1.49002 55818 75
43	1.09655 76707 45	0.90279 45618 48	0.63682 79995 32	1.50925 80877 33
44	1.11243 84477 29	0.91061 49195 95	0.65014 55033 01	1.52855 29395 35
45	1.12792 74027 94	0.91805 41397 05	0.66332 11137 28	1.54788 67142 95

K = 2.90256 49406 70027   E = 1.06105 93337 53857
K'= 1.59125 43820 13687   E'= 1.55073 19509 84013

r	u=(r/90)K=F(φ,k)	sn u	cn u	dn u
45	1.45128 24703 35	0.90352 59535 63	0.42853 33723 73	0.47429 00529 67
46	1.48353 31918 98	0.90989 63045 33	0.41483 57687 04	0.46258 34957 99
47	1.51578 39134 61	0.91590 94702 53	0.40138 49054 22	0.45117 64416 84
48	1.54803 46350 24	0.92158 29487 89	0.38818 14891 27	0.44007 12924 50
49	1.58028 53565 87	0.92693 36098 81	0.37522 53761 06	0.42926 96821 44
50	1.61253 60781 50	0.93197 76857 88	0.36251 56454 47	0.41877 25499 82
51	1.64478 67997 13	0.93673 07669 34	0.35005 06681 59	0.40858 02094 61
52	1.67703 75212 76	0.94120 78017 34	0.33782 81722 35	0.39869 24135 75
53	1.70928 82428 39	0.94542 31000 34	0.32584 53036 68	0.38910 84161 41
54	1.74153 89644 02	0.94939 03396 58	0.31409 86834 80	0.37982 70292 99
55	1.77378 96859 65	0.95312 25755 77	0.30258 44608 12	0.37084 66772 30
56	1.80604 04075 28	0.95663 22512 71	0.29129 83622 14	0.36216 54462 34
57	1.83829 11290 91	0.95993 12118 97	0.28023 57372 39	0.35378 11312 60
58	1.87054 18506 54	0.96303 07189 19	0.26939 16004 96	0.34569 12790 50
59	1.90279 25722 17	0.96594 14658 76	0.25876 06703 13	0.33789 32280 39
60	1.93504 32937 80	0.96867 35950 18	0.24833 74041 80	0.33038 41451 75
61	1.96729 40153 43	0.97123 67145 66	0.23811 60311 24	0.32316 10598 19
62	1.99954 47369 06	0.97363 99163 77	0.22809 05812 10	0.31622 08948 91
63	2.03179 54584 69	0.97589 17938 23	0.21825 49123 15	0.30956 04954 38
64	2.06404 61800 32	0.97800 04597 23	0.20860 27343 60	0.30317 66547 66
65	2.09629 69015 95	0.97997 35641 90	0.19912 76311 53	0.29706 61383 24
66	2.12854 76231 58	0.98181 83122 63	0.18982 30800 14	0.29122 57054 69
67	2.16079 83447 21	0.98354 14812 20	0.18068 24693 21	0.28565 21292 74
68	2.19304 90662 84	0.98514 94374 97	0.17169 91141 48	0.28034 22145 33
69	2.22529 97878 47	0.98664 81531 22	0.16286 62701 12	0.27529 28140 69
70	2.25755 05094 10	0.98804 32216 15	0.15417 71455 83	0.27050 08435 16
71	2.28980 12309 73	0.98933 98732 97	0.14562 49123 79	0.26596 32946 53
72	2.32205 19525 36	0.99054 29899 71	0.13720 27150 61	0.26167 72474 45
73	2.35430 26740 99	0.99165 71189 44	0.12890 36789 55	0.25763 98808 75
74	2.38655 33956 62	0.99268 64863 59	0.12072 09169 96	0.25384 84826 69
75	2.41880 41172 25	0.99363 50098 23	0.11264 75355 01	0.25030 04580 24
76	2.45105 48387 88	0.99450 63103 14	0.10467 66389 69	0.24699 33374 04
77	2.48330 55603 51	0.99530 37233 62	0.09680 13339 90	0.24392 47835 01
78	2.51555 62819 14	0.99603 03094 92	0.08901 47323 43	0.24109 25974 29
79	2.54780 70034 77	0.99668 88639 30	0.08130 99533 76	0.23849 47242 11
80	2.58005 77250 40	0.99728 19255 72	0.07368 01257 25	0.23612 92576 40
81	2.61230 84466 03	0.99781 17852 13	0.06611 83884 42	0.23399 44445 44
82	2.64455 91681 66	0.99828 04930 40	0.05861 78916 09	0.23208 86885 29
83	2.67680 98897 29	0.99868 98653 96	0.05117 17964 78	0.23041 05532 32
84	2.70906 06112 92	0.99904 14908 19	0.04377 32752 10	0.22895 87651 26
85	2.74131 13328 55	0.99933 67353 46	0.03641 55102 54	0.22773 22159 18
86	2.77356 20544 18	0.99957 67471 15	0.02909 16934 26	0.22672 99645 62
87	2.80581 27759 81	0.99976 24602 36	0.02179 50247 30	0.22595 12389 22
88	2.83806 34975 44	0.99989 45979 61	0.01451 87109 70	0.22539 54371 03
89	2.87031 42191 07	0.99997 36751 45	0.00725 59641 90	0.22506 21284 66
90	2.90256 49406 70	1.00000 00000 00	0.00000 00000 00	0.22495 10543 44

q = 0.17865 56628 04652 6   D(90) = 2.10841 44475 37723
q' = 0.00324 54674 43524 990   1/D(90) = 0.47429 00529 67448

r	ϕ	$E(\phi,k)$	A(r)	D(r)
45	1.12792 74027 94	0.91805 41397 05	0.66332 11137 28	1.54788 67142 95
46	1.14303 40257 68	0.92513 06305 63	0.67634 81165 73	1.56723 58854 98
47	1.15776 79258 71	0.93186 22347 02	0.68921 96955 78	1.58657 68516 20
48	1.17213 88031 87	0.93826 62093 80	0.70192 89422 83	1.60588 59650 11
49	1.18615 64226 78	0.94435 92131 86	0.71446 88662 61	1.62513 95611 12
50	1.19983 05906 12	0.95015 72980 22	0.72683 24057 44	1.64431 39879 61
51	1.21317 11332 77	0.95567 59058 02	0.73901 24386 11	1.66338 56359 57
52	1.22618 78778 62	0.96092 98692 99	0.75100 17937 24	1.68233 09678 25
53	1.23889 06353 81	0.96593 34165 78	0.76279 32625 68	1.70112 65487 65
54	1.25128 91855 11	0.97070 01785 16	0.77437 96111 71	1.71974 90767 17
55	1.26339 32632 26	0.97524 31989 64	0.78575 35922 79	1.73817 54127 07
56	1.27521 25470 99	0.97957 49471 16	0.79690 79577 51	1.75638 26112 37
57	1.28675 66491 66	0.98370 73317 32	0.80783 54711 42	1.77434 79506 44
58	1.29803 51062 36	0.98765 17168 60	0.81852 89204 39	1.79204 89634 19
59	1.30905 73725 35	0.99141 89387 78	0.82898 11309 23	1.80946 34663 91
60	1.31983 28135 93	0.99501 93238 78	0.83918 49781 27	1.82656 95907 68
61	1.33037 07012 65	0.99846 27072 62	0.84913 34008 37	1.84334 58119 53
62	1.34068 02098 04	1.00175 84518 54	0.85881 94141 26	1.85977 09790 96
63	1.35077 04128 97	1.00491 54678 40	0.86823 61223 75	1.87582 43443 35
64	1.36065 02815 78	1.00794 22322 91	0.87737 67322 45	1.89148 55916 57
65	1.37032 86829 54	1.01084 68088 41	0.88623 45655 70	1.90673 48653 43
66	1.37981 43796 62	1.01363 68673 05	0.89480 30721 37	1.92155 27979 38
67	1.38911 60299 94	1.01631 97031 40	0.90307 58423 15	1.93592 05376 85
68	1.39824 21886 39	1.01890 22566 91	0.91104 66195 07	1.94981 97753 93
69	1.40720 13079 70	1.02139 11321 41	0.91870 93123 83	1.96323 27706 54
70	1.41600 17398 35	1.02379 26161 28	0.92605 80068 67	1.97614 23773 99
71	1.42465 17378 06	1.02611 26959 88	0.93308 69778 43	1.98853 20687 00
72	1.43315 94598 26	1.02835 70775 94	0.93979 07005 55	2.00038 59608 06
73	1.44153 29712 37	1.03053 12027 87	0.94616 38616 56	2.01168 88363 38
74	1.44978 02481 27	1.03264 02663 62	0.95220 13698 94	2.02242 61666 07
75	1.45790 91809 84	1.03468 92326 29	0.95789 83663 93	2.03258 41330 17
76	1.46592 75786 13	1.03668 28515 45	0.96325 02345 08	2.04214 96474 88
77	1.47384 31722 89	1.03862 56744 16	0.96825 26092 25	2.05111 03718 77
78	1.48166 36201 22	1.04052 20691 84	0.97290 13860 75	2.05945 47363 49
79	1.48939 65116 16	1.04237 62353 23	0.97719 27295 55	2.06717 19566 51
80	1.49704 93723 85	1.04419 22183 51	0.98112 30810 09	2.07425 20502 67
81	1.50462 96690 22	1.04597 39239 81	0.98468 91659 71	2.08068 58514 14
82	1.51214 48141 02	1.04772 51319 45	0.98788 80009 27	2.08646 50248 36
83	1.51960 21712 85	1.04944 95094 97	0.99071 68995 01	2.09158 20783 84
84	1.52700 90605 25	1.05115 06246 45	0.99317 34780 30	2.09603 03743 49
85	1.53437 27633 64	1.05283 19591 19	0.99525 56605 24	2.09980 41395 09
86	1.54170 05282 93	1.05449 69211 22	0.99696 16829 86	2.10289 84738 94
87	1.54899 95761 73	1.05614 88578 85	0.99829 00970 91	2.10530 93582 29
88	1.55627 71057 03	1.05779 10680 54	0.99923 97732 15	2.10703 36600 45
89	1.56354 02989 33	1.05942 68139 55	0.99980 99027 91	2.10806 91384 49
90	1.57079 63267 95	1.06105 93337 54	1.00000 00000 00	2.10841 44475 38

K = 2.97856 89511 81384   E = 1.05377 69204 07046
K'= 1.58819 72125 27520   E'= 1.55368 08919 36509

r	u=(r/90)K=F(ϕ,k)	sn u	cn u	dn u
0	0.00000 00000 00	0.00000 00000 00	1.00000 00000 00	1.00000 00000 00
1	0.03309 52105 69	0.03308 33938 05	0.99945 25947 01	0.99947 62637 38
2	0.06619 04211 37	0.06609 60083 42	0.99781 32679 42	0.99790 78934 93
3	0.09928 56317 06	0.09896 76685 31	0.99509 06494 31	0.99530 33680 19
4	0.13238 08422 75	0.13162 93967 49	0.99129 89972 31	0.99167 66965 59
5	0.16547 60528 43	0.16401 39845 64	0.98645 80137 38	0.98704 72389 11
6	0.19857 12634 12	0.19605 65330 27	0.98059 25942 29	0.98143 94595 71
7	0.23166 64739 81	0.22769 49525 20	0.97373 25138 85	0.97488 26217 03
8	0.26476 16845 49	0.25887 04144 05	0.96591 20604 62	0.96741 04280 01
9	0.29785 68951 18	0.28952 77480 53	0.95716 96208 65	0.95906 06164 57
10	0.33095 21056 87	0.31961 57784 26	0.94754 72305 81	0.94987 45198 54
11	0.36404 73162 56	0.34908 76009 29	0.93709 00953 90	0.93989 65981 52
12	0.39714 25268 24	0.37790 07918 81	0.92584 60949 29	0.92917 39531 61
13	0.43023 77373 93	0.40601 75545 09	0.91386 52775 06	0.91775 58346 80
14	0.46333 29479 62	0.43340 48017 99	0.90119 93551 80	0.90569 31469 26
15	0.49642 81585 30	0.46003 41788 81	0.88790 12074 89	0.89303 79634 46
16	0.52952 33690 99	0.48588 20287 02	0.87402 44013 67	0.87984 30579 03
17	0.56261 85796 68	0.51092 93056 97	0.85962 27338 66	0.86616 14571 90
18	0.59571 37902 36	0.53516 14428 70	0.84474 98032 35	0.85204 60223 08
19	0.62880 90008 05	0.55856 81781 64	0.82945 86127 97	0.83754 90613 71
20	0.66190 42113 74	0.58114 33463 23	0.81380 12110 00	0.82272 19780 08
21	0.69499 94219 42	0.60288 46425 07	0.79782 83699 07	0.80761 49574 04
22	0.72809 46325 11	0.62379 33638 52	0.78158 93034 16	0.79227 66912 33
23	0.76118 98430 80	0.64387 41349 43	0.76513 14255 41	0.77675 41418 11
24	0.79428 50536 48	0.66313 46228 07	0.74850 01483 20	0.76109 23450 39
25	0.82738 02642 17	0.68158 52465 93	0.73173 87181 41	0.74533 42509 59
26	0.86047 54747 86	0.69923 88866 04	0.71488 80887 67	0.72952 06002 45
27	0.89357 06853 54	0.71611 05967 73	0.69798 68288 08	0.71368 98344 19
28	0.92666 58959 23	0.73221 73241 10	0.68107 10611 03	0.69787 80373 12
29	0.95976 11064 92	0.74757 76380 98	0.66417 44311 67	0.68211 89050 03
30	0.99285 63170 60	0.76221 14723 96	0.64732 81017 76	0.66644 37413 49
31	1.02595 15276 29	0.77613 98807 56	0.63056 07706 64	0.65088 14761 66
32	1.05904 67381 98	0.78938 48085 06	0.61389 87083 39	0.63545 87031 31
33	1.09214 19487 67	0.80196 88805 30	0.59736 58131 00	0.62019 97345 35
34	1.12523 71593 35	0.81391 52062 98	0.58098 36804 56	0.60512 66701 85
35	1.15833 23699 04	0.82524 72021 05	0.56477 16843 27	0.59025 94778 52
36	1.19142 75804 73	0.83598 84304 35	0.54874 70675 82	0.57561 60829 07
37	1.22452 27910 41	0.84616 24560 80	0.53292 50396 83	0.56121 24649 42
38	1.25761 80016 10	0.85579 27184 76	0.51731 88794 20	0.54706 27594 24
39	1.29071 32121 79	0.86490 24195 22	0.50194 00409 46	0.53317 93626 12
40	1.32380 84227 47	0.87351 44260 80	0.48679 82615 32	0.51957 30382 14
41	1.35690 36333 16	0.88165 11862 20	0.47190 16696 69	0.50625 30244 21
42	1.38999 88438 85	0.88933 46582 62	0.45725 68923 63	0.49322 71402 05
43	1.42309 40544 53	0.89658 62516 07	0.44286 91606 20	0.48050 18898 93
44	1.45618 92650 22	0.90342 67783 68	0.42874 24123 27	0.46808 25652 52
45	1.48928 44755 91	0.90987 64148 00	0.41487 93918 61	0.45597 33444 16

q = 0.18728 51836 10216 8   D(90) = 2.19311 06549 24674
q'= 0.00276 18093 29251 567   1/D(90) = 0.45597 33444 15832

r	ϕ	$E(\phi,k)$	A(r)	D(r)
0	0.00000 00000 00	0.00000 00000 00	0.00000 00000 00	1.00000 00000 00
1	0.03308 94318 03	0.03308 36548 53	0.01509 04838 02	1.00035 38636 25
2	0.06614 42286 09	0.06609 80940 83	0.03018 06650 26	1.00141 50582 00
3	0.09912 99429 01	0.09897 46931 29	0.04527 02295 42	1.00318 23951 41
4	0.13201 24996 82	0.13164 59988 61	0.06035 88401 60	1.00565 38945 22
5	0.16475 83767 25	0.16404 62889 00	0.07544 61251 83	1.00882 67866 38
6	0.19733 47777 53	0.19611 21001 75	0.09053 16670 62	1.01269 75142 14
7	0.22970 97964 76	0.22778 27179 29	0.10561 49911 93	1.01726 17352 33
8	0.26185 25695 93	0.25900 06175 63	0.12069 55548 81	1.02251 43264 08
9	0.29373 34171 46	0.28971 18530 86	0.13577 27365 11	1.02844 93872 99
10	0.32532 39688 65	0.31986 63873 88	0.15084 58249 49	1.03506 02450 72
11	0.35659 72754 65	0.34941 83611 74	0.16591 40092 17	1.04233 94599 16
12	0.38752 79041 41	0.37832 62989 26	0.18097 63684 67	1.05027 88311 14
13	0.41809 20178 46	0.40655 32517 91	0.19603 18622 80	1.05886 94037 92
14	0.44826 74381 92	0.43406 68787 21	0.21107 93213 33	1.06810 14763 30
15	0.47803 36921 49	0.46083 94684 65	0.22611 74384 45	1.07796 46084 66
16	0.50737 20429 21	0.48684 79060 95	0.24114 47600 48	1.08844 76300 85
17	0.53626 55056 56	0.51207 35886 73	0.25615 96780 96	1.09953 86507 08
18	0.56469 88488 06	0.53650 22953 44	0.27116 04224 42	1.11122 50696 95
19	0.59265 85821 40	0.56012 40176 28	0.28614 50537 14	1.12349 35871 52
20	0.62013 29325 27	0.58293 27559 51	0.30111 14566 99	1.13633 02155 74
21	0.64711 18087 00	0.60492 62885 56	0.31605 73342 70	1.14972 02922 16
22	0.67358 67562 72	0.62610 59188 59	0.33098 02018 71	1.16364 84922 00
23	0.69955 09042 96	0.64647 62070 58	0.34587 73825 71	1.17809 88423 79
24	0.72499 89046 67	0.66604 46915 22	0.36074 60027 29	1.19305 47359 41
25	0.74992 68656 26	0.68482 16049 75	0.37558 29882 48	1.20849 89477 89
26	0.77433 22805 87	0.70281 95900 66	0.39038 50614 71	1.22441 36506 68
27	0.79821 39534 43	0.72005 34183 13	0.40514 87387 02	1.24078 04320 75
28	0.82157 19214 25	0.73653 97158 85	0.41987 03283 80	1.25758 03119 32
29	0.84440 73765 00	0.75229 66991 18	0.43454 59299 07	1.27479 37610 31
30	0.86672 25862 07	0.76734 39220 91	0.44917 14331 44	1.29240 07202 61
31	0.88852 08147 30	0.78170 20381 17	0.46374 25185 68	1.31038 06205 93
32	0.90980 62449 05	0.79539 25764 71	0.47825 46581 11	1.32871 24038 49
33	0.93058 39017 68	0.80843 77352 81	0.49270 31166 71	1.34737 45442 22
34	0.95085 95781 55	0.82086 01911 04	0.50708 29542 91	1.36634 50705 68
35	0.97063 97627 86	0.83268 29253 57	0.52138 90290 25	1.38560 15894 36
36	0.98993 15711 64	0.84392 90675 26	0.53561 60004 59	1.40512 13088 48
37	1.00874 26795 62	0.85462 17547 75	0.54975 83339 08	1.42488 10628 08
38	1.02708 12623 01	0.86478 40074 44	0.56381 03052 62	1.44485 73365 16
39	1.04495 59324 45	0.87443 86197 23	0.57776 60064 82	1.46502 62922 93
40	1.06237 56860 05	0.88360 80647 04	0.59161 93517 32	1.48536 37961 84
41	1.07934 98496 81	0.89231 44129 08	0.60536 40841 41	1.50584 54452 14
42	1.09588 80321 37	0.90057 92633 65	0.61899 37831 59	1.52644 65952 90
43	1.11200 00787 67	0.90842 36862 52	0.63250 18725 25	1.54714 23897 11
44	1.12769 60298 87	0.91586 81761 26	0.64588 16287 96	1.56790 77882 68
45	1.14298 60822 46	0.92293 26147 95	0.65912 61904 38	1.58871 75968 93

K = 2.97856 89511 81384 E = 1.05377 69204 07046
K'= 1.58819 72125 27520 E'= 1.55368 08919 36509

r	u=(r/90)K=F(φ,k)	sn u	cn u	dn u
45	1.48928 44755 91	0.90987 64148 00	0.41487 93918 61	0.45597 33444 16
46	1.52237 96861 59	0.91595 46715 80	0.40128 17459 24	0.44417 73871 80
47	1.55547 48967 28	0.92168 03719 94	0.38795 01151 96	0.43269 69262 58
48	1.58857 01072 97	0.92707 16371 64	0.37488 42215 48	0.42153 33542 50
49	1.62166 53178 65	0.93214 58774 66	0.36208 29506 12	0.41068 73061 26
50	1.65476 05284 34	0.93691 97893 81	0.34954 44296 04	0.40015 87371 28
51	1.68785 57390 03	0.94140 93570 44	0.33726 61003 87	0.38994 69960 71
52	1.72095 09495 71	0.94562 98578 33	0.32524 47877 74	0.38005 08940 45
53	1.75404 61601 40	0.94959 58713 92	0.31347 67631 51	0.37046 87686 14
54	1.78714 13707 09	0.95332 12915 29	0.30195 78035 38	0.36119 85435 98
55	1.82023 65812 78	0.95681 93405 07	0.29068 32462 17	0.35223 77846 00
56	1.85333 17918 46	0.96010 25852 63	0.27964 80390 99	0.34358 37504 14
57	1.88642 70024 15	0.96318 29551 62	0.26884 67870 10	0.33523 34405 20
58	1.91952 22129 84	0.96607 17609 42	0.25827 37940 85	0.32718 36388 32
59	1.95261 74235 52	0.96877 97145 15	0.24792 31024 82	0.31943 09539 15
60	1.98571 26341 21	0.97131 69493 73	0.23778 85276 04	0.31197 18558 64
61	2.01880 78446 90	0.97369 30413 39	0.22786 36900 61	0.30480 27100 45
62	2.05190 30552 58	0.97591 70294 66	0.21814 20445 44	0.29791 98079 06
63	2.08499 82658 27	0.97799 74369 07	0.20861 69058 42	0.29131 93950 52
64	2.11809 34763 96	0.97994 22915 90	0.19928 14721 76	0.28499 76967 72
65	2.15118 86869 64	0.98175 91465 83	0.19012 88460 49	0.27895 09412 05
66	2.18428 38975 33	0.98345 51000 27	0.18115 20527 91	0.27317 53803 24
67	2.21737 91081 02	0.98503 68145 54	0.17234 40569 72	0.26766 73089 03
68	2.25047 43186 70	0.98651 05361 10	0.16369 77768 43	0.26242 30816 31
69	2.28356 95292 39	0.98788 21121 29	0.15520 60969 68	0.25743 91285 25
70	2.31666 47398 08	0.98915 70089 93	0.14686 18791 90	0.25271 19687 76
71	2.34975 99503 76	0.99034 03287 67	0.13865 79720 70	0.24823 82231 76
72	2.38285 51609 45	0.99143 68251 45	0.13058 72189 23	0.24401 46252 37
73	2.41595 03715 14	0.99245 09186 26	0.12264 24645 82	0.24003 80311 22
74	2.44904 55820 82	0.99338 67108 64	0.11481 65609 97	0.23630 54285 08
75	2.48214 07926 51	0.99424 79982 18	0.10710 23717 69	0.23281 39444 55
76	2.51523 60032 20	0.99503 82844 78	0.09949 27757 34	0.22956 08523 96
77	2.54833 12137 89	0.99576 07927 65	0.09198 06696 62	0.22654 35783 26
78	2.58142 64243 57	0.99641 84766 26	0.08455 89701 84	0.22375 97062 54
79	2.61452 16349 26	0.99701 40303 01	0.07722 06150 07	0.22120 69830 09
80	2.64761 68454 95	0.99754 98981 98	0.06995 85634 90	0.21888 33224 52
81	2.68071 20560 63	0.99802 82835 52	0.06276 57966 59	0.21678 68091 44
82	2.71380 72666 32	0.99845 11563 08	0.05563 53167 22	0.21491 57015 47
83	2.74690 24772 01	0.99882 02602 11	0.04856 01461 30	0.21326 84347 73
84	2.77999 76877 69	0.99913 71191 23	0.04153 33262 59	0.21184 36229 46
85	2.81309 28983 38	0.99940 30425 80	0.03454 79157 47	0.21064 00612 06
86	2.84618 81089 07	0.99961 91305 81	0.02759 69885 49	0.20965 67273 78
87	2.87928 33194 75	0.99978 62776 37	0.02067 36317 41	0.20889 27833 45
88	2.91237 85300 44	0.99990 51760 67	0.01377 09431 30	0.20834 75761 37
89	2.94547 37406 13	0.99997 63185 60	0.00688 20287 12	0.20802 06387 70
90	2.97856 89511 81	1.00000 00000 00	0.00000 00000 00	0.20791 16908 18

q = 0.18728 51836 10216 8   D(90) = 2.19311 06549 24674
q'= 0.00276 18093 29251 567   1/D(90) = 0.45597 33444 15832

r	ϕ	$E(\phi,k)$	A(r)	D(r)
45	1.14298 60822 46	0.92293 26147 95	0.65912 61904 38	1.58871 75968 93
46	1.15788 05537 63	0.92963 62428 59	0.67222 85674 49	1.60954 64978 35
47	1.17238 98513 44	0.93599 76390 53	0.68518 16514 92	1.63036 90803 29
48	1.18652 44416 51	0.94203 47065 01	0.69797 82265 21	1.65115 98717 12
49	1.20029 48246 75	0.94776 46650 89	0.71061 09798 60	1.67189 33689 59
50	1.21371 15099 68	0.95320 40491 91	0.72307 25137 24	1.69254 40705 87
51	1.22678 49953 67	0.95836 87100 50	0.73535 53571 41	1.71308 65088 97
52	1.23952 57480 80	0.96327 38221 72	0.74745 19782 47	1.73349 52824 93
53	1.25194 41879 57	0.96793 38931 31	0.75935 47969 40	1.75374 50890 51
54	1.26405 06728 27	0.97236 27762 63	0.77105 61978 27	1.77381 07582 69
55	1.27585 54857 32	0.97657 36857 66	0.78254 85434 71	1.79366 72849 58
56	1.28736 88239 33	0.98057 92137 58	0.79382 41878 71	1.81328 98622 30
57	1.29860 07895 54	0.98439 13489 26	0.80487 54901 60	1.83265 39147 08
58	1.30956 13817 32	0.98802 14964 13	0.81569 48284 77	1.85173 51317 22
59	1.32026 04901 62	0.99148 04986 45	0.82627 46139 84	1.87050 95004 28
60	1.33070 78899 08	0.99477 86568 36	0.83660 73049 80	1.88895 33387 88
61	1.34091 32373 89	0.99792 57529 47	0.84668 54210 88	1.90704 33283 62
62	1.35088 60674 31	1.00093 10718 87	0.85650 15574 70	1.92475 65468 50
63	1.36063 57912 94	1.00380 34238 14	0.86604 83990 32	1.94207 05003 10
64	1.37017 16955 80	1.00655 11663 64	0.87531 87345 86	1.95896 31550 23
65	1.37950 29419 53	1.00918 22267 11	0.88430 54709 30	1.97541 29689 08
66	1.38863 85675 87	1.01170 41233 54	0.89300 16468 06	1.99139 89224 53
67	1.39758 74862 72	1.01412 39875 42	0.90140 04466 98	2.00690 05490 95
68	1.40635 84901 20	1.01644 85842 87	0.90949 52144 40	2.02189 79649 78
69	1.41496 02518 05	1.01868 43329 07	0.91727 94665 88	2.03637 18980 42
70	1.42340 13272 93	1.02083 73270 67	0.92474 69055 30	2.05030 37163 83
71	1.43169 01590 01	1.02291 33542 85	0.93189 14322 85	2.06367 54558 13
72	1.43983 50793 46	1.02491 79149 02	0.93870 71589 74	2.07646 98465 77
73	1.44784 43146 42	1.02685 62404 88	0.94518 84209 13	2.08867 03391 71
74	1.45572 59893 14	1.02873 33117 10	0.95132 97883 04	2.10026 11291 85
75	1.46348 81303 75	1.03055 38756 40	0.95712 60774 88	2.11122 71811 52
76	1.47113 86721 65	1.03232 24625 34	0.96257 23617 36	2.12155 42513 19
77	1.47868 54612 96	1.03404 34020 96	0.96766 39815 39	2.13122 89093 11
78	1.48613 62617 90	1.03572 08392 39	0.97239 65543 74	2.14023 85586 33
79	1.49349 87603 98	1.03735 87493 67	0.97676 59839 21	2.14857 14559 68
80	1.50078 05720 51	1.03896 09532 18	0.98076 84687 03	2.15621 67292 20
81	1.50798 92454 55	1.04053 11312 78	0.98440 05101 20	2.16316 43942 74
82	1.51513 22687 96	1.04207 28378 03	0.98765 89198 73	2.16940 53704 27
83	1.52221 70755 37	1.04358 95144 89	0.99054 08267 27	2.17493 14944 56
84	1.52925 10503 07	1.04508 45038 12	0.99304 36826 33	2.17973 55332 96
85	1.53624 15348 61	1.04656 10620 73	0.99516 52681 52	2.18381 11952 94
86	1.54319 58340 96	1.04802 23721 94	0.99690 36972 01	2.18715 31400 11
87	1.55012 12221 23	1.04947 15562 86	0.99825 74210 79	2.18975 69865 64
88	1.55702 49483 76	1.05091 16880 32	0.99922 52317 89	2.19161 93204 69
89	1.56391 42437 57	1.05234 58049 29	0.99980 62646 19	2.19273 76989 82
90	1.57079 63267 95	1.05377 69204 07	1.00000 00000 00	2.19311 06549 25

K = 3.06172 86120 38789   E = 1.04678 64993 44049
K′= 1.58539 41637 75538   E′= 1.55639 97977 70947

r	u=(r/90)K=F(φ,k)	sn u	cn u	dn u
0	0.00000 00000 00	0.00000 00000 00	1.00000 00000 00	1.00000 00000 00
1	0.03401 92068 00	0.03400 63280 05	0.99942 16175 65	0.99944 26812 26
2	0.06803 84136 01	0.06793 55234 22	0.99768 97136 17	0.99777 39205 26
3	0.10205 76204 01	0.10171 11517 03	0.99481 39733 74	0.99500 32607 47
4	0.13607 68272 02	0.13525 81609 94	0.99081 03904 81	0.99114 64610 26
5	0.17009 60340 02	0.16850 35404 62	0.98570 10484 18	0.98622 52822 73
6	0.20411 52408 03	0.20137 69402 06	0.97951 38222 37	0.98026 71944 86
7	0.23813 44476 03	0.23381 12418 83	0.97228 20080 46	0.97330 50131 64
8	0.27215 36544 03	0.26574 30707 45	0.96404 38892 24	0.96537 64736 42
9	0.30617 28612 04	0.29711 32415 56	0.95484 22496 37	0.95652 37534 18
10	0.34019 20680 04	0.32786 71328 02	0.94472 38449 56	0.94679 29533 99
11	0.37421 12748 05	0.35795 49856 45	0.93373 88437 09	0.93623 35494 50
12	0.40823 04816 05	0.38733 21260 77	0.92194 02497 50	0.92489 78257 24
13	0.44224 96884 06	0.41595 91106 63	0.90938 33175 60	0.91284 03010 11
14	0.47626 88952 06	0.44380 17980 42	0.89612 49712 26	0.90011 71586 88
15	0.51028 81020 06	0.47083 13499 43	0.88222 32370 05	0.88678 56900 71
16	0.54430 73088 07	0.49702 41667 70	0.86773 66983 40	0.87290 37598 08
17	0.57832 65156 07	0.52236 17639 11	0.85272 39809 01	0.85852 93007 88
18	0.61234 57224 08	0.54683 05956 66	0.83724 32738 71	0.84371 98446 58
19	0.64636 49292 08	0.57042 18342 23	0.82135 18923 35	0.82853 20927 16
20	0.68038 41360 09	0.59313 11113 21	0.80510 58842 06	0.81302 15305 60
21	0.71440 33428 09	0.61495 82302 79	0.78855 96838 62	0.79724 20886 09
22	0.74842 25496 09	0.63590 68558 15	0.77176 58133 96	0.78124 58494 09
23	0.78244 17564 10	0.65598 41887 49	0.75477 46313 38	0.76508 28015 57
24	0.81646 09632 10	0.67520 06321 37	0.73763 41277 10	0.74880 06391 62
25	0.85048 01700 11	0.69356 94547 66	0.72038 97635 41	0.73244 46049 55
26	0.88449 93768 11	0.71110 64572 89	0.70308 43522 66	0.71605 73745 72
27	0.91851 85836 12	0.72782 96455 07	0.68575 79799 91	0.69967 89790 12
28	0.95253 77904 12	0.74375 89146 35	0.66844 79612 52	0.68334 67619 78
29	0.98655 69972 12	0.75891 57476 40	0.65118 88266 73	0.66709 53685 70
30	1.02057 62040 13	0.77332 29300 79	0.63401 23388 50	0.65095 67617 13
31	1.05459 54108 13	0.78700 42832 26	0.61694 75327 64	0.63496 02627 18
32	1.08861 46176 14	0.79998 44167 11	0.60002 07771 56	0.61913 26124 46
33	1.12263 38244 14	0.81228 85013 89	0.58325 58533 87	0.60349 80496 87
34	1.15665 30312 15	0.82394 20626 94	0.56667 40485 71	0.58807 84035 82
35	1.19067 22380 15	0.83497 07943 76	0.55029 42599 55	0.57289 31971 36
36	1.22469 14448 16	0.84540 03922 01	0.53413 31078 16	0.55795 97591 34
37	1.25871 06516 16	0.85525 64069 28	0.51820 50544 03	0.54329 33420 28
38	1.29272 98584 16	0.86456 41156 90	0.50252 25267 21	0.52890 72436 57
39	1.32674 90652 17	0.87334 84107 68	0.48709 60412 58	0.51481 29309 06
40	1.36076 82720 17	0.88163 37046 23	0.47193 43289 82	0.50102 01636 87
41	1.39478 74788 18	0.88944 38500 00	0.45704 44592 13	0.48753 71178 63
42	1.42880 66856 18	0.89680 20738 84	0.44243 19611 85	0.47437 05059 61
43	1.46282 58924 19	0.90373 09240 87	0.42810 09423 60	0.46152 56947 37
44	1.49684 50992 19	0.91025 22272 57	0.41405 42026 99	0.44900 68188 38
45	1.53086 43060 19	0.91638 70571 39	0.40029 33443 22	0.43681 68899 85

$q = 0.19656\ 76611\ 43642\ 2$ $D(90) = 2.28928\ 87681\ 91522$
$q' = 0.00231\ 79450\ 15820\ 765$ $1/D(90) = 0.43681\ 68899\ 85432$

r	ϕ	$E(\phi,k)$	$A(r)$	$D(r)$
0	0.00000 00000 00	0.00000 00000 00	0.00000 00000 00	1.00000 00000 00
1	0.03401 28857 43	0.03400 65667 99	0.01486 01947 52	1.00038 07801 42
2	0.06798 78886 55	0.06793 74312 15	0.02972 05707 72	1.00152 27001 43
3	0.10188 73428 30	0.10171 75761 35	0.04458 12965 41	1.00342 44990 34
4	0.13567 40132 32	0.13527 33418 60	0.05944 25150 04	1.00608 40762 03
5	0.16931 13037 47	0.16853 30723 89	0.07430 43308 95	1.00949 84929 01
6	0.20276 34565 93	0.20142 77240 06	0.08916 67981 73	1.01366 39743 57
7	0.23599 57405 47	0.23389 14254 80	0.10402 99076 14	1.01857 59125 09
8	0.26897 46257 11	0.26586 19807 63	0.11889 35745 75	1.02422 88693 39
9	0.30166 79428 92	0.29728 13067 75	0.13375 76269 94	1.03061 65808 50
10	0.33404 50259 96	0.32809 58008 10	0.14862 17936 40	1.03773 19616 65
11	0.36607 68362 39	0.35825 66340 61	0.16348 56926 52	1.04556 71102 69
12	0.39773 60673 55	0.38771 99697 68	0.17834 88204 12	1.05411 33149 06
13	0.42899 72313 83	0.41644 71063 59	0.19321 05407 73	1.06336 10601 36
14	0.45983 67249 61	0.44440 45477 14	0.20807 00746 78	1.07330 00340 66
15	0.49023 28764 40	0.47156 40042 43	0.22292 64902 06	1.08391 91362 73
16	0.52016 59744 04	0.49790 23297 42	0.23777 86930 67	1.09520 64864 19
17	0.54961 82784 91	0.52340 14000 62	0.25262 54175 86	1.10714 94335 84
18	0.57857 40136 23	0.54804 79403 71	0.26746 52181 93	1.11973 45663 24
19	0.60701 93489 33	0.57183 33082 85	0.28229 64614 51	1.13294 77234 70
20	0.63494 23628 36	0.59475 32403 90	0.29711 73186 52	1.14677 40056 81
21	0.66233 29957 70	0.61680 75696 65	0.31192 57589 91	1.16119 77877 63
22	0.68918 29921 71	0.63799 99211 27	0.32671 95433 59	1.17620 27317 70
23	0.71548 58332 99	0.65833 73926 31	0.34149 62187 61	1.19177 18009 01
24	0.74123 66624 63	0.67783 02272 70	0.35625 31133 77	1.20788 72741 97
25	0.76643 22041 76	0.69649 14832 00	0.37098 73323 06	1.22453 07620 65
26	0.79107 06786 80	0.71433 67060 55	0.38569 57539 74	1.24168 32226 20
27	0.81515 17131 91	0.73138 36083 92	0.40037 50272 51	1.25932 49788 72
28	0.83867 62511 15	0.74765 17599 31	0.41502 15692 69	1.27743 57367 56
29	0.86164 64603 49	0.76316 22916 19	0.42963 15639 64	1.29599 46040 15
30	0.88406 56416 82	0.77793 76158 93	0.44420 09613 41	1.31498 01099 45
31	0.90593 81381 80	0.79200 11649 25	0.45872 54774 74	1.33437 02259 93
32	0.92726 92463 04	0.80537 71480 24	0.47320 05952 44	1.35414 23872 32
33	0.94806 53294 12	0.81809 03289 13	0.48762 15658 14	1.37427 35146 88
34	0.96833 27341 86	0.83016 58231 28	0.50198 34108 50	1.39474 00385 40
35	0.98807 97103 79	0.84162 89154 52	0.51628 09254 76	1.41551 79221 67
36	1.00731 43342 54	0.85250 48969 52	0.53050 86819 71	1.43658 26870 52
37	1.02604 54359 28	0.86281 89209 63	0.54466 10341 82	1.45790 94385 31
38	1.04428 23307 98	0.87259 58771 62	0.55873 21226 79	1.47947 28923 68
39	1.06203 47551 46	0.88186 02827 33	0.57271 58806 05	1.50124 74021 46
40	1.07931 28059 63	0.89063 61895 18	0.58660 60402 36	1.52320 69874 63
41	1.09612 68849 77	0.89894 71059 85	0.60039 61402 27	1.54532 53629 07
42	1.11248 76468 20	0.90681 59328 29	0.61407 95335 27	1.56757 59677 84
43	1.12840 59512 62	0.91426 49109 91	0.62764 93959 50	1.58993 19965 88
44	1.14389 28193 70	0.92131 55809 30	0.64109 87353 85	1.61236 64301 72
45	1.15895 93934 69	0.92798 87519 84	0.65442 04016 10	1.63485 20675 95

315

K = 3.06172 86120 38789   E = 1.04678 64993 44049
K' = 1.58539 41637 75538   E' = 1.55639 97977 70947

r	u=(r/90)K=F(φ,k)	sn u	cn u	dn u
45	1.53086 43060 19	0.91638 70571 39	0.40029 33443 22	0.43681 68899 85
46	1.56488 35128 20	0.92215 57119 58	0.38681 88760 96	0.42495 79012 42
47	1.59890 27196 20	0.92757 76998 80	0.37363 03128 56	0.41343 09260 62
48	1.63292 19264 21	0.93267 17315 37	0.36072 62690 64	0.40223 62119 45
49	1.66694 11332 21	0.93745 57186 86	0.34810 45468 01	0.39137 32685 89
50	1.70096 03400 22	0.94194 67781 68	0.33576 22180 94	0.38084 09505 36
51	1.73497 95468 22	0.94616 12403 57	0.32369 57016 19	0.37063 75343 77
52	1.76899 87536 22	0.95011 46614 02	0.31190 08339 02	0.36076 07906 01
53	1.80301 79604 23	0.95382 18386 19	0.30037 29351 55	0.35120 80502 66
54	1.83703 71672 23	0.95729 68284 40	0.28910 68699 60	0.34197 62666 62
55	1.87105 63740 24	0.96055 29664 27	0.27809 71029 85	0.33306 20721 81
56	1.90507 55808 24	0.96360 28888 66	0.26733 77499 90	0.32446 18306 24
57	1.93909 47876 25	0.96645 85555 66	0.25682 26243 42	0.31617 16851 87
58	1.97311 39944 25	0.96913 12734 85	0.24654 52793 17	0.30818 76023 66
59	2.00713 32012 25	0.97163 17208 94	0.23649 90464 07	0.30050 54120 39
60	2.04115 24080 26	0.97396 99718 02	0.22667 70699 21	0.29312 08439 63
61	2.07517 16148 26	0.97615 55204 15	0.21707 23380 87	0.28602 95609 39
62	2.10919 08216 27	0.97819 73054 45	0.20767 77109 37	0.27922 71888 79
63	2.14321 00284 27	0.98010 37340 86	0.19848 59451 70	0.27270 93440 00
64	2.17722 92352 28	0.98188 27055 40	0.18948 97162 43	0.26647 16573 73
65	2.21124 84420 28	0.98354 16339 58	0.18068 16378 91	0.26050 97970 35
66	2.24526 76488 28	0.98508 74707 26	0.17205 42792 80	0.25481 94878 55
67	2.27928 68556 29	0.98652 67259 98	0.16360 01799 85	0.24939 65293 54
68	2.31330 60624 29	0.98786 54894 37	0.15531 18629 72	0.24423 68116 53
69	2.34732 52692 30	0.98910 94501 01	0.14718 18457 59	0.23933 63297 08
70	2.38134 44760 30	0.99026 39154 60	0.13920 26498 98	0.23469 11959 95
71	2.41536 36828 31	0.99133 38294 98	0.13136 68089 45	0.23029 76517 79
72	2.44938 28896 31	0.99232 37899 08	0.12366 68750 43	0.22615 20771 20
73	2.48340 20964 31	0.99323 80643 49	0.11609 54242 37	0.22225 09997 06
74	2.51742 13032 32	0.99408 06057 83	0.10864 50606 65	0.21859 11026 65
75	2.55144 05100 32	0.99485 50668 80	0.10130 84197 01	0.21516 92314 31
76	2.58545 97168 33	0.99556 48135 09	0.09407 81701 73	0.21198 23997 74
77	2.61947 89236 33	0.99621 29373 05	0.08694 70157 44	0.20902 77950 76
78	2.65349 81304 34	0.99680 22673 51	0.07990 76955 30	0.20630 27829 34
79	2.68751 73372 34	0.99733 53809 62	0.07295 29840 51	0.20380 49111 66
80	2.72153 65440 34	0.99781 46136 01	0.06607 56905 74	0.20153 19132 78
81	2.75555 57508 35	0.99824 20679 32	0.05926 86579 21	0.19948 17114 52
82	2.78957 49576 35	0.99861 96220 30	0.05252 47607 97	0.19765 24191 20
83	2.82359 41644 36	0.99894 89367 62	0.04583 69037 13	0.19604 23431 46
84	2.85761 33712 36	0.99923 14623 47	0.03919 80185 29	0.19464 99856 87
85	2.89163 25780 37	0.99946 84441 12	0.03260 10616 95	0.19347 40457 44
86	2.92565 17848 37	0.99966 09274 62	0.02603 90112 16	0.19251 34204 47
87	2.95967 09916 37	0.99980 97620 57	0.01950 48633 92	0.19176 72061 03
88	2.99369 01984 38	0.99991 56052 22	0.01299 16293 74	0.19123 46990 15
89	3.02770 94052 38	0.99997 89245 93	0.00649 23315 81	0.19091 53961 11
90	3.06172 86120 39	1.00000 00000 00	0.00000 00000 00	0.19080 89953 77

q = 0.19656 76611 43642 2   D(90) = 2.28928 87681 91522
q' = 0.00231 79450 15820 765   1/D(90) = 0.43681 68899 85432

r	ϕ	$E(\phi,k)$	$A(r)$	$D(r)$
45	1.15895 93934 69	0.92798 87519 84	0.65442 04016 10	1.63485 20675 95
46	1.17361 69007 20	0.93430 44807 28	0.66760 70967 04	1.65736 15586 08
47	1.18787 66201 74	0.94028 20572 98	0.68065 13860 27	1.67986 74367 52
48	1.20174 98530 94	0.94593 99986 84	0.69354 57097 33	1.70234 21530 13
49	1.21524 78963 68	0.95129 60481 05	0.70628 23947 97	1.72475 81100 12
50	1.22838 20188 36	0.95636 71796 12	0.71885 36675 30	1.74708 76966 64
51	1.24116 34403 28	0.96116 96071 64	0.73125 16665 34	1.76930 33232 75
52	1.25360 33132 40	0.96571 87974 79	0.74346 84560 88	1.79137 74570 26
53	1.26571 27065 26	0.97002 94860 27	0.75549 60399 09	1.81328 26577 76
54	1.27750 25915 10	0.97411 56956 08	0.76732 63752 70	1.83499 16141 53
55	1.28898 38306 17	0.97799 07570 06	0.77895 13874 32	1.85647 71798 56
56	1.30016 71667 58	0.98166 73312 81	0.79036 29843 44	1.87771 24101 22
57	1.31106 32153 21	0.98515 74333 04	0.80155 30715 97	1.89867 05982 89
58	1.32168 24573 64	0.98847 24561 98	0.81251 35675 67	1.91932 53123 95
59	1.33203 52342 97	0.99162 31963 81	0.82323 64187 20	1.93965 04317 58
60	1.34213 17438 61	0.99461 98789 67	0.83371 36150 47	1.95962 01834 47
61	1.35198 20373 02	0.99747 21832 90	0.84393 72055 64	1.97920 91786 09
62	1.36159 60176 08	1.00018 92683 91	0.85389 93138 64	1.99839 24485 53
63	1.37098 34387 25	1.00277 97982 90	0.86359 21536 63	2.01714 54805 47
64	1.38015 39056 54	1.00525 19669 29	0.87300 80442 95	2.03544 42532 39
65	1.38911 68753 38	1.00761 35226 82	0.88213 94261 33	2.05326 52716 47
66	1.39788 16582 62	1.00987 17923 40	0.89097 88758 74	2.07058 56016 33
67	1.40645 74206 97	1.01203 37045 22	0.89951 91216 64	2.08738 29038 07
68	1.41485 31875 18	1.01410 58124 50	0.90775 30580 04	2.10363 54667 73
69	1.42307 78455 26	1.01609 43160 56	0.91567 37604 19	2.11932 22396 59
70	1.43114 01472 41	1.01800 50834 16	0.92327 44998 28	2.13442 28638 62
71	1.43904 87150 93	1.01984 36714 68	0.93054 87565 89	2.14891 77039 29
72	1.44681 20459 77	1.02161 53460 48	0.93749 02341 76	2.16278 78775 21
73	1.45443 85161 28	1.02332 51012 18	0.94409 28724 58	2.17601 52843 77
74	1.46193 63862 79	1.02497 76779 23	0.95035 08605 26	2.18858 26342 33
75	1.46931 38070 67	1.02657 75819 75	0.95625 86490 54	2.20047 34736 19
76	1.47657 88246 62	1.02812 91014 00	0.96181 09621 44	2.21167 22114 75
77	1.48373 93865 84	1.02963 63231 67	0.96700 28086 30	2.22216 41435 38
78	1.49080 33476 87	1.03110 31493 34	0.97182 94928 09	2.23193 54754 26
79	1.49777 84762 98	1.03253 33126 30	0.97628 66245 64	2.24097 33443 87
80	1.50467 24604 66	1.03393 03915 31	0.98037 01288 58	2.24926 58396 39
81	1.51149 29143 43	1.03529 78248 40	0.98407 62545 72	2.25680 20212 82
82	1.51824 73846 38	1.03663 89258 25	0.98740 15826 53	2.26357 19376 99
83	1.52494 33571 66	1.03795 68959 48	0.99034 30335 61	2.26956 66414 51
84	1.53158 82634 60	1.03925 48382 24	0.99289 78739 87	2.27477 82035 82
85	1.53818 94874 42	1.04053 57702 50	0.99506 37228 28	2.27919 97263 39
86	1.54475 43721 41	1.04180 26369 48	0.99683 85563 99	2.28282 53542 50
87	1.55129 02264 54	1.04305 83230 56	0.99822 07128 64	2.28565 02835 45
88	1.55780 43319 33	1.04430 56654 13	0.99920 88958 86	2.28767 07698 97
89	1.56430 39496 04	1.04554 74650 83	0.99980 21774 70	2.28888 41344 59
90	1.57079 63267 95	1.04678 64993 44	1.00000 00000 00	2.28928 87681 92

11   317

ELLIPTIC FUNCTIONS TABLE $\theta = 80°$

K = 3.15338 52518 87839   E = 1.04011 43957 06010
K′= 1.58284 28043 38351   E′= 1.55888 71966 01596

r	u=(r/90)K=F(φ,k)	sn u	cn u	dn u
0	0.00000 00000 00	0.00000 00000 00	1.00000 00000 00	1.00000 00000 00
1	0.03503 76139 10	0.03502 34991 11	0.99938 64890 57	0.99940 49941 83
2	0.07007 52278 20	0.06996 24729 16	0.99754 96240 21	0.99762 35999 03
3	0.10511 28417 30	0.10473 32099 70	0.99450 03543 13	0.99466 66335 59
4	0.14015 04556 39	0.13925 36099 56	0.99025 67506 03	0.99055 19468 63
5	0.17518 80695 49	0.17344 39483 26	0.98484 37423 21	0.98530 41684 17
6	0.21022 56834 59	0.20722 75934 38	0.97829 27601 27	0.97895 43517 03
7	0.24526 32973 69	0.24053 16629 05	0.97064 12927 24	0.97153 95387 49
8	0.28030 09112 79	0.27328 76078 92	0.96193 23694 38	0.96310 22507 25
9	0.31533 85251 89	0.30543 17164 33	0.95221 39815 17	0.95368 99182 00
10	0.35037 61390 99	0.33690 55293 66	0.94153 84560 83	0.94335 42648 15
11	0.38541 37530 09	0.36765 61650 41	0.92996 17972 30	0.93215 06586 19
12	0.42045 13669 18	0.39763 65515 71	0.91754 30087 22	0.92013 74453 17
13	0.45548 89808 28	0.42680 55677 78	0.90434 34122 69	0.90737 52771 89
14	0.49052 65947 38	0.45512 80962 08	0.89042 59744 88	0.89392 64505 93
15	0.52556 42086 48	0.48257 49934 89	0.87585 46544 14	0.87985 42637 36
16	0.56060 18225 58	0.50912 29848 92	0.86069 37819 31	0.86522 24049 16
17	0.59563 94364 68	0.53475 44911 56	0.84500 74758 18	0.85009 43798 23
18	0.63067 70503 78	0.55945 73964 70	0.82885 91083 75	0.83453 29847 26
19	0.66571 46642 87	0.58322 47670 04	0.81231 08217 63	0.81859 98306 33
20	0.70075 22781 97	0.60605 45295 21	0.79542 30995 18	0.80235 49218 05
21	0.73578 98921 07	0.62794 91194 52	0.77825 43950 27	0.78585 62904 11
22	0.77082 75060 17	0.64891 51074 31	0.76086 08173 30	0.76915 96876 65
23	0.80586 51199 27	0.66896 28126 87	0.74329 58732 85	0.75231 83305 04
24	0.84090 27338 37	0.68810 59109 41	0.72561 02640 73	0.73538 27018 10
25	0.87594 03477 47	0.70636 10436 22	0.70785 17331 00	0.71840 04012 91
26	0.91097 79616 56	0.72374 74342 71	0.69006 49617 15	0.70141 60434 80
27	0.94601 55755 66	0.74028 65171 16	0.67229 15086 31	0.68447 11988 19
28	0.98105 31894 76	0.75600 15818 58	0.65456 97886 62	0.66760 43734 82
29	1.01609 08033 86	0.77091 74378 31	0.63693 50862 12	0.65085 10234 80
30	1.05112 84172 96	0.78506 00998 94	0.61941 95989 42	0.63424 35985 07
31	1.08616 60312 06	0.79845 64976 56	0.60205 25071 38	0.61781 16111 51
32	1.12120 36451 16	0.81113 42089 76	0.58486 00644 85	0.60158 17272 15
33	1.15624 12590 26	0.82312 12181 21	0.56786 57062 01	0.58557 78731 87
34	1.19127 88729 35	0.83444 56984 39	0.55109 01708 03	0.56982 13571 65
35	1.22631 64868 45	0.84513 58190 48	0.53455 16320 82	0.55433 09998 93
36	1.26135 41007 55	0.85521 95746 77	0.51826 58382 42	0.53912 32728 93
37	1.29639 17146 65	0.86472 46375 77	0.50224 62555 04	0.52421 24410 36
38	1.33142 93285 75	0.87367 82302 09	0.48650 42138 14	0.50961 07072 39
39	1.36646 69424 85	0.88210 70173 18	0.47104 90526 46	0.49532 83573 02
40	1.40150 45563 95	0.89003 70158 90	0.45588 82651 99	0.48137 39032 18
41	1.43654 21703 04	0.89749 35214 97	0.44102 76395 77	0.46775 42235 58
42	1.47157 97842 14	0.90450 10494 96	0.42647 13958 29	0.45447 46998 33
43	1.50661 73981 24	0.91108 32896 07	0.41222 23179 29	0.44153 93479 34
44	1.54165 50120 34	0.91726 30724 24	0.39828 18800 39	0.42895 09439 90
45	1.57669 26259 44	0.92306 23464 97	0.38465 03665 40	0.41671 11441 60

318

q = 0.20660 97552 00965 0   D(90) = 2.39974 38369 84197
q′ = 0.00191 35945 90170 284   1/D(90) = 0.41671 11441 59753

r	ϕ	$E(\phi,k)$	A(r)	D(r)
0	0.00000 00000 00	0.00000 00000 00	0.00000 00000 00	1.00000 00000 00
1	0.03503 06633 02	0.03502 37151 76	0.01460 06854 45	1.00041 13181 84
2	0.07001 96737 73	0.06996 41989 64	0.02920 20956 40	1.00164 48264 18
3	0.10492 56318 53	0.10473 90215 22	0.04380 49411 68	1.00369 91860 32
4	0.13970 76408 28	0.13926 73397 48	0.05840 99043 21	1.00657 21668 33
5	0.17432 55490 82	0.17347 06503 65	0.07301 76250 54	1.01026 06484 98
6	0.20874 01816 37	0.20727 34962 05	0.08762 86870 63	1.01476 06225 30
7	0.24291 35578 57	0.24060 41126 34	0.10224 36040 28	1.02006 71947 87
8	0.27680 90925 41	0.27339 50030 26	0.11686 28060 50	1.02617 45885 78
9	0.31039 17780 73	0.30558 34344 89	0.13148 66263 38	1.03307 61483 64
10	0.34362 83457 56	0.33711 18475 26	0.14611 52881 71	1.04076 43440 46
11	0.37648 74049 37	0.36792 81758 77	0.16074 88921 76	1.04923 07758 73
12	0.40893 95590 56	0.39798 60752 89	0.17538 74039 69	1.05846 61799 74
13	0.44095 74982 07	0.42724 50623 91	0.19003 06421 81	1.06846 04345 39
14	0.47251 60683 10	0.45567 05669 56	0.20467 82669 11	1.07920 25666 55
15	0.50359 23173 85	0.48323 39027 87	0.21932 97686 45	1.09068 07598 28
16	0.53416 55198 39	0.50991 21639 41	0.23398 44576 64	1.10288 23622 03
17	0.56421 71799 75	0.53568 80542 63	0.24864 14539 85	1.11579 38954 94
18	0.59373 10162 20	0.56054 96589 68	0.26329 96778 53	1.12940 10646 65
19	0.62269 29277 82	0.58449 01675 32	0.27795 78408 22	1.14368 87683 66
20	0.65109 09455 68	0.60750 75572 74	0.29261 44374 54	1.15864 11101 47
21	0.67891 51693 32	0.62960 42468 66	0.30726 77376 53	1.17424 14104 83
22	0.70615 76929 94	0.65078 67286 44	0.32191 57796 67	1.19047 22196 11
23	0.73281 25201 25	0.67106 51879 72	0.33655 63637 78	1.20731 53312 22
24	0.75887 54715 05	0.69045 31172 18	0.35118 70467 05	1.22475 17970 11
25	0.78434 40865 64	0.70896 69310 09	0.36580 51367 30	1.24276 19421 12
26	0.80921 75204 50	0.72662 55886 00	0.38040 76895 73	1.26132 53814 35
27	0.83349 64382 84	0.74345 02282 26	0.39499 15050 34	1.28042 10369 23
28	0.85718 29080 36	0.75946 38174 21	0.40955 31244 01	1.30002 71557 41
29	0.88028 02933 22	0.77469 08224 37	0.42408 88286 55	1.32012 13294 15
30	0.90279 31472 16	0.78915 68990 73	0.43859 46374 69	1.34068 05139 40
31	0.92472 71080 62	0.80288 86064 88	0.45306 63090 05	1.36168 10508 44
32	0.94608 87980 91	0.81591 31449 46	0.46749 93405 34	1.38309 86892 51
33	0.96688 57255 18	0.82825 81178 35	0.48188 89698 55	1.40490 86089 17
34	0.98712 61906 41	0.83995 13178 65	0.49623 01775 38	1.42708 54442 65
35	1.00681 91963 75	0.85102 05369 20	0.51051 76899 74	1.44960 33094 01
36	1.02597 43635 02	0.86149 33987 30	0.52474 59832 38	1.47243 58241 35
37	1.04460 18508 48	0.87139 72132 93	0.53890 92877 52	1.49555 61409 72
38	1.06271 22804 99	0.88075 88517 81	0.55300 15937 51	1.51893 69730 87
39	1.08031 66680 97	0.88960 46405 49	0.56701 66575 20	1.54255 06232 66
40	1.09742 63581 81	0.89796 02727 89	0.58094 80084 24	1.56636 90137 97
41	1.11405 29645 13	0.90585 07363 35	0.59478 89566 80	1.59036 37172 99
42	1.13020 83152 43	0.91330 02561 26	0.60853 26018 84	1.61450 59884 56
43	1.14590 44027 77	0.92033 22498 72	0.62217 18422 54	1.63876 67966 53
44	1.16115 33381 52	0.92696 92954 96	0.63569 93845 75	1.66311 68594 61
45	1.17596 73097 11	0.93323 31090 20	0.64910 77548 37	1.68752 66769 58

319

K = 3.15338 52518 87839   E = 1.04011 43957 06010
K'= 1.58284 28043 38351   E'= 1.55888 71966 01596

r	u=(r/90)K=F(ϕ,k)	sn u	cn u	dn u
45	1.57669 26259 44	0.92306 23464 97	0.38465 03665 40	0.41671 11441 60
46	1.61173 02398 54	0.92850 21646 85	0.37132 69855 19	0.40482 05980 19
47	1.64676 78537 64	0.93360 26785 81	0.35830 99755 06	0.39327 90553 77
48	1.68180 54676 74	0.93838 31398 89	0.34559 67053 84	0.38208 54664 31
49	1.71684 30815 83	0.94286 19077 39	0.33318 37675 14	0.37123 80752 99
50	1.75188 06954 93	0.94705 64609 98	0.32106 70641 51	0.36073 45070 14
51	1.78691 83094 03	0.95098 34147 43	0.30924 18873 38	0.35057 18481 63
52	1.82195 59233 13	0.95465 85401 44	0.29770 29924 77	0.34074 67213 71
53	1.85699 35372 23	0.95809 67870 81	0.28644 46658 35	0.33125 53538 86
54	1.89203 11511 33	0.96131 23088 92	0.27546 07862 70	0.32209 36405 42
55	1.92706 87650 43	0.96431 84887 47	0.26474 48814 64	0.31325 72013 84
56	1.96210 63789 52	0.96712 79671 68	0.25429 01789 73	0.30474 14342 82
57	1.99714 39928 62	0.96975 26703 16	0.24408 96524 11	0.29654 15628 19
58	2.03218 16067 72	0.97220 38386 91	0.23413 06630 82	0.28865 26797 79
59	2.06721 92206 82	0.97449 20559 46	0.22442 19973 56	0.28106 97865 38
60	2.10225 68345 92	0.97662 72775 95	0.21493 99001 06	0.27378 78286 44
61	2.13729 44485 02	0.97861 88593 61	0.20568 21044 78	0.26680 17278 95
62	2.17233 20624 12	0.98047 55850 35	0.19664 08582 95	0.26010 64111 69
63	2.20736 96763 21	0.98220 56936 67	0.18780 83473 35	0.25369 68362 83
64	2.24240 72902 31	0.98381 69059 99	0.17917 67157 60	0.24756 80151 33
65	2.27744 49041 41	0.98531 64500 31	0.17073 80839 15	0.24171 50343 39
66	2.31248 25180 51	0.98671 10856 53	0.16248 45637 28	0.23613 30736 22
67	2.34752 01319 61	0.98800 71282 95	0.15440 82719 24	0.23081 74221 28
68	2.38255 77458 71	0.98921 04715 46	0.14650 13412 34	0.22576 34928 76
69	2.41759 53597 81	0.99032 66087 24	0.13875 59297 94	0.22096 68355 22
70	2.45263 29736 91	0.99136 06533 74	0.13116 42288 94	0.21642 31475 97
71	2.48767 05876 00	0.99231 73586 97	0.12371 84692 33	0.21212 82843 81
72	2.52270 82015 10	0.99320 11358 98	0.11641 09258 20	0.20807 82675 40
73	2.55774 58154 20	0.99401 60714 79	0.10923 39216 59	0.20426 92926 67
74	2.59278 34293 30	0.99476 59434 63	0.10217 98303 33	0.20069 77358 43
75	2.62782 10432 40	0.99545 42365 87	0.09524 10775 98	0.19736 01593 17
76	2.66285 86571 50	0.99608 41564 73	0.08841 01420 86	0.19425 33164 24
77	2.69789 62710 60	0.99665 86427 95	0.08167 95552 25	0.19137 41558 01
78	2.73293 38849 69	0.99718 03814 66	0.07504 19004 31	0.18871 98250 12
79	2.76797 14988 79	0.99765 18158 64	0.06848 98116 81	0.18628 76736 30
80	2.80300 91127 89	0.99807 51571 28	0.06201 59715 20	0.18407 52558 65
81	2.83804 67266 99	0.99845 23935 35	0.05561 31085 67	0.18208 03327 72
82	2.87308 43406 09	0.99878 52989 79	0.04927 39945 87	0.18030 08741 14
83	2.90812 19545 19	0.99907 54405 88	0.04299 14411 81	0.17873 50599 14
84	2.94315 95684 29	0.99932 41854 70	0.03675 82961 35	0.17738 12817 37
85	2.97819 71823 39	0.99953 27066 40	0.03056 74394 97	0.17623 81437 46
86	3.01323 47962 48	0.99970 19881 08	0.02441 17793 91	0.17530 44635 54
87	3.04827 24101 58	0.99983 28291 71	0.01828 42476 45	0.17457 92729 02
88	3.08331 00240 68	0.99992 58479 02	0.01217 77952 41	0.17406 18181 89
89	3.11834 76379 78	0.99998 14838 57	0.00608 53876 37	0.17375 15608 56
90	3.15338 52518 88	1.00000 00000 00	0.00000 00000 00	0.17364 81776 67

ELLIPTIC FUNCTIONS TABLE $\theta = 80°$

q = 0.20660 97552 00965 0   D(90) = 2.39974 38369 84197
q' = 0.00191 35945 90170 284   1/D(90) = 0.41671 11441 59753

r	ϕ	$E(\phi,k)$	A(r)	D(r)
45	1.17596 73097 11	0.93323 31090 20	0.64910 77548 37	1.68752 66769 58
46	1.19035 85458 70	0.93914 45316 12	0.66238 93095 10	1.71196 65668 41
47	1.20433 92817 38	0.94472 35246 21	0.67553 62474 62	1.73640 67003 01
48	1.21792 17293 69	0.94998 91714 90	0.68854 06224 72	1.76081 71386 00
49	1.23111 80514 00	0.95495 96855 58	0.70139 43563 10	1.78516 78703 25
50	1.24394 03378 58	0.95965 24228 28	0.71408 92523 61	1.80942 88492 63
51	1.25640 05858 93	0.96408 38988 81	0.72661 70097 48	1.83357 00328 32
52	1.26851 06822 44	0.96826 98091 91	0.73896 92379 25	1.85756 14210 33
53	1.28028 23881 95	0.97222 50521 89	0.75113 74717 00	1.88137 30958 56
54	1.29172 73268 39	0.97596 37544 87	0.76311 31866 54	1.90497 52610 62
55	1.30285 69724 65	0.97949 92977 51	0.77488 78149 12	1.92833 82823 10
56	1.31368 26418 55	0.98284 43467 86	0.78645 27612 31	1.95143 27275 32
57	1.32421 54873 59	0.98601 08784 27	0.79779 94193 51	1.97422 94074 96
58	1.33446 64915 60	0.98901 02109 22	0.80891 91885 84	1.99669 94164 90
59	1.34444 64633 94	0.99185 30335 11	0.81980 34905 83	2.01881 41730 46
60	1.35416 60355 80	0.99454 94359 69	0.83044 37862 54	2.04054 54606 31
61	1.36363 56632 35	0.99710 89379 13	0.84083 15927 61	2.06186 54682 25
62	1.37286 56235 59	0.99954 05176 94	0.85095 85005 88	2.08274 68307 05
63	1.38186 60164 71	1.00185 26407 65	0.86081 61905 95	2.10316 26689 58
64	1.39064 67661 09	1.00405 32873 96	0.87039 64510 50	2.12308 66296 40
65	1.39921 76230 92	1.00614 99796 61	0.87969 11945 55	2.14249 29244 98
66	1.40758 81674 64	1.00814 98076 43	0.88869 24748 52	2.16135 63691 65
67	1.41576 78122 53	1.01005 94547 94	0.89739 25034 51	2.17965 24213 63
68	1.42376 58075 59	1.01188 52224 43	0.90578 36660 21	2.19735 72184 06
69	1.43159 12451 24	1.01363 30534 19	0.91385 85385 31	2.21444 76139 45
70	1.43925 30633 19	1.01530 85547 90	0.92160 99030 63	2.23090 12138 53
71	1.44676 00525 07	1.01691 70197 36	0.92903 07632 73	2.24669 64111 77
72	1.45412 08607 17	1.01846 34485 47	0.93611 43594 56	2.26181 24200 83
73	1.46134 39996 17	1.01995 25687 82	0.94285 41831 64	2.27622 93087 04
74	1.46843 78507 19	1.02138 88546 15	0.94924 39913 49	2.28992 80308 15
75	1.47541 06718 09	1.02277 65453 90	0.95527 78199 76	2.30289 04562 76
76	1.48227 06035 55	1.02411 96634 23	0.96094 99970 83	2.31509 94001 50
77	1.48902 56762 82	1.02542 20310 95	0.96625 51552 45	2.32653 86504 35
78	1.49568 38168 77	1.02668 72872 60	0.97118 82434 04	2.33719 29943 46
79	1.50225 28558 13	1.02791 89030 28	0.97574 45380 41	2.34704 82430 85
80	1.50874 05342 80	1.02912 01969 52	0.97991 96536 39	2.35609 12550 18
81	1.51515 45113 87	1.03029 43496 69	0.98370 95524 44	2.36430 99572 35
82	1.52150 23714 51	1.03144 44180 35	0.98711 05534 48	2.37169 33654 10
83	1.52779 16313 32	1.03257 33488 13	0.99011 93406 13	2.37823 16019 26
84	1.53402 97478 24	1.03368 39919 36	0.99273 29702 84	2.38391 59122 22
85	1.54022 41250 87	1.03477 91134 12	0.99494 88777 86	2.38873 86793 06
86	1.54638 21221 14	1.03586 14079 06	0.99676 48831 75	2.39269 34364 20
87	1.55251 10602 17	1.03693 35110 53	0.99817 91961 33	2.39577 48777 98
88	1.55861 82305 42	1.03799 80115 34	0.99919 04199 96	2.39797 88675 21
89	1.56471 09015 98	1.03905 74629 74	0.99979 75548 93	2.39930 24464 12
90	1.57079 63267 95	1.04011 43957 06	1.00000 00000 00	2.39974 38369 84

321

K = 3.25530 29421 43555   E = 1.03378 94623 90754
K'= 1.58054 09338 95721   E'= 1.56114 17453 51334

r	u=(r/90)K=F(ϕ,k)	sn u	cn u	dn u
0	0.00000 00000 00	0.00000 00000 00	1.00000 00000 00	1.00000 00000 00
1	0.03617 00326 90	0.03615 44603 35	0.99934 62137 81	0.99936 22181 74
2	0.07234 00653 81	0.07221 56793 01	0.99738 90392 74	0.99745 30156 10
3	0.10851 00980 71	0.10809 13748 08	0.99414 09631 90	0.99428 47561 39
4	0.14468 01307 62	0.14369 11624 38	0.98962 25794 90	0.98987 78316 37
5	0.18085 01634 52	0.17892 74528 04	0.98386 22701 54	0.98426 03467 91
6	0.21702 01961 43	0.21371 62892 95	0.97689 57711 50	0.97746 76905 10
7	0.25319 02288 33	0.24797 81097 36	0.96876 56357 92	0.96954 20060 06
8	0.28936 02615 24	0.28163 84182 22	0.95952 06101 91	0.96053 15740 81
9	0.32553 02942 14	0.31462 83564 39	0.94921 49373 69	0.95049 01259 81
10	0.36170 03269 05	0.34688 51671 17	0.93790 76078 35	0.93947 61034 06
11	0.39787 03595 95	0.37835 25456 14	0.92566 15748 90	0.92755 18836 97
12	0.43404 03922 86	0.40898 08789 57	0.91254 29527 68	0.91478 29881 14
13	0.47021 04249 76	0.43872 73747 29	0.89862 02149 20	0.90123 72902 66
14	0.50638 04576 67	0.46755 60849 29	0.88396 34084 32	0.88698 42405 23
15	0.54255 04903 57	0.49543 78322 95	0.86864 33988 30	0.87209 41204 61
16	0.57872 05230 48	0.52235 00484 04	0.85273 11574 77	0.85663 73393 97
17	0.61489 05557 38	0.54827 65342 40	0.83629 71015 14	0.84068 37828 64
18	0.65106 05884 29	0.57320 71548 04	0.81941 04940 03	0.82430 22205 72
19	0.68723 06211 19	0.59713 74797 19	0.80213 89096 13	0.80755 97791 34
20	0.72340 06538 10	0.62006 83817 96	0.78454 77690 35	0.79052 14827 08
21	0.75957 06865 00	0.64200 56050 96	0.76669 99432 80	0.77324 98626 94
22	0.79574 07191 91	0.66295 93134 13	0.74865 54272 55	0.75580 46358 90
23	0.83191 07518 81	0.68294 36291 26	0.73047 10804 93	0.73824 24490 04
24	0.86808 07845 72	0.70197 61713 37	0.71220 04316 72	0.72061 66862 12
25	0.90425 08172 62	0.72007 76010 51	0.69389 35426 02	0.70297 73354 78
26	0.94042 08499 53	0.73727 11799 09	0.67559 69266 33	0.68537 09086 70
27	0.97659 08826 43	0.75358 23478 27	0.65735 35160 36	0.66784 04100 71
28	1.01276 09153 34	0.76903 83237 16	0.63920 26725 97	0.65042 53476 27
29	1.04893 09480 24	0.78366 77323 81	0.62118 02357 00	0.63316 17812 34
30	1.08510 09807 15	0.79750 02597 15	0.60331 86021 94	0.61608 24024 90
31	1.12127 10134 05	0.81056 63374 46	0.58564 68326 56	0.59921 66405 28
32	1.15744 10460 95	0.82289 68579 15	0.56819 07789 06	0.58259 07889 05
33	1.19361 10787 86	0.83452 29187 53	0.55097 32280 93	0.56622 81488 88
34	1.22978 11114 76	0.84547 55967 70	0.53401 40590 53	0.55014 91849 03
35	1.26595 11441 67	0.85578 57499 81	0.51733 04071 18	0.53437 16883 90
36	1.30212 11768 57	0.86548 38463 59	0.50093 68340 33	0.51891 09467 36
37	1.33829 12095 48	0.87459 98176 76	0.48484 55000 52	0.50377 99144 15
38	1.37446 12422 38	0.88316 29366 45	0.46906 63357 54	0.48898 93839 02
39	1.41063 12749 29	0.89120 17154 76	0.45360 72115 09	0.47454 81543 12
40	1.44680 13076 19	0.89874 38239 45	0.43847 41029 08	0.46046 31961 07
41	1.48297 13403 10	0.90581 60250 56	0.42367 12507 98	0.44673 98105 30
42	1.51914 13730 00	0.91244 41264 52	0.40920 13148 84	0.43338 17827 46
43	1.55531 14056 91	0.91865 29457 89	0.39506 55201 28	0.42039 15279 11
44	1.59148 14383 81	0.92446 62883 69	0.38126 37953 82	0.40777 02296 44
45	1.62765 14710 72	0.92990 69354 73	0.36779 49039 33	0.39551 79705 65

322

q = 0.21754 89496 99726 3
q′= 0.00154 85045 16579 192

D(90) = 2.52833 01251 02273
1/D(90) = 0.39551 79705 65473

r	ϕ	$E(\phi,k)$	A(r)	D(r)
0	0.00000 00000 00	0.00000 00000 00	0.00000 00000 00	1.00000 00000 00
1	0.03616 23414 93	0.03615 46532 38	0.01430 61216 34	1.00044 63616 92
2	0.07227 85957 82	0.07221 72201 55	0.02861 35823 81	1.00178 49727 65
3	0.10830 29745 81	0.10809 65619 40	0.04292 37056 44	1.00401 44114 43
4	0.14419 02827 58	0.14370 34141 58	0.05723 77834 51	1.00713 23088 97
5	0.17989 62033 73	0.17895 12731 10	0.07155 70608 83	1.01113 53504 44
6	0.21537 75692 15	0.21375 72232 91	0.08588 27206 26	1.01601 92772 38
7	0.25059 26169 86	0.24804 26897 19	0.10021 58677 03	1.02177 88884 53
8	0.28550 12206 77	0.28173 41015 35	0.11455 75144 32	1.02840 80439 86
9	0.32006 51013 31	0.31476 34563 30	0.12890 85656 34	1.03589 96676 76
10	0.35424 80109 35	0.34706 87779 33	0.14326 98041 58	1.04424 57510 69
11	0.38801 58888 58	0.37859 44637 15	0.15764 18767 43	1.05343 73577 43
12	0.42133 69899 16	0.40929 15207 27	0.17202 52802 70	1.06346 46282 12
13	0.45418 19837 41	0.43911 76930 48	0.18642 03484 44	1.07431 67854 38
14	0.48652 40257 72	0.46803 74854 08	0.20082 72389 32	1.08598 21409 67
15	0.51833 88006 92	0.49602 20904 65	0.21524 59210 15	1.09844 81017 24
16	0.54960 45396 29	0.52304 92289 49	0.22967 61637 68	1.11170 11774 89
17	0.58030 20128 22	0.54910 29132 48	0.24411 75248 24	1.12572 69890 88
18	0.61041 44997 82	0.57417 31458 30	0.25856 93397 38	1.14051 02773 19
19	0.63992 77391 97	0.59825 55643 44	0.27303 07119 95	1.15603 49126 63
20	0.66882 98609 81	0.62135 10451 93	0.28750 05036 91	1.17228 39057 84
21	0.69711 13029 68	0.64346 52769 92	0.30197 73269 07	1.18923 94188 73
22	0.72476 47147 20	0.66460 83146 88	0.31645 95358 17	1.20688 27778 61
23	0.75178 48509 07	0.68479 41241 72	0.33094 52195 42	1.22519 44855 21
24	0.77816 84566 01	0.70404 01261 96	0.34543 21957 91	1.24415 42355 11
25	0.80391 41466 76	0.72236 67472 45	0.35991 80052 84	1.26374 09273 63
26	0.82902 22813 76	0.73979 69838 10	0.37439 99070 09	1.28393 26824 68
27	0.85349 48398 69	0.75635 59853 32	0.38887 48743 04	1.30470 68610 80
28	0.87733 52934 68	0.77207 06599 59	0.40333 95917 91	1.32604 00803 50
29	0.90045 15171 99	0.78696 93061 61	0.41779 04531 80	1.34790 82334 37
30	0.92314 04801 22	0.80108 12723 07	0.43222 35599 40	1.37028 65097 05
31	0.94511 84979 81	0.81443 66454 34	0.44663 47208 58	1.39314 94160 26
32	0.96649 07448 00	0.82706 59696 99	0.46101 94524 93	1.41647 07992 08
33	0.98726 63283 39	0.83899 99943 57	0.47537 29805 15	1.44022 38695 75
34	1.00745 51473 76	0.85026 94506 15	0.48969 02419 47	1.46438 12256 83
35	1.02706 77920 47	0.86090 48562 90	0.50396 58883 01	1.48891 48802 07
36	1.04611 54502 01	0.87093 63468 71	0.51819 42896 09	1.51379 62869 96
37	1.06460 98199 28	0.88039 35313 83	0.53236 95393 34	1.53899 63692 88
38	1.08256 30282 69	0.88930 53712 73	0.54648 54601 70	1.56448 55490 98
39	1.09998 75560 74	0.89770 00804 78	0.56053 56107 07	1.59023 37777 55
40	1.11689 61688 98	0.90560 50447 66	0.57451 32929 45	1.61621 05676 01
41	1.13330 18537 59	0.91304 67584 87	0.58841 15606 64	1.64238 50248 11
42	1.14921 77615 51	0.92005 07768 97	0.60222 32286 02	1.66872 58833 39
43	1.16465 71548 72	0.92664 16822 93	0.61594 08824 50	1.69520 15399 50
44	1.17963 33609 98	0.93284 30622 89	0.62955 68896 17	1.72178 00903 19
45	1.19415 97297 24	0.93867 74986 75	0.64306 34107 62	1.74842 93661 65

ELLIPTIC FUNCTIONS   TABLE $\theta = 81°$

$K = 3.25530\ 29421\ 43555$

$K' = 1.58054\ 09338\ 95721$

$E = 1.03378\ 94623\ 90754$

$E' = 1.56114\ 17453\ 51334$

r	u=(r/90)K=F(ϕ,k)	sn u	cn u	dn u
45	1.62765 14710 72	0.92990 69354 73	0.36779 49039 33	0.39551 79705 65
46	1.66382 15037 62	0.93499 66418 96	0.35465 65657 70	0.38363 38547 25
47	1.69999 15364 53	0.93975 61413 55	0.34184 55715 47	0.37211 61218 87
48	1.73616 15691 43	0.94420 51585 34	0.32935 78883 18	0.36096 22537 64
49	1.77233 16018 34	0.94836 24266 55	0.31718 87572 24	0.35016 90723 61
50	1.80850 16345 24	0.95224 57095 72	0.30533 27833 71	0.33973 28306 87
51	1.84467 16672 15	0.95587 18275 22	0.29378 40182 00	0.32964 92961 12
52	1.88084 16999 05	0.95925 66857 19	0.28253 60346 98	0.31991 38267 42
53	1.91701 17325 96	0.96241 53051 34	0.27158 19958 03	0.31052 14411 37
54	1.95318 17652 86	0.96536 18548 32	0.26091 47164 03	0.30146 68817 92
55	1.98935 17979 77	0.96810 96853 71	0.25052 67193 16	0.29274 46727 42
56	2.02552 18306 67	0.97067 13628 00	0.24041 02856 37	0.28434 91717 03
57	2.06169 18633 58	0.97305 87028 84	0.23055 74998 62	0.27627 46171 26
58	2.09786 18960 48	0.97528 28052 31	0.22096 02901 43	0.26851 51705 44
59	2.13403 19287 39	0.97735 40870 63	0.21161 04640 66	0.26106 49545 75
60	2.17020 19614 29	0.97928 23163 85	0.20249 97402 85	0.25391 80869 44
61	2.20637 19941 20	0.98107 66444 07	0.19361 97763 63	0.24706 87108 36
62	2.24254 20268 10	0.98274 56370 35	0.18496 21931 32	0.24051 10219 20
63	2.27871 20595 00	0.98429 73053 48	0.17651 85958 62	0.23423 92923 24
64	2.31488 20921 91	0.98573 91349 52	0.16828 05925 37	0.22824 78918 52
65	2.35105 21248 81	0.98707 81141 62	0.16023 98094 83	0.22253 13066 94
66	2.38722 21575 72	0.98832 07609 53	0.15238 79046 03	0.21708 41558 81
67	2.42339 21902 62	0.98947 31486 64	0.14471 65784 35	0.21190 12056 97
68	2.45956 22229 53	0.99054 09304 26	0.13721 75832 38	0.20697 73822 65
69	2.49573 22556 43	0.99152 93623 31	0.12988 27303 20	0.20230 77825 00
70	2.53190 22883 34	0.99244 33253 19	0.12270 38957 40	0.19788 76835 89
71	2.56807 23210 24	0.99328 73458 27	0.11567 30245 97	0.19371 25511 72
72	2.60424 23537 15	0.99406 56151 99	0.10878 21340 05	0.18977 80463 72
73	2.64041 23864 05	0.99478 20078 85	0.10202 33149 21	0.18608 00317 89
74	2.67658 24190 96	0.99544 00984 64	0.09538 87329 30	0.18261 45766 08
75	2.71275 24517 86	0.99604 31775 08	0.08887 06281 09	0.17937 79608 99
76	2.74892 24844 77	0.99659 42663 31	0.08246 13140 58	0.17636 66792 41
77	2.78509 25171 67	0.99709 61306 49	0.07615 31762 01	0.17357 74437 32
78	2.82126 25498 58	0.99755 12931 76	0.06993 86694 36	0.17100 71864 83
79	2.85743 25825 48	0.99796 20452 07	0.06381 03152 07	0.16865 30616 67
80	2.89360 26152 39	0.99833 04571 93	0.05776 06980 65	0.16651 24471 75
81	2.92977 26479 29	0.99865 83883 65	0.05178 24617 85	0.16458 29459 60
82	2.96594 26806 20	0.99894 74954 11	0.04586 83050 91	0.16286 23871 01
83	3.00211 27133 10	0.99919 92402 50	0.04001 09770 37	0.16134 88266 33
84	3.03828 27460 01	0.99941 48969 16	0.03420 32720 99	0.16004 05482 03
85	3.07445 27786 91	0.99959 55575 80	0.02843 80250 12	0.15893 60635 63
86	3.11062 28113 82	0.99974 21377 28	0.02270 81053 93	0.15803 41129 39
87	3.14679 28440 72	0.99985 53805 15	0.01700 64121 86	0.15733 36653 05
88	3.18296 28767 63	0.99993 58603 00	0.01132 58679 68	0.15683 39185 83
89	3.21913 29094 53	0.99998 39853 93	0.00565 94131 32	0.15653 42997 72
90	3.25530 29421 44	1.00000 00000 00	0.00000 00000 00	0.15643 44650 40

324

q = 0.21754 89496 99726 3   D(90) = 2.52833 01251 02273
q' = 0.00154 85045 16579 192   1/D(90) = 0.39551 79705 65473

r	ϕ	$E(\phi,k)$	A(r)	D(r)
45	1.19415 97297 24	0.93867 74986 75	0.64306 34107 62	1.74842 93661 65
46	1.20824 95957 80	0.94416 65654 07	0.65645 24120 48	1.77511 69733 75
47	1.22191 62455 24	0.94933 08343 94	0.66971 56781 02	1.80181 03310 89
48	1.23517 28876 31	0.95418 98878 80	0.68284 48256 43	1.82847 67116 96
49	1.24803 26274 73	0.95876 23363 12	0.69583 13177 53	1.85508 32816 84
50	1.26050 84449 22	0.96306 58407 25	0.70866 64787 40	1.88159 71432 97
51	1.27261 31752 97	0.96711 71387 68	0.72134 15095 75	1.90798 53769 46
52	1.28435 94932 01	0.97093 20735 96	0.73384 75038 55	1.93421 50842 94
53	1.29575 98990 00	0.97452 56249 53	0.74617 54642 46	1.96025 34319 67
54	1.30682 67077 05	0.97791 19418 58	0.75831 63193 79	1.98606 76958 04
55	1.31757 20400 46	0.98110 43763 86	0.77026 09411 41	2.01162 53055 88
56	1.32800 78155 32	0.98411 55181 05	0.78200 01623 27	2.03689 38901 66
57	1.33814 57472 97	0.98695 72287 96	0.79352 47945 97	2.06184 13228 81
58	1.34799 73385 69	0.98964 06771 52	0.80482 56466 99	2.08643 57672 36
59	1.35757 38805 86	0.99217 63731 84	0.81589 35429 11	2.11064 57226 97
60	1.36688 64518 14	0.99457 42021 35	0.82671 93416 41	2.13444 00705 53
61	1.37594 59183 35	0.99684 34577 09	0.83729 39541 48	2.15778 81197 23
62	1.38476 29352 57	0.99899 28745 05	0.84760 83633 31	2.18065 96524 44
63	1.39334 79490 65	1.00103 06595 16	0.85765 36425 27	2.20302 49697 15
64	1.40171 12007 70	1.00296 45226 47	0.86742 09742 79	2.22485 49364 17
65	1.40986 27297 91	1.00480 17061 73	0.87690 16690 18	2.24612 10260 09
66	1.41781 23784 69	1.00654 90131 09	0.88608 71835 98	2.26679 53646 93
67	1.42556 97971 38	1.00821 28344 72	0.89496 91396 53	2.28685 07749 57
68	1.43314 44496 83	1.00979 91754 31	0.90353 93417 06	2.30626 08183 86
69	1.44054 56195 24	1.01131 36803 47	0.91178 97949 96	2.32499 98376 55
70	1.44778 24159 71	1.01276 16567 23	0.91971 27229 58	2.34304 29975 91
71	1.45486 37808 96	1.01414 80980 93	0.92730 05843 18	2.36036 63252 18
72	1.46179 84956 77	1.01547 77058 73	0.93454 60897 54	2.37694 67486 78
73	1.46859 51883 82	1.01675 49102 12	0.94144 22180 70	2.39276 21349 43
74	1.47526 23411 51	1.01798 38898 97	0.94798 22318 49	2.40779 13262 12
75	1.48180 82977 51	1.01916 85913 40	0.95415 96925 20	2.42201 41749 20
76	1.48824 12712 63	1.02031 27467 03	0.95996 84748 25	2.43541 15772 56
77	1.49456 93519 08	1.02141 98912 07	0.96540 27806 23	2.44796 55051 11
78	1.50080 05149 53	1.02249 33796 80	0.97045 71519 94	2.45965 90363 73
79	1.50694 26287 08	1.02353 64023 93	0.97512 64836 16	2.47047 63834 99
80	1.51300 34625 95	1.02455 20002 32	0.97940 60343 77	2.48040 29202 76
81	1.51899 06952 57	1.02554 30792 62	0.98329 14381 74	2.48942 52067 13
82	1.52491 19227 26	1.02651 24247 37	0.98677 87138 91	2.49753 10119 92
83	1.53077 46666 10	1.02746 27146 08	0.98986 42745 12	2.50470 93354 31
84	1.53658 63823 21	1.02839 65325 69	0.99254 49353 40	2.51095 04253 76
85	1.54235 44673 15	1.02931 63807 16	0.99481 79213 21	2.51624 57960 07
86	1.54808 62693 46	1.03022 46918 47	0.99668 08734 19	2.52058 82419 87
87	1.55378 90947 42	1.03112 38414 64	0.99813 18540 48	2.52397 18509 24
88	1.55947 02166 75	1.03201 61595 33	0.99916 93515 45	2.52639 20136 15
89	1.56513 68834 51	1.03290 39420 38	0.99979 22836 48	2.52784 54320 43
90	1.57079 63267 95	1.03378 94623 91	1.00000 00000 00	2.52833 01251 02

K = 3.36986 80266 68445   E = 1.02784 36197 40833
K' = 1.57848 65776 88648   E' = 1.56316 22295 18261

r	u=(r/90)K=F(ϕ,k)	sn u	cn u	dn u
0	0.00000 00000 00	0.00000 00000 00	1.00000 00000 00	1.00000 00000 00
1	0.03744 29780 74	0.03742 56590 93	0.99929 94146 11	0.99931 29890 20
2	0.07488 59561 48	0.07474 76346 03	0.99720 24825 09	0.99725 67425 79
3	0.11232 89342 22	0.11186 33886 64	0.99372 35945 05	0.99384 55395 92
4	0.14977 19122 96	0.14867 26480 47	0.98888 64665 48	0.98910 29121 71
5	0.18721 48903 70	0.18507 84705 48	0.98272 37453 83	0.98306 12551 89
6	0.22465 78684 45	0.22098 82351 92	0.97527 64735 74	0.97576 12966 00
7	0.26210 08465 19	0.25631 45355 59	0.96659 34299 70	0.96725 14444 42
8	0.29954 38245 93	0.29097 59592 05	0.95673 03649 23	0.95758 70296 38
9	0.33698 68026 67	0.32489 77402 95	0.94574 91519 17	0.94682 94660 56
10	0.37442 97807 41	0.35801 22770 48	0.93371 68786 54	0.93504 53506 37
11	0.41187 27588 15	0.39025 95100 34	0.92070 49010 56	0.92230 55268 28
12	0.44931 57368 89	0.42158 71616 96	0.90678 78831 86	0.90868 41340 99
13	0.48675 87149 63	0.45195 08414 55	0.89204 28447 72	0.89425 76650 16
14	0.52420 16930 37	0.48131 40241 82	0.87654 82360 52	0.87910 40493 99
15	0.56164 46711 11	0.50964 79127 03	0.86038 30571 77	0.86330 17826 33
16	0.59908 76491 86	0.53693 11971 68	0.84362 60365 28	0.84692 91123 42
17	0.63653 06272 60	0.56314 97256 50	0.82635 48792 74	0.83006 32946 66
18	0.67397 36053 34	0.58829 61011 20	0.80864 55944 40	0.81277 99282 91
19	0.71141 65834 08	0.61236 92202 33	0.79057 19057 18	0.79515 23714 64
20	0.74885 95614 82	0.63537 37689 88	0.77220 47485 49	0.77725 12444 46
21	0.78630 25395 56	0.65731 96895 93	0.75361 18534 59	0.75914 40174 29
22	0.82374 55176 30	0.67822 16317 46	0.73485 74135 38	0.74089 46818 06
23	0.86118 84957 04	0.69809 84001 79	0.71600 18321 68	0.72256 35009 31
24	0.89863 14737 78	0.71697 24087 84	0.69710 15457 18	0.70420 68351 70
25	0.93607 44518 52	0.73486 91500 46	0.67820 89149 44	0.68587 70350 09
26	0.97351 74299 26	0.75181 66869 08	0.65937 21781 26	0.66762 23953 38
27	1.01096 04080 01	0.76784 51726 29	0.64063 54586 42	0.64948 71636 84
28	1.04840 33860 75	0.78298 64027 83	0.62203 88195 74	0.63151 15950 47
29	1.08584 63641 49	0.79727 34021 69	0.60361 83580 65	0.61373 20461 48
30	1.12328 93422 23	0.81074 00483 08	0.58540 63324 47	0.59618 11021 66
31	1.16073 23202 97	0.82342 07321 23	0.56743 13155 87	0.57888 77294 75
32	1.19817 52983 71	0.83535 00556 13	0.54971 83684 29	0.56187 74484 30
33	1.23561 82764 45	0.84656 25655 94	0.53228 92282 73	0.54517 25207 86
34	1.27306 12545 19	0.85709 25220 84	0.51516 25069 70	0.52879 21469 81
35	1.31050 42325 93	0.86697 36994 58	0.49835 38947 86	0.51275 26690 81
36	1.34794 72106 67	0.87623 92182 35	0.48187 63663 30	0.49706 77758 18
37	1.38539 01887 41	0.88492 14051 78	0.46574 03854 71	0.48174 87066 72
38	1.42283 31668 16	0.89305 16792 59	0.44995 41067 41	0.46680 44525 27
39	1.46027 61448 90	0.90066 04610 48	0.43452 35711 72	0.45224 19508 68
40	1.49771 91229 64	0.90777 71030 91	0.41945 28949 75	0.43806 62739 41
41	1.53516 21010 38	0.91442 98389 22	0.40474 44498 57	0.42428 08086 91
42	1.57260 50791 12	0.92064 57484 73	0.39039 90340 90	0.41088 74275 99
43	1.61004 80571 86	0.92645 07377 72	0.37641 60337 74	0.39788 66498 65
44	1.64749 10352 60	0.93186 95309 47	0.36279 35739 40	0.38527 77925 97
45	1.68493 40133 34	0.93692 56727 57	0.34952 86593 81	0.37305 91118 85

q = 0.22956 71598 81194 2   D(90) = 2.68054 03437 23203
q′= 0.00122 24470 64293 800   1/D(90) = 0.37305 91118 84518

r	ϕ	$E(\phi,k)$	A(r)	D(r)
0	0.00000 00000 00	0.00000 00000 00	0.00000 00000 00	1.00000 00000 00
1	0.03743 44015 00	0.03742 58284 61	0.01396 87845 54	1.00048 71378 75
2	0.07481 74152 99	0.07474 89873 10	0.02793 96080 60	1.00194 80481 28
3	0.11209 80111 33	0.11186 79415 32	0.04191 44920 29	1.00438 12208 16
4	0.14922 58676 02	0.14868 33987 61	0.05589 54231 37	1.00778 41399 55
5	0.18615 17117 89	0.18509 93653 23	0.06988 43359 24	1.01215 32844 14
6	0.22282 76415 96	0.22102 41268 31	0.08388 30956 48	1.01748 41291 76
7	0.25920 74259 00	0.25637 11328 46	0.09789 34813 16	1.02377 11469 75
8	0.29524 67782 27	0.29105 97687 38	0.11191 71689 64	1.03100 78103 44
9	0.33090 36004 69	0.32501 60020 06	0.12595 57152 16	1.03918 65940 75
10	0.36613 81939 49	0.35817 28947 14	0.14001 05411 82	1.04829 89781 23
11	0.40091 34360 33	0.39047 09781 38	0.15408 29167 22	1.05833 54509 80
12	0.43519 49213 53	0.42185 84899 97	0.16817 39451 35	1.06928 55135 46
13	0.46895 10675 04	0.45229 14785 68	0.18228 45483 18	1.08113 76835 40
14	0.50215 31858 98	0.48173 37814 06	0.19641 54524 19	1.09387 95004 64
15	0.53477 55190 94	0.51015 68892 24	0.21056 71740 45	1.10749 75311 85
16	0.56679 52465 49	0.53753 97076 55	0.22474 00070 60	1.12197 73761 50
17	0.59819 24611 86	0.56386 82310 90	0.23893 40099 97	1.13730 36762 94
18	0.62895 01195 47	0.58913 51436 34	0.25314 89941 49	1.15346 01206 72
19	0.65905 39685 59	0.61333 93624 23	0.26738 45123 40	1.17042 94548 66
20	0.68849 24520 55	0.63648 55382 52	0.28163 98484 46	1.18819 34902 07
21	0.71725 66002 85	0.65858 35276 81	0.29591 40076 67	1.20673 31138 60
22	0.74533 99055 53	0.67964 78497 23	0.31020 57075 99	1.22602 82998 24
23	0.77273 81870 54	0.69969 71388 29	0.32451 33701 33	1.24605 81208 84
24	0.79944 94477 92	0.71875 36043 93	0.33883 51141 93	1.26680 07615 60
25	0.82547 37262 31	0.73684 25054 30	0.35316 87493 61	1.28823 35321 12
26	0.85081 29451 23	0.75399 16474 63	0.36751 17703 87	1.31033 28836 27
27	0.87547 07596 46	0.77023 09071 45	0.38186 13526 22	1.33307 44242 44
28	0.89945 24067 57	0.78559 17887 06	0.39621 43483 84	1.35643 29365 48
29	0.92276 45573 51	0.80010 70149 89	0.41056 72842 70	1.38038 23961 82
30	0.94541 51725 75	0.81381 01547 17	0.42491 63594 37	1.40489 59916 99
31	0.96741 33654 04	0.82673 52865 88	0.43925 74448 48	1.42994 61457 07
32	0.98876 92683 20	0.83891 67000 23	0.45358 60835 06	1.45550 45373 14
33	1.00949 39077 55	0.85038 86316 26	0.46789 74916 73	1.48154 21259 23
34	1.02959 90857 48	0.86118 50359 72	0.48218 65610 74	1.50802 91763 80
35	1.04909 72691 09	0.87133 93888 47	0.49644 78620 97	1.53493 52855 09
36	1.06800 14862 27	0.88088 45208 46	0.51067 56479 77	1.56222 94100 44
37	1.08632 52315 54	0.88985 24790 10	0.52486 38599 66	1.58987 98959 65
38	1.10408 23776 66	0.89827 44140 96	0.53900 61334 70	1.61785 45092 48
39	1.12128 70947 42	0.90618 04910 55	0.55309 58051 60	1.64612 04680 29
40	1.13795 37772 25	0.91359 98203 13	0.56712 59210 30	1.67464 44761 79
41	1.15409 69773 81	0.92056 04075 20	0.58108 92453 89	1.70339 27582 74
42	1.16973 13454 21	0.92708 91195 63	0.59497 82707 72	1.73233 10959 58
43	1.18487 15758 45	0.93321 16647 30	0.60878 52287 48	1.76142 48656 61
44	1.19953 23596 32	0.93895 25851 04	0.62250 21016 01	1.79063 90776 59
45	1.21372 83419 03	0.94433 52593 90	0.63612 06348 56	1.81993 84164 46

K = 3.36986 80266 68445   E = 1.02784 36197 40833
K'= 1.57848 65776 88648   E'= 1.56316 22295 18261

r	u=(r/90)K=F(φ,k)	sn u	cn u	dn u
45	1.68493 40133 34	0.93692 56727 57	0.34952 86593 81	0.37305 91118 85
46	1.72237 69914 08	0.94164 15399 79	0.33661 73052 39	0.36122 79338 04
47	1.75981 99694 82	0.94603 83601 76	0.32405 46575 42	0.34978 07755 23
48	1.79726 29475 57	0.95013 62365 15	0.31183 51039 59	0.33871 34568 06
49	1.83470 59256 31	0.95395 41774 36	0.29995 23751 40	0.32802 12022 54
50	1.87214 89037 05	0.95751 01301 49	0.28839 96370 71	0.31769 87347 32
51	1.90959 18817 79	0.96082 10170 20	0.27716 95749 05	0.30774 03604 26
52	1.94703 48598 53	0.96390 27740 74	0.26625 44687 55	0.29814 00460 23
53	1.98447 78379 27	0.96677 03909 13	0.25564 62619 60	0.28889 14885 14
54	2.02192 08160 01	0.96943 79514 68	0.24533 66223 23	0.27998 81781 34
55	2.05936 37940 75	0.97191 86750 97	0.23531 69968 29	0.27142 34549 17
56	2.09680 67721 49	0.97422 49575 97	0.22557 86603 29	0.26319 05593 81
57	2.13424 97502 23	0.97636 84117 92	0.21611 27586 56	0.25528 26777 83
58	2.17169 27282 97	0.97835 99074 22	0.20691 03466 45	0.24769 29824 27
59	2.20913 57063 72	0.98020 96100 77	0.19796 24214 67	0.24041 46674 28
60	2.24657 86844 46	0.98192 70190 22	0.18925 99516 92	0.23344 09803 57
61	2.28402 16625 20	0.98352 10037 57	0.18079 39024 68	0.22676 52501 34
62	2.32146 46405 94	0.98499 98392 01	0.17255 52571 63	0.22038 09115 33
63	2.35890 76186 68	0.98637 12394 39	0.16453 50358 06	0.21428 15266 29
64	2.39635 05967 42	0.98764 23899 66	0.15672 43106 30	0.20846 08034 90
65	2.43379 35748 16	0.98881 99784 03	0.14911 42190 09	0.20291 26124 02
66	2.47123 65528 90	0.98991 02236 78	0.14169 59740 38	0.19763 09998 84
67	2.50867 95309 64	0.99091 89036 62	0.13446 08729 93	0.19261 02007 38
68	2.54612 25090 38	0.99185 13812 88	0.12740 03039 11	0.18784 46483 39
69	2.58356 54871 12	0.99271 26291 67	0.12050 57504 54	0.18332 89833 88
70	2.62100 84651 87	0.99350 72527 28	0.11376 87952 65	0.17905 80612 83
71	2.65845 14432 61	0.99423 95119 35	0.10718 11219 72	0.17502 69582 97
72	2.69589 44213 35	0.99491 33415 98	0.10073 45159 81	0.17123 09766 96
73	2.73333 73994 09	0.99553 23703 44	0.09442 08642 01	0.16766 56489 38
74	2.77078 03774 83	0.99609 99382 76	0.08823 21538 17	0.16432 67410 84
75	2.80822 33555 57	0.99661 91133 69	0.08216 04702 27	0.16121 02555 10
76	2.84566 63336 31	0.99709 27066 61	0.07619 79942 27	0.15831 24330 45
77	2.88310 93117 05	0.99752 32862 62	0.07033 69985 49	0.15562 97546 05
78	2.92055 22897 79	0.99791 31902 47	0.06456 98438 17	0.15315 89424 06
79	2.95799 52678 53	0.99826 45384 57	0.05888 89740 01	0.15089 69608 35
80	2.99543 82459 28	0.99857 92432 60	0.05328 69114 26	0.14884 10170 32
81	3.03288 12240 02	0.99885 90193 08	0.04775 62513 98	0.14698 85612 45
82	3.07032 42020 76	0.99910 53923 15	0.04228 96564 95	0.14533 72870 06
83	3.10776 71801 50	0.99931 97069 12	0.03687 98505 70	0.14388 51311 72
84	3.14521 01582 24	0.99950 31335 76	0.03151 96125 06	0.14263 02738 64
85	3.18265 31362 98	0.99965 66746 95	0.02620 17697 59	0.14157 11383 45
86	3.22009 61143 72	0.99978 11697 65	0.02091 91917 26	0.14070 63908 59
87	3.25753 90924 46	0.99987 72997 60	0.01566 47829 71	0.14003 49404 57
88	3.29498 20705 20	0.99994 55906 71	0.01043 14763 22	0.13955 59388 25
89	3.33242 50485 94	0.99998 64162 58	0.00521 22258 88	0.13926 87801 41
90	3.36986 80266 68	1.00000 00000 00	0.00000 00000 00	0.13917 31009 60

ELLIPTIC FUNCTIONS TABLE $\theta = 82°$

q = 0.22956 71598 81194 2

q' = 0.00122 24470 64293 800

D(90) = 2.68054 03437 23203

1/D(90) = 0.37305 91118 84518

r	ϕ	$E(\phi,k)$	A(r)	D(r)
45	1.21372 83419 03	0.94433 52593 90	0.63612 06348 56	1.81993 84164 46
46	1.22747 40846 79	0.94938 19145 44	0.64963 23506 21	1.84928 72823 63
47	1.24078 40343 52	0.95411 36447 32	0.66302 85617 23	1.87864 98344 61
48	1.25367 24935 18	0.95855 04363 13	0.67630 03865 86	1.90799 00345 33
49	1.26615 35968 06	0.96271 11976 64	0.68943 87648 38	1.93727 16922 75
50	1.27824 12903 68	0.96661 37928 09	0.70243 44735 88	1.96645 85114 95
51	1.28994 93147 09	0.97027 50779 71	0.71527 81443 47	1.99551 41373 29
52	1.30129 11905 59	0.97371 09402 42	0.72796 02805 45	2.02440 22043 65
53	1.31228 02074 83	0.97693 63376 98	0.74047 12755 99	2.05308 63856 27
54	1.32292 94149 88	0.97996 53403 96	0.75280 14314 85	2.08153 04423 06
55	1.33325 16158 58	0.98281 11717 47	0.76494 09777 78	2.10969 82741 84
56	1.34325 93614 92	0.98548 62498 72	0.77688 00910 87	2.13755 39706 26
57	1.35296 49490 48	0.98800 22285 86	0.78860 89148 61	2.16506 18620 74
58	1.36238 04201 77	0.99037 00377 45	0.80011 75794 93	2.19218 65719 17
59	1.37151 75611 82	0.99259 99227 34	0.81139 62226 78	2.21889 30686 58
60	1.38038 79044 44	0.99470 14829 04	0.82243 50099 70	2.24514 67182 47
61	1.38900 27309 53	0.99668 37088 45	0.83322 41554 85	2.27091 33364 84
62	1.39737 30738 25	0.99855 50183 78	0.84375 39426 82	2.29615 92413 76
63	1.40550 97226 74	1.00032 32912 11	0.85401 47451 80	2.32085 13053 27
64	1.41342 32287 40	1.00199 59022 00	0.86399 70475 48	2.34495 70070 49
65	1.42112 39106 60	1.00357 97532 04	0.87369 14660 09	2.36844 44830 74
66	1.42862 18608 21	1.00508 13035 23	0.88308 87690 00	2.39128 25787 37
67	1.43592 69521 78	1.00650 65989 36	0.89217 98975 41	2.41344 08985 23
68	1.44304 88455 13	1.00786 12993 53	0.90095 59853 34	2.43488 98556 44
69	1.44999 69970 30	1.00915 07051 20	0.90940 83785 66	2.45560 07207 35
70	1.45678 06662 66	1.01037 97820 20	0.91752 86553 33	2.47554 56695 33
71	1.46340 89242 42	1.01155 31850 07	0.92530 86446 42	2.49469 78294 32
72	1.46989 06618 42	1.01267 52807 38	0.93274 04449 44	2.51303 13247 96
73	1.47623 45983 46	1.01375 01689 44	0.93981 64421 22	2.53052 13208 99
74	1.48244 92901 23	1.01478 17027 15	0.94652 93269 15	2.54714 40663 92
75	1.48854 31394 24	1.01577 35077 48	0.95287 21116 97	2.56287 69341 77
76	1.49452 44032 80	1.01672 90006 14	0.95883 81465 85	2.57769 84605 88
77	1.50040 12024 54	1.01765 14061 27	0.96442 11348 15	2.59158 83827 62
78	1.50618 15304 59	1.01854 37738 51	0.96961 51473 50	2.60452 76741 10
79	1.51187 32626 11	1.01940 89938 31	0.97441 46366 78	2.61649 85777 89
80	1.51748 41651 06	1.02024 98115 84	0.97881 44497 49	2.62748 46380 79
81	1.52302 19041 17	1.02106 88424 39	0.98280 98400 30	2.63747 07295 88
82	1.52849 40549 02	1.02186 85852 58	0.98639 64786 29	2.64644 30841 91
83	1.53390 81109 12	1.02265 14356 20	0.98957 04644 59	2.65438 93156 44
84	1.53927 14929 05	1.02341 96985 07	0.99232 83334 20	2.66129 84417 93
85	1.54459 15580 48	1.02417 56005 66	0.99466 70665 62	2.66716 09043 23
86	1.54987 56090 18	1.02492 13019 91	0.99658 40972 03	2.67196 85859 79
87	1.55513 09031 02	1.02565 89080 81	0.99807 73170 03	2.67571 48252 33
88	1.56036 46612 79	1.02639 04805 40	0.99914 50809 38	2.67839 44283 32
89	1.56558 40773 06	1.02711 80485 58	0.99978 62112 04	2.68000 36787 09
90	1.57079 63267 95	1.02784 36197 41	1.00000 00000 00	2.68054 03437 23

329

ELLIPTIC FUNCTIONS   TABLE $\theta = 83°$

K = 3.50042 24991 71838

K'= 1.57667 79815 92838

E = 1.02231 25881 67584

E'= 1.56494 75629 69419

r	u=(r/90)K=F(φ,k)	sn u	cn u	dn u
0	0.00000 00000 00	0.00000 00000 00	1.00000 00000 00	1.00000 00000 00
1	0.03889 35833 24	0.03887 41290 63	0.99924 41153 64	0.99925 53460 49
2	0.07778 71666 48	0.07763 18122 83	0.99698 20969 92	0.99702 69861 29
3	0.11668 07499 72	0.11615 79948 27	0.99323 07487 38	0.99333 16240 63
4	0.15557 43332 97	0.15434 03687 17	0.98801 77379 91	0.98819 67630 92
5	0.19446 79166 21	0.19207 06598 69	0.98138 10990 73	0.98166 02130 34
6	0.23336 14999 45	0.22924 58156 18	0.97336 85612 46	0.97376 94233 93
7	0.27225 50832 69	0.26576 90661 68	0.96403 67230 91	0.96458 06640 04
8	0.31114 86665 93	0.30155 08385 68	0.95345 00992 50	0.95415 80790 19
9	0.35004 22499 17	0.33650 95075 70	0.94168 00684 50	0.94257 26429 43
10	0.38893 58332 41	0.37057 19738 30	0.92880 37533 37	0.92990 10490 00
11	0.42782 94165 65	0.40367 40660 06	0.91490 28628 41	0.91622 45603 58
12	0.46672 29998 90	0.43576 07690 61	0.90006 25267 99	0.90162 78536 69
13	0.50561 65832 14	0.46678 62862 70	0.88437 01504 18	0.88619 78823 55
14	0.54451 01665 38	0.49671 39468 35	0.86791 43131 78	0.87002 27840 12
15	0.58340 37498 62	0.52551 59745 11	0.85078 37331 15	0.85319 08527 41
16	0.62229 73331 86	0.55317 31352 11	0.83306 63133 75	0.83578 95931 67
17	0.66119 09165 10	0.57967 42830 83	0.81484 82837 51	0.81790 48687 60
18	0.70008 44998 34	0.60501 58252 71	0.79621 34457 37	0.79962 01529 28
19	0.73897 80831 58	0.62920 11253 80	0.77724 25257 42	0.78101 58874 99
20	0.77787 16664 83	0.65223 98648 68	0.75801 26375 44	0.76216 89496 61
21	0.81676 52498 07	0.67414 73801 83	0.73859 68520 05	0.74315 22253 83
22	0.85565 88331 31	0.69494 39916 91	0.71906 38694 94	0.72403 42848 27
23	0.89455 24164 55	0.71465 43384 30	0.69947 77884 71	0.70487 91532 26
24	0.93344 59997 79	0.73330 67305 09	0.67989 79621 91	0.68574 61692 68
25	0.97233 95831 03	0.75093 25288 29	0.66037 89345 12	0.66668 99220 14
26	1.01123 31664 27	0.76756 55596 35	0.64097 04452 33	0.64776 02568 86
27	1.05012 67497 52	0.78324 15694 37	0.62171 74952 55	0.62900 23410 44
28	1.08902 03330 76	0.79799 77240 38	0.60266 04619 77	0.61045 67786 86
29	1.12791 39164 00	0.81187 21537 78	0.58383 52558 04	0.59215 97671 70
30	1.16680 74997 24	0.82490 35457 82	0.56527 35091 59	0.57414 32854 58
31	1.20570 10830 48	0.83713 07828 08	0.54700 27901 90	0.55643 53070 97
32	1.24459 46663 72	0.84859 26274 30	0.52904 68341 01	0.53906 00307 38
33	1.28348 82496 96	0.85932 74495 30	0.51142 57859 00	0.52203 81220 45
34	1.32238 18330 20	0.86937 29945 87	0.49415 64491 97	0.50538 69616 33
35	1.36127 54163 45	0.87876 61898 59	0.47725 25364 64	0.48912 08945 18
36	1.40016 89996 69	0.88754 29853 68	0.46072 49169 77	0.47325 14773 14
37	1.43906 25829 93	0.89573 82264 66	0.44458 18593 33	0.45778 77200 87
38	1.47795 61663 17	0.90338 55547 55	0.42882 92660 96	0.44273 63204 60
39	1.51684 97496 41	0.91051 73342 28	0.41347 08986 98	0.42810 18880 88
40	1.55574 33329 65	0.91716 45995 91	0.39850 85911 97	0.41388 71581 39
41	1.59463 69162 89	0.92335 70238 93	0.38394 24519 73	0.40009 31928 50
42	1.63353 04996 14	0.92912 29028 19	0.36977 10527 57	0.38671 95705 77
43	1.67242 40829 38	0.93448 91531 56	0.35599 16047 24	0.37376 45620 64
44	1.71131 76662 62	0.93948 13232 08	0.34260 01216 32	0.36122 52939 19
45	1.75021 12495 86	0.94412 36131 31	0.32959 15701 72	0.34909 78994 57

330

q = 0.24291 29743 06665 4   D(90) = 2.86452 59726 74201
q'= 0.00093 52197 97815 9662   1/D(90) = 0.34909 78994 56796

r	ϕ	$E(\phi,k)$	$A(r)$	$D(r)$
0	0.00000 00000 00	0.00000 00000 00	0.00000 00000 00	1.00000 00000 00
1	0.03888 39268 11	0.03887 42746 13	0.01357 81428 40	1.00053 54142 45
2	0.07771 00017 72	0.07763 29746 02	0.02715 91293 93	1.00214 11229 83
3	0.11642 08074 67	0.11616 19060 04	0.04074 57839 75	1.00481 55242 95
4	0.15495 97874 63	0.15434 96012 76	0.05434 08921 61	1.00855 59485 78
5	0.19327 16573 48	0.19208 85967 60	0.06794 71815 46	1.01335 86589 52
6	0.23130 27931 52	0.22927 66113 76	0.08156 73026 57	1.01921 88518 32
7	0.26900 15907 90	0.26581 76001 80	0.09520 38100 79	1.02613 06577 19
8	0.30631 87910 87	0.30162 26615 55	0.10885 91438 35	1.03408 71421 89
9	0.34320 77660 03	0.33661 07824 84	0.12253 56110 80	1.04308 03071 54
10	0.37962 47628 42	0.37070 94124 72	0.13623 53681 45	1.05310 10923 89
11	0.41552 91044 08	0.40385 48626 69	0.14996 04030 00	1.06413 93773 84
12	0.45088 33442 32	0.43599 25324 92	0.16371 25181 63	1.07618 39835 64
13	0.48565 33771 26	0.46707 69712 05	0.17749 33141 21	1.08922 26769 08
14	0.51980 85063 07	0.49707 17862 38	0.19130 41732 96	1.10324 21710 33
15	0.55332 14692 31	0.52594 94135 80	0.20514 62446 07	1.11822 81307 83
16	0.58616 84249 94	0.55369 07680 34	0.21902 04286 70	1.13416 51763 89
17	0.61832 89067 42	0.58028 47927 12	0.23292 73636 78	1.15103 68882 56
18	0.64978 57429 38	0.60572 79278 21	0.24686 74120 09	1.16882 58124 32
19	0.68052 49515 70	0.63002 35186 15	0.26084 06475 84	1.18751 34668 32
20	0.71053 56115 31	0.65318 11815 84	0.27484 68440 36	1.20708 03482 82
21	0.73980 97153 40	0.67521 61465 74	0.28888 54637 02	1.22750 59404 33
22	0.76834 20072 79	0.69614 85907 71	0.30295 56474 91	1.24876 87226 33
23	0.79612 98107 78	0.71600 29784 52	0.31705 62056 50	1.27084 61798 16
24	0.82317 28486 28	0.73480 74182 76	0.33118 56094 60	1.29371 48134 66
25	0.84947 30592 34	0.75259 30476 79	0.34534 19838 87	1.31735 01537 36
26	0.87503 44117 96	0.76939 34518 51	0.35952 31012 21	1.34172 67727 77
27	0.89986 27229 07	0.78524 41227 92	0.37372 63757 18	1.36681 82993 51
28	0.92396 54766 90	0.80018 19621 42	0.38794 88592 70	1.39259 74347 72
29	0.94735 16502 50	0.81424 48298 91	0.40218 72381 17	1.41903 59702 61
30	0.97003 15458 49	0.82747 11397 54	0.41643 78306 23	1.44610 48057 38
31	0.99201 66309 08	0.83989 95007 96	0.43069 65861 26	1.47377 39701 33
32	1.01331 93866 63	0.85156 84040 70	0.44495 90848 64	1.50201 26432 52
33	1.03395 31660 17	0.86251 59522 43	0.45922 05390 04	1.53078 91792 36
34	1.05393 20609 47	0.87277 96297 22	0.47347 57947 55	1.56007 11316 71
35	1.07327 07795 81	0.88239 61104 09	0.48771 93355 88	1.58982 52803 64
36	1.09198 45329 59	0.89140 11000 00	0.50194 52865 41	1.62001 76598 33
37	1.11008 89313 03	0.89982 92096 37	0.51614 74196 30	1.65061 35895 21
38	1.12759 98895 54	0.90771 38577 30	0.53031 91603 34	1.68157 77057 62
39	1.14453 35418 36	0.91508 71968 09	0.54445 35951 59	1.71287 39954 98
40	1.16090 61644 31	0.92198 00624 05	0.55854 34802 68	1.74446 58317 70
41	1.17673 41068 36	0.92842 19411 27	0.57258 12511 48	1.77631 60109 66
42	1.19203 37304 12	0.93444 09552 67	0.58655 90333 15	1.80838 67918 22
43	1.20682 13541 42	0.94006 38615 14	0.60046 86540 16	1.84063 99361 59
44	1.22111 32069 94	0.94531 60615 26	0.61430 16549 18	1.87303 67513 43
45	1.23492 53863 94	0.95022 16223 81	0.62804 93057 43	1.90553 81344 13

K = 3.50042 24991 71838   E = 1.02231 25881 67584
K′= 1.57667 79815 92838   E′= 1.56494 75629 69419

r	u=(r/90)K=F(φ,k)	sn u	cn u	dn u
45	1.75021 12495 86	0.94412 36131 31	0.32959 15701 72	0.34909 78994 57
46	1.78910 48329 10	0.94843 89033 65	0.31696 00078 63	0.33737 76572 59
47	1.82799 84162 34	0.95244 87895 74	0.30469 87089 55	0.32605 91178 90
48	1.86689 19995 58	0.95617 36226 72	0.29280 02788 70	0.31513 62193 11
49	1.90578 55828 82	0.95963 25527 01	0.28125 67577 79	0.30460 23916 00
50	1.94467 91662 07	0.96284 35755 02	0.27005 97139 79	0.29445 06516 06
51	1.98357 27495 31	0.96582 35812 61	0.25920 03277 00	0.28467 36881 95
52	2.02246 63328 55	0.96858 84041 56	0.24866 94660 27	0.27526 39387 67
53	2.06135 99161 79	0.97115 28724 46	0.23845 77495 91	0.26621 36576 80
54	2.10025 34995 03	0.97353 08584 60	0.22855 56116 69	0.25751 49772 31
55	2.13914 70828 27	0.97573 53860 40	0.21895 33503 17	0.24915 99618 23
56	2.17804 06661 51	0.97777 83890 59	0.20964 11741 26	0.24114 06558 87
57	2.21693 42494 75	0.97967 13387 45	0.20060 92421 64	0.23344 91261 44
58	2.25582 78328 00	0.98142 47095 57	0.19184 76986 35	0.22607 74987 13
59	2.29472 14161 24	0.98304 83134 59	0.18334 67027 41	0.21901 79915 81
60	2.33361 49994 48	0.98455 12844 54	0.17509 64542 18	0.21226 29428 78
61	2.37250 85827 72	0.98594 21192 93	0.16708 72149 63	0.20580 48353 87
62	2.41140 21660 96	0.98722 87162 98	0.15930 93271 51	0.19963 63176 89
63	2.45029 57494 20	0.98841 84122 79	0.15175 32281 94	0.19375 02223 01
64	2.48918 93327 44	0.98951 80175 37	0.14440 94628 82	0.18813 95811 33
65	2.52808 29160 69	0.99053 38489 53	0.13726 86929 98	0.18279 76385 74
66	2.56697 64993 93	0.99147 17612 15	0.13032 17046 87	0.17771 78624 79
67	2.60587 00827 17	0.99233 71761 94	0.12355 94138 19	0.17289 39533 07
68	2.64476 36660 41	0.99313 51105 37	0.11697 28695 80	0.16831 98516 41
69	2.68365 72493 65	0.99387 02015 25	0.11055 32564 86	0.16398 97442 85
70	2.72255 08326 89	0.99454 67312 48	0.10429 18950 05	0.15989 80691 35
71	2.76144 44160 13	0.99516 86491 68	0.09818 02409 49	0.15603 95189 85
72	2.80033 79993 37	0.99573 95931 33	0.09220 98837 87	0.15240 90444 18
73	2.83923 15826 62	0.99626 29088 96	0.08637 25440 04	0.14900 18559 13
74	2.87812 51659 86	0.99674 16682 21	0.08066 00696 26	0.14581 34252 94
75	2.91701 87493 10	0.99717 86856 16	0.07506 44320 16	0.14283 94866 33
76	2.95591 23326 34	0.99757 65337 73	0.06957 77210 36	0.14007 60366 79
77	2.99480 59159 58	0.99793 75577 70	0.06419 21396 46	0.13751 93349 38
78	3.03369 94992 82	0.99826 38880 74	0.05889 99980 33	0.13516 59034 37
79	3.07259 30826 06	0.99855 74524 26	0.05369 37073 10	0.13301 25262 71
80	3.11148 66659 31	0.99881 99866 37	0.04856 57728 67	0.13105 62489 81
81	3.15038 02492 55	0.99905 30443 47	0.04350 87874 07	0.12929 43778 05
82	3.18927 38325 79	0.99925 80057 91	0.03851 54237 10	0.12772 44788 73
83	3.22816 74159 03	0.99943 60856 14	0.03357 84271 86	0.12634 43773 58
84	3.26706 09992 27	0.99958 83397 68	0.02869 06082 25	0.12515 21566 37
85	3.30595 45825 51	0.99971 56715 15	0.02384 48343 89	0.12414 61574 86
86	3.34484 81659 75	0.99981 88365 84	0.01903 40224 73	0.12332 49773 29
87	3.38374 17491 99	0.99989 84474 84	0.01425 11304 56	0.12268 74695 75
88	3.42263 53325 24	0.99995 49770 09	0.00948 91493 63	0.12223 27430 46
89	3.46152 89158 48	0.99998 87609 46	0.00474 10950 60	0.12196 01615 21
90	3.50042 24991 72	1.00000 00000 00	0.00000 00000 00	0.12186 93434 05

q = 0.24291 29743 06665 4
q′= 0.00093 52197 97815 9662

D(90) = 2.86452 59726 74201
1/D(90) = 0.34909 78994 56796

r	ϕ	$E(\phi,k)$	A(r)	D(r)
45	1.23492 53863 94	0.95022 16223 81	0.62804 93057 43	1.90553 81344 13
46	1.24827 38223 27	0.95480 33050 83	0.64170 26188 32	1.93810 46178 67
47	1.26117 42465 94	0.95908 25995 44	0.65525 23645 92	1.97069 64170 44
48	1.27364 21667 82	0.96307 97646 45	0.66868 90878 03	2.00327 34790 40
49	1.28569 28445 01	0.96681 38721 46	0.68200 31247 29	2.03579 55331 27
50	1.29734 12775 07	0.97030 28533 94	0.69518 46210 09	2.06822 21425 70
51	1.30860 21853 17	0.97356 35479 28	0.70822 35502 74	2.10051 27577 97
52	1.31948 99979 66	0.97661 17532 06	0.72110 97334 46	2.13262 67708 14
53	1.33001 88475 84	0.97946 22748 08	0.73383 28586 69	2.16452 35708 00
54	1.34020 25624 85	0.98212 89765 83	0.74638 25018 28	2.19616 26007 58
55	1.35005 46634 95	0.98462 48302 87	0.75874 81475 88	2.22750 34151 44
56	1.35958 83622 62	0.98696 19643 63	0.77091 92109 21	2.25850 57383 43
57	1.36881 65613 18	0.98915 17115 68	0.78288 50590 38	2.28912 95238 94
58	1.37775 18556 84	0.99120 46552 35	0.79463 50336 92	2.31933 50143 33
59	1.38640 65358 26	0.99313 06739 84	0.80615 84737 72	2.34908 28015 23
60	1.39479 25917 91	0.99493 89847 84	0.81744 47381 51	2.37833 38873 58
61	1.40292 17183 68	0.99663 81842 61	0.82848 32286 92	2.40704 97446 80
62	1.41080 53211 34	0.99823 62882 13	0.83926 34133 88	2.43519 23782 99
63	1.41845 45232 66	0.99974 07693 05	0.84977 48495 40	2.46272 43859 42
64	1.42588 01730 06	1.00115 85929 56	0.86000 72069 29	2.48960 90190 11
65	1.43309 28516 71	1.00249 62514 16	0.86995 02909 03	2.51581 02429 91
66	1.44010 28821 44	1.00375 97960 91	0.87959 40653 31	2.54129 27973 49
67	1.44692 03377 46	1.00495 48681 40	0.88892 86753 44	2.56602 22547 99
68	1.45355 50514 33	1.00608 67274 19	0.89794 44698 00	2.58996 50797 45
69	1.46001 66252 58	1.00716 02798 24	0.90663 20234 21	2.61308 86857 88
70	1.46631 44400 51	1.00818 01031 02	0.91498 21585 29	2.63536 14921 14
71	1.47245 76652 53	1.00915 04712 07	0.92298 59663 13	2.65675 29786 30
72	1.47845 52688 98	1.01007 53772 69	0.93063 48275 82	2.67723 37396 94
73	1.48431 60276 75	1.01095 85552 64	0.93792 04329 29	2.69677 55362 93
74	1.49004 85370 74	1.01180 35004 39	0.94483 48022 53	2.71535 13465 24
75	1.49566 12215 62	1.01261 34886 02	0.95137 03035 82	2.73293 54142 37
76	1.50116 23447 97	1.01339 15943 20	0.95751 96711 42	2.74950 32957 08
77	1.50656 00198 50	1.01414 07081 21	0.96327 60226 16	2.76503 19042 04
78	1.51186 22194 11	1.01486 35527 66	0.96863 28755 47	2.77949 95523 13
79	1.51707 67860 02	1.01556 26986 66	0.97358 41628 30	2.79288 59919 24
80	1.52221 14421 53	1.01624 05785 12	0.97812 42472 54	2.80517 24517 39
81	1.52727 38005 53	1.01689 95011 87	0.98224 79350 40	2.81634 16721 95
82	1.53227 13741 83	1.01754 16650 30	0.98595 04883 53	2.82637 79377 22
83	1.53721 15863 99	1.01816 91705 15	0.98922 76367 30	2.83526 71062 10
84	1.54210 17809 94	1.01878 40324 13	0.99207 55874 03	2.84299 66356 26
85	1.54694 92322 27	1.01938 81914 82	0.99449 10344 77	2.84955 56076 79
86	1.55176 11548 16	1.01998 35257 78	0.99647 11669 52	2.85493 47484 85
87	1.55654 47139 06	1.02057 18616 15	0.99801 36755 38	2.85912 64461 48
88	1.56130 70350 19	1.02115 49842 43	0.99911 67582 73	2.86212 47652 26
89	1.56605 52139 73	1.02173 46483 13	0.99977 91248 98	2.86392 54580 22
90	1.57079 63267 95	1.02231 25881 68	1.00000 00000 00	2.86452 59726 74

333

K = 3.65185 59694 78752   E = 1.01723 69183 41019
K'= 1.57511 36077 77251   E'= 1.56649 67877 60132

r	u=(r/90)K=F(ϕ,k)	sn u	cn u	dn u
0	0.00000 00000 00	0.00000 00000 00	1.00000 00000 00	1.00000 00000 00
1	0.04057 61774 39	0.04055 40450 29	0.99917 73463 36	0.99918 63384 74
2	0.08115 23548 77	0.08097 56425 80	0.99671 60805 91	0.99675 20198 11
3	0.12172 85323 16	0.12113 40697 70	0.99263 61554 67	0.99271 69094 59
4	0.16230 47097 55	0.16090 20054 05	0.98697 03869 20	0.98711 36803 91
5	0.20288 08871 93	0.20015 71143 06	0.97976 38131 68	0.97998 71756 88
6	0.24345 70646 32	0.23878 34978 98	0.97107 28299 83	0.97139 35486 52
7	0.28403 32420 71	0.27667 29761 77	0.96096 41326 57	0.96139 92106 72
8	0.32460 94195 09	0.31372 61736 04	0.94951 35006 92	0.95007 96227 12
9	0.36518 55969 48	0.34985 33897 58	0.93680 44650 17	0.93751 79699 82
10	0.40576 17743 87	0.38497 52442 39	0.92292 68992 30	0.92380 37610 86
11	0.44633 79518 25	0.41902 30937 90	0.90797 55761 42	0.90903 13926 70
12	0.48691 41292 64	0.45193 92274 94	0.89204 87288 55	0.89329 87186 35
13	0.52749 03067 02	0.48367 68528 07	0.87524 66521 27	0.87670 56594 06
14	0.56806 64841 41	0.51419 98908 69	0.85767 03750 45	0.85935 28821 77
15	0.60864 26615 80	0.54348 26038 30	0.83942 04306 15	0.84134 05775 43
16	0.64921 88390 18	0.57150 90797 66	0.82059 57419 73	0.82276 73521 63
17	0.68979 50164 57	0.59827 26022 61	0.80129 26390 43	0.80372 92511 68
18	0.73037 11938 96	0.62377 49319 27	0.78160 40137 43	0.78431 89183 97
19	0.77094 73713 34	0.64802 55262 70	0.76161 86166 99	0.76462 48973 85
20	0.81152 35487 73	0.67104 07225 75	0.74142 04938 13	0.74473 10714 79
21	0.85209 97262 12	0.69284 29060 98	0.72108 85573 00	0.72471 62377 11
22	0.89267 59036 50	0.71345 96830 33	0.70069 62827 69	0.70465 38060 55
23	0.93325 20810 89	0.73292 30746 94	0.68031 15217 17	0.68461 16135 05
24	0.97382 82585 28	0.75126 87462 39	0.65999 64173 57	0.66465 18409 43
25	1.01440 44359 66	0.76853 52802 59	0.63980 74108 65	0.64483 10199 72
26	1.05498 06134 05	0.78476 35027 40	0.61979 53249 00	0.62520 01166 36
27	1.09555 67908 44	0.79999 58663 51	0.60000 55114 92	0.60580 46791 85
28	1.13613 29682 82	0.81427 58937 79	0.58047 80519 62	0.58668 50376 24
29	1.17670 91457 21	0.82764 76819 32	0.56124 79974 07	0.56787 65436 53
30	1.21728 53231 60	0.84015 54662 75	0.54234 56393 19	0.54940 98406 06
31	1.25786 15005 98	0.85184 32433 30	0.52379 68010 53	0.53131 11541 71
32	1.29843 76780 37	0.86275 44484 09	0.50562 31420 24	0.51360 25958 06
33	1.33901 38554 76	0.87293 16850 15	0.48784 24677 05	0.49630 24719 79
34	1.37959 00329 14	0.88241 65018 66	0.47046 90396 14	0.47942 55934 28
35	1.42016 62103 53	0.89124 92132 75	0.45351 38805 33	0.46298 35797 41
36	1.46074 23877 92	0.89946 87585 32	0.43698 50711 70	0.44698 51554 60
37	1.50131 85652 30	0.90711 25959 47	0.42088 80353 19	0.43143 64348 09
38	1.54189 47426 69	0.91421 66273 98	0.40522 58113 57	0.41634 11928 82
39	1.58247 09201 07	0.92081 51493 82	0.38999 93085 49	0.40170 11217 69
40	1.62304 70975 46	0.92694 08268 77	0.37520 75471 91	0.38751 60706 75
41	1.66362 32749 85	0.93262 46865 68	0.36084 78820 83	0.37378 42695 15
42	1.70419 94524 23	0.93789 61263 29	0.34691 62092 15	0.36050 25358 70
43	1.74477 56298 62	0.94278 29381 38	0.33340 71558 26	0.34766 64654 74
44	1.78535 18073 01	0.94731 13419 18	0.32031 42542 46	0.33527 06066 42
45	1.82592 79847 39	0.95150 60280 91	0.30763 01001 30	0.32330 86192 29

334

ELLIPTIC FUNCTIONS TABLE $\theta = 84°$

q = 0.25794 01957 66336 7
q' = 0.00068 66451 27304 8341

D(90) = 3.09301 99212 91430
1/D(90) = 0.32330 86192 28831

r	ϕ	$E(\phi,k)$	A(r)	D(r)
0	0.00000 00000 00	0.00000 00000 00	0.00000 00000 00	1.00000 00000 00
1	0.04056 51693 35	0.04055 41666 06	0.01311 92586 45	1.00059 38572 14
2	0.08106 43983 40	0.08097 66132 91	0.02624 22974 28	1.00237 49857 89
3	0.12143 22858 48	0.12113 73352 97	0.03937 28748 75	1.00534 13261 64
4	0.16160 44983 49	0.16090 97109 46	0.05251 47063 44	1.00949 04191 86
5	0.20151 82775 33	0.20017 20772 99	0.06567 14425 85	1.01481 81886 02
6	0.24111 29173 67	0.23880 91728 14	0.07884 66484 59	1.02131 95491 27
7	0.28033 02022 67	0.27671 34123 07	0.09204 37818 92	1.02898 82841 36
8	0.31911 47992 77	0.31378 59669 06	0.10526 61730 98	1.03781 70450 07
9	0.35741 45987 05	0.34993 76299 51	0.11851 70041 43	1.04779 73504 29
10	0.39518 09993 03	0.38508 94583 85	0.13179 92888 91	1.05891 95857 49
11	0.43236 91357 82	0.41917 31875 99	0.14511 58533 94	1.07117 30023 83
12	0.46893 80480 38	0.45213 14255 84	0.15846 93167 72	1.08454 57173 66
13	0.50485 07930 29	0.48391 76390 53	0.17186 20726 40	1.09902 47131 03
14	0.54007 45015 70	0.51449 59498 98	0.18529 62711 32	1.11459 58373 94
15	0.57458 03834 43	0.54384 07645 72	0.19877 38015 61	1.13124 38038 05
16	0.60834 36851 80	0.57193 62618 52	0.21229 62757 82	1.14895 21924 64
17	0.64134 36055 03	0.59877 57659 00	0.22586 50122 86	1.16770 34513 74
18	0.67356 31738 71	0.62436 10317 37	0.23948 10210 79	1.18747 88983 26
19	0.70498 90978 19	0.64870 14694 14	0.25314 49893 93	1.20825 87235 01
20	0.73561 15847 52	0.67181 33314 02	0.26685 72682 61	1.23002 19928 59
21	0.76542 41437 76	0.69371 88853 67	0.28061 78600 04	1.25274 66524 11
22	0.79442 33727 98	0.71444 55917 07	0.29442 64066 65	1.27640 95334 67
23	0.82260 87358 07	0.73402 53021 79	0.30828 21794 25	1.30098 63589 57
24	0.84998 23347 24	0.75249 34928 88	0.32218 40690 42	1.32645 17509 31
25	0.87654 86797 61	0.76988 85418 98	0.33613 05773 26	1.35277 92393 28
26	0.90231 44616 49	0.78625 10589 30	0.35011 98097 11	1.37994 12721 07
27	0.92728 83286 19	0.80162 32720 77	0.36414 94689 13	1.40790 92268 49
28	0.95148 06704 54	0.81604 84742 39	0.37821 68497 36	1.43665 34239 05
29	0.97490 34115 10	0.82957 05301 02	0.39231 88350 11	1.46614 31411 90
30	0.99756 98141 00	0.84223 34429 21	0.40645 18927 20	1.49634 66307 06
31	1.01949 42932 92	0.85408 09791 51	0.42061 20743 01	1.52723 11368 73
32	1.04069 22437 84	0.86515 63480 23	0.43479 50141 49	1.55876 29167 48
33	1.06117 98792 26	0.87550 19324 99	0.44899 59303 33	1.59090 72622 03
34	1.08097 40841 14	0.88515 90676 05	0.46320 96265 28	1.62362 85241 22
35	1.10009 22781 44	0.89416 78618 87	0.47743 04951 67	1.65689 01386 82
36	1.11855 22927 76	0.90256 70576 58	0.49165 25218 16	1.69065 46557 70
37	1.13637 22595 77	0.91039 39257 35	0.50586 92907 72	1.72488 37695 75
38	1.15357 05098 57	0.91768 41905 09	0.52007 39918 67	1.75953 83513 95
39	1.17016 54850 05	0.92447 19813 95	0.53425 94284 90	1.79457 84846 90
40	1.18617 56568 99	0.93078 98069 72	0.54841 80267 92	1.82996 35023 95
41	1.20161 94577 13	0.93666 85483 93	0.56254 18460 73	1.86565 20265 04
42	1.21651 52184 76	0.94213 74689 76	0.57662 25903 25	1.90160 20099 40
43	1.23088 11156 79	0.94722 42371 66	0.59065 16209 18	1.93777 07806 76
44	1.24473 51252 95	0.95195 49603 82	0.60461 99703 89	1.97411 50881 16
45	1.25809 49835 46	0.95635 42275 37	0.61851 83573 17	2.01059 11516 96

335

K = 3.65185 59694 78752   E = 1.01723 69183 41019
K'= 1.57511 36077 77251   E'= 1.56649 67877 60132

r	u=(r/90)K=F(ϕ,k)	sn u	cn u	dn u
45	1.82592 79847 39	0.95150 60280 91	0.30763 01001 30	0.32330 86192 29
46	1.86650 41621 78	0.95539 02068 98	0.29534 64957 71	0.31177 34188 35
47	1.90708 03396 17	0.95898 56628 00	0.28345 45793 31	0.30065 73070 69
48	1.94765 65170 55	0.96231 28125 26	0.27194 49408 40	0.28995 20887 29
49	1.98823 26944 94	0.96539 07655 11	0.26080 77258 55	0.27964 91767 92
50	2.02880 88719 33	0.96823 73857 09	0.25003 27276 87	0.26973 96861 13
51	2.06938 50493 71	0.97086 93538 91	0.23960 94690 86	0.26021 45167 22
52	2.10996 12268 10	0.97330 22297 21	0.22952 72742 39	0.25106 44275 77
53	2.15053 74042 49	0.97555 05130 32	0.21977 53319 26	0.24228 01016 19
54	2.19111 35816 87	0.97762 77038 12	0.21034 27506 22	0.23385 22029 00
55	2.23168 97591 26	0.97954 63605 57	0.20121 86062 93	0.22577 14265 51
56	2.27226 59365 65	0.98131 81566 91	0.19239 19835 87	0.21802 85422 82
57	2.31284 21140 03	0.98295 39348 44	0.18385 20110 70	0.21061 44320 64
58	2.35341 82914 42	0.98446 37588 52	0.17558 78911 16	0.20352 01226 03
59	2.39399 44688 81	0.98585 69633 65	0.16758 89250 04	0.19673 68131 59
60	2.43457 06463 19	0.98714 22010 22	0.15984 45337 25	0.19025 58992 25
61	2.47514 68237 58	0.98832 74871 63	0.15234 42749 77	0.18406 89925 23
62	2.51572 30011 96	0.98942 02421 00	0.14507 78567 62	0.17816 79377 59
63	2.55629 91786 35	0.99042 73309 67	0.13803 51479 67	0.17254 48265 08
64	2.59687 53560 74	0.99135 51012 02	0.13120 61862 87	0.16719 20085 84
65	2.63745 15335 12	0.99220 94177 37	0.12458 11837 90	0.16210 21012 17
66	2.67802 77109 51	0.99299 56959 44	0.11815 05304 10	0.15726 79963 08
67	2.71860 38883 90	0.99371 89324 53	0.11190 47956 24	0.15268 28660 31
68	2.75918 00658 28	0.99438 37338 96	0.10583 47285 29	0.14834 01670 00
69	2.79975 62432 67	0.99499 43436 87	0.09993 12565 28	0.14423 36432 23
70	2.84033 24207 06	0.99555 46669 22	0.09418 54827 97	0.14035 73279 95
71	2.88090 85981 44	0.99606 82934 91	0.08858 86827 00	0.13670 55449 35
72	2.92148 47755 83	0.99653 85194 84	0.08313 22992 85	0.13327 29082 72
73	2.96206 09530 22	0.99696 83669 94	0.07780 79379 82	0.13005 43225 42
74	3.00263 71304 60	0.99736 06023 81	0.07260 73606 28	0.12704 49817 84
75	3.04321 33078 99	0.99771 77530 96	0.06752 24788 96	0.12424 03683 57
76	3.08378 94853 38	0.99804 21231 29	0.06254 53472 25	0.12163 62514 58
77	3.12436 56627 76	0.99833 58071 62	0.05766 81553 26	0.11922 86854 16
78	3.16494 18402 15	0.99860 07034 89	0.05288 32203 10	0.11701 40078 42
79	3.20551 80176 54	0.99883 85257 79	0.04818 29785 21	0.11498 88376 91
80	3.24609 41950 92	0.99905 08137 20	0.04355 99770 99	0.11315 00732 85
81	3.28667 03725 31	0.99923 89426 24	0.03900 68653 31	0.11149 48903 54
82	3.32724 65499 70	0.99940 41320 26	0.03451 63858 16	0.11002 07401 24
83	3.36782 27274 08	0.99954 74533 26	0.03008 13654 79	0.10872 53475 01
84	3.40839 89048 47	0.99966 98365 26	0.02569 47064 59	0.10760 67093 64
85	3.44897 50822 85	0.99977 20760 78	0.02134 93769 00	0.10666 30930 09
86	3.48955 12597 24	0.99985 48358 98	0.01703 84016 51	0.10589 30347 58
87	3.53012 74371 63	0.99991 86535 55	0.01275 48529 11	0.10529 53387 53
88	3.57070 36146 01	0.99996 39436 70	0.00849 18408 12	0.10486 90759 49
89	3.61127 97920 40	0.99999 10005 40	0.00424 25039 68	0.10461 35833 15
90	3.65185 59694 79	1.00000 00000 00	0.00000 00000 00	0.10452 84632 68

336

q = 0.25794 01957 66336 7   D(90) = 3.09301 99212 91430
q′= 0.00068 66451 27304 8341   1/D(90) = 0.32330 86192 28831

r	ϕ	$E(\phi,k)$	A(r)	D(r)
45	1.25809 49835 46	0.95635 42275 37	0.61851 83573 17	2.01059 11516 96
46	1.27097 81538 35	0.96044 51583 10	0.63233 72022 47	2.04715 47116 58
47	1.28340 17992 34	0.96424 94574 95	0.64606 66446 27	2.08376 10819 74
48	1.29538 27599 86	0.96778 74729 80	0.65969 65607 25	2.12036 52053 36
49	1.30693 75355 21	0.97107 82561 46	0.67321 65824 67	2.15692 17101 56
50	1.31808 22704 95	0.97413 96236 37	0.68661 61171 82	2.19338 49695 00
51	1.32883 27444 13	0.97698 82196 58	0.69988 43681 66	2.22970 91618 60
52	1.33920 43644 42	0.97963 95780 62	0.71301 03560 57	2.26584 83336 72
53	1.34921 21610 35	0.98210 81836 83	0.72598 29409 30	2.30175 64634 70
54	1.35887 07860 32	0.98440 75324 16	0.73879 08450 76	2.33738 75275 60
55	1.36819 45129 26	0.98655 01897 03	0.75142 26764 11	2.37269 55670 85
56	1.37719 72390 33	0.98854 78471 46	0.76386 69524 33	2.40763 47563 54
57	1.38589 24892 96	0.99041 13770 22	0.77611 21246 82	2.44215 94722 84
58	1.39429 34215 19	0.99215 08845 83	0.78814 66036 36	2.47622 43648 14
59	1.40241 28328 18	0.99377 57580 21	0.79995 87839 62	2.50978 44281 20
60	1.41026 31671 18	0.99529 47160 71	0.81153 70700 73	2.54279 50724 87
61	1.41785 65235 28	0.99671 58532 25	0.82286 99019 05	2.57521 21966 47
62	1.42520 46654 69	0.99804 66825 71	0.83394 57808 54	2.60699 22604 19
63	1.43231 90304 19	0.99929 41763 99	0.84475 32957 90	2.63809 23574 73
64	1.43921 07401 65	1.00046 48039 29	0.85528 11490 88	2.66847 02880 19
65	1.44589 06114 77	1.00156 45683 24	0.86551 81825 86	2.69808 46312 52
66	1.45236 91671 11	1.00259 90395 82	0.87545 34034 12	2.72689 48173 45
67	1.45860 81657 07	1.00357 33868 78	0.88507 60095 95	2.75486 11988 06
68	1.46476 30200 87	1.00449 24083 63	0.89437 54153 91	2.78194 51210 05
69	1.47069 79951 83	1.00536 05592 18	0.90334 12762 50	2.80810 89916 69
70	1.47647 10334 18	1.00618 19779 46	0.91196 35133 46	2.83331 63491 57
71	1.48209 13596 29	1.00696 05110 26	0.92023 23376 07	2.85753 19293 23
72	1.48756 79742 24	1.00769 97360 09	0.92813 82731 67	2.88072 17307 62
73	1.49290 96649 69	1.00840 29831 65	0.93567 21801 71	2.90285 30782 70
74	1.49812 50187 50	1.00907 33557 66	0.94282 52768 67	2.92389 46843 14
75	1.50322 24333 04	1.00971 37491 21	0.94958 91609 21	2.94381 67083 38
76	1.50821 01288 79	1.01032 68684 24	0.95595 58298 82	2.96259 08137 30
77	1.51309 61598 48	1.01091 52455 32	0.96191 77007 48	2.98019 02222 79
78	1.51788 84262 35	1.01148 12547 42	0.96746 76285 61	2.99658 97659 47
79	1.52259 46851 74	1.01202 71276 49	0.97259 89239 86	3.01176 59358 10
80	1.52722 25622 84	1.01255 49671 81	0.97730 53698 10	3.02569 69280 17
81	1.53177 95629 63	1.01306 67608 60	0.98158 12363 14	3.03836 26866 18
82	1.53627 30836 08	1.01356 43933 94	0.98542 12954 82	3.04974 49431 31
83	1.54071 04227 54	1.01404 96586 46	0.98882 08339 80	3.05982 72527 32
84	1.54509 87921 44	1.01452 42710 63	0.99177 56648 88	3.06859 50269 44
85	1.54944 53277 36	1.01498 98766 25	0.99428 21381 36	3.07603 55627 28
86	1.55375 71006 41	1.01544 80633 78	0.99633 71496 16	3.08213 80678 89
87	1.55804 11280 19	1.01590 03716 25	0.99793 81489 36	3.08689 36827 03
88	1.56230 43839 20	1.01634 83038 11	0.99908 31458 05	3.09029 54977 15
89	1.56655 38101 00	1.01679 33341 96	0.99977 07150 12	3.09233 85676 34
90	1.57079 63267 95	1.01723 69183 41	1.00000 00000 00	3.09301 99212 91

K = 3.83174 19997 84146   E = 1.01266 35062 34396
K'= 1.57379 21309 24768   E'= 1.56780 90739 77622

r	u=(r/90)K=F(φ,k)	sn u	cn u	dn u
0	0.00000 00000 00	0.00000 00000 00	1.00000 00000 00	1.00000 00000 00
1	0.04257 49111 09	0.04254 93032 18	0.99909 43683 13	0.99910 12506 98
2	0.08514 98222 17	0.08494 54017 04	0.99638 56074 48	0.99641 31122 38
3	0.12772 47333 26	0.12703 72893 27	0.99189 79418 87	0.99195 97355 51
4	0.17029 96444 35	0.16867 82904 44	0.98567 11593 29	0.98578 07880 13
5	0.21287 45555 44	0.20972 80618 26	0.97775 97558 10	0.97793 06018 87
6	0.25544 94666 52	0.25005 44079 88	0.96823 17868 39	0.96847 70298 94
7	0.29802 43777 61	0.28953 48625 91	0.95716 74688 08	0.95750 00520 59
8	0.34059 92888 70	0.32805 79998 93	0.94465 75827 81	0.94509 01856 96
9	0.38317 41999 78	0.36552 44525 92	0.93080 17375 13	0.93134 67551 76
10	0.42574 91110 87	0.40184 76252 40	0.91570 65502 05	0.91637 60797 89
11	0.46832 40221 96	0.43695 41046 11	0.89948 38022 24	0.90028 96366 65
12	0.51089 89333 05	0.47078 37795 71	0.88224 86230 61	0.88320 22518 68
13	0.55347 38444 13	0.50328 96923 86	0.86411 77498 10	0.86523 03667 39
14	0.59604 87555 22	0.53443 76507 93	0.84520 79018 89	0.84649 04190 68
15	0.63862 36666 31	0.56420 56353 07	0.82563 43022 72	0.82709 73702 53
16	0.68119 85777 39	0.59258 30392 68	0.80550 93677 74	0.80716 34008 82
17	0.72377 34888 48	0.61956 97800 18	0.78494 15823 42	0.78679 67886 57
18	0.76634 83999 57	0.64517 53188 11	0.76403 45594 26	0.76610 09747 13
19	0.80892 33110 66	0.66941 76247 89	0.74288 62925 25	0.74517 38174 08
20	0.85149 82221 74	0.69232 21149 80	0.72158 85871 53	0.72410 70268 86
21	0.89407 31332 83	0.71392 05982 32	0.70022 66628 89	0.70298 57690 94
22	0.93664 80443 92	0.73425 02465 20	0.67887 89107 68	0.68188 84245 95
23	0.97922 29555 00	0.75335 26124 74	0.65761 67890 79	0.66088 64852 69
24	1.02179 78666 09	0.77127 27075 70	0.63650 48393 83	0.64004 45708 33
25	1.06437 27777 18	0.78805 81512 37	0.61560 08043 11	0.61942 05467 67
26	1.10694 76888 27	0.80375 83974 66	0.59495 58290 35	0.59906 57256 43
27	1.14952 25999 35	0.81842 40422 23	0.57461 47292 86	0.57902 51347 71
28	1.19209 75110 44	0.83210 62123 22	0.55461 63100 88	0.55933 78344 16
29	1.23467 24221 53	0.84485 60341 90	0.53499 37209 84	0.54003 72723 93
30	1.27724 73332 61	0.85672 41792 79	0.51577 48352 12	0.52115 16625 72
31	1.31982 22443 70	0.86776 04816 40	0.49698 26420 56	0.50270 43765 38
32	1.36239 71554 79	0.87801 36223 15	0.47863 56432 92	0.48471 43393 79
33	1.40497 20665 88	0.88753 08746 96	0.46074 82462 93	0.46719 64221 85
34	1.44754 69776 96	0.89635 79047 38	0.44333 11478 04	0.45016 18252 97
35	1.49012 18888 05	0.90453 86199 28	0.42639 17037 87	0.43361 84477 32
36	1.53269 67999 14	0.91211 50610 19	0.40993 42818 82	0.41757 12393 24
37	1.57527 17110 22	0.91912 73308 59	0.39396 05940 56	0.40202 25331 97
38	1.61784 66221 31	0.92561 35549 63	0.37847 00078 86	0.38697 23569 92
39	1.66042 15332 40	0.93160 98689 30	0.36345 98356 24	0.37241 87220 16
40	1.70299 64443 49	0.93715 04282 29	0.34892 56007 67	0.35835 78900 43
41	1.74557 13554 57	0.94226 74363 39	0.33486 12823 48	0.34478 46179 78
42	1.78814 62665 66	0.94699 11876 96	0.32125 95374 88	0.33169 23809 17
43	1.83072 11776 75	0.95135 01223 06	0.30811 19030 30	0.31907 35744 47
44	1.87329 60887 83	0.95537 08893 08	0.29540 89772 88	0.30691 96971 85
45	1.91587 09998 92	0.95907 84171 47	0.28314 05830 36	0.29522 15147 10

q = 0.27517 98048 73562 8   D(90) = 3.38728 70037 34678
q'= 0.00047 65699 16866 8574   1/D(90) = 0.29522 15147 09986

r	ϕ	$E(\phi,k)$	A(r)	D(r)
0	0.00000 00000 00	0.00000 00000 00	0.00000 00000 00	1.00000 00000 00
1	0.04256 21525 39	0.04254 94008 49	0.01256 98449 75	1.00066 67395 62
2	0.08504 78919 04	0.08494 61810 72	0.02514 45764 92	1.00266 63651 92
3	0.12738 14929 22	0.12703 99102 84	0.03772 90569 66	1.00599 70973 93
4	0.16948 85914 04	0.16868 44721 28	0.05032 81006 09	1.01065 59692 32
5	0.21129 68277 45	0.20974 00585 88	0.06294 64494 88	1.01663 88246 99
6	0.25273 64478 78	0.25007 49784 15	0.07558 87497 47	1.02394 03164 59
7	0.29374 08300 47	0.28956 72325 35	0.08825 95280 81	1.03255 39030 09
8	0.33424 70678 79	0.32810 58204 99	0.10096 31685 01	1.04247 18453 15
9	0.37419 61825 69	0.36559 17544 79	0.11370 38894 54	1.05368 52029 72
10	0.41353 36594 53	0.40193 87699 65	0.12648 57213 64	1.06618 38299 49
11	0.45220 96066 97	0.43707 37345 88	0.13931 24846 40	1.07995 63700 19
12	0.49017 89562 01	0.47093 67675 43	0.15218 77682 14	1.09499 02519 32
13	0.52740 15689 28	0.50348 10914 77	0.16511 49086 59	1.11127 16844 46
14	0.56384 22687 49	0.53467 26460 39	0.17809 69699 56	1.12878 56513 13
15	0.59947 08103 72	0.56448 94974 70	0.19113 67239 43	1.14751 59063 21
16	0.63426 17880 91	0.59292 10815 43	0.20423 66315 17	1.16744 49685 22
17	0.66819 44928 46	0.61996 73181 44	0.21739 88246 26	1.18855 41177 66
18	0.70125 27255 06	0.64563 76349 26	0.23062 50891 14	1.21082 33906 55
19	0.73342 45744 20	0.66994 99352 43	0.24391 68484 55	1.23423 15770 74
20	0.76470 21650 60	0.69292 95422 03	0.25727 51484 37	1.25875 62174 17
21	0.79508 13892 64	0.71460 81466 41	0.27070 06428 21	1.28437 36006 52
22	0.82456 16209 54	0.73502 27823 60	0.28419 35800 40	1.31105 87633 80
23	0.85314 54246 02	0.75421 48474 23	0.29775 37909 63	1.33878 54900 11
24	0.88083 82618 96	0.77222 91858 75	0.31138 06777 75	1.36752 63142 21
25	0.90764 82013 44	0.78911 32401 22	0.32507 32039 96	1.39725 25218 23
26	0.93358 56347 37	0.80491 62805 03	0.33882 98856 89	1.42793 41552 02
27	0.95866 30036 46	0.81968 87153 83	0.35264 87838 76	1.45954 00194 53
28	0.98289 45384 50	0.83348 14823 79	0.36652 74982 01	1.49203 76903 59
29	1.00629 60117 33	0.84634 55191 86	0.38046 31618 57	1.52539 35243 46
30	1.02888 45073 27	0.85833 13107 64	0.39445 24378 17	1.55957 26705 56
31	1.05067 82057 84	0.86948 85084 11	0.40849 15163 63	1.59453 90851 36
32	1.07169 61866 44	0.87986 56154 08	0.42257 61139 62	1.63025 55479 01
33	1.09195 82475 00	0.88950 97333 97	0.43670 14734 82	1.66668 36814 47
34	1.11148 47396 01	0.89846 63634 17	0.45086 23657 63	1.70378 39728 42
35	1.13029 64194 93	0.90677 92555 07	0.46505 30925 64	1.74151 57979 82
36	1.14841 43160 25	0.91449 03009 28	0.47926 74908 66	1.77983 74486 97
37	1.16585 96119 37	0.92163 94613 33	0.49349 89385 58	1.81870 61626 95
38	1.18265 35391 62	0.92826 47295 77	0.50774 03614 88	1.85807 81563 96
39	1.19881 72868 98	0.93440 21172 64	0.52198 42418 74	1.89790 86607 20
40	1.21437 19215 24	0.94008 56646 01	0.53622 26280 69	1.93815 19598 70
41	1.22933 83174 03	0.94534 74685 31	0.55044 71456 60	1.97876 14331 46
42	1.24373 70976 32	0.95021 77256 39	0.56464 90098 96	2.01968 95998 00
43	1.25758 85838 48	0.95472 47866 77	0.57881 90394 02	2.06088 81669 46
44	1.27091 27542 23	0.95889 52200 24	0.59294 76711 78	2.10230 80805 09
45	1.28372 92088 30	0.96275 38817 43	0.60702 49768 27	2.14389 95792 07

K = 3.83174 19997 84146   E = 1.01266 35062 34396
K' = 1.57379 21309 24768   E' = 1.56780 90739 77622

r	u=(r/90)K=F(ϕ,k)	sn u	cn u	dn u
45	1.91587 09998 92	0.95907 84171 47	0.28314 05830 36	0.29522 15147 10
46	1.95844 59110 01	0.96249 59883 57	0.27129 59129 73	0.28396 92061 05
47	2.00102 08221 10	0.96564 53172 72	0.25986 36589 27	0.27315 24943 70
48	2.04359 57332 18	0.96854 66292 57	0.24883 21260 52	0.26276 07619 64
49	2.08617 06443 27	0.97121 87403 01	0.23818 93332 79	0.25278 31527 37
50	2.12874 55554 36	0.97367 91360 29	0.22792 31012 01	0.24320 86614 23
51	2.17132 04665 44	0.97594 40493 66	0.21802 11285 79	0.23402 62118 83
52	2.21389 53776 53	0.97802 85362 71	0.20847 10585 20	0.22522 47251 59
53	2.25647 02887 62	0.97994 65490 72	0.19926 05353 83	0.21679 31783 69
54	2.29904 51998 70	0.98171 10070 75	0.19037 72533 36	0.20872 06554 00
55	2.34162 01109 79	0.98333 38641 79	0.18180 89974 64	0.20099 63902 68
56	2.38419 50220 88	0.98482 61733 68	0.17354 36782 18	0.19360 98039 63
57	2.42676 99331 97	0.98619 81479 62	0.16556 93599 58	0.18655 05355 12
58	2.46934 48443 05	0.98745 92196 00	0.15787 42842 50	0.17980 84679 30
59	2.51191 97554 14	0.98861 80929 61	0.15044 68885 38	0.17337 37496 94
60	2.55449 46665 23	0.98968 27972 62	0.14327 58207 21	0.16723 68122 51
61	2.59706 95776 31	0.99066 07346 07	0.13634 99501 59	0.16138 83841 04
62	2.63964 44887 40	0.99155 87252 69	0.12965 83755 25	0.15581 95018 91
63	2.68221 93998 49	0.99238 30500 26	0.12319 04299 12	0.15052 15188 67
64	2.72479 43109 58	0.99313 94896 55	0.11693 56835 52	0.14548 61111 51
65	2.76736 92220 66	0.99383 33617 18	0.11088 39444 51	0.14070 52820 62
66	2.80994 41331 75	0.99446 95547 60	0.10502 52572 28	0.13617 13648 07
67	2.85251 90442 84	0.99505 25600 64	0.09934 99004 06	0.13187 70238 01
68	2.89509 39553 92	0.99558 65010 78	0.09384 83823 60	0.12781 52548 19
69	2.93766 88665 01	0.99607 51606 55	0.08851 14361 30	0.12397 93841 91
70	2.98024 37776 10	0.99652 20062 25	0.08333 00132 60	0.12036 30672 15
71	3.02281 86887 19	0.99693 02130 19	0.07829 52767 98	0.11696 02859 25
72	3.06539 35998 27	0.99730 26854 75	0.07339 85936 18	0.11376 53463 77
73	3.10796 85109 36	0.99764 20769 10	0.06863 15261 32	0.11077 28755 43
74	3.15054 34220 45	0.99795 08075 99	0.06398 58235 28	0.10797 78179 39
75	3.19311 83331 53	0.99823 10813 29	0.05945 34125 92	0.10537 54320 62
76	3.23569 32442 62	0.99848 49005 38	0.05502 63882 00	0.10296 12867 25
77	3.27826 81553 71	0.99871 40801 22	0.05069 70035 30	0.10073 12573 60
78	3.32084 30664 80	0.99892 02599 92	0.04645 76600 61	0.09868 15223 39
79	3.36341 79775 88	0.99910 49164 53	0.04230 08973 81	0.09680 85593 77
80	3.40599 28886 97	0.99926 93724 78	0.03821 93828 73	0.09510 91420 54
81	3.44856 77998 06	0.99941 48069 34	0.03420 59012 73	0.09358 03365 00
82	3.49114 27109 14	0.99954 22628 22	0.03025 33441 55	0.09221 94982 73
83	3.53371 76220 23	0.99965 26545 87	0.02635 46993 51	0.09102 42694 61
84	3.57629 25331 32	0.99974 67745 27	0.02250 30403 23	0.08999 25760 32
85	3.61886 74442 41	0.99982 52983 64	0.01869 15155 00	0.08912 26254 50
86	3.66144 23553 49	0.99988 87899 97	0.01491 33375 98	0.08841 29045 80
87	3.70401 72664 58	0.99993 77054 72	0.01116 17729 14	0.08786 21778 93
88	3.74659 21775 67	0.99997 23961 98	0.00743 01306 23	0.08746 94859 76
89	3.78916 70886 75	0.99999 31114 25	0.00371 17520 60	0.08723 41443 74
90	3.83174 19997 84	1.00000 00000 00	0.00000 00000 00	0.08715 57427 48

q = 0.27517 98048 73562 8   D(90) = 3.38728 70037 34678
q'= 0.00047 65699 16866 8574   1/D(90) = 0.29522 15147 09986

r	ϕ	$E(\phi,k)$	A(r)	D(r)
45	1.28372 92088 30	0.96275 38817 43	0.60702 49768 27	2.14389 95792 07
46	1.29605 71416 10	0.96632 39902 40	0.62104 06800 08	2.18561 22515 09
47	1.30791 53182 38	0.96962 72038 56	0.63498 41750 50	2.22739 50955 41
48	1.31932 20592 09	0.97268 36999 92	0.64884 45467 01	2.26919 65818 62
49	1.33029 52275 60	0.97551 22546 04	0.66261 05909 64	2.31096 47190 44
50	1.34085 22206 60	0.97813 03211 44	0.67627 08369 75	2.35264 71219 57
51	1.35100 99655 58	0.98055 41081 79	0.68981 35698 54	2.39419 10826 59
52	1.36078 49174 55	0.98279 86551 06	0.70322 68545 05	2.43554 36437 71
53	1.37019 30608 66	0.98487 79055 01	0.71649 85602 68	2.47665 16742 04
54	1.37924 99131 15	0.98680 47777 78	0.72961 63863 98	2.51746 19470 98
55	1.38797 05298 27	0.98859 12329 03	0.74256 78882 74	2.55792 12198 10
56	1.39636 95121 25	0.99024 83390 09	0.75534 05042 90	2.59797 63157 86
57	1.40446 10152 74	0.99178 63328 37	0.76792 15833 52	2.63757 42081 36
58	1.41225 87585 32	0.99321 46779 44	0.78029 84129 00	2.67666 21047 12
59	1.41977 60360 08	0.99454 21197 05	0.79245 82473 92	2.71518 75345 04
60	1.42702 57283 52	0.99577 67371 49	0.80438 83371 57	2.75309 84351 21
61	1.43402 03151 13	0.99692 59917 03	0.81607 59575 55	2.79034 32411 53
62	1.44077 18876 31	0.99799 67729 39	0.82750 84383 38	2.82687 09731 79
63	1.44729 21623 47	0.99899 54414 28	0.83867 31931 60	2.86263 13271 86
64	1.45359 24944 21	0.99992 78688 40	0.84955 77491 16	2.89757 47641 48
65	1.45968 38915 78	1.00079 94753 99	0.86014 97762 59	2.93165 25995 40
66	1.46557 70281 00	1.00161 52648 45	0.87043 71169 85	2.96481 70925 09
67	1.47128 22589 05	1.00237 98570 02	0.88040 78152 06	2.99702 15344 64
68	1.47680 96336 52	1.00309 75182 69	0.89005 01452 37	3.02822 03368 24
69	1.48216 89108 41	1.00377 21896 61	0.89935 26402 87	3.05836 91176 62
70	1.48736 95718 46	1.00440 75133 67	0.90830 41204 96	3.08742 47869 86
71	1.49242 08348 83	1.00500 68571 27	0.91689 37204 10	3.11534 56304 05
72	1.49733 16688 62	1.00557 33370 48	0.92511 09158 21	3.14209 13909 23
73	1.50211 08071 14	1.00610 98388 17	0.93294 55498 97	3.16762 33485 95
74	1.50676 67609 89	1.00661 90374 51	0.94038 78585 05	3.19190 43978 22
75	1.51130 78332 95	1.00710 34156 95	0.94742 84946 61	3.21489 91220 16
76	1.51574 21315 92	1.00756 52811 76	0.95405 85520 29	3.23657 38654 12
77	1.52007 75813 19	1.00800 67824 04	0.96026 95873 92	3.25689 68017 94
78	1.52432 19387 78	1.00842 99237 44	0.96605 36420 32	3.27583 79999 16
79	1.52848 28039 47	1.00883 65794 11	0.97140 32619 41	3.29336 94853 98
80	1.53256 76331 56	1.00922 85066 17	0.97631 15168 07	3.30946 52989 08
81	1.53658 37516 08	1.00960 73579 19	0.98077 20177 18	3.32410 15504 21
82	1.54053 83657 68	1.00997 46928 72	0.98477 89335 13	3.33725 64693 99
83	1.54443 85756 25	1.01033 19890 44	0.98832 70057 51	3.34891 04507 04
84	1.54829 13868 32	1.01068 06524 85	0.99141 15622 22	3.35904 60961 04
85	1.55210 37227 39	1.01102 20277 01	0.99402 85289 85	3.36764 82512 34
86	1.55588 24363 35	1.01135 74072 05	0.99617 44408 76	3.37470 40378 77
87	1.55963 43221 03	1.01168 80407 24	0.99784 64504 49	3.38020 28814 71
88	1.56336 61278 04	1.01201 51441 00	0.99904 23353 50	3.38413 65337 43
89	1.56708 45662 12	1.01233 99079 64	0.99976 05040 55	3.38649 90903 86
90	1.57079 63267 95	1.01266 35062 34	1.00000 00000 00	3.38728 70037 35

K = 4.05275 81695 49437   E = 1.00864 79569 07096
K′= 1.57271 24349 95227   E′= 1.56888 37196 07763

r	u=(r/90)K=F(ϕ,k)	sn u	cn u	dn u
0	0.00000 00000 00	0.00000 00000 00	1.00000 00000 00	1.00000 00000 00
1	0.04503 06463 28	0.04500 03078 28	0.99898 69730 36	0.99899 19048 77
2	0.09006 12926 57	0.08981 91718 67	0.99595 80896 63	0.99597 77971 74
3	0.13509 19389 85	0.13427 80629 31	0.99094 36925 56	0.99098 79606 16
4	0.18012 25853 13	0.17820 41821 07	0.98399 35312 18	0.98407 20485 00
5	0.22515 32316 42	0.22143 30842 95	0.97517 55683 87	0.97529 78930 45
6	0.27018 38779 70	0.26381 10273 44	0.96457 43837 84	0.96474 99131 13
7	0.31521 45242 98	0.30519 69797 39	0.95228 92436 43	0.95252 71885 27
8	0.36024 51706 27	0.34546 42380 41	0.93843 19156 10	0.93874 12804 01
9	0.40527 58169 55	0.38450 16250 48	0.92312 43146 70	0.92351 38829 45
10	0.45030 64632 83	0.42221 42595 77	0.90649 60667 37	0.90697 43931 30
11	0.49533 71096 12	0.45852 39073 97	0.88868 20727 04	0.88925 74808 62
12	0.54036 77559 40	0.49336 89391 37	0.86982 01480 16	0.87050 07344 91
13	0.58539 84022 68	0.52670 39341 77	0.85004 88019 65	0.85084 24457 42
14	0.63042 90485 97	0.55849 89790 96	0.82950 52081 51	0.83041 95853 59
15	0.67545 96949 25	0.58873 87151 85	0.80832 34038 69	0.80936 60071 46
16	0.72049 03412 53	0.61742 11919 48	0.78663 27426 02	0.78781 09045 17
17	0.76552 09875 82	0.64455 65828 55	0.76455 66110 48	0.76587 75309 63
18	0.81055 16339 10	0.67016 58164 60	0.74221 14108 85	0.74368 21846 34
19	0.85558 22802 38	0.69427 91708 91	0.71970 57960 50	0.72133 34478 43
20	0.90061 29265 67	0.71693 48734 27	0.69714 01489 40	0.69893 16649 35
21	0.94564 35728 95	0.73817 77398 45	0.67460 62736 13	0.67656 86366 46
22	0.99067 42192 23	0.75805 78810 36	0.65218 72806 18	0.65432 75056 64
23	1.03570 48655 52	0.77662 94974 91	0.62995 76363 74	0.63228 28063 65
24	1.08073 55118 80	0.79394 97757 84	0.60798 33497 16	0.61050 06514 01
25	1.12576 61582 08	0.81007 78955 48	0.58632 22690 16	0.58903 90286 41
26	1.17079 68045 37	0.82507 41505 78	0.56502 44650 00	0.56794 81836 18
27	1.21582 74508 65	0.83899 91837 16	0.54413 26765 81	0.54727 10648 75
28	1.26085 80971 93	0.85191 33320 83	0.52368 27996 21	0.52704 38121 76
29	1.30588 87435 21	0.86387 60768 42	0.50370 44012 72	0.50729 62702 60
30	1.35091 93898 50	0.87494 55901 00	0.48422 12452 64	0.48805 25135 58
31	1.39595 00361 78	0.88517 83704 96	0.46525 18161 23	0.46933 13698 79
32	1.44098 06825 06	0.89462 89584 97	0.44680 98327 24	0.45114 69334 99
33	1.48601 13288 35	0.90334 97222 95	0.42890 47437 72	0.43350 90602 62
34	1.53104 19751 63	0.91139 07053 76	0.41154 21997 26	0.41642 38392 19
35	1.57607 26214 91	0.91879 95272 22	0.39472 44973 10	0.39989 40369 80
36	1.62110 32678 20	0.92562 13291 65	0.37845 09941 77	0.38391 95123 22
37	1.66613 39141 48	0.93189 87580 57	0.36271 84924 05	0.36849 75997 62
38	1.71116 45604 76	0.93767 19811 22	0.34752 15904 35	0.35362 34617 04
39	1.75619 52068 05	0.94297 87260 95	0.33285 30037 90	0.33929 04094 86
40	1.80122 58531 33	0.94785 43414 06	0.31870 38554 49	0.32549 01942 13
41	1.84625 64994 61	0.95233 18719 05	0.30506 39371 57	0.31221 32686 64
42	1.89128 71457 90	0.95644 21462 14	0.29192 19432 42	0.29944 90218 18
43	1.93631 77921 18	0.96021 38723 81	0.27926 56786 76	0.28718 59877 65
44	1.98134 84384 46	0.96367 37390 56	0.26708 22432 39	0.27541 20308 25
45	2.02637 90847 75	0.96684 65198 45	0.25535 81936 47	0.26411 45087 72

q = 0.29548 83855 58691 4   D(90) = 3.78623 65253 90837
q′= 0.00030 48651 48813 9401   1/D(90) = 0.26411 45087 72474

r	ϕ	$E(\phi,k)$	A(r)	D(r)
0	0.00000 00000 00	0.00000 00000 00	0.00000 00000 00	1.00000 00000 00
1	0.04501 55094 96	0.04500 03818 21	0.01189 42847 41	1.00076 14948 26
2	0.08994 03815 37	0.08981 97623 83	0.02379 47903 18	1.00304 53670 90
3	0.13468 48915 33	0.13428 00479 33	0.03570 77105 80	1.00684 97793 82
4	0.17916 11183 48	0.17820 88610 44	0.04763 91854 62	1.01217 16668 13
5	0.22328 37913 36	0.22144 21577 62	0.05959 52741 84	1.01900 67332 24
6	0.26697 10744 83	0.26382 65710 31	0.07158 19286 40	1.02734 94459 44
7	0.31014 52710 68	0.30522 14134 92	0.08360 49670 37	1.03719 30291 42
8	0.35273 34355 76	0.34550 02909 82	0.09567 00478 43	1.04852 94558 49
9	0.39466 78833 32	0.38455 22977 93	0.10778 26441 10	1.06134 94387 25
10	0.43588 65922 37	0.42228 27845 74	0.11994 80182 38	1.07564 24196 96
11	0.47633 34947 67	0.45861 37084 18	0.13217 11972 26	1.09139 65585 41
12	0.51595 86619 94	0.49348 35908 83	0.14445 69484 86	1.10859 87205 90
13	0.55471 83845 03	0.52684 71228 48	0.15680 97562 75	1.12723 44636 51
14	0.59257 51576 94	0.55867 44646 80	0.16923 37987 92	1.14728 80243 28
15	0.62949 75809 45	0.58895 02960 75	0.18173 29260 24	1.16874 23038 93
16	0.66546 01815 29	0.61767 26723 57	0.19431 06383 70	1.19157 88538 87
17	0.70044 31749 42	0.64485 17433 75	0.20697 00661 19	1.21577 78616 31
18	0.73443 21735 91	0.67050 83879 53	0.21971 39498 32	1.24131 81358 38
19	0.76741 78555 27	0.69467 28118 27	0.23254 46216 69	1.26817 70925 35
20	0.79939 56043 93	0.71738 31506 37	0.24546 39877 46	1.29633 07414 92
21	0.83036 51308 07	0.73868 41125 98	0.25847 35115 29	1.32575 36733 67
22	0.86033 00844 00	0.75862 56882 90	0.27157 41983 56	1.35641 90477 96
23	0.88929 76644 90	0.77726 19480 82	0.28476 65811 06	1.38829 85826 29
24	0.91727 82361 83	0.79464 99413 28	0.29805 07070 78	1.42136 25445 53
25	0.94428 49574 58	0.81084 87057 76	0.31142 61261 09	1.45557 97412 97
26	0.97033 34216 35	0.82591 83908 26	0.32489 18799 90	1.49091 75156 67
27	0.99544 13185 65	0.83991 94943 11	0.33844 64932 04	1.52734 17416 01
28	1.01962 81169 08	0.85291 22093 29	0.35208 79650 29	1.56481 68224 87
29	1.04291 47690 26	0.86495 58753 82	0.36581 37630 43	1.60330 56919 30
30	1.06532 34393 16	0.87610 85264 08	0.37962 08180 49	1.64276 98171 87
31	1.08687 72561 82	0.88642 65272 80	0.39350 55204 74	1.68316 92054 64
32	1.10760 00873 83	0.89596 42898 27	0.40746 37182 32	1.72446 24132 61
33	1.12751 63381 05	0.90477 40592 92	0.42149 07161 06	1.76660 65589 53
34	1.14665 07708 18	0.91290 57623 05	0.43558 12766 42	1.80955 73387 68
35	1.16502 83457 67	0.92040 69078 70	0.44972 96225 84	1.85326 90463 24
36	1.18267 40808 11	0.92732 25333 93	0.46392 94408 59	1.89769 45958 75
37	1.19961 29292 35	0.93369 51884 44	0.47817 38881 08	1.94278 55493 84
38	1.21586 96741 24	0.93956 49496 25	0.49245 55977 80	1.98849 21475 61
39	1.23146 88379 03	0.94496 94606 69	0.50676 66887 83	2.03476 33449 45
40	1.24643 46056 34	0.94994 39925 40	0.52109 87756 73	2.08154 68491 31
41	1.26079 07607 63	0.95452 15190 49	0.53544 29803 96	2.12878 91642 07
42	1.27456 06320 39	0.95873 28040 63	0.54978 99455 47	2.17643 56384 38
43	1.28776 70503 99	0.96260 64970 15	0.56412 98491 35	2.22443 05162 58
44	1.30043 23147 35	0.96616 92339 20	0.57845 24208 30	2.27271 69945 41
45	1.31257 81654 79	0.96944 57415 81	0.59274 69596 63	2.32123 72831 93

K = 4.05275 81695 49437   E = 1.00864 79569 07096
K′= 1.57271 24349 95227   E′= 1.56888 37196 07763

r	u=(r/90)K=F(φ,k)	sn u	cn u	dn u
45	2.02637 90847 75	0.96684 65198 45	0.25535 81936 47	0.26411 45087 72
46	2.07140 97311 03	0.96975 51789 55	0.24407 96855 35	0.25328 04160 19
47	2.11644 03774 31	0.97242 09765 58	0.23323 25971 01	0.24289 65085 90
48	2.16147 10237 60	0.97486 35726 68	0.22280 26361 72	0.23294 94126 27
49	2.20650 16700 88	0.97710 11285 42	0.21277 54323 27	0.22342 57180 76
50	2.25153 23164 16	0.97915 04048 83	0.20313 66156 49	0.21431 20591 17
51	2.29656 29627 45	0.98102 68562 99	0.19387 18835 22	0.20559 51827 52
52	2.34159 36090 73	0.98274 47216 31	0.18496 70568 14	0.19726 20069 04
53	2.38662 42554 01	0.98431 71099 05	0.17640 81266 49	0.18929 96692 22
54	2.43165 49017 30	0.98575 60817 59	0.16818 12928 82	0.18169 55677 04
55	2.47668 55480 58	0.98707 27262 91	0.16027 29952 68	0.17443 73941 43
56	2.52171 61943 86	0.98827 72333 52	0.15266 99382 28	0.16751 31612 90
57	2.56674 68407 15	0.98937 89613 36	0.14535 91100 19	0.16091 12245 59
58	2.61177 74870 43	0.99038 65005 97	0.13832 77970 44	0.15462 02989 86
59	2.65680 81333 71	0.99130 77326 21	0.13156 35939 19	0.14862 94720 98
60	2.70183 87797 00	0.99214 98851 31	0.12505 44099 00	0.14292 82132 69
61	2.74686 94260 28	0.99291 95832 92	0.11878 84721 52	0.13750 63800 65
62	2.79190 00723 56	0.99362 28972 28	0.11275 43263 18	0.13235 42220 45
63	2.83693 07186 85	0.99426 53860 29	0.10694 08347 83	0.12746 23823 94
64	2.88196 13650 13	0.99485 21384 48	0.10133 71729 71	0.12282 18977 65
65	2.92699 20113 41	0.99538 78104 96	0.09593 28239 79	0.11842 41966 19
66	2.97202 26576 70	0.99587 66601 16	0.09071 75718 18	0.11426 10963 38
67	3.01705 33039 98	0.99632 25791 25	0.08568 14934 79	0.11032 47993 49
68	3.06208 39503 26	0.99672 91226 06	0.08081 49500 32	0.10660 78884 66
69	3.10711 45966 55	0.99709 95359 13	0.07610 85769 26	0.10310 33216 23
70	3.15214 52429 83	0.99743 67794 66	0.07155 32736 37	0.09980 44261 60
71	3.19717 58893 11	0.99774 35514 76	0.06714 01927 92	0.09670 48927 96
72	3.24220 65356 40	0.99802 23087 51	0.06286 07288 79	0.09379 87694 01
73	3.28723 71819 68	0.99827 52857 20	0.05870 65066 29	0.09108 04546 73
74	3.33226 78282 96	0.99850 45117 95	0.05466 93691 57	0.08854 46918 09
75	3.37729 84746 25	0.99871 18271 98	0.05074 13659 15	0.08618 65622 33
76	3.42232 91209 53	0.99889 88973 47	0.04691 47405 22	0.08400 14794 62
77	3.46735 97672 81	0.99906 72259 23	0.04318 19185 08	0.08198 51831 48
78	3.51239 04136 10	0.99921 81666 85	0.03953 54950 15	0.08013 37333 56
79	3.55742 10599 38	0.99935 29341 39	0.03596 82224 73	0.07844 35051 10
80	3.60245 17062 66	0.99947 26131 23	0.03247 29982 85	0.07691 11832 40
81	3.64748 23525 94	0.99957 81673 87	0.02904 28525 31	0.07553 37575 67
82	3.69251 29989 23	0.99967 04472 28	0.02567 09357 02	0.07430 85184 39
83	3.73754 36452 51	0.99975 01962 29	0.02235 05064 85	0.07323 30526 46
84	3.78257 42915 79	0.99981 80571 70	0.01907 49195 75	0.07230 52397 27
85	3.82760 49379 08	0.99987 45771 33	0.01583 76135 55	0.07152 32486 83
86	3.87263 55842 36	0.99992 02118 57	0.01263 20988 07	0.07088 55351 09
87	3.91766 62305 64	0.99995 53293 66	0.00945 19454 76	0.07039 08387 55
88	3.96269 68768 93	0.99998 02129 01	0.00629 07714 63	0.07003 81815 16
89	4.00772 75232 21	0.99999 50631 82	0.00314 22304 59	0.06982 68658 67
90	4.05275 81695 49	1.00000 00000 00	0.00000 00000 00	0.06975 64737 44

ELLIPTIC FUNCTIONS   TABLE $\theta = 86°$

$q = 0.29548\ 83855\ 58691\ 4$
$q' = 0.00030\ 48651\ 48813\ 9401$

$D(90) = 3.78623\ 65253\ 90837$
$1/D(90) = 0.26411\ 45087\ 72474$

r	ϕ	$E(\phi,k)$	$A(r)$	$D(r)$
45	1.31257 81654 79	0.96944 57415 81	0.59274 69596 63	2.32123 72831 93
46	1.32422 57650 96	0.97245 89430 81	0.60700 23531 50	2.36993 26699 87
47	1.33539 56845 93	0.97523 00630 16	0.62120 70977 90	2.41874 35896 45
48	1.34610 78952 93	0.97777 87312 42	0.63534 93209 13	2.46760 96970 57
49	1.35638 17651 42	0.98012 30841 81	0.64941 68038 11	2.51646 99445 79
50	1.36623 60589 41	0.98227 98629 36	0.66339 70061 17	2.56526 26632 92
51	1.37568 89419 24	0.98426 45076 95	0.67727 70913 67	2.61392 56480 90
52	1.38475 79861 81	0.98609 12480 27	0.69104 39536 88	2.66239 62464 64
53	1.39346 01794 88	0.98777 31888 26	0.70468 42455 39	2.71061 14508 00
54	1.40181 19361 45	0.98932 23917 71	0.71818 44064 54	2.75850 79940 16
55	1.40982 91094 77	0.99074 99522 30	0.73153 06926 90	2.80602 24483 31
56	1.41752 70056 99	0.99206 60716 43	0.74470 92077 26	2.85309 13269 39
57	1.42492 03988 74	0.99328 01254 50	0.75770 59335 13	2.89965 11883 57
58	1.43202 35467 44	0.99440 07266 66	0.77050 67624 07	2.94563 87431 85
59	1.43885 02072 27	0.99543 57852 70	0.78309 75296 84	2.99099 09630 12
60	1.44541 36554 13	0.99639 25635 55	0.79546 40465 60	3.03564 51911 76
61	1.45172 67009 13	0.99727 77276 39	0.80759 21336 09	3.07953 92550 84
62	1.45780 17054 35	0.99809 73953 18	0.81946 76544 93	3.12261 15797 79
63	1.46365 06004 77	0.99885 71804 79	0.83107 65499 11	3.16480 13024 33
64	1.46928 49050 56	0.99956 22342 47	0.84240 48716 49	3.20604 83874 32
65	1.47471 57433 94	1.00021 72830 96	0.85343 88166 51	3.24629 37417 14
66	1.47995 38625 02	1.00082 66640 99	0.86416 47609 98	3.28547 93300 07
67	1.48500 96496 06	1.00139 43575 15	0.87456 92936 95	3.32354 82896 31
68	1.48989 31493 88	1.00192 40169 05	0.88463 92501 60	3.36044 50444 79
69	1.49461 40809 94	1.00241 89969 34	0.89436 17453 19	3.39611 54178 44
70	1.49918 18548 01	1.00288 23790 57	0.90372 42061 99	3.43050 67437 18
71	1.50360 55889 16	1.00331 69952 25	0.91271 44039 15	3.46356 79762 01
72	1.50789 41254 02	1.00372 54497 73	0.92132 04849 58	3.49524 97966 73
73	1.51205 60462 14	1.00411 01396 44	0.92953 10016 76	3.52550 47183 61
74	1.51609 96888 59	1.00447 32730 60	0.93733 49418 60	3.55428 71879 60
75	1.52003 31617 64	1.00481 68867 99	0.94472 17573 28	3.58155 36839 73
76	1.52386 43593 70	1.00514 28621 77	0.95168 13914 29	3.60726 28114 13
77	1.52760 09769 51	1.00545 29398 48	0.95820 43053 60	3.63137 53925 72
78	1.53125 05251 67	1.00574 87335 47	0.96428 15032 34	3.65385 45535 20
79	1.53482 03443 77	1.00603 17428 54	0.96990 45557 86	3.67466 58060 53
80	1.53831 76186 94	1.00630 33650 81	0.97506 56226 70	3.69377 71247 88
81	1.54174 93898 34	1.00656 49063 82	0.97975 74732 49	3.71115 90191 46
82	1.54512 25707 45	1.00681 75921 44	0.98397 35058 25	3.72678 45999 69
83	1.54844 39590 44	1.00706 25767 63	0.98770 77652 34	3.74062 96405 31
84	1.55172 02502 88	1.00730 09528 62	0.99095 49587 52	3.75267 26317 22
85	1.55495 80510 74	1.00753 37600 32	0.99371 04702 62	3.76289 48312 27
86	1.55816 38920 13	1.00776 19931 52	0.99597 03726 26	3.77128 03064 98
87	1.56134 42405 75	1.00798 66103 67	0.99773 14382 30	3.77781 59713 92
88	1.56450 55138 40	1.00820 85407 75	0.99899 11476 52	3.78249 16163 16
89	1.56765 40911 65	1.00842 86918 85	0.99974 76964 47	3.78529 99318 02
90	1.57079 63267 95	1.00864 79569 07	1.00000 00000 00	3.78623 65253 91

345

K = 4.33865 39759 99725   E = 1.00525 85872 09152
K' = 1.57187 36105 14009   E' = 1.56972 01504 23979

r	u=(r/90)K=F(ϕ,k)	sn u	cn u	dn u
0	0.00000 00000 00	0.00000 00000 00	1.00000 00000 00	1.00000 00000 00
1	0.04820 72664 00	0.04817 00085 22	0.99883 91513 55	0.99884 23328 22
2	0.09641 45328 00	0.09611 72967 40	0.99537 00142 50	0.99538 27254 36
3	0.14462 17992 00	0.14362 32444 91	0.98963 24386 57	0.98966 09842 86
4	0.19282 90656 00	0.19047 72725 34	0.98169 16056 73	0.98174 22196 41
5	0.24103 63320 00	0.23648 04751 48	0.97163 62410 25	0.97171 50615 99
6	0.28924 35984 00	0.28144 88157 62	0.95957 62419 46	0.95968 92902 66
7	0.33745 08648 00	0.32521 57843 79	0.94563 98329 13	0.94579 29954 80
8	0.38565 81312 00	0.36763 44480 45	0.92997 03826 52	0.93016 93982 63
9	0.43386 53976 00	0.40857 88601 21	0.91272 30220 95	0.91297 34735 34
10	0.48207 26640 00	0.44794 48277 89	0.89406 12010 69	0.89436 85116 43
11	0.53027 99304 00	0.48565 00676 44	0.87415 33113 80	0.87452 27462 38
12	0.57848 71968 00	0.52163 38044 03	0.85316 94873 26	0.85360 61593 27
13	0.62669 44632 00	0.55585 58866 56	0.83127 86736 53	0.83178 75534 41
14	0.67490 17296 00	0.58829 55056 48	0.80864 60276 50	0.80923 19574 99
15	0.72310 89960 00	0.61894 96085 73	0.78543 06984 37	0.78609 84093 64
16	0.77131 62624 00	0.64783 10975 17	0.76178 40042 23	0.76253 81358 46
17	0.81952 35288 00	0.67496 69000 20	0.73784 80086 56	0.73869 31312 78
18	0.86773 07952 00	0.70039 59885 27	0.71375 44810 76	0.71469 51194 79
19	0.91593 80616 00	0.72416 74149 68	0.68962 42129 59	0.69066 48714 50
20	0.96414 53280 00	0.74633 84145 35	0.66556 66540 55	0.66671 18423 49
21	1.01235 25944 00	0.76697 26203 49	0.64167 98264 20	0.64293 40860 02
22	1.06055 98608 00	0.78613 84189 41	0.61805 04722 64	0.61941 84029 28
23	1.10876 71272 00	0.80390 74657 79	0.59475 43917 16	0.59624 06780 60
24	1.15697 43936 00	0.82035 33708 59	0.57185 69287 16	0.57346 63664 05
25	1.20518 16600 00	0.83555 05567 20	0.54941 35666 00	0.55115 10882 80
26	1.25338 89264 00	0.84957 32852 10	0.52747 05992 35	0.52934 13000 18
27	1.30159 61928 00	0.86249 48448 12	0.50606 58481 58	0.50807 50106 55
28	1.34980 34592 00	0.87438 68871 60	0.48522 94009 67	0.48738 25198 57
29	1.39801 07256 00	0.88531 88993 67	0.46498 43507 30	0.46728 71569 13
30	1.44621 79920 00	0.89535 77977 56	0.44534 75204 79	0.44780 60048 47
31	1.49442 52584 00	0.90456 76282 86	0.42633 01606 22	0.42895 05975 39
32	1.54263 25248 00	0.91300 93592 54	0.40793 86104 73	0.41072 75810 38
33	1.59083 97912 00	0.92074 07525 69	0.39017 49179 00	0.39313 93330 97
34	1.63904 70576 00	0.92781 63008 70	0.37303 74134 59	0.37618 45372 88
35	1.68725 43240 00	0.93428 72188 89	0.35652 12372 64	0.35985 87099 66
36	1.73546 15904 00	0.94020 14787 20	0.34061 88183 47	0.34415 46798 29
37	1.78366 88568 00	0.94560 38798 51	0.32532 03074 07	0.32906 30209 78
38	1.83187 61232 00	0.95053 61460 51	0.31061 39646 75	0.31457 24412 03
39	1.88008 33896 00	0.95503 70423 27	0.29648 65052 31	0.30067 01278 25
40	1.92829 06560 00	0.95914 25061 95	0.28292 34044 92	0.28734 20538 22
41	1.97649 79224 00	0.96288 57884 93	0.26990 91667 93	0.27457 32471 47
42	2.02470 51888 00	0.96629 75997 56	0.25742 75601 12	0.26234 80263 00
43	2.07291 24552 00	0.96940 62589 77	0.24546 18199 58	0.25065 02051 63
44	2.12111 97216 00	0.97223 78421 43	0.23399 48253 82	0.23946 32700 56
45	2.16932 69880 00	0.97481 63285 67	0.22300 92499 42	0.22877 05318 50

346

q = 0.32040 03371 34866 4   D(90) = 4.37119 23555 58983
q' = 0.00017 14256 42257 4727   1/D(90) = 0.22877 05318 50027

r	ϕ	$E(\phi,k)$	A(r)	D(r)
0	0.00000 00000 00	0.00000 00000 00	0.00000 00000 00	1.00000 00000 00
1	0.04818 86565 45	0.04817 00596 18	0.01102 97158 42	1.00089 26934 41
2	0.09626 59125 84	0.09611 77043 73	0.02206 73088 58	1.00357 01695 46
3	0.14412 16529 50	0.14362 46139 25	0.03312 06260 37	1.00803 06141 01
4	0.19164 82972 13	0.19048 04978 42	0.04419 74540 67	1.01427 09982 37
5	0.23874 19790 67	0.23648 67232 20	0.05530 54893 38	1.02228 70706 97
6	0.28530 36251 68	0.28145 95059 32	0.06645 23081 33	1.03207 33471 03
7	0.33123 99088 96	0.32523 25644 19	0.07764 53370 73	1.04362 30963 01
8	0.37646 40524 77	0.36765 91673 47	0.08889 18238 72	1.05692 83238 99
9	0.42089 64855 34	0.40861 35409 49	0.10019 88084 67	1.07197 97531 29
10	0.46446 53188 07	0.44799 16354 85	0.11157 30945 89	1.08876 68031 83
11	0.50710 66682 34	0.48571 12806 22	0.12302 12218 34	1.10727 75652 21
12	0.54876 48143 36	0.52171 17846 93	0.13454 94382 90	1.12749 87762 20
13	0.58939 22147 03	0.55595 30516 70	0.14616 36738 04	1.14941 57909 10
14	0.62894 93831 66	0.58841 43016 96	0.15786 95139 21	1.17301 25520 26
15	0.66740 46528 57	0.61909 24865 65	0.16967 21745 82	1.19827 15591 22
16	0.70473 38419 21	0.64800 04911 31	0.18157 64776 33	1.22517 38362 37
17	0.74091 98411 22	0.67516 52065 23	0.19358 68272 04	1.25369 88986 93
18	0.77595 21422 56	0.70062 55523 14	0.20570 71870 20	1.28382 47193 23
19	0.80982 63252 33	0.72443 05137 97	0.21794 10587 14	1.31552 76944 56
20	0.84254 35201 18	0.74663 72483 67	0.23029 14611 83	1.34878 26099 67
21	0.87410 98585 39	0.76730 93026 43	0.24276 09110 66	1.38356 26077 47
22	0.90453 59267 76	0.78651 49702 08	0.25535 14043 83	1.41983 91529 13
23	0.93383 62307 39	0.80432 58091 76	0.26806 43994 09	1.45758 20021 29
24	0.96202 86809 43	0.82081 53295 95	0.28090 08008 25	1.49675 91733 67
25	0.98913 41036 94	0.83605 78530 34	0.29386 09452 03	1.53733 69174 82
26	1.01517 57829 09	0.85012 75406 90	0.30694 45878 85	1.57927 96919 36
27	1.04017 90354 89	0.86309 75818 46	0.32015 08912 94	1.62255 01370 42
28	1.06417 08218 41	0.87503 95312 97	0.33347 84147 30	1.66710 90550 64
29	1.08717 93920 80	0.88602 27824 23	0.34692 51057 05	1.71291 53925 15
30	1.10923 39675 38	0.89611 41614 88	0.36048 82928 39	1.75992 62260 03
31	1.13036 44565 86	0.90537 76284 85	0.37416 46803 83	1.80809 67519 36
32	1.15060 12032 21	0.91387 40701 50	0.38795 03443 83	1.85738 02804 06
33	1.16997 47665 48	0.92166 11714 26	0.40184 07305 36	1.90772 82335 66
34	1.18851 57350 39	·0.92879 33526 83	0.41583 06537 55	1.95909 01487 67
35	1.20625 45313 44	0.93532 17611 24	0.42991 42994 78	2.01141 36867 42
36	1.22322 13313 53	0.94129 43060 23	0.44408 52267 40	2.06464 46450 86
37	1.23944 58852 56	0.94675 57286 91	0.45833 63730 25	2.11872 69772 62
38	1.25495 74483 88	0.95174 76992 62	0.47266 00609 14	2.17360 28173 47
39	1.26978 46937 60	0.95630 89335 20	0.48704 80065 32	2.22921 25107 08
40	1.28395 56462 96	0.96047 53240 28	0.50149 13298 08	2.28549 46507 68
41	1.29749 76309 27	0.96428 00807 84	0.51598 05665 33	2.34238 61220 12
42	1.31043 72328 37	0.96775 38774 46	0.53050 56822 28	2.39982 21493 27
43	1.32280 02683 20	0.97092 49999 32	0.54505 60877 83	2.45773 63537 79
44	1.33461 17648 29	0.97381 94948 10	0.55962 06568 77	2.51606 08148 75
45	1.34589 59489 43	0.97646 13154 83	0.57418 77451 40	2.57472 61393 35

347

K = 4.33865 39759 99725   E = 1.00525 85872 09152
K'= 1.57187 36105 14009   E'= 1.56972 01504 23979

r	u=(r/90)K=F(φ,k)	sn u	cn u	dn u
45	2.16932 69880 00	0.97481 63285 67	0.22300 92499 42	0.22877 05318 50
46	2.21753 42544 00	0.97716 37434 30	0.21248 76902 93	0.21855 52558 05
47	2.26574 15208 00	0.97930 02953 97	0.20241 27748 80	0.20880 07716 13
48	2.31394 87872 00	0.98124 45084 58	0.19276 72550 53	0.19949 05659 52
49	2.36215 60536 00	0.98301 33474 32	0.18353 40806 77	0.19060 83596 52
50	2.41036 33200 00	0.98462 23367 90	0.17469 64621 69	0.18213 81713 78
51	2.45857 05864 00	0.98608 56726 12	0.16623 79206 71	0.17406 43695 52
52	2.50677 78528 00	0.98741 63276 57	0.15814 23279 07	0.16637 17140 73
53	2.55498 51192 00	0.98862 61496 05	0.15039 39371 00	0.15904 53892 00
54	2.60319 23856 00	0.98972 59526 35	0.14297 74061 89	0.15207 10288 44
55	2.65139 96520 00	0.99072 56025 52	0.13587 78144 09	0.14543 47353 38
56	2.69960 69184 00	0.99163 40957 25	0.12908 06732 09	0.13912 30926 72
57	2.74781 41848 00	0.99245 96321 27	0.12257 19323 42	0.13312 31750 09
58	2.79602 14512 00	0.99320 96827 84	0.11633 79818 68	0.12742 25512 46
59	2.84422 87176 00	0.99389 10519 50	0.11036 56506 94	0.12200 92862 52
60	2.89243 59840 00	0.99450 99343 44	0.10464 22022 44	0.11687 19393 59
61	2.94064 32504 00	0.99507 19677 42	0.09915 53277 10	0.11199 95605 89
62	2.98885 05168 00	0.99558 22812 62	0.09389 31373 23	0.10738 16850 43
63	3.03705 77832 00	0.99604 55396 27	0.08884 41500 00	0.10300 83258 29
64	3.08526 50496 00	0.99646 59837 00	0.08399 72816 75	0.09886 99658 26
65	3.13347 23160 00	0.99684 74675 71	0.07934 18325 85	0.09495 75485 85
66	3.18167 95824 00	0.99719 34924 46	0.07486 74737 29	0.09126 24685 75
67	3.22988 68488 00	0.99750 72375 99	0.07056 42327 01	0.08777 65609 91
68	3.27809 41152 00	0.99779 15885 98	0.06642 24790 55	0.08449 20912 84
69	3.32630 13816 00	0.99804 91630 34	0.06243 29093 32	0.08140 17445 68
70	3.37450 86480 00	0.99828 23339 53	0.05858 65318 78	0.07849 86150 22
71	3.42271 59144 00	0.99849 32511 64	0.05487 46515 26	0.07577 61953 83
72	3.47092 31808 00	0.99868 38606 04	0.05128 88542 39	0.07322 83666 37
73	3.51913 04472 00	0.99885 59219 16	0.04782 09917 61	0.07084 39879 62
74	3.56733 77136 00	0.99901 10243 83	0.04446 31663 37	0.06863 38869 92
75	3.61554 49800 00	0.99915 06013 51	0.04120 77155 29	0.06657 68504 55
76	3.66375 22464 00	0.99927 59432 65	0.03804 71971 68	0.06467 36152 20
77	3.71195 95128 00	0.99938 82094 22	0.03497 43744 55	0.06291 98597 96
78	3.76016 67792 00	0.99948 84385 55	0.03198 22012 34	0.06131 15963 04
79	3.80837 40456 00	0.99957 75583 20	0.02906 38074 30	0.05984 51629 40
80	3.85658 13120 00	0.99965 63937 91	0.02621 24846 76	0.05851 72169 66
81	3.90478 85784 00	0.99972 56750 11	0.02342 16721 13	0.05732 47282 21
82	3.95299 58448 00	0.99978 60436 91	0.02068 49423 58	0.05626 49731 77
83	4.00120 31112 00	0.99983 80591 02	0.01799 59876 44	0.05533 55295 43
84	4.04941 03776 00	0.99988 22032 07	0.01534 86061 12	0.05453 42714 29
85	4.09761 76440 00	0.99991 88850 96	0.01273 66882 42	0.05385 93650 66
86	4.14582 49104 00	0.99994 84447 48	0.01015 42034 16	0.05330 92650 96
87	4.19403 21768 00	0.99997 11561 54	0.00759 51865 93	0.05288 27114 27
88	4.24223 94432 00	0.99998 72298 50	0.00505 37250 73	0.05257 87266 60
89	4.29044 67096 00	0.99999 68148 45	0.00252 39453 47	0.05239 66140 83
90	4.33865 39760 00	1.00000 00000 00	0.00000 00000 00	0.05233 59562 43

q = 0.32040 03371 34866 4
q'= 0.00017 14256 42257 4727

D(90) = 4.37119 23555 58983
1/D(90) = 0.22877 05318 50027

r	ϕ	$E(\phi,k)$	A(r)	D(r)
45	1.34589 59489 43	0.97646 13154 83	0.57418 77451 40	2.57472 61393 35
46	1.35667 62411 22	0.97887 24646 05	0.58874 52110 26	2.63366 15363 73
47	1.36697 52562 42	0.98107 31315 77	0.60328 04383 75	2.69279 48994 57
48	1.37681 48089 90	0.98308 18242 85	0.61778 03606 04	2.75205 28944 72
49	1.38621 59233 56	0.98491 54945 23	0.63223 14865 00	2.81136 10542 02
50	1.39519 88455 00	0.98658 96567 40	0.64661 99275 43	2.87064 38789 97
51	1.40378 30594 13	0.98811 84999 58	0.66093 14267 17	2.92982 49434 65
52	1.41198 73048 15	0.98951 49928 03	0.67515 13887 24	2.98882 70090 05
53	1.41982 95968 54	0.99079 09817 48	0.68926 49115 55	3.04757 21419 54
54	1.42732 72472 06	0.99195 72826 98	0.70325 68193 17	3.10598 18371 00
55	1.43449 68862 21	0.99302 37661 59	0.71711 16962 47	3.16397 71462 89
56	1.44135 44858 47	0.99399 94362 35	0.73081 39218 30	3.22147 88118 02
57	1.44791 53830 74	0.99489 25037 56	0.74434 77069 08	3.27840 74041 78
58	1.45419 43036 85	0.99571 04538 34	0.75769 71307 09	3.33468 34641 23
59	1.46020 53861 49	0.99646 01081 89	0.77084 61786 74	3.39022 76481 09
60	1.46596 22055 05	0.99714 76825 45	0.78377 87809 77	3.44496 08772 54
61	1.47147 77971 16	0.99777 88394 33	0.79647 88516 45	3.49880 44890 59
62	1.47676 46801 92	0.99835 87367 07	0.80893 03281 35	3.55168 03915 41
63	1.48183 48810 14	0.99889 20720 78	0.82111 72112 82	3.60351 12192 94
64	1.48669 99557 78	0.99938 31239 63	0.83302 36054 65	3.65422 04909 88
65	1.49137 10130 30	0.99983 57889 20	0.84463 37589 00	3.70373 27678 11
66	1.49585 87356 36	1.00025 36159 37	0.85593 21039 09	3.75197 38123 28
67	1.50017 34022 79	1.00063 98378 26	0.86690 32970 52	3.79887 07472 47
68	1.50432 49084 53	1.00099 73999 52	0.87753 22589 97	3.84435 22135 45
69	1.50832 27869 46	1.00132 89865 19	0.88780 42139 81	3.88834 85274 31
70	1.51217 62278 20	1.00163 70446 16	0.89770 47287 63	3.93079 18355 93
71	1.51589 40978 74	1.00192 38062 21	0.90721 97509 15	3.97161 62681 99
72	1.51948 49596 10	1.00219 13083 24	0.91633 56463 33	4.01075 80891 06
73	1.52295 70897 01	1.00244 14113 54	0.92503 92358 55	4.04815 58427 39
74	1.52631 84969 94	1.00267 58160 49	0.93331 78308 38	4.08375 04971 32
75	1.52957 69400 41	1.00289 60789 13	0.94115 92675 99	4.11748 55825 80
76	1.53273 99441 90	1.00310 36263 96	0.94855 19405 80	4.14930 73254 29
77	1.53581 48182 63	1.00329 97679 10	0.95548 48341 43	4.17916 47764 95
78	1.53880 86708 24	1.00348 57078 06	0.96194 75528 68	4.20700 99336 27
79	1.54172 84260 86	1.00366 25564 00	0.96793 03502 55	4.23279 78579 84
80	1.54458 08394 48	1.00383 13401 57	0.97342 41557 38	4.25648 67835 66
81	1.54737 25127 30	1.00399 30111 19	0.97842 05999 00	4.27803 82195 95
82	1.55010 99090 86	1.00414 84556 59	0.98291 20378 13	4.29741 70453 64
83	1.55279 93676 59	1.00429 85026 39	0.98689 15704 10	4.31459 15971 80
84	1.55544 71179 82	1.00444 39310 50	0.99035 30638 26	4.32953 37470 88
85	1.55805 92941 63	1.00458 54771 94	0.99329 11666 21	4.34221 89730 52
86	1.56064 19488 74	1.00472 38414 80	0.99570 13248 47	4.35262 64203 44
87	1.56320 10671 77	1.00485 96948 95	0.99757 97948 74	4.36073 89538 93
88	1.56574 25802 10	1.00499 36852 02	0.99892 36539 61	4.36654 32013 94
89	1.56827 23787 68	1.00512 64429 31	0.99973 08085 14	4.37002 95870 14
90	1.57079 63267 95	1.00525 85872 09	1.00000 00000 00	4.37119 23555 59

349

K = 4.74271 72652 78886   E = 1.00258 40855 27552
K'= 1.57127 49523 72225   E'= 1.57031 79198 97448

r	u=(r/90)K=F(ϕ,k)	sn u	cn u	dn u
0	0.00000 00000 00	0.00000 00000 00	1.00000 00000 00	1.00000 00000 00
1	0.05269 68585 03	0.05264 81632 62	0.99861 31237 40	0.99861 48140 92
2	0.10539 37170 06	0.10500 54466 21	0.99447 16467 45	0.99447 83988 33
3	0.15809 05755 09	0.15678 73632 72	0.98763 23823 76	0.98764 75400 23
4	0.21078 74340 12	0.20772 19163 12	0.97818 79193 10	0.97821 47817 04
5	0.26348 42925 15	0.25755 51263 16	0.96626 36063 25	0.96630 54128 16
6	0.31618 11510 19	0.30605 57606 11	0.95201 35878 22	0.95207 35051 77
7	0.36887 80095 22	0.35301 90945 66	0.93561 61172 57	0.93569 72298 36
8	0.42157 48680 25	0.39826 96034 68	0.91726 84028 97	0.91737 37060 30
9	0.47427 17265 28	0.44166 25536 38	0.89718 12463 01	0.89731 36430 31
10	0.52696 85850 31	0.48308 45267 87	0.87557 37204 71	0.87573 60216 29
11	0.57966 54435 34	0.52245 29669 74	0.85266 81050 10	0.85286 30324 92
12	0.63236 23020 37	0.55971 48814 14	0.82868 52548 00	0.82891 54478 00
13	0.68505 91605 40	0.59484 48532 85	0.80384 05317 73	0.80410 85556 29
14	0.73775 60190 43	0.62784 25368 33	0.77834 03811 59	0.77864 87384 51
15	0.79045 28775 46	0.65872 98042 15	0.75237 95883 98	0.75273 07318 88
16	0.84314 97360 50	0.68754 77020 53	0.72613 92135 14	0.72653 55605 38
17	0.89584 65945 53	0.71435 33568 59	0.69978 51681 37	0.70022 91160 73
18	0.94854 34530 56	0.73921 69451 11	0.67346 73771 32	0.67396 13195 95
19	1.00124 03115 59	0.76221 88186 04	0.64731 94517 13	0.64786 57952 04
20	1.05393 71700 62	0.78344 68509 52	0.62145 87932 71	0.62205 99740 16
21	1.10663 40285 65	0.80299 40483 14	0.59598 70454 74	0.59664 55462 74
22	1.15933 08870 68	0.82095 64475 76	0.57099 08153 23	0.57170 91822 63
23	1.21202 77455 71	0.83743 13088 83	0.54654 25901 99	0.54732 34491 20
24	1.26472 46040 74	0.85251 55966 43	0.52270 17863 76	0.52354 78590 53
25	1.31742 14625 77	0.86630 47337 31	0.49951 58739 38	0.50042 99939 42
26	1.37011 83210 81	0.87889 16072 92	0.47702 15326 70	0.47800 66609 12
27	1.42281 51795 84	0.89036 58007 19	0.45524 58027 38	0.45630 50427 32
28	1.47551 20380 87	0.90081 30246 26	0.43420 72024 54	0.43534 38153 36
29	1.52820 88965 90	0.91031 47195 19	0.41391 67928 79	0.41513 42122 51
30	1.58090 57550 93	0.91894 78037 58	0.39437 91753 73	0.39568 10220 33
31	1.63360 26135 96	0.92678 45422 50	0.37559 34134 75	0.37698 35101 15
32	1.68629 94720 99	0.93389 25134 53	0.35755 38747 05	0.35903 62606 56
33	1.73899 63306 02	0.94033 46547 86	0.34025 09911 94	0.34182 99372 94
34	1.79169 31891 05	0.94616 93690 59	0.32367 19404 82	0.32535 19641 63
35	1.84439 00476 08	0.95145 06769 72	0.30780 12496 56	0.30958 71303 21
36	1.89708 69061 12	0.95622 84030 90	0.29262 13271 87	0.29451 81219 67
37	1.94978 37646 15	0.96054 83847 80	0.27811 29275 96	0.28012 59875 61
38	2.00248 06231 18	0.96445 26955 33	0.26425 55544 91	0.26639 05414 02
39	2.05517 74816 21	0.96797 98757 13	0.25102 78076 52	0.25329 07113 32
40	2.10787 43401 24	0.97116 51652 63	0.23840 76797 85	0.24080 48361 74
41	2.16057 11986 27	0.97404 07340 77	0.22637 28083 46	0.22891 09183 39
42	2.21326 80571 30	0.97663 59068 16	0.21490 06875 70	0.21758 68366 89
43	2.26596 49156 33	0.97897 73797 65	0.20396 88454 38	0.20681 05244 37
44	2.31866 17741 36	0.98108 94280 60	0.19355 49899 85	0.19656 01164 40
45	2.37135 86326 39	0.98299 41021 67	0.18363 71288 87	0.18681 40698 73

q = 0.35316 56482 96037 1   D(90) = 5.35291 58734 13650
q' = 0.00007 61698 24679 77407   1/D(90) = 0.18681 40698 72965

r	ϕ	$E(\phi,k)$	A(r)	D(r)
0	0.00000 00000 00	0.00000 00000 00	0.00000 00000 00	1.00000 00000 00
1	0.05267 25156 01	0.05264 81929 35	0.00984 61866 48	1.00109 49202 26
2	0.10519 93779 38	0.10500 56832 18	0.01970 23988 45	1.00437 91719 14
3	0.15743 69399 50	0.15678 81573 99	0.02957 86286 56	1.00985 12248 70
4	0.20924 55000 57	0.20772 37843 26	0.03948 48012 24	1.01750 85180 26
5	0.26049 11117 21	0.25755 87393 50	0.04943 07414 52	1.02734 74434 00
6	0.31104 72083 02	0.30606 19307 18	0.05942 61408 42	1.03936 33237 80
7	0.36079 59990 39	0.35302 87585 76	0.06948 05245 47	1.05355 03842 86
8	0.40962 96047 67	0.39828 38052 04	0.07960 32187 03	1.06990 17179 86
9	0.45745 09155 90	0.44168 24251 62	0.08980 33180 92	1.08840 92457 97
10	0.50417 41662 24	0.48311 12693 30	0.10008 96541 84	1.10906 36709 29
11	0.54972 52369 59	0.52248 78321 43	0.11047 07636 30	1.13185 44281 77
12	0.59404 16986 35	0.55975 91531 88	0.12095 48572 58	1.15676 96283 94
13	0.63707 26280 81	0.59489 98312 25	0.13154 97896 30	1.18379 59985 17
14	0.67877 82260 24	0.62790 95208 21	0.14226 30292 33	1.21291 88175 49
15	0.71912 92725 61	0.65881 00809 28	0.15310 16293 46	1.24412 18489 38
16	0.75810 64560 93	0.68764 25332 92	0.16407 21996 68	1.27738 72698 08
17	0.79569 96106 29	0.71446 39697 72	0.17518 08787 61	1.31269 55975 46
18	0.83190 68938 40	0.73934 45242 57	0.18643 33073 77	1.35002 56142 54
19	0.86673 39347 91	0.76236 44997 66	0.19783 46027 27	1.38935 42896 07
20	0.90019 29761 69	0.78361 17165 81	0.20938 93337 79	1.43065 67026 80
21	0.93230 20315 30	0.80317 91244 18	0.22110 14976 35	1.47390 59633 26
22	0.96308 40737 79	0.82116 27018 99	0.23297 44970 65	1.51907 31336 87
23	0.99256 62671 16	0.83765 96501 86	0.24501 11192 67	1.56612 71504 59
24	1.02077 92510 15	0.85276 68749 11	0.25721 35159 20	1.61503 47485 11
25	1.04775 64816 67	0.86657 97411 45	0.26958 31846 05	1.66576 03864 92
26	1.07353 36336 97	0.87919 10798 13	0.28212 09516 56	1.71826 61750 44
27	1.09814 80627 60	0.89069 04201 33	0.29482 69565 14	1.77251 18082 49
28	1.12163 83280 15	0.90116 34209 55	0.30770 06376 58	1.82845 44989 38
29	1.14404 37721 49	0.91069 14736 65	0.32074 07201 62	1.88604 89184 61
30	1.16540 41557 89	0.91935 14503 17	0.33394 52049 64	1.94524 71415 57
31	1.18575 93425 03	0.92721 55724 04	0.34731 13598 89	2.00599 85968 81
32	1.20514 90302 85	0.93435 13778 95	0.36083 57125 08	2.06825 00238 02
33	1.22361 25252 71	0.94082 17666 20	0.37451 40448 70	2.13194 54360 16
34	1.24118 85534 21	0.94668 51066 47	0.38834 13901 72	2.19702 60925 12
35	1.25791 51060 69	0.95199 53866 97	0.40231 20314 22	2.26343 04764 13
36	1.27382 93153 84	0.95680 24020 13	0.41641 95021 20	2.33109 42821 78
37	1.28896 73560 98	0.96115 19631 84	0.43065 65890 34	2.39995 04116 14
38	1.30336 43700 94	0.96508 61193 41	0.44501 53370 65	2.46992 89791 22
39	1.31705 44107 63	0.96864 33887 87	0.45948 70562 76	2.54095 73265 75
40	1.33007 04043 37	0.97185 89915 66	0.47406 23310 73	2.61296 00481 53
41	1.34244 41256 88	0.97476 50797 21	0.48873 10315 81	2.68585 90254 55
42	1.35420 61863 76	0.97739 09619 85	0.50348 23272 23	2.75957 34731 50
43	1.36538 60329 67	0.97976 33205 36	0.51830 47024 98	2.83401 99953 68
44	1.37601 19539 06	0.98190 64181 15	0.53318 59749 73	2.90911 26530 22
45	1.38611 10934 28	0.98384 22944 13	0.54811 33154 69	2.98476 30421 53

K = 4.74271 72652 78886
K'= 1.57127 49523 72225

E = 1.00258 40855 27552
E'= 1.57031 79198 97448

r	u=(r/90)K=F(φ,k)	sn u	cn u	dn u
45	2.37135 86326 39	0.98299 41021 67	0.18363 71288 87	0.18681 40698 73
46	2.42405 54911 43	0.98471 14129 27	0.17419 36659 36	0.17755 12618 46
47	2.47675 23496 46	0.98625 95048 95	0.16520 34775 79	0.16875 10671 79
48	2.52944 92081 49	0.98765 48179 09	0.15664 59723 76	0.16039 34191 68
49	2.58214 60666 52	0.98891 22370 79	0.14850 11358 73	0.15245 88558 54
50	2.63484 29251 55	0.99004 52315 37	0.14074 95630 95	0.14492 85539 98
51	2.68753 97836 58	0.99106 59823 75	0.13337 24805 89	0.13778 43526 87
52	2.74023 66421 61	0.99198 55003 11	0.12635 17596 77	0.13100 87682 50
53	2.79293 35006 64	0.99281 37336 27	0.11966 99223 77	0.12458 50019 36
54	2.84563 03591 67	0.99355 96670 00	0.11331 01412 49	0.11849 69416 12
55	2.89832 72176 70	0.99423 14118 05	0.10725 62342 28	0.11272 91585 61
56	2.95102 40761 74	0.99483 62884 94	0.10149 26553 78	0.10726 69003 01
57	3.00372 09346 77	0.99538 09016 49	0.09600 44823 57	0.10209 60802 29
58	3.05641 77931 80	0.99587 12082 51	0.09077 74012 41	0.09720 32647 59
59	3.10911 46516 83	0.99631 25797 20	0.08579 76893 11	0.09257 56585 26
60	3.16181 15101 86	0.99670 98582 26	0.08105 21962 42	0.08820 10881 47
61	3.21450 83686 89	0.99706 74077 54	0.07652 83241 29	0.08406 79849 37
62	3.26720 52271 92	0.99738 91603 79	0.07221 40066 66	0.08016 53669 42
63	3.31990 20856 95	0.99767 86581 46	0.06809 76877 66	0.07648 28205 57
64	3.37259 89441 98	0.99793 90909 74	0.06416 82998 56	0.07301 04819 79
65	3.42529 58027 01	0.99817 33309 06	0.06041 52420 20	0.06973 90186 94
66	3.47799 26612 05	0.99838 39630 66	0.05682 83581 71	0.06665 96111 49
67	3.53068 95197 08	0.99857 33136 01	0.05339 79153 46	0.06376 39347 60
68	3.58338 63782 11	0.99874 34748 96	0.05011 45822 46	0.06104 41423 46
69	3.63608 32367 14	0.99889 63283 07	0.04696 94080 79	0.05849 28470 86
70	3.68878 00952 17	0.99903 35646 56	0.04395 38017 77	0.05610 31060 67
71	3.74147 69537 20	0.99915 67026 78	0.04105 95116 20	0.05386 84044 76
72	3.79417 38122 23	0.99926 71056 21	0.03827 86052 97	0.05178 26404 69
73	3.84687 06707 26	0.99936 59961 78	0.03560 34504 28	0.04984 01107 60
74	3.89956 75292 29	0.99945 44698 89	0.03302 66955 45	0.04803 54969 50
75	3.95226 43877 32	0.99953 35071 69	0.03054 12515 47	0.04636 38526 02
76	4.00496 12462 36	0.99960 39840 86	0.02814 02736 07	0.04482 05910 82
77	4.05765 81047 39	0.99966 66819 99	0.02581 71435 32	0.04340 14741 64
78	4.11035 49632 42	0.99972 22961 63	0.02356 54525 56	0.04210 26014 11
79	4.16305 18217 45	0.99977 14433 91	0.02137 89845 54	0.04092 04003 14
80	4.21574 86802 48	0.99981 46688 57	0.01925 16996 37	0.03985 16172 00
81	4.26844 55387 51	0.99985 24521 15	0.01717 77181 30	0.03889 33089 04
82	4.32114 23972 54	0.99988 52123 92	0.01515 13048 84	0.03804 28351 86
83	4.37383 92557 57	0.99991 33132 22	0.01316 68539 07	0.03729 78519 01
84	4.42653 61142 60	0.99993 70664 61	0.01121 88732 80	0.03665 63049 10
85	4.47923 29727 63	0.99995 67357 38	0.00930 19703 32	0.03611 64247 24
86	4.53192 98312 66	0.99997 25393 70	0.00741 08370 36	0.03567 67218 77
87	4.58462 66897 70	0.99998 46527 77	0.00554 02356 06	0.03533 59830 18
88	4.63732 35482 73	0.99999 32104 22	0.00368 49842 51	0.03509 32677 31
89	4.69002 04067 76	0.99999 83073 03	0.00183 99430 63	0.03494 79060 49
90	4.74271 72652 79	1.00000 00000 00	0.00000 00000 00	0.03489 94967 03

q = 0.35316 56482 96037 1
q' = 0.00007 61698 24679 77407

D(90) = 5.35291 58734 13650
1/D(90) = 0.18681 40698 72965

r	ϕ	$E(\phi,k)$	A(r)	D(r)
45	1.38611 10934 28	0.98384 22944 13	0.54811 33154 69	2.98476 30421 53
46	1.39570 94712 11	0.98559 09510 35	0.56307 32704 20	3.06088 03833 90
47	1.40483 20066 35	0.98717 05247 67	0.57805 17864 04	3.13737 16225 18
48	1.41350 25466 81	0.98859 74490 76	0.59303 42367 79	3.21414 15421 36
49	1.42174 38966 34	0.98988 66040 59	0.60800 54504 15	3.29109 28843 01
50	1.42957 78529 04	0.99105 14551 44	0.62294 97424 51	3.36812 64840 09
51	1.43702 52373 39	0.99210 41810 05	0.63785 09470 28	3.44514 14133 27
52	1.44410 59325 61	0.99305 57912 09	0.65269 24519 31	3.52203 51359 02
53	1.45083 89178 86	0.99391 62341 57	0.66745 72350 59	3.59870 36715 54
54	1.45724 23054 82	0.99469 44959 12	0.68212 79026 49	3.67504 17705 76
55	1.46333 33764 89	0.99539 86905 32	0.69668 67291 49	3.75094 30973 28
56	1.46912 86168 60	0.99603 61424 82	0.71111 56986 52	3.82630 04226 69
57	1.47464 37527 33	0.99661 34617 33	0.72539 65477 77	3.90100 58246 86
58	1.47989 37851 96	0.99713 66120 95	0.73951 08098 70	3.97495 08971 80
59	1.48489 30243 12	0.99761 09733 36	0.75343 98604 28	4.04802 69652 71
60	1.48965 51223 30	0.99804 13975 88	0.76716 49635 85	4.12012 53074 88
61	1.49419 31060 12	0.99843 22605 25	0.78066 73195 43	4.19113 73836 29
62	1.49851 94080 26	0.99878 75077 65	0.79392 81127 99	4.26095 50676 65
63	1.50264 58973 82	0.99911 06969 08	0.80692 85610 09	4.32947 08849 06
64	1.50658 39088 91	0.99940 50356 06	0.81964 99643 54	4.39657 82526 41
65	1.51034 42716 57	0.99967 34160 21	0.83207 37552 30	4.46217 17234 00
66	1.51393 73365 80	0.99991 84459 96	0.84418 15481 06	4.52614 72299 91
67	1.51737 30029 22	1.00014 24772 55	0.85595 51893 94	4.58840 23314 34
68	1.52066 07439 17	1.00034 76309 00	0.86737 68071 40	4.64883 64588 87
69	1.52380 96314 82	1.00053 58204 71	0.87842 88603 89	4.70735 11606 65
70	1.52682 83600 39	1.00070 87727 85	0.88909 41880 33	4.76385 03454 26
71	1.52972 52694 88	1.00086 80467 96	0.89935 60569 84	4.81824 05226 12
72	1.53250 83673 64	1.00101 50506 35	0.90919 82094 93	4.87043 10392 04
73	1.53518 53502 17	1.00115 10570 43	0.91860 49094 42	4.92033 43119 04
74	1.53776 36242 53	1.00127 72173 27	0.92756 09874 50	4.96786 60538 01
75	1.54025 03252 70	1.00139 45740 11	0.93605 18846 21	5.01294 54946 61
76	1.54265 23379 34	1.00150 40723 03	0.94406 36947 66	5.05549 55939 34
77	1.54497 63144 41	1.00160 65704 98	0.95158 32049 59	5.09544 32456 51
78	1.54722 86925 91	1.00170 28494 40	0.95859 79342 51	5.13271 94743 65
79	1.54941 57133 23	1.00179 36211 34	0.96509 61704 20	5.16725 96213 52
80	1.55154 34377 57	1.00187 95366 09	0.97106 70045 94	5.19900 35203 07
81	1.55361 77637 70	1.00196 11931 07	0.97650 03636 29	5.22789 56618 15
82	1.55564 44421 57	1.00203 91406 89	0.98138 70401 14	5.25388 53459 20
83	1.55762 90924 10	1.00211 38883 16	0.98571 87198 81	5.27692 68221 56
84	1.55957 72181 61	1.00218 59094 82	0.98948 80069 22	5.29697 94164 67
85	1.56149 42223 13	1.00225 56474 61	0.99268 84456 08	5.31400 76444 71
86	1.56338 54219 23	1.00232 35202 12	0.99531 45401 28	5.32798 13106 13
87	1.56525 60628 46	1.00238 99250 12	0.99736 17710 64	5.33887 55927 77
88	1.56711 13342 04	1.00245 52428 62	0.99882 66090 49	5.34667 11120 07
89	1.56895 63826 93	1.00251 98427 06	0.99970 65254 46	5.35135 39870 36
90	1.57079 63267 95	1.00258 40855 28	1.00000 00000 00	5.35291 58734 14

$K = 5.43490\ 98296\ 25564$

$K' = 1.57091\ 59581\ 27243$

$E = 1.00075\ 15777\ 01834$

$E' = 1.57067\ 67091\ 27960$

r	$u=(r/90)K=F(\phi,k)$	sn u	cn u	dn u
0	0.00000 00000 00	0.00000 00000 00	1.00000 00000 00	1.00000 00000 00
1	0.06038 78869 96	0.06031 45996 20	0.99817 94172 76	0.99817 99723 06
2	0.12077 57739 92	0.12019 20251 58	0.99275 06620 94	0.99275 28782 04
3	0.18116 36609 88	0.17920 76862 76	0.98381 12650 20	0.98381 62364 46
4	0.24155 15479 83	0.23696 13981 57	0.97151 90660 94	0.97152 78681 18
5	0.30193 94349 79	0.29308 77575 26	0.95608 55434 47	0.95609 92262 83
6	0.36232 73219 75	0.34726 45333 98	0.93776 72119 69	0.93778 67959 93
7	0.42271 52089 71	0.39921 87218 77	0.91685 57204 40	0.91688 21929 53
8	0.48310 30959 67	0.44873 01212 09	0.89366 73197 11	0.89370 16333 58
9	0.54349 09829 63	0.49563 24816 75	0.86853 23500 65	0.86857 54228 94
10	0.60387 88699 58	0.53981 24529 69	0.84178 53144 48	0.84183 80315 46
11	0.66426 67569 54	0.58120 66750 13	0.81375 59836 46	0.81381 92001 92
12	0.72465 46439 50	0.61979 74308 04	0.78476 18395 22	0.78483 63850 64
13	0.78504 25309 46	0.65560 73037 70	0.75510 20217 45	0.75518 87054 87
14	0.84543 04179 42	0.68869 32648 19	0.72505 28166 92	0.72515 24335 49
15	0.90581 83049 38	0.71914 05666 03	0.69486 46238 41	0.69497 79610 72
16	0.96620 61919 33	0.74705 67563 24	0.66476 02596 65	0.66488 81038 65
17	1.02659 40789 29	0.77256 60444 33	0.63493 44115 64	0.63507 75558 63
18	1.08698 19659 25	0.79580 41934 43	0.60555 40320 22	0.60571 32833 59
19	1.14736 98529 21	0.81691 40249 90	0.57675 94609 32	0.57693 56472 95
20	1.20775 77399 17	0.83604 15877 37	0.54866 60765 66	0.54886 00541 43
21	1.26814 56269 13	0.85333 29851 75	0.52136 62977 34	0.52157 89579 21
22	1.32853 35139 08	0.86893 18307 58	0.49493 17867 10	0.49516 40629 62
23	1.38892 14009 04	0.88297 72768 20	0.46941 57311 17	0.46966 86056 50
24	1.44930 92879 00	0.89560 25517 32	0.44485 51104 93	0.44512 96208 44
25	1.50969 71748 96	0.90693 39347 79	0.42127 28782 46	0.42157 01237 24
26	1.57008 50618 92	0.91709 00984 46	0.39868 00112 02	0.39900 11592 64
27	1.63047 29488 88	0.92618 17515 42	0.37707 73967 11	0.37742 36893 08
28	1.69086 08358 84	0.93431 15225 66	0.35645 75413 71	0.35683 03013 04
29	1.75124 87228 79	0.94157 40297 86	0.33680 60961 91	0.33720 67335 25
30	1.81163 66098 75	0.94805 60920 10	0.31810 32008 69	0.31853 32194 52
31	1.87202 44968 71	0.95383 70413 29	0.30032 46553 12	0.30078 56594 51
32	1.93241 23838 67	0.95898 91059 85	0.28344 29300 61	0.28393 66313 91
33	1.99280 02708 63	0.96357 78376 17	0.26742 80292 97	0.26795 62538 98
34	2.05318 81578 59	0.96766 25625 69	0.25224 82210 08	0.25281 29168 14
35	2.11357 60448 54	0.97129 68415 19	0.23787 06490 00	0.23847 38935 35
36	2.17396 39318 50	0.97452 89255 32	0.22426 18409 40	0.22490 58494 35
37	2.23435 18188 46	0.97740 21998 48	0.21138 81258 09	0.21207 52597 42
38	2.29473 97058 42	0.97995 56092 33	0.19921 59730 88	0.19994 87491 80
39	2.35512 75928 38	0.98222 40608 10	0.18771 22648 26	0.18849 33645 49
40	2.41551 54798 34	0.98423 88018 54	0.17684 45105 87	0.17767 67902 21
41	2.47590 33668 29	0.98602 77712 85	0.16658 10140 91	0.16746 75153 70
42	2.53629 12538 25	0.98761 59245 11	0.15689 09992 74	0.15783 49606 79
43	2.59667 91408 21	0.98902 55319 69	0.14774 47024 87	0.14874 95712 20
44	2.65706 70278 17	0.99027 64521 85	0.13911 34366 17	0.14018 28813 13
45	2.71745 49148 13	0.99138 63805 13	0.13096 96321 00	0.13210 75563 22

354

q = 0.40330 93063 38377 8   D(90) = 7.56958 97179 80109
q' = 0.00001 90395 55386 95351   1/D(90) = 0.13210 75563 21671

r	ϕ	$E(\phi,k)$	A(r)	D(r)
0	0.00000 00000 00	0.00000 00000 00	0.00000 00000 00	1.00000 00000 00
1	0.06035 12288 68	0.06031 46107 82	0.00797 98676 37	1.00148 76066 46
2	0.12048 13075 09	0.12019 21140 72	0.01597 27569 58	1.00595 04087 69
3	0.18018 10407 35	0.17920 79842 03	0.02399 16544 17	1.01338 83449 42
4	0.23923 69708 95	0.23696 20973 14	0.03204 94760 29	1.02380 12862 07
5	0.29745 48291 47	0.29308 91057 88	0.04015 90321 80	1.03718 89963 49
6	0.35465 25227 10	0.34726 68277 22	0.04833 29924 93	1.05355 10765 65
7	0.41066 45601 57	0.39922 23008 08	0.05658 38507 53	1.07288 68948 08
8	0.46534 38564 15	0.44873 53568 36	0.06492 38899 14	1.09519 55001 78
9	0.51856 28993 52	0.49563 97714 14	0.07336 51472 15	1.12047 55227 94
10	0.57021 42967 31	0.53982 22115 10	0.08191 93794 31	1.14872 50596 62
11	0.62021 07530 67	0.58121 93267 03	0.09059 80282 80	1.17994 15471 59
12	0.66848 45486 37	0.61981 34026 98	0.09941 21860 32	1.21412 16207 65
13	0.71498 66071 26	0.65562 70194 96	0.10837 25613 55	1.25126 09628 17
14	0.75968 52444 34	0.68871 71393 40	0.11748 94454 27	1.29135 41390 77
15	0.80256 46902 65	0.71916 90019 10	0.12677 26783 91	1.33439 44250 04
16	0.84362 34677 80	0.74709 01380 44	0.13623 16161 75	1.38037 36226 57
17	0.88287 27065 87	0.77260 47392 91	0.14587 50977 59	1.42928 18692 53
18	0.92033 44522 39	0.79584 85475 06	0.15571 14129 49	1.48110 74384 19
19	0.95604 00225 52	0.81696 43625 97	0.16574 82707 13	1.53583 65352 76
20	0.99002 84486 30	0.83609 82110 03	0.17599 27681 75	1.59345 30864 97
21	1.02234 50269 96	0.85339 61739 93	0.18645 13603 46	1.65393 85265 78
22	1.05303 99993 82	0.86900 18431 77	0.19712 98306 58	1.71727 15815 41
23	1.08216 73684 50	0.88305 43497 31	0.20803 32624 22	1.78342 80513 96
24	1.10978 38512 63	0.89568 69017 74	0.21916 60112 85	1.85238 05926 49
25	1.13594 79673 49	0.90702 57594 00	0.23053 16788 02	1.92409 85022 25
26	1.16071 92547 23	0.91718 95770 70	0.24213 30872 13	1.99854 75041 71
27	1.18415 76048 73	0.92628 90467 87	0.25397 22555 53	2.07568 95405 09
28	1.20632 27063 80	0.93442 67814 83	0.26605 03771 90	2.15548 25676 48
29	1.22727 35861 75	0.94169 73850 86	0.27836 77989 16	2.23788 03597 33
30	1.24706 82374 23	0.94818 76632 59	0.29092 40017 03	2.32283 23203 32
31	1.26576 33233 17	0.95397 69361 04	0.30371 75832 44	2.41028 33038 34
32	1.28341 39467 03	0.95913 74209 61	0.31674 62423 94	2.50017 34479 23
33	1.30007 34762 13	0.96373 46596 02	0.33000 67656 31	2.59243 80184 62
34	1.31579 34204 38	0.96782 79694 65	0.34349 50156 56	2.68700 72680 94
35	1.33062 33425 87	0.97147 09032 14	0.35720 59222 33	2.78380 63098 26
36	1.34461 08088 96	0.97471 17047 34	0.37113 34753 98	2.88275 50068 21
37	1.35780 13649 60	0.97759 37528 41	0.38527 07211 32	2.98376 78795 62
38	1.37023 85348 65	0.98015 59865 80	0.39960 97596 03	3.08675 40315 02
39	1.38196 38387 61	0.98243 33079 96	0.41414 17460 71	3.19161 70942 33
40	1.39301 68251 19	0.98445 69598 70	0.42885 68945 57	3.29825 51931 62
41	1.40343 51145 04	0.98625 48771 69	0.44374 44843 37	3.40656 09345 56
42	1.41325 44521 88	0.98785 20118 42	0.45879 28693 52	3.51642 14147 86
43	1.42250 87673 61	0.98927 06313 19	0.47398 94905 99	3.62771 82524 58
44	1.43123 02370 79	0.99053 05915 33	0.48932 08915 37	3.74032 76440 61
45	1.43944 93534 06	0.99164 95856 32	0.50477 27365 71	3.85412 04436 23

ELLIPTIC FUNCTIONS   TABLE $\theta = 89°$

K= 5.43490 98296 25564   E = 1.00075 15777 01834
K'= 1.57091 59581 27243   E'= 1.57067 67091 27960

r	u=(r/90)K=F(φ,k)	sn u	cn u	dn u
45	2.71745 49148 13	0.99138 63805 13	0.13096 96321 00	0.13210 75563 22
46	2.77784 28018 09	0.99237 10749 45	0.12328 68590 44	0.12449 74156 18
47	2.83823 06888 04	0.99324 45604 74	0.11603 98340 60	0.11732 74403 02
48	2.89861 85758 00	0.99401 93135 87	0.10920 44148 16	0.11057 37687 15
49	2.95900 64627 96	0.99470 64284 26	0.10275 75848 66	0.10421 36822 70
50	3.01939 43497 92	0.99531 57661 58	0.09667 74308 56	0.09822 55837 44
51	3.07978 22367 88	0.99585 60890 18	0.09094 31139 01	0.09258 89697 97
52	3.14017 01237 84	0.99633 51804 15	0.08553 48365 67	0.08728 43991 72
53	3.20055 80107 79	0.99675 99524 17	0.08043 38066 83	0.08229 34577 97
54	3.26094 58977 75	0.99713 65418 16	0.07562 21989 60	0.07759 87217 81
55	3.32133 37847 71	0.99747 03959 17	0.07108 31152 13	0.07318 37191 01
56	3.38172 16717 67	0.99776 63490 72	0.06680 05438 52	0.06903 28906 34
57	3.44210 95587 63	0.99802 86909 00	0.06275 93191 48	0.06513 15510 77
58	3.50249 74457 59	0.99826 12270 66	0.05894 50806 84	0.06146 58501 50
59	3.56288 53327 55	0.99846 73333 85	0.05534 42333 34	0.05802 27344 25
60	3.62327 32197 50	0.99865 00039 67	0.05194 39079 90	0.05478 99100 36
61	3.68366 11067 46	0.99881 18940 30	0.04873 19232 53	0.05175 58064 60
62	3.74404 89937 42	0.99895 53579 63	0.04569 67482 06	0.04890 95415 20
63	3.80443 68807 38	0.99908 24831 43	0.04282 74663 74	0.04624 08877 12
64	3.86482 47677 34	0.99919 51199 78	0.04011 37409 41	0.04374 02399 27
65	3.92521 26547 30	0.99929 49085 79	0.03754 57812 37	0.04139 85846 13
66	3.98560 05417 25	0.99938 33024 40	0.03511 43105 45	0.03920 74704 09
67	4.04598 84287 21	0.99946 15894 48	0.03281 05351 83	0.03715 89802 41
68	4.10637 63157 17	0.99953 09105 21	0.03062 61148 80	0.03524 57048 94
69	4.16676 42027 13	0.99959 22761 39	0.02855 31343 96	0.03346 07180 22
70	4.22715 20897 09	0.99964 65809 90	0.02658 40763 55	0.03179 75525 92
71	4.28753 99767 05	0.99969 46169 58	0.02471 17952 50	0.03025 01787 14
72	4.34792 78637 00	0.99973 70846 23	0.02292 94925 67	0.02881 29828 37
73	4.40831 57506 96	0.99977 46034 36	0.02123 06929 80	0.02748 07482 58
74	4.46870 36376 92	0.99980 77207 29	0.01960 92215 63	0.02624 86369 30
75	4.52909 15246 88	0.99983 69196 76	0.01805 91819 55	0.02511 21724 93
76	4.58947 94116 84	0.99986 26263 22	0.01657 49354 37	0.02406 72245 31
77	4.64986 72986 80	0.99988 52157 87	0.01515 10808 43	0.02310 99939 80
78	4.71025 51856 75	0.99990 50177 28	0.01378 24352 66	0.02223 69996 72
79	4.77064 30726 71	0.99992 23211 42	0.01246 40154 89	0.02144 50659 72
80	4.83103 09596 67	0.99993 73785 74	0.01119 10200 97	0.02073 13114 68
81	4.89141 88466 63	0.99995 04098 00	0.00995 88121 95	0.02009 31386 93
82	4.95180 67336 59	0.99996 16050 31	0.00876 29027 00	0.01952 82248 41
83	5.01219 46206 55	0.99997 11276 83	0.00759 89341 33	0.01903 45134 54
84	5.07258 25076 51	0.99997 91167 63	0.00646 26648 66	0.01861 02070 45
85	5.13297 03946 46	0.99998 56888 95	0.00534 99537 76	0.01825 37606 53
86	5.19335 82816 42	0.99999 09400 19	0.00425 67452 43	0.01796 38762 92
87	5.25374 61686 38	0.99999 49467 94	0.00317 90544 43	0.01773 94982 83
88	5.31413 40556 34	0.99999 77677 13	0.00211 29529 01	0.01757 98094 58
89	5.37452 19426 30	0.99999 94439 58	0.00105 45542 25	0.01748 42282 17
90	5.43490 98296 26	1.00000 00000 00	0.00000 00000 00	0.01745 24064 37

356

q = 0.40330 93063 38377 8   D(90) = 7.56958 97179 80109
q'= 0.00001 90395 55386 95351   1/D(90) = 0.13210 75563 21671

r	ϕ	$E(\phi,k)$	A(r)	D(r)
45	1.43944 93534 06	0.99164 95856 32	0.50477 27365 71	3.85412 04436 23
46	1.44719 49924 95	0.99264 33697 61	0.52032 98326 40	3.96896 22667 88
47	1.45449 44845 79	0.99352 59674 00	0.53597 61539 15	4.08471 36195 99
48	1.46137 36840 42	0.99430 98538 38	0.55169 48696 35	4.20123 00521 40
49	1.46785 70389 18	0.99500 61223 20	0.56746 83750 42	4.31836 23371 11
50	1.47396 76592 99	0.99562 46334 07	0.58327 83254 27	4.43595 66732 41
51	1.47972 73842 44	0.99617 41490 07	0.59910 56732 16	4.55385 49133 44
52	1.48515 68468 98	0.99666 24524 86	0.61493 07080 69	4.67189 48166 94
53	1.49027 55375 83	0.99709 64561 41	0.63073 30999 11	4.78991 03252 47
54	1.49510 18647 24	0.99748 22972 83	0.64649 19448 08	4.90773 18631 47
55	1.49960 47321 21	0.99782 54240 22	0.66218 58136 09	5.02518 66587 72
56	1.50394 60020 97	0.99813 06718 22	0.67779 28032 12	5.14209 90885 11
57	1.50799 57357 62	0.99840 23317 30	0.69329 05903 51	5.25829 10412 70
58	1.51181 70582 94	0.99864 42111 85	0.70865 64877 41	5.37358 23026 49
59	1.51542 38013 62	0.99885 96881 40	0.72386 75024 29	5.48779 09575 60
60	1.51882 90314 85	0.99905 17592 43	0.73890 03961 81	5.60073 38099 68
61	1.52204 50948 02	0.99922 30826 85	0.75373 17477 05	5.71222 68183 28
62	1.52508 36596 89	0.99937 60163 08	0.76833 80165 32	5.82208 55451 76
63	1.52795 57573 04	0.99951 26514 72	0.78269 56083 16	5.93012 56192 34
64	1.53067 18201 39	0.99963 48431 54	0.79678 09413 51	6.03616 32083 10
65	1.53324 17186 65	0.99974 42366 94	0.81057 05140 61	6.14001 55011 89
66	1.53567 47961 66	0.99984 22915 41	0.82404 09732 17	6.24150 11966 22
67	1.53797 99018 31	0.99993 03023 59	0.83716 91826 41	6.34044 09974 68
68	1.54016 54222 20	1.00000 94177 57	0.84993 22921 19	6.43665 81080 01
69	1.54223 93111 68	1.00008 06569 38	0.86230 78062 82	6.52997 87323 06
70	1.54420 91182 24	1.00014 49244 69	0.87427 36531 61	6.62023 25717 09
71	1.54608 20157 16	1.00020 30234 15	0.88580 82521 65	6.70725 33191 09
72	1.54786 48245 11	1.00025 56670 01	0.89689 05811 93	6.79087 91481 05
73	1.54956 40385 63	1.00030 34889 71	0.90750 02426 14	6.87095 31947 96
74	1.55118 58483 20	1.00034 70528 11	0.91761 75278 33	6.94732 40301 18
75	1.55273 61630 77	1.00038 68599 38	0.92722 34801 86	7.01984 61206 63
76	1.55422 06323 29	1.00042 33570 06	0.93629 99558 84	7.08838 02758 76
77	1.55564 46662 24	1.00045 69424 00	0.94482 96827 54	7.15279 40796 56
78	1.55701 34551 50	1.00048 79720 46	0.95279 63165 14	7.21296 23043 63
79	1.55833 19885 66	1.00051 67645 91	0.96018 44943 54	7.26876 73053 68
80	1.55960 50730 93	1.00054 36060 51	0.96697 98855 62	7.32009 93943 07
81	1.56083 73499 77	1.00056 87539 76	0.97316 92390 02	7.36685 71893 23
82	1.56203 33119 43	1.00059 24412 11	0.97874 04272 04	7.40894 79406 62
83	1.56319 73195 29	1.00061 48792 82	0.98368 24868 89	7.44628 78300 97
84	1.56433 36169 42	1.00063 62614 93	0.98798 56557 37	7.47880 22427 77
85	1.56544 63474 97	1.00065 67657 37	0.99164 14052 32	7.50642 60102 18
86	1.56653 95686 97	1.00067 65570 92	0.99464 24694 41	7.52910 36232 87
87	1.56761 72669 97	1.00069 57902 36	0.99698 28695 94	7.54678 94141 62
88	1.56868 33723 22	1.00071 46116 99	0.99865 79343 39	7.55944 77064 13
89	1.56974 17723 75	1.00073 31619 99	0.99966 43156 10	7.56705 29324 78
90	1.57079 63267 95	1.00075 15777 02	1.00000 00000 00	7.56958 97179 80

357

APPENDIX

In the Legendre-Jacobi-Abel system for computing elliptic functions, the following formulas, and tables, will be found useful. The formulas were compiled from the following list of reference texts:

Smithsonian Mathematical Formulae, Edwin P. Adams, Ph.D.
Theory of Elliptic Functions, Harris Hancock, Ph.D.
Elliptic Functions, Alfred Cordew Dixon, M.A.
Functions of Complex Variable, James Pierpont, L.L.D.
Advanced Calculus, Edwin Bidwell Wilson, Ph.D.

Our use of the notations snh (u, κ), cn h (u, κ), dnh (u, κ) in the formulas below may be strange to the reader, but they seem to be a natural extension of the hyperbolic notation to the sn (u, κ), cn (u, κ), dn (u, κ) elliptic functions. We have used them for years; we hope they will be acceptable to other computers.

The basic number q may be computed as follows: given the modular angle θ, the number l is computed from

$$l = \tfrac{1}{2} \cdot \frac{1 - \sqrt{\cos \theta}}{1 + \sqrt{\cos \theta}}, \text{ whence}$$

$$q = l + 2l^5 + 15l^9 + 150l^{13} + 1707l^{17} + 20910l^{21} + 268616l^{25} + \ldots$$

For 16-place accuracy this becomes difficult, if not impossible, for $\theta > 70°$; for these we may use the relation

$$ln \; q \cdot ln \; q' = \pi^2$$

The Jacobi θ functions:

$\theta_1(v, q) = 2q^{\frac{1}{4}}(\sin \pi v - q^2 \sin 3\pi v + q^6 \sin 5\pi v - q^{12} \sin 7\pi v + \ldots)$
$\theta_2(v, q) = 2q^{\frac{1}{4}}(\cos \pi v + q^2 \cos 3\pi v + q^6 \cos 5\pi v + q^{12} \cos 7\pi v + \ldots)$
$\theta_3(v, q) = 1 + 2q \cos 2\pi v + 2q^4 \cos 4\pi v + 2q^9 \cos 6\pi v + 2q^{16} \cos 8\pi v + \ldots$
$\theta_0(v, q) = 1 - 2q \cos 2\pi v + 2q^4 \cos 4\pi v - 2q^9 \cos 6\pi v + 2q^{16} \cos 2\pi v - \ldots$

whence

$$\theta_2(q) = 2q^{\frac{1}{4}}(1 + q^2 + q^6 + q^{12} + q^{20} + q^{30} + q^{42} + \ldots)$$
$$\theta_3(q) = 1 + 2q + 2q^4 + 2q^9 + 2q^{16} + 2q^{25} + 2q^{36} + \ldots$$
$$\theta_0(q) = 1 - 2q + 2q^4 - 2q^9 + 2q^{16} - 2q^{25} + 2q^{36} - \ldots$$

To compute K, K' we have

$$\sqrt{\frac{2K}{\pi}} = \theta_3(q), \text{ and, since } q = e^{-\pi \frac{K'}{K}}, \text{ it follows that } K' = -\frac{K}{\pi} ln \; q.$$

To compute E, E' we have

$$1 - \frac{E'}{K} = \frac{2\pi^2}{K^2} \left[\frac{q - 4q^4 + 9q^9 - 16q^{16} + 25q^{25} - \ldots}{1 - 2q + 2q^4 - 2q^9 + 2q^{16} - 2q^{25} + \ldots} \right]$$

359

Check formula:

$$KE' + K'E - KK' = \frac{\pi}{2}$$

For reader's convenience

$$\pi = 3.14159\ 26535\ 89793\ 23846$$
$$\pi^2 = 9.86960\ 44010\ 89358\ 62$$
$$\frac{\pi}{2} = 1.57079\ 63267\ 94896\ 61923$$

(A)

$$\operatorname{sn}(u, \kappa) = \frac{\theta_3(q)}{\theta_2(q)} \cdot \frac{\theta_1(v, q)}{\theta_0(v, q)}$$

$$= \frac{1 + 2q + 2q^4 + 2q^9 +.}{1 + q^2 + q^6 + q^{12} +.} \cdot \left[\frac{\sin \pi v - q^2 \sin 3\pi v + q^6 \sin 5\pi v - q^{12} \sin 7\pi v\ .}{1 - 2q \cos 2\pi v + 2q^4 \cos 4\pi v - 2q^9 \cos 6\pi v\ .} \right]$$

$$\operatorname{cn}(u, \kappa) = \frac{\theta_0(q)}{\theta_2(q)} \cdot \frac{\theta_2(v, q)}{\theta_0(v, q)}$$

$$= \frac{1 - 2q + 2q^4 - 2q^9}{1 + q^2 + q^6 + q^{12}} \cdot \left[\frac{\cos \pi v + q^2 \cos 3\pi v + q^6 \cos 5\pi v + q^{12} \cos 7\pi v +.}{1 - 2q \cos 2\pi v + 2q^4 \cos 4\pi v - 2q^9 \cos 6\pi v +.} \right]$$

$$\operatorname{dn}(u, \kappa) = \frac{\theta_0(q)}{\theta_3(q)} \cdot \frac{\theta_3(v, q)}{\theta_0(v, q)}$$

$$= \frac{1 - 2q + 2q^4 - 2q^9}{1 + 2q + 2q^4 + 2q^9} \cdot \left[\frac{1 + 2q \cos 2\pi v + 2q^4 \cos 4\pi v + 2q^9 \cos 6\pi v +.}{1 - 2q \cos 2\pi v + 2q^4 \cos 4\pi v - 2q^9 \cos 6\pi v +.} \right]$$

where $v = \frac{u}{2K}$. There are similar expansions for $\operatorname{sc}(u\,\kappa)$, $\operatorname{sd}(u, \kappa)$, $\operatorname{cd}(u\,\kappa)$.

These expansions imply similar ones for $\operatorname{sn}(u, \kappa')$, $\operatorname{cn}(u\,\kappa')$, $\operatorname{dn}(u\,\kappa')$ etc., where q' and v' are substituted for q and v and $v' = \frac{u}{2K'}$.

Also these expansions are true for the imaginary argument iu.
Thus:

(B)

$$-i\operatorname{sn}(iu, \kappa) = \operatorname{snh}(u, \kappa)$$

$$= \frac{\theta_3(q)}{\theta_2(q)} \left[\frac{\sinh \pi v - q^2 \sinh 3\pi v + q^6 \sinh 5\pi v - q^{12} \sinh 7\pi v +. .}{1 - 2q \cosh 2\pi v + 2q^4 \cosh 4\pi v - 2q^9 \cosh 6\pi v +. . . .} \right]$$

$$\operatorname{cn}(iu, \kappa) = \operatorname{cnh}(u, \kappa)$$

$$= \frac{\theta_0(q)}{\theta_2(q)} \left[\frac{\cosh \pi v + q^2 \cosh 3\pi v + q^6 \cosh 5\pi v + q^{12} \cosh 7\pi v +. . . .}{1 - 2q \cosh 2\pi v + 2q^4 \cosh 4\pi v - 2q^9 \cosh 6\pi v +. . . .} \right]$$

$$\operatorname{dn}(iu, \kappa) = \operatorname{dnh}(u, \kappa)$$

$$= \frac{\theta_0(q)}{\theta_3(q)} \left[\frac{1 + 2q \cosh 2\pi v + 2q^4 \cosh 4\pi v + 2q^9 \cosh 6\pi v +. . . .}{1 - 2q \cosh 2\pi v + 2q^4 \cosh 4\pi v - 2q^9 \cosh 6\pi v +. . . .} \right]$$

where $v = \frac{u}{2K}$.

These, of course, imply similar expansions for $-i\operatorname{sn}(iu, \kappa')$, $\operatorname{cn}(iu, \kappa')$ and $\operatorname{dn}(iu, \kappa')$ where q' and v' are substituted for v and q and $v' = \frac{u}{2K'}$.

360

For values of $\operatorname{sn}(u, \kappa)$, $\operatorname{cn}(u, \kappa)$, $\operatorname{dn}(u, \kappa)$ where the modular angle θ lies between tabulated values, and where interpolation fails, direct computation may be employed up to, and including, $\theta = 89°$, using equations (A) above. Values, 15-places correct, can be thus computed without prohibitive labor. That, in fact, was the way our tables were computed.

For values of θ between $89°$ and $90°$ we may resort to Jacobi's imaginary transformation equations:

(C)

$$\operatorname{sn}(u, \kappa) = \frac{-i \operatorname{sn}(iu, \kappa')}{\operatorname{cn}(iu, \kappa')} = \frac{\operatorname{snh}(u, \kappa')}{\operatorname{cnh}(u, \kappa')}$$

$$\operatorname{cn}(u, \kappa) = \frac{1}{\operatorname{cn}(iu, \kappa')} = \frac{1}{\operatorname{cnh}(u, \kappa')}$$

$$\operatorname{dn}(u, \kappa) = \frac{\operatorname{dn}(iu, \kappa')}{\operatorname{cn}(iu, \kappa')} = \frac{\operatorname{dnh}(u, \kappa')}{\operatorname{cnh}(u, \kappa')}$$

together with

(D)

$$\operatorname{sn}(K - u, \kappa) = \frac{\operatorname{cn}(u, \kappa)}{\operatorname{dn}(u, \kappa)}$$

$$\operatorname{cn}(K - u, \kappa) = \frac{\kappa', \operatorname{sn}(u, \kappa)}{\operatorname{dn}(u, \kappa)}$$

$$\operatorname{dn}(K - u, \kappa) = \frac{\kappa'}{dn(u, \kappa)}$$

Confining our attention to $\operatorname{sn}(u, \kappa)$, we may obtain from these, written out for ready use

(E)

$$\operatorname{sn}(u, \kappa) = \frac{\operatorname{snh}(u, \kappa')}{\operatorname{cnh}(u, \kappa')}$$
$$= \frac{\theta_3(q')}{\theta_0(q')} \left[\frac{\sinh \pi v' - q'^2 \sinh 3\pi v' + q'^6 \sinh 5\pi v' - q'^{12} \sinh 7\pi v' \ldots}{\cosh \pi v' + q'^2 \cosh 3\pi v' + q'^6 \cosh 5\pi v' + q'^{12} \cosh 7\pi v' \ldots} \right]$$

where $v' = \dfrac{u}{2K'}$

and also $\operatorname{sn}(K - u, \kappa) = \dfrac{\operatorname{cn}(u, \kappa)}{\operatorname{dn}(u, \kappa)} = \dfrac{1}{\operatorname{cn}(iu, \kappa')} \cdot \dfrac{\operatorname{cn}(iu, \kappa')}{\operatorname{dn}(iu, \kappa')} = \dfrac{1}{\operatorname{dnh}(u, \kappa')}$,

that is

(F)

$$\operatorname{sn}(K - u, \kappa) = \frac{\theta_3(q')}{\theta_0(q')} \left[\frac{1 - 2q' \cosh 2\pi v' + 2q'^4 \cosh 4\pi v' - 2q'^9 \cosh 6\pi v' + \ldots}{1 + 2q' \cosh 2\pi v' + 2q'^4 \cosh 4\pi v' + 2q'^9 \cosh 6\pi v' + \ldots} \right]$$

where $v' = \dfrac{u}{2K'}$.

The following two examples will be used to illustrate this method, first, because the results can be readily checked by reference to our tables, and, secondly, because the fundamental values q, q', K, K' are available without preliminary computation.

Example (1): Compute sn$(44°, 89°)$.

For $\theta = 89°$ we have

$$q = 0.40330, 93063, 38377, 8$$
$$q' = 0.00001, 90395, 55386, 95351$$
$$K = 5.43490, 98296, 25564$$
$$K' = 1.57091, 59581, 27243$$

Also $u = \dfrac{44}{90} K$.

Using equation (E) above, we have

$$\text{sn}(44°, 89°) = \frac{\theta_3(q')}{\theta_0(q')} \frac{\left[\sinh\left(44° \dfrac{K}{K'}\right) - q'^2 \sinh 3\left(44° \dfrac{K}{K'}\right) + \text{etc.} \right]}{\left[\cosh\left(44° \dfrac{K}{K'}\right) + q'^2 \cosh 3\left(44° \dfrac{K}{K'}\right) + \text{etc.} \right]}$$

To explain the argument $\left(44° \dfrac{K}{K'}\right)$ we note

$$u = \frac{44}{90} K \text{ and } v' = \frac{u}{2K'}, \text{ whence } \pi v' = \frac{44}{90} \cdot \frac{\pi}{2} \cdot \frac{K}{K'} = 44° \frac{K}{K'}$$

This change from the rational argument $44°$ on the left side of the equation to the irrational argument $44° \dfrac{K}{K'}$ on the right side is unfortunate for the computer, but seems to be unavoidable.

Example (2): Compute sn$(88°, 89°)$

Here setting $u = \dfrac{2}{90} K$, and using equation (F) above, we have

$$\text{sn}(88°, 89°) = \frac{\theta_3(q')}{\theta_0(q')} \cdot \frac{\left[1 - 2q' \cosh 2\left(2° \dfrac{K}{K'}\right) + 2q'^4 \cosh 4\left(2° \dfrac{K}{K'}\right) \ldots \right]}{\left[1 + 2q' \cosh 2\left(2° \dfrac{K}{K'}\right) + 2q'^4 \cosh 4\left(2° \dfrac{K}{K'}\right) \ldots \right]}$$

Using this method the authors were able to compute sn$(89° \ 59' \ 59'', 89° \ 59' \ 59'')$ with no extravagant amount of computing.

For computing $E(u, \kappa)$ we have

$$E(u, \kappa) = Z(u, \kappa) + \frac{E}{K} \cdot u$$

where

$$Z(u, \kappa) = \frac{2\pi}{K} \left[\frac{q \sin 2\pi v - 2q^4 \sin 4\pi v + 3q^9 \sin 6\pi v}{1 - 2q \cos 2\pi v + 2q^4 \cos 4\pi v - 2q^9 \cos 6\pi v} \right.$$
$$\left. \frac{-4q^{16} \sin 8\pi v + 5q^{25} \sin 10\pi v - \ldots}{+2q^{16} \cos 8\pi v - 2q^{25} \cos 10\pi v + \ldots} \right]$$

in which $v = \dfrac{u}{2K}$.

For computing the $E(u, \kappa)$ column in our tables we used also

$$E(u+v, \kappa) = E(u, \kappa) + E(v, \kappa) - \kappa^2 \operatorname{sn}(u, \kappa) \operatorname{sn}(v, \kappa) \operatorname{sn}(u+v, \kappa)$$

For tabulating $\operatorname{sn}(u, \kappa)$, $\operatorname{cn}(u, \kappa)$, $\operatorname{dn}(u, \kappa)$, $E(u, \kappa)$, $\phi = \sin^{-1}(\operatorname{sn}(u, \kappa))$ we set $u = \dfrac{r}{90}$ $K = r°$, whence $\pi v = \dfrac{r}{90} \cdot \dfrac{\pi}{2} = r°$ for sin, cos, sinh, cosh.

Also $\kappa = \sin \theta°$
   $\kappa' = \cos \theta°$
Again, we write

$$A(r°) = \frac{\sin r° - q^2 \sin 3r° + q^6 \sin 5r° - q^{12} \sin 7r° + q^{20} \sin 9r° \; \dots}{1 + q^2 + q^6 + q^{12} + q^{20} + \; \dots}$$

$$B(r°) = A(90° - r°)$$

$$D(r°) = \frac{1 - 2q \cos 2r° + 2q^4 \cos 4r° - 2q^9 \cos 6r° + 2q^{16} \cos 8r° - \; \dots}{1 - 2q + 2q^4 - 2q^9 + 2q^{16} - \; \dots}$$

$$C(r°) = D(90° - r°)$$

whence

$$\operatorname{sn}(r°, \theta°) = D(90°) \cdot \frac{A(r°)}{D(r°)}$$

$$\operatorname{cn}(r°, \theta°) = \frac{B(r°)}{D(r°)}$$

$$\operatorname{dn}(r°, \theta°) = \frac{1}{D(90°)} \cdot \frac{C(r°)}{D(r°)}$$

Also $Z(r°, \theta°) = \dfrac{2\pi}{K} \left[\dfrac{q \sin 2r° - 2q^4 \sin 4r° + 3q^9 \sin 6r°}{1 - 2q \cos 2r° + 2q^4 \cos 4r° - 2q^9 \cos 6r°} \right.$

$$\left. \frac{-4q^{16} \sin 8r° + 5q^{25} \sin 10r° - \; \dots}{+2q^{16} \cos 8r° - 2q^{25} \cos 10r° + \; \dots} \right]$$

whence

$$E(r°, \theta°) = Z(r°, \theta°) + \frac{r}{90} \cdot E$$

Beginning with $r° = 1°$ we obtain succeeding values $E(2°)$, $E(3°)$, etc., by means of $E(r° + 1°) = E(r°) + E(1°) - \kappa^2 \operatorname{sn}(r°) \cdot \operatorname{sn}(1°) \cdot \operatorname{sn}(r° + 1°)$.
The ϕ column was computed from the relation

$$\sin \phi = \operatorname{sn} u$$

that is, $\phi(r°, \theta°) = \sin^{-1}(\operatorname{sn}(r°, \theta°))$

r°	radians	sinh r	cosh r
1	0.01745 32925 19943	0.01745 41786 29595	1.00015 23125 76256
2	0.03490 65850 39887	0.03491 36742 41017	1.00060 92967 03268
3	0.05235 98775 59830	0.05238 38054 35780	1.00137 10915 89893
4	0.06981 31700 79773	0.06986 98940 55263	1.00243 79292 98016
5	0.08726 64625 99716	0.08737 72668 01878	1.00381 01348 13236
6	0.10471 97551 19660	0.10491 12568 61719	1.00548 81261 43867
7	0.12217 30476 39603	0.12247 72055 29182	1.00747 24144 48275
8	0.13962 63401 59546	0.14008 04638 34058	1.00976 36041 90587
9	0.15707 96326 79490	0.15772 63941 71594	1.01236 23933 24828
10	0.17453 29251 99433	0.17542 03719 36010	1.01526 95735 07533
11	0.19198 62177 19376	0.19316 77871 57981	1.01848 60303 38910
12	0.20943 95102 39320	0.21097 40461 46575	1.02201 27436 32611
13	0.22689 28027 59263	0.22884 45731 36153	1.02585 07877 14211
14	0.24434 60952 79206	0.24678 48119 38725	1.03000 13317 48475
15	0.26179 93877 99149	0.26480 02276 02271	1.03446 56400 95511
16	0.27925 26803 19093	0.28289 63080 75536	1.03924 50726 95930
17	0.29670 59728 39036	0.30107 85658 79793	1.04434 10854 85117
18	0.31415 92653 58979	0.31935 25397 88101	1.04975 52308 36746
19	0.33161 25578 78923	0.33772 37965 12546	1.05548 91580 35670
20	0.34906 58503 98866	0.35619 79324 00012	1.06154 46137 80336
21	0.36651 91429 18809	0.37478 05751 36959	1.06792 34427 14875
22	0.38397 24354 38753	0.39347 73854 63767	1.07462 75879 91022
23	0.40142 57279 58696	0.41229 40588 99132	1.08165 90918 60056
24	0.41887 90204 78639	0.43123 63274 75069	1.08902 00962 94915
25	0.43633 23129 98582	0.45030 99614 83032	1.09671 28436 42697
26	0.45378 56055 18526	0.46952 07712 31691	1.10473 96773 07736
27	0.47123 88980 38469	0.48887 46088 16893	1.11310 30424 65463
28	0.48869 21905 58412	0.50837 73699 04367	1.12180 54868 07263
29	0.50614 54830 78356	0.52803 49955 25681	1.13084 96613 16572
30	0.52359 87755 98299	0.54785 34738 88040	1.14023 83210 76429
31	0.54105 20681 18242	0.56783 88421 98436	1.14997 43261 08744
32	0.55850 53606 38185	0.58799 71885 02740	1.16006 06422 45537
33	0.57595 86531 58129	0.60833 46535 40269	1.17050 03420 32397
34	0.59341 19456 78072	0.62885 74326 14412	1.18129 66056 64466
35	0.61086 52381 98015	0.64957 17774 79873	1.19245 27219 55198
36	0.62831 85307 17959	0.67048 39982 47118	1.20397 20893 38221
37	0.64577 18232 37902	0.69160 04653 04585	1.21585 82169 02579
38	0.66322 51157 57845	0.71292 76112 59275	1.22811 47254 61695
39	0.68067 84082 77789	0.73447 19328 96275	1.24074 53486 56359
40	0.69813 17007 97732	0.75623 99931 57849	1.25375 39340 92087
41	0.71558 49933 17675	0.77823 84231 42676	1.26714 44445 11201
42	0.73303 82858 37618	0.80047 39241 25845	1.28092 09589 99980
43	0.75049 15783 57562	0.82295 32696 00232	1.29508 76742 31252
44	0.76794 48708 77505	0.84568 33073 39883	1.30964 89057 42804
45	0.78539 81633 97448	0.86867 09614 86010	1.32460 90892 52006

r°	radians	sinh r	cosh r
46	0.80285 14559 17392	0.89192 32346 56263	1.33997 27820 07041
47	0.82030 47484 37335	0.91544 72100 77902	1.35574 46641 75159
48	0.83775 80409 57278	0.93925 00537 45530	1.37192 95402 68370
49	0.85521 13334 77221	0.96333 90166 04027	1.38853 23406 07022
50	0.87266 46259 97165	0.98772 14367 57379	1.40555 81228 21700
51	0.89011 79185 17108	1.01240 47417 04044	1.42301 20733 93909
52	0.90757 12110 37051	1.03739 64505 99555	1.44089 95092 36003
53	0.92502 45035 56995	1.06270 41765 47046	1.45922 58793 10854
54	0.94247 77960 76938	1.08833 56289 16394	1.47799 67662 91741
55	0.95993 10885 96881	1.11429 86156 92686	1.49721 78882 62973
56	0.97738 43811 16825	1.14060 10458 54728	1.51689 51004 61762
57	0.99483 76736 36768	1.16725 09317 84321	1.53703 43970 61876
58	1.01229 09661 56711	1.19425 63917 07028	1.55764 19129 99612
59	1.02974 42586 76654	1.22162 56521 65200	1.57872 39258 42656
60	1.04719 75511 96598	1.24936 70505 23975	1.60028 68577 02386
61	1.06465 08437 16541	1.27748 90375 11061	1.62233 72771 90208
62	1.08210 41362 36484	1.30600 01797 91033	1.64488 19014 18521
63	1.09955 74287 56428	1.33490 91625 74955	1.66792 75980 46920
64	1.11701 07212 76371	1.36422 47922 66118	1.69148 13873 74254
65	1.13446 40137 96314	1.39395 59991 42686	1.71555 04444 77190
66	1.15191 73063 16258	1.42411 18400 78090	1.74014 21013 95919
67	1.16937 05988 36201	1.45470 15012 99973	1.76526 38493 67679
68	1.18682 38913 56144	1.48573 43011 88551	1.79092 33411 08779
69	1.20427 71838 76087	1.51721 96931 15221	1.81712 83931 45802
70	1.22173 04763 96031	1.54916 72683 22302	1.84388 69881 96724
71	1.23918 37689 15974	1.58158 67588 44765	1.87120 72776 02641
72	1.25663 70614 35917	1.61448 80404 74852	1.89909 75838 10881
73	1.27409 03539 55861	1.64788 11357 70500	1.92756 64029 10227
74	1.29154 36464 75804	1.68177 62171 08455	1.95662 24072 19038
75	1.30899 69389 95747	1.71618 36097 83039	1.98627 44479 27059
76	1.32645 02315 15690	1.75111 37951 51493	2.01653 15577 91711
77	1.34390 35240 35634	1.78657 74138 26863	2.04740 29538 89703
78	1.36135 68165 55577	1.82258 52689 19396	2.07889 80404 24780
79	1.37881 01090 75520	1.85914 83293 27442	2.11102 64115 92479
80	1.39626 34015 95464	1.89627 77330 78853	2.14379 78545 02768
81	1.41371 66941 15407	1.93398 47907 23910	2.17722 23521 61443
82	1.43116 99866 35350	1.97228 09887 80799	2.21131 00865 11199
83	1.44862 32791 55294	2.01117 79932 34694	2.24607 14415 33312
84	1.46607 65716 75237	2.05068 76530 91508	2.28151 70064 10857
85	1.48352 98641 95180	2.09082 20039 87402	2.31765 75787 54441
86	1.50098 31567 15123	2.13159 32718 55138	2.35450 41678 91425
87	1.51843 64492 35067	2.17301 38766 48408	2.39206 79982 19646
88	1.53588 97417 55010	2.21509 64361 25265	2.43036 05126 26646
89	1.55334 30342 74953	2.25785 37696 91808	2.46939 33759 75466
90	1.57079 63267 94897	2.30129 89023 07295	2.50917 84786 58057

CIRCULAR FUNCTIONS

r°	sin r	r°	cos r	r°
1	0.01745 24064 37283 51281 94190	89	0.99984 76951 56391 23915 70116	1
2	0.03489 94967 02500 97164 59952	88	0.99939 08270 19095 73000 62434	2
3	0.05233 59562 42943 83272 21186	87	0.99862 95347 54573 87378 44921	3
4	0.06975 64737 44125 30077 59588	86	0.99756 40502 59824 24761 31627	4
5	0.08715 57427 47658 17355 80643	85	0.99619 46980 91745 53229 50104	5
6	0.10452 84632 67653 47139 98342	84	0.99452 18953 68273 33692 26919	6
7	0.12186 93434 05147 48111 28939	83	0.99254 61516 41322 03498 00616	7
8	0.13917 31009 60065 44411 24967	82	0.99026 80687 41570 31508 37749	8
9	0.15643 44650 40230 86901 01053	81	0.98768 83405 95137 72619 00402	9
10	0.17364 81776 66930 34885 17166	80	0.98480 77530 12208 05936 67430	10
11	0.19080 89953 76544 81240 51405	79	0.98162 71834 47663 95349 65049	11
12	0.20791 16908 17759 33710 17423	78	0.97814 76007 33805 63792 85667	12
13	0.22495 10543 43864 99805 11072	77	0.97437 00647 85235 22853 96945	13
14	0.24192 18955 99667 72256 04424	76	0.97029 57262 75996 47230 63779	14
15	0.25881 90451 02520 76234 88988	75	0.96592 58262 89068 28674 97432	15
16	0.27563 73558 16999 18564 99716	74	0.96126 16959 38318 86191 64970	16
17	0.29237 17047 22736 72809 74687	73	0.95630 47559 63035 48133 86508	17
18	0.30901 69943 74947 42410 22934	72	0.95105 65162 95153 57211 64393	18
19	0.32556 81544 57156 66871 40089	71	0.94551 85755 99316 81034 81247	19
20	0.34202 01433 25668 73304 40996	70	0.93969 26207 85908 38405 41093	20
21	0.35836 79495 45300 27348 41378	69	0.93358 04264 97201 74899 00431	21
22	0.37460 65934 15912 03541 49638	68	0.92718 38545 66787 40080 64745	22
23	0.39073 11284 89273 75506 20846	67	0.92050 48534 52440 32739 68947	23
24	0.40673 66430 75800 20775 39860	66	0.91354 54576 42600 89550 21276	24
25	0.42261 82617 40699 43618 69785	65	0.90630 77870 36649 96324 25527	25
26	0.43837 11467 89077 41745 27345	64	0.89879 40462 99166 99278 22957	26
27	0.45399 04997 39546 79156 04084	63	0.89100 65241 88367 86235 97096	27
28	0.46947 15627 85890 77595 94623	62	0.88294 75928 58926 94203 21714	28
29	0.48480 96202 46337 02907 53796	61	0.87461 97071 39395 80028 46370	29
30	0.50000 00000 00000 00000 00000	60	0.86602 54037 84438 64676 37232	30
31	0.51503 80749 10054 21008 16319	59	0.85716 73007 02112 28746 52180	31
32	0.52991 92642 33204 95404 67812	58	0.84804 80961 56425 97038 61762	32
33	0.54463 90350 15027 08222 40837	57	0.83867 05679 45424 02963 75909	33
34	0.55919 29034 70746 83016 04281	56	0.82903 75725 55041 69200 63368	34
35	0.57357 64363 51046 09610 80319	55	0.81915 20442 88991 78968 44884	35
36	0.58778 52522 92473 12916 87060	54	0.80901 69943 74947 42410 22934	36
37	0.60181 50231 52048 27991 79770	53	0.79863 55100 47292 84628 40008	37
38	0.61566 14753 25658 27966 88111	52	0.78801 07536 06721 95669 39778	38
39	0.62932 03910 49837 45270 59025	51	0.77714 59614 56970 87997 99377	39
40	0.64278 76096 86539 32632 26434	50	0.76604 44431 18978 03520 23927	40
41	0.65605 90289 90507 28478 24960	49	0.75470 95802 22771 99794 29842	41
42	0.66913 06063 58858 21382 62733	48	0.74314 48254 77394 23501 46970	42
43	0.68199 83600 62498 50044 22258	47	0.73135 37016 19170 48328 75436	43
44	0.69465 83704 58997 28665 64063	46	0.71933 98003 38651 13935 60547	44
45	0.70710 67811 86547 52440 08444	45	0.70710 67811 86547 52440 08444	45